HOSPITAL AND COMMUNITY

Studies in External Relationships
of the Administrator

Hospital and Community

STUDIES IN EXTERNAL RELATIONSHIPS OF THE ADMINISTRATOR

Laura G. Jackson, B.S., M.I.C.S.(Hon.)

Associate Professor Emeritus and formerly Associate
Director, Program in Hospital Administration, Northwestern University, Chicago, Illinois

THE MACMILLAN COMPANY, NEW YORK
COLLIER-MACMILLAN LIMITED, LONDON

First Printing

Library of Congress catalog card number: 64-14969

The Macmillan Company, New York
Collier-Macmillan Canada, Ltd., Toronto, Ontario

Printed in the United States of America

DESIGNED BY RONALD FARBER

A new profession is being born—the calling of
Administrator in the House of Healing—and this,
to possess the attributes of a true and worthy
profession, must number among its members those who
not only profess unselfishly to serve, but—of
equal importance—those who can demonstrate an
unusual ability based on special training for this
work. It is fast being proven that those, ofttimes
overrated, affixes: "M.D.," "R.N.," "D.D.," "PH.D."
are in no way a guarantee that the possessor
of one or all of them can understand the psychology
of those who either live or labor in the temples
of Aesculapius.

JOSEPH C. DOANE, M.D.
Pre-convention Message of the President.
Bulletin, American Hospital Association,
July, 1928.

Foreword

The external environmental relationships of the hospital administrator are all too often obscured by the internal complexities of his work. The administrator of the hospital of today and tomorrow must, of necessity, confront, deal with, and succeed in his outside public relationships.

This book deals with the vital role that the administrator plays in community relationships and focuses its attention on the various publics with which he must work.

In the education of students for careers in health administration it is imperative that they be made fully aware of the social, economic, and political forces that affect the health institution, and that they be stimulated to visualize their future roles from a broad community service standpoint. Miss Jackson's long experience in directing public relations for medical organizations and in developing and teaching courses in hospital administration gives her exceptional perspective for presenting a needed community relations text.

EDGAR O. MANSFIELD, M.S.H.A., DR.P.H.
President, Alumni Association, Program in
Hospital Administration, Northwestern University
Administrator, Riverside Methodist Hospital, Columbus, Ohio

Preface

Work in the health field has a fascination, not only for those who are engaged in it but for those who are preparing to enter it, that produces an insularity which is out of accord with the spirit of the times. Cognizance of this is shown in the developing concepts of comprehensive medicine and of area-wide planning of health services. Only slowly, however, is it being realized that progress toward these goals depends upon leadership by persons whose education has given them vision of the *total* needs and problems of the community. The remedy lies in undergraduate, graduate, and postgraduate education and self-teaching that have breadth and depth.

These studies are designed to indicate the background needed to understand the relationships of health service administration to other fields. They are introductory only and necessarily incomplete. The literature of the separate disciplines must be explored to supplement them. In a few fields, such as law, discussion is omitted because texts exist, as shown in the bibliography, that relate them to health services.

The range of subject matter has made it necessary and desirable to draw upon the research and ideas of many authors. Among the major contributors are alumni of the Northwestern University program in hospital administration. Dr. Arthur J. Glazebrook's thesis on pharmacology has been used almost in full in two different sections. Robert J. Marsh is responsible for almost the entire chapter on administration. Dr. Frederick N. Elliott has been quoted from liberally on medical staff relationships and medical records. There is a long quotation from Augustine Gunn's thesis on medical social service, and another from Karl Glunz's discussion of treating the alcoholic in the general hospital. Bessie Covert's history of *The Modern Hospital* is given in full. George H. Yeckel's ideas on the "wholistic" concept in medicine and its implications for hospital service are incorporated in the discussion of comprehensive medicine in the final chapter. Ewell Singleton's report on disparity of charges is summarized.

Other lengthy quotations from papers by former students include those of Donald Arnwine, on the administrative residency; Gordon Boughton, on inhalation therapy; George Brotherton, on the development of the medical library; Neil Cooper, on the therapeutic community; Roy House, on fraternal and civic organizations; Virginia Jones on morale surveys; Norbert Lindskog, on dental service; Freeman May, on the American National Red Cross; Frank Meisamer, on the Hill-Burton Act; Dr. J. Pagan-Carlo, on the history of medical records; O. K. Stephens, on wage and salary administration; David Stickney, on planning the laboratory; Masaichi Tasaka, on suburban hospitals; and Patrick Wade, on data processing.

Grateful acknowledgment is extended for these and many shorter quotations from other alumni and faculty; for permission from the Board of Hospitals and Homes of the Methodist Church to reproduce the address by Bishop William T. Watkins on church and state relations and from the editor of the *Journal of the International College of Surgeons* to use extracts from E. Todd Wheeler's article, "The Hospital of the Future" and to all the hospital journals and a number of other publications for quotations and references that enable a much broader view of events and prospects than any individual author could present.

Finally, indebtedness is acknowledged for ideas and inspiration gained from long association with one of the great hospital leaders of all time, Dr. Malcolm T. MacEachern.

LAURA G. JACKSON

Contents

PART FIVE. THE EDUCATIONAL, RESEARCH, AND COMMUNICATIONS ENVIRONMENT

PART SIX. THE HEALTH SERVICE COMMUNITY

Introduction

UNTIL HIS position is firmly established, and sometimes even then, an administrator in the health and medical care field is walking a tightrope the end of which is hidden in a haze. On one side is the pull of internal administrative responsibilities; on the other that of external interests and obligations. No sharply defined rules exist to help him to keep his balance and to focus on his goal.

In this relatively new profession which impinges on other professions much more solidly entrenched by virtue of precedence and recognized high status, every decision the administrator makes faces the possibility that somebody may rebel against it. When should he stand firm? When should he relax, concede, compromise? His footing is precarious unless he has developed the confidence that comes from knowing precisely what and where his immediate goal is and from being sure that he has the physical and mental prowess to avoid critical missteps.

How to develop this confidence that a successful administrator must have is a question that has no simple answer. Only prolonged study can show the way through the mist. The medical service administrator of the nineteen sixties should be at home in the whole wide world. The walls of his institution must melt away before his penetrating vision of the external forces that profoundly affect what happens within them. His concept of what constitutes his community must not only overpass town and city limits, county and state boundaries, and lines that separate nations; it must transcend geographic notions entirely and embrace spheres of thought and action that make the community, and society, what they were yesterday, what they are today, and what they are likely to be tomorrow. The term "community" has multiple aspects.

This is why formal education and continuing study are more necessary than ever before to prepare the administrator for and to support him on his perilous tightrope journey. Breadth and depth of knowledge and understanding are the resources upon which he should be able to draw to keep his balance and to press forward toward his goals. Since the welfare of his organization is so increasingly dependent upon good administration, his fall could have far-reaching and tragic consequences for many others besides himself.

Time was, and not too long ago, when the administrator in this field could virtually isolate himself in his institution and satisfactorily operate it. Hospitals in particular existed in isolation. "Houses of death" they were considered by most

I

people and were shunned by all but the disease-ravaged, hopeless, poor. The twentieth century turnabout, to a stage at which overutilization by private patients is the complaint, has been accomplished without completely killing the traditional attitude of aloofness on the part of those who work in them. The public has learned to use hospitals but not to trust them completely—a state of affairs growing out of the aloofness and lack of effective communication.

There are some justifications for the clinging of hospital people to their separatist feeling. One is the gravity of their main objective—saving lives. Another is the suffering and fear in the atmosphere, minimized though these are by modern medical strategy. Still another is the intense strife that goes on to find ever-better ways to combat disease and death. How grim the battles are few people outside realize. They are waged in a setting of scientific, technological, and sociological complexity and behind a mask of personal imperturbability that is a protection against emotional collapse. The administrative staff imbibes the tension in the air and shares the feeling of exhaustion upon release from duty, all of which tends to stifle desire to be very active in the world outside.

This tendency must be fought. People in medical service, for the sake of their own and their patients' advancement, must deliberately instigate interaction between their institutions and external forces. Unless they cooperate and communicate convincingly with people in other circles, medical service facilities will retrogress from lack of public support. Gone under modern conditions is the security once enjoyed because of self-immolating service to the sick which was supposed to speak for itself. Nothing speaks for itself nowadays.

Medical institutions have progressed to their present stage mainly because of some eminent leaders who are and who have been spokesmen as well as men and women of action. They have had the vision to recognize that the public must be made aware of the extent to which it is being served. Fortunately for hospitals, the example of the Good Samaritan has been followed by countless devoted souls who have through the ages toiled and given generously of themselves and their wealth without waiting for full understanding. But the present day is one of great questioning and of great competition. Philanthropy must now be courted and be given solid, substantiated facts. Aloofness must be replaced by frank and friendly interrelationships.

THREE STEPS TO INTERACTION

The initial step in breaking down isolation was the forming of ties between similar agencies through organizing associations. For hospitals in the United States this did not occur until 1899 with the organization by ten active members and one honorary of the Association of Hospital Superintendents, the name of which was changed in 1907 to the American Hospital Association. At that time there were 273 active and 13 honorary members. Its development, concurrent with that of related groups and the hospital standardization program of the

American College of Surgeons, now conducted by the Joint Commission on Accreditation of Hospitals, has brought about a goodly measure of coordination. Today's administrator is beginning to think as often in terms of hospitals in general as he does in terms of just his own institution.

Influenced by what he learns from the associations, the administrator may even proceed to the next step and think and act in the light of the needs of his community. This requires analysis of the elements of which the community is composed. Here is where the dizziness that may lead the administrator to disaster threatens. It takes knowledge to make this analysis correctly and to act wisely on the findings. It takes understanding of underlying economic, sociological, psychological, political, religious, educational, and scientific forces. It takes the sensitivity that is developed through studying and trying to understand people and what motivates them to participate in community affairs. It takes skill in communications in order to give to them and to get from them genuine interest and support. There is no easy way, no blithely opportunistic approach, to successful community relations.

The third step takes the administrator beyond the local community. A community can no longer be an isolated unit, any more than can the health institution. It is tightly linked with neighboring communities, with the region, with the nation, and with the world. Nor can it be studied as a world in miniature and conclusions drawn therefrom of world-wide significance. Communities differ from each other. Community citizenship is different from world citizenship. For the broad perspective demanded by conditions as they affect the health field, the administrator needs to study economics, sociology, psychology, government, religion, education, communications, science and the arts, on the world as well as on the local level.

EDUCATION FOR ADMINISTRATION

Clearly the new approach to education for administration must be to build study of administrative concepts and procedures upon a base of knowledge of the field and of all related fields insofar as it is possible to squeeze them into the curriculum. Orientation to the specific field, be it business, government, school, church, or medical service, is not sufficient. Only by trying to understand life and society in their completeness can a person truly comprehend the interaction of forces that affect all of the seemingly distinct fields and utilize these forces to the best advantage of his own enterprise.

Where is the niche in the whole complex into which health service fits? What is the administrator's role in making it fit as perfectly as possible?

In preparing students for careers in administration, it is easy for both teacher and pupil to become so engrossed in study of the complicated inside workings of such an institution as the hospital that the environment, the external relationships, the community needs which are its reason for existence, are relegated to a subordinate role when actually they should be the primary consideration. It is like ignoring that an individual's importance depends upon his impact on society and that the hermit's life is a wasted one. In itself, viewed as a detached unit of the social structure designed as a repair shop for out-of-order members of the populace, the hospital is not too significant an institution. To the degree that its detachment is lessened does its effectiveness increase.

Yet study of the specific field must not be slighted. Long since it was discovered that persons well trained for executive responsibility in government, schools, churches, and industry may fail dismally in administering a hospital. They do not learn quickly enough that the same principles cannot always be applied. They cannot readily adjust themselves to the medically dominated atmosphere. If the hospital is a business, as in some respects it certainly is, it is a queer business. It has an equal right to be classified as a scientific, social, or educational institution—and sometimes as a religious or governmental one. As many speakers and writers have said before, it is an anomaly, crossing the boundaries of artificial separation of fields more than do other activities. So many kinds of disciplines and endeavors are involved that the administrator, in order to run it successfully, must learn to make decisions in a staggering variety of situations involving widely different types of people.

In no academic program, however well planned and extended through undergraduate, master's, and doctorate stages, can the prospective administrator expect to gain more than introductory insight into most of the subjects he would benefit by mastering. Yet everything learned can be used at some time to advantage. Knowledge of this is his spur to keep studying.

A Needed Quality—Balance

A word of caution is necessary. To return to the tightrope simile, balance is a major quality for the administrator to cultivate. External aspects could conceivably absorb a disproportionate amount of his interest and activity. An outgoing personality especially could enjoy too much the role of leadership in the community. He might subordinate his hospital duties to interprofessional affairs. If he permits ambition to become the president of the Elks, Rotary, school board, or even the state hospital association to dominate his thoughts and to usurp an exorbitant share of his time, he is doing his hospital, and himself as an administrator, more harm than good.

Furthermore, it should be borne in mind that the obligation and the privilege of participating in community affairs are not by any means to be abrogated by the administrator as his own personal functions alone. He is considered here as the director of such participation by the entire personnel of his institution in appropriate degrees according to their positions and talents. It is one of his specific duties to encourage and to help his associates to assume related outside responsibilities of many kinds. He contributes more sometimes by promoting civic and professional engagements for his trustees, doctors, nurses, therapists, dietitians, technicians, business personnel, and auxiliary members than he does by accepting them himself. This is one of his functions as an educator and a leader.

Like other aspects of the space age, promoting interaction between an institution and the community in its broad sense has grown into an acute problem, for help in the solution of which experts in human relations and in communications should be developed and used. Industry has grown painfully conscious of this need. Within reasonable limits the administrator can learn these skills. Beyond these limits he is well advised to employ the services of persons who have concentrated on acquiring them, just as he does in delegating business responsibilities to a comptroller and medical care to specially trained medical and allied professional personnel.

Again it is a matter of balance. He can stretch himself too far by trying to *do* everything. But he needs the background in theory in a great many fields that will enable him to do the over-all planning, organizing, managing, and controlling.

AIM OF THESE STUDIES

This series of studies is inescapably but a lifting of the curtain for a glimpse of the vast areas which the present and prospective administrator would benefit by exploring deeply. It is launched with the thought that opportunities for administrators in the health field are increasing far more rapidly than the facilities and faculties for training them. Therefore the breadth of the preparation required needs to be publicized, to the end that better integration may be effected with existing faculties in the universities. The specialized instruction directed by authorities in the health field should not be subordinated, but it can be conducted as supplemental to a basic cross-disciplinary curriculum utilizing existing courses.

The hospital for care of the acutely ill being the most complicated of all health facilities, it naturally becomes the primary model for study. What is learned in programs in hospital administration can be applied to the direction of any health organization. Graduates of the hospital courses are therefore being sought by every conceivable type of health and welfare agency. This is one result of the hospital's rather new interaction with other community agencies in area-wide planning.

Hospitals and medical services in general are being studied by a growing number of students and practitioners in other fields. The reason for this is the new appreciation of health and its preservation as a basic consideration in all human endeavor. Careerists in medicine, public health, social work, government, business, education, religion, personnel, and public relations are studying operation of hospitals because they are likely to be or already are working in or with them. Engineers, architects, and scientists in several fields are showing a high degree of interest. For these side-line students the overview presented in these studies, without the procedural detail required in a text on internal functioning, should be an introduction to study of the place of the medical service institution in the community at large.

Emphasized throughout, as it deserves to be, is the contribution made by individuals to progress in the various fields.

Part one

THE WORLD
OF MEDICINE
AND ITS
CITIZENS

Interdependence of Doctor and Hospital

> In the hospital of our grandfathers' or even fathers' time, the physician was an adjunct service given on a now and then basis. In those same times, a hospital was not often used in the practice of medicine. Today, hospital service is really medical and becoming increasingly so. We have experienced such remarkable changes in medical science, medical practice and socioeconomics that we find the physician and the hospitals with their functions so intermingled that their relationship is undergoing a needed thorough re-examination.
> RUSSELL NELSON, M.D.[1]

THE LOGICAL starting point for the administrator's exploration of the outer world is *medicine* because it is the dominant power within the medical institution. He needs to look beyond the frequently baffling relationships with his medical staff and to view medicine objectively as a natural science, as a social science, as a profession, and as a fascinating historical and biographical study. He needs to trace its evolution and to try to see where it is going in a changing society. With the insight thus gained, he can undertake more intelligently and more sympathetically his responsibilities in furthering the medical purposes which are the reasons for his institution's existence.

It is through this kind of study that the administrator will find out why as the coordinator of the conglomeration of duties and of people in the hospital it is up to him to see that the medical care is safeguarded by high professional standards,

---

[1] President and chief executive officer, Johns Hopkins Hospital, Baltimore; past president, American Hospital Association. From *Hospitals,* October 16, 1961, p. 45.

proper staff organization, comprehensive and accurate medical records, thorough and continuous medical audits, well-defined and implemented educational and research programs, and so on. This responsibility he cannot completely delegate even to a medical director. He alone is at the helm. The authority is his as the one to whom it was delegated by the governing board. It has to be exercised judiciously and tactfully. Ability to do this can be developed by learning to subjugate personality difficulties to the primary purpose of promoting what Dr. Alan Gregg called "great medicine."

In every decision the administrator needs to remember that scientific medical care of patients is his institution's aim. All other aspects of operation are incidental and contributory to this. Important as many of them are, their significance in the total picture is measurable only by their help in attaining the primary objective. That objective is the maximum possible improvement in the physical and mental condition of the maximum possible number of patients served. The advancement of "great medicine" depends in high degree upon how well this objective is attained in individual medical service institutions.

By "great medicine" Dr. Gregg said he meant "the whole of medicine." He summarized medicine's status as follows:[2]

It has made progress to a degree not now understood or appreciated.

It offers the means for modern man to have life and have it more abundantly.

It offers these means with such certainty and in such abundance that medical care (both preventive and curative) deserves to be held on a par with food, clothing, and housing as one of the essentials of keeping alive.

It is the prevailing concept of disease that determines how much and how wisely medical science and art will be used and added to.

Serious and even threatening factors are now affecting the teaching and practice of medicine and medical research.

A way exists that would solve the cost of adequate medical care, medical education, and research.

We must provide for the training and future careers of all the professions involved in curative and preventive medicine and in the rehabilitation of the handicapped if we wish to avoid a state of frustration bordering on disaster.

These statements Dr. Gregg presented as challenges. Expansion of the voluntary prepayment idea was what he referred to as the "way" that would solve the cost. Every one of the challenges implies that planning and action are imperative to meet them. They are obviously challenges to the administrator of medical services as well as to the physician, since he explicitly refers in the last statement to "all the professions involved in curative and preventive medicine and in the rehabilitation of the handicapped."

It is in no passive sense therefore that the administrator should view the province of medicine. Perhaps as one not directly involved in its techniques his influence can be greater than that of the individual practitioners. He should prepare himself to play an important part in its drama, and not alone in the single institution scene.

[2] *Challenges to Contemporary Medicine.* New York, Columbia University Press, 1956, pp. 3-4.

Value to the Physician of Hospital Affiliation

Doctors and hospitals in this modern age are indispensable to each other. The lone worker, the physician who has no institutional affiliation, is handicapped because his perspective is limited. The surroundings and the associations of medical care in the hospital are educational and broadening. The unattached physician not only lacks many of the technical aids but also misses the insight gained through daily contact with colleagues who exchange ideas and experiences.

The modern hospital revolves around the physician and his patient. In many a hospital of the past a physician was rarely seen. Care was of a custodial nature, usually limited to the indigent sick, almost up to the present century in some places. Until the physician appeared in the hospital as a central figure, it was not a hospital as it is conceived of today. Scientific methods were unknown. Shelter, food, sometimes a little nursing care and certain religious rituals were all hospitals attempted to provide. They were social, not medical, phenomena.

Rulers and wealthy citizens in early civilizations had physicians who served them in their palaces and homes. The public seldom benefited from their knowledge. Only when physicians and hospitals became welded together did people in general begin to receive scientific medical treatment.

Many physicians are most reluctant to recognize the necessity for centralized authority in the hospital, which in some respects entails a certain subjugation of personal interests. By tradition doctors are individualists and they cling to this heritage. Their education and their outlook from the time they choose their profession are distinctive.

Yet much of the stupendous advance of medical science may be credited to the physician's individualism. On the other hand, it may be blamed for some of the lag between the acquisition of new knowledge and its application.

The physician, especially in the United States, still has independence far beyond that enjoyed by most members of any other profession or vocation as a whole. The truly dedicated doctor uses this independence to expend and exhaust himself in ceaseless labor to increase his knowledge, to improve his insight and methods, to advance his profession, and to wage continuous warfare against disease, disability, and death.

The restrictions of institutionalized medical practice naturally tend to limit individualism, yet its advantages in interplay of effort are obvious. In general, the physician remains a much freer worker than are most people.

The sometimes resentful attitude of physicians toward administrative controls may perhaps be traced to inheritance of ideals of independence dating back to kitchen-table surgery days. Nobody was forever hounding the horse-and-buggy doctor to dictate his medical records or to attend medical staff conferences. No one barred him from attempting surgery that was too complicated for his training and which should have been referred to somebody better qualified than he who was available to do it. A tradition of self-sufficiency under all conditions is hard to live down. Administrators should cultivate understanding of and make allowances for this heritage from the not too remote past.

The overburdened medical school curriculum permits little indoctrination in administrative concepts. The graduate emerges almost wholly dependent upon the hospital for orientation in this respect during his internship and residency, his only previous contact usually having been through a clerkship as a medical student. Since medical education is practically turned over to the medical staff during the intern-resident periods, the new doctor gains even then little perception of the role of administration unless the administrator assumes the responsibility for teaching medical staff–administrative relationships. This is seldom done on any more than the most casual scale.

The atmosphere of the hospital has a powerful influence upon the satisfactions which the physician derives from his staff connection. How this varies in different institutions is well expressed in the following:[3]

> The totality of the patient care given in a particular hospital is a reflection of the cumulated philosophies of the medical staff members, upon which restrictions are imposed by the hospital facilities. The interactions between physicians, and the use of common facilities tend to produce homogeneity within the hospital staff so that an overview of any one hospital's experience is partly a reflection of group medical philosophy. That this may vary markedly from hospital to hospital is obvious.

The kind of skill which should be developed in relationships between the administrator and the medical staff is indicated in Dr. Lucius W. Johnson's answer[4] to the question, "Should the administrator take an active part in the revision of the bylaws or should this be left to the staff alone?"

> The administrator has a great personal interest in the bylaws, because it will be his duty to enforce them and to fit his administrative practices into the framework of the bylaws. Also, he is more familiar with the standard bylaws than the medical staff. Therefore, he should guide and advise the medical staff during the revision without being too insistent. There will be more harmony and better obedience to the bylaws if the staff members believe they have done the revision.

Although this is an internal matter, and external relationships are the subject of these studies, it is necessary to become familiar with the thinking and attitude of physicians in general in order to develop adeptness in gaining medical staff cooperation. Dr. Johnson's answer gives a clue that it would be wise to follow in all relationships with the staff.

ATTITUDE TOWARD "LAY" PERSONNEL BY SOME DOCTORS

The lay administrator suffers, along with other "outsiders," from the "outside the pale" attitude of many medical and allied professional workers. Although

[3] From Report No. 26, May 1, 1958, of the Commission on Professional and Hospital Activities, Inc.—a nonprofit organization sponsored by the American College of Physicians, the American College of Surgeons, the American Hospital Association, and the Southwestern Michigan Hospital Council.

[4] *Mod. Hosp.,* August, 1957, p. 100.

sometimes it is politic for him to accept this attitude, depending upon the individual who seems to have it, it is also imperative for him to acquire sufficient familiarity with what goes on in the world of medicine to feel entitled to a kind of citizenship in it himself. Thus he can avoid developing an inferiority complex in the medical atmosphere. He then has a right to consider himself, along with the technologist, the psychologist, and the nurse, as a member of a profession not only closely allied to medicine but inseparable from it.

Many a physician has gone on record scorning the presumption of the lay administrator who professes any knowledge of medical science. Even the medical administrator shares some of the opprobrium because he is supposed to have lost touch with advances since he is no longer in practice. In other fields there is nowhere near this degree of separation between those who practice a profession or an art and those who appreciate and promote it. In art, in music, in literature, in religion, and in the other sciences, a warm welcome from the doers is extended to the organizers and supporters, with credit to them for their understanding despite their inability to perform in the field of their enthusiasms. In medicine the attitude toward hospital trustees and administrators by a few physicians is one of toleration of a more or less necessary encroachment upon their domain. Although this is an increasingly minority group, the hospital suffers from its attitude, and administrators should try to change it. Hospitals are not without blame for it; too frequently the staff is slighted by not being given enough voice in major policy decisions; too often communications are poor.

The Joint Commission on Accreditation of Hospitals states:[5]

A physician when accepting a hospital appointment assumes responsibility for supporting medical staff and hospital policies. He becomes a creative force in formulating future policies and standards of patient care. He works through the staff organization to maintain high standards. He supervises those less experienced and accepts supervision from those more experienced. He accepts controls as a protection to himself as well as to others. He contributes to the teamwork required in the modern practice of medicine. He makes it possible for the medical staff to be truly self-appraising and self-regulatory.

In his presidential address delivered before the American Hospital Association's House of Delegates on August 26, 1959, Dr. Russell A. Nelson[6] said emphatically:

Hospital service is medical—and is becoming increasingly so. Our new services to the public will be mainly medical in nature and will require closer work with our medical staffs. For instance, expansion in outpatient, diagnostic, and rehabilitation services must occur in our hospitals and requires some new approaches to medical staff–hospital relations. . . . The public and hospitals will continue to press for these improvements and understandings with medical groups. On the one hand, we want the benefits of the hospital organization extended beyond its beds; on the other, we—and the medical staff—want to preserve the basic personal nature of medical practice. . . . Hospitals need more help from doctors in

[5] In Explanatory Supplement, *Standard for Accreditation of Medical Staff*, December 1, 1960.
[6] *Hospitals*, October 16, 1959.

day-to-day management. . . . Hospital doctors need more responsibility and authority in hospital affairs. Medical practice is and will continue to be more hospital oriented. We need their participation . . . .

The educated, perceptive administrator can further this closer alliance by gaining so much knowledge of medicine and of medical affairs in general that he becomes a zealot for promoting medical progress in his institution. He directs his main administrative effort toward this end. His relations with the medical staff will be harmonious when they realize that his goal is the same as theirs and that his paramount concern is not the financial balance sheet. Administrative practices that seemed to them before to be obstructive begin to be accepted when they see their desirability from an over-all efficiency standpoint. Open minds follow confidence won through proof that the administrator is with them all the way in promoting the best possible care of patients and that he appreciates the scientific and technical knowledge which they possess and employ.

Of course, it must always be taken into consideration that the physician is in a unique position. Since the primary function of the hospital is the best possible care of the sick, it follows that the staff physician heads all other personnel. The chief of the medical staff is the real czar of this domain. He and his fellows are in most hospitals in a peculiarly independent position, because although they are rendering the most important service offered, they are not beholden to the institution for their livelihood because they are not on its payroll. Furthermore, in a great many instances they do not even receive remuneration from the patient. Administrative control is therefore unbuttressed by financial dependence and is an extremely delicate responsibility. Its exercise is more of an art than a science. Woe to the administrator who lacks the discernment to know that here he treads softly and rules by the most inconspicuous direction, whether or not he is himself a physician.

The administrator who is a physician or a nurse has some advantage in communications. This may be offset by need to appreciate economic, human relations, social, and other aspects. The person of nonprofessional background faces an unending learning process in medical affairs and will find himself overwhelmed by the subject matter unless he keeps his interest under reasonable control. The layman who pretends to know as much about diagnosis and treatment as the doctor, and who takes pride in showing off his knowledge of medical terminology, is regarded with amusement rather than admiration. This is an area in which a little knowledge is not as dangerous perhaps as too much, and in which caution must be exercised in disclosing what is known. The background should be sufficient to bring about the humility that comes from realizing how much more there is to know and yet to grasp the theories of disease and its treatment and the main trends in the advance of medical science in order that full cooperation can be extended.

As Dr. Anthony J. J. Rourke[7] said in an address at the Tenth Annual Institute

[7] *Hospitals,* April 1, 1955.

for Hospital Administrators sponsored by the Maine Hospital Association in September, 1954:

> Although it is true that no one outside the medical field can tell a surgeon how better to remove a stomach, there are hundreds who can tell him about group participation, delegation, follow-up, and many other techniques he has been deprived of much too long.
> It is in this area that all advances in belt line production can be employed to the greatest advantage in all hospitals. The new and younger trustees, realizing that the methods used on Main Street and at the factory can be very successfully applied to *some* parts of hospital activity, are insisting that this be done. Although I want all the savings that modern management can yield, I want also the freedom of rugged individual action that the doctor needs to have preserved securely.

Expressions of this kind *by physicians* in particular fortify the administrator in his approach to medical staff relations problems. Dr. Frederick N. Elliott, assistant to the director of the American Hospital Association and director of its hospital counseling program, stated his views as follows in his thesis submitted in 1960 as final requirement for his master's degree in hospital administration from Northwestern University:

> Among the obstacles to the ideal functioning of the medical staff are many which are administrative and mechanical, as well as the frequent exigencies of time. Hardly less palpable are factors inherent in the very traditions of medicine and the character of physicians. Ignorance of the ultimate responsibility borne by the trustees of the hospital and of the lines of authority which must result, is widespread, and for this the medical curriculum must be held to account. From few medical schools do graduates come prepared with any knowledge of the organizational structure of the hospital and their place and responsibilities in it.
> Then, too, the valid premise of the profession that only those within it can admit, or judge unworthy and exclude, has been in many cases corrupted by extension to a doctrine which makes the only judge of a physician himself. In this frame of reference, then, the requirement to scrutinize the work of others, and to submit it to appraisal, is doubly repugnant.
> With this background, the vital distinction between the physician as an individual and as a member of the organized medical staff, acting under the ultimate authority and on behalf of the trustees of the institution, goes uncomprehended. It is apparent that these obstacles will be removed only with time for education and attrition. In extenuation we must reflect that the concepts upon which the medical staff functions as formulated in the accreditation standards require, from individuals essentially in competition, standards of honesty, humility, and principled behavior which, when achieved as they already are in many hospitals, are almost unique in human society and worthy of the greatest respect.

The basic causes of conflict between administrators and physicians were concisely listed by John M. Danielson,[8] then administrator, now vice president, of Evanston (Illinois) Hospital, and Dr. David N. Danforth, chairman of the hospital's department of obstetrics and gynecology:

[8] *Mod. Hosp.,* August, 1960.

The Administrator
—Fails to keep physicians and trustees informed on important details of costs and operation.
—Fails to educate physicians and trustees on their proper responsibilities for hospital policy.
—Curtails or increases services without consulting the responsible physicians.
—Resists efforts of physicians and trustees to communicate with one another directly.
—Dimisses physicians' suggestions without giving them careful consideration and a forthright answer.

The Physician
—Criticizes administrative policies without informing himself as to the reasons for them.
—Insists on certain policies or expenditures in his own area of the hospital without regard to their effect on the total hospital operation.
—Either fails to let administration make administrative decisions or insists that the administrator take responsibility for decisions that belong to the physician.
—Criticizes the hospital to everyone except the people to whom criticism should be made.
—Regards the hospital as a threat to the private practice of medicine rather than as its greatest ally.

Enlarging on the need for cooperation the authors stated:

Ironically, in an age when the prerogatives of management are held to be so priceless, we in hospitals need to return to the sharing of these prerogatives with the physician. We have said "return" because most surely the great hospitals of the past were built on the philosophy that the hospital and its physicians were one and the same. Witness the era of Osler, Halsted, Kelly and Welch—the Johns Hopkins. Witness the Mayo Clinic, built on a site no modern management consultant or community survey group would consider sane. Yet its greatness rested in something other than the proper selection of the site. It was, in fact, its physicians. . . . Hospitals must understand that the physician can no longer be merely associated with the staff, but must be concerned with management, budget and policies, both professional and administrative.

It is the physician who controls the quality of the product we sell. He is our most effective public relations counselor. The physician is responsible for our vast educational responsibilities. He is the user and controller of the largest part of our budget, and, most important, the physician is the conscience which dictates the kind of treatment our patients receive. In a society moving at a frightening pace toward government and state control, a recognition of the hospital-physician marriage could well be an important factor in stopping this trend. . . .

Occasionally the conflict between doctor and hospital breaks out publicly and criticisms both reasonable and unreasonable are aired. For example, at a meeting of the Ontario Hospital Association back in 1954, an officer of the province's medical association charged that hospitals were invading the practice of medicine by extending Blue Cross coverage for medical care in hospitals. It developed that this was done only after conferences with the medical association had failed to produce an alternative plan to meet public demand. The physician also said that in many hospitals the president of the medical staff was not notified of meetings of the board of governors, nor was his attendance sought, and that physicians often learned of changes in hospital regulations and policies through a nurse. He listed other charges, concluding by calling on the hospital association to "restore the dignity of the medical profession in your hospitals and acknowledge the profession's place as director of clinical matters in the hospital, including the services of the auxiliary profession, nursing."

For such extreme resentment there must be causes, and remedies must be sought, but there remains the fact to be faced that a few individual physicians have determined to be irreconcilable to change.

The problem did not begin in the twentieth century. Illustrative of an early American physician's rebellion against a hospital board's interference in medical affairs is Dr. Marion Sims' statement on November 19, 1874, at the nineteenth annual meeting of the board of governors of the Woman's Hospital, New York, of which he was then honorary chief consulting surgeon and a board member:

> You have transcended the bounds of your authority in the matter of excluding cancer patients . . . and when you see fit to invade the sanctity of our operating room and to dictate to us who shall be present . . . you evidently overstep the limits of your authority.

The second reference was to a regulation limiting observers at operations. Angry discussion followed Dr. Sims' statement which led to his offer to resign. To his dismay the offer was accepted. His status in the profession, however, was unimpaired, for a few months later the American Medical Association elected him president.

Many physicians are well aware of the problems which their profession creates for administration. Said Dr. Dermont W. Melick,[9] chief of surgery and former chief of staff, Good Samaritan Hospital, Phoenix, Arizona:

> It has been stated that the physician is the last of the autocrats in our Western culture and, as such, still holds to the authoritarian tradition in medicine. This authoritarian attitude now keeps colliding with a new democratic concept of management, and from this clash all problems arise.

Dr. Melick went on to say that he did not believe having a physician on the board is the answer because of possible embarrassing situations with his colleagues, lack of business acumen, and tendency to emphasize the clinical aspects. He advocates patience, persistence, and persuasiveness on the part of the administrator—a good summing up of the qualities it will always take to win and to keep the cooperation of the members of the medical staff.

The aid of local or state medical associations should be sought in attempts to improve medical staff–administrative relationships. A good example of cooperation in this area is the California Medical Association's *Guiding Principles for Physician-Hospital Relations,* released in 1960 after two years of study. Among

[9] *Hospitals,* May 1, 1959.

the major objectives of these principles is "the acceptance of responsibility by the self-governing medical staff in the hospital, rather than the simple verbalizing of this concept without acting upon it, which is all too common." The association hopes to have these principles so widely accepted that they can be presented to the public as supplementary to accreditation by the Joint Commission as additional evidence of concern for patient welfare. State, county, and area hospital inspection committees are part of the plan.

PHYSICIANS ON THE HOSPITAL BOARD

Reference was made in the comment on Dr. Melick's article to his belief that having a physician on the board was not the solution to better physician-hospital relationships. There has long been controversy over whether or not this is good policy. Trustees are in an important way part of the external environment of the hospital, since they serve usually on a purely voluntary basis and their main interest lies elsewhere. They represent the community. The medical staff member, on the other hand, has a deep personal concern in his relationships with the hospital. Although not a paid employee as a rule, his livelihood and his career are certainly intermeshed with its operation.

It is argued that membership on the board gives a physician unfair advantage over other members of the medical staff, and there are other valid and obvious objections. Yet on the main premise that trustees need firsthand knowledge of medical affairs beyond that which a liaison committee can provide, and that more power should be given physicians in directing hospital policies, opinion is shifting somewhat. The trend is a manifestation of the growing appreciation that the goal of the whole operation is the highest possible quality of medical service for the benefit of the patient.

To quote again from Dr. Lucius W. Johnson,[10] formerly a member of the hospital standardization staff of the American College of Surgeons, who summarized as follows the answer given to this problem at an institute for hospital administrators in 1957:

> Should doctors be on the governing board? A year ago the answer would have been "No!" and, as authority, the ten reasons against it in Dr. MacEachern's book would have been quoted, with the comment that eight of these ten reasons involve jealousy created within the medical staff. Six months ago the answer would have been that if a doctor is to be a member of the board he should (1) be elected to that duty by the medical staff, not selected by the board, and (2) serve for one year only and not succeed himself. . . . Today the answer is: Why not try it? The pressure by doctors for positions on governing boards of hospitals is very great. In the Massachusetts Memorial Hospital, Boston, the chiefs of the three clinical services have been added to the board. The Stover Committee of the American Medical Association that spent a year studying criticisms of the Joint Commission recommended that "Physicians should be on the governing

[10] *Mod. Hosp.,* August, 1957.

boards of hospitals, with or without a vote." The committee also urged medical staff members to request their boards of trustees to accept a medical member, even if he serves as a nonvoting member. . . . Dr. Kenneth Babcock, director of the Joint Commission on Accreditation of Hospitals, has commented, "An individual should not be elected to the governing board because he has the title of physician, lawyer or union representative, but because he has the ability and time to make a contribution of his knowledge and judgment." *Bulletin No. 12* of the Joint Commission, August, 1956, states: "Very close liaison between the medical staff and the governing board must be maintained. The method used to accomplish this should be determined locally."

THE MEDICAL STAFF

The medical staff is an internal body in the hospital, but the thinking behind its organization and functioning is so generally dictated by outside organizations and authorities that it has to be considered from an external viewpoint.

In his review of Dr. Malcolm T. MacEachern's revision of Dr. Thomas R. Ponton's *Medical Staff in the Hospital*,[11] published originally in 1939, George Bugbee, then director of the American Hospital Association, stated that this "valuable aid" brought up-to-date all of the material bearing upon hospital-physician relations, "by far the most important problem before any hospital administrator and his governing board." In a foreword to the revised edition, Ritz E. Heerman, then president of the association and general manager of The California Hospital and Santa Monica Hospital, said, "'It is well recognized that the medical staff program is the key to good hospital administration."

The 1953 edition is a decade old, yet it remains an authoritative guide, representing as it does the balanced viewpoint of two thoroughly experienced physicians who were equally appreciative of the administrative and the medical aspects of hospital care. The obligations of the governing body and of the medical staff are clearly delineated and in substance are unlikely to be radically changed as the years pass. The discussions of selection and appointment, organization, bylaws, meetings, medical records, professional accounting and medical audit, and the resident medical staff are in general in line with current ideas and practices. A number of events have occurred, especially in the medical audit area, that should be studied as additions to the text, certain references would be strengthened by knowledge of recent actions, and some of the material in the addenda has been replaced by revisions; but on the whole this book gives the basic picture of medical-hospital relationships so presented that trustee, administrator, physician, and student can readily grasp their significance.

It is a paradox that most of the controls over medical staff organization and functioning have been imposed by physicians' own professional groups. Through these groups highly significant progress in medical staff–administrative relationships and in improved patient care has been made. When physicians get

[11] Chicago, Physicians' Record Co., 1953; 2nd ed. completely revised by Malcolm T. MacEachern.

together and study a problem objectively their viewpoint broadens. It is the individual who resists controls. Small committees and individual members of the American Medical Association periodically attack policies and practices of the Joint Commission on Accreditation of Hospitals on the ground that hospitals are trying to dominate medicine, forgetting that the commission is medically directed and that under its corporate structure the American Medical Association has 7 votes, the American College of Surgeons and the American College of Physicians each 3, and the American Hospital Association 7—a 13 to 7 ratio of representatives and voting power on the Board of Commissioners.

Appointments to medical staffs constitute an acute professional and public problem from the standpoint of physicians who do not have them. Nearly a third of the physicians in New York City, for example, are in this predicament. When their patients require hospital service, they must turn them over to other physicians. The doctors themselves suffer from the lack of the educational and inspirational advantages of the hospital environment and associations.

The restriction on hospital appointments has advantages from many points of view. It enables hospitals to set high standards of education, training, ability and reputation for members of their medical staffs. It gives patients confidence in the quality of medical care that they will receive in certain hospitals. Sometimes, however, less laudable reasons exist for denying privileges to some applicants. One of them is fear of competition on the part of older staff members. Another which is a leading factor in the New York situation is objection to group medical practice. Doctors associated with the nonprofit Health Insurance Plan of Greater New York may have difficulty in obtaining hospital appointments. The problem of closed hospital staffs was publicized nationally in an article "Why Hospitals Lock Out Doctors" in the January 17, 1961 issue of *Look*.

Besides the wish to maintain high quality medical service through restricting privileges not only for admission to the staff but for kinds of services performed, a hospital for reasons of efficiency needs to control staff membership numerically. Some hospitals have more staff members than they have beds—occasionally one is found that has twice as many. The result is dissatisfied doctors who cannot get beds and a constant turmoil for which the administrator is blamed. Yet he can do nothing more than try to persuade the board and the medical staff to correct the situation.

The Hospital Council of Greater New York was founded in 1937 after the report, *Hospital Survey for New York,* disclosed critical deficiencies in the methods and distribution of medical and hospital care. One of the chief recommendations made by the council in a report published in 1951 was:

> For the benefit of the community and of the practicing physicians, it is desirable for all doctors in active practice to have hospital connections which afford them not only the privilege of caring for their private patients, but also the educational advantages gained from working in wards and outpatient departments.

The report disclosed that in 1948 regular hospital appointments were not held by 28.6 per cent of physicians in active practice in New York City. Another study ten years later showed that the situation was even a little worse, with regular hospital appointments not being held by 29.1 per cent. Most of these physicians, the report indicated, would like to have hospital affiliations.

It is recognized in the report that limitation of privileges in a given hospital may have the effect of maintaining high quality of patient care but that from an over-all community standpoint the effect of exclusion is to lower the standards of care.

A plan for a category of "referring physicians" that has area-wide acceptance and significance was started in 1960 by Detroit Memorial Hospital, Detroit, Michigan. Under this plan special courtesy staff privileges are extended to qualified physicians who want to admit patients who require special services not available in the hospitals where they are regular staff members.

In response to the pressures, a few hospitals which previously had "closed" staffs are opening them to all qualified physicians in their communities, and intensive studies are being made of the consequences.

One of the obvious reasons why great care must be exercised in granting surgical privileges in particular is that even the best-trained and experienced surgeon not infrequently finds on operation a complication greater than he anticipated. Sometimes unexpected disease is disclosed, and what may in advance have appeared to call for only a minor procedure turns out to require major surgery. On opening an abdomen for removal of the appendix, for example, there may be found a gangrenous gallbladder, a perforated ulcer, a tumor, or other condition that had escaped attention in the preoperative examination. One surgeon when operating for what he believed to be an ovarian follicle or ruptured cyst that was bleeding excessively found a ruptured spleen. In such emergencies, which may occur at any time, quick action and the utmost skill are needed or a life is lost.

Working with the medical staff was given as the hospital administrator's major problem in interviews with 100 administrators conducted in 1948 by the Joint Commission on Education[12] which was sponsored by the American Hospital Association and the American College of Hospital Administrators. Fortunately the administrator has external agencies upon which to lean for support when principles are being questioned. Foremost among them is the Joint Commission on Accreditation of Hospitals which has drawn up a *Standard for Accreditation of Medical Staff*. The commission and its work are described in Chapter 23.

---

[12] *Problems of Hospital Administration*. Chicago, Physicians' Record Co., 1948. For description of other activities of this commission see Chapter 18.

CHAPTER 2

Organized Medicine

> It took a long time to demonstrate that the advancement of internal medicine as a science can never be accomplished by hugging some pet theory out of a regard for its author's personality, but only through the performance of a vast amount of chemical, physical, and biological research by thousands of willing workers.
>
> FIELDING H. GARRISON, M.D.[1]

IT IS customary to think of modern medicine as not beginning until just before the twentieth century with the introduction of anesthesia, antisepsis, and asepsis in surgery, laboratory diagnosis, x-ray, and so on—the dazzling atmosphere and armamentaria of the modern hospital, the exit of kitchen-table surgery and the horse-and-buggy doctor.

Leading up to these developments, and doubtless of as much importance as all of them combined, was the growth of the concept of group cooperation. In order to be effective, the groups had to be organized, whether on a small scale as in a laboratory or on a large one as in national societies. Garrison heads his chapter on the modern period, "The Nineteenth Century: the Beginnings of Organized Advancement of Science."

The individual scientist began in the 1840's to be submerged to a much greater degree than before in group activities. For the first time in history, large numbers of men made plans to work together systematically for the sake of progress. This was, of course, facilitated by the concomitant improvements in transportation and communications.

---

[1] *An Introduction to the History of Medicine,* 4th ed. Philadelphia, W. B. Saunders Company, 1929, p. 408.

LABORATORIES

Laboratories for teaching and research purposes were one of the most important early manifestations of the trend toward teamwork in medical science. For Johannes Purkinje, professor of physiology at Prague, the founder of laboratory training in connection with teaching in the German medical schools, the Prussian government erected a physiological institute at Breslau in 1824 after the work done by him and his pupils in his private laboratory attracted national attention.

Napoleon III in 1869 gave Claude Bernard, professor of physiology at the College of France, two fine laboratories, one at the Sorbonne, the other at the Museum of Natural History. Didactic teaching began to disappear with the foundation of these laboratories and Virchow's, founded in 1856 at Berlin.

In the United States also, laboratories were founded by Bowditch at Harvard in 1871, by Welch at Baltimore in 1884, and by William Pepper at Philadelphia in 1895. The Wistar Institute of Anatomy and Biology was established at Philadelphia in 1892, the Rockefeller Institute at New York in 1901, the John McCormick Institute for Infectious Diseases at Chicago in 1902, the Henry Phipps Institute for Tuberculosis at Philadelphia in 1903, the Carnegie Institute at Washington in 1903, the Rudolf Spreckels Laboratory in 1910, the Henry Phipps Psychiatric Clinic of Baltimore in 1913, the Otho S. A. Sprague Institute in 1911, and many others at later dates.

MEDICAL CONGRESSES

What appears to have been an epochal event but which must have been purely local in character was the holding of the first medical congress at Rome in 1681. It lasted from March 10, 1681, to June 8, 1682, with three to four meetings a month and a total attendance of 46 physicians.

The first international medical congress was held at Paris in 1867. Succeeding ones met at Florence in 1869, Vienna in 1873, Brussels in 1875, Genoa in 1877, Amsterdam in 1879, London in 1881, Copenhagen in 1884, Washington in 1887, Berlin in 1890, Rome in 1894, Moscow in 1897, Paris in 1900, Madrid in 1903, Lisbon in 1906, Budapest in 1909, and in other cities every few years since that time.

The calendar of international medical congresses of major importance, including those on basic sciences, is so full in the modern period that the profession has a most difficult time keeping up with the developments that are reported through this valuable device.

CLINICAL RESEARCH TEAMS

Group investigative activity within the hospital came late in the history of medicine because of the physician's strong tendency to individualism. It was an innovation when in 1842 Richard Bright (of Bright's disease fame) set aside two clinical wards at Guy's Hospital, London, for study of renal disease. Between the two wards were a consulting room and a laboratory. This, historians say, was the first cooperative investigation of disease ever undertaken in a clinical setting.

SCIENTIFIC SOCIETIES

Scientific societies were not a new development in the nineteenth century but their number and scope were greatly increased during this period. The Barbers' Company of London and the Fellowship or Guild of Surgeons which merged with it in 1540 were early societies. Porta's Secret Academy was formed at Naples in 1560, the Academy of the Lynxes at Rome in 1603, and the Academy of Experiment at Florence in 1657. One called an "Invisible College" was founded at London in 1645, combining later with an Oxford "Philosophical Society" and getting a charter from Charles II in 1662 as the Royal Society of London. Publication of its celebrated *Philosophical Transactions* began in 1664.

In other countries likewise, societies, mostly of a local character, were founded from time to time.

In 1800 the Royal College of Surgeons was established at London. The British Medical Association came into being in 1832.

In the United States the first medical society was organized in Boston in 1735, with other eastern cities following its example soon afterward. The first state society was that of New Jersey, started in 1766. The American Medical Association was organized in 1847, the American College of Surgeons in 1913, and the American College of Physicians in 1915.

National and international organizations have played so large a part in medical progress that the activities of a few of the leading ones should be familiar to every medical service administrator. Digests follow.

American Medical Association

More than 160,000 physicians who belong to some 1,900 county medical societies in the United States are members of the American Medical Association, which conducts a gigantic program of professional and public education, information, and consultation; encourages "rational therapeutics" in medical practice; evaluates drugs, foods, medical devices and equipment, and chemical products; assembles, correlates, and analyzes research data; operates a grant-in-aid program for research; inspects medical schools and hospitals which have interns and residents; approves schools for the training of allied professional personnel; wages war on quacks; participates in the work of the Joint Commission on Accreditation of Hospitals; cooperates with industry, labor, and state and federal governments in programs of medical care; helps communities to attract physicians when needed; studies ways to improve distribution of medical personnel;

promotes development and extension of voluntary health insurance; proposes legislation on health affairs when in accord with its policies and opposes legislation which it deems contrary to the best interests of the profession and the public; cooperates with other organizations on current health problems; publishes a large amount of professional and public literature; and constantly combats any project that might lead to socialized medicine.

This prodigious activity has grown slowly and intermittently through the years.

Largely through the efforts of Dr. Nathan Smith Davis, then a New Yorker, later a Chicagoan, the association was organized in 1847. The British Medical Association had been founded only fifteen years earlier.

The influence of the American Medical Association was relatively minor until its reorganization in 1901. Originally its membership was confined to specially elected delegates. Since 1901 membership has been based upon membership in the county societies.

Early interest of the association in hospitals was evidenced by publication of a survey made by Dr. J. M. Toner in 1873—the first in the United States. The survey showed 178 hospitals with a total of 34,453 beds; 146,472 patients were treated in hospitals that year, one out of every 263 people (1870 census, 38,558,-000). One-third of the beds were for the insane. Dr. Toner conducted the survey under the auspices of the United States Office of Education.

A second attempt to list hospitals was made in 1903 when the *Standard Medical Directory* was published by G. P. Engelhard and Company. A year later the American Medical Association took over the directory files and in 1906 brought out the *American Medical Directory,* in which were listed 2,411 hospitals. By 1924, when the third presentation of hospital data was published, the number of hospitals had increased to 6,830, total bed capacity was 755,722, and the daily average number of patients was 533,133.

In 1904 the association formed a Council on Medical Education, the name of which was changed in 1920 to the Council on Medical Education and Hospitals. Work of this council in connection with medical and hospital schools is described in later chapters.

Hospital internship began to be required for the M.D. degree or for licensure in 1914, when Pennsylvania became the first state to require it; a year later the University of Minnesota became the first medical school to require it for the degree. Before that time, however, internships were elected by 70 per cent of graduates.

Improved standards being obviously necessary, the council began surveys of training programs in hospitals and in 1914 published the first list of approved internship hospitals, totaling 603. Since 1928 a staff of hospital inspectors has been maintained whose function is to improve the educational standards in hospitals.

After considerable preliminary study, the council began in 1927 the listing of hospitals approved for residencies in the various medical specialties. The first list included 270 hospitals. Currently more than 1,200 hospitals are approved for the training of residents. The council was authorized in 1933 to "express its approval of such special examining boards as conform to the standards of administration formulated by the Council" and about the same time the Advisory Board for Medical Specialties was organized with representation from each of the approved boards, to "act in an advisory capacity to such organizations as may seek its advice concerning the coordination of the education and certification of medical specialists." The purposes of the boards are stated as follows:

> An American Board in a specialty is organized to assist in improving the quality of graduate education in that field, to establish minimum educational and training standards in the specialty, to determine whether candidates have received adequate preparation as defined by the Board, to provide comprehensive examinations to determine the ability and fitness of such candidates, and to certify to the competence of those physicians who have satisfied the requirements of the Board, as a protection to the public and the profession.

In Chapter 3 will be found further discussion of the specialty boards and of the educational activities of the Association.

As its activities began to extend into the hospital field, the council recognized a need to participate in the improvement of hospitals and to collect and publish data about them beyond the listing for internships and residencies. The *American Medical Directory* was therefore started, as previously mentioned, in 1906. Beginning in 1928 the council maintained a hospital register in which names of hospitals and statistical information about them were published. This was discontinued after the American Hospital Association started in 1945 to publish "The American Hosptial Directory," now called the "Guide Issue" of *Hospitals,* Part 2 of the August issue.

The association had no headquarters, and its chief publications were the annual transactions, until 1883 when Dr. Nathan Smith Davis, who had been so active in its founding, led an organization movement and became the first editor of the *Journal.* The editorial offices were moved several times as expansion became necessary. The original building of the present headquarters at 535 North Dearborn Street, Chicago, was erected in 1903.

The membership plan should be understood by administrators. A physician who becomes a member of a local county or district medical society automatically becomes a member of the constituent state medical association of which the local society is a component unit; he becomes a member of the American Medical Association when officially reported by his constituent association. State medical associations have councilor districts, composed of county medical societies. These districts elect councilors for the state medical society. The county societies elect delegates to the houses of delegates of the state societies. The state societies elect delegates to the House of Delegates of the A. M. A. The House of Delegates meets annually at the time of the convention and may also be called in special session.

Responsible to the House of Delegates are the Board of Trustees and three councils: judicial, scientific assembly, and medical education and hospitals. Responsible through the Board of Trustees are the *Journal;* the special journals; the library; the committee on scientific exhibit; the chemical laboratory; the committee on rehabilitation; the bureaus of investigation; health education, legal medicine and legislation, and medical economics; the councils on medical service, medical education and hospitals, pharmacy and chemistry, medical physics, physical medicine, foods, mental health, industrial health, and the department of nursing, etc.[2]

For some 16 years the association has been disseminating information on new medical motion pictures. The one-thousandth film review appeared in the *Journal* in late 1961. A film library of more than 1,200 prints of nearly 300 different subjects is maintained. More than 10,000 showings were booked through the film library in 1961. The British Medical Association reprints the reviews in its publication *Medical and Biological Illustration.*

Among the many publications of the American Medical Association is a monthly health magazine, established in 1923, to give reliable information about health and its protection to the public. This was first called *Hygeia* and is now known as *Today's Health.*

American College of Physicians

The American College of Physicians was chartered in 1915 "to maintain and advance high standards in medical education, medical practice and clinical research; to perpetuate the history and best traditions of medicine and medical ethics; and to maintain both the dignity and the efficiency of internal medicine in its relationship to the public welfare."

The college is one of the four organizational members of the Joint Commission on Accreditation of Hospitals.

One of the recent major activities of the college has been a study of standards of practice of internal medicine and methods of assessing the quality of practice in hospitals. The third and fourth years of the study were conducted with the aid of a grant from the Department of Health, Education, and Welfare. A "Medical Care Appraisal Plan" which was developed as a result of the study is being tried out in selected hospitals. In essence the plan provides that (1) self-evaluation be done by staff physicians who practice general medicine; (2) quality of medical care be judged, not the quality of record-keeping; and (3) anonymity of the patient, attending physician, and appraiser be preserved.

In an editorial[3] about the study the following statement was made:

It is the consensus of opinion among informed students of the subject that reliable and valid methods of measuring the quality of medical care objectively

[2] See *AMA, Voice of American Medicine,* by James G. Burrow, for "The eventful and turbulent history of the American Medical Association, its attitudes, policies, and politics." Baltimore, The Johns Hopkins Press, 1963.
[3] *Ann. Int. Med.,* October, 1959 (preprint).

do not exist. There is doubt that they can be devised for use even within a given specialty. It is obviously most difficult to quantitate quality. On the other hand, there is good reason to believe that virtually all effort to appraise quality leads automatically to improvement in medical care even though the validity of the methods used is not established.

National Medical Association

The National Medical Association, with headquarters in Washington, D.C., was organized by Negro physicians in 1895. It publishes a monthly journal.

The first medical degree conferred upon a Negro in the United States was given by Rush Medical College in 1847 to David J. Peck. There are now some 5,000 Negro physicians in the country.

Provident Hospital, Chicago, was founded by a Negro surgeon, Dr. Daniel Hale Williams. The first blood bank for the American Red Cross was established by a Howard University professor of surgery, Dr. Charles Richard Drew.

Today's Negro medical graduate has no trouble getting appointed to an internship because of the shortage of applicants. In other respects he suffers from discrimination, but not more so than the woman physician. The situation is one which shortages will help to remedy.

The first Imhotep National Conference on Hospital Integration was held in Washington, D.C., in 1957. It was sponsored by the National Medical Association, the Medico-Chirurgical Society of the District of Columbia, and the National Association for the Advancement of Colored People. The National Urban League has participated in later meetings.

There are two predominantly Negro medical schools, Howard and Meharry.

American Osteopathic Association

The rigid bars between osteopaths and doctors of medicine are being broken down here and there, the most conspicuous example being the plan approved in the spring of 1961 and put into effect in July, 1962, by the California Medical Association and the California Osteopathic Association, whereby the osteopaths gave up their association and were eligible to join the medical organization, and the College of Osteopathic Physicians and Surgeons at Los Angeles became the California College of Medicine.

The largest single doctorate class in medical history—nearly 2,000—resulted from the granting of M.D. degrees by this college in June, 1962, to practicing osteopaths who had met the academic requirements.

The state medical association has nearly 18,000 members, the osteopathic association had around 2,200.

The American Medical Association during its June, 1961, convention adopted a recommendation which established the new era in relationships. The gist of the recommendation was that a

... policy should now be applied individually at state level according to the facts as they exist ... the test now should be: does the individual doctor of osteopathy practice osteopathy, or does he in fact practice a method of healing founded on a scientific basis? If he practices osteopathy he practices a cult system of healing and all voluntary associations with him are unethical. If he bases his practice on the same scientific principles as those adhered to by members of the American Medical Association, voluntary professional relationship with him should not be deemed unethical.

The American Osteopathic Association violently opposed the American Medical Association recommendation, calling it an attempt to "create a medical monopoly." It also attacked the action in California, arguing that it was aimed to "absorb, amalgamate or destroy" the organization. Announcement was made of a campaign to combat attempts by organized medicine to absorb members of the American Osteopathic Association.

Osteopathy was founded by Andrew Taylor Still in 1874 on the theory that the human body is self-healing and its adequate functioning depends on its unimpaired structure and an uninterrupted nerve and blood supply to tissues. Besides the school in Los Angeles, there are schools in Des Moines, Iowa; Kansas City, Missouri; Philadelphia, Pennsylvania; and Kirksville, Missouri, the last-named being the original school. There are some 13,500 doctors of osteopathy, constituting about 8 per cent of doctors in the United States; around 10,000 of them are licensed to practice the healing art without limitation. In some states they are given unrestricted licenses to practice; in others they are not licensed or are restricted. There are around 400 osteopathic hospitals located in 22 states with bed capacity total estimated at 12,000.

All references to Andrew Taylor Still, the founder of osteopathy, were eliminated from its constitution by the American Osteopathic Association in July, 1958. However, there was still insistence that there was room for two distinct branches of medicine, and the association continued teaching that a physician can manipulate his patient out of any disease.

It is generally conceded that education in osteopathic schools has been greatly improved in late years.

American College of Surgeons

The American College of Surgeons was organized in 1913. Two medical events led to its founding. In 1905 Dr. Franklin H. Martin of Chicago established a journal, *Surgery, Gynecology and Obstetrics,* for the exchange of practical surgical information. Among the sponsors were Drs. Nicholas Senn who headed the editorial board, George Crile, John B. Murphy, and W. J. and C. H. Mayo. Eligibility for the editorial board and the editorial staff was limited to actual practitioners of surgery. Dr. Murphy was one of the chief financial backers. Dr. Martin was the managing editor and Dr. Allen B. Kanavel the associate editor. The journal flourishes today, with an international circulation, under the editorship of Dr. Loyal Davis.

Five years after starting the journal Dr. Martin conceived the idea of inviting the subscribers to a series of surgical clinics in Chicago. His purpose was to extend to all progressive specialists the advantages of firsthand observation of the work of good surgeons which was being enjoyed by a select group belonging to the Society of Clinical Surgery which had been founded in 1903. Thirteen hundred surgeons registered on the opening day of the new clinics, held from November 7 to 19, 1910. Operative clinics extended from 8:00 A.M. to 5:00 P.M. each day during the two weeks.

"Let us perpetuate these clinics," urged the surgeons. Accordingly there was organized on the next to the last day the Clinical Congress of Surgeons of North America with Dr. Albert J. Ochsner of Chicago as president. Fifteen hundred surgeons enrolled at the second congress at Philadelphia, November 7 to 16, 1911, and around 3,000 at the third congress at New York, November 11 to 26, 1912, with headquarters at the old Waldorf-Astoria Hotel.

It becoming apparent that general regulations and control of clinicians and of attendance were needed, Dr. Martin developed a plan for a new organization which would have qualifications for membership. It involved the following elements as outlined by him in the chapter on the American College of Surgeons in his autobiography:[4]

1. A standard of professional, ethical, and moral requirements for every authorized graduate in medicine who practices general surgery or any of its specialties, insofar as feasible along the lines of the Royal Colleges of Surgeons of England, Ireland, and Scotland

2. A supplementary degree for operating surgeons.

3. Special letters to indicate fellowship in the college

4. A published list of members of the college

5. The appointment of a committee of twelve members of the clinical congress with full power to proceed with the plan, if careful consideration proved its worth.

The story of the battle against opposition to the proposed college is a dramatic one. The plan was approved at the 1912 congress in New York. After preliminary consultation by Dr. Martin with Dr. Murphy and with Dr. Edward Martin of Philadelphia who was the second president of the Clinical Congress of Surgeons of North America, the American College of Surgeons was born. Its Illinois charter is dated November 25, 1912. Its bylaws were accepted at a meeting in Washington, D.C., on May 5, 1913; and Dr. John M. T. Finney of Baltimore was elected the first president. Prior to this meeting Dr. Martin had personally visited and invited to the conference the leading surgeons of the chief cities of the United States and Canada.

[4] *The Joy of Living.* Garden City, New York, Doubleday & Co., 1933, vol. 1, p. 410.

The Clinical Congress of Surgeons of North America continued as an independent organization until 1917, when it was absorbed by the college. Of historic interest is the fact that the 1914 congress was held at London in July and 1,100 American doctors were stranded there by the declaration of war.

It is significant that the surgeons, even before organizing the college, had recognized that many hospitals had many deficiencies. How could good surgical clinics be held in poorly organized, equipped, and operated hospitals? Furthermore, they jumped immediately from the selfish motive of wanting better hospitals so that they could have good clinics to that of wanting better hospitals so that the surgical patient would have a greater chance of recovery.

Dr. Allen B. Kanavel made the following proposal to the November, 1912, clinical congress:

> Some system of standardization of hospital equipment and hospital work should be developed, to the end that those institutions having the highest ideals may have proper recognition before the profession and that those of inferior equipment and standards should be stimulated to raise the quality of their work.

Dr. Ernest Amory Codman, of Boston, headed the committee which was then appointed to carry out the spirit of this resolution. Dr. Codman had already propounded the need for standardization of hospitals. He made progress reports to the clinical congress in 1913 and in 1915.

The plan for the hospital standardization program of the American College of Surgeons was adopted at its 1913 business meeting on motion of Dr. E. Payne Palmer, of Arizona.

The war into which the United States was plunged in 1914 delayed the hospital standardization program as an organized effort. It strongly emphasized the need for it, however. This view is expressed in an article in the 1917–1918 *Year Book* of the college:

> With some impatience the Fellows of the College looked forward to an active campaign throughout the continent for the betterment of hospitals. Then came the war and its quick effect to vitalize a high ideal of service not only in the profession and among hospitals, but throughout every phase of our national life. In the fluid state of mind thus created, soldiers, sailors, and the general public realized with new force that they are entitled to the best in medical science; and the profession in turn by this awakening was struck with a keener sense of the debt which the practice of medicine demands. Almost in a single morning all shadows of doubt as to whether a continent-wide standardization of hospitals could be entered into with continent-wide good will were cleared away.

Because hospital standardization proved to be so vital a force in the improvement of hospital care, its story is deferred to Chapter 23. Suffice it to say here that when on October 14, 1957, President Dwight D. Eisenhower's personal greeting to the clinical congress in Atlantic City was read it contained a statement that the college had reason to be especially proud "of its standardization program for American hospitals, inaugurated early in the College's history, maintained for many years by the College's efforts alone, but now recognized everywhere as a massive contribution toward improving the care of America's sick."[5]

Among other activities of the college of great importance to medical progress is the protection afforded the public through its primary function of screening applicants for fellowship with the object of assuring that "F.A.C.S." after a surgeon's name means, in the eyes of the profession and of the informed public, competence and high ethical standing.

Another vital activity is the effort to improve the care of cancer patients, partly through an approval program for cancer clinics. This work is described in Chapter 7.

The study of medical motion pictures for the profession and the laity was undertaken by the college in 1926. Specific fundamental requirements concerned with selection of the subject matter, preparation of the scenario, ethics, illustration by animation or drawings, photography, and teaching value were developed by the college for use in evaluating films. Films are reviewed by committees of recognized authorities on the subject matter portrayed. They are approved if they meet the standards from the standpoint of professional technique, general teaching value, and photographic quality. The author of the film is then authorized to insert a legend showing such approval. A list of approved films is published in the annual "approval number" of the college's *Bulletin*.

A special committee of the college is concerned with problems related to nutrition of the surgical patient. Another committee has an ambitious and effective program for improving the care of the injured, aimed at educating not only the practicing physician, intern, resident, and medical student, but also the public. This activity is described in Chapter 7.

The educational function has been dominant in the efforts of the college to elevate the standard of surgery. It has been furthered through all of its activities, beginning with the establishment of qualifications for fellowship, which must be high but must also be attainable so that they may be enforced. Helping the prospective fellow to gain the requisite training has always been a concern of the college. Beginning in 1930, special committees were appointed to study the problems. In 1937 the Committee on Graduate Training in Surgery was appointed to investigate, analyze, and evaluate opportunities for the training of surgeons in hospitals of the United States and Canada.

Personal surveys of selected hospitals were begun by a field staff in 1937, in connection with the work of hospital standardization. As one of the results of these surveys, information was gathered for the development of fundamental requirements upon which acceptable plans of training should be based. The "Fundamental Requirements for Graduate Training in Surgery" are published in the annual "approval number" of the college's *Bulletin*.

[5] *Bull. Am. Coll. Surgeons*, 43: 5, 1958.

In 1950 the college collaborated in the establishment of the Conference Committee on Graduate Training in Surgery. This committee is composed of representatives of the American Medical Association, American Board of Surgery, and the college. Its first action was to adopt standards for approved residencies in general surgery acceptable to all three organizations. Similar conference committees were later established in the surgical specialties.

Further reference to graduate and postgraduate training in surgery is made in Chapter 8.

The splitting of fees between surgeons and the referring physicians was attacked at the first formal conference of the regents which was held on June 7, 1913, in Minneapolis. The discussion led to the adoption of an oath against fee-splitting which every candidate for fellowship would be required to take. With some slight revisions this is still a part of the induction into fellowship. Continuously through the years the college has fought fee-splitting as "traffic in patients," and not infrequently a member is dropped when it has been proved that he indulges in this practice.

Besides its monthly scientific journal, *Surgery, Gynecology and Obstetrics,* the college publishes a bimonthly *Bulletin,* a directory of fellows, a catalogue of films in its motion picture library, and, from time to time, various manuals.

Other educational activities are the holding of an annual clinical congress, several sectional meetings yearly, one or more of which is outside the United States, and meetings of local chapters.

Particularly noteworthy as a promotion device for research is the Forum on Fundamental Surgical Problems which is held in connection with the clinical congress, with publication afterward of the research reports.

A rather new activity in which the college is engaged with the American College of Physicians, the American Hospital Association, and the Southwestern Michigan Hospital Council is a project for the collection and processing of objective data from patients' records under the direction of the Commission on Professional and Hospital Activities, Inc. As a separate activity the commission in collaboration with the college conducts a medical audit program. The work of the commission is described in Chapter 8.

International Federation of Surgical Colleges and Societies

The International Federation of Surgical Colleges and Societies was founded in 1958 to improve world standards of surgery. It is composed of some 30 surgical organizations located in 27 countries on the six continents, and is recognized as the nongovernmental affiliate in surgery of the World Health Organization. The federation conducts a program for facilitating the interchange of surgeons between countries.

The American College of Surgeons is the United States member of the federation.

American Psychiatric Association

The oldest national medical association in the United States is the American Psychiatric Association. It was founded in 1844, three years before the American Medical Association. It has a long, crowded history of effort to improve the care of the patient who is mentally ill and to prevent mental illness.

In 1962 the association endorsed and urged the implementation of the basic recommendations in the final report of the Joint Commission on Mental Illness and Health. The report, *Action for Mental Health*, 100,000 words in length, was made to Congress, the governors, and the legislatures of the United States, and was published by Basic Books, Inc., New York, in 1961. Its instigation came from the 1953-1954 president of the American Psychiatric Association, Dr. Kenneth E. Appel, who with others in the association succeeded in getting Congress to establish in 1955 the Joint Commission on Mental Illness and Health. The association with the Council on Mental Health of the American Medical Association took the leadership in the study, with the participation of 36 other professional and lay organizations.

A national overhauling of training, research, and treatment services for the mentally ill, based on increases in federal, state, and local expenditures, is recommended in the report, a 1,000 word digest of which was published in the March, 1961, issue of *The Modern Hospital*.

Cuban Medical Association in Exile

The Cuban Medical Association in Exile deserves mention because of its peculiar nature and its significance to administrators of medical service institutions in the nations of the western hemisphere. The association was formed in January, 1962, and the American Medical Association contributed $1,000 per month for six months to underwrite expenses of establishing a headquarters office at Coral Gables, Florida.

In a letter to hospital administrators in January, 1962, Dr. Edwin L. Crosby, director of the American Hospital Association, stated in part:

> Recognizing the plight of these exiles, we encourage employment of these Cuban physicians wherever legitimately possible and practical. However, hospitals cannot afford to jeopardize their standards of medical and patient care by employment of unqualified Cuban physicians in exile in positions where direct patient care responsibility must be exercised. The standards and requirements of the Educational Council for Foreign Medical Graduates, listing by the American Hospital Association, accreditation by the Joint Commission on Accreditation of Hospitals, and approval for internships and residencies by the American Medical Association should not and have not been waived for these exiles. The hospitals of the United States must continue to guard assiduously the standards of care provided to the patients they serve. To lower them could result in loss of various approvals and could create unfortunate medico-legal problems for hospitals in which unqualified physicians are giving patient care.

How then may hospitals assist in helping to meet the economic and professional needs and desires of these physicians? If the Cuban physician has been qualified under ECFMG, or has a valid license to practice from one of the states, he can be given patient care responsibilities. Those Cuban physicians who do not qualify for patient care may be employed in several ways, i.e., in technical positions in laboratories, x-ray, pharmacy, medical records, etc. It is also possible for them to serve as interpreters, providing their command of English permits accurate communication with members of the medical staff, nursing and other hospital personnel.

In conclusion the letter urged that the hospitals extend assistance "in every way practical and possible" in view of the fact that the Cuban physicians in exile deserve every aid that can properly be offered to them.

The Royal College of Surgeons of England

In 1540 the Barbers' Company of London and the Fellowship or Guild of Surgeons merged, after long years of rivalry. A charter under which an examining board was set up for surgeons was granted by Charles I in 1629. If approved by the examiners, a surgeon could practice anywhere in England. The surgeons again separated from the barbers in 1745, and in 1800 reincorporated under the name of the Royal College of Surgeons in London. The name was changed in 1843 to the Royal College of Surgeons of England and a class of members called "fellows" was instituted. In 1875 a joint examining board with the Royal College of Physicians of London was established.

Besides the qualifying examination function, activities of the college include arranging memorial orations, lectures, and demonstrations; awarding medals, prizes, and scholarships; administering of trusts and bequests for the purposes designated; maintaining the Hunterian and other collections; conducting a library which was formed in 1805; and operating research laboratories.

Extensive damage to the college buildings was suffered through bombing and subsequent fires on May 10 and 11, 1941. A rehabilitation fund to which the American College of Surgeons contributed enabled restoration of the properties after the end of the war.

The history of the college is well presented in a recent book written by a surgeon in his fiftieth year of fellowship, Sir Zachary Cope.[6] Biographical notes on the great surgeons of England are included in its text.

Royal College of Surgeons of Edinburgh

The Royal College of Surgeons of Edinburgh received its charter from George III in 1778, although its beginnings are traced back to the year 1505 when the town council granted a petition of the surgeons and barbers to incorporate

---

[6] Zachary Cope: *The History of the Royal College of Surgeons of England.* Springfield, Ill., Charles C Thomas, 1959.

for the purpose of teaching. The college has always had a close connection with the faculty of medicine of Edinburgh University.

In 1695 the surgeons were authorized to conduct examinations of all who practiced anatomy, surgery, and pharmacy in the surrounding counties.

The college early in the nineteenth century was unsuccessful in persuading the university to separate the teaching of surgery from anatomy by establishing a distinct chair, so in 1804 it established a post of professor of surgery in the college, an arrangement which continued for 27 years. Among the professors were John Thomson, John William Turner, and Lord Lister. Thomson became the first to occupy the chair of surgery in the university when it was finally established in 1831.

The college is now a national institution. It has a large library and museum. Clinical and scientific conferences are held, and a program of postgraduate instruction is conducted.

Royal College of Physicians and Surgeons of Canada

The Royal College of Physicians and Surgeons of Canada (Le College Royal des Medecins et Chirurgiens du Canada) was founded in 1929. Its stated purpose is:

> Because of the growth and development of the Science and Art of Medicine and its division into various specialties, it is considered necessary and advisable that a practising physician essaying to do "special work" should have the opportunity of obtaining a distinguishing designation . . . whereby it may be known that he is properly qualified.

The letters F.R.C.P.(C) and F.R.C.S.(C) following a doctor's name provide this "distinguishing designation."

Applicants are examined both for admission to the fellowship and for certification. Fellowship examinations are in medicine and general surgery, with modifications for certain specialties; those for certification are in the approved specialties.

The certifying function was assumed by the college in 1939 at the invitation of the Canadian Medical Association. Certification is not a degree, and it does not admit the holder to fellowship.

The regulations and requirements relating to surgery and its specialties state:

> The standards required for admission to Fellowship are higher than those for Certification. Candidates for Certification examinations must demonstrate a knowledge of general medical and/or surgical principles and of basic science necessary to the proper understanding and practice of their specialty, as well as a full technical knowledge of the specialty. Candidates for the Fellowship examinations are required to display equal or greater clinical proficiency, and to have a keener appreciation and a broader understanding of basic science and fundamental principles of medicine and/or surgery. . . . In addition to meeting the requirements as to training, a candidate must, before admission to any examina-

tion conducted by the College, provide evidence . . . of satisfactory moral and ethical standing. . . .

The college has headquarters at 150 Metcalfe Street, Ottawa 4, Ontario.

The proposal to form the college was first presented as a resolution at a meeting of the Canadian Medical Association at Vancouver in 1920, as follows:

Whereas Canada has now assumed the status of nationhood within the British Empire, and Whereas the events co-incident with the Great War have brought about a closer union and deeper appreciation between the Medical men of the Old Country and those of Canada and Whereas it is desirable that the best means of stimulating and promoting advanced study of, and Post Graduate work in Medicine and Surgery, be adopted, to the end that as large a number as possible of the Medical men of Canada should engage in such advanced studies.

Be it Resolved that it is now the opportune time to promote a closer alliance between those great institutions which are furthering and teaching the study of Surgery and Medicine in the Old Country with those furthering and teaching it in Canada. In furtherance of this idea It Is Resolved that a special Committee be appointed at this meeting in Vancouver, to consider the problem of founding a Canadian Royal College of Surgeons and Physicians in some way affiliated with those of British origin.

Nine years later the proposed college became a reality. Seventy-two doctors, (the nucleus of 554 now regarded as charter fellows) met in Ottawa to complete its organization. The first president was Dr. Jonathan Meakins of Montreal.

The World Medical Association

Organized in 1947 to promote closer liaison between the physicians of all countries, the World Medical Association at the end of its first 15 years of life had as members more than fifty national medical associations whose combined memberships were close to a million physicians. The United States is represented by the American Medical Association. Each member association sends two delegates and may send in addition two alternate delegates and as many observers as it may wish to the annual general assembly. Observers may also be sent by international and national organizations which do not belong, official membership being open only to the medical organization in each country which best represents its medical profession as a whole. The headquarters is in New York City where the secretary-general is located, with regional secretaries in Australasia, Asia, Latin America, and Europe and a full-time liaison officer in Geneva.

The aims of the association are stated as follows:

To bring the physicians of the world in closer liaison
To serve as a forum for discussion of international medical problems
To distribute information
To protect the interests of the medical profession
To raise the standards of medical care, medical education, and health throughout the world

To speak for the practising medical profession before other international bodies
To promote better international relations

The World Medical Association differs from the World Health Organization, with which it is frequently confused, in that it is nongovernmental, is an instrument of the medical profession through its national associations, and is supported by dues and contributions. The World Health Organization, which will be discussed in Chapter 15, represents governments in the field of health and medicine and is supported mainly by government funds.

The United States Committee of the World Medical Association, membership on which is open to individuals and corporations, supports the *World Medical Journal* and the secretariat.

International College of Surgeons

The International College of Surgeons was founded in Geneva, Switzerland, in 1935, by Dr. Max Thorek. It has organized sections in some 45 countries. Each of the sections holds a national assembly each year and international congresses are held biennially. A number of the sections also hold regional meetings and conduct postgraduate courses.

In a building adjoining the Chicago headquarters of the college is housed the International Surgeons' Hall of Fame and School of the History of Surgery and Related Sciences.

The *Journal of the International College of Surgeons* was founded by Dr. Andre Crotti and is edited by Dr. Philip Thorek. The college also publishes a monthly *Bulletin*.

Joint Commission on Accreditation of Hospitals

The hospital standardization program of the American College of Surgeons was taken over in 1952 by the Joint Commission on Accreditation of Hospitals.

Although the sponsorship of this organization is predominantly medical, description of its activities is deferred to Chapter 23 in view of its work with and influence upon hospitals.

CHAPTER 3

Specialization and Group Practice

Specialization is inevitable and necessary in the complexity
of today's existence. The danger is not in the fact that men are
learning more about less and less. That is to be expected.
The real danger lies in the specialist himself and the loss to
the society which developed him if he crawls into the shell of
his primary interest and, like the hibernating bear,
withdraws completely from the reality of the outside world
unless his dream state is encroached upon from without. It is
my greatest criticism of the specialist today, and particularly
the medical specialist, that he becomes so engrossed in the
little world he builds around him that he forgets that his own
orbit is but a tiny one in a swirling galaxy.

J. ROSCOE MILLER, M.D.[1]

BESIDES THE disadvantages from civic and social standpoints that
specialization in medicine brings, it produces conflict within the profession itself.
Overlapping of specialties is an obvious reason for some of the strife that goes
on in hospitals. It is a problem for which there is not now and doubtless never
will be an easy solution. Each time it arises it has to be approached on an individual plane. Shall the otorhinolaryngologist or the plastic surgeon undertake
reconstruction of a patient's nose? Shall the thoracic surgeon or the otorhinolaryngologist do bronchoscopy? Shall the oral surgeon or the tumor specialist
operate on a tumor of the jaw? Making decisions in such disputes would tax
the wisdom of a Solomon. It is no wonder that medical staff committees and
boards of trustees sometimes flounder in this kind of crisis, leaving hurt feelings
that take a long time to heal.

---

[1] President of Northwestern University. From an address, The Doctor as Citizen, presented at the
Convocation, American College of Surgeons, San Francisco, November 9, 1951.

So staggering are the medical specialty problems caused by traffic accidents, for example, that a new medical specialty to deal with them, "medicotrafficology," has been rather facetiously suggested by one general practitioner. In an article in the October 27, 1956, *Journal of the American Medical Association* entitled "The Automobile—A Challenge to Medicine," essentials of a number of specialties are mentioned as included in this area, such as preventive medicine, psychiatry, epidemiology, neurosurgery, ophthalmology, toxicology, orthopedics, and industrial health. The chairman of the association's Committee on Medical Aspects of Automobile Injuries and Deaths is quoted as saying:

> When one car in twelve is involved in a serious crash each year, when speed is a factor in one-third of our fatal accidents, when the drinking driver is in one-fourth of our fatal accidents, when the automobile death rate as figured in man-years of life lost ranks next to our main killers of cardiovascular disease and cancer, it is time indeed to answer Cain's query and say: "Yes, I am my brother's keeper."

Speaking on the same subject, treating accident victims, Dr. Preston A. Wade,[2] professor of clinical surgery, Cornell University Medical College, put the specialization problems in these words:

> The general surgeon has resisted the efforts of the orthopedic surgeon to enter general surgical fields, and the orthopedic surgeon's claim to fractures is still resisted. The inclusion of hand surgery in orthopedic training is often resisted by the plastic surgeon as well as the general surgeon. The neurosurgeon feels that the orthopedist should not attempt to repair nerves or operate upon intervertebral discs. The vascular surgeon believes the orthopedist to be out of his field if he performs vascular grafts when treating other injuries to a limb. What a troubled state for the poor patient with many injuries!

Dr. Wade proposes the establishment of specialized accident hospitals, in which experienced surgeons can treat every kind of trauma, saying that such hospitals have been operating successfully in Austria and Hungary for many years and are now in operation in some communities in England, and that a few communities in the United States have set up regional medical trauma centers. He admits, however, that there is a problem in training the surgeons to staff such a facility, since over and above the customary training of the general surgeon would be needed training in the treatment of bones and joints and enlargement of his horizon in neurosurgery. He suggests that it might be a good idea to establish a certification in trauma as an additional qualification in every surgical specialty as well as in general surgery.

Multiple injuries are the most glaring of the conditions in which fragmentation in medical practice is a critical problem, but there are others, a few of them with almost as many emergency characteristics, in which a superior sort of medical coordinator would be a boon to mankind. He is an impossibility. The field is too vast. Consultation and improved teamwork are the only answers.

[2] From the 29th Oration on Trauma, The Injured Patient and The Specialist, presented at the Clinical Congress of the American College of Surgeons, October 4, 1961, published in the March–April, 1962, *Bull. Am. Coll. Surgeons,* pp. 79–82, 94.

Of course, specialization is not new. Speaking on "The Rise of Specialism in Modern Society" at the 55th Annual Congress on Medical Education and Licensure of the American Medical Association in 1959, Paul M. Gross,[3] of Durham, North Carolina, remarked:

Faced with the bewildering complexity of our own social structure, its profusion of implements, machines, instruments, devices, gadgets, and specialisms, we are prone to think the latter are characteristic of our time. Anyone who has visited the Museum of Egyptian Antiquities in Cairo and seen the high state of development of household and fine arts in such exhibits as those of the Tutankhamen tomb (1350 B.C.) must realize this civilization had its full quota of specialists of all kinds. These must have included not only highly developed specialties among artisans and craftsmen but a professional type of specialization in architecture and engineering. All evidence points to a similar high degree of development of specialism in the household arts, agriculture, and the fine arts. Thus, one must speak with caution of the "rise" of specialism in our times. It has been a continuing component of civilization, at least in historic times. . . . The highly organized civilization of the Roman Empire must have required a great degree of specialism among its citizenry to sustain its roads, aqueducts, commerce and food supply, logistics of the support of its armies, and the government of its far-flung colonies and provinces—not to speak of the high state of development of the fine arts and literature of its age. . . .

DEVELOPMENT OF MEDICAL SPECIALIZATION

The following discussion of the general aspects of medical specialization is adapted in some degree from an independent study project submitted by the late Edward M. Leveroos, M.D., while a student in Northwestern University's Program in Hospital Administration and a member of the staff of the Council on Medical Education and Hospitals of the American Medical Association.

The emphasis on prolonged and specialized training occupies the forefront in considering the preparation of the medical student for his career as a practicing physician. His four years in medical school and one or two years' internship no longer are considered adequate for the embryo doctor to take his place alongside his professional colleagues, many of whom, while highly successful, have had considerably less formal training. Equipped as he is with his diploma from a Class A medical school, a certificate from the Basic Science Board, and a license to practice from the state, nonetheless, in the eyes of his profession, and, increasingly, in the eyes of the public, this man is competent to treat only routine cases and take care of such minor surgery as may be carried out in his office.

Specialism in medicine, while becoming of increasing importance in the past 25 years, is hardly to be considered a new idea in medicine. In ancient times among the disciples of Aesculapius there were physicians who confined their practice to a definite category of disease. Special medical societies and special

[3] *From* Selected Papers from the Annual Congress on Medical Education and Licensure on Specialism in Medicine, held February 8–9, 1959, in Chicago. *J.A.M.A.,* May 16, 1959, pp. 285–86.

hospitals were established in accordance with the existing level of medical knowledge. The Royal Ophthalmic Hospital was founded in London in 1804, the
Royal Hospital for Diseases of the Chest ten years later. In New York City
in 1925 a hospital for the care and treatment of fever cases only was established,
and the Lying-in Hospital in Boston was founded a short while after. As early
as 1866, less than twenty years after its founding, the American Medical Association took cognizance of specialization and a considerable portion of the annual
reports was given over to its discussion.

During the ensuing years, specialists arose in various fields of medicine; some
of them were well qualified for their special practice; many were not. Training
and experience in the specialties were acquired in various ways. The usual
method was that of prolonged assistantships under the tutelage of some already
recognized specialist, working up through dispensary services and assistant
hospital ward appointments to direct associateships, with gradually increasing
responsibilities, opportunities, and clinical privileges. Internships and residencies
in the various specialties were relatively uncommon, and the opportunities for
what is now considered intensive training through the special residency system
were distinctly limited in number.

Short refresher courses or visits to clinics in the larger centers in the United
States and overseas were considered desirable in rounding out special training.
Longer courses, and even hospital services, were obtainable chiefly on the European continent. Several postgraduate schools were established in the United
States in an effort to supply partially the demand for graduate medical education.
The entire situation was chaotic. There were no standards or formal appraisal
of qualifications to gauge or establish a doctor's right to call himself a specialist
in any branch of medicine. Both the lay and medical public had little else by
which to judge capability than an individual's self-appraisal and his own announcement that he was a specialist.

In 1913 the American Ophthalmological Society, the Section on Ophthalmology of the American Medical Association, and the American Academy of
Ophthalmology and Otolaryngology appointed committees to consider standards.
The committees reported in 1914 to their different societies, recommending that
medical schools of the first class establish graduate courses in ophthalmology,
that these courses represent not less than two years of systematic work subsequent
to taking the degree of M.D., and that such courses lead to an appropriate degree.
This plan, however, did not solve the problem of differentiating between the
competent and incompetent already engaged in the practice of ophthalmology.
(It is worthy of note that this earliest attempt at specialty regulation was based
on educational considerations; the educational aspect was the primary principle
in the creation of later boards.)

The committees were continued and in 1915 made further recommendations
as a result of which a joint board was created consisting of three representatives
from each of the three special societies. After considerable preliminary work,

this was finally organized as the American Board for Ophthalmic Examinations, later to become the American Board of Ophthalmology. It consisted of nine members, three from each of the national societies, chosen in the same manner as their presiding officers are chosen. One is elected each year by each society to serve for three years, and no member can serve for more than six years continuously. Thus was the first specialty board organized, and it set the pattern for those which followed. This board, composed of outstanding and recognized ophthalmologists, undertook to formulate certain minimum training requirements and then to examine and certify as specialists those who applied voluntarily to the board for such recognition. The American Board of Otolaryngology was created along similar lines with identical objectives in 1924; it was followed in 1930 by the American Board of Obstetrics and Gynecology and in 1932 by the American Board of Dermatology and Syphilology.

In 1933 these four boards, as well as leaders of interested groups, such as the Association of American Medical Colleges, the American Hospital Association, the Federation of State Medical Boards of the U.S.A., and the National Board of Medical Examiners, had become concerned over the threat that various informal groups without authoritative sponsorship were about to organize similar examining and certifying boards in specialties or subspecialties which might soon nullify the effect and force of the movement because they lacked proper backing or sponsorship from strong national societies. The four original boards were composed of men officially appointed by the recognized national societies in the given specialty and the related special section of the American Medical Association.

At about this same time, it appeared that various state legislatures were prepared to take action on the qualifications of those claiming to be specialists; such legislation was introduced in New Jersey; New York State was entertaining similar proposals. It was, however, the opinion of the members of the Council on Medical Education and Hospitals of the A.M.A. that it would be disastrous for the states to assume the function of designating qualified specialists. First, it was apparent that standards of specialization should be uniform throughout the country and that probable divergent requirements of the various states, with resultant confusion, should be avoided. Since the national government could not undertake this work, it seemed necessary that voluntary agencies be created to function extralegally but with the force of public opinion behind them. Second, it was realized that while a populous state like New York might conceivably set up some machinery for identifying specialists, it would be wholly impossible in many states to find a group of highly trained specialists capable of conducting the necessary examinations. Third, it was realized that if the states should undertake the certification of specialists, the procedure would necessarily be subject to political influence; and since no one of the states had yet been able to create a satisfactory system of testing the applicants for the general medical license, it seemed much less likely that they would succeed in the far more difficult task of conducting examinations for each of the specialties.

With the threat of government interference, and the formation of numerous quasi-official and irresponsible boards, it was clear that steps had to be taken to establish the official and formal nature of any and all boards subsequently to be organized. Consequently, a meeting was called of representatives from the four boards and the other interested groups of state and national medical examiners, the American Hospital Association, and the Association of American Medical Colleges. From this meeting in 1933 a liaison organization was formed termed the Advisory Board for Medical Specialties. The major medical specialties were defined and named, rules and regulations for the official formation of new boards were adopted, and election of new boards to membership in the advisory board was stipulated to be based on adherence to the high standards established by the four certifying boards then in existence.

Simultaneously, the House of Delegates of the American Medical Association, through the Council on Medical Education and Hospitals, adopted an identical set of regulations, and the council agreed not to recognize any group which had not been previously approved and recommended by the advisory board. The mechanism had become established for the control of examination and certification of specialists. By 1940, 15 major specialties were represented by recognized specialty boards. Beginning in 1946, certain of the boards undertook to certify candidates in subspecialties. Certification in the basic board is a prerequisite for subsequent certification in the subspecialty. These subspecialties are fully recognized by the Council on Medical Education and Hospitals of the American Medical Association.

That certification of specialists is fundamentally an educational movement, and that it has resulted in a pronounced improvement in qualification for special practice, can be verified by study of the graduates seeking special training and of the institutions which provide the clinical facilities for the graduate medical education. In 1930 only 278 hospitals were providing a total of 1,776 residencies and fellowships in the specialties approved by the Council on Medical Education and Hospitals of the American Medical Association. By 1940 there were 4,392 residencies and 726 fellowships, a total of 5,118 in 587 hospitals in the United States. On demobilization, upward of 20,000 medical officers of the armed forces were seeking residencies and other postgraduate medical courses.

Facilities for adequate training were greatly expanded when the Veterans Administration allied itself with medical schools throughout the country and, through the deans' committees of forty medical schools, established extensive and complete resident training programs in the larger Veterans Administration hospitals. This forward step had two major results: first, it provided a well-trained and supervised staff at a time when the patient load in veterans' hospitals had increased tremendously; second, it provided for the absorption of a large proportion of medical officers requesting postgraduate work on their release from the armed services.

While the formation of the specialty boards may be considered essentially an educational movement, it should be evident that certification itself is not considered in the same sense as would the conferring of a degree: e.g., a Ph.D. in Surgery. This point is clearly stated in the bylaws of several of the boards. The American Board of Pathology defines its position as follows:

> The board is in no sense an educational institution and the certificates of the board are not to be considered degrees. Therefore, the certificate does not confer on any person legal qualifications, privileges or license to practice medecine or the specialty of pathology. The board does not purport in any way to interfere with or limit the professional activities of any licensed physician. Its chief aim is to standardize the qualification for the specialty of pathology and to issue certificates to those voluntarily complying with the requirements of the board.

A corollary function of the specialty boards and the one with which they are most closely associated in the lay as well as the professional mind is that of certification of diplomates who have successfully passed the necessary requirements. In the certification of specialists each board recognizes the necessity of adopting accepted standards to meet the situation of those doctors already in practice who are partially trained in a special field and also that group of older physicians who are well recognized in their specialty. The latter constitute the founder groups in the different fields and the former will gradually disappear as the younger graduates complete the more formal type of training which is recognized by the specialty boards as most desirable. The older specialists of unquestioned ability have been quick to see the advantages of the movement to succeeding generations of physicians, and many applied for certification which obviously these men did not need merely to prove their worth. In so doing they added their prestige and influence to the structure of better service for the sick and improved standards of medical practice.

A third and by no means unimportant function of the examining boards is that of publishing a register listing those who are considered properly qualified in each specialty.

The boards must of necessity have close working relationships with hospitals, in which most of the graduate preparation is provided. Faced with the necessity of meeting the council's requirements in order to obtain interns and residents, hospitals have had to elevate their standards and enlist the aid of the professional staff in carrying out their teaching programs. This results in direct benefit to the public in better care provided, to the staff itself in stimulating professional interest, and directly, of course, to the residents.

A second effect and one which poses several difficult problems is that of the place of diplomates on the hospital staff. Shall key positions on the staff, such as chiefs of the major services, be restricted to board men? In several hospitals in the larger cities, staffs are already being closed to all but certified specialists. While from the long-range view this policy may or may not be justified, as an immediate problem to the hospital administrator it may be responsible for many difficult decisions.

The war years brought into sharp focus thinking regarding the role of the general practitioner. Because of the method of duty assignment and classification employed by the Surgeon General's office, most nonspecialists, although they may have been highly competent, found themselves in combat units where their professional experience was confined to dispensary or office type treatment, or assigned to administrative, sanitary, and staff positions. This concept has carried over into the policy in effect in Veterans Administration hospitals. The law under which the Department of Medicine and Surgery of this agency functions provides a 25 per cent increase in base pay and original appointments at a higher grade for men certified by specialty boards.

This trend is also apparent in medical teaching centers in which interns and residents are trained, setting a pattern for their thinking. Again, it has become generally accepted that small clinics, consisting of seven or eight doctors restricting their practice more or less to a specialty, result in a higher type of care for the sick. The net effect has been to create in the minds of the public the thought that only specialists are competent to treat patients.

The basic policy of the private practice of medicine still rests on the assumption that the general practitioner will take care of the routine ills of all members of the family and refer them to appropriate specialists only when the occasion demands.

The preceding paragraph ends the adaptation of Dr. Leveroos' paper. Since he wrote it there was a determined effort to establish a Board of Abdominal Surgery which, after considerable controversy, was finally disapproved as a recognized specialty board by the House of Delegates of the American Medical Association at the 1962 convention. Under consideration by the Board of Preventive Medicine is a subspecialty in administrative medicine. Full-time medical directors and directors of medical education in hospitals and related institutions and organizations including public health agencies are being studied by those who recognize that education in administrative skills is needed if they are to function effectively.

The nineteen examining boards in the medical specialties which have been approved by the A.M.A.'s Council on Medical Education and Hospitals and the Advisory Board for Medical Specialties are:

Name of Board	*Year of Incorporation*
American Board of Ophthalmology	1917
American Board of Otolaryngology	1924
American Board of Obstetrics and Gynecology	1930
American Board of Dermatology and Syphilology	1932
American Board of Pediatrics*	1933
American Board of Orthopaedic Surgery	1934
American Board of Radiology	1934
American Board of Psychiatry and Neurology	1934

Name of Board	Year of Incorporation
American Board of Urology	1935
American Board of Internal Medicine†	1936
American Board of Pathology	1936
American Board of Anesthesiology	1937
American Board of Surgery	1937
American Board of Plastic Surgery	1937
American Board of Neurological Surgery	1940
American Board of Physical Medicine and Rehabilitation	1947
American Board of Preventive Medicine‡	1948
Board of Thoracic Surgery (an affiliate of the American Board of Surgery)	1948
American Board of Colon and Rectal Surgery§	1949

* Certifies specialists in allergy.
† Certifies specialists in allergy, cardiovascular disease, gastroenterology and pulmonary disease.
‡ Certifies specialists in aviation medicine, occupational medicine and public health.
§ Formerly the American Board of Proctology.

THE MEDICAL SPECIALTIES

Besides the medical specialties for which there are approved boards, there are a few others which have developed to meet specific needs, and more of them will appear to meet new demands for particular skills. One of them, already discussed, may lead to recognition of a traumatologist as a specialist. There are physicians who specialize in the treatment of tuberculosis; others who specialize in tropical medicine—a specialty that becomes tremendously important when global war descends or impends, and which in any case is increasing in recognition with the mobility of peoples resulting from the jet age. Then there are specialties such as geriatrics which, like traumatology, cross the lines of all the specialties by concentrating upon the kind of patient involved rather than the type of his affliction. A book has recently been published about what the author terms "mediatrics"—a specialty that is concerned with the health problems of persons in the middle-age group!

The administrator needs to watch these developments, besides keeping up with those in the presently recognized fields as described in the following brief studies.

Dermatology and Syphilology

Robert Willan (1757–1812), of Yorkshire, England, is considered to be the founder of modern dermatology. He established a definite classic nomenclature and divided skin diseases into eight classifications. For this work he was awarded in 1790 the Fothergillian gold medal. He clarified the nature of eczema and lupus. His classification, which still retains some usefulness, is based on objective appearances. He produced a famous text *On Cutaneous Diseases,* which was published in part before his death and finished afterward by his pupil Thomas Bateman (1778–1821), who is also noted for his contributions to this field.

Jean-Louis Alibert (1768–1837) founded the modern French school of dermatology. A new phase in the development of dermatology based on histology was introduced by Ferdinand von Hebra (1816–1880) of Vienna, who classified skin diseases according to their pathological anatomy. Considering most of them to be purely local, his treatment was mainly by local remedies, although he was a great believer in the healing power of Nature unassisted. He revived the use of mercurials in syphilis.

The first American books on dermatology (1714) and syphilis (1727) were published by Daniel Turner.

In the latter part of the nineteenth century Paul Gerson Unna of Hamburg and Raymond Sabouraud of Paris were among those who inaugurated the scientific or parasitic period of dermatology, tracing many cutaneous diseases to microscopic organisms. Unna founded a private clinic in 1881 and a hospital for skin diseases in 1884 in Hamburg and published several valuable works on his specialty.

The first dermatological clinic in the United States, Broom Street Infirmary, New York, was established in 1836.

Treatment of syphilis was revolutionized by the discoveries in 1906 by Schaudinn of the parasite of the disease, in 1907 by Wassermann of the reliable diagnostic test which bears his name, in 1910 by Ehrlich and Hata of Salvarsan (606) for treatment, and in latter days by a number of workers of modifications of the tests and of the value of the "wonder drugs" in treatment.

Increasingly the dermatologist recognizes the general physical and mental condition of the patient as a fundamental consideration in his diagnosis and treatment of a skin disorder. He obtains a medical history and sometimes asks the patient to undergo a general medical examination. He performs skin biopsies and tests sensitivity of the skin, coordinating results of the physical examination and of the tests to determine whether the complaint is internal or external in origin, and whether the cause is chemical, parasitic, or neoplastic. Neurological or psychiatric origin of the condition is considered as a possibility. In his diagnosis he decides whether the skin disorder is primarily of the skin and skin appendages or is a cutaneous manifestation of systemic disease. Having made his diagnosis, he prescribes medicine for internal use if indicated and local applications for external treatment and advises the use of or employs physical agents, such as cryotherapy, roentgen therapy, radium irradiation, diathermy, electric cautery, iontophoresis or electrophoresis, hyperprexia, and actinotherapy. He also advises the patient, when the need is evident, on matters of nutrition and hygiene.

The American Dermatological Association was organized in 1876 to advance knowledge, teaching, and research. Membership is considered an honorary award. Candidates must be diplomates of the American Board of Dermatology and Syphilology and must have had outstanding records in practice, teaching, and research. Membership is around 300.

The American Academy of Dermatology and Syphilology was organized in 1936 "to educate physicians in dermatology and syphilology." The fellowship requirements include certification by the American Board and three years' full-time experience either as practitioner, teacher, or graduate student in the specialty and limitation of practice for three years preceding application. Membership is around 1,600.

Pediatrics

Pediatrics is an ancient art. Susruta includes a praiseworthy section on infant hygiene and nutrition. Soranus of Ephesus in the second century A.D. wrote excellent precepts on the same subjects and also on infants' diseases, one of these being recognizable from the description as rickets. Paul of Aegina (A.D. 625–690) summarized in his seven-volume *Epitome* of medicine all that was known in his day about pediatrics. Little more happened in the field up to the fifteenth century when a few treatises on the subject began to appear. The output of literature gradually increased until by the nineteenth century a notable collection had accumulated, with the most recent contributions those of Eduard Heinrich Henoch of Berlin (series of essays on children's diseases from 1861 to 1868 and lectures on pediatrics 1881); Alois Bednar of Vienna (treatise on diseases of infants from 1850 to 1853); Theodor Escherich of Munich (treatise on the intestinal bacteria of infants, 1886); and Adalbert Czerny with Arthur Keller (a great treatise on the disorders of infantile nutrition). In Germany in particular great pediatricians appeared in the late nineteenth and early twentieth centuries.

Pre-eminent in pediatrics in America in his day was Abraham Jacobi (1830–1919) who immigrated to New York from Germany in 1953 and taught the subject in different medical schools in that city for 42 years. He wrote a monograph on the history of American pediatrics in 1913. Through his efforts the New York Medical College started the first pediatric clinic in the United States in 1860. He was a founder and editor of the *American Journal of Obstetrics*.

In response to the unique needs of small children—consider, for example, the necessity for smaller-sized instruments and supplies—the specialty of pediatric surgery has arisen. A prominent pediatric surgeon has said that he never ceases to marvel at the terrific ability of little children to stage a comeback after surgery. He attributes this mainly to the fact that a child has only the inborn desire to live, has no preconceived fears, and cannot talk over his operation in advance! The same surgeon predicts that pediatric surgery will progress rapidly in the next fifteen years and points to an urgent need for more research and more technical aids.

The pediatricians are saying that the "new pediatrics" requires sensitivity to the psychological and emotional aspects of illness and also increased integration from a consultative and referral standpoint with other medical specialties. In turn they anticipate more referrals to them. For example, special techniques are needed in treating allergies peculiar to children.

The American Academy of Pediatrics was organized in 1930 to foster and stimulate interest in pediatrics and all aspects of work for children's welfare. Requirements for membership, which is around 3,000, are five years' work in pediatrics and certification by the board.

The American Academy of Allergy was organized in 1943 to advance knowledge and practice of allergy through discussion, education, encouragement of cooperation among those in the field, and promotion of research and study. Requirements for membership (around 900) are a minimum of five years in allergy work after medical school graduation. Allergies are major problems in the field of pediatrics.

Canada was host in 1960 to the ninth meeting of the International Congress of Paediatrics, which attracted delegates from 63 countries.

Psychiatry and Neurology

Psychiatry may be considered the earliest of the distinct medical specialties, because lunatics were isolated usually in separate institutions from other victims of illness. Treatment was seldom given these patients; nevertheless a few physicians began to study and to try to help them. One of the first actions was to classify them according to type of disorder—Emil Kraepelin (1856–1927), of Germany, did this and attempted prognoses. His classification was according to clinical manifestations, some of them observed at autopsy. He is considered to be the "great systematist" of psychiatry.

Early in the twentieth century, psychology began to enter the concept of mental illness—emotional factors came to be recognized as responsible for many conditions. Freud and others propounded completely new ideas. Circumstances which led to the breakdown were explored in many cases rather than evidence of brain damage alone. There was a movement toward a germ theory of mental disease when in 1913 in cases of pareses Noguchi and Moore discovered the syphilitic spirochete in the brain. That this applied only to one kind of condition was gradually recognized, especially after Adolf Meyer between 1900 and 1915 divulged his views of individualizing the patient and considering all factors, such as heredity, body build, medical status, prepsychotic personality.

In two of Oliver Wendell Holmes' "medicated novels" the effects of fright in infancy upon personality are traced. Walter B. Cannon, of Boston, studied the physiology of the emotions and in 1915 published a book about the results of emotional excitement. During World Wars I and II in particular it became clear that stress caused physical disability and actual diseases such as goiter and diabetes.

The psychiatrist is increasingly being utilized almost routinely in the treatment of patients before and after surgery and in many other circumstances in which there is no surface indication of need for treatment of anything but the physical disorder. Mental and physical health are in the new thinking linked as intensely affecting each other.

The extent of mental illness—estimated to involve at least one person in every ten—is placing the psychiatrist in a conspicuous position.

Marti-Ibanez declares that in neurology, and consequently in psychiatry, "progress was impeded by the notion, metaphysical in the conceptual sense and emotional in its personal connotations, that the organs that are studied in neurology, such as the brain and the nervous-system organs, regulate internally man's organism and externally his relationship with his environment, with God and Nature." This, he says, is the reason for the "historical clash between the two principal attitudes governing neurological thought—the metaphysico-religious and the empirico-scientific."

The dramatic effectiveness of new psychopharmacological agents—tranquilizers and antidepressants—has enormously brightened the prospect for the conquest of many types of mental illness. Nevertheless, psychiatrists warn that drugs are only "an adjunct to treatment" and can perpetuate the neurosis of a person with a chronic neurotic problem by "lulling him into lassitude."

The first World Congress of Psychiatry was held in 1950 in Paris, the third in 1961 in Montreal with some 3,000 psychiatrists from 62 nations in attendance.

As mentioned in Chapter 2, the American Psychiatric Association, founded in 1844, is the oldest national medical association in the United States.

Internal Medicine

The requirements for certification by the American Board of Internal Medicine show the wide range of practice embraced by this specialty:

> One-year internship; three years' residency or fellowship in internal medicine; two years of practice of clinical internal medicine. The board will accept, as the equivalent of one year only of the residency, 12 months' internship in the medical service and the medical specialties, or one year of approved residency in allergy, cardiovascular disease, gastroenterology, hematology, pulmonary diseases, neurology, pediatrics, psychiatry, dermatology and syphilology, or one year of approved residency in pathology, or one year as a graduate student or as an instructor in an approved medical school on a fulltime basis in bacteriology, biochemistry, pathology, pharmacology, physiology or internal medicine, or an advanced degree in the fundamental sciences; written and oral examinations. Candidates in the sub-specialties must pass examinations in internal medicine before admission to examination in the specialty applied for. The specialty examinations are oral only.

The specialist in internal medicine diagnoses and treats disorders due to infections and to systemic, allergic, metabolic, nutritional, and physical and chemical agents, including diseases of the respiratory tract, endocrine glands, alimentary tract, blood, spleen and reticule, and locomotor and nervous systems. He takes complete histories and conducts physical examinations. He performs or orders various laboratory tests to aid diagnosis. He prescribes treatment such as use of counterirritants, diet, bed rest, massage, medications, roentgen ray, ultraviolet irradiation, transfusion and physiotherapy, and surgical intervention when indicated.

The leading organization of this specialty is the American College of Physicians, described in Chapter 2. One of the requirements for fellowship is certification by the recognized board in the candidate's particular field. Membership is around 8,000.

Among the organizations representing the subspecialties are the American Academy of Allergy organized in 1943; the American College of Allergists organized in 1942; the American Gastroenterological Association organized in 1897; and the National Gastroenterological Association, Inc., organized in 1934.

Physical Medicine and Rehabilitation

As a specialty physical medicine is new, although much of its philosophy and many of the procedures which it employs are as old as medicine itself. It took a World War with its tragic aftermath of mutilation and disability to bring it to the fore as a distinct science and art. Dr. John S. Coulter, then assistant professor of physical therapy, Northwestern University Medical School, Chicago, said in 1928:

> We are now ten years past the greatest revival of physical therapy that the medical world has ever seen, and today physical therapy is on a better basis than it has ever been. It is now recognized that it is not a specific for any medical or surgical condition but that it is capable of benefiting along with other medical and surgical treatment a wide range of conditions.

Placed in charge of all physical therapy in the United States Army hospitals during World War I was Dr. Frank B. Granger, who was already developing physical therapy in Boston when the war broke out. It became through his efforts and enthusiasm a service in every army hospital in the theaters of war and was continued in the regular military hospitals after the end of the war.

"Physical therapy" was soon replaced as the term to designate this service by "physical medicine," which had long been in use in England. Besides physical therapy, physical medicine embraces occupational therapy and the employment of physical agents for diagnostic purposes, plus reconditioning of the convalescent patient.

Following World War II when there was a resurgence of interest the Council on Physical Medicine of the American Medical Association voted to sponsor the designation "physiatrist" to describe the physician who specializes in physical medicine. Bernard M. Baruch, who had been impressed with the possibilities of physical medicine by his father, Dr. Simon Baruch, appointed a committee headed by Dr. Ray Lyman Wilbur to make a survey and to report on the programs deemed best for adequate development of physical medicine in the United States. Forty scientists divided into eight subcommittees made the survey in consultation with 400 other outstanding scientists. The chief needs decided upon were:

1. An adequate supply of physicians who can teach and use physical medicine
2. More extensive basic and clinical research in physical medicine
3. Proper use of physical medicine in relation to rehabilitation

The A.M.A.'s Council on Physical Medicine states that physical medicine is the broadest of all medical specialties. Hence it was a complicated task to activate the recommendations of the Baruch committee's report, for which he gave the initial sum of $1,100,000. One of the first projects, for which $400,000 was allocated, was establishment of a model center for basic research and teaching of physical medicine at Columbia University College of Physicians and Surgeons. Additional teaching and research centers were established at Harvard Medical School, the University of Minnesota Medical School, the Massachusetts Institute of Technology, the University of California, the Medical College of Virginia, and the New York University College of Medicine. A few other universities received minor grants. Spurred by the Baruch committee's activities, other sponsors of major teaching and research projects, particularly the National Foundation for Infantile Paralysis, made large grants to several universities.

Among those who should be credited as pioneers of the new profession are Dr. George Deaver, of the Institute for the Crippled and Disabled, New York; Dr. John S. Coulter, of Northwestern University, Chicago; Dr. Ben Boynton, formerly of the Veterans Administration and Northwestern; Dr. A. B. C. Knudson, of the Veterans Administration; Dr. Edward E. Gordon, of Michael Reese Medical Center, Chicago; Dr. Frank H. Krusen, of the Mayo Foundation, University of Minnesota; Dr. Henry Kessler, of the Kessler Institute, Orange, New Jersey; Dr. Gustave Gingras, of the Rehabilitation Institute of Montreal, Quebec; and Dr. Howard A. Rusk of the Institute of Rehabilitation and Physical Medicine, New York University College of Medicine.

An annual Congress of Physical Medicine and Rehabilitation has been held in the United States since 1922. Other organizations are the American Academy of Physical Medicine and Rehabilitation and the Association for Physical and Mental Rehabilitation.

Preventive Medicine

Public health, practiced in olden times but neglected during the middle ages, was revived in the eighteenth century and was given great impetus in the nineteenth with the discovery of bacteria and their role in the transmission of disease.

Preventive medicine is supposed to be practiced at every possible opportunity by every physician. The preventive medicine or public health specialist, however, is of fairly recent origin. Lay persons and lay organizations have been active in the field. Lemuel Shattuck, considered to be the father of public health in the United States, was a teacher, merchant, editor, and bookseller at the time of his appointment to head a survey of sanitary conditions in Massachusetts in 1849. Stephen Smith, however, who crusaded against slum conditions in New York because he connected them with the high incidence of typhus fever, was a medical intern at the time, 1850, and went on to become a surgeon, although he never lost his interest in the improvement of environmental conditions. Probably the first physician who might be considered a preventive medicine and public health specialist was Dr. John Woodworth, a Civil War army officer, who was appointed in 1870 Surgeon General of the Marine Hospital Service, predecessor of the United States Public Health Service.

In other countries, however, there were a few physicians who concentrated their efforts on public health at an earlier period. Edwin Chadwick, who started the crusade in England in 1828, was a lawyer, but when he was asked to have a study made of the causes of disease among the working population he appointed three well-known doctors to conduct it, among them Southwood Smith who founded the Health of Towns Association in 1839 and the Association for Improving the Dwellings of the Industrial Classes in 1842 and wrote a *Philosophy of Health*. A lecturer in surgery at St. Thomas' Hospital, John Simon, was the first appointee as Medical Officer of Health for the City of London, serving in that capacity from 1848 to 1855.

In Germany, Max von Pettenkofer, who graduated in medicine at Munich in 1843, gave up ten years later his teaching of dietetic chemistry for that of hygiene. Preceding him by many years was Johann Peter Frank (1745–1828), who produced a great work on public hygiene which constitutes a plan for a model system of health administration. He also carried out many practical reforms.

In France several important treatises on public hygiene were published in the first half of the nineteenth century, and all the large towns of southern France had bureaus of health.

Some confusion exists between the scope, respectively, of preventive medicine and of public health. Stieglitz[4] in predicting the "future strategy of preventive medicine" says that it "falls into two clearly separable major divisions: (1) public health activities which have to do primarily with mass measures to minimize health hazards in the environment and (2) private health efforts concerned directly with the *individual*" and declares that "a full measure of success cannot be anticipated unless both the 'wholesale' or *'en masse'* and 'retail' or 'individual' approaches are developed to their maximum capacity and utilized cooperatively."

With this outlook, preventive medicine is clearly comprehensive in its inclu-

---

[4] *A Future for Preventive Medicine*. New York, The Commonwealth Fund, 1945, pp. 39, 40.

sion of aviation medicine, occupational medicine, and public health, in each of which certification is available.

Among the organizations whose members are specialists in preventive medicine are the American Academy of Occupational Medicine, American Association of Public Health Physicians, the American College of Preventive Medicine, the American School Health Association, Association of State and Territorial Health Officers, Industrial Medical Association, and Western Industrial Medical Association. Organizations whose membership is not restricted to physicians are the American Public Health Association, Inc., and the Canadian Public Health Association.

In 1953 a new medical specialty, aeromedicine, was established when the Council on Medical Education and Hospitals of the A.M.A. approved the request of the American Board of Preventive Medicine for authorization to examine and certify physicians who had concentrated their interest on aviation medicine. The council later developed standards under which schools of aviation medicine and training programs in hospitals would be approved. The new specialty was also sponsored by the American and Canadian Public Health Associations, the Aero Medical Association, the Southern Medical Association, and the Association of Schools of Public Health.

Anesthesiology

The suffering of the patient in preanesthetic days was the main reason for the lightning speed for which surgeons strove in operating. It was told of Dr. George McClellan, whose work was exceptionally fast and dexterous, that while he operated he kept saying over and over to the patient: "Courage, my good fellow; be brave, for we wound but to heal; courage, my dear fellow; it will soon be over."

Sir Clifford Allbutt, in an article in the *Johns Hopkins Hospital Bulletin* in 1898, wrote:

> When I was a boy, surgeons operating upon the quick were pitted one against the other like runners on time. He was the best surgeon, both for patient and onlooker, who broke the three-minute record in an amputation or a lithotomy. What place could there be in record-breaking operations for the fiddle-faddle of antiseptic precautions? The obvious boon of immunity from pain, precious as it was, when we look beyond the individual, was less than the boon of time. With anesthetics ended slapdash surgery; anesthesia gave time for the theories of Pasteur and Lister to be adopted in practice.

An account of the discovery and early use of ether anesthesia is given in Chapter 6. Sir James Young Simpson used ether in obstetrical practice for the first time in England on January 19, 1847, but in the fall of the same year he substituted chloroform. A French and a German scientist working independently of each other had discovered this anesthetic agent. The hazards of both ether and chloroform soon manifested themselves, and refinements in both agent and manner of administration were developed. But these came slowly and painfully. As Dr. Howard W. Haggard, then director of the Laboratory of Applied Physiology at Yale University, told members of the American Society of Anesthetists at their 1939 meeting, anesthesia "got off to a bad start" because "it was a technical procedure carried out by rule of thumb by men or women who had no special knowledge of the respiratory and circulatory physiology and of the pharmacology that today are the primary requirements of the professional anesthetist. Anesthesia was the giving of a dose of medicine which could be administered by the nurse or intern and in an emergency by a layman." Those were what is known as the "rag-and-bottle" days of anesthesia.

Advances in the last twenty years have been rapid, continually making anesthesiology a profession the practice of which requires a prodigious amount of knowledge and skill. From the gas oxygen mixture introduced by Dr. Edmund Andrews of Chicago in 1868 and revived by Drs. Goldmann, Halsted, and Crile in 1900 to conduction anesthesia, nerve-blocking, spinal, intravenous, intramuscular, and rectal types of administration, and a great number of synthetic drugs for local use, analgesia and anesthesia have become constantly more complicated and individualized. At least 400 compounds are marketed.

It has been improvements in anesthesia that have made possible a number of operations that were previously not attempted because of the hazards. Until the 1930's the surgeon could not enter the chest because once it was opened the lungs, no longer in a partial vacuum, would collapse and breathing would cease. The chief innovation was the increased use of tubes which can be slipped down the windpipe to permit the anesthetist to rhythmically force air and oxygen into the lungs.

Refrigeration anesthesia sounds rather simple but, if properly done, requires, in the words of Dr. A. J. Polderman,[5] of The Netherlands, "meticulous preparation and control and is time-consuming; on a percentile basis, only for very few patients is it strictly indicated."

The anesthesiologist prescribes sedatives for preoperative and postoperative care of the patient and during surgery initiates such remedial measures as administration of oxygen, saline solution, whole blood, or blood plasma. He also supervises all inhalation therapy service in the hospital. Oxygen is prescribed almost routinely to take the strain off the heart and lungs when the patient's breathing is impaired. Aerosol therapy—the inhalation through a mask by the patient of drugs in the form of a mist—is proving exceptionally effective in treating conditions in which lung function is not normal. Medical hypnosis is another innovation in the realm of the anesthesiologist, as is also the use of electricity as an anesthetic.

The relationship between anesthesiologist and surgeon must be very close if the

[5] From a paper read at the Second Congress of the European Federation, International College of Surgeons, Amsterdam, May, 1962.

best results are to be obtained. Originally the American Board of Anesthesiology was formed (1937) as an affiliate of the American Board of Surgery. In June, 1940, the American Medical Association established its Section on Anesthesiology and a separate board was formed. The first department of anesthesia in a university in the United States was founded by Dr. Ralph Waters in 1927 at the University of Wisconsin.

In an article, "Anesthesia Is a Part of Surgery," Dr. Francis D. Moore,[6] surgeon-in-chief, Peter Bent Brigham Hospital, Boston, contends that the profession of anesthesia is a part of surgery "because it is wholly involved in the care of surgical patients" and is "an indispensable part of surgical operations; it is involved with the resuscitation of the wounded and injured; it is as 'surgical' as many other activities of surgeons who are involved in the care of their patients." Dr. Moore believes that it is unfortunate to place anesthesia with pathology and radiology, since the two latter are "wholly devoted to the application of special laboratory techniques to the care of the sick and neither of them partake of the continuous intimate physician-patient contact so important in anesthesia."

Great Britain long preceded America in having full-time anesthetists. The first physician to devote all of his time to anesthesia was John Snow of London, who besides administering it conducted laboratory and clinical investigation in anesthesia. In 1853 and in 1857 he administered chloroform to the Queen in childbirth.

The Society of Anesthetists was organized in London in 1893, twelve years before Dr. A. F. Erdmann founded the first American organization, the American Society of Anesthetists (now Anesthesiologists). From 90 members in 1905 it has grown to a total of more than 7,000. The American Association of Anesthetists was formed in 1913, changing its name in 1926 to the Associated Anesthetists of the United States and Canada. Its secretary, Dr. Francis McMechan, founded in 1922 the National Anesthesia Research Society, which in 1925 became the International Anesthesia Research Society. Dr. McMechan was also instrumental in the founding of the Canadian Society of Anesthetists.

The American College of Anesthesiologists was founded in 1947. The formation of a European Board of Anesthesiology is being promoted in Europe. The World Federation of Societies of Anesthesiologists was registered in The Netherlands in 1955 "to make available the highest standards of anesthesia to all peoples throughout the world." This activity is being conducted largely through the World Health Organization. Founding of the federation was a result of experience with a course in Copenhagen initiated by a religious group, the trainees being mostly from Russia and middle European countries. W.H.O. contributes by recruiting "prominent teaching-investigative anesthesiologists" to spend three-month periods there. Improved standards have resulted throughout Europe. Decision was made at the 1960 Congress of the Federation in Toronto to establish centers in the Orient and in the western portions of South America.

[6] *Bull. Am. Coll. Surgeons*, May–June, 1955.

Societies of anesthesiologists from 40 countries, with a membership of more than 13,000, are members of the World Federation.[7]

That the advances in anesthesia have intensified its problems and its mystery is strikingly expressed by Dr. Basile Yanovsky,[8] of New York:

> Anesthesia may be characterized by the fact that a variety of medical problems requiring *immediate solution* meet very dramatically at the anesthesiologist's end of the table; problems of general physiology and physiologic nature of specific organs (even cells); of cardiology, endocrinology, ophthalmology, otology, rhinology, laryngology, pediatrics, geriatrics, psychiatry, allergy, neurology, and biochemistry. These multiple disciplines converge suddenly, occupying, as it were, the same space at the same time. This *simultaneity* constitutes a definite, specific trait of anesthesia, its distinctive stamp. The question of how to deal with it is not only a technical challenge and a demand on scientific knowledge but a philosophical problem: *Time acquires a new meaning, which must be explored.* . . . Another inherent trait of anesthesia which again, and in an even more pointed way, brings up the problem of time, is its *reversibility.* The abolition of the vital reflexes, as well as all possible complications, such as apnea, tachycardia, bradycardia or anoxia, are expected to disappear without leaving any traces. . . .
> . . . the activity of an anesthesiologist is close to that realm "from which no traveler returns"; daily, under his direction, the most fascinating and daring drama is enacted, in which the seemingly passive main character is led through a number of dangerous adventures (approaching cellular death or old age), and then brought back to his former status. . . . While the internist may deal with a mild chronic disease and the surgeon with a minor operation, there is hardly any quantitative difference in the administration of anesthesia; what counts mostly is its induction and end. The only parallel that comes to mind is not from a medical field but from aeronautics, in which take-off and landing are the crucial stages.

Pathology

The usually behind-the-scenes pathologist was appropriately glorified in the 1961 motion picture production, "The Young Doctors." Surgeons are familiar personalities, and operating rooms are common scenes for theater and television; but now the pathological laboratory and the autopsy room in the morgue have had their secrets exposed. There was even a medical staff conference at which the pathologist pointed out the mistaken diagnoses, a truly more shattering event in real life than the best actors can reproduce on stage or screen. Although certainly morbid for popular showing, this film doubtless has public education value in its revelation that much more goes on for his benefit in the hospital than the patient and his visitors imagine.

The role of the pathologist in the hospital is extremely important. He is the basic scientist whose scientific endeavors are concentrated on disease in its multitudinous manifestations, and his objective analyses are the tests of the competence

[7] Some of the information on the various organizations was abstracted from an article, The World-Wide Growth of Organized Anesthesiology, by R. S. Sappenfield, M.D., of Miami. *J. Internat. Coll. Surgeons,* November, 1961, pp. 677–81.

[8] Toward a Philosophy of Anesthesia. *J. Internat. Coll. Surgeons,* May, 1962, pp. 501–6.

of the physicians, as well as, frequently, their guides to diagnosis and treatment. The pathologist of today and his predecessors are the physicians whose names appear most prominently on many of the milestones in medicine, as will be indicated in Chapter 6. Up to the present century the pathologist was usually also a practicing physician or surgeon, and he had little or no laboratory space in the hospital. Nowadays demands upon the laboratory are increasing so fast that planners all seem to be too conservative in estimating space requirements for its growth, as will be further discussed in Chapter 9.

Organization of specialists in this field in the United States began in 1900 with the founding of the American Association of Pathologists and Bacteriologists, followed in 1922 by the formation of the American Society of Clinical Pathologists. The College of American Pathologists was organized in 1946, ten years after the board, certification by which is required for admission to fellowship.

The pathologist works in cooperation with several other medical scientists, such as bacteriologists, epidemiologists, biochemists, clinical hematologists, biophysicists, and biomedical engineers, in the typical teaching hospital.

Radiology

Radiology is defined by the Council on Medical Education and Hospitals of the American Medical Association as "that branch of medicine which deals with the diagnostic and therapeutic application of radiant energy, including Roentgen rays, radium, ultra-violet, and other spectral radiation." Roentgenology is that phase of radiology which deals with the diagnostic and therapeutic application of roentgen rays only.

Wilhelm Conrad Roentgen (1845–1923), professor of physics successively at Strassburg, Giessen, Würzburg, and Munich, gave medicine one of its greatest aids, the x-ray. In December, 1895, he made the startling announcement of his discovery of a new kind of ray to the Physical Medicine Society of Würzburg. He had been experimenting with a Crookes tube when he got strange shadows of solid objects. He reported that the ray could penetrate a shield known to be absolutely impervious to light and that with its aid he could see the bones of his hand. He did not know what to call it so he named it "x" ray.

The members of the society seem immediately to have grasped the possibilities of this ray in medicine and surgery, and one of them moved that it be called the "roentgen" ray.

The world seemed to be ready for this development. No time was lost in putting it to use; in fact this was being done within thirty days. Within a year a French doctor used it in treating a carcinoma of the stomach. Within two and a half years a roentgenologist on an American hospital ship during the Spanish-American War reported its use in locating bullets and diagnosing fractures.

Physiologists began to use x-ray in their experiments. As early as 1898 W. B. Cannon employed it to study the movements of the stomach in animals by using bismuth paste. In 1906 E. Beck carried over this method to surgery.

It should be noted that overdependence by physicians upon roentgenograms is deplored by many eminent physicians, who while acknowledging their great value, urge that they should not precede a thorough clinical examination and should always be interpreted in the light of the condition of the person as a whole.

The Nobel prize, his only financial gain from his work, was awarded to Roentgen in 1901. Fame and publicity were painful to him, however, especially when there was some implication that an assistant had made the discovery. He retired from teaching, his wife died, his friends neglected him, and he died lonely and unhappy over the war and its aftermath.

Improvement of the apparatus to obtain higher voltage and to permit absolute control became almost frenzied. Unaware of the dangers, many of the experimenters as well as physicians who used the rays in practice suffered serious burns from overexposure, and means had to be devised to protect workers. One example will illustrate the courage and sacrifice shown by many of those who advanced this science.

Dr. Emil H. Grubbe, who died in Chicago on March 26, 1960, at the age of 85, was working in 1895 in the manufacture of vacuum tubes but knew nothing about the rays emanating from them. He is believed to have been the first person in America exposed to x-rays. When in December of 1895 Roentgen announced his discovery, Dr. Grubbe began within a few weeks to apply x-rays to pathologic lesions. The dermatitis of the left hand which was a result of his experiments disclosed both the danger of the rays and the possibilities of using them for therapy in certain conditions.

On January 29, 1896, Dr. Grubbe treated a cancer of the breast with x-rays. The next day he treated a tuberculous skin condition with them. By this time he was using lead as a protective device. Dr. Grubbe is believed to have been the first professor of roentgenology in any medical college. He received citations from the Chicago Medical Society in 1946 and from the American Cancer Society in 1960. But over the years he underwent surgery 93 times for radiation burns, and lost first his left hand, then the fingers of the right hand, and afterward parts of his nose, lips, and adjacent structures.

The fact that the hazards continue must be faced, however. Dr. Shields Warren,[9] of Boston, pointed out that studies have indicated that deaths from leukemia occur from six to ten times as frequently among radiologists as among other physicians and that in general they die younger than do nonradiologists from every major cause of death except anemia. He expressed a belief that standards for protection appear adequate but that more determined effort should be made to live up to them.

Partly as a result of the arousing of public fear of radiation because of publicity on fall-out, there is a strong trend to reduce radiation exposure for patients. This trend was well under way, however, before the fall-out scare began. Cost is

[9] Longevity and Causes of Death from Irradiation in Physicians. *J.A.M.A.*, September 29, 1956.

a factor in the more conservative approach. Smaller-sized films prevent needless irradiation and save money.

Among the numerous new devices is the Sanchez-Perez automatic serialograph by means of which twelve films can be taken in a few seconds. It is used in taking x-rays of the intracranial circulation of the brain and x-rays of the aorta, the main artery which carries blood from the heart down through the center of the body.

Madame Marie Curie isolated the chemical element radium a few years after Roentgen's discovery. This was the birth of the science of radiology, which has expanded to include the man-made radioactive substances known as "isotopes." Radioisotope facilities are found even in many small hospitals. They must be approved by the Atomic Energy Commission before the use of isotopes is authorized.

Emerging as a distinct professional group, radiologists of the United States organized the American College of Radiologists in 1923. The American Medical Association established a Section on Radiology in 1925. Preceding this action three groups had been founded: the American Roentgen Ray Society, the American Radium Society, and the Radiological Society of North America. An Inter-Society Committee on Radiology was created to effect cooperation between the four organizations.

THE SURGICAL SPECIALTIES

Specialization in surgery, except for general surgery, is different from specialization in most other branches of medicine in that it is based on areas or specific parts of the body. Less restricted in area than the other specialties are orthopedic, plastic, and neurological surgery, but even these are more sharply defined in scope than most major nonsurgical specialties. The justifiable inclination, therefore, is to view surgery as one kind of approach to therapy. The special field is a secondary consideration, although the administrator should be thoroughly aware of the main divisions listed earlier in this chapter.

In Chapter 6 a few of the highlights in the progress of surgery are mentioned. Here the concern is mainly with organizational aspects.

As early as 1849, only two years after its own beginning, the American Medical Association established a Section on Obstetrics and Gynecology. In 1876 came the formation of the American Gynecological Society and in 1888 that of the American Association of Obstetricians and Gynecologists.

The American Ophthalmological Society dates from 1865, and this was the first surgical specialty to organize a board—1917. The American Otological Society, Inc., was organized in 1868, the American Laryngological Association in 1879, the American Laryngolical, Rhinological and Otological Society in 1895, and the American Academy of Ophthalmology and Otolaryngology in 1896. Otolaryngologists founded the second specialty board in 1924.

Also dating back to the nineteenth century is the American Orthopaedic Association which was organized in 1887.

The other surgical specialists have likewise formed societies, associations, academies, and colleges, among them the Society of Neurological Surgeons, the Academy of Neurological Surgery, the Neurosurgical Society of America, the American Association for Thoracic Surgery, the American Association of Plastic Surgeons, the American Society of Plastic and Reconstructive Surgery, the American Urological Association, and the Natonal Proctologic Association.

Over-all organizations in surgery include the American Surgical Association, the Society of Clinical Surgery, the American College of Surgeons, and the International College of Surgeons.

In the annual "Guide Issue" of *Hospitals* the leading medical organizations are listed with the names of officers, addresses, and telephone numbers.

In other countries similar organizations exist, most of them, of course, long predating their counterparts in America.

Surgery must always be thought of as an aid to medicine. It cannot stand alone. The surgeon is first of all a physician. His special approach to therapy is an added skill. The surgical specialties have arisen from the growth of medical knowledge in the fields which they represent. Frequently developments in medicine make surgery unnecessary—for example, the decline in surgery for tuberculosis and for mastoid conditions with the advent of new drugs to control infection. Again they bring about possibilities for effective surgical intervention that hitherto did not exist—for example, brain, lung, and heart surgery, interdicted, before improved aseptic, anesthetic, radiological, and chemotherapeutic procedures were introduced. Hence the nonsurgical and the surgical specialties are in a constant seesaw relationship as medical science advances. No one can predict what the future has in store for the surgical specialist.

GROUP PRACTICE

Specialism in medicine has been the chief cause of the development of group practice. Dr. Alan Gregg,[10] former vice-president of the Rockefeller Foundation, in discussing factors affecting medicine, had this to say about group practice:

> The most nearly satisfactory practical corrective of the defects of specialism is group practice. More than one reason supports such an opinion, though in other countries than the United States group practice has made but little headway. First, the skills as well as the knowledge in all the fields of Great Medicine exceed, by an indisputable margin, the abilities of any one man to master. Secondly, it is possible for professional men to collaborate effectively in the care of any patient. Thirdly, group practice encourages, facilitates, and improves such collaboration, and to the advantage of the patient. . . .
> There are, also, less evident advantages. Perhaps these can best be brought out by the sarcastic remark I once heard that there's very little difference between

[10] *Challenges to Contemporary Medicine.* New York, Columbia University Press, 1956, pp. 59–62.

group practice and fee-splitting unless the performance of every member of the group is held to a high level. In other words, the service given a patient by group practice gains in quality by the criticism of the other members of the group, whether the criticism be tacit or fully expressed. . . .

The similarity between group practice and practice in a well-organized teaching hospital with full-time staff has had two results, as I see it. The first is that the transition to group practice from working in a good teaching hospital as a student, intern, resident, or young instructor proves to be fraught with fewer risks and difficulties than going into practice alone. Thus one could say that group practice is growing because medical education under full-time teachers prepares a young man almost specifically for group practice. . . .

Dr. Gregg pointed out, however, contraindications for certain kinds of clinics, one of them being the organization of schools of medicine around the structure of group practice. He observed that "group practice centers logically and appropriately around the care of the patient and little else, whereas the task of a clinician in a teaching hospital involves two additional duties—teaching and research."

Only two years after the publication of Dr. Gregg's book, the Association of American Medical Colleges approved in principle group practice of medicine by full-time clinical teachers in American medical schools. The reason for this action was partly to provide a way to supplement the comparatively low base salaries paid by universities or medical schools to full-time faculty members. Yet medical educators are undoubtedly fully aware of dangers such as the jealousy and even opposition of the practitioners in the community who are not on the faculty.

The growth in group practice, especially since the war, has been impressive. Answers to questionnaires sent in 1945 by a committee on postwar medical service to all medical officers on duty concerning practice after the war disclosed that 8,041 wished to engage in the individual practice of medicine and 10,994 wished to practice as a member of a group.

A study[11] reported in 1947 mentioned that a 1927 publication stated that one group clinic existed in 1877 and that a survey of some New England clinics made in 1946 disclosed that such groups had existed since 1916. The American Medical Association listed 134 names and locations of group clinics in 1922. The Modern Hospital Publishing Company listed 240 clinics in 1925. A directory of "medical groups in the United States," published by the Public Health Service, listed 386 formal organizations having at least three full-time physician members each, in 1947, with a total of 3,084 full-time physicians. Nurses employed totaled 1,469.

By 1963, the National Association of Clinic Managers, organized in 1933, had some 500 members representing that number of group practice clinics. Undoubtedly there are more clinics whose managers do not belong to the association.

[11] Hunt and Goldstein: Group Practice in the United States, *J.A.M.A.*, December 6, 1947, pp. 904–9.

Some 130 clinics are represented in the membership of the American Association of Medical Clinics, which admits only physicians.

The American Association of Medical Clinics gives as its chief aims:

To raise standards of private group clinics
To foster and improve graduate medical education in such clinics
To promote clinical research work
To encourage an interchange of group practice ideas and experiences

The Federal Health Benefits Act of 1959, which became effective in July, 1960, caused membership gains by most group practice prepayment medical care plans. The recognition by Congress of the value of these plans has stimulated their development. The plans have extended the type and extent of benefits to other employee groups as a result of the benefits covered in government-negotiated contracts under the Act for Federal Employees, 90 per cent of whom are enrolled in an insurance plan. In the nine geographic areas in which 13 group practice plans are available, 73,000, or 13 per cent, of the federal employees eligible are enrolled in them. More than half of the total number of federal employees are enrolled in the government-wide service benefit plan.

The economic aspects of prepaid group practice are a large factor in the growth of this type of plan, represented by such organizations as the Health Insurance Plan of Greater New York; the Kaiser Foundation Health Plan; the Metropolitan Hospital and Clinics of Detroit; the Group Health Cooperative of Puget Sound; the Group Health Association of America, Inc., Washington, D.C.; and the United Mine Workers Welfare and Retirement Fund hospitals. Some four million persons are enrolled in prepaid group practice plans. Most of these are sponsored by union, industrial, or consumer groups rather than by physicians and contract with physicians for medical care.

There are several different kinds of clinics; the main groups may be classified as private, industrial, consumer, hospital, medical school faculty, and government. There are service groups which furnish complete family medical care to a permanent clientele; reference groups which give specialized care to patients referred to them; and diagnostic groups which specialize in diagnostic work. Such organizations as the Mayo Clinic, the University of Chicago Clinics, and the Lahey Clinic are reference groups to which referrals are made by service groups or by individual practicing physicians and are paid fees for services.

Besides having senior and junior partners, many of the private groups employ physicians on a salary basis, sometimes as a probationary device before admission for a permanent connection.

Research is an important activity in a number of the larger group clinics. The Lovelace Foundation for Medical Education and Research, a nonprofit corporation in Albuquerque, New Mexico, was created in September, 1947, a quarter of a century after the Lovelace Clinic was founded by Dr. W. R. Lovelace. The creation of the foundation marked the end of private ownership of the clinic and set up a philanthropic foundation in which no individual has an equity. The example of the Mayo Clinic–Mayo Foundation was followed in the reorganization. All net earnings of the clinic are paid to the foundation as rental for grounds, buildings, and equipment. The clinic is a voluntary association of salaried physicians engaged in the private practice of group medicine. Staff members of the clinic, individuals, and friends supplement the funds by donations. Besides the Baird Memorial Research Laboratory, the foundation has a library. Students are trained in the basic sciences in cooperation with the University of New Mexico.

The fame of the Mayo Clinic is world-wide. It was established during the period 1915 to 1917. It was formed by William W. Mayo and his two sons as a result of their experience in treating the casualties of a tornado which leveled a large part of the city of Rochester. The growth in size and prestige of the Mayo Clinic undoubtedly gave impetus to the group movement in other parts of the country. It has been said that of all the unlikely places in the world for a medical service project to thrive, Rochester, Minnesota, was the unlikeliest, but the organizing genius of the Mayos coupled with their scientific knowledge and skill brought the world to Rochester.

Standards for group practice do not exist. Several times study committees have been established for the purpose of formulating them, and as far back as 1940 one of them did so. How to implement them is the problem. The variations in types of group clinics make application of standards seem impossible, although the subject is one that is continually being brought up for discussion.

Clinic Management

The National Association of Clinic Managers has been mentioned. This is a comparatively new field of administration. Quite a number of physicians have become uncomfortably aware of the problems of administration through their participation in group practice. In the hospital they view administration at a distance usually as something which does not affect them too much personally; in the clinic where the profit and loss statement directly touches their pocketbooks, they are gaining insight into business affairs. They are having to seek persons with administrative skills to manage these clinics as they realize their own inadequacies and the time-consuming details involved. A few of them who are aware of the courses for hospital administrators express preference for applicants who are graduates of such courses.

Clinic managers themselves agree that the problems are different and less complex than those of the hospital administrator. Donald A. Starr,[12] business manager for the Tucson, Arizona, Clinic, cites one difference as that of size, the clinic being in general about a fifth as large as the average hospital; another, that of the physical plant, the clinic needing about a tenth "as many bricks" as the hospital;

[12] *Hospitals*, January 16, 1963, pp. 44–47.

a third, the complexity, the clinic needing far less equipment and not being beset by such problems as those of food service; and a fourth, the relationships, the clinic being run by the doctors, for profit, and not having a board. Mr. Starr ends his article with statements about the limitations of clinic management that give insight into the needs (here, of course, the private clinic is meant):

> A particular limitation of clinic management today may be that it is too specifically business-oriented. When we recall . . . that a few years ago 40 per cent of clinic managers were former accountants or bankers, the likelihood of bias appears clear. There is room in clinic management for the cultivation of greater understanding of the medical side of the clinic function, the relationship of physician to patient, and the nonbusiness satisfactions the physician hopes to achieve from his association with a group. As in hospital administration, the responsibilities of directing the administrative affairs of a medical clinic are complex, challenging and, to most of its practitioners, intensely interesting and satisfying. As medical group practice grows to become, as it is predicted it will, the predominant form of medical practice in this country, opportunities for men and women of ability in medical administration will greatly multiply. . . .

Relationship of Clinics to Hospitals

Diagnosis and preventive medicine are the chief functions of a considerable proportion of group practice clinics. Therapy, especially surgery, is usually delegated to an affiliated hospital unless the clinic group maintains a hospital of its own. A few of them have tried to do this to their regret. Operating a hospital without losing money is not easy, they have discovered. Physicians like the feeling of control of hospital policies that owning the inpatient facilities gives; they do not like the problems. Circumstances govern, however, and in some instances combined clinic-hospital operation is proving successful.

In general, the relationship between group practice clinics and hospitals is cooperative rather than competitive.

CHAPTER 4

The Professions Allied to Medicine

In the early days of medicine the doctor did all of the work—diagnosed the illness, prescribed and prepared the medicines and administered them to the patient. Now, the pharmacist takes a big load off the doctor's shoulders.

Occupational therapists are medical associates who help smooth out the wrinkles from worried brows, wrinkles caused by crippled legs, arms, hands and bodies.

The patient is on the table. It is an important operation, and the surgeon has discovered unforeseen complications that perhaps have never arisen before. It is an unusual case and one that should be reported thoroughly in the annals of surgery. This is where medical artists are almost indispensable . . . many a life is saved due to the knowledge imparted by doctors of medicine aided by medical artists.
MICHIGAN STATE MEDICAL SOCIETY[1]

IT HAS been estimated that there are some 180 types of work conducted in hospitals. The main classifications of personnel who perform them number at least fifty. The Tri-State Hospital Assembly has 36 sections of personnel who plan their own programs for the annual meeting.

All of the workers in medical service institutions are in a sense allied to the medical profession in that every one of them contributes in some way to the welfare of the patient. In this chapter, however, the concern is with those professions whose members directly aid the physician in ways that affect his treatment.

[1] Extracts from 3 of the 22 descriptions of careers as "medical associates" in a brochure published by the society as an aid to recruitment of ancillary personnel (undated).

Unification of effort by these different professional personnel is obviously necessary. However, in this chapter there is a deliberate lack of uniformity in the pattern of presentation of the sections into which it is divided. Each section is a study in itself, approached and developed as a separate entity, with the focus on the distinctive aspects.

The beginnings of the ancillary or auxiliary medical professions in the early years of the twentieth century were concisely traced by Dr. Arthur C. Bachmeyer:[2]

The x-ray service was meager and limited for the most part to the examination of the bony structures. The equipment was crude and its operation hazardous to roentgenologist and often to the patient. Roentgen ray therapy was in its early infancy and was seldom utilized. Radium and radium therapy were unknown.

Physical therapy was limited to the use of fomentations, Priessnitz applications, baths, douches, baking, massage, and in a restricted measure to Galvanic and Faradic electrical currents. Separate departments were found only in special institutions. There was no diathermy, no ultra-violet, infra-red or other radiation therapy.

Clinical laboratories were crude and poorly equipped when compared with those of today. For the most part such facilities were located in remote rooms. The equipment in most of them consisted of a poor microscope or two, a small and inefficient centrifuge, a few slides, test tubes, beakers and pipettes, a few reagents and stains and possibly a crude incubator that seldom was in order. Tests made consisted of rough hemoglobin determinations, red, white and differential blood counts, urine and gastric analyses, which for the most part were qualitative and less often of roughly quantitative type. There was little bacteriologic work done, no serological analyses, no blood chemistry. There were no trained technicians. To substantiate this statement I might cite the experience in a teaching institution in which the number of examinations in the clinical laboratories in 1910 did not exceed 1,500, whereas in the same institution in 1934 the total exceeded 42,000.

The hospital of 25 years ago [1915] had no laboratory for the determination of basal metabolism, no electrocardiograph. Many other diagnostic instruments now in general use were not to be found. Biopsy examinations were infrequent and in most instances there was comparatively little pathological work performed. . . . Few biological products were available and serious reactions frequently followed their administration. There has been an enormous increase in hypodermic, intramuscular and intravenous medication. These developments have called for new aptitudes on the part of nurses.

Though occupational therapy may be said to date from 1904 when Dr. Herbert J. Hall established his first workshop, it was not until after the War that such departments were instituted in hospitals generally.

Medical records, when made, were very meager and little attention was paid to their filing and study.

Though the use of diet in treatment is not new, there were but few dietitians employed in hospitals 25 years ago and special diets were few and far between. . . .

Nurses labored at the bedside twelve or more hours per day. Student nurses received little instruction in classroom or laboratory. Few of the students had sufficient education to profit by such teaching had it been given. Though the

[2] Talk before the Iowa Hospital Association in Iowa City. *Bull. Am. Hosp. A.*, July, 1935.

standards for admission to nursing schools have been raised and hours of duty shortened, it is to be regretted that *the training of the nurse has not kept pace* with the advances that have been made in other fields of education. Nurses have been and remain the victims of a faulty method of education. . . .

Another major development of this period was that of the social service department. Here a whole new field of human endeavor has become well established, largely due, in my opinion, to the passing of the old type of physician and to the fact that the modern practitioner of medicine, especially the type we see in our hospitals, devotes his primary attention to the science of medicine and to organic pathology. Busily occupied by these interests, he is prone to pass over the social aspects of his patients' needs and has left their solution to some other person. The social worker soon developed to serve in this capacity. . . .

Note particularly the reference to nursing education in the light of the tumult that began reaching a peak a quarter of a century after this talk. The nurse, having preceded all of the other ancillary professional members as an assistant to the doctor, was the first one for whom a training program was conducted, and much of its nineteenth-century pattern remains despite strenuous efforts to remold it in accordance with the academic standards of other medical auxiliary groups.

MEDICAL RELATIONSHIPS WITH THE ALLIED PROFESSIONS

By undertaking the responsibility of inspecting, reporting, and approving schools for the training of their prospective members, the Council on Medical Education and Hospitals of the American Medical Association has created a strong link between the medical and several of the allied professions. It has further strengthened this link by formulating its "essentials" for approval with the cooperation of the respective national associations of these professions. They, in turn, have coordinated their membership and registration requirements with its educational standards.

It was pointed out by a speaker[3] at a symposium held in London, England, on "the use of medical auxiliary services," that while the organizations whose members rendered these services had done much "to raise the standards of training and ethical conduct," there were those who had little or no training who "took advantage of the lack of statutory control to practice various methods of treatment on the unsuspecting public." The ultimate responsibility, this speaker declared, belonged to the medical profession, from whose point of view it was essential "that a doctor should be able to refer a patient for treatment to persons in whom he could have absolute confidence that they fully understood the kind of treatment required, and that they were qualified to undertake such treatment." Accordingly in the early 1930's the British Medical Association held conferences to study training programs and registration, feeling that it was not "the best of arrangements" for organizations to train and register their own members and

[3] A. M. A. Moore, Consultant Surgeon, London Hospital, and President, Board of Registration of Medical Auxiliaries: *J. Roy. Soc. Health,* **79:** 847, 1959.

that "a separate controlling registering body is surely the best guarantee of the maintenance of adequate standards."

Although the American Medical Association does not follow this idea to the extent of registration, the fact that the organizations accept as basic to registration the association's essentials for training makes the practice similar to that of the British Board of Registration of Medical Auxiliaries, which was established in 1936.

The professions for which the A.M.A. conducts an educational approval program are:

Medical Records (librarians and technicians), in collaboration with the Committee on Education and Registration of the American Association of Medical Record Librarians (programs in Canada are approved by the Canadian Association of Medical Record Librarians)

Medical Technology, in collaboration with the Board of Schools of Medical Technology, American Society of Clinical Pathologists (programs in Canada are approved by the Committee on Approval of Schools for Laboratory Technologists of the Canadian Medical Association)

Occupational Therapy, in collaboration with the American Occupational Therapy Association (programs in Canada are approved by the Canadian Association of Occupational Therapy)

Physical Therapy, in collaboration with the American Physical Therapy Association (programs in Canada are approved by the Canadian Physiotherapy Association)

X-ray Technology, in collaboration with the American College of Radiology (programs in Canada are approved by the Canadian Medical Association and the Canadian Society of Radiological Technicians)

Approval programs for schools for other professions allied to medicine are conducted by the following:

Dentistry—Council on Dental Education of the American Dental Association (includes Canada)

Dietetics—American Dietetic Association (in Canada, Canadian Dietetic Association)

Hospital and Medical Librarianship—American Library Association

Nurse Anesthetists—American Association of Nurse Anesthetists

Practical Nursing—The respective state, territorial, or provincial approving authorities, or (in Colorado, District of Columbia and West Virginia) the National Association for Practical Nurse Education. Reported for the United States by National League for Nursing; for Canada by the Canadian Hospital Association

Professional Nursing—The respective state, territorial, or provincial approving authorities. Reported for the United States by National League for Nursing; for Canada by the Canadian Hospital Association

Pharmacy—American Council on Pharmaceutical Education (in Canada, Canadian Hospital Association)

Social Work—Council on Social Work Education

Lists of A.M.A. approved schools are published in the annual "Educational Number" of the *Journal of the American Medical Association*. Lists of all of the approved schools are published in the annual "Guide Issue" of *Hospitals,* the journal of the American Hospital Association.

The Joint Commission on Accreditation of Hospitals and the Canadian Council on Hospital Accreditation, following the pattern established by the American College of Surgeons, recognize and promote in their accreditation programs the standards for the education of personnel promulgated by the associations concerned. The educational element is emphasized in the respective standards for conduct of the department in which the personnel function.

The American Hospital Association and the Canadian Hospital Association likewise in their meetings and publications stress education, basic and continuing.

This intermeshing of interest and activity in striving for high quality of preparation for the allied professions has contributed immeasurably to their advancement for the ultimate good of the patient and the public.

Dentistry

In dentistry, as in other professions allied to medicine, there is an acute shortage of personnel. To offset this somewhat by conserving the time of the dentist, auxiliary personnel are increasingly being utilized—dental assistants, dental technicians, dental hygienists. Whether he practices in an office or in a hospital the dentist is becoming the head of a staff. Like the physician, he needs to have in his educational preparation some orientation to administrative techniques and relationships. The administrator likewise needs to be acquainted with the world of dentistry, its history, its organization, its personnel, its expanding future. The American Dental Association and its local societies are a significant part of his professional public.

Dentistry as a profession distinct from medicine, or from just tooth-pulling performed by barbers or itinerants, began in the middle of the eighteenth century. Nevertheless, numerous evidences have been found that dentistry was skillfully practiced from earliest times, especially by the Etruscans in Italy.

The first dental school and society were founded by Chapin A. Harris at Baltimore in 1840. In 1900 Edwin Hartley Angle, of Philadelphia, organized a School of Orthodontia and in 1901 a Society of Orthodontists, one of the first of the specialized groups. The American Dental Association had been founded in 1859, more than twenty years before the start of the bacteriological age when dentistry acquired new significance from the standpoint of its relationship to health as a whole.

As the third largest profession, with some 100,000 members, dentistry has progressed rapidly through research, improved educational methods, development of new anesthetics and techniques of treatment, technological advancement, and public education. The American Dental Association has councils on research, therapeutics, and dental health. It is generally recognized that the United States has led the world in dental progress.

About one-fourth of the acute general hospitals in the United States have dental departments, and one-third of *all* United States hospitals. Convinced that as a community health center, practically every hospital should include dentistry among its services, Norbert F. Lindskog chose as the subject for his thesis submitted to Northwestern University in 1960, "A Study of the Role of the Dentist on the Hospital Staff." (Mr. Lindskog is now assistant director, Louis A. Weiss Memorial Hospital, Chicago.) The following is adapted from that part of his paper which deals with the general background rather than the internal operational aspects of this service.

The first hospital to be exclusively devoted to the practice of dentistry was recently opened in Los Angeles. It provides dentists and oral surgeons with the facilities and staff privileges which are customarily accorded medical doctors in a general hospital. John May,[4] president of the firm which manages the dental hospital, stated: "It is our belief that the best way to bring dental service to the public and still achieve the objectives desired by the dental profession is for doctors of dentistry to have their own hospitals."

This is a step further than hospital dentistry has gone in other areas.[5] In fact, in many hospitals in the United States the dentist is not admitted to the staff and must confine his work to clinics and his own office. Many dentists feel that they should be admitted to the hospital staff—that their services are only one facet of health care necessary in providing complete services to the hospitalized patient. They point to the transfer of obstetrics from the home to the hospital and of surgical service from the doctor's office to the hospital as steps toward better patient care. They contend that transfer of oral surgery and complicated dental cases from the dentist's office to the hospital is a logical step in the same direction.

Generally, the medical profession does not dispute that dental services should be offered in the hospital, especially the long-term hospital. They contend, however, that dentists are not doctors of medicine and that doctors of dental surgery cannot be given complete admitting rights.

Most hospital administrators agree that offering dental facilities is necessary in providing complete hospital services, but feel that the administrative and financial obstacles may be greater than the advantages offered for their particular operation.

From the standpoint of all groups interested, there seems to be common agreement that "the problems involved in initiating and operating a hospital dental service are great. . . . It is these problems, rather than a lack of interest or desire, which have kept dentistry out of the majority of our hospitals."[6]

[4] New Hospital Designed for Dental Patients Only. *Hospitals,* **33:** 102, 1959.
[5] Early in 1961 the first round-the-clock emergency dental care clinic in the United States was established at Hollywood Presbyterian Hospital–Olmstead Memorial, Los Angeles. The hospital had 53 members on its dental staff.
[6] Alfred E. Maffly and Robert A. Craig: What's Keeping Dentistry out of the General Hospital? *Mod. Hosp.,* **85:** 82, 1955.

Status of Dentistry in Hospitals

Latest figures indicate that about one-third of the hospitals in the United States have a dental department. Size and services vary greatly, some having one practitioner giving very limited service, others having many dentists giving complete dental services. In late 1957, 2,241 of 6,966 hospitals had organized dental departments. Formal approval had been extended by the Council on Hospital Dental Service of the American Dental Association to 430 of the institutions which had dental departments. Besides maintaining dental departments, 190 of the hospitals had dental internship and residency training programs.[7] Only about 6 per cent of the total hospitals in the United States had dental departments approved by the American Dental Association, and only about 3 per cent offered approved training programs. Dental services are available in more long-term than short-term institutions—from 50 to 90 per cent of the long-term general, psychiatric, tuberculosis, and federal hospitals, compared with about 25 per cent of the short-term acute hospitals.[8]

Many hospitals which have less than 150 beds extend "courtesy" privileges to dentists who are professionally acceptable. Basically, these dentists act as consultants for medical doctors. Because of lack of funds and the limited needs for complete dental services, this type of courtesy privilege is probably satisfactory in smaller hospitals. It should not suffice for larger ones, especially if outpatient service exists.

Need for Better Dental Service in Hospitals

Dental offices and dental clinics no longer are adequate to meet the needs of some of the more serious dental problems. It is impossible to separate the practice of dentistry completely from the practice of medicine. Very often a diagnosis of a malfunction in a patient entails combining these services. If dental services were more commonly available in hospitals, many patients suffering from diseases which have oral manifestations would receive a *total* treatment which would aid in their recovery. Including dental records in the medical records kept in the hospital, and consultation between doctors and dentists, could improve treatment and shorten the length of hospital stay in many instances. Reasons why dentistry should be practiced in the hospital are:

1. Availability of laboratory service and medical consultation.
2. Availability of operating rooms and endotracheal anesthesia for more complicated oral surgery.
3. Availability of postoperative care to speed recovery of the patient through controlled medication, good nursing care, constant observation, and correct diet.

[7] Hospital Dental Service—A Progress Report to the Profession. *ADA Information Bulletin*. Chicago, American Dental Association, p. 1.
[8] Rudolph H. Friedrich: Dentistry in Hospitals. *Hospitals,* **31**: 36, 1957.

4. Possibility of complete extensive oral surgery in one stage rather than in several episodes as would be necessary in the dentist's office.

5. Possibility of controlling infection through constant observation of patients with complicated conditions which require a series of dental treatments.

The dentist, physician, and administration must understand that "legally, a dentist can never be a member of the *medical* staff since he is not a licensed physician. If such an appointment is made and the dentist, in his treatment of the patient, is negligent, in some states the hospital can be held liable if the staff bylaws provide that only licensed physicians are eligible for appointment as members."[9] To avoid this contingency, the hospital staff should be a medical and dental staff, and the bylaws should limit the rights of dentists on the basis of their education and experience the same as physicians are limited on this basis. Dental service should be included in the title of the bylaws. Questions about authority can be avoided by including the following statement, approved by the American Hospital Association and the Joint Commission on Accreditation of Hospitals, in the hospital bylaws:

> In all cases, the hospitalized dental patient must have an admission history and physical examination done by a physician on the medical staff of the hospital, and likewise, a physician on the medical staff of the hospital shall be responsible for the patient's medical care throughout his entire stay.[10]

A dentist "should be appointed to the dental staff of the hospital and given such privileges as he is competent to have on the dental staff. Usually a dentist attends the medical staff meetings in his capacity as a dental staff member, participates in medical staff discussions, and may even hold office."[11] An authority[12] states: "Limitations of dental practice are determined by the location of the disease and not by the nature of the problem or the method of treatment. All acute diseases of the mouth and jaws are either medical or surgical interferences with the pathological process." This indicates that the physician's services are as necessary in the treatment of acute dental problems as are those of the dentist.

It has been suggested that routine dental examinations be included as part of the physical examination given medical, surgical, and obstetrical patients upon admission. Early detection of systemic diseases manifested through oral symptoms can help to eliminate complicated medical conditions before they become major problems. This concept has not been widely accepted in the hospital field because dentistry as such has not been integrated into the total care programs of many general hospitals.

Most states permit a dentist to administer an anesthetic as incidental to the practice of dentistry; however, most hospitals do not consider it good practice

---

[9] Dental Privileges. *Trustee,* **7**: 25, 1955.
[10] *Ibid.*
[11] Dentist's Position in the Hospital. *Hospitals,* **29**: 32, 1955.
[12] Friedrich, *op. cit.,* p. 36.

for a dentist to administer a general anesthetic while also doing dental work.[13] Many oral surgical procedures, however, do not require comprehensive anesthetics as given by the anesthesiologist. Many minor oral surgery and exodontia cases as well as minor problems of general surgery could be done on an outpatient basis, and cooperative effort by the dentist and anesthesiologist could help to bring about this economy.

Qualifications

All dentists privileged to practice in the hospital should be graduates of dental schools recognized at the time of graduation by the Council on Dental Education of the American Dental Association and legally licensed to practice in the locality; should be members of the American Dental Association or the National Dental Association, or eligible for membership in these associations; and should be worthy in personal character and in professional ethics.

Standards for Accreditation

The boards of the American Dental Association and the Joint Commission on Accreditation of Hospitals approved the following interpretation of the dental staff standards:[14]

Depending upon the local situations and the qualifications of the individuals involved, a "surgical service" may be the oral surgical service to which the members of the dental staff admit and discharge dental patients, provided that this service is the responsibility of the chief of the department of surgery and that . . . an adequate medical survey, by a member of the service to which admitted, shall be done on each patient before dental surgery. Indicated consultations shall be held in complicated cases . . . the bylaws of the staff would indicate that the staff of the hospital would be a "medical and dental" staff and that within the framework of the hospital's staff bylaws, dentists would be appointed to and hold appointments in the division of oral surgery just as physicians and surgeons are appointed to other services of the hospital.

Dental Specialties

The American Dental Association suggests that the dental service should develop programs in the following areas in accordance with local needs and facilities available: dentistry for children (pedodontics); restorative dentistry; periodontics; dental roentgenology; oral surgery; and oral pathology.

Seven boards of specialties have been recognized by the Council on Dental Education of the American Dental Association. They include the American Board of Dental Public Health, American Board of Oral Pathology, American

---

[13] *Ibid.*
[14] Report on Conference between American Dental Association and the Joint Commission on Accreditation of Hospitals. *J. Am. Dental A.*, **48**: 314, 1954.

Board of Oral Surgery, American Board of Orthodontics, American Board of Pedodontics, American Board of Periodontology, and American Board of Prosthodontics. These boards are concerned primarily with the training of residents and usually certify only graduates of hospital programs approved by the board concerned.

Dietetics

The profession of dietetics developed from the cooking schools of London, Boston, New York, and Philadelphia. It was a slow development. Ellen H. Richards, who in 1871 was a special student in chemistry at the Massachusetts Institute of Technology, commented: "Life is conditioned on the food supply, and the first place in which all the scientific knowledge of food as a remedial agent should be applied is in the hospital kitchen. But as the old adage, 'Shoemaker's children go barefoot,' so the hospital is the last to show the effects of modern science."

Sarah Tyson Rorer was a pioneer dietitian before the name was coined. She opened a diet kitchen in the 1870's in Philadelphia at the request of three physicians. Physicians sent their patients to her with prescriptions for food. In those days wealthy patients shunned hospitals and stayed at home or in hotels. She also held classes for doctors and encouraged them to experiment with foods.

The graduates of the cooking schools gradually began to be sought by hospitals. Besides organizing the dietary service at Johns Hopkins Hospital in 1889, Mary Boland, a graduate of the Boston Cooking School, taught nurses how to cook for the sick. The Presbyterian Hospital at Philadelphia organized a diet kitchen in 1893.

In Canada, the first dietitian, a graduate of a course in nutrition and dietetics at the University of Toronto, was appointed to the Hospital for Sick Children, Toronto, in 1907.

Back of these beginnings of the profession of dietetics was a long history of research and study of the relationships between nutrition and disease by medical scientists. The Mosaic code, with its taboos, is an early example of an effort to regulate diet because of discoveries of harmful substances that were consumed as food. As Celsus commented: "In this way, medicine had its rise from the experience of the recovery of some, of the death of others, distinguishing the hurtful from the salutary things."

The American Dietetic Association was organized in 1917 and the Canadian Dietetic Association in 1935. More than half of the membership of both are hospital dietitians. Both exercise strong influence in raising the standards of education and training for this profession. Membership requirements are based on these standards plus satisfactory experience.

Attendance at the third International Congress of Dietetics, held at London in July, 1961, totaled 839 dietitians from 40 countries. The theme was "Tradition, Science, and Practice in Dietetics." Most of those countries which do not yet require a university or equivalent education for the profession reported that they were working toward establishment of that level. In France the profession has existed only since 1953, which contrasts with Japan in which a school of dietetics at Tokyo was established in 1924. In 1965 the congress is scheduled to be held in Stockholm, Sweden; in 1969 in the United States.

Trends

The shortage of dietitians is acute. For some reason the profession is losing its attractiveness, and recruitment needs to be stepped up. Each year the number of vacancies in hospital internships grows larger. The shortage, plus the rapid turnover, is causing hospitals and other medical service institutions to devise new ways of keeping the food service going. Some share dietitians with other hospitals; others use consultant dietitians; many employ food service managers; a few contract with outside catering services. The latter two methods do not dispense with the need for a professional dietitian or dietetic consultant, but they do reduce the number of dietitians required.

Strong objections to these devices are expressed at organization meetings and in articles in the association journals. Recognizing, however, that some of the fault lies in the inadequate preparation of the dietitian for administrative responsibility, the associations are advocating more training in this area both before and after graduaton. For example, a 12-month correspondence course for the training of food service supervisors was started in October, 1960, by the American Dietetic Association with the help of a grant from the W. K. Kellogg Foundation.

Emphasis on nutrition—the scientific aspect—rather than just on food service is the great need in strengthening the profession from both the standpoint of recruitment and that of patient welfare. This need is well expressed in the final statement of a two-part article, "Role and Status of the Professional Dietitian," prepared by the Quebec Dietetic Association:[15]

> The professional aspect of hospital dietetics should be strengthened by including dietitians as members of the hospital medical team as much as possible. The importance of nutrition in its preventive and curative roles should be stressed in medical education, and dietitians should be given an opportunity to assist in this part of the program, so that their role in the hospital will be understood by medical personnel.

Publications

The American Dietetic Association publishes manuals from time to time and also a monthly periodical, the *Journal*.

[15] *Canad. Hosp.*, January, 1961 (p. 54); February, 1961 (pp. 84–85). Article extracted from a brief which contained organizational charts and salary recommendations, obtainable in either English or French from Miss H. Neilson, Box 285, Macdonald College, Ste. Anne de Bellevue, Province of Quebec, Canada.

INHALATION THERAPY

The introduction of inhalation therapy must be hailed as a lifesaving and discomfort-relieving procedure. The groundwork was laid in 1774 when Joseph Priestley, of Leeds, England, proved that oxygen was a necessity for animal life. That the air contained two gases had been stated in the late fifteenth century by Leonardo da Vinci and that oxygen could be liberated from seven different substances had been demonstrated about the same time by Karl Scheele, of Sweden. The latter's work, however, was not published until 1777, so that it is generally conceded that Priestley takes precedence as the discoverer of oxygen.

Lavoisier also experimented with oxygen. No noteworthy practical results followed until the time of World War I, when J. S. Haldane popularized oxygen therapy. Alvan L. Barach, in connection with air warfare, showed that at elevations of 10,000 feet or more, aviators needed a supply of oxygen. Understanding of its value physiologically was increased by the experiments of C. K. Drinker and J. Bancroft. Several other scientists contributed to knowledge of inhalation therapy procedures by demonstrating the improved results obtained by giving 5 to 7 per cent carbon dioxide with oxygen. The benefits were increasing the average depth of respiration 250 per cent, increasing the average respiratory rate 50 per cent, and increasing the cerebral blood flow 75 per cent.

Gordon S. Boughton,[16] now administrator of Madison County Community Hospital, Anderson, Indiana, summed up a discussion of the physiology of respiration by stating:

It is apparent that the oxygen and carbon dioxide diffusion process is dependent on the correct number of red cells, the adequate percentage of hemoglobin in the blood, and the proper viscosity and specific gravity of the blood. Therefore when conditions exist causing marked diminution in the red cell count, reduction in the hemoglobin content, and higher viscosity, immediate therapeutic measures must be initiated to get oxygen to and carbon dioxide from the tissues. Otherwise deterioration in the condition of the tissues of the various organs of the body can be expected, and permanent damage of the tissues is a very real possibility.

Later in his paper, speaking of the basic problem of medical staff acceptance, Mr. Boughton states:

Volumes have been written relative to the application of basic physiological concepts in the clinical practice of medicine. Water-salt regulation and acid-base balance have been reduced to simple rules and chemical equivalents. Shock and dehydration are now measured in terms of specific gravity and by hematocrit index. Yet with all these developments and advances, one of the most life-sustaining and live-giving agents, oxygen, has been neglected by most physicians. Following the works of Priestley and Lavoisier, oxygen was hailed as a panacea for all the ills of man, but before long oxygen therapy fell into dis-

[16] In his thesis, A Study of Oxygen Therapy in the General Hospital, submitted to Northwestern University in 1957.

repute. Interest in oxygen from a therapeutic standpoint was revived during World War I. Rapid progress has been made in the development of oxygen therapy techniques and of equipment for administering oxygen. Happily this has been paralleled by the rapid development of technical personnel in more recent years. Unfortunately, it is all too common to find physicians and surgeons indifferent to or unaware of the great value of oxygen therapy. If interested at all, a verbal order is given without specific direction as to method of administration, concentration desired, and suggested rate of flow. Others seem to believe that oxygen is to be given only when the patient is in *extremis*.

The administrator who wishes to gain a general knowledge of the rather new realm of inhalation therapy should familiarize himself with the history and activities of the American Association of Inhalation Therapists. The work of this organization has had much to do with the growing acceptance by physicians of this mode of treatment.

Leading anesthesiologists and a few other interested physicians actively promoted the group in its infancy, helped it to organize, and regularly appear on its programs. Dr. Malcolm T. MacEachern gave it, like many other groups, its first powerful boost when in 1948 he created a place for it as a distinct section on the program of the Tri-State Hospital Assembly. Thus he planted the idea of a formal organization which was born the following year under the name of Inhalation Therapy Association with Rev. Brother Roland Maher, R.N., of Alexian Brothers Hospital, Chicago, as the first president. National organization soon followed. Late in 1963 A.M.A. approved a school survey and accreditation program in cooperation with the association, the American College of Chest Physicians and the American Society of Anesthesiologists.

Without the therapists, advance in inhalation therapy would have been slow and slight. As in physical medicine, the procedures are too exacting and too time-consuming to be undertaken by physicians alone. Aids were essential in both areas, and their origin may be traced to the wars, when soldiers and sailors were assigned to new services born of the emergencies.

What is the nature of the inhalation therapist's duties? Picking up again the Boughton thesis referred to, we quote his summary:

> The average patient receiving oxygen therapy is generally a mighty sick person. He is often restless, apprehensive, emotionally upset and confused. There is the constant risk that in his threshing about, the set-up of oxygen equipment will be disarranged, and the effectiveness of the administration of oxygen will be reduced. Obviously the equipment must be checked and rechecked often.
>
> There is danger in having dual responsibility for checking oxygen equipment. However, the equipment can never be checked too often. Ward nurses under adequate supervision can discover quickly and correct any leaks or other reasons for inadequate administration. The technicians when making their rounds can note deficiencies and report them immediately to the nurses. . . .
>
> The most commonly used methods for the administration of oxygen are: (1) oropharyngeal insufflation by catheter at a flow of six liters per minute to attain 50 to 70 per cent concentration; (2) face mask at a flow of from 6 to 10 liters per minute for the highest concentration of any method (also most efficient);

(3) oxygen tent at a flow of 10 to 12 liters per minute for a 40 to 60 per cent concentration (the most comfortable but least efficient method).

When a call is received, the therapist enters the patient's name and location, name of attending physician, method of administration, name of the caller, and time of call. Before taking the administering apparatus into the patient's room, he checks with the section supervisor, and the private nurse if there is one. If the patient is conscious, he introduces himself when he enters the room and explains what is to be done. He notices whether it will be necessary to rearrange the furniture. . . . When possible, it is advisable to have the supervisor and the attending nurse present when therapy is started to be sure that the physician's orders are properly interpreted. . . . After starting therapy, the therapist should remain with the patient until the prescribed concentration is actually being delivered, and he is thoroughly satisfied that the apparatus is functioning properly and is understood by the nurses. He also makes certain that everyone, including the patient, is acquainted with all safety precautions, particularly the "no smoking" rule. . . . He should revisit the patient within the first hour, if possible, and certainly within three hours. It is in this period that treatment is most difficult for the patient and the administering apparatus is most likely to need attention. A mask or catheter may not be fitted comfortably. Temperature or humidity of a tent may have to be adjusted to suit the patient's condition or wants. . . . Subsequent visits should ideally be made every four hours but at least once every eight hours. These visits provide an opportunity to make sure that the patient is tolerating the therapy well; that the administering techniques are still proper for the patient's present condition; and that all details of the treatment are correct. He should not make changes from those prescribed without consulting the attending physician however.

Mr. Boughton suggests as solutions to the problem that hospitals organize oxygen therapy committees of their medical staffs and that skilled inhalation therapy technicians cooperate with these committees in acquainting the physicians with the benefits of treatment administered by skilled personnel in accordance with rapidly increasing knowledge.

Inhalation therapy is commonly prescribed for such conditions as pneumonia, emphysema, bronchial obstructions, bronchial asthma, pulmonary edema, severe anemia, respiratory paralysis, bronchial infections in the newborn, premature birth, asphyxia, and heart disease. Severe oxygen deficiency damages the brain, adrenals, heart, kidney, and liver.

The anesthesiologist is the physician who is the most logical head of the inhalation therapy division, the two fields being most closely allied in their physiological aspects. In those hospitals which have a bronchoesophagologist, he is also a good choice for director of the department.

Recognizing the lag in utilization of inhalation therapy in their country, the Canadian Medical Association and the Canadian Anaesthetists' Society appointed in 1962 a pilot committee to study the problems and to work toward their solution. The therapists are organized in the Canadian Association of Inhalation Therapists with some 60 members, but there are no standards for their training and qualification. A course was started around 1947 at the Queen

Mary Veterans Hospital, Montreal, but few Canadian hospitals have established inhalation therapy departments. The situation will improve with the new support of the medical organizations to recruit and train therapists.

MEDICAL LIBRARIANSHIP

"The rise of the medical librarian to professional status, like that of many members of other professions allied to the medical world, really came as a result of a need for persons who could help the doctor in the indexing and cataloguing of research." So begins a talk given by George Brotherton in 1950 to Alpha Delta Mu Fraternity at Northwestern University. The following account of the history of this profession is adapted from Mr. Brotherton's paper.

History of the Medical Library Association

The Medical Library Association was organized in 1898 through the efforts of four lay people and four doctors. Margaret Charlton, librarian of the McGill University Medical School, Montreal, Canada, is credited with originating the idea. She belonged to the American Library Association, but she realized this did not fill the specialized needs of her professional work. Equal credit goes to Drs. William Osler and George M. Gould, who initiated the action for its formation. (Dr. Gould was then editor of the *Philadelphia Medical Journal* and later of *American Medicine*.) Seven libraries were represented at the first meeting in Dr. Gould's office, at which time he outlined eight activities that an association of medical libraries could carry on through committees:

1. Exchange of material between libraries
2. Obtaining of libraries from retired or deceased doctors
3. Distribution of minutes of medical society meetings
4. Establishment of a committee on rare books and auction sales
5. Obtaining of endowments for medical libraries
6. Compiling of a united catalogue of rare items
7. Abstracting of special information
8. Formation of a committee on library management

These recommendations were accepted, were implemented after the association was organized, and have been followed through the years.

As a result of this meeting, the association was formed under the name of Association of Medical Librarians, which was changed in the first decade of the twentieth century to Medical Library Association. The executive committee consisted of Miss Charlton and three doctors. Dr. Gould was elected president and served in that capacity for three years. He submitted a resolution to the American Medical Association for the organization of the group which was unanimously approved with an agreement to encourage the formation of medical libraries and to furnish member libraries with complimentary copies of the A.M.A. *Journal.*

In 1928 the bylaws were revised to include three classifications of members: library or institutional members; supporting members—any person interested in medical or allied libraries; and professional members or trained medical librarians. The institutional members were the voting members. In 1931 the association was incorporated in Maryland and the constitution amended to provide for honorary membership.

Until 1933 all of the presidents were physicians. Since that year, with the exception of two years, the president has been a professional medical librarian.

About 1933 the dental libraries became active in the association, followed in 1937 by the hospital libraries. This is one of the allied medical professions that was formed primarily outside of the hospital but nevertheless has been of great benefit to the hospital library.

From 1898 to 1902 the official organ of the association was *Medical Libraries.* Its successor was the *Medical Library and Historical Journal.* Since 1911 the official publication is the *Bulletin.* In 1943 was published the *Handbook of Medical Library Practice,* which had been originally proposed in 1920. It is based on the preliminary manuscript of M. Irene Jones, edited by Janet Doe with the aid of a special committee. (A second edition of the *Handbook* was published in 1956, edited by Janet Doe and M. L. Marshall.)

The "exchange" recommended by Dr. Gould came into being in December, 1899. It was popular from the first and has served to hold the association together whenever there was danger of dissolution.

Acceptance of the Profession

Of all the people of the medical school faculty or hospital staff, the librarian is undoubtedly the one who will help the most in making the medical student a good scholar. Her public is the doctor and the medical student, chiefly. Her work has a direct bearing on good patient care, which is recognized by the American College of Surgeons in its surveys for approval of hospitals (and since the transfer of hospital standardization, by the Joint Commission on Accreditation of Hospitals).

Certification Program of the Medical Library Association

In the chapter on hospital libraries which she contributed to Dr. MacEachern's *Hospital Organization and Management,* L. Margueriete Prime, librarian of the American College of Surgeons until her retirement in 1960, describes courses in medical librarianship offered by several schools and refers to the certification program of the Medical Library Association which was established to encourage special training. She states:[17]

[17] Hospital Libraries, in *Hospital Organization and Management,* 3rd ed., 1957, p. 842.

Charter certification, which was initiated in 1949, was closed as of April 13, 1954. Thereafter certification is open only to persons who have taken courses in medical librarianship or have, in exceptional cases, presented other credentials acceptable to the subcommittee on certification. The Medical Library Association concurrently initiated and put into effect an aggressive recruitment program. It is hoped that this program will provide more well-trained librarians for the medical library field.

MEDICAL RECORD LIBRARIANSHIP

A librarian does not write the books in her library. Neither does the medical record librarian write the medical records in her department. Many persons outside the hospital have this misconception of her duties, vaguely likening her to the bookkeeper who makes the entries in the financial ledgers. There is no parallel. The doctors write and have the full responsibility for the essential part of the record. Nurses' and other notes may be attached but are supplemental.

The significant difference between the two kinds of librarians is that the regular librarians' material is completed when she receives it; the medical record librarian has to work unceasingly upon her "authors" to get them to do their writing. She has to know in general what should go into the record and has to prod the doctor subtly and constantly to produce an accurate, thorough case history. When her efforts are in vain, she has to have the administrator join her in the prodding, working through the medical records committee of the medical staff. Frequently he has to threaten withdrawal of privileges before he gets action; sometimes he has to carry out the threat. On every medical staff there are delinquents in this respect. As Dr. MacEachern once remarked, "The medical record library is probably the top ranking place in the world for the delivery of alibis."

As will be discussed in Chapter 8, the medical record is the measuring rod of the quality of medical care in the hospital. Education of the physician to the point at which he appreciates this fact is the solution to the medical record problem. Some forty years ago it began to be realized that a specially trained person had to be entrusted with the responsibility of making certain that the doctor wrote his records promptly and properly, turned them in, and used them to study and improve his work. The medical record librarian came into being to make the record room a vital spot for making records available for review and for clinical research, as well as for the safekeeping and quick accessibility of classified case histories. She combines with the physician's record the nurses' notes, the laboratory and x-ray reports, and records of any special services, so that the complete story of treatment of a given patient is assembled. It is necessary on occasion for her to bring the record to court when litigation is involved.

The profession of medical record librarianship began in 1897 when Massachusetts General Hospital employed a librarian to catalogue and file the medical records. She was Mrs. Grace Whiting Myers. She was called a records clerk, and soon other hospitals in the Boston area copied the idea. In 1913 a group of these records clerks began to hold regular meetings in Boston. In the same year, 1913, the American College of Surgeons was founded. Records of 50 major operations performed by the surgeon, and 50 other major operations in which he was the assistant, were supposed to accompany applications for fellowships. Few surgeons could produce the complete, scientific records desired. Suddenly, in a very practical way, the deficiencies of recordkeeping in the hospitals were disclosed. The college acted upon the disclosure by drawing up and making available forms on which to record the information needed.

World War I interrupted civilian activity in this direction, but this was more than made up for by the insistence of the medical department of the United States Army upon painstaking recording of case histories and continued critical review of them. Undoubtedly since most of the fellows of the college were involved directly or indirectly in war duty, this led to the strong emphasis on medical records in the Minimum Standard for Hospitals which the college formulated when it started hospital standardization in 1918. The January, 1921, *Bulletin* made clear the part in this of the records clerk:

> The old saying that everybody's business is nobody's business applies to case records. If the records are worth keeping and if they are worth keeping so that their contents are available for study and review, then somebody must have charge of them; somebody must check them up, see that they are all promptly completed, conveniently accessible, and protected from misuse.

Massachusetts General Hospital stars again in laying the foundation for the new profession. In 1917 it started an "in-service" training program which was ultimately to become an affiliation with three colleges—Simmons College, Boston; Colby Junior College, New London, New Hampshire; and Rosary Hill College, Buffalo, New York—all of which offer a four-year program in medical record administration leading to a Bachelor of Science or Arts degree. The hospital also offers a certificate program for college graduates.

In the August, 1926, *Bulletin of the American Hospital Association,* page 53, appears this indication of early interest in records:

> The Association is developing a division of clinical records . . . the aim of this department is two-fold. First, it hopes to aid the hospitals throughout the country to establish and to maintain record departments that meet all requirements for classification and all demands of the individual staff. Second, it hopes to organize the clinical record librarians into a group for the purpose of concentrating on their problems and working them out for the mutual benefit of institution and individual.

The clerkship stage lasted until 1928 when Dr. MacEachern acted upon his idea that the importance of this group to hospitals and patients as well as to themselves would be furthered by organization. He invited all of the records room clerks to meet with the American College of Surgeons at its annual congress. At this meeting the Association of Medical Record Librarians of North

America (changed later to American Association of Medical Record Librarians) was organized and elected as its first president the first records room clerk, Mrs. Grace Whiting Myers.

For many years the medical record librarians held their annual meeting with the clinical congress of the college and basked in the high favor of Dr. Mac-Eachern, whom they considered their godfather. In his position of liaison between medicine and hospitals he probably more than any other one person recognized the heavy and delicate responsibility that rests upon this group and appreciated the part which they play in the improvement of medical care.

The association labored long on an educational program and curriculum. It formed a committee composed of representatives of the American College of Surgeons, the American Medical Association, and the American Hospital Association. A registry was organized in 1933. Examination was offered after a stipulated number of years' experience. Successful candidates had the privilege of using "R.R.L." (Registered Record Librarian) after their names. In 1934 a curriculum was adopted and approval of schools started. The first approved school, opened in 1935, was at the Rochester General Hospital, Rochester, New York. In 1941 the responsibility for inspection and approval of schools was assumed by the Council on Medical Education and Hospitals of the American Medical Association.

As in nursing, shortages of trained personnel have led to the use of aids. The American Medical Association publishes, besides the "Essentials" and list of approved schools for the professional group, "Essentials for the Training of Medical Record Technicians" and lists of approved schools for these technicians.

After January 1, 1965, only graduates of approved schools for medical record librarians will be permitted to write the registration examination of the American Association of Medical Record Librarians to qualify for the professional designation "R.R.L."

A special higher rank is possible for a few librarians. The "Certified Record Librarian" (C.R.L.) has, in addition to qualifications as a Registered Record Librarian, a minimum of five years' experience and has submitted evidence of additional study or achievement in this field.

In 1959 the W. K. Kellogg Foundation awarded a four-year, $88,540 grant on a decreasing basis to the association to start an extension-correspondence course designed to upgrade the work of medical record librarian personnel. A similar grant from the same foundation made possible in 1953 the inauguration by the Canadian Hospital Association of a home study program in Canada, which has been very successful.

Canada has a Canadian Association of Medical Record Librarians, although originally membership in the American association was extended to them. In Australia, the first medical record librarians' school was established at Royal Prince Alfred Hospital in 1950–1952 with the assistance of Sara McKinney, prominent medical record librarian from the United States, who since 1959 has conducted the extension-correspondence course for the American association. Mrs. Edna K. Huffman, author of *Manual for Medical Record Librarians,* spent six months in 1949 and a year in 1960 in Australia teaching and promoting medical record work generally. Mrs. Huffman is also the author of *Medical Records in Nursing Homes.*

In England there is an Association of Medical Records Officers which was organized in 1948. Most of its members are men.

Four international congresses have been held: in 1952 in London, England; in 1956 in Washington, D.C.; in 1960 in Edinburgh, Scotland; and in 1963 in Chicago.

The official journal of the American association is *Medical Record News,* published bimonthly.

SOCIAL SERVICE

In introducing her thesis, "An Evaluation of Medical Social Work in the Short Term, General, Non-Profit Hospital," Augustine Gunn (Northwestern '56, presently administrative assistant, Chicago Wesley Memorial Hospital) used as a definition of social work the following quotation from Arthur J. Altmeyer:[18]

> Our evolving concept of social work is dependent upon our evolving ideas of the responsibility of community and state in promoting the well-being of its members. As our sense of social responsibility develops, our concept of social work inevitably grows. At one time, not long ago, our concept of social work included almost exclusively, relief and service to the underprivileged and disadvantaged. Our concept was based rather largely upon the spirit of *noblesse oblige.* Our attention was focussed upon the needs of the specific individual rather than upon the social institutions, the presence or absence of which affected the needs of individuals. Social work was thought of largely in terms of adjusting the individual to his environment rather than in terms of bringing environmental forces into play to assist the individual. . . .
>
> The newer concept of social work, as I view it, is that it consists not only of counselling and assisting the individual and family in making the necessary adjustments to environment, but more importantly, it consists of marshalling community resources to promote the well-being of individuals and of families generally. In other words, we do not think any longer in terms of a few underprivileged and disadvantaged persons, but we think in terms of *all* individuals and families. We think not in terms of "cure" or even "prevention" but in affirmative terms of actively promoting well-being rather than simply avoiding ill-being.

The following discussion of social work is adapted from the sections of Miss Gunn's thesis which deal with general background aspects of this profession.

[18] Quoted in Arthur E. Fink: *The Field of Social Work.* New York, Henry Holt & Co., rev. 1949, p. 5.

History

The development of social work has been made possible through two chan-nels—private charities and public welfare. Private social work, referring to nongovernmental persons and agencies, is as old as humanity itself. Some form of social work has always been present—alms to the beggar, incomplete glean-ing of crops so that the poor could collect the scattered grain, etc. However, the earliest actually "private" agencies that ministered to the poor were the churches and church societies which flourished first in Europe and later in America. Although America was a new land, the Industrial Revolution brought problems of pauperization, health, sanitation, housing, child welfare, etc., as early as the 1820's. Many church societies sprang up, each ministering to a particular need. Problems of coordination and organization arose, developing especially during the depression of 1873.

In 1877, the Charity Organization Society, patterned after the London Charity Organization Society, originated in Buffalo, New York, with the purpose of organizing existing charities. Arthur E. Fink[19] points out:

Private charity, which had made a thousand beginnings in as many places, had incorporated the individualism of industrialists who had grown wealthy in an expanding economy. Each prosperous donor had sought to impress his par-ticular private philanthropy upon any relief society willing to accept his largess. As a result there was such an over-lapping and waste of private and charity funds that more needs were unmet than met.

The Charity Organization concept of coordination and organization grew rapidly in the United States and within six years, 25 cities had adopted the principles of the movement: (1) investigation of every applicant; (2) central registration; (3) cooperation of all relief agencies; (4) the use in the main of volunteer friendly visitors. These principles remain applicable today.

Although the original Charity Organization Society had intended to coordi-nate relief-giving instead of dispensing it, within a quarter of a century about half of the societies were giving direct relief. This development occurred fre-quently when it was the only agency in the community and there was a definite need to be met.

At this stage of development, Mr. Fink[20] points out, two well-defined divergent trends could be identified: (1) those who advocated correction of the external factors in society which were responsible for poverty and its concomitant prob-lems; and (2) those who

. . . restricted their labors to the individual client with the aim of effecting a change within the individual which would enable him to utilize to the full his

[19] *Ibid.*, p. 103.
[20] *Ibid.*, p. 108.

own potentialities. Quite naturally this latter group developed a more intensive approach to the individual client and gave form to the specialization of social case work within the larger field of social work.

History has shown the validity of both positions. Social casework has assisted the individual in developing the capacities within himself so that he has become a more competent and creative individual; social action has developed as another form of social work which is directed toward an attack on basic social problems "to make possible a world in which the individual can function more effectively. It is therefore necessary to stress the complementary nature of these positions rather than their apparent incompatibility."[21]

In contrast to private charities the term "public welfare" has come to be used as the general designation for a wide variety of governmental services to people which may be provided at the federal, state, or local level, or through a combination of these various levels of government.

These services today, as exemplified in the various functions of government under the direction of the Department of Health, Education and Welfare, are a far cry from the early beginnings of governmental responsibility for the individual. When the original colonists came to America they brought with them not only the concept of private welfare, as exemplified in the church societies, but the public concept of the care of the poor as practiced in England under the Elizabethan Poor Law which was passed in 1601. Public services for the needy, the delinquent, and the handicapped of all kinds began in the local community and expanded outward to state areas to serve those categories of individuals whose numbers were too small for development of local facilities. Institutions for the care of the insane were among the first to be established on a state level.

Public care for the unfortunate individual developed in a haphazard manner and was often associated with corruption and graft. It remained for the stock market crash of 1929 and the subsequent economic depression of the thirties to prove the inadequacy of existing agencies to meet the needs of unemployment. Private charities had been developing in a more orderly way than public welfare; however, private charity could not begin to meet the financial needs of the unemployed in the thirties. The depression disproved individual responsibility or "character flaw" as a cause of unemployment; it developed the concept of the responsibility of the state for the welfare of the individual and laid the foundation for the expansion of welfare services by the Social Security Act of 1935.

The public welfare agencies drew largely upon the private agencies for personnel and organization principles during the transitional and chaotic periods of the early 1930's. However, neither the private nor the public agencies submerged the other, and experiences proved the value of both types to the community welfare.

[21] *Ibid.*, p. 108.

Earlier mention was made of social casework as developing in the larger field of social work. Social casework is that form of social work directed toward the individual rather than toward the socioeconomic problems which may have contributed to his difficulties. Social group work, another specialization of social work, is also directed toward the individual himself but in a little different way. The settlements and community centers are the main media within which this type of social work operates.

Community Organization for Social Welfare. This is the opposite of social casework. It is

> . . . the process by which people of communities, as individual citizens or as representatives of groups, join together to determine social welfare needs, plan ways of meeting them, and mobilize the necessary resources. The focus of the effort may be a functional field of social welfare, for example leisure time and recreation, or a geographical area, such as a neighborhood, city, or county.[22]

Social Research. Since social work is a comparatively new discipline and has attained the status of a profession only recently, little thought has been given to social research as it specifically relates to social work practice. There is need for more factually substantiated practice, and research is developing as a distinct entity in the field.

Social Service Administration. Likewise, social service administration has come to be recognized as a specialized area.

These classifications may be further divided into family social work, child welfare work, medical social work, psychiatric social work, school social work, and others. These may seem to complicate and confuse the person seeking to learn the meaning and methods of social work. Closer scrutiny will disclose that there is little basic difference—each is concerned with the welfare of the individual in relation to himself and his environment. The lines of demarcation are breaking down, evidence of which is the emergence of schools of social work which emphasize "generic" rather than "specialized" social work; and also the various professional societies representing each group have merged into one professional group, The National Association of Social Workers, which was accomplished only as recently as July 7, 1955.

Social Trends

Since social work is concerned with the individual, the economic, cultural, and social forces which affect the individual must concern the social worker too and must be viewed in perspective if he is to function with maximum skill. Social work, which concerns itself largely with the well-being of the individual, should have unprecedented growth in an era of scientific, technological, and industrial revolution. Among the factors listed in *Recent Social Trends in the United States* (Report of the 1933 President's Research Committee on Social

[22] *Ibid.*, p. 121.

Trends) are spectacular increase in efficiency and productivity, tragic spread of unemployment and business distress, the experiment of prohibition, birth control, race riots, stoppage of immigration, women's suffrage, governmental corruption, crime and racketeering, sprawl of great cities, rise and weakening of organized labor, expansion of education, growth of spectacular fortunes, advance of medical science, and renewed interest in child welfare.

The years following 1933 have modified a few of the earlier problems and created many others: organized labor, instead of weakening, rose rapidly as a result of the economic depression; large individual fortunes have given way to spectacular earnings of large corporations; a second World War spread destruction and hate, dislocating entire races of people, keeping alive international problems and tensions, engendering the cold war. The problem of racial discrimination continues and medical care remains inadequate for large segments of the population despite medical advances. On the other hand, the war accelerated business efficiency and productivity; gave birth to the electronics era, precipitated rapid development of medical and related sciences, and brought about drastic changes in transportation and communication. All of these developments have created new socioeconomic problems.

Medical Social Work

Medical social work, as defined by the American Association of Medical Social Workers, is "a professional service to patients, physicians, hospital administrators and the community which has developed in hospitals, clinics, and sanatoria to help patients with environmental and personal difficulties related to their illness, recovery and preservation of health." At first, medical social work was found almost exclusively in hospitals and clinics, but the field has been considerably broadened. It has five essential functions: (1) practice of social casework; (2) participation in program planning and policy formulation of the agency; (3) participation in the development of social and health programs in the community; (4) participation in the educational program for professional personnel; (5) social research.

The origin of medical social work is usually attributed to one person, Dr. Richard Clark Cabot, who recognized the relationship of the patient's social situation to the total medical problem, and under whose leadership a department of social service was begun at Massachusetts General Hospital, Boston, in 1905. Of medical social work Dr. Cabot said:[23]

> To make the doctor's work worthwhile to himself and to the patient, it must be done (in hospitals) in cooperation with some one who has time and ability to teach hygiene and to see that it is carried out (for instance in tuberculosis), to

[23] *Social Service and the Art of Healing.* New York, Moffat, Yard and Company, 1917, p. 178. Quoted by Louise C. Odencrantz in *The Social Worker.* New York, Harper and Brothers, 1929, p. 151.

study the home conditions and report upon their part in causing or prolonging disease, and to help modify those conditions, financial, mental, moral, which stand between the patient and recovery. The "some one" is the social worker—a man or woman trained to think of a human being as a whole just as naturally as the physician concentrates upon a part.

Although Dr. Cabot's name is always linked with the history of medical social work, there were prior and parallel developments. Medical social service began in the Berkeley Infirmary in Boston one day earlier, October 7, 1905, than it did in the outpatient department of Massachusetts General Hospital. As far back as 1886 the Children's Hospital of San Francisco gave a type of service similar to what is now called medical social service. Ida Cannon, one of the medical social work pioneers, described the forerunners of medical social work in the following order: "services for the after care of the insane; those furnished by the lady almoners in London hospitals; nursing in its various forms; and the field work training of medical students in at least one medical school as early as 1902."

The movement for the aftercare of the insane had extended from Germany in the early part of the nineteenth century. It was given serious attention in the United States by psychiatrists and neurologists before the end of that century. In England a Guild of Friends of the Infirm in Mind was founded and later a Society for After Care of Poor Persons Discharged Recovered from Insane Asylums.

The original duty of the lady almoners in London hospitals was inquiry into the financial status of the patient and his worthiness of free care. Later they assisted in instructing the patients in fulfilling the doctors' recommendations, and in referring patients to appropriate sources for other types of aid.

The visiting nurse movement, independent of hospital connections, began in 1893; later it was incorporated as part of the formal instruction at Presbyterian Hospital, New York City, when the training of nurses included visits to patients in their own homes. The same hospital in 1907 placed the supervision of the social aspects of nursing under the direction of a special nurse. In a few hospitals today the social service work is done by a person trained in nursing, although this practice is disappearing.

The field training of medical students was initiated at Johns Hopkins Medical School in 1902 when social work was included in the curriculum. Medical students were assigned as friendly visitors to families known to the Charity Organization Society.

Medical social work developed slowly. Ten years after the establishment of the first department there were only some dozen hospitals which had one. Growth was greatly stimulated by a statement by Dr. Malcolm T. MacEachern which appeared in the 1929 edition of the *Report of Hospital Standardization* published by the American College of Surgeons:

The American College of Surgeons, in its survey of hospitals, is directing attention to the development of medical social service activities in relation to the physical care of the patient before, during, and after hospitalization. It is now fully realized that the trained medical social worker, cooperating with the physician in attendance, is of valuable assistance in diagnosis, treatment, and follow-up not to say anything of the many advantages directly to the general welfare of the patients, and to the more efficient administration of the hospital in rendering its fullest community service. The social worker thus becomes an important link in the hospital system, particularly in rounding out the service rendered the patient.

Medical specialization has affected the physician-patient relationship, notwithstanding the fact that the social sciences which have contributed to the understanding of the individual emphasize that the physician's function is to treat people, not diseases. As one result of the trend toward comprehensive medicine, new attention is being directed at the medical social worker as a person particularly qualified to help in offsetting the specialized doctor problem.

The field of medical social service has been broadened through such concepts as that of the World Health Organization which defines health as "a state of complete physical, mental and social well-being and not merely the absence of disease or infirmity." Medical social workers have become active as consultants in public health programs at all geographic levels; also in public welfare agencies, rehabilitation services, voluntary health organizations, and in community organizations. They are also participating in educational programs for various medical disciplines, including medicine, nursing, public health, and hospital administration.

In the current definition of medical social work, and in the enlarging scope of its functions, it seems to take over from many of the social sciences, besides being an adjunct of medical science, and in some ways to lose its identity. Mary L. Hemmy,[24] executive director of the American Association of Medical Social Workers, clarifies this in the following statement:

> The peculiar contribution and competence of medical social work lies not in any one part of its knowledge and skill but in the particular combination and application of bodies of knowledge and skills which individually are found in many other professions. These are: knowledge of the social, cultural, and psychological factors in human development and behavior; knowledge of the interrelationship between these factors and health, disease and disability, and the impact of the details of medical care, including the hospital environment, on the patient as a social being; knowledge of the dynamics of group interaction and the forces which shape community action; skill in helping individuals and groups assess their situations, define their problems and possible methods of their solution, and assisting them to take action toward the solution. . . . However, fundamental to all of this, there is the need for medical social service departments to look up from their preoccupation with the day to day problems and to see more clearly their opportunities now for adding, independently and jointly with the other professions, in an orderly way to the knowledge of man in relation to health and illness.

[24] In an Integrated Total Treatment Program, What Is the Role of Medical Social Service? *South. Hosp.*, December, 1954.

The medical social worker, from experience with sick people, knows that the ill person is a troubled person. Deep emotions may be stirred producing debilitating fears of operations, possible death, or invalidism which in turn give way to helplessness and hopelessness. These fears may be based on reality, depending upon the diagnosis and the prognosis for the patient, or they may be entirely disproportionate to the medical facts. In either situation the medical social worker seeks to help the patient understand his feelings and attitudes which may be preventing him from using to the fullest his capacity to contribute, in conjunction with the physician and other medical personnel, toward his own recovery.

Medical social workers are most likely to be concerned with the patient who is facing a long convalescence, extended treatment, or a chronic illness which may or may not be progressive. These situations produce varying degrees of frustration. It becomes necessary for the social worker to study and try to understand the structure of the personality of each patient with whom she works. To do this she draws upon the disciplines of psychology, psychiatry, sociology, and anthropology. The social worker cannot demonstrate with test tube and formulas the particular processes which she uses and the results which she obtains. She seeks out the patient's feelings about his illness, information that details his economic, domestic, and industrial status, his relationship to his family, his work, his church, and his recreation, but none of these is a separate entity. They all have to be integrated.

The fact that the social worker does not represent the authoritarian forces in the hospital environment as do the physician, nurse, or other medical personnel (whose functions often require that the patient adhere to strict rules and regulations of treatment) contributes to her usefulness to the patient in permitting him to give vent to his feelings which may be retarding his recovery. But if the worker permits the patient's problems to become entangled with her own personal problems and does not understand her own reactions, she may become enmeshed emotionally to the point that she will be of little value, and possibly of harm, to the patient. Education of self is the difficult part of the social work discipline.

The social worker does not assume any responsibility for the patient without the knowledge and approval of the physician. It is usually the physician who asks the worker to interview a patient, or he may have given his over-all consent for interviews with each patient in a particular diagnostic group or within other specific classifications or limitations. The patient may be referred to the social worker by hospital personnel other than the doctor, by members of the patient's family or other members of the community; but the physician is apprised of the referral, and the medical situation is incorporated into any procedure followed. The physician is recognized as "the captain" of the team responsible for the total care. The social work process is such that the patient is given time, which the busy physician might not have, to express his misunderstandings and trepidation.

The administrator must cooperate with the social service department in stimulating its further development, and he can do this only if he has a clear understanding of the social work function, is convinced of its value, and finds this attitude reflected in the medical staff and governing board. The social worker takes a part in creating the atmosphere which prevails in the hospital. She serves in a public relations capacity, since she is frequently the interpreter of hospital policies and procedures as they affect the patient and the community. She can assist in establishing policies, particularly those which affect specific groups such as the indigent, the chronically ill, or the physically handicapped. Although a hospital may have no formalized program for the care of the indigent, nevertheless applications may be received for free care in individual situations, and even in these there should be a policy base. Planning for the chronically ill and the physically handicapped in particular must be done with full awareness of all the community health and welfare resources available.

The medical social worker is in a position to test constantly the adequacies of community resources in relation to the needs of the individual patient. When community resources are unorganized or too limited she should accept this as a challenge and not as a cause for retreat. It is her obligation to interpret, aggressively, the needs to the community and thus to be a strong influence in its development.

The shift in emphasis from curative to preventive and comprehensive medicine will gradually redefine the place of the hospital within the community health picture. The transition will be accompanied by problems of planning, integration, and implementation of all community resources for the improvement of community health and welfare. The medical social worker should be in a position to contribute to this planning, which should transfer the needs of the individual into services for the larger group.

MEDICAL TECHNOLOGY

In 1928 in Denver, Colorado, the American Society of Clinical Pathologists created the Board of Registry of Medical Technologists to set and supervise standards for medical technology. Five years later the American Society of Medical Technologists was organized. A new profession was on its way.

By 1962 more than 42,000 medical technologists had been certified by the board of registry and were entitled to use the designation M.T. (A.S.C.P.) after their names. The society has a membership of around 9,000. To qualify for active membership a technologist must either be certified by the registry or have at least a master's degree in one of the fields of medical technology: serology, microbiology, hematology, biochemistry, histology, etc.

The fact that certification is conducted by a medical organization rather than by its own society is a differentiating factor for this group compared with most paramedical groups. The advantage in closer relationships between the pathologist and his staff of professional assistants is obvious.

The association in 1962 established two new membership classifications: affiliate member—technologists with a year's schooling in an approved United States military training program and recommended by an association member; and associate members—persons actively engaged in medical laboratory work and having the recommendation of two active association members.

In 1962, for the second time, the American Society of Medical Technologists and the Canadian Society of Laboratory Technologists met together for the North American Conference of Medical Laboratory Technologists. The sessions were chaired alternately by the presidents of the two associations.

Soon after it was established, the board of registry began formal recognition of schools of medical technology by issuing an approved list. Previously training had simply been under individual pathologists in laboratories, and personal knowledge of their standing by members of the board was at first the only criterion of the quality of the training. The Council on Medical Education and Hospitals of the American Medical Association soon took over the setting of standards for the schools by issuing "Essentials" and publishing lists. In 1954, aroused by the extreme shortage of technologists, the American Society of Clinical Pathologists' Board of Schools prepared and published a booklet, "How to Organize an Approved School of Medical Technology," with the hope that more schools would be established by "medical schools, hospitals or other acceptable laboratories suitably organized in accordance with present educational standards." Accredited schools now total 770.

In 1940 Dr. Lall G. Montgomery became chairman of the Board of Registry of Medical Technologists, succeeding Dr. Philip Hilkowitz who was retiring after having served as chairman since the board was organized in 1928. Dr. Montgomery was then, and still is, director of pathology at the Ball Memorial Hospital in Muncie, Indiana, and the board headquarters were established in that city. A new building was dedicated on April 14, 1962. The board has nine members, including Dr. Montgomery; five of them represent the American Society of Clinical Pathologists, and four the American Society of Medical Technologists.

The board of registry sets up requirements and examinations for other types of certificates besides medical technology. One of these is blood banking—certification is given to ASCP-certified medical technologists who receive additional training and experience to meet special requirements arranged in cooperation with the American Association of Blood Banks. Specialist certification without the requirement of first being an ASCP-certified medical technologist is granted to those with a master's degree or doctorate in chemistry or microbiology from an accredited college or university. In chemistry and in microbiology there is also arrangement for certification of persons who have bachelor's degrees from an accredited college or university with majors in either of these fields plus the necessary experience in an acceptable medical laboratory. Histological technique and exfoliative cytology are other specialties in which examination and certification is open to candidates with certain stipulated backgrounds.

Two rather new developments are benefiting the profession: the raising of the requirement for admission to training in medical technology from two to three years of college work, effective January 1, 1962; and the creation of a professional category for registered medical technologists by Civil Service— formerly they were in a subprofessional category for government employment.

At the dedication of the new building, Dr. Richard Palmer, president of the American Society of Clinical Pathologists, referred to the registry as the "guardian of laboratory integrity" during the last 34 years and warned that "clinical laboratory diagnosis can produce tragic mistakes if careless, inadequately trained, or otherwise incompetent workers are allowed to assume the responsibilities of the ASCP-registered medical technologists who should conduct the complicated tests upon which the diagnosis and treatment of disease by modern medicine so largely depends."

The work of the registry is extremely important in view of the rise of a great many commercial medical technology schools and of outside so-called accrediting agencies which have no standing.[25]

Medical Technology in England

In England medical technologists organized as far back as 1912 when they founded the Institute of Medical Laboratory Technology. When it was incorporated in 1942 it had about 1,000 members. Currently it has nearly 6,000 qualified members and some 1,500 registered students.

As in the United States, many of the technologists are employed by pharmaceutical and other industrial firms, medical schools, public health services, etc., and the shortage of qualified personnel in hospitals is acute.

Ministry of Health figures showed that in the period from 1953 to 1957 the units of laboratory work undertaken in hospitals increased by 56 per cent, while technical staffs increased by only 18 per cent.

The trend toward specialization in the laboratory is recognized in England. Comments that have universal application were made by W. H. Valentine:[26]

> Even in the general hospital laboratory the technical staff tend to specialize after a few years' training and to work in one section of the department devoted to a particular subject, e.g., histopathology, bacteriology. Nor does the process stop there. However well equipped the large general hospital laboratory may be, it will need to turn, not infrequently, to a reference laboratory specializing in a narrower field. For example, an organism of the food poisoning group may be sent for final identification to a particular laboratory within the Public Health Laboratory Service; a specimen of blood may be sent to the regional centre of the National Blood Transfusion Service for antigen analysis; or, blood or other

---

[25] *See* Commercial Medical Technology Schools. *Mod. Hosp.,* December, 1961, pp. 98–112. Also a report of an interview with Dr. Montgomery, Evolution of the Medical Technologist. *Hospitals,* December 1, 1962, pp. 47–51.

[26] *J. Roy. Soc. Health,* November/December, 1959, pp. 869–70.

specimens will often require the specialized facilities of a virological laboratory in order to establish a firm diagnosis. The number of such reference laboratories will continue to grow.

There are thus two ways in which the medical laboratory technician is being affected. The increased demand for laboratory investigations has meant that he has had to assume increasing responsibility for the technical work of the department. The pathologist has found his time more and more absorbed by non-technical matters so that the days have gone when he could be pathologist and technician in one. This process is bound to continue and it seems reasonable that it should do so.

Another way in which the technician is affected is that the growing complexity of investigations demands a standard of training and qualification which must be subject to constant review. One sometimes gets the impression, even from those who should be better informed, that the technician is thought to do little more than count red blood cells or estimate a blood urea percentage. In point of fact he has to undertake work of considerable responsibility and requiring a high degree of technical competence. The theoretical background of his subject is always expanding and his work is never static. His contributions to original work may be found in the medical press and in the journal of his own Institute. Anyone who wants to know the standards required of the technician should study carefully the questions set in final examinations of the Institute of Medical Laboratory Technology. . . .

Having seen so much change in laboratory practice in the last few years, it is interesting to speculate on the future. It seems likely that at least two factors may have an important influence on the medical laboratory services. One is the changing conception of the functions of hospitals: the idea that the hospital's chief duty was to provide beds in which people recovered—or did not recover—with medical and nursing assistance has, at least in great measure, given place to the conception of the hospital as a centre of diagnosis and treatment where most of the patients remain as outpatients, being admitted to wards only as a necessity and for as short a time as possible. In other words the hospital stands at the back of the large amount of curative work which is done elsewhere. There are many advantages in keeping patients out of hospital and it is possible that the future may see a greater amount of laboratory work done for patients outside hospitals than at present.

The growing number of older people in the population is bound to affect the laboratory as it will medicine generally. As the results of fundamental research are applied to maintaining health among the elderly and, as early diagnostic procedures become possible for some of the major diseases of middle life and beyond, so the laboratory will have to show its adaptability and extend its techniques.

In the laboratory, as elsewhere, automation will have a place in the future. Already there are automatic tissue processors and section staining machines, electronic blood cell counters, semi-automatic titrators and a number of instruments for speeding up chemical analyses and eliminating chance variation of the human eye for colour changes. To employ these developments is good capital investment; their use will allow more profitable allocation of the technician's time and may give that much-wanted extra bit of time, now often denied to the routine laboratory, in which to work out adaptation of techniques and to ponder some of the findings which are worth pursuing.

The use of these devices in the laboratory does not mean that technical staffs with less skill or training will be needed. All the evidence points to the contrary, and medical laboratory technicians are well prepared to meet what may be required of them by future standards. It is perhaps worth observing that the impetus to improve standards of training and qualifications has always come from within the body corporate of technicians and has never been in the nature of an external compulsion. In this connection it may be noted that the self-imposed code of ethics to which all I.M.L.T. members must subscribe is a stringent one which ensures a high standard of professional behaviour. . . .

NURSING

The *South African Nursing Journal* reported that Professor Sir James Learmonth, giving the Lister Oration at the Royal College of Surgeons in London, and wishing to record his ever-increasing debt to the nursing profession, said:

> Nursing is at once an art and a science. The existence of a highly trained and devoted body of women and men is inseparable from and indispensable to the practice of modern surgery. In both ward and operating theater it is never easy to draw a dividing line between surgical care and nursing care, nor is it desirable to attempt to do so for they are one. When on occasions formal treatments and remedies fail, it is possible for a patient to be nursed back to life and health.

Far outnumbering all other auxiliary medical professional members of the hospital staff is the graduate nurse. The average hospital in the continental United States has 44 full-time graduate professional nurses supplemented by 67 practical nurses, nurses' aides and attendants, orderlies, and other nursing assistants, or a total of 111 personnel with nursing duties. In addition it has 10 graduate nurses and 5 other nursing personnel who serve part-time. All other auxiliary medical professional personnel combined total 7 full-time workers in the average hospital supplemented by 10 unregistered or uncertified full-time assistants or technicians—a ratio of 111 full-time nursing personnel to 17 technical, dietary, medical records, etc., staff members. When administrative and other operational employees are added to the latter group, the nursing personnel still outnumber them all by 111 to 94.

Numerically, then, the nurse is the most conspicuous figure in the hospital, particularly since so many of the other workers are behind the scenes. She is also, even more than the doctor, the personification of the hospital to the patient, the visitor, and the public in general. With few exceptions, she lives up to her importance in a most admirable way.

Why, then, the furor about the nursing profession? What are the external disturbing factors that must be understood in order to maintain a superior quality of nursing service within our institutions?

A primary problem is the shortage of nurses, which creates a highly competitive situation among hospitals. For the nurses this is obviously good, resulting in an upward trend not only in salaries and benefits of various kinds, but in much needed recognition and appreciation. Back in June, 1928, the director of the Committee on the Grading of Nursing Schools, May Ayres Burgess,

Ph.D., strongly urged, in an address at the annual convention of nursing organizations at Louisville, that the supply of nurses be reduced by curtailing admission to the schools because "there is serious unemployment in nursing." Of course, that was a period of economic depression; unemployment was serious in every line of work. When war came, a critical shortage immediately arose. As an expedient to relieve it the United States Cadet Nurse Corps was organized in 1943. The postwar boom swallowed up the augmented supply of nurses as new needs for them grew in public health, clinics, schools, and industry. The nurse is now in a position to advance her profession and herself. What wonder that she is taking advantage of group action? The cries of overproduction and predictions of an alarming surplus made in 1928 have not only not come to pass but are completely the opposite of prevailing conditions because unforeseen trends and events have reversed the current.

Not that the recommendations of that committee to upgrade standards of nursing education were without value. Its nearly ten years of work started an analysis of nursing schools that has continued to this day, with recent acceleration. The final report of the committee emphasized that the oversupply consisted of poorly selected and trained personnel and that there was a real shortage of highly qualified nurses. This conclusion could be parried with the truism that this is a universal situation in all fields. Yet there can be no quarrel with the ambition of a group to elevate itself through better education and training. The people whom it serves will be the ultimate beneficiaries.

Bedside nursing disappearing? The paramount fear, so commonly expressed that it becomes tiresome, is that "bedside nursing" is disappearing because nurses are being better educated and consequently all want supervisory or administrative positions. The kind of bedside nursing that most of these critics have in mind *should* disappear as a function of the graduate nurse who, along with other highly trained personnel in fields allied to medicine, is now needed for new responsibilities thrust upon her by advances in medical science. Other skilled workers are being relieved of routine labor; why not the nurse? The doctor delegates many of his duties of former days to interns, residents, junior associates, nurses, and others.

Thinking persons whose voices are almost drowned by the tumult recognize that under supervision assistants can perform the routine nursing tasks. The fact that the aides already outnumber graduate nurses by 50 per cent in the average hospital shows that practice is in this regard ahead of the tradition-bound theorists.

The Brown Report

Esther Lucile Brown of the Russell Sage Foundation, in her report, published in 1948 when she served as director of the National Nursing Council study of nursing education, told of strong feeling among certain doctors and administrators in support of better education for nurses. One professor of preventive medicine went so far as to say that medical and nursing education should be placed on an "absolutely comparable basis." On the whole she found nurses discontented with their lack of participation in hospital planning and policy, and doctors and administrators unsympathetic toward their desire for more opportunity to present ideas and exercise initiative.

This famous "Brown Report"[27] is one that all students in administration should read in order to acquire familiarity with the underlying problems of nursing. Bringing these forcibly to light made the report a potent instrument in starting a new crusade for better nursing schools and for raising the status of nursing. Miss Brown's virtual commitment to the idea of eventual closing of hospital schools, disastrous though she felt too abrupt termination would be, naturally aroused a storm of opposition. Nevertheless, many hospital schools have been closed since the report was published.

In January, 1949, the year following publication of the report, the joint board of the six national nursing organizations approved the National Nursing Accrediting Service, which released in the October, 1949, issue of the *American Journal of Nursing* an approved list of programs of nursing education. This list included those programs formerly recognized by the Association of Collegiate Schools of Nursing, the Conference of Catholic Schools of Nursing, the National League of Nursing Education, and the National Organization for Public Health Nursing, and recommended by them to the new accrediting service. The list of 190 programs was represented to be only "partial." The accrediting function was assumed in 1952 by the National League for Nursing, which was a merger of the old accrediting organizations—the Association of Collegiate Schools of Nursing, the National League for Nursing Education, and the National Organization for Public Health Nursing.

Accreditation

Accreditation is such a prominent and controversial issue at present that a study of nursing is forced to focus upon it. Some physicians and hospital administrators have expressed themselves as violently opposed to the way in which the National League for Nursing is conducting the program. An "independent joint commission on accreditation of hospital schools of nursing" was demanded in a resolution passed by the House of Delegates of the American Hospital Association at its annual meeting in September, 1958. The plan was to have the association, the American Medical Association, and the National League for Nursing compose the joint commission. (In 1953 the A.H.A. had endorsed the N.L.N. accreditation program.) The league rejected the joint commission idea but established a policy committee within the league to which A.H.A. should appoint seven members and the league should appoint seven. A.H.A. has

[27] *Nursing for the Future.* New York, Russell Sage Foundation, 1948.

gone along with this compromise arrangement, not without objections from individual members.

An uncomfortable situation also exists between the league and the American Nurses' Association. The latter at its biennial meeting in May, 1960, made responsibility in nursing education a part of its platform, and the delegates expressed the conviction that there should be only one organization in nursing —the A.N.A. Its house of delegates adopted a report of the Committee on Current and Long-Term Goals in which this statement was made: "The A.N.A. shall promote the baccalaureate program so that in due course it becomes the basic educational foundation for professional nursing."

Ardent proponents of the traditional hospital school notwithstanding, the trend in nursing education seems therefore to be toward the baccalaureate program. The two- or three-year hospital diploma schools are clearly on the defensive, yet in a fairly strong position still because of the shortage of nurses. This is recognized by the league. There were 51,219 admissions to the 1,126 professional nursing programs in 1961, of which 39,464 were to diploma (hospital) schools, 2,846 more than the admissions five years earlier, in 1957, when total admissions were 44,281. Admissions to associate degree programs rose in the five-year period from 770 to 2,468, and to bachelor's degree programs from 6,893 to 9,287. Hospital school admissions in 1961 constituted 77 per cent of the total, associate degree programs 4.8 per cent, and baccalaureate degree programs 18.2 per cent. Commenting on these figures the National League for Nursing[28] states:

> These figures fall far short of N.L.N. estimates that 33 per cent of the professional nursing force should be prepared in college and university programs to meet the requirements for beginning jobs in public health nursing and for the graduate study desirable in the other leadership areas where shortages are pressing—teaching, administration, expert clinical practice, and research.

Graduations in 1961 totaled 30,267. The 550,000 total of licensed professional nurses employed in the United States in 1962 was 90,000 more than four years earlier. Licensed practical nurses total around 250,000 and auxiliary nursing workers in hospitals close to 400,000.

Special Fields of Nursing

Need for supplementary training and continuing education is recognized in several special fields of nursing, the main ones being anesthesia, operating room, industrial, public health, obstetrics, mental, heart disease, school, administration, and education. Besides their common interest in the broad base of nursing each of these groups has distinct interests, one of which is strong tie-ins with non-nursing and even, for some of them, nonmedical fields.

Education was the first specialty field to organize nationally. In 1893 during

[28] *Fact Sheet,* June, 1962, Committee on Careers.

the World's Fair in Chicago, the National League for Nursing Education was founded, merging sixty years later into the National League for Nursing. Public health was next, forming in 1912 the National Organization for Public Health Nursing. It, too, merged with the N.L.N. Nurse anesthetists created the American Association of Nurse Anesthetists in 1931. It survived a campaign for amalgamation and currently has nearly 10,000 members. Also a survivor after a determined struggle is the American Association of Industrial Nurses, which was organized in 1942. Organized after the merger was the Association of Operating Room Nurses, growing from a small beginning in 1954 to some 3,500 members in less than a decade.

The creation of "one national organization for nurses and nursing" strongly urged by some members of the American Nurses' Association seems unrealistic in so large and diversified a profession. Medicine, law, engineering, education, all have a great many autonomous specialty organizations with distinct functions. As Janet Geister, consultant in organization, National League for Nursing, and a former board member of the American Nurses' Association, pointed out in a talk at the Association of Operating Room Nurses' Congress in 1959:

> In the wide expansion and in the very nature of the health movement, the growth of specialties within medicine and nursing was inevitable. They are a product of the space age, of the health revolution. . . . No day passes without an addition to scientific knowledge, nor one that doesn't demand greater, more intensified skills. . . . As the lines that mark off the special area become clearer, workers in these areas recognize needs—a need to work out their own standards of practice; their basic principles; the education requirements that are peculiar to the group. . . . Nursing is moving out into a broader, more skilled service to society than it's ever known, and more specialist groups within it are a certainty. How the workers within these groups handle internal affairs is anybody's guess. Mine is that we'll have more national specialist associations.

The Nurse Anesthetist. An example of an effective educational program by a specialized nursing group, a program which an over-all organization could not have planned and conducted as effectively, is that of the nurse anesthetist. Soon after the introduction of anesthesia in surgery she appeared on the scene. Because of greater experience accumulated through everyday practice and concentration of interest, she became recognized as superior to the physician who had no special training. With the development of anesthesiology as a medical specialty, she has remained because the supply of medically trained personnel has never been anywhere near sufficient to meet the need. In hospitals in which there is an anesthesiologist, she works under his direction; in others the department is headed by a physician who has acquired some background in the specialty. In view of the rapid developments in the field and the dangers to the patient in unskilled administration of anesthesia, the shortage of both anesthesiologists and of well-trained nurse anesthetists is critical.

Formal training of the nurse anesthetist began in 1911 when under the direction of Dr. George W. Crile a school was started at Lakeside, now University

Hospitals, Cleveland. Agatha Hodgins was appointed to head the school. In World War I Miss Hodgins worked as an anesthetist with Dr. Crile overseas, including teaching in her functions, and very rapidly thereafter the use of nurses in anesthesia increased. As schools for training them began to spring up, the need for standards became obvious and was the chief impetus to the founding of the American Association of Nurse Anesthetists in 1931. The association drew up standards of education and practice, and has revised and raised them from time to time.

Some 120 hospitals have schools for nurse anesthetists which are approved by the American Association of Nurse Anesthetists. New minimum standards were adopted by the association for schools established after January 1, 1960. Schools already in existence had until July 1, 1962, to change to the new requirements. The main change is expansion of the former 12-month course to 18 months. The clinical experience must include 450 cases totaling 500 hours of clinical instruction. Class hours must total 250 hours and must follow a prescribed course outline. A visitation plan is included in the approval program.

The association has an official publication, the *Journal of the American Association of Nurse Anesthetists*. It sponsors meetings and institutes and encourages participation in the programs of other organizations. The Joint Commission on Accreditation of Hospitals and the Department of Health, Education and Welfare recognize its standards.

More than half of the anesthetics in the United States are administered by nurse anesthetists. In Canada, Great Britain, and certain other countries, however, only physicians may give anesthetics.

The Operating Room Nurse. Edith Dee Hall was the guiding spirit in organizing in 1954 the Association of Operating Room Nurses, and she served as its executive secretary until 1962. This, like anesthesia, is a field in which the shortage of skilled personnel is serious. As surgery has advanced, so has the need for expert nursing assistance in the operating room.

The A.O.R.N. conducts an educational program through annual congresses, workshops, participation in meetings of other organizations, and articles published in a special section of *Hospital Topics* each month. It publishes an official journal, *Operating Room Nursing.*

There are few formally organized courses in operating room nursing. Training in operating room supervision and nursing is conducted more or less informally in many hospitals, and the need for developing special skills and for acquiring greater knowledge of the principles underlying aseptic techniques is well recognized. There is also a trend to broaden the scope of responsibility to include preoperative and postoperative care as recognized in the American Nurses' Association section on surgical nursing.

As in other fields of nursing, attempts to offset the shortage are being made by training and utilizing aides, or, as they are usually called, surgical technicians.

The Industrial Nurse. Of the three nationally organized special nursing fields, industrial nursing has the broadest scope. Its association was organized in 1942 and its official publication is *American Association of Industrial Nurses' Journal*. The changes which have occurred in this field are shared to a considerable degree by nursing in general. Miss Geister, in the same talk presented at the 1959 A.O.R.N. Congress, not only points this out but also credits organized effort for stimulating the changes, when she says that the American Association of Industrial Nurses

> . . . has been a strong force in moving the nurse with the iodine swab with an indeterminate position at the edge of the plant, right into the center of the plant, a definite part of production. The iodine swab may still be around, but the industrial nurse's main job is treating the whole man, not his cut finger—helping him with his physical, social, psychological, and rehabilitation problems.

The Public Health Nurse. With increasing emphasis on preventive medicine, the role of the public health nurse becomes more important than ever before. She represents a broad range of services including education, administration, and all kinds of duties from counseling to bedside care. The origin and development of public health nursing is exceptionally interesting, beginning as it did with the ministrations of the visiting nurse, and expanding to include the far-flung governmental services. Emilie G. Sargent[29] traces the history as follows:

> Visiting Nursing began in England ninety years ago and in the United States seventy-one years ago. The first salaried service was started by William Rathbone in Liverpool, England, in 1859. His action, like most humanitarian movements, was prompted by a personal experience. His wife had been very ill and her last days were made more comfortable by good nursing care. In his gratitude he wanted to help the sick who could not afford nursing care. He turned to his friend, Florence Nightingale, for advice and for some of her graduate nurses to staff the undertaking. Out of this collaboration of layman and nurse, the pattern of visiting nursing, or district nursing as the English called it, was established. The Liverpool District Nursing Organization was soon copied by other cities. Mr. Rathbone and Florence Nightingale also helped to establish the first postgraduate district nursing training program, the Metropolitan and National Nursing Association, in London in 1874. Queen Victoria's interest was enlisted, and through her influence, substantial financial aid was given from the Women's Jubilee Offering. In recognition of this help, the Queen Victoria Jubilee Institute for Nurses was created, absorbing the Metropolitan and National Nursing Association. This organization still functions under the name of the Queen's Institute of District Nursing. . . .
> The development of visiting nurse service in the United States followed the pattern of the Liverpool District Nursing Organization but not that of the Queen's Institute standardization and control. New York City had the first salaried visiting nurse service, inaugurated by the Women's Branch of the New York City Mission in 1877. . . . In 1885 Buffalo formed a visiting nurse association, followed in 1886 by Boston and Philadelphia, and in 1889 by Chicago. By 1890 the idea had really taken root, for there were 21 organizations. In 1893 the Visiting Nurse Service of the Henry Street Settlement in New York City was

[29] In Emerson: *Administrative Medicine.* New York, Thomas Nelson Sons, 1951. Ch. 10, pp. 135–43.

organized by Lillian D. Wald whose leadership in public health nursing continued for a half century.

Reference should be made to Miss Sargent's account in detail[30] of the development of visiting nursing and the events which led to the founding in 1912 of the National Organization for Public Health Nursing, since merged with the National League for Nursing.

The expanding responsibilities of the public health nurse are well described in an article by Zella Bryant.[31]

Nurse-Midwifery. Resurrected in the sixties is the ancient profession of midwifery—a resurrection virtually confined to the United States because it never died in most other countries. Births are increasing; obstetricians are decreasing. Esteemed in Europe, the midwife in America has been known only in the backwoods and the hill country or in the mission field. Urgent need for better use of the nurse trained in obstetrics spurred the establishment of a school for nurse-midwives by the University of the State of New York in 1931. Affiliated with it was a clinic. Gradually the number of midwife training programs increased to seven.

The midwife can give the patient more personal attention than can the physician, be with her more so as to note quickly any abnormal condition, and can relieve the doctor of many procedures yet have the benefit of his direction and of his help should any difficulties arise.

Other Specialties. Among the other important nursing specialties is central service supervision. Although this specialty is organized nationally in the National Association of Central Service Personnel, its membership includes supervisors who are not nurses.

A new and exciting specialty is space nursing. The nurses on the space projects say that their work is not very different from that of other nurses. The uniqueness is in the environment, in the fact that the doctors they work with are space surgeons, and in the highly research-centered aspects of their work with the patients, the astronauts. Their special flight nurses' courses provide the needed surgical background.

Psychiatric nursing is an expanding specialty. In 1963 a new publication, *Journal of Psychiatric Nursing,* was launched.

Male Nurses

The shortage of nurses has focused attention on a promising recruitment source—men. The January, 1960, issue of *Reader's Digest* carried an article, condensed from the December, 1959, issue of *The Modern Hospital,* entitled "*Men Can Beat the Nurse Shortage,*" by Allen Rankin.

In 1961 there were only about 4,000 registered and employed male nurses—

[30] *Ibid.,* pp. 135–43.
[31] *Pub. Health Rep.,* October, 1961, pp. 857–60.

about one per cent of the total professional nurses. This is a downtrend from a historical standpoint. D. L. McAllen, Jr., in the December, 1961, issue of *Hospital Progress,* called attention to the fact that men have assumed nursing duties since early Christian times, citing "the brotherhood known as Parabolani in the third century, St. Basil's monks in the sixth century, the Benedictines, the Order of St. John and Teutonic Knights during the Crusades, the Alexian brothers from the fourteenth century," and the nursing brotherhood that staffed the Jesus of Nazareth Hospital built in 1524 in Mexico City by Cortez.

More than half of the nursing schools in the United States admit men, and most hospitals and other health agencies are willing to employ them. The chief barrier is the tradition that has grown that nursing is a woman's profession.

Evolution of Nursing[32]

The precursor of the American Nurses' Association was the Nurses' Associated Alumnae of the United States and Canada, organized in 1896 with the support of the American Society of Superintendents of Training Schools for Nurses of the United States and Canada, which had been founded in 1893. The alumnae group changed its name to American Nurses' Association in 1911 after the Canadian group had withdrawn in 1908 to form the Canadian Nurses' Association. In 1912 the name of the school superintendents' association was changed to National League for Nursing Education, which in 1952 merged with other organizations, as mentioned before, into the National League for Nursing.

Effective work has been done by the American Nurses' Association in raising the standards of nursing care and in promoting the nursing profession. Besides its monthly *Journal,* it publishes the quarterly *Nursing Research* and an annual edition of *Facts about Nursing,* which currently runs around 250 pages in length. It constantly instigates studies on nursing subjects and publishes or arranges publication of the reports. Through joint committees it cooperates with other medical, nursing, and allied health organizations in surveys and in problem solving. As a federation of nursing associations of 50 states and the District of Columbia, the Panama Canal Zone, Puerto Rico, and the Virgin Islands, it has more than 170,000 members. A current important activity to which members are contributing funds is the American Nurses' Foundation, founded in 1955, which, as funds become available, makes grants to research teams, to colleges and universities, to hospitals, to special study groups, and to selected individuals, in the promotion of an expanded nursing research program. The foundation has a board of directors which represents both nursing and the general public. In the first five years some $300,000 was spent for research, and the total initial goal is $1,000,000.

Another major nursing project is a National Fund for Graduate Nursing Edu-

---

[32] For general historical background, the chapter on the nursing department in MacEachern's *Hospital Organization and Management,* 3rd ed. (Berwyn, Ill., Physician's Record Co., 1957, pp. 509–11) gives a brief outline. Several excellent histories of nursing, a few of which are listed in the Bibliography (pp. 787–811), are readily available.

cation with a goal of $1,000,000 for the first year, established in 1960. Its establishment was the result of studies conducted by Teachers College, Columbia University, which disclosed that there was need for four times the 1,100 nurses a year who are receiving master's degrees in thirty accredited graduate nursing education programs. The fund has been endorsed by the Secretary of Health, Education and Welfare; the Surgeon General of the Public Health Service; the American Medical Association; American Hospital Association; American Council on Education; National League for Nursing; and the American Nurses' Association.

Canadian Nurses' Association

The Canadian Nurses' Association has, like the A.N.A., a broad program. The main difference is that it is undertaking, after considerable study, an evaluation of schools of nursing with the objective of establishing an accreditation program. The C.N.A. is a federation of the ten provincial nurses' associations and has almost 70,000 members. It publishes in both English and French editions a journal, *The Canadian Nurse*. It is represented on the board of governors of the Victorian Order of Nurses of Canada, another national organization of nurses.

As in the United States, hospital administrators are concerned about the effect upon hospital nursing schools of pressure from the nursing group for university education.

> The Canadian Conference of University Schools of Nursing has recommended in its brief to the Royal Commission on Health Services that one-quarter of our nurses should be prepared through university programs and that this be done by increased grants, bursaries and the like. We have no fault to find with this recommendation except that it states one method of accomplishing this objective would be for selected hospital schools of nursing to abdicate the field of nursing education and make their facilities available to university schools of nursing. In our opinion while there is room for more university-trained nurses, this should not be done at the expense of the diploma school. This would involve giving up a familiar and much-needed system without adequate provision for replacing it and we cannot see the logic in that.[33]

International Council of Nurses

Nurses have been organized internationally since 1899. The International Council of Nurses was proposed by Mrs. Bedford Fenwick of what was then the British College of Nurses, at a meeting of the Matrons' Council of Great Britain and Ireland, held that year in London. The first meeting was held at Buffalo in 1901, but no countries affiliated, which was believed to have been because nurses were not sufficiently organized in their own countries to enter into international relations. In 1904 the United States, Germany, and Great Britain affiliated, and in

[33] Editorial. *Canad. Hosp.*, November, 1962.

1909, four more countries. At the close of the congress in Helsingfors in 1925, 19 countries were affiliated. Currently it has some 55 full and 20 associate members.

Membership in the council is open to one nursing association in a country. It represents nursing in many international organizations, including the World Health Organization, the World Medical Association, and the International Hospital Federation. Congresses are held every four years, with occasional interim meetings. The thirteenth congress will be held in Germany in 1965.

The council's publication is *International Nursing Review*. It maintains headquarters at 1 Dean Trench Street, Westminster, London, S.W.1, England.

Comprehensive Nursing

In nursing the same concept has developed as in medicine—comprehensive care. It was expressed in the definition of nursing formulated in 1953 by the Joint Commission for the Improvement of the Care of the Patient:[34]

> Comprehensive nursing should be designed to provide physical and emotional care for the patient; care of his immediate environment; carrying out the treatment prescribed by the physician; teaching the patient and his family the essentials of nursing that they must render; giving general health instruction and supervision of auxiliary workers.

Trends in nursing were spelled out in an intriguing way by Miss Geister in the previously mentioned A.O.R.N. talk: "Yesterday, when our patients were all prostrate, we did everything *for* the patient; today, in the maze of procedures and the need to get the work done, we do everything *to* him; tomorrow, as today's inequities are dropped out, and as a patient is re-emerging as a patient, we will do everything *with* him."

The inevitable conclusion: medicine is changing, nursing is changing, and the patient is changing along with them. He is in the act—no longer an inert object. He cannot be rehabilitated unless he works at it along with the medical, nursing, and physical and occupational therapy team. Early ambulation and self-help as therapeutic aids are destroying the hospital and even the nursing home as places in which to rest and be waited on. Bedside nursing appears to have a diminishing place in the hospital of the future because most patients most of the time will be using beds only for sleeping.

OCCUPATIONAL THERAPY

World Wars I and II, especially II, brought to all therapy involved in rehabilitation the recognition of the benefits of medical supervision of the total programs. An occupational therapist needs the direction of a licensed physician in prescribing treatment adapted to the individual patient.

[34] Report approved by the boards of trustees of the American Medical Association, the American Hospital Association, and the boards of directors of the American Nurses' Association and the National League for Nursing. New York, National League for Nursing, 1953.

The psychosomatic medical theories developed during the past few decades call further attention to those aspects of treatment that are not furthered by surgery and pharmaceuticals. The occupational therapy program should be thoroughly correlated with nursing, physical therapy, and social service.

The American Occupational Therapy Association was founded in 1917. The American Medical Association began accreditation of schools in 1923. In its early years the association met with the annual conference of the American Hospital Association. On the program of its 1927 session in Minneapolis appear such subjects as:

Muscle Training by Occupational Treatment
Occupational Therapy in Tuberculosis
The Junior League's Occupational Therapy Work with Children
Relating Occupational Therapy to Rehabilitation
Corrective Work for Children
Medical and Social Considerations
When Is Occupation Curative?
Therapeutic Occupations for Mental Patients
The Psychological Basis of Occupational Therapy
Occupational Therapy in Relation to Agriculture
Organized Methods and Work in Mental Hospitals
Occupational Therapy in Industrial Accident Cases
Habit Training: Methods and Results
Training the Occupational Therapist
Methods, Crafts and Equipment
The Hospital's Role in Training the Therapist
The Preindustrial Shop

These are not unlike topics appearing on the programs of this group in the 1960's. They show that although this profession was born in military hospitals during World War I, it developed quickly.

In 1930, Dr. Walter S. Goodale,[35] superintendent of the Buffalo, New York, City Hospital, said that the original exponents of occupational therapy held that work so designated "should have for its sole purpose therapy of the disease involved, and that under no circumstances should it constitute a gainful occupation." He declared a conviction that a broader outlook was desirable, saying that the hand work carried on in his hospital was not only "designed as an aid to recovery, but it also has in mind the economic improvement of the patient who is handicapped by disease, accident, retarded mentality, or lack of opportunity." He told of a tuberculosis patient who had been employed for two years in the hospital print shop and who upon discharge "was fully equipped to take his place in a commercial shop."

Almost imperceptibly, therefore, occupational therapy leads into vocational rehabilitation for many patients, without the latter always being initially a primary aim. Dr. Goodale emphasized, "No patient is permitted to do work that will in any way hinder his cure." The patients were offered a financial incentive for their work by being permitted to earn a maximum of one dollar a day

[35] *Bull. Am. Hosp. A.,* January, 1930.

through sales of their products. At that time, 1930, this 863-bed hospital had 29 teachers on its educational extension division staff. The Department of Public Instruction selected and paid the book work teachers; the hospital the hand work teachers.

In 1931 the American Occupational Therapy Association established its registry for occupational therapists. It has established reciprocity with international occupational therapy groups. Its official publication is *American Journal of Occupational Therapy*. Another publication in this field is *Occupational Therapy and Rehabilitation*. The association publishes each year a *Yearbook* with alphabetical and geographical listings of registered occupational therapists. From time to time it publishes a revised list of colleges and universities offering courses in occupational therapy which are approved by the Council on Medical Education and Hospitals of the American Medical Association. There are certificate courses, degree courses with a major in O.T., and advanced standing courses for college graduates. Two or three of the colleges offering the latter have master's degree programs, but most of them are certificate programs.

A neurologist, Dr. Goldwin W. Howland, was the founder of occupational therapy in Canada. Mainly through his efforts the first occupational therapy department in a general hospital in Canada was established in 1919 at the Toronto General Hospital. In 1921 he became a member of the honorary advisory board of the Ontario Society of Occupational Therapy when it was first organized. As chairman of the society's educational committee he was instrumental in having a course in occupational therapy established at the University of Toronto in 1926, the same year in which the Dominion Association of Occupational Therapists was founded, of which he was elected the first president, an office he held for 22 years. Publication of *The Canadian Journal of Occupational Therapy* began in 1933.

The World Federation of Occupational Therapists issues publications from time to time. Designed for countries in which the service is new are *Establishment of a Program for the Education of Occupational Therapists* and *Organization of an Occupational Therapy Department*.

THERAPEUTIC RECREATION

An interesting activity related to occupational therapy is "therapeutic recreation," organized nationally in the United States as "Comeback, Inc.," with headquarters in New York City. In 1959 the National Recreation Association published *Recreation in Hospitals: Report of a Study of Organized Recreation Programs in Hospitals and of Personnel Conducting Them*. Included in this report are findings of a survey of colleges and universities offering preparation in therapeutic recreation. These findings disclosed complete lack of uniformity in curricula of the different schools. Studies and meetings followed which culminated in the holding of a "Therapeutic Recreation Curriculum Development

Conference" in New York City February 16 to 18, 1961, the report of which was published and distributed by Comeback, Inc. Fifteen universities were represented by educators at the meeting, which was financed by the Avalon Foundation. Others attending were practitioners and consultants.

The "Recommended Essentials for Institutions Offering a Curriculum in Therapeutic Recreation," presented at the conference, stipulate that the "minimum length of full-time education should be the equivalent of a regular master's degree program which is at least 30 semester-hours, with clinical experience and a thesis in addition. Section X, "Clinical Experiences and Hospital Affiliation," specifies a minimum of eight weeks for assignment to a clinical training center.

This is an example of one of the latest of the many rather new allied professions which are struggling for higher standards through organizing to improve the educational and training programs which prepare practitioners.

PHARMACY

The pharmacy department in a hospital is relatively small and inconspicuous. Its professional staff is also small, for in all of the United States there are only around 6,000 registered pharmacists working full-time in hospitals, and about a fifth as many working part-time. Yet this behind-the-scenes department wages a tremendously effective war on pain and disease and represents a giant industrial and research effort. There is no more thrilling study than that of following the day-by-day discoveries that the laboratories announce and watching the benefits to patients of the quick application of new medications as prescribed by the physician.

The hospital pharmacy market is approaching the $500 million figure in the United States alone. In 1929 it was $8 million. A service that has grown sixty times in monetary terms in less than four decades merits the administrator's study of its broad background, in order that, for one thing, he may have the vision to anticipate new developments that will affect his whole operation.

Hospital administrators need to watch developments in attempts to solve the problem of evaluation of new drugs. In a summary of the situation as reported at the conference of the American Public Health Association in the fall of 1960, *Public Health Reports* for February, 1961, said:

> An effective program for clinical evaluation of drugs requires that medical need and scientifically established criteria be the primary factors governing the development, production, and trial of new products, according to Dr. Mindel C. Sheps, associate research professor of biostatistics in the Graduate School of Public Health and associate research professor of preventive medicine in the School of Medicine, University of Pittsburgh.
>
> The clinical value and limitations of a drug can be determined only by comparing its effect with the effect of alternative methods of treatment, after extensive experience and cirtical evaluation, Sheps said. However, the number of new drugs being developed and the acceleration in their rate of obsolescence have

resulted in increased pressure for each new drug to go on the market quickly, and lasting value has become a secondary consideration, he stated.

Of the nearly 6,000 new products introduced in the twelve years 1948–59, only 491 were new chemical entities. Of the 63 new chemical entities introduced in 1959, only 29, or 46 per cent, were truly new; the remainder were either new salts of old products or derivatives of known drugs.

Hospital staffs, administrators of medical care programs, and individual physicians all must demand convincing evidence of the value of a drug before they accept it, Sheps said.

At present no organization, official or unofficial, is responsible for testing all drugs for chemical effectiveness, although a number of medical centers are studying methods of refining techniques for evaluating drugs and are training physicians in these methods. However, these centers investigate only drugs of interest to themselves, and their findings usually are not immediately available.

In Sheps' opinion it is an essential requirement of a rational, scientific, and ethical program for the clinical evaluation of drugs and their subsequent utilization in practice that a way be found to govern the development, production, and trial of new drugs, primarily according to medical need and scientifically, established criteria.

Chauncey D. Leake,[36] director of the research training program at the University of California Medical School, introduced a talk on "What We Should Know about Drugs" by saying:

Drugs, of course, are chemical agents. To use them satisfactorily all members of the health professions must really know a great deal more about them, in a general and fundamental way, than we now know. Always, of course, drug action depends upon the physical chemical characteristics of the drug, and these must be known in much wider detail than is now the case. If you are following the pharmacological reports and reviews, you will observe that it is, increasingly, the recognition of the characteristic of the chemical of the drug, the physical chemical characteristic of the compound that is being studied that determines its reactivity with specific chemicals in the living tissue to which it is applied. So, through the study of the action of drugs we are learning a great deal more about the physical chemical characteristic of living material.

The hospital pharmacist needs to learn how to dispense and assay radioactive materials and to understand the health problems involved in the handling and disposing of such materials. The Atomic Energy Commission has on occasion made grants to colleges of pharmacy for training students in the handling of radioisotopes.

The most widely used isotope is radioactive iodine. It is used to locate brain tumors, to evaluate renal and liver function, and to determine fat absorption in the gastrointestinal tract. By far its greatest use, however, is in the diagnosis of thyroid disorders. It is also employed in the treatment of certain thyroid disorders, particularly thyroid carcinoma.

[36] At the 1962 Pharmacy Assembly of the New York State Council of Hospital Pharmacists, in cooperation with Pfizer Laboratories, held in New York City, September 22. *Hosp. Topics,* December, 1962, p. 63.

Growth of the American Pharmaceutical Industry[37]

Since academic medicine was born in Philadelphia, it is not surprising that the city also became the "Cradle of Pharmacy." Christopher Marshall set up the first American apothecary shop at the "Sign of the Golden Ball." His son Charles was the first president of the pioneer Philadelphia College of Pharmacy, and his daughter Elizabeth the nation's first woman pharmacist. Benjamin Franklin, who helped establish the Pennsylvania Hospital at Philadelphia, also persuaded the governing board to appoint a pharmacist to the hospital to take over the task of compounding medications from the doctors.

In 1825, Elias Durand, pharmacist to Napoleon's Grand Army, set up a store in Philadelphia. He collected American herbs for the College of Pharmacy and helped to publish a *Materia Medica*. John Farr, an Englishman, and Abraham Kunzie, a Swiss, started to make quinine in Philadelphia in 1818. The partnership was an American root of a major drug house, the firm of Merck, Sharpe, and Dohme, which was established in Philadelphia in 1853.

Another famous drug house was started by George K. Smith who commenced business on Arch Street, Philadelphia. Cancellation of heavy orders from the South at the start of the Civil War nearly caused his failure, but he formed a partnership with his accountant, Mahler N. Kline, which later took in the perfume manufactory of Harry B. French. Smith, Kline, and French were to become the leading makers of tranquilizers in the 1950's.

William R. Warner, a student of the College of Pharmacy, invented a process for sugar-coating pills before the Civil War. After its close, he began to make drugs in Philadelphia under his own name. At the Philadelphia Centennial in 1876, he exhibited a model drugstore that was years ahead of its time, and founded the present-day Warner-Lambert Pharmaceutical Company.

A fourth famous Philadelphia venture commenced in 1860, when Frank and John Wyeth opened a pharmacy shop at 1410 Walnut Street. Although John had graduated from the Philadelphia College of Pharmacy and not Frank, it was the former who became the businessman of the enterprise, and the latter the chemist. In 1872 their employees designed the first rotary press for making tablets. This can be seen in the Smithsonian Institution, while their drugstore on Walnut survives in the Wanamaker department store. Their business went on to become the Wyeth Laboratories, division of American Home Products Corporation, and the Wyeth name is now attached to pharmaceutical sales of the same order as those of Smith, Kline and French.

While Philadelphia nourished the beginnings of the industry, major enterprises also became established in other places. Brooklyn saw Charles Pfizer and

[37] The following account of the growth of the American pharmaceutical industry is taken from a thesis, "Pharmaceutical Research and its Impact upon Hospitals," submitted to Northwestern University by Dr. A. J. Glazebrook, visiting psychiatrist in research, Brooklyn State Hospital, as his final project to qualify him for his master's degree in hospital administration in 1961.

Company, Inc., commence operations in 1849, and E. R. Squibb and Sons in 1858. Parke Davis and Company was founded in Detroit in 1866; Eli Lilly and Company in Indianapolis in 1876; the Upjohn Company in Kalamazoo in 1882; Abbott Laboratories and G. D. Searle in Chicago in 1888 and 1891; Lederle Laboratories in Pearl River, New York, in 1906; S. B. Penwick and Company in New York City in 1914; and the Sterling Drug Company, Inc., in Attica, Indiana, in 1887.

Steady evolution has occurred during the last hundred years, but the greatest advances took place in times of national emergency. During the Civil War, medicines had to be made available for troops on widely scattered fronts and pharmacy moved from a local to a national level. The Confederacy became cut off from the major suppliers of drugs, and this stimulated a search for new sources. In the North, the war started a movement toward standardization of products.

Even so, at the outbreak of World War I, the production of the major medicinal chemicals was still centered in Germany. As a result, alarming rumors circulated of the possibility, for instance, that surgical operations might have to be done without an anesthetic. The price of Salvarsan, Ehrlich's silver bullet against syphilis, went to more than $35 a dose. Although the German submarine *Deutschland* succeeded in running the British blockade with cargoes of drugs, the entry of the United States into the war as a combatant cut off this precious source.

American chemists had to apply themselves to making German drugs in American plants. Salvarsan was produced within six months and was soon followed by procaine (German, Novocain) and by barbital (German, Veronal). Soon the gap made by loss of German imports was filled.

The six years of World War II marked the greatest medical progress of any comparable period in history. In contrast to the Civil War, the problem was that of supplying medicines for soldiers fighting all over the world instead of within the nation. The tactical values of succoring wounded men with rapidity had been shown in the Spanish Civil War, by blood transfusions on the field of battle. That disease killed or disabled more men than cannon had been noted in the American Civil War and in the Crimean War. Thus, efficient medicine became a recognized tool for attaining victory, and scientific, medical, industrial, and governmental sources were mobilized for this war effort. The impetus raised research and development in this country to a higher plane, and among the important developments were blood plasma and its fractions; manufacture of penicillin; and production of new drugs for the control of tropical diseases. When the war ended, the making of drugs had become established as a major industry, and business drive maintained the rate of growth. The prospect of large profits led to the development of extremely costly and complicated programs. Major breakthroughs were soon announced. New antibiotics of extreme potency, antihistamines, synthetic steroid hormones, hypotensive agents, new vaccines, tranquilizers, and the use of radioisotopes for diagnosis and treatment were among them.

Mass production and assaying techniques, with exacting quality control procedures, were introduced to complement the research effort. These lowered the cost of expensive drugs and helped to ensure that the American pharmaceutical industry retained the leading place it had gained in World War II.

Since the growth of the industry has had considerable impact upon the ability of hospitals to serve the people, an estimate of further growth which is likely to take place up to the last quarter of the century is of interest.

G. B. Stone[38] has studied five different projections of the annual sales value of the products of the ethical drug industry.

The first is an economic one, based upon a composite index trend of six primary sources of data during the period 1939 to 1956. The six sources mentioned are the *Annual Prescription Survey,* prepared by Topics Publishing Company, Inc., New York; a study of the ethical drug industry prepared by Arthur D. Little, Inc., Cambridge, Massachusetts; the corporate sales of the major ethical drug companies for the period 1946 to 1956; government statistics, from the *Census of Manufacturing* for 1947 to 1950; reports from *F-D-C,* a weekly trade letter; and a survey carried out by the Medimetric Institute of New York. This provides an estimate of annual sales for 1965 amounting to $2.85 billion; $4.10 billion in 1970; and $5.63 billion in 1975.

The second projection is based upon the trend in average cost of prescriptions, the trend in the annual per capita number of prescriptions, and published population forecasts. This provides estimates of sales values amounting to $2.66 billion in 1965; $3.70 billion in 1970; and $5.05 billion in 1975.

The third approach uses the trend observed in the per capita expenditure for drugs, including over-the-counter purchases without prescriptions. The figures have been made available yearly by the Department of Commerce since 1929. Again applying published projections for population growth in the United States, estimates by this method furnish totals of $2.83 billion in 1965, $3.50 billion in 1970, and $4.27 billion in 1975.

Concomitant with the fall in the death rate from 11.55 per 1,000 in 1936, to 9.36 per 1,000 in 1956, the drug industry expanded fifteenfold, and new drugs have been a vital factor in this lowering of the mortality rate.

The fourth projection is based upon the assumption that new drugs will continue to be a factor in the further reduction of the mortality rate. The composite annual sales value of the industry is divided by the annual crude mortality rate per 1,000 population. This series of statistics from 1936 to 1956 is then projected in five-year periods to 1975.

Multiplying these by projections for the mortality rate up to 1975, published by

---

[38] A Long Range Economic Outlook for the Drug Industry, thesis submitted to Massachusetts Institute of Technology (1958).

the Social Security Administration, estimates averaging $2.84 billion in 1965, $3.78 billion in 1970, and $4.84 billion in 1975 are furnished.

The final calculation uses the assumption that advances will occur in the treatment of five important medical problems during the next fifteen years. These problems are cancer, heart disease, mental disease, arthritis, and viral infections. Major discoveries for the chemotherapeutic treatment of cancer were forecast for 1965, for heart disease in 1962, for mental disease in 1962, for arthritis in 1962, and for viral infections (common cold vaccines) in 1966. These assumptions regarding new product development are considered together with forecasts of sales of existing major drug categories on the basis of population growth, economic growth, and mortality reduction. Summation provides sales estimates for ethical drugs of $2.73 billion in 1965, $3.80 billion in 1970; and $5.50 billion in 1975.

The last projection is based upon assumptions drawn from opinions, and not from facts. However, the opinions are in turn based upon the present progress being made by the major research facilities. The history of the last 25 years tends to show that forecasts of the timing of major advances have erred on the pessimistic side, if at all. Stone has not included in his assumptions, for instance, the possibility that a safe oral contraceptive may become available, which would have enormous sales potential in view of the present rate of population expansion. G. D. Searle and Company appear to have already accomplished the production of such a substance in Enovid. At present it is too expensive for world-wide use, but it cannot be doubted that means will be found to manufacture a cheap, reliable, and safe oral contraceptive.

On the other hand, it is perhaps unrealistic to believe that a "wonder drug" for the cure of cancer will suddenly emerge. Cancer is not a single disease entity, but a whole family of diseases. Each member of the family will probably have to be subdued by an individual approach, unless one current concept of immunotherapy to cancerous change can be applied as a general measure.

Other scientific objections can be made to Stone's forecasts, but it is interesting that the five are in rather close agreement. The median is given value of $2.8 billion in 1965, $3.8 billion in 1970, and $5.2 billion in 1975, and the variations from this median are only plus 10 per cent for periods up to 1970, and plus 20 per cent up to 1975.

A factor which may influence the predictions to a significant extent is increased federal regulation of the drug industry. This may have a very adverse effect upon growth, particularly if pricing regulations force down the funds available for research and if profit-cutting reduces the drive to discover new drugs.

The preceding statement concludes the extract from Dr. Glazebrook's thesis. Since he wrote it, the thalidomide tragedies triggered action for tighter controls over testing of new drugs in clinical trials.

Dr. Sarah H. Knutti[39] summarizes the problem as follows:

[39] How to Promote and Assure Rational Drug Therapy. *Mod. Hosp.*, July, 1959, p. 89.

Many new drugs are not only potent therapeutically but capable of doing great harm in over-dosage or if too long continued or through unforeseeable but dangerous individual idiosyncrasy. Often new drugs, extensively tested, are used rather freely for some time before untoward effects are appreciated. (A good example is meperidine, once thought nonhabit forming.) Not only do we have these problems with drugs which have been clinically investigated and released by the Federal Food and Drug Administration for general use, but, also, obviously, the increased production of new drugs means that more must be clinically tested, somewhere, and on someone.

Dr. Kenneth B. Babcock[40] in the next article in the same series remarks: "Thanks to the rapid developments in the drug industry, the pharmacist has switched roles—from humble apothecary to the modern 'Sorcerer's Apprentice,' if not the Sorcerer himself."

Organization

The American Pharmaceutical Association was founded in 1852. The first object of the association as stated under Article II of its constitution is:

To improve and promote the public health by aiding in the establishment of satisfactory standards for drugs, and to aid in the detection and prevention of adulteration and misbranding of drugs and medicines, and to take such steps as an Association and in cooperation with other organizations as will assure the production and distribution of drugs and medicines of the highest quality.

The second stated object is:

To foster and encourage interprofessional relations to the end that pharmacists, physicians, and members of other allied professions may contribute to the promotion of the public health and welfare in fullest measure.

A staggering ethical problem confronts the association and the profession. The traffic in counterfeit drugs is conservatively estimated to amount to $50 million a year, with indications that the true figure may be three times as large. Where there are sellers there are buyers, and pharmacists in hospitals, mail-order houses, and drugstores are buying these bootleg drugs, known as "zombies." *Parade* magazine in its issues of October 23, 1960, and January 15, 1961, publicized the racket. Jack Anderson who directed *Parade's* investigation, reported in the February, 1961, issue of *Hospital Topics* that the District of Columbia Pharmaceutical Association, "anxious to purge an honorable profession of its shady operators," organized a committee and set up a Washington pilot project in which pharmacists sign a "Pledge of Ethical Practice" and agree to forfeit a $10,000 bond if, knowingly, that pledge is broken. Those who sign are issued blue-and-white seals, the issuance of which is the responsibility of a three-man, not-for-profit committee—the National Committee Against Counterfeit Drugs. The association named to active membership on this committee Mr. Anderson,

[40] Rx for Accreditation: Keep Drug Standards High. *Mod. Hosp.*, July, 1959, p. 90.

a prominent Washington attorney who had no connection with the drug industry, and the then president-elect of the pharmaceutical association. Mr. Anderson also reported: "Certain drug manufacturers have expressed willingness to provide shoppers, investigators, and testing facilities to police the program. Committee investigators will spot-shop drug stores. Any complaint that a pharmacist is violating his pledge will be thoroughly investigated."

Hospital Pharmacists. Agitation began in the late 1930's and early 1940's for the establishment of a hospital pharmacy section within the American Pharmaceutical Association. Finally an affiliate was founded in 1942, the American Society of Hospital Pharmacists. The society has its own periodical, the *American Journal of Hospital Pharmacy.* In 1950, after long study of previous standard-setting activities, the society published a minimum standard for pharmacies in hospitals which was submitted to various agencies for approval and has since been revised from time to time. In the 1950 presentation, the following account of "The First Minimum Standard" was contributed by Edward Spease, formerly dean of the School of Pharmacy at Western Reserve University, Cleveland:

> The first Minimum Standard for Hospital Pharmacies was offered to the eighteenth annual Hospital Standardization Conference of the American College of Surgeons held in San Francisco and Oakland, California, in 1935. The standard as presented consisted of five principles.
>
> Credit for suggesting that a Minimum Standard for Hospital Pharmacies be established goes to Dr. Malcolm T. MacEachern, formerly director of the American College of Surgeons. Preparation of the original standard was done by Edward Spease, then directing pharmacist of the University Hospitals of Cleveland, and by Robert M. Porter, then chief pharmacist. Dr. MacEachern, on visiting the pharmacy department at the University Hospitals in Cleveland in 1935, issued an invitation to prepare a standard and present it in written form at the Hospital Standardization Conference. The paper as presented at the Conference was read by Dr. Troy C. Daniels, dean of the College of Pharmacy of the University of California.
>
> Adoption of the standard by the American College of Surgeons soon followed, and while neither Dr. MacEachern as a hospital authority, nor those of us interested, expected the adoption to have the force of law immediately, it is now apparent that the suggestions offered in the standard and the frequent publication and discussion of the principles set forth, have led to something that is permanent and good.

The American Association for the Advancement of Science includes a hospital pharmacy session in its annual meeting.

Formularies

In any study of pharmacy, however condensed, some consideration must be given to formularies. The situation is "turbulent," to use the description employed by a staff member of the National Pharmaceutical Council.[41] In 1960 the

---

[41] William E. Woods, assistant to the executive vice president, in a talk at a branch meeting of the American Pharmaceutical Association, Philadelphia, January, 1962.

American Hospital Association and the American Society of Hospital Pharmacists approved twelve guiding principles, the fourth one of which reads:

> The medical staff should adopt the policy of, and formulate the procedure for, including drugs in the formulary and dispensing of such drugs by their non-proprietary names, even though brand-name drugs are and will continue to be in common use in the hospital. The writing of prescriptions and medication orders by their nonproprietary names is preferred, although not required as a universal practice.

The nonproprietary name is customarily known as the "generic" name. The pharmaceutical industry is concerned about the limiting of the number of brands in a formulary system, which would restrict the physician's choice of a drug. Obviously economy and efficiency are involved. The hospital must have some control, exercised through a committee which functions as recommended in the "Statement on the Pharmacy and Therapeutics Committee" adopted in 1959 by the American Hospital Association and the American Society of Hospital Pharmacists and advocated by the Joint Commission on Accreditation of Hospitals.

After extended discussion of the controversial aspects of the "guiding principles," a five-point statement of operation for the hospital formulary system was jointly announced by the American Pharmaceutical Association, its affiliate the American Society of Hospital Pharmacists, the American Hospital Association, and the American Medical Association, during the meeting of the two pharmacy associations in Miami Beach, May 12-17, 1963. The statement, which was published in the June 1, 1963, issue of *Hospitals,* "clears the way for the four organizations to revise the guiding principles."

PHYSICAL THERAPY

The American Medical Association and the medical profession in general have demonstrated in conspicuous ways a particular appreciation of the value of the physical therapist as a co-worker in promoting the rehabilitation of patients. The doctor prescribes the treatment as he does in other allied services, but more than in most of the others, physical therapy frequently brings dramatic, readily appreciable benefits. That fact is one of the main satisfactions to the therapist.

The association's Council on Physical Therapy published in 1938 its recommendations for physical therapy departments in hospitals with fifty or more beds, concluding them with the statement ". . . 90 per cent of the physical therapy in a general hospital can be done with the simplest physical agents: heat, massage and exercise. The most important factors in a hospital physical therapy department are competent medical direction and efficient physical therapy technicians."[42] In other words, in the opinion of that experienced group, the personal element dominates the scene, and the departmental layout, furnishings and equipment, important as they are, are decidedly secondary.

[42] *J.A.M.A.,* March 19, 1938, pp. 896-88.

The emphasis on the personal element led to the interest of the medical profession in the training of the therapist. His potentialities in lessening disability after injury were demonstrated in World War I, and soon thereafter the Council on Medical Education and Hospitals of the American Medical Association, in collaboration with the American Physical Therapy Association, organized in 1921, began its approval program for schools.

In 1962 there were 39 approved schools in continental United States, 1 in Puerto Rico, and 6 in Cuba. The American Physical Therapy Association issues an *Organizational Guide for Physical Therapy Schools.* The Canadian Physiotherapy Association, which was organized in 1920, conducts the approval program for schools in Canada.

Concurrently with establishment of the approval program for schools, the American Congress of Physical Medicine set up the American Registry of Physical Therapists. Besides conforming to certain educational and experience requirements, the registrant signs the following code of ethics:

> All registered technicians shall be required strictly to observe the Code of Ethics as defined by the American Congress of Physical Medicine: namely, that they shall practice only under the prescription and direction of a licensed physician and shall under no circumstances on their own initiative treat patients or operate an office independently.

Since 1958 physical therapists trained in Canada may be registered with the American registry provided they are graduates of a course of study approved by the Canadian Medical Association and meet all other requirements established for United States registrants.

The American College of Surgeons included a "Minimum Standard for Physical Therapy Departments in Hospitals" in its *Manual of Hospital Standardization.* The surgeons also recognized the pre-eminence of the personal element in this profession; the elaboration of the five-clause Minimum Standard in the 1946 edition of the *Manual* included the statement: "It is important that well-trained technicians be available to assist the director in the treatment of these cases." The Joint Commission on Accreditation of Hospitals continues to emphasize high standards in the operation and control of physical therapy.

The American Hospital Association issued in 1949 and reissued in 1957 (the latter rewritten rather than revised), *Physical Therapy: Essentials of a Hospital Department.* The manual was prepared by a joint committee with the American Physical Therapy Association. A review by June M. Schroeder, R.P.T., chief physical therapist, University of Illinois Research and Educational Hospitals, Chicago, said in part:

> It assists the hospital administrator in assessing the justification for a physical therapy department and provides guide lines for the appropriate establishment and maintenance of this service once it has been justified. The need for clearly defined policies and for their development jointly by the responsible physician, the hospital administrator, and the physical therapist has been emphasized.[43]

[43] *Hosp. Topics,* October, 1958.

Although some aspects of physical therapy were discussed under physiatry in the preceding chapter, it is important to bear in mind that the therapist must have varied knowledge and skills in order to escape the dangers and give the greatest benefits through his treatment of the patient. The scope is vast. In an outline furnished to university programs in hospital administration by the American Physical Therapy Association are listed five physical agents that are employed: heat and cold, electricity, water, massage, and therapeutic exercise; and five aims: to combat the cumulative effects of prolonged physical and mental illness; to shorten the hospital stay; to reduce physical disability; to hasten convalescence; and to contribute to the return of patients to normal living economically and socially. A number of types of treatment and of specific aims are listed under each of the five physical agents. Several tests are described. Outlined are the major conditions in which physical therapy is of value in treating patients. Programs are indicated with which the therapist should cooperate within and without the hospital.

Obviously physical therapists must have exceptional understanding of anatomy, biology, pathology, physiology, and physics, before they can be entrusted with the application of the physical agents used in therapy. To the uninitiated, for example, massage may seem a simple procedure, but for maximum effectiveness it requires a wealth of knowledge and skill, as set forth in *Massage, Principles and Techniques,* by Gertrude Beard and Elizabeth Wood. Philadelphia, W. B. Saunders Company, 1964.

X-ray Technology

In the early days of x-ray described in the preceding chapter, physicians were the sole manipulators of the equipment. As the novelty began to wear off, the time taken from their practices for the mechanical work was begrudged, and they looked around the institution for assistants. At first almost any attendant was assigned for certain of the duties. This casual answer to the problem quickly proved wrong as the equipment and procedures became more complex. The need for trained technicians was apparent. An organization was needed to establish standards for training.

Through the joint efforts of the Radiological Society of North America and the American Roentgen Ray Society, the American Registry of X-ray Technicians was founded in 1922. The Roentgen Ray Society soon withdrew. An American Society of X-ray Technicians was organized in 1920, and in 1926 adopted a requirement that all of its members be registered technicians. In 1936 it became a co-sponsor of the registry, the other co-sponsor of which is the American College of Radiology.

The registry recognizes as "affiliated registered technicians" those who are engaged in x-ray work for manufacturers or distributors of x-ray equipment and accessories. X-ray technicians in other industries are not eligible.

Approval of the training schools has been assumed by the American Medical Association in collaboration with the American College of Radiology.

The Canadian Society of Radiological Technicians was formed in 1943. Its story[44] is an illuminating account of the maneuvering typically involved in the upgrading of a profession.

Prior to the formation of the Canadian Society of Radiological Technicians in 1943 there were no generally accepted standards of technician training. Some provinces set their own qualifying examinations and in others technicians registered with the American Society of X-ray Technicians, a body established in 1920. The important events for the period 1943–1959 when more and more attention was being paid to technician training in Canada are outlined in the following.

In 1943, the Canadian Society of Radiological Technicians was established by a federal charter with the Central and Provincial Examining Board appointed by the C.S.R.T. The year 1944 saw the Provincial Boards dissolved and one standard examination set by the Central Examining Board (Committee on Qualifications) leading to the granting of the "R.T." certificate in Diagnostic Radiography and Radiotherapy.

In the next two years a C.S.R.T. syllabus of training was published and a C.S.R.T. committee on technicians' training was established to study current training and make recommendations.

In 1948 the Canadian Association of Radiologists' Standing Committee on Technicians was established on the recommendation of the chairman of the C.S.R.T. Its purpose lay in drawing up a detailed curriculum and in acting as a liaison between the C.A.R. and the C.S.R.T. Following this in 1950 the C.A.R. *Instructors' Curriculum in Radiological Technique* was adopted by the C.S.R.T. and the next year it was published jointly by the C.A.R. and the C.S.R.T.

In 1955 a separation of training and examinations for diagnostic and therapeutic technique was proposed, agreed upon, and the necessary revisions were begun. The C.A.R. Committee on Technicians and the C.S.R.T. Committee on Technical Training were also amalgamated to form the Joint Committee on Technical Training with the object of formulating a plan for setting up approved schools. Two years later the minimal requirements for approved schools and the proposed plan for establishing approved schools were presented by the J.C.T.T. to their associations. A separate syllabus as well for training in radiotherapeutic technique was adopted and published jointly. . . . May of 1958 saw the first separate examinations held in radiotherapeutic technique (R.T.T.). The Joint Committee on Technical Training became the Joint Council on Technical Training, C.S.R.T. and C.A.R., with the status of a special committee of the two associations. In June of that year authorization was given to the J.C.T.T. to act as the official agent of the C.S.R.T. and the C.A.R. for "Approval and Accreditation of Training Schools." Questionnaires and invitations to apply for approval of schools in either diagnostic or radio therapeutic technique issued by the J.C.T.T. were put out in August.

Then, in December, the Canadian Medical Association was approached by the C.A.R. at the request of the J.C.T.T. with a view to undertaking the accreditation of such schools. Following this in January, 1959, the revised *Syllabus in Radiographic Technology* was published jointly again by the C.A.R. and the

[44] *Canad. Hosp.,* May, 1960, p. 78.

C.S.R.T., and the C.S.R.T. *Log Books for Diagnostic or Radiotherapeutic Technique* was introduced for student technicians as well. Finally in June a Standing Committee of the Canadian Medical Association on "Approval of Schools for the Training of Radiological Technicians" was established and in November, 1959, publication of the J.C.T.T. list of official "Interim Approved Training Schools in Diagnostic or Radiotherapeutic Technique" came about. A brochure describing the basic requirements and minimum standards which must be met by hospital schools for approval by the Canadian Medical Association committee is being distributed together with an application form for approval.

A similar "story" of the rise of the profession is told in other countries. W. J. Ashworth,[45] of Kent, England, past president of the Society of Radiographers, says:

> The radiologist of the early days was usually a man of considerable technological understanding and dexterity, but he nevertheless often found it a great convenience to employ and train a lay assistant to help with the apparatus and the darkroom. Gradually these assistants began to relieve the radiologist of the burden of actually taking the pictures or preparing the apparatus, and in time they too felt the need of professional status and came to call themselves radiographers. The First World War gave considerable impetus to radiology and radiography, and after 1918, members of both professions were more or less agreed that the radiographer's contribution was so essential that training, qualification and ethical control must be established and standardized. Therefore on 19th July, 1920, the Society of Radiographers was inaugurated, one of the original subscribers being Campbell Swinton, who had made the first radiograph in England nearly 25 years earlier. From then until the present day the Society has maintained the closest relationship with its radiological colleagues, and became affiliated to the British Institute of Radiology in 1927. More recently the Society has enjoyed the additional support of the Faculty of Radiologists and the Hospital Physicists' Association. The Council of the Society and its Education Committee and Board of Examiners include radiologists, radiotherapists and physicists, reflecting in the professional organization the close team work that has been developed in the hospital departments.

Mr. Ashworth continues his article with an account of the establishment of standards for training, of the function of the radiographer, and of the scope and organization of the diagnostic and therapeutic services in the National Health Service, stating that "with a few minor exceptions, the Society's examination is compulsory for employment in the National Health Service."

The American College of Radiology is concerned about the registration of x-ray technicians by organizations other than the American Registry of X-ray Technicians. In 1962 it passed a resolution aimed at clarifying the use and meaning of the title, "Registered Technician." Following explanation of the processes of approved training and registration, the resolution closes with the statement:

> The College is not in sympathy with x-ray technician registration by organizations lacking recognition of the American Medical Association. The College

[45] Radiography in the National Health Service, *J. Roy. Soc. Health,* November/December, 1959, pp. 854–55.

does not believe the public interest is served by beclouding the meaning of "RT, Registered Technician," by attributing to the initials some other title such as "radiographic technologist," etc. Such activities tend to confuse those concerned with competence in x-ray technique, radiation protection, and high standards of patient care.

An interesting development was the inauguration in 1959 of joint annual conventions by the Canadian Society of Radiological Technicians and the American Society of X-ray Technicians.

The profession is organized on a world-wide scale through the International Secretariat of Radiographers and Radiological Technicians which was formed at the Ninth International Congress of Radiology at Munich and met in conjunction with the Tenth Congress in Montreal in 1962.

OTHER ALLIED MEDICAL PROFESSIONS

With the shortage of physicians and the ever-increasing complexities of medical service a demand grows for assistants who can take a greater share of the responsibility for treatment than is now the case. Unquestionably hospitals are on the brink of change in this respect. A member of the Council on Medical Service of the American Medical Association, Dr. Charles L. Hudson,[46] advocates

> . . . externs-assistants with special training, intermediate between that of technician and doctor, who could not only handle the technical procedures listed above (assist at the actual operation as well as merely in the operating room; help cast and suture; dress and redress wounds; do lumbar puncture, venipuncture, transfusion, infusion, venous pressure, circulation time, intubation, catheterization, and charting) but could also take some degree of medical responsibility.

He conditions this recommendation by saying:

> Local attempts at implementation should be made only by collaboration between the hospital's nursing profession, the administration, and the medical profession. Certainly, there should be no reassignment of new groups of medical assistants without the advice and consent of the hospital administrator.

However far this expansion proposed for auxiliary groups may go, it is obvious that in the foregoing sections of this chapter a number of existing ones that should be mentioned are not included, and a few of them are here briefly described.

Medical Scientists

The American Medical Association has a special committee to study how to break down the barriers between physicians and their colleagues who contribute to health care in other fields, such as biophysics, biochemistry, microbiology.

Their associations identify a few of these highly educated groups, who are not

---
[46] *Hosp. Topics.,* June, 1962, p. 22.

generally M.D.'s, yet who are contributing more and more to medical progress and who are becoming staff members of leading hospitals:

American Electroencephalographic Society
American Physiological Society
American Psychological Association
American Psychosomatic Society, Inc.
American Society for Microbiology
American Society of Biological Chemists, Inc.
American Speech and Hearing Association
American Veterinary Medical Association

Except from the standpoint of coordination, these groups differ from those such as dentists, podiatrists, and therapists who are subject to the direction of the physician. They have more, though not complete, autonomy. The relationships are more difficult to define. Only the future can show how they will be fitted into the medical service picture, although in a few places like rehabilitation centers the psychologist, the vocational counselor, and the speech specialist are being absorbed into a well-coordinated team.

Chaplains

As the concept of comprehensive medicine penetrates more deeply into care of the patient, the chaplain's role is no longer separate from the other professional aspects of treatment; he is accepted as part of the team. He has had a more prominent place in the past in Catholic hospitals than in those of other sects, but the latter are integrating him more and more into hospital life. The subject is discussed in more detail in Chapter 16.

Podiatrists

Podiatrists, more commonly known as chiropodists, are a comparatively new group on hospital medical staffs, although from time immemorial this art has been practiced. Mounting interest in the services of the profession comes partly from the highlighting in the 1960's of care of the aged, some 85 per cent of whom are estimated to be afflicted with foot troubles. Skilled treatment of these is conceded to be an appreciable factor in keeping the aged mobile for the longest possible time, besides being a major contribution to their comfort.

Another factor that is pushing podiatry to the fore is the abuse of feet through ill-fitting and style-dictated footwear such as excessively high heels and pointed toes. Less than 10 per cent of persons who go barefoot have foot defects.

The podiatrist who functions in a hospital is under the direction and supervision of a doctor of medicine. When the podiatrist performs surgery, a surgeon should be present.

The American Podiatry Association is the new name for the former National Association of Chiropodists. There are five accredited schools which confer a degree of Doctor of Surgical Podiatry after completion of two years of college preprofessional study and four years' training in podiatry. A state board examination is required in all of the states, and a year of intern or resident training is required in some states before a license is issued.

The American College of Foot Surgeons confers fellowship upon properly qualified podiatrists.

Medical Illustrators

An interesting, rather recent addition as an aide on a full-time basis in medical service and research in the hospital is the medical illustrator. Some ten universities in the United States offer training in this field. The medical textbook illustrator plays a more static role than this new type artist, who is comparable to the journalist, working with the new developments that occur from day to day.

Shortly after Max Broedel organized the first department of medical illustration at Johns Hopkins University, Thomas S. Jones created in 1914 his famous department at the University of Illinois, of which he was made head in 1925, becoming full professor in 1942. He was elected president of the Association of Medical Illustrators in 1946 and up to his death in 1961 was also active in the Biologic Photographic Association. To his influence can be credited much of the progress in this field, one about which long ago the librarian Claudius Mayer wrote: "Only a new renaissance can resuscitate the now dead art of medical book illustration." The renaissance came with such leaders as Tom Jones and the doctor-artist F. H. Netter.

The medical illustrator not only functions in such complicated areas as surgery but can assist in the making of graphs, charts, slides, and films. He can help in preparing literature and lectures, can take photographs, can prepare exhibits. When all the possible uses for his talent are considered, even a small hospital can use a full-time illustrator—if he can be obtained. The demand is great, the supply small. The preparation, of course, requires intensive and continuous study of anatomy and pathology.

The sculptor also is important in medical art. Joseph Paderewski's postoperative and postaccident life masks at the John Sealy Hospital at the University of Texas Medical Center, considered in connection with his finished prostheses, show what an aid the sculptor can be to the plastic surgeon in the work of restoration and reconstruction. He supplies ears and other missing parts, made from clay, which can be attached with adhesive.

Medical Rehabilitation Coordinators

So many different professional groups are involved in the process of rehabilitation that need appeared, and was particularly recognized by the Veterans Administration, for a coordinator in each medical service institution. The Association of Medical Rehabilitation Directors and Coordinators, Inc., was organized in 1948 "to foster the concept of total rehabilitation for all disabled persons through unified and coordinated methods and to provide a means for the professional growth and advancement of medical rehabilitation directors and coordinators."

In connection with an honorary membership and a citation by the association in 1961 to Dr. J. T. Naramore, superintendent of Larned State Hospital, Larned, Kansas, the following statement was made which discloses the growth of the rehabilitation concept:

> Starting twelve years ago, the adjunctive therapy program at Larned State Hospital was managed by one occupational therapist with one per cent of the patients participating out of a population of 1,800. The other 99 per cent sat in their rocking chairs ten hours a day with no activity or diversion to break the monotony. Today there are 31 employees in this program, as well as a full time coordinator, who cover 98 per cent of the patient population. Dr. Naramore has pioneered in many phases of rehabilitation activities such as cosmetology care of female patients, special patient rehabilitation hospital projects, sheltered workshops, alerting citizens to hospital problems, and helping communities to understand their role in providing opportunities for the rehabilitated mental patient.

Wanted, but not yet achieved, are special university training courses for coordinators, most if not all of whom have a background of training in one of the therapies. The skill many of them miss is administration, and this they are striving to acquire through short courses and workshops. Success in coordination needs combined skills, as do many of the other medical-administrative combinations that are developing.

Part two

MEDICAL SCIENCE
AND SCIENTISTS

The Basic Science Foundation

Science no longer needs to be explained just to laymen and citizens and children; it now needs to be explained to statesmen and philosophers and even to scientists themselves! The poor scientist can never keep up with the hundred thousand research papers that are published every year, and so he becomes a layman too, in every field but his own, and an important part of the mass audience. There will have to be writing up as well as writing down. There is a need and an audience at every level of sophistication from the nursery school to the graduate school. . . . To say that basic science is exciting may sound like a contradiction. We are used to the really spectacular excitements of the engineers with their radar and rockets; and the life-and-death excitements of the doctors, the biological engineers, in their white coats. By contrast, the intellectual excitement of a man sitting over a microscope in a university basement tracking down a clue may seem pretty tame. . . . The thrill of a detective story and the pleasure of watching a play by George Bernard Shaw . . . are exactly the excitements basic science has to offer. . . . It is a thrilling thing to be participating as actor or observer in the scientific revolution of our time, as science enters and transforms the life of man.

JOHN R. PLATT, PH.D.[1]

DR. PLATT thinks that there are three particular qualities of basic science that a citizen in a scientific society "should be shown over and over until he begins to feel them for himself. The first quality is the excitement of science,

---

[1] From an address, The Sweep and Excitement of Science, given by Dr. Platt, professor of physics, University of Chicago before the Thomas Alva Edison Foundation meeting, on The Mass Media and the Image of Science, in Washington, D.C., November 6, 1959. *Pub. Health Rep.*, June, 1960, pp. 495–500.

the second is the sweep of science, and the third is the incompleteness of science." He asserts that when the word leaks out to the children that personalities in basic science are having fun doing exactly what they like to do, there will not be laboratories enough to hold the budding scientists.

Although he is unlikely to be an actor himself in the scientific aspects of medicine, the administrator should know enough about them to promote vigorously high standards of medical education, medical research, and medical practice in his institution. This for many students is a most difficult part of their orientation. The reason is that medical science is not a pure science. It may be considered application of what is learned in pathology, and pathology is not a pure science either, but a mixture. Both rest upon a foundation of basic sciences. Anatomy, biology, chemistry, physics, and their branches constitute the indispensable preface to and constant ingredients of medical science.

Depth of knowledge is not required but full awareness of their underlying importance is essential. The kind of medicine that was practiced before the great discoveries in the basic sciences was not scientific. It required neither institutions nor administrators for its practice. Physicians—and administrators—have to keep reminding themselves that they must keep informed of new discoveries about normal structure and functions in order to make progress in treating abnormal conditions. The institutions in which medicine is practiced must undergo constant adaptation to new developments in the basic sciences which affect medical science.

Dr. John B. Murphy laid down as a law many years ago, "The best surgery is a good physiology, the best you can buy." It should be added that the physiology textbook needs to be frequently replaced with revisions as new discoveries are made. The good physician will study the basic sciences intensively to the end of his days. The hospital should provide incentives and resources for such study. The whole atmosphere should be that of a research institution.

A down-to-earth reason for the strong current emphasis on the physician's need for a firm foundation in science is the requirement by the certifying boards and by many medical societies for passing examinations in the basic sciences as a condition of acceptance for certification and membership. These examinations come several years after graduation from medical school. Thus continuing study is made practically compulsory for the doctor who wishes to have qualifications beyond his M.D. degree. Instruction in the basic sciences is being provided in many hospitals not only for interns and residents but also for regular staff members. In some instances hospitals have joined forces for this purpose.

Like medical practice, the basic sciences have proliferated into many specialized areas. The fundamental four have each branched out spectacularly, within the memory of living scientists. A speaker at the Congress on Medical Education and Licensure in 1959, Moody E. Prior, Dean of the Graduate School of Northwestern University, told of an incident which illustrates one of the minor problems resulting: "At the dedication of the Midwest Library Center a few years ago, one of the visiting librarians was introduced to a distinguished scientist who was described as a mathematical biophysicist. The librarian was annoyed. He said, 'Why can't you fellows stay within the system of classification established by the Library of Congress?' "[2]

Most of the early basic scientists, like the founder of practically all science, Aristotle, were medically trained individuals whose interests and discoveries covered several fields. To Aristotle are traced the beginnings of botany, zoology, comparative anatomy, embryology, teratology and physiology. Erasistratus of Alexandria, in the fourth century B.C., is hailed as the first experimental physiologist; he was also an anatomist and a physician. Galen was for centuries the voice of authority in experimental physiology, anatomy, pathology, and pharmacy. The cranial nerves and the sympathetic system were first described by him. The mechanism of respiration had its first valid explanation from him. Many of his other discoveries were firsts, although in general his reasoning is obscured by his speculative and philosophic tendencies.

The celebrated Jewish physician of Cordova, Maimonides (1135–1204) was a mathematician, astronomer, and philosopher. The English Franciscan, Roger Bacon (1210–1243), was noted as a comparative philologist, mathematician, astronomer, physicist, physical geographer, chemist, and physician. In earlier days there was not the separation that is now so hard to bridge by anyone who is trying to see science and the human being as a whole. One of the lasting evidences of the genius of the great classic figures in medical science is the skill they displayed for inventing not only new techniques but often whole new concepts in fields quite outside their own area of interest when the solution of the problem at hand needed it. They set an impressive record by their contributions to the sister sciences when the problem could not be solved readily by scientific principles known at the time.

For example, physics was enriched by the contribution of von Helmholtz to the theory of sound, by the precise experimental definition of the laws of fluid flow by Poiseuille, by a quantitative description of the elasticity of solids by Young, by the first statement of the first law of thermodynamics by Mayer. Even the founder of the *American Journal of Mineralogy,* Archibald Bruce, was a physician. All science has advanced immeasurably through the straying of medical scientists into bordering fields and through their need for amalgamation of scientific knowledge in order to give the patient the best possible medical care. "With today's pharmacopeia," says a surgeon currently writing about steroid therapy, "the surgeon as well as the internist must have fundamental, practical knowledge of endocrinology and its older brother, biochemistry."

So let us include the basic sciences in the administrator's study of medical

[2] From *Selected Papers*, Annual Congress on Medical Education and Licensure, Conference on Specialism in Medicine, February 8, 1959, *J.A.M.A.*, May 16, 1959.

science, indicating here only the beginnings of the paths to be followed. Books are available which are not too technical for the layman to understand, some of which are listed in the bibliography. An especially good summary is William Cecil Dampier's *A Shorter History of Science,* a paperback published by Meridian Books, New York, 1957.

The administrator has little need to think in terms of differentiation between body structure and function, or between chemical and physical aspects, his concern being to gain a comprehensive concept of the normal human being on which to gain insight into pathology and treatment of disease. Yet it is helpful to know something about the progress of each of the basic sciences and to keep abreast of new developments. One of the most interesting ways for the adult student to do this is to learn to attach names to the main discoveries, thus emphasizing the personal element which makes them dramatic. True, many a name of an ardent worker is hidden behind that of the one who finally got the credit, and group effort is increasingly necessary in all scientific research; yet as in other fields the individual medical scientist who has imagination and courage still is a most significant figure in progress.

ANATOMY

Anatomy is in a sense *the* basic science in the study of man because bones are all that remain after centuries to tell the story of changes in structure, if any, and of prehistoric medicine. From them the ancients could study the differences between skeletons of animals and of men. They show that prehistoric man suffered from rickets and arthritis just as modern man does. They disclose that surgery was practiced before the dawn of history. Skulls show evidences of trephining. Arm and leg bones show that fractures were set. It is obvious from the remains that patients survived these procedures. The reason for the extensive employment of trephining, it is surmised, was the belief that this let out the demons who were causing headaches and attacks of epilepsy and madness, besides repairing the damage done by injuries received in warfare and in hunting and sports. Of course, the skeleton in a living human being could not be seen and studied until the discovery of x-rays in 1895.

Erasistratus and Herophilus of Alexandria in the fourth century B.C. were, as far as our knowledge goes, the originators of dissecting, and the latter has been called the "Father of Scientific Anatomy." Celsus of Rome, the historian, writing about them in the first century A.D., charged them with human vivisection. The cerebrum and the cerebellum were differentiated by Herophilus, who also described a number of bones, organs, and glands. It has been through the records of later writers rather than any writings of their own that remain that the work of these early Alexandrian physicians is known.

The Greek physicians and surgeons learned much of their anatomy from the sculptors, whose painstaking study of athletes in action is clearly shown in the art treasures that remain. They observed how the muscles manipulate the skeleton. The great age of Greek sculpture was coincident with the era of intense interest in athletics, not only from a contest standpoint but from that of the contribution of gymnastics regularly practiced for development of the body and the correction of certain weaknesses or defects.

Aristotle (384–322 B.C.) taught anatomy by dissection of animals. He also used anatomical diagrams. He was a far better direct observer than was his master Plato, who was more a philosopher than a scientist. In Aristotle's *Historia Animalium* he describes some five hundred kinds of animals.

Galen, born in Greece (A.D. 131–201), who practiced mostly in Rome, wrote nine books on anatomy. Some of his descriptions, especially those of the motor and locomotor systems, are excellent. Many others, however, are wrong or partly so because his dissections were practically limited to hogs and apes, although it was said that he once dissected the skeleton of a robber he found on a lonely hillside and that he may have come across a few other stray skeletons. He knew most of the muscles. His chief contribution to anatomy was his description of the nervous system, and he is the recognized founder of neurological anatomy.

Twelve centuries elapsed after Galen before anyone made a significant contribution to anatomy or any other science basic to medicine. Although there were other causes for this in the general social environment of those centuries, Galen's assumption of a position of final authority was placidly accepted, and it became treason for any doctor to disagree with him in any respect.

An artist was the one who first broke the tradition. Leonardo da Vinci (1452–1519), great artist and scientist of the Italian Renaissance, founded physiological anatomy. His sketches were made at the dissection table and more than 750 of them have been found. He made his own deductions, irrespective of Galen, with whose work he was undoubtedly familiar. He originated cross-sectional anatomy. William Hunter called Leonardo "the greatest anatomist of his epoch," when he came across his chalk drawings in the year 1784.

In the Ospedale Santa Maria Nuova at Florence, in the Ospedale Maggiore at Milan, and in the Ospedale Santo Spirito at Rome, Leonardo made his dissections and carried on the anatomic studies which resulted in the drawings and descriptions on which the teaching of anatomy came later to be based. But those drawings were buried for more than two hundred years.

A physician and surgeon was the next to release anatomy—and medicine—from the Galenic superstitions and domination. Andreas Vesalius (1514–1564), Flemish born of German ancestry, student and later teacher at Padua, "alone made anatomy what it is today—a living, working science," in the words of Garrison.[3] He made a boyhood hobby of animal dissection. Later he had to steal human skeletons from graveyards. He dissected and taught students to dissect and to inspect the human body. His publication of *De Fabrica Humani Corporis*

[3] Fielding H. Garrison: *An Introduction to the History of Medicine.* Philadelphia: W. B. Saunders Co., 1929, p. 218.

in 1543, which broke completely with Galen, aroused such a storm that he burned his manuscripts and left Padua to become court physician to Emperor Charles V. Authorities said that the anatomy of men must have changed if it was different from that described by Galen. Osler called Vesalius' *Fabrica* "the greatest book ever written, from which modern medicine dates."

An anatomist who opposed Vesalius but made some important contributions to the science was Bartolommeo Eustachi (1524–1574) who was professor at the Collegia della Sapienza at Rome. He discovered the eustachian tube; also the thoracic duct, the suprarenal bodies, and the abducens nerve. He described the origin of the optic nerves, the cochlea, the pulmonary veins, and the muscles of the throat and neck. The first correct description of the uterus and the best treatise on the structure of the teeth were contributed by him.

Vesalius' loyal pupil, Gabriele Falloppio (1523–1562), discovered and described the ovaries (fallopian tubes); also the chorda tympana, the semicircular canals, the sphenoid sinus, the round ligaments, and the trigeminal, auditory, and glossopharyngeal nerves. He named the vagina and placenta. His pupil Fabricius ab Aquapendente (1537–1619) built at his own expense a fine anatomic theater at Padua. Here Morgagni afterward worked and William Harvey came to study under him.

Variolus (1543–1575), physician to Pope Gregory XIII, investigated the nervous system, describing the crura cerebri, the commissure, and the pons. Falloppio's pupil Coiter (1534–1600) of Groningen, Holland, studied the formation and growth of bones and described the muscles of the nose and the eyelids.

Important indeed were the contributions to anatomy of illustrators whose productions became so voluminous beginning with Vesalius' *Fabrica*. His illustrations were woodcuts. The drawings are believed to have been made by Titian's pupil, Jan Kalkar. In the seventeenth century the illustrations were copperplate engravings, some of the original drawings being the work of the authors, others by professional artists, including the painter Rubens. Albinus (1697–1770), who held the chair of anatomy and surgery at the University of Leyden, was one of the greatest anatomic illustrators of his time. He published atlases of the bones, the muscles, the veins and arteries of the intestines, the fetal bones, the skeleton and skeletal muscles, and the gravid uterus.

A professor of anatomy at Bologna, Pisa, and Messina, Marcello Malpighi (1628–1694), was the founder of histology. He described the red blood corpuscles in 1665, calling them "fat globules looking like a rosary of red coral." In 1660 he discovered the capillaries. His investigations of the embryology of the chick and the histology and physiology of the glands and viscera were history making. He is also known as the founder of descriptive embryology.

Jan Swammerdam (1637–1680), of Amsterdam, who studied medicine but labored all his life in minute anatomy and embryology, discovered and described the red blood corpuscles seven years before Malpighi. He also discovered the valves of the lymphatic glands. A method of injecting blood vessels with wax was devised by him in 1667. An interesting personal side light on this scientist was his sudden conviction in 1680, the year of his death, that anatomy was impious. This came at the same time that he joined a fanatical religious sect.

Edward Tyson (1650–1708), of the University of Cambridge, who lectured on anatomy to the Barber-Surgeons up to 1699, was a remarkable comparative anatomist. He compared the anatomy of man with that of monkeys in his *Orang-Outang, sive Home Sylvestris,* the first important work in comparative morphology.

In the British Isles, as on the continent, anatomy had come to be recognized as a distinct subject to be taught in medical schools. An example of the establishment of such departments is the University of Edinburgh where the three Monros, Alexander I (1697–1767), Alexander II (1737–1817), and Alexander III (1773–1859), succeeded each other over 126 years as heads of the department —a dynasty of anatomists who were also surgeons.

Prominent as an illustrator of his own books was Antonio Scarpa (1747–1832), of Venice, who trained the engraver for his drawings. The first proper delineation of the nerves of the heart is contained in his beautifully illustrated *Tabulae Neurologicoe.* He discovered the membranous labyrinth, the nasopalatine nerve, and the triangle in the thigh which is named for him. His artistic talent is said to be unexcelled among medical men who have illustrated their own books.

Although best known as a physiologist, Albrecht von Haller (1708–1777), of Switzerland, who taught all branches of medicine at Göttingen, must be included among the anatomists. His *Icones Anatomicae,* published from 1743 to 1756, is authoritative for study of the blood vessels, the viscera, and other structures. Because of his wide range of interests, he will be referred to again in the sections on physiology, public health, and medical history. He was the principal founder of medical and scientific bibliography.

Although they must be highlighted again under "Milestones," the Hunter brothers—John (1728–1793), William (1718–1783)—belong also among the great basic scientists because with them, so Garrison[4] affirms, "surgery ceased to be regarded as a mere technical mode of treatment, and began to take its place as a branch of scientific medicine, firmly grounded on physiology and pathology." Ball[5] declared that those who "walked the hospital" with John Hunter "carried his spirit of inquiry and love of truth through England and to the New World. Many became teachers in new medical schools: Sir Astley Cooper at Guy's, Cline at St. Thomas', Abernethy at St. Bartholomew's, Sir Anthony Carlisle at Westminster; others like Philip Physick carried his message to America." Ball also stated that from 1746 to 1783 John Hunter is said to have delivered the most complete course of anatomical lectures ever given in London and in between times "enriched the science of medicine by some of the most valuable contributions ever made."

[4] *Ibid.,* pp. 344–45.
[5] Otho F. Ball: John and William Hunter, *Mod. Hosp.,* November, 1952.

William was John's first teacher. William was a scholar; John disliked books and in consequence was ill at ease as a lecturer, although his bedside and clinical demonstrations were excellent.

There was neither public nor professional encouragement of the work of these brothers until their contributions were so patently outstanding that recognition could not be denied. Difficulties and inattention were their lot while they endeavored to teach anatomy and physiology and the best principles of pathology upon a solid foundation. Besides their teaching activities, the Hunters built up vast anatomical museums. William's collection included specimens of natural history, works of art, shells and corals, an assortment of coins and medals, and several hundred Egyptian medallions. His museum with 8,000 pounds in addition for maintenance was willed to the University of Glasgow. John's collection was concentrated on human and comparative anatomy and physiology. Six years after his death the Parliament purchased it and placed it under the care of the Royal College of Surgeons.

What is termed a "monumental" treatise on anatomy was published between 1791 and 1796 by Samuel Thomas von Soemmering (1755–1830), of Western Prussia. He did notable research on the brain, the eye, the ear, the throat, and the nose. He was a good artist and his fame is assured by his remarkably accurate anatomical illustrations.

Coming to the nineteenth century, the earliest name in anatomy and scientific medicine in France is that of Marie-Francois-Xavier Bichat (1771–1802), who founded descriptive anatomy. His publications were epoch-making. In 1800 appeared his *Traite des Membranes,* in 1803 the last of his five-volume *Anatomie Descriptive,* and in 1802 his general anatomy applied to physiology and medicine. They contained the first detailed description of the parts and tissues of the body in both health and disease.

The leading British anatomist of the early nineteenth century was Sir Charles Bell (1774–1842). His brother, John Bell, a surgeon, opened a private school of anatomy at Edinburgh in 1790. Sir Charles taught anatomy and lectured to anatomists in London. He published books on the anatomy of the brain and the nervous system. In Scotland, Robert Knox (1791–1862) supported Bichat's ideas, and the descriptive, histological, and comparative aspects of general anatomy were first taught by him. He was a showman type of lecturer, however, and came to disaster through an incident involving body-snatching and suspicion of murder. Lord Warburton's Anatomy Act of 1832, which provided that medical schools should receive all unclaimed bodies, was a result of this episode, bringing practically to an end the nefarious traffic in bodies procured by ruffians who were well paid by prominent surgeons and anatomists, including the Hunters.

Great works on comparative anatomy were published by Georges Cuvier (1769–1832), of France, from 1801 to 1805, and by Sir Richard Owen (1804–1892), of England, from 1866 to 1868. Geoffroy Saint-Hilaire (1772–1844), French zoologist, laid the basis for scientific anatomy by announcing his theory of the unity of organic structure.

America can lay claim to a few of the pioneers in anatomy. Casper Wistar (1760–1818) taught anatomy at the University of Pennsylvania for twenty years and published a *System of Anatomy*. The wistaria vine was named after him. In his memory the Wistar Institute of Anatomy and Biology was established at Philadelphia in 1892. William Edmond Horner was appointed professor of anatomy at the University of Pennsylvania in 1891 and made several important anatomical discoveries. John D. Godman (1794–1830) of Annapolis was a talented anatomist, and produced three important works, including *Contributions to Physiological and Pathological Anatomy* published in 1825. Samuel George Morton (1799–1851) of Philadelphia wrote a treatise on general and microscopic anatomy, and was a craniologist, paleontologist, and phthisiologist.

Joseph Leidy (1823–1891), of Philadelphia, followed Horner as professor of anatomy at the University of Pennsylvania and was the leading American anatomist of his time, doing research on the comparative anatomy of the liver and the bones and publishing an *Elementary Treatise on Human Anatomy,* illustrated by himself. Oliver Wendell Holmes (1809–1894), of Boston, was Parkman professor of anatomy at the Harvard Medical School for 35 years up to 1882. In his *The Autocrat of the Breakfast Table* he shows his scientific indoctrination by referring frequently to anatomical and physiological findings —for example, in one place he remarks:

> The more we study the body and the mind, the more we find both to be governed, not *by* but *according to* laws, such as we observe in the large universe. . . . You think you know all about walking, don't you, now? Well, how do you suppose your lower limbs are held to your body? They are sucked up by two cupping vessels, ("cotyloid"—cup-like—cavities), and held there as long as you live, and longer. At any rate, you think you move them backward and forward at such a rate as your will determines, don't you? On the contrary, they swing just as any other pendulums swing, at a fixed rate, determined by their length. You can alter this by muscular power, as you can take hold of the pendulum of a clock and make it move faster or slower; but your ordinary gait is timed by the same mechanism as the movements of the solar system.

In this outpouring of wisdom for the edification of the uninitiated he gave credit to the Webers (Ernst Heinrich and Eduard Friedrich), German contemporaries who were making outstanding anatomical and physiological discoveries.

Carl Ernst von Baer (1792–1876), of Russia, founded modern embryology. He established the theory of the germ layers, and the beginnings of histogenesis, organogenesis, and morphogenesis may be credited to him. He is considered a genius by all who study his infinitely painstaking work. He cooperated with Rudolf Wagner in assembling in 1861 the first Congress of Anthropologists.

"One of the greatest anatomists of all time," Garrison[6] terms Jacob Henle (1809–1885), of Germany, and also "the greatest German histologist of his time." He was successively professor of anatomy at Zurich, Heidelberg, and Göttingen.

[6] *Ibid.,* p. 457.

Knowledge of the epithelial tissues of the body is founded on his descriptions. His *Handbook of Systematic Anatomy,* published from 1866 to 1871 in three volumes, is considered a production of the highest scientific value. He did his own illustrating.

Botanists developed the cell theory which is so important in medical science. It is significant that the Hamburg botanist, Matthias Jacob Schleiden (1804–1861) had studied medicine and was a physiological botanist, disdaining the mere collector of herbs. After a discussion with Theodor Schwann (1810–1882) of the latter's discovery of nucleated cells in animal tissues, he began to look for cells in all tissues. As a result he formulated what is considered to be the most important generalization in the science of morphology: "There is one universal principle of development for the elementary parts of organisms, however different, and that principle is the formation of the cells."

Schwann was professor of anatomy and physiology at Liege beginning in 1848. He had published his treatise on the cell theory in 1839. Among his anatomic discoveries was the sheath of the axis cylinder of nerves, which is named after him, and the striped muscle in the upper part of the esophagus.

Joseph Hyrtl (1810–1894), of Hungary, was the first and greatest teacher of regional anatomy. In 1836 he was appointed professor of anatomy at Prague and in 1844 at Vienna. He is said to have been for thirty years the most popular lecturer on anatomy in Europe. In 1847 he published the first topographical anatomy in German. In 1860 he produced a classic manual of dissecting. His preferred fields of investigation were the vascular and osseous systems. His final works were three masterpieces on Hebraic and Arabic elements in anatomy, on anatomical terminology, and on old German anatomical expressions.

Thomas Henry Huxley (1825–1895) graduated in medicine from London University, and as a surgeon in the Royal Navy became interested in marine biology and subsequently in science in general. He produced a textbook on vertebrate and invertebrate anatomy, gave lectures on the theory of the vertebrate skull, and wrote famous essays on the comparative anatomy of man and the higher apes.

Wilhelm Waldeyer (1837–1921), professor at Berlin, is considered the leading German anatomist of recent times, reporting on his research on the development of cancer, retroperitoneal hernia, ovary and ovum, the topographical relations of the pregnant uterus, pelvic viscera, and pelvis, and the neuron theory. Karl von Bardeleben (1849–1918), professor at Jena, wrote a topographical atlas, a manual of dissecting, edited a handbook of anatomy, and investigated the skeletal, muscular, and vascular systems.

Later British anatomists include Henry Gray (1825–1861), who wrote on the optic nerves and the spleen; John Goodsir (1814–1867), who succeeded Alexander Monro III to the chair of anatomy at Edinburgh and restored its prestige, its decline under the third Monro bearing likeness to the disappointing end-result of many other inherited posts; Sir William Turner (1832–1916), who was

Goodsir's assistant and finally his successor and brought the Edinburgh anatomical school to the top rank in Great Britain; and Sir Arthur Keith (1866–1955), professor at the Royal College of Surgeons, who discovered with Flack the sinoatrial node in the heart. He wrote on the anthropoid apes, human embryology and morphology, the antiquity of man, and the endocrine aspects of race.

Recent advances tend, philosophically speaking, to merge anatomy with physiology, structure with function, normalcy with disease, so that physiological anatomy is becoming the leading study. This goes back to Galen, founder of neurological anatomy, the chief latter-day star of which is Santiago Ramón y Cajal of Spain (1852–1946). A leading histologist, he made discoveries in all parts of the nervous system, and in 1906 with Golgi was awarded the Nobel prize in medicine.

Among procedures which have helped to advance experimental anatomy have been methods of staining tissues and cells, microdissection and injection, experimental cytology and tissue cultivation.

BIOLOGY

The biological sciences include botany, zoology, physiology, and their subdivisions. (See also Chap. 6.)

Jean Fernel (1506–1588) a member of the Faculty of Medicine in Paris and the greatest French physician of the Renaissance, seems to have been first to use the word "physiology." This was in 1542. He limited it to the functioning of the body in a state of health and credited Aristotle as its founder.

Aristotle's physiology was based on the theory of the humors. This theory was promulgated by Hippocrates, reaffirmed by Galen, and not discarded until the seventeenth century. The four humors were blood, black bile, yellow bile, and phlegm, and health depended upon their equilibrium. The blood was supposed to carry the other humors—hence the vogue of bloodletting to drain off the excessive humor.

After Aristotle, in the fourth century B.C., in the medical school of Alexandria, human dissection and animal vivisection were carried on for the first time. Among others whose theories differed from those of Aristotle, Herophilus of Chalcedon, referred to previously as an anatomist, declared that the brain, not the heart, was the seat of intelligence and sensation. Another Alexandrian, Erasistratus of Chios, is sometimes called the Father of Physiology. He described the cardiac valves, distinguished between motor and sensory nerves, and had some idea of metabolism. These two Alexandrians, however, theorized that in every organ there were three kinds of tubes—veins, arteries, and hollow nerves—in which there were blood and two kinds of pneuma. Vital spirit, a form of pneuma, resulted when air passed from the lungs into the left ventricle of the heart. This vital spirit was then distributed throughout the body by the arteries.

The pulse, body heat, digestion, nutrition, assimilation, all resulted from this force. In the brain it became another pneuma called animal spirit, which produced sensation.

These false theories, with some changes and some additional findings and ideas contributed by Galen (A.D. 130–200) misled scientists for nearly two thousand years. Galen's views were progressive, however. He was one of the earliest experimental physiologists and the first experimental neurologist. The stagnation of medical science in the following centuries was more the result of the decadence of culture in general than it was of his influence, commonly blamed though he is.

Interesting as the occasional contributions are which were made by such men as Ibn Nafis who in the thirteenth century described the circulation, and Leonardo da Vinci who produced such amazing anatomical drawings, they had no great influence because of the indifference of the times and poor communications.

At the beginning of the sixteenth century in the medical schools of the universities of Padua and Bologna, a few human dissections were done and a little progress was made in anatomy; and toward the middle of the century Andreas Vesalius was contributing some original discoveries.

Michael Servetus (1509–1553) published a theological treatise in 1553 in which he described the pulmonary circulation, but Servetus retained the Aristotelian theory of a "vital spirit" in the blood.

A Spanish anatomist, Juan Valverde, and two Italians, Realdo Colombo (1516–1559) and Andrea Cesalpino (1524–1603), further expounded on the pulmonary circulation idea, the latter Italian sometimes being declared as Harvey's predecessor in discovering the general circulation of the blood. Physiologists in general point out his faulty description of the cardiovascular system and do not support him as a true predecessor, some even declaring that Colombo's contribution had a greater influence than Cesalpino's upon Harvey.

Through vivisection, mainly, Vesalius made many important physiological discoveries. Sanctorius (1561–1636), of Padua, was a pioneer in the investigation of metabolism and was the first physiologist to have scientific instruments made especially for his studies.

René Descartes (1596–1650), of France, for his book *De Homine,* is credited with having produced the first treatise of modern times on physiology, but Descartes was a Galenist and the book is elementary.

William Harvey (1578–1657) demonstrated the circulation of the blood in 1628 after he had stated his theories twelve years earlier. A native of Folkestone in Kent, student of medicine under Cesalpino at Padua, he won little notice as a practicing physician. As an experimenter and physiologist of the first rank he earned enduring fame. Others before him had observed that the blood is in motion. Harvey proved mathematically that it moves in a circle. Despite the proof, there were those of high rank in medicine who opposed his theory.

Then in 1661 Malpighi (1628–1694), of Bologna, who figured in the discussion of anatomy, and in 1688 van Leeuwenhoek (1632–1723), of Delft, Holland, announced discoveries of the capillaries.

Stephen Hales (1677–1761), of England, contributed a theory of blood pressure which was credited with being the greatest addition to knowledge of the vascular system after Harvey.

Malpighi has a prominent place in physiology by virtue of his work on the spleen, liver, and kidneys. Also using the microscope, with lenses he had ground himself, van Leeuwenhoek reported his discovery of what we call bacteria, a discovery then unheralded and unappreciated. He gave the first complete description of the red blood corpuscles and discovered the striped character of voluntary muscle, the sarcolemma, and the structure of the crystalline lens. He will be referred to again in the next chapter in the discussion of bacteriology.

In the light of present-day knowledge it is astonishing that the importance of air for the existence of life was not demonstrated until 1660 and 1682 when Robert Boyle proved, by employing an air pump to create a pressure vacuum, that the resulting lack of air extinguished at the same time the light of a candle and the life of a mouse.

Textbooks of physiology appeared in the eighteenth century—Boerhaave's *Medical Institutes* in 1708 and von Haller's *Elements of Physiology* in 1757.

Von Haller's is a name on which to pause. Called by Garrison[7] "one of the most imposing figures in all medical history" and "the master physiologist of his time," he has already been mentioned in the discussion of anatomy, and will be referred to again in later sections. His accomplishments in the 65 years of his life (1708–1877) sound impossible. At 10 years of age he was writing Latin verses and a Chaldee grammar. At 16 he successfully contested his professor's contention that the lingual vein was a salivary duct. After graduating at Leyden, he became widely known as a poet and botanist.

Called to the newly established university at Göttingen, von Haller taught for 17 years, as noted before, *all branches of medicine*. He established botanic gardens and churches. He wrote some 13,000 scientific papers. He constantly conducted experiments.

Getting homesick at the age of 45 in 1753, he returned to Bern. There he became public health officer and assumed countless other activities which will be described in later sections. For his contributions to physiology a quotation from Garrison[8] is enlightening:

> To read Professor Kronecker's *Haller redivivus* is to see how many apparently "new" discoveries of modern observers had already been accounted for by this great master and are now forgotten, doubtless because humanity does not take kindly to the theorist on his pedestal. They include a reassertion of the myogenic theory (muscular autonomy) of the heart's action (1736), and the first experimental injections of putrid matter into the living body (1760). In his concern about sensibility and irritability, Haller saw the parts of the nervous system as

[7] *Ibid.*, p. 317.
[8] *Ibid.*, p. 318.

tissues, and thus failed to get at some of their functions as organs. . . . Akin to the French Encyclopedists in his grasp of detail Haller was the best historian of medicine after Guy de Chauliac.

William Hewson (1739-1774) of England did important work on the properties of the blood. Luigi Galvani (1737-1798) of Italy founded electrophysiology through his summarization of experiments on muscle-nerve preparation and his discovery of the electric properties of excised tissues. Lavoisier (1743-1794) of France discovered the nature of the interchange of gases in the lungs.

Francois Magendie (1783-1855) of Bordeaux was the pioneer of experimental physiology in France. In his investigations he used both chemical and physical procedures. Experimental pharmacology was founded by him. He founded the first periodical devoted exclusively to physiology, the *Journal de Physiologie Expérimentale.*

Johannes Evangelista Purkinje (1787-1869), of Bohemia, was a renowned physiologist. The Prussian government erected a physiological institute for him at Breslau in 1842. Previously he had set up a laboratory in his own home. He was the founder of laboratory training in connection with teaching in the German universities. He pioneered in the use of the microscope.

For a most exciting development, a jump to America is in order. By a rare opportunity of which he took full advantage, William Beaumont (1785-1853) studied digestion and the movement of the stomach in a live human being, the first to do so. The subject was a Canadian Indian, Alexis St. Martin. As a surgeon in the United States Army, Beaumont had operated on him in 1825 for an accidental gastric fistula. An opening remained, a sort of window through which observations and tests could be made. The surgery was performed on Mackinac Island, then an isolated military post. The patient's home was in Canada, and for continued observation he had to be enticed to travel two thousand miles to Plattsburgh, New York, where Beaumont was later stationed, or Beaumont had to go to him.

With due credit to previous investigators of digestion, such as Regner de Graaf who experimented with a dog, Beaumont reported his findings. He showed that only when food is present is gastric juice secreted; that congestion is produced by mechanical irritation of the mucous membrane but only limited local secretion of gastric juice; that different foods vary in digestive values—the foundation of dietetics; and that the gastric juice contains free hydrochloric acid plus some other chemical substance (pepsin, as Schwann discovered in 1835).

Herman von Helmholtz (1821-1894), of Potsdam, professor of physiology at, successively, Königsberg, Bonn, and Heidelberg, and afterward for 23 years, from 1871 to 1894, professor of physics at Berlin, demonstrated in 1848 that the muscles are the main source of animal heat. Around 1850 he invented the pendulum myograph, with which he measured the velocity of the nervous impulse. In 1851 he invented the ophthalmometer, with which he could determine the optical constants and explain the mechanism of accommodation. In 1856-1857 he published his great *Handbook of Physiological Optics*. Claude Bernard, Carl Ludwig and von Helmholtz are considered the masters of physiology of the last half of the nineteenth century.

Crossing to America again, we find Henry Pickering Bowditch (1840–1911), of Boston, conducting experiments with the nerves, culminating in the final demonstration of their indefatigability. This was in 1885. In 1871 he founded the first physiological laboratory in the United States. He was the first to investigate the staircase phenomenon and the "all-or-none" principle of contraction in the heart muscle. He was an early investigator of the growth of children, especially as it is related to nutrition and to disease. His experiments in functional nerve blocking led to such later developments as Halsted and Cushing's conduction anesthesia and Crile's shockless surgery.

Another prominent American physiologist was Jacques Loeb (1859–1924), graduate in medicine at Strassburg, professor of biology and physiology at, successively, Bryn Mawr, the University of Chicago, and the University of California, before he became head of the department of experimental biology in the Rockefeller Institute in 1910. Among his extensive investigations were those of the functions of the brain, the chain reflexes, and the effects of electrolytic, thermal, and radiant energy upon living matter.

Claude Bernard (1813–1878), professor of physiology at the College of France, was the greatest physiologist of modern France and the founder of experimental medicine. Napoleon III gave him two fine laboratories and made him a senator. Often quoted is his statement of his attitude toward scientific investigation:

> Put off your imagination, as you take off your overcoat, when you enter the laboratory; but put it on again, as you do your overcoat, when you leave the laboratory. Before the experiment and between whiles, let your imagination wrap you round; put it right away from you during the experiment itself lest it hinder your observing power.

Jean-Baptiste Dumas (1800–1884) said of Bernard: "He is not only a great physiologist: he is physiology itself." It has been said that all of his great discoveries were based upon facts which he discovered accidentally and then proceeded to use as clues for further investigations. Among his outstanding research activities were studies of the pancreatic juice, of the vasomotor mechanism, and of the glycogenic function of the liver.

Considered the greatest teacher of physiology who ever lived was Carl Ludwig (1816–1895), professor of physiology at Leipzig for thirty years and founder of the Physiological Institute there. He inspired and directed investigations by his students and most of his own work is said to be buried under publications that bear their names. He was unambitious except for his pupils and was completely unselfish.

One of the great physiological discoveries, the inhibitory power of the vagus nerve, was made in 1845. The discoverer was Ernst Heinrich Weber (1795–1878), professor of anatomy and physiology at Leipzig for 45 years. Problems such as the motion of the heart and the nature of fever were brought nearer to solution by this knowledge. With his brother, Eduard Friedrich, he conducted many experiments, among them one leading to the measurement for the first time of the velocity of the pulse wave, and another to the measurement and comparison of the velocity of the blood and lymph corpuscles in the capillaries. In 1850 Ernst Weber made a model to illustrate the hydrodynamics of the circulation. In 1846 he produced a great work on touch and temperature sense. He stated what is known as Weber's law, that intensity of sensation is not directly proportional to the degree of stimulus but depends upon its mode of application.

The discoveries of the Webers came about through applying the methods of laboratory physics to physiological problems. In England, Marshall Hall (1790–1857) also employed physical experimentation. Among his contributions was establishment of the difference between volitional action and unconscious reflexes.

The study of blood pressure and of the viscosity of the blood was furthered by Jean-Leonard-Marie Poiseuille (1799–1869), of Paris. A career devoted entirely to teaching and experimenting was that of William Sharpey (1802–1880), of Scotland, professor of physiology at University College, London, who wrote on cilia and ciliary motion and discovered the "fibers of Sharpey." Also prominent in physiology in this period in England, as he was also in anatomy, was Thomas Henry Huxley (1825–1895).

The brilliant work of the Russian surgeon and physiological experimentalist, Ivan Petrovich Pavlov (1849–1936), director of the Institute for Experimental Medicine at Leningrad, is widely known, particularly his experiments with dogs in his studies of the digestive system. He especially studied the changes in the salivary reflex produced by psychic influence. As a result of his experiments he founded the theory of conditioned reflexes. His pupils continued to experiment along similar lines and contribute constantly to knowledge of nutrition, digestion, and reflexes. In 1904 Pavlov received the Nobel prize in medicine and physiology.

Sir James Mackenzie (1853–1925), an Edinburgh graduate who went to London as consultant in 1907, investigated the energetics of the heart muscle. In 1919 he started the Institute for Clinical Research at St. Andrews, to which he donated some 10,000 pounds. He wrote excellent books on the pulse and on heart disease.

Noted for his research on the capillaries was August Krogh (1874–1949), Danish physiologist, who received the Nobel prize for medicine and physiology in 1920. Otto Fritz Meyerhof (1884–1951), of Germany, who with Archibald Vivian Hill received the Nobel prize for medicine and physiology in 1922, did notable work on the metabolism of muscles. Hill's chief work was on the heat loss in muscle contraction.

These names and discoveries represent but an infinitesimal fraction of the persons and the work that have gone into the development of the science of physiology. They are guide posts only. Every one of them has served to open up new vistas for further research, so that now much more is known to be unknown than when this fascinating science was new. One of the most challenging vistas is that opened up by the science of endocrinology.

A physician at the court of Louis XV, Theophile de Bordeu (1722–1776), studied cellular tissue and advanced some theories, unsupported by experiment, that may be considered a prelude to endocrinology, such as that certain secretions affect the masculinity and femininity of the individual.

Around 1850 A. A. Berthold, a German physician, transplanted sex glands in chickens and noted changes in sexual characteristics.

The real starting point of endocrinology as a science, however, was Claude Bernard's work, from 1848 to 1857, on the glycogenic function and Thomas Addison's description of disease of the suprarenal capsules resulting from research between 1849 and 1855. Then in 1889 von Mering and Minkowski by removing the pancreas produced diabetes experimentally.

An important name in the dawn of this science is that of Charles-Edouard Brown-Sequard (1817–1894), of Mauritius, who with Claude Bernard is credited with being the founder of the doctrine of the internal secretions. He produced experimentally in animals a form of Addison's disease by excising the suprarenal capsules. He theorized that the kidney has an internal secretion. He treated acromegaly by animal extracts in 1893. He used testicular and other organic juices with some notion of the possibilities of rejuvenation.

Another pioneer was Moritz Schiff (1823–1896), of Frankfort, who studied the effects of removal of the thyroid gland in dogs and the prevention of these effects by thyroid grafts and by injections of thyroid juices.

In America John Jacob Abel, of Cleveland, in 1897 isolated and named the blood-pressure–raising constituent of the suprarenal capsule *epinephrine*. Jokichi Takamine was the first to isolate epinephrine in crystalline form in 1901. He named the pressor substance of the adrenal gland *adrenaline*. This hormone is now produced synthetically.

In 1899 Pavlov discovered enterokinase. Sir William M. Bayliss and Ernest H. Starling early in the twentieth century developed their theory that "hormones," which are distributed from the organs and glands by the blood channels, chemically control the body. Charles E. de M. Sajous, of Philadelphia, published in 1903 a system of medicine based upon the internal secretions, theorizing that the immunizing mechanism of the body is controlled by the suprarenal, pituitary, and thyroid bodies.

The thyroid hormone known as thyroxin, now also prepared synthetically, was isolated by E. C. Kendall, of Rochester, Minnesota, in 1914. Sir E. S. Schafer suggested in 1913 that what he called "insulin" was secreted in the pancreas, and in 1921 came the well-known achievement of Banting and Best of Canada, who were the first to extract insulin and prepare it for general use.

The growth hormone in the anterior pituitary was demonstrated in 1921 by Drs. Evans and Long of the University of California.

The pituitary gland was also the subject of deep study and extensive experiment by Dr. Harvey Cushing, of Boston, who produced a great text on it. The supreme importance of this pea-sized gland at the base of the brain as the controller of growth and sexual development had not been fully appreciated until his book appeared in 1912. He visualized it as "conductor of the endocrine orchestra." Early authorities knew that it existed. Galen thought its function was to filter into the throat a cerebrospinal fluid which he called "pituita." Vesalius thought it was the source of the mucous fluid discharged from the nose. The French called it the enigmatic organ, giving up entirely. Cushing climaxed his work by brilliant surgery on the pituitary.

The discovery of the ovarian hormone was announced by two St. Louis doctors in 1923 and its crystallization by the same physicians in 1930. The parathyroid hormone was isolated in 1924 and a gonad-stimulating hormone from the placenta in 1931 by Dr. J. B. Collip, of Canada.

The Ascheim-Zondek pregnancy test resulted from the discovery by these physicians in 1926 of sex-gland–stimulating substances in the urine of pregnant women. In 1935 Laqueur isolated the hormone known as testosterone, which now can be prepared synthetically.

A stupendous amount of research continues. The new science of endocrinology is in its infancy. Closely identified with it because their value would be small without the endocrine secretions is the work on vitamins. Hormones and vitamins function interdependently. Both physiology and chemistry are involved in the process.

Takaki, medical inspector in the Japanese Navy, made some observations between 1882 and 1886 which convinced him that beriberi was caused by a diet lacking in fats and protein. Although he proved his theory by a cruise in which milk and meat were added to the rice diet, and one in which the traditional rice diet was employed, with only 14 cases developing on the former cruise and 169 on the latter, both having crews of 276 men, few believed him. Eijkman, a Dutch physician practicing in Java, observed in 1897 the difference between chickens fed polished rice and those fed unhusked rice, but his published results were also overlooked until in 1908 two doctors in the Malay peninsula cured natives of beriberi by repeating his experiments.

Casimir Funk, the physiologist, discovered and finally isolated something from brewers' yeast that had similar effects to the rice husks. This he called "vitamin"—vita meaning life, amine its chemical nature. And thus vitamin research and therapy began and feverishly continues.

One of the world's best-known biochemists, Conrad Arnold Elvehjam (1901–1962), president of the University of Wisconsin at the time of his death, was the discoverer of niacin. In 1937 after years of research and experiment, he isolated an enzyme found in fresh meat and yeast—nicotinic acid—which came to be known as niacin. Lack of the vitamin in human nutrition was found to be the main cause of pellagra, once a major health problem, particularly in the southern part of the United States. Patients suffering from the critical dementia stage of this disease were restored to normalcy within 24 hours after nicotinic acid was administered. Dr. Elvehjam was, however, opposed to supplemental vitamins as a general rule, and he criticized food fads. He was a charter member of the National Food and Nutrition Board of the National Research Council.

CHEMISTRY AND PHARMACOLOGY

Chemistry is a broad and complicated science. Dorland[9] calls it "the science which treats of the elements and atomic relations of matter, and of the various compounds of the elements," and lists 18 kinds of chemistry: analytical, applied, biological, colloid, dental, forensic, gross, industrial, inorganic, medical, metabolic, mineral, organic, pharmaceutical, physical, physiological, structural, and synthetic.

Although strict separation is impossible, here the main considerations will be the developments in pharmaceutical and physiological chemistry.

Study of herbs for medicinal purposes long preceded any truly scientific concept of chemistry. In ancient Egypt, so papyri disclose, as well as in China, Japan, India, and the Aztec Empire, extensive use was made of drugs, and botanic gardens flourished. Poisons had been identified. The American Indian taught herb-lore to the pilgrims. Many of the concoctions were efficacious, and some of them are in the pharmacopeia today.

The first systematic treatise on plants and plant-lore was compiled by Theophrastus of Eresos (370–286 B.C.), the friend and pupil of Aristotle, who left his library and botanic garden to him. Theophrastus, like Aristotle, was a physician. Some 500 plants are described in his books, which relate all that was known of their medicinal properties.

The originator of the materia medica was Pedacius Dioscorides, Greek army surgeon of the first century A.D., in the service of Nero. He wrote on medical botany, describing some 600 plants and plant principles. Hippocrates had been acquainted with 150 of them. About one-sixth are now in use. Dioscorides recognized natural families of plants. For hundreds of years, in fact up to the seventeenth century, his book was copied or used for commentaries, and much that is in it is still of value.

Pliny the Elder, Roman contemporary of Dioscorides, wrote a natural history in which are included many facts about plants and drugs. Five of the books compose an herbal, taken mainly from Theophrastus. Much erroneous information was included and was not questioned until the fifteenth century.

An important Persian work on pharmacology was produced around 970 by

[9] *Dorland's Illustrated Medical Dictionary,* 23rd ed. Philadelphia, W. B. Saunders Co., 1957.

Abu Mansur, and an apothecary's manual appeared in the tenth or eleventh century credited to Mesue, Junior—exactly who he was is not known.

Alchemy was founded in the eighth century by Jabir, or Geber (702–776). He discovered nitric acid and described such aspects of chemical procedure as distillation, filtration, water baths, and sublimation.

Along with the alchemist's search for gold through transmutation of metals went the quest for an elixir which would cure all diseases and give immortal youth. Despite these unattainable goals which were its object, the study of alchemy resulted in many significant chemical discoveries.

Roger Bacon (1214–1294) thought that medicine was a means of prolonging life through alchemy.

Sodium sulfate, known as Glauber's salt, was discovered by Johann Rudolph Glauber (1604–1688), of Carlstadt, who also made sulfate of copper, arsenic chloride, and zinc chloride. He distilled ammonia from bones. By distilling sulfuric acid with sea salt he obtained hydrochloric acid. He published an encyclopedia of chemical procedures.

Arnold, of Villanova (1235–1311) in Spain, studied Arabian chemistry and wrote on alchemy. He is believed to have been the first to introduce tinctures and brandy into the pharmacopeia.

The first formulary was published by Nicolaus Salernitanus in Venice in 1471. Many new Eastern drugs were included in it.

These early alchemists and chemists had little effect that can be called scientific on medical practice. Yet they laid a foundation. Not until Paracelsus (1493–1541) appeared to bring a new spirit of original investigation into the field did progress begin, and even then, right through to the present day, the most absurd beliefs and superstitions have surrounded the use of chemicals to attack disease. This is a sphere in which the public is most gullible, and fortunes continue to be made in quack remedies. Antimony and arsenic were often ingredients in drugs dispensed by charlatans in the same periods in which chemists were making their poisonous qualities known.

There was Mrs. Joanna Stephens, of London, who won fame and fortune (even a 5,000-pound payment from Parliament) for a solvent for the stone which turned out to be composed of snail shells, egg shells, and soap. The first London pharmacopeia, published in 1618, carried through many editions vile and filthy remedies which had become entrenched through the centuries. Among them were the gall of a bull mixed in vinegar, unicorn's horn, powder supposed to be made from mummies, lice, preparations of toad, the bowels of moles, oil of swallows, and viper wine.

The poor people fared better than the rich. Their home remedies were for the most part harmless, whereas the wealthy were dosed with strange nostrums by quacks who charged heavily for their prescriptions.

Early in the sixteenth century the Royal College of Physicians began its long battle for licensure and control of the practice of medicine and surgery, including authority to search apothecaries' shops for poisons and bad drugs. The deceptions went on, however. In the seventeenth century Sir Kenelm Digby concocted a "sympathetic powder," specific for almost any malady, which he claimed to have originated with a Carmelite monk in Florence. Said to have been only green vitriol, dissolved in water and afterward crystallized in the sun, its users attributed to it marvelous healing powers.

Leonicenus (1428–1524), professor of medicine at Padua, Bologna, and Ferrara, served science well by correcting the botanical errors in Pliny's natural history. This took courage and aroused a storm of protest because, like Galen's, Pliny's statements were considered authoritative and almost sacred.

Paracelsus, born in Switzerland, studied under Leonicenus at Ferrara, obtaining his doctor's degree in 1515. Extensive travel greatly enlarged his store of knowledge. He was an innovator in chemical therapeutics, introducing into the pharmacopeia opium, mercury, lead, sulfur, iron, arsenic, copper sulfate, and potassium sulfate. He popularized tinctures and alcoholic extracts. He was one of the first to analyze and prescribe the use of mineral baths. He discredited alchemy. In his writings he surrounds his discoveries and beliefs with mysticism. Nevertheless, when his strange delusions are stripped away, much that remains is an important contribution to knowledge.

Alchemy continued to flourish despite Paracelsus for a long time. The Rosicrucians incorporated it into their religious beliefs. Monarchs encouraged it, especially the German emperor Rudolph II (1576–1612). He spent his life and fortune, calling to his court many scholars and impostors, seeking the elixir of life, the philosopher's stone, and a way of changing baser metals into gold.

During the same period a physician and teacher, Libavius (1546–1616), of Coburg, had a well-equipped laboratory for chemical experimentation. He analyzed mineral waters with the balance, discovered stannic chloride, wrote a city pharmacopeia, and was among the first to mention blood transfusion. He wrote the first systematic treatise on chemistry in 1595. Part of his book deals with instruments, furnaces, and other laboratory equipment and procedures, and the rest with descriptions of chemical substances, but 80 pages of the latter have to do with the philosopher's stone.

A little later Van Helmont (1577–1644), of Belgium, began the idea of physiological chemistry, albeit in a confused way. Yet he was the first to use the term "gas" and knew about hydrogen, carbon dioxide, and sulfur dioxide. Clarification occurred with Sylvius (1614–1672), of Leyden, who firmly declared the identity of organic and inorganic processes in chemistry and stated his conviction of the importance of the saliva and pancreatic juice in digestion.

The chemist Robert Boyle (1627–1691) first defined the chemical elements. He founded analytic chemistry. Around the same time Minderer discovered ammonium acetate, Nicolas Lemery discovered iron in the blood, and Thomas Willis the sweetish taste of diabetic urine.

The historian Ralph Major[10] comments as follows on the use of drugs by North American Indians and by the Aztecs:

> The history of American medicine is a true mirror of the progress of civilization and culture in the Western hemisphere. The earliest American inhabitants of whom we have written record were the Indians, the very numerous tribes of North America and the much more advanced and gifted Mayas, Aztecs, and Incas of Mexico, Central America, and Peru.
>
> While sand paintings, weird ritual dances, and the terrifying costumes of the North American Indian medicine man were long considered the chief healing measures of these Indians, later studies have brought a complete reappraisal. The North American Indians, nomadic and warlike, inured to the accidents of the hunt and the wounds of battle, developed much skill in the treatment of wounds and fractures. They also employed many drugs quite rationally—as cathartics, cascara podophyllin and jalop; as diuretics, wintergreen, sarsaparilla, and juniper; as a remedy for high fever and for "rheumatism," willow bark, the original source of salicylates. They were familiar with the effects of the peyote bean, the active principle of which, mescaline, has been the object of much recent pharmacological study.
>
> If the materia medica of the North American Indian is surprising, that of the Aztecs is amazing. The Spanish conquerors of Mexico in their search for gold were quite unprepared for the wealth of drugs they found, for, as Moll remarked, "Rich as the Potosi mines proved, their value could not approach that contained in the depths of the New World forests." Francisco Hernandez described more than 3,000 plants used by the Indians in the treatment of disease. Their materia medica included remedies of vegetable, mineral, and animal origin —poisons, antidotes, anthelmintics, aphrodisiacs, tonics, hemostatics, laxatives, oxytocics, antiseptics, and anesthetics. The knowledge of these drugs was rapidly disseminated throughout Europe, and at one time it was estimated that more than one half of the drugs in the pharmacopeias of Europe were of American origin—a statement that may still be valid.

The *Chicago Tribune* Press Service on April 28, 1961, in a summary of a National Geographic Society report, indicated a return to some of the remedies used by our forefathers:

> Wahoo bark may be on the way out, but snakeroot and other old remedies are coming into their own as medicines.
>
> Wahoo bark, once widely used to stimulate the liver, has waned in popularity. A species of snakeroot, however, is increasingly in demand as a source of tranquilizing drugs.
>
> For centuries medicine men in India prescribed snakeroot for emotional disturbances, the National Geographic Society reports. However, the root did not come to the attention of western chemists until about ten years ago when their tests showed it contains reserpine, a sedative.
>
> The success of snakeroot has aroused new interest in medicinal plants and has touched off a wide search for them. Most folk remedies have proved largely useless; many are dangerous. Others, however, are beneficial.
>
> In the past decade, the value of drugs produced from plants has risen from about 50 million dollars a year to 250 million. Pharmaceutical firms send scouts

[10] *A History of Medicine.* 2 vols. Springfield, Illinois, Charles C Thomas, 1954, Vol. 1, p. 8.

to the jungles of Africa, South America, India, and to the hills of Kentucky. They talk shop with medicine men and herbalists, and look for promising plants.

The Mexican yam is an important find. The tuber is a source of diosgenin, which yields cortisone as well as other hormones and steroids used in treating rheumatic diseases and some forms of cancer.

African natives long have used willow bark tea to relieve the pain of rheumatism. They say the graceful, flexible willow transfers its attributes to the stiff joints of the patient. Physicians scoffed until they found salicin, a pain killing drug, in the bark.

Africans also treat rheumatism with meadow saffron. The British find it valuable for gout, an affliction more common in England than in Africa. As long as 5,000 years ago, Chinese doctors dispensed mahuang, an herbal drug containing ephedrine, now prescribed in combating asthma and hay fever. The Collahuaya Indians of South America are known as the "druggists of the Amazon." They make excellent cough medicine from certain tree barks, an invigorating tonic from sarsaparilla roots, and a powerful poison, curare, from plants of the strychnos family. Curare is widely used as a muscle relaxer.

While herb hunters concentrate on the profusion of plants in tropical regions, they do not ignore the temperate zones. Fox-glove tea, for example, was recommended for weak hearts in Wales long before chemists discovered digitalis, a heart stimulant, in leaves of the plant.

Hermann Boerhaave (1668–1738) is renowned as an experimental chemist. Besides medicine, he taught chemistry, physics, and botany. His book on the elements of chemistry is considered to be by far the best produced in the eighteenth century.

Francois Magendie (1783–1855), who was a physiologist and has been mentioned as such, must also be included among the great chemists because in his investigations he used both physical and chemical procedures. He is conceded to be the founder of modern experimental pharmacology. He introduced bromine, iodine compounds, strychnine, morphine, veratrine, brucine, piperine, and emetine into medical practice.

In the nineteenth century, physiology and chemistry became more closely allied than ever. One of the principal founders of modern physiological chemistry was Justus von Liebig (1803–1873), of Darmstadt. He did research on the chemistry of the carbon compounds. He originated laboratory teaching in chemistry, his laboratory at Giessen founded in 1826 having been the first connected with a university. He founded a journal of chemistry which lasted 42 years. He conducted famous investigations, including those on the cyanides and the benzoates. In 1842 he published a book, *Organic Chemistry in Its Applications to Physiology and Pathology,* which was the first formal text of its kind. In it he introduced the concept of metabolism.

Liebig's associate, Friedrich Wohler (1800–1882), of Hesse-Nassau, besides his work with Liebig, made investigations of uric acid, the cyanogen compounds, the artificial synthesis of sugar, morphine, and salicin. Two epochmaking achievements were an artificial synthesis of urea by heating ammonium cyanate, and the discovery that the benzoic acid taken in with food appears as hippuric acid in the urine. This was the beginning of the modern chemistry of metabolism, and of the idea of producing artificial foods from elementary materials.

A thesis prepared for graduation in 1803, reporting on chemical investigation of digestion, was an important advance in physiology. It was by John R. Young, of Maryland, and was entitled "An Experimental Inquiry into the Principles of Nutrition and the Digestive Process." He deduced that the flow of gastric juice and of saliva are associated and synchronous. This was later demonstrated by Pavlov, of Russia. Young, however, thought that phosphoric acid was the acid principle of the stomach. William Prout proved in 1824 that free hydrochloric acid is the acid of the gastric juice. Beaumont's experiments, mentioned under "Physiology," gave further light on the intricacies of the digestive process.

Garrison[11] terms Felix Hoppe-Seyler (1825–1895), of Saxony, the greatest physiological chemist between Liebig and Emil Fischer. He was professor of physiological chemistry at Strassburg for 23 years. Over a period of 30 years he made analyses of the blood, and many of his discoveries led to further ones by his students and others. His pupil Albrecht Koessel (1853–1927) worked on the chemistry of the cell and its nucleus and did important research on the chemistry of metabolism. For his research on the chemistry of cells and proteins he was awarded the Nobel prize in 1910.

Numerous new compounds were discovered in the nineteenth century and valuable work was done in food chemistry. The work of Magendie in experimental pharmacology was continued by a great number of scientists, many of whom fused their work with that of others in the great laboratories that arose, so that individual discoveries are often lost in the joint effort that was, and today continues to be, involved. Especially important and going on in accelerated fashion now has been the work of the so-called "destructive" critics employed in reducing the overgrowth of materia medica to reasonable and practical proportions.

In a lifetime which spanned the latter nineteenth and early twentieth centuries (1852–1919), Emil Fischer became known as the leading physiological chemist. He was successively professor of chemistry at Munich, Erlangen, Wurzburg, and Berlin. His work on carbohydrates alone was spectacular. He engineered the manufacture of synthetic substances for animal fats and foodstuffs which were in scarce supply during World War I. Among his other synthetic achievements was Veronal (1904). In 1902 he received the Nobel prize for chemistry. His work on nutrition was continued by his pupil Emil Abderhalden of Switzerland who in 1917 wrote a book on the subject and in 1911 produced a *Biochemical Dictionary*.

A significant trend should be mentioned in connection with the work of Paul Ehrlich (1854–1915), of Silesia. He led and many follow in emphasizing the biochemical as opposed to the bacterial theory of disease. In this direction he

[11] *Op. cit.*, p. 566.

and his successors have opened up many questions which show how much more is unknown than known in the biological sciences.

A speaker at the 1960 conference of the American Public Health Association, J. F. Follmann, Jr., told the assembly that physicians are prescribing more drugs than ever before, and that between 1929 and 1956 the prescription volume in drugstores increased 1,000 per cent. Mr. Follmann, who is director of information and research, Health Insurance Foundation of America, predicted that "protection against the costs of out-of-hospital prescription drugs will be included in all major medical care insurance in the future."

Spectacular among the recent drugs are those designed to relieve tension, anxiety, and even more severe behavior disturbances. The implications for the relief of mental illness are impressive. They are useful likewise in the treatment of the anxious patient who is to undergo surgery or other procedure that he fears.

Cortisone, found to be effective in treating some forms of arthritis, later was hailed as limiting the effects of apoplectic stroke. The antibiotics and certain other drugs hold promise in the fight against cancer. New drugs are being used against amebic dysentery and hepatitis; others are used in treating high blood pressure and to dissolve or prevent blood clots. The list is endless. Hundreds of antibiotics have been isolated and identified since 1941 when Florey and Heatley instigated the production of penicillin in the United States.

A product has even been developed for use in a test to determine whether or not a patient has been taking his medicine! This test can be used on tuberculous patients who are under antimicrobial therapy. Dr. Julius B. Novak[12] states: "Drug evasion is especially high when medicines have to be taken over a long period of time as with anticoagulants, tranquilizers, and the anti-tuberculosis drugs."

Victories over disease which have resulted from the introduction of new pharmaceuticals can be counted in the hundreds. One of them is the virtual elimination of mastoid operations through the use of antibiotics. Another is the dramatic decrease in poliomyelitis effected through the use of vaccines. As Dr. C. H. McCuiston, Jr.,[13] Austin, Texas, dermatologist, said in concluding an article on the effectiveness of griseofulvin in treating superficial fungal infections of the skin: "One wonders if perhaps a cure for cancer, tuberculosis, diabetes or mental illness is not now on the chemist's shelf."

A new drug is being introduced about every eight days. Each one is multiplied several times under the trade names of the different manufacturers. How is the physician to keep up with the flood?

A new telephone service is attempting to give a solution to the problem. Doctors may subscribe to Mediphone—a drug information service in Washington, D.C. They may call day or night, according to an item in a telephone

[12] Drug Evasion—a Headache for Doctors. *The Challenge,* September, 1960. Published by the Tuberculosis Institute of Chicago and Cook County.
[13] *J.A.M.A.,* December 19, 1959.

company publication, and get the facts about drug reactions, unusual uses, and the effects of overdosage, on some 9,000 drugs.

Building on the work of the pioneers, discarding what prove to have been erroneous conclusions, chemists and physicians continue to collaborate in advancing the science. They need to be fully cognizant of its interrelationships with its sister basic sciences, anatomy, physiology, and physics, and of its development of new branches such as biochemical genetics which is a dazzling field of exploration.

GENETICS

In a news release by the American Medical Association on medical advances during 1959, based on a poll of the deans of 84 medical schools, the dean of the University of Maryland School of Medicine, Dr. William S. Stone, was quoted as saying: "The biggest single achievement in the field of scientific medicine in 1959 has been the increase in our knowledge of the chemistry of genetics." Commenting on this statement, the report said that nearly all of the deans agreed that the intensive medical investigation going on in many quarters in the field of biochemical genetics was a most important development.

Dr. Severo Ochoa, of the New York College of Medicine, one of two winners of the 1959 Nobel prizes in medicine, is quoted in the report as saying: "All life is chemistry. The more we know of these chemical reactions, the more we know of life."

The emphasis on the medical implications of genetics was foreshadowed in 1937 by the British surgeon Sir Lockhart-Mummery:[14]

A new branch of biology which has recently engaged the attention of scientists throughout the world is destined, in my opinion, to have a profound influence upon medicine and surgery in the near future. I refer to the science of genetics, the means by which heredity works to transmit characteristics from the parent to the offspring. At first it may seem that this has little to do with the healing art, but it is generally recognized that it is as much the duty of doctors to prevent disease as to cure it and anything which will assist us to understand how diseased conditions arise, or are transmitted from one generation to another, the better equipped we shall be to combat them.

There is much yet to be discovered in the field of human genetics, but thanks largely to the brilliant work of Morgan, de Vries, Mueller, Loeb, Maud Slye and their coworkers, a great deal has already been discovered.

In the science of genetics . . . we have, I believe, found the key which will open that door, so long closed to us, behind which is to be found the explanation of the cause of tumors. Ever since human diseases began to be studied scientifically instead of empirically the chief problem that has intrigued everyone has been that of the origin of tumors. A vast amount of time and money has been spent during the last twenty-five years in attempting to elucidate this problem, and, although no definite result has been reached, the inquiry has been consider-

[14] Address at Convocation of the American College of Surgeons at Chicago, October 25, 1937. From the original manuscript.

ably narrowed. We now know that tumors occur in all vertebrate animals, that they are species specific and cannot be transmitted from one species of animal to another, that if left alone they continue to grow indefinitely during the life of the organism in which they arise, and that if completely removed they do not tend to recur. We know that by selective breeding, mice can be obtained that are predisposed almost 100 per cent to the formation of spontaneous tumors, or are almost entirely immune to the development of such tumors. . . .

These implications were slower in being detected than might have been expected after Darwin's exposition of his theory of evolution in 1859; Mendel's enunciation of his mathematical law concerned with the inheritance of dominant and recessive characteristics derived from his study of plants (1865); Sir Francis Galton's (Darwin's cousin) announcement of a statistical law of inheritance following his study of the pedigrees of hounds (1897); and Hugo De Vries' advancement of his hypothesis of mutation following experiments with the primrose (1901). These reductions of heredity to mechanistic formulas tended to dissolve its mystical and speculative quality and to make it a scientific study. In 1904 Galton established the Eugenics Laboratory in London.

Such illuminating discoveries as Thomas Hunt Morgan made with his work on the fruit fly, and Maude Slye in her experiments on malignant tumors in mice, plus the application to genetics of the science of biometrics created by Galton and his pupil Karl Pearson, paved the way for intense activity in this field.

The reviewer[15] of a book entitled *The Metabolic Basis of Inherited Disease,* published in 1960, made this comment on the speed with which the science of genetics suddenly developed:

> That a book of 1,477 pages can be written on the subject of human biochemical genetics testifies to the rapid advances made in this subject in the last few years. . . . After two introductory chapters on inherited variations and on the biochemistry of human genetics, the remaining 44 chapters . . . cover inherited diseases involving primarily the following types of metabolism: carbohydrates, amino acids, lipids, steroids, purines and pyrimidines, metals, porphyrins, blood formation, renal tubules and plasma proteins. It is remarkable that some of the diseases unknown a few years ago and found only in isolated cases, such as maple syrup urine disease and oroticaciduria, have already been thoroughly explored and the chemical lesion pinpointed. On the other hand, the lengthy and learned discussions of diabetes and gout fail to hide the dismal truth that the profession still has no accurate knowledge of the causation of these most common diseases. . . . For those interested in learning how far the scientific world has advanced in understanding of the biochemical basis of disease, this book is an intellectual treat of the highest order.

It was to a research worker in genetics that the American Association for the Advancement of Science presented its 1961 Theobald Smith Award for promising work by a young medical scientist. Samuel Weiss, University of Chicago

---

[15] William S. Hoffman: *J. Internat. Coll. Surgeons,* February, 1961, pp. 264–65. John B. Stanbury, James B. Wyngaarden, and Donald S. Frederickson: *The Metabolic Basis of Inherited Disease.* New York, The McGraw-Hill Book Company, 1960.

biochemist and a research associate at the Argonne Cancer Research Hospital, was the recipient. His studies were on the chain of command within the cell: how orders are relayed from deoxyribonucleic acid, the genetic material in the nucleus, to other parts of the living cell where basic biological processes take place. The award was established in 1936 by Eli Lilly and Company. In the association's announcement on December 30, 1961, was the following statement: "The tremendous current interest in biochemical genetics has led to major developments in many laboratories. The contributions of Dr. Weiss in regard to RNA (ribonucleic acid) biosynthesis are among the most outstanding in this field."

The old argument over which is the more important, heredity or environment, is stirred up in the present emphasis on genetics. The sanitarians like Edwin Chadwick and later Pasteur, Semmelweis and other proponents of the germ theory of disease, swung the pendulum far toward environmental factors as the most important. Few took much note of Karl Pearson's statement in 1910:

> It appears to me that the whole of the liberal and philanthropic social reformation of the past half century and more has been based not on the hypothesis that both nature and nurture contribute to the progress of the race, but solely on the assumption that improving the environment would indefinitely raise us in the scale of nations.

Sir Francis Galton's studies in 1873 convinced him that nature was far stronger than nurture, and later Pearson declared that the influence of environment was not one-fifth that of heredity and possibly not one-tenth.

Another branch of science that is still in its infancy is medical anthropology. Darwin, Huxley, Lyell, Spencer, Prichard, and Tylor developed the science in England; Virchow, an expert in craniology, was its leading spirit in Germany; Paul Broca, founder of the modern surgery of the brain, its originator, in the modern sense, in France; and Cesare Lombroso in Italy.

PHYSICS

The relation of the science of physics to physiology and therapy is not as easily discerned at first as that of chemistry. The foundation was a kind of atomic theory developed by the ancient Greeks Leucippus and Democritus, in the fifth, and Epicurus in the fourth, centuries B.C. The atoms they conceived were all the same in composition but varied in size and shape. Their reasoning was entirely speculative and that of Aristotle in challenging it was equally unscientific.

Probably the earliest approach to what was to become the science of physics was made by Archimedes (287–212 B.C.), the great mathematician who understood that the rise or fall of matter depends on the weight per unit volume compared with that of the surrounding medium. Archimedes is credited with laying the foundations of mechanics and hydrostatics.

No noteworthy advance in physics occurred for twelve centuries. Rhazes, of Persia, the leading physician of Islam in the tenth century, has some claim to being called a physicist, since he used the hydrostatic balance. In Egypt in the same period there was an Arabic physicist who devoted most of his study to optics, Ibn-al-Haitham (965–1020). His writings were translated into Latin and influenced the English Franciscan Roger Bacon (1214–1294), who in his period excelled all others in all science. He advanced the theory of lenses and vision.

Leonardo da Vinci (1452–1519) also included physics among his many interests. He was a keen observer and an untiring experimenter, well acquainted with the writings of Archimedes. The principle of inertia and the impossibility of perpetual motion as a power source were understood by him. From his studies he deducted the law of the lever. Hydrostatics and hydrodynamics were other fields of his interest and experiments.

A collection of information about magnetism was published by the English physician William Gilbert (1540–1603) following investigations of the forces between magnets. He coined the term "electricity" to describe the forces shown when amber was rubbed, and he measured these forces with a suspended needle.

Galileo (1546–1642) is conceded to have been the scientist who gave the chief impetus to physics. The theories of Copernicus were tested by him with the aid of the telescope. His work on dynamics was outstanding, combining experimental and mathematical procedures.

René Descartes (1596–1650) made improvements in the mathematics used in physics. Blaise Pascal (1623–1662) originated the theory of probability so valuable in all the sciences, and Sir Isaac Newton (1642–1727) stated the law of gravity.

These and numerous other basic discoveries had to precede and form the foundation for application of physical science to medicine. About the earliest work of a biological nature was that of Luigi Galvani (1737–1798), of Bologna, a physician who summarized the experiments on muscle-nerve preparations and is credited with being the founder of the science of animal electricity.

Galvani was followed by Alessandro Volta (1745–1827), of Pavia, who showed that a muscle can be thrown into continuous contraction by electric stimulations. He devised the electric battery.

Robert Mayer, of Heilbronn, and James Joule demonstrated in 1842 the physical principle of conservation of energy. Von Helmholtz in 1847 applied this principle to the entire field of chemistry and physics. Among the latter's countless contributions to the advancement of physical science in his 23 years as professor of physics at Berlin was his demonstration in 1848 that the muscles are the main source of animal heat.

When in the last five years of the nineteenth century the chemical atom, believed by Dalton to be indivisible, was disintegrated as a result of new research, thinking in the physical sciences had to be radically changed.

The most spectacular discovery from a physical-medical standpoint was an accident—Wilhelm Konrad Roentgen's discovery of x-rays in 1895. Roentgen (1845–1922) was a professor of physics to whom recent surgery owes more than to any other individual. The effect of his work upon the development of hospitals has been dramatic.

Roentgen was educated at Utrecht in Holland. He came under the influence of Clausius, the physicist of Zurich who with Helmholtz and Sir William Thomson had worked out about 1850 the mathematical relations of the laws governing heat transformations. Caloric heat had previously been regarded as a material substance, an idea which severely retarded medical progress.

Basing his experiments on the new theories, Carl Reinhold August Wunderlich (1815–1877) produced a treatise in 1868 on the relations of animal heat and disease. Garrison[16] comments that Wunderlich "found fever a disease and left it a symptom."

Thomson and Rutherford experimented with the x-rays newly discovered by Roentgen. The end result of this and later research was the electronic theory.

In 1896 Henri Becquerel found that uranium gives out rays, and in 1900 the Curies discovered radium. Crookes, Rutherford, and others further developed these discoveries, leading to the discovery of positive rays and isotopes and the development of the cyclotron. A curious result has been the final realization of the alchemist's dream—transmutation of elements—accomplished with bombardment by atomic energy. Some 300 new radioactive substances have been recorded through recent research in this field.

BIONICS

The new science of bionics, a term first assigned to it in 1960, is a merger of biological and industrial research. Realizing finally that living organisms demonstrate special adaptation mechanisms more effective than any they can devise, industrial engineers are studying the animal kingdom, a vast laboratory heretofore given scant attention. The mysteries of the selectivity of the frog's eye are being probed for possible use in developing a map-reading eye for missiles and a pattern-recognition eye for the basic air-defense system, according to James Poling in the May, 1962, *Rotarian*. Possibility of application to automatic monitors for air-traffic radarscopes is also envisioned. Bats, mosquitoes, fish, snakes, and moths are among the numerous other subjects of study.

Two of the developments already achieved are an "eye" that "can peer through a microscope and distinguish cancerous from healthy cells" and one that "can detect abnormal patterns in an electroencephalogram." Speaking of the brain which is "the ultimate challenge to the bionicist," Mr. Poling quotes a statement by one of the great computer-scientists, Dr. Warren S. McCulloch: "Actually computers are clumsy, stupid beasts in a hazardous world. They haven't the brains of a retarded ant. And they can't do the jobs that must be done."

[16] *Op. cit.*, p. 431.

Another term for bionics is biomedical engineering. The scientists in this field are called "dry" biophysicists. One of them developed the heart pacemaker which keeps alive persons whose hearts tend to stop. A so-called wet biophysicist unlocked DNA, the genetic key to life. "Wet" biophysicists do the more basic research. Russia has a biophysics research center which houses 1,000 people. University faculty members who are teaching biomedical engineering hope that through the cooperative efforts of engineers and physicians there will emerge new applications of computers to medicine, such as a method of modifying listening equipment for screening tape recordings of heart beats so it will signal sounds indicating a defective heart, and automatic techniques for telemetering the physical state and depth of anesthesia in patients during an operation.

Basic Science Organizations

The basic scientists are organized in practically every nation. There is room to mention only two of the broadest types of societies, two which are typical of those in other countries.

The British Association for the Advancement of Science was organized in 1831. Its stated object is

> . . . to give a stronger impulse and a more systematic direction to scientific inquiry; to promote the intercourse of those who cultivate science in different parts of the British Empire with one another and with foreign philosophers; to obtain a more general attention to the objects of science and a removal of any disadvantages of a public kind which impede its progress.

Annual meetings are held in a different city each year, special conferences are arranged throughout the year, publications are issued, and funds are granted to scientists to pursue specific investigations.

The American Association for the Advancement of Science is patterned after the British association and is an affiliation of associations in the natural sciences. It has sections for each of the sciences. It was organized under its present title in 1847, developing out of the original Association of American Geologists, founded at Philadelphia in 1840. It holds an annual winter session and occasional summer meetings.

The Basic Scientist

Basic scientists need not be and usually are not isolated human beings confined to their laboratories, as they are sometimes imagined to be. Teamwork is as characteristic of scientific research as it is of the modern hospital. Yet a high degree of individualization is essential in any kind of detective work, solitude being necessary for the concentration which is required. The individual explorer is still very important. As a sort of image of the basic scientist of the twentieth century, Dr.

Anton Julius Carlson, known in his later years as a "Grand Old Man of Science" (he died in Chicago at the age of 81 on September 2, 1956), is presented as the climax to this chapter.

Dr. Carlson won international renown for his discoveries and fundamental biological research. For 52 years he was on the faculty of the University of Chicago. He was born in Sweden. He came to the United States at the age of 16. His bachelor's and master's degrees in philosophy were received from Augustana College and his Ph.D. in biology from Stanford University. When he came to the University of Chicago a year later he was already well known for having proved that the heart beat begins in the nerve and then reaches out to trigger the heart muscle.

Dr. Carlson's M.D. was honorary, as were also his degrees in law and science from seven universities and colleges.

The fact that hunger is automatic and independent of appetite was one of his discoveries. Among his literary accomplishments was his famous work on nutrition, *The Control of Hunger in Health and Disease.*

His was not a placid temperament. He fought boldly for many causes, and he opposed violently some others, such as cradle-to-the-grave security, insisting that people were put into the world to work. Adulterated and devitalized foods, especially white bread, aroused him to battle. Probably his most belligerent crusade was against the antivivisectionists. He used every weapon he could command—the press, the lecture platform, radio, and organized action. He and the dog heroes which he used as exhibits, along with a child who had benefited from the results of animal experimentation, were well known to many a public audience. No other single person so effectively blocked the antivivisectionists as did this fighting scientist.

Dr. Carlson's investigations altered certain physiological concepts. His research covered many areas, among them the nerves of the heart, the aging process, the functioning of the parathyroid glands, and the distribution of immune substances in the body fluids.

One of Dr. Carlson's colleagues, Dr. Lester R. Dragstedt, said of him in a tribute published in the *Proceedings of the Institute of Medicine of Chicago,* "It is probable that no man in America not engaged in clinical practice had so great an effect on medicine."

CHAPTER 6

Milestones in Medical Science

Nothing contributes so much to the appreciation of a science
or an art as a knowledge of its history. The architect goes
back to the days of Greece and the medieval cathedrals
for an understanding of his art, and although he plans with
the most modern of materials and methods and in designs
quite different from those of his ancestors, there is the
feeling that he is the present culmination of a long line of
architects reaching back into history. In art the student
likewise feels himself the descendant of all artists who have
gone before. It was long felt that medicine is such a rapidly
growing art and science that a knowledge of its history,
while interesting, had little bearing on present-day problems.
The great volume of literature—some 3,000 medical journals
and a comparable number of books, monographs, and
systems—published each year taxed one's capacity to
assimilate them even partially. Material only two or three
years old was thought to be already as obsolete as yesterday's
airplanes. However, with the current emphasis on the
humanities which educators are promoting, interest in the
history of medicine has been aroused.
MICHAEL L. MASON, M.D.[1]

THE EFFECT of disease upon the history of mankind is strikingly illustrated by the decline of early European civilization in the fourth century B.C.
Then malaria mosquitoes, as they are now recognized, penetrated Greece. Greek
farmers, so the records show, fled from marshy regions. This, besides the effects
of the disease, caused food shortages that affected the health of the populace.

[1] Resurgence of Interest in Medical History. *Bull. Am. Coll. Surgeons*, May–June, 1959, p. 153.

Twenty-four hundred years ago Empedocles tried to protect Selinus in his native land, Sicily, against "bad air" by draining the swamps from which the mists and "bad air" came. He succeeded in checking disease, because by drainage he robbed the mosquitoes of their breeding grounds.

Alexander the Great died at the age of 33 by the waters of Babylon—the cause, malaria. A few years ago *Surgery, Gynecology and Obstetrics* published a series of articles on the causes of death of great men of the past, the reading of which gives rise to speculation on how the course of history would have been changed had present-day knowledge of disease and its treatment been available in their times.

Authorities believe that the decline of Rome, as well as that of Greece and the Hanseatic Empire in China, resulted from weakening of the populace through malaria acquired from mosquitoes infesting the undrained swamplands.

Sixty million persons are said to have perished from the Black Death, over a fourth of the earth's population at the time, in the epidemics which raged in Asia, Africa, and Europe in the fourteenth century and which broke out spasmodically to the end of the seventeenth. In the Venetian Republic, more than 500,000 and in Milan 80,000 died in the epidemic of 1630.

In London alone, 69,000 died in the Great Plague of 1665; in Vienna, 70,000 in 1679; in Prague, 83,000 in 1681. In the early sixteenth century typhus fever and diphtheria were epidemic in Italy, Spain, and England. Leprosy, scourge of the ancient Hebrews, Greeks, and Romans, appeared in Europe in the sixth and seventh centuries A.D. and spread terribly during and probably as a result of the Crusades. The building of leprosaria shows that there was some inkling that segregation checked the spread of the disease. There were some 2,000 lazar houses in France, between 200 and 300 in England, many more in other countries. Smallpox ravaged all the earth until vaccination was made compulsory in many countries. And everywhere there was tuberculosis, "Captain of the Men of Death."

Willison[2] in his tale of the landing of the pilgrims, *Saints and Strangers,* says:

> The delay in providing warm and adequate shelter was at once the cause and the effect of the "general sickness" . . . disease reached epidemic proportions and appears to have been a powerful combination of scurvy, pneumonia, and tuberculosis in a particularly virulent form, brought on by months of bad diet, cramped and unsanitary quarters, exposure and over-exertion in all kinds of weather. . . .

And from a note in the old records of the pilgrims: "This month thirteen of our number die. And in three months past dies halfe our company. . . . Of a hundred persons, scarce fifty remain, the living scarce able to bury the dead."

Harry Hansen[3] records an incident that throws an interesting side light on theories of disease in the 1830's. An outbreak of cholera occurred at Fort Armstrong at Rock Island, Illinois. In his battle against the epidemic, General Win-

[2] George F. Willison: *Saints and Strangers.* New York, Renal & Hitchcock, 1945, p. 166.
[3] Harry Hansen: *The Chicago.* New York, Farrar & Rinehart, 1942, p. 105.

field Scott published a famous order in which he declared that alcoholism must be associated with the spread of cholera, and ordered that "every soldier, or ranger, found drunk or sensibly intoxicated, be compelled, as soon as his strength will permit, to dig a grave at a suitable burying place, large enough for his own reception, as such grave cannot fail to be soon wanted for the drunken man himself or some drunken companion."

The colossal tragedies of epidemics and the frantic searchings for their cause, prevention, and cure are milestones—dread ones—on the highway of medicine. Heroic measures to prevent their reappearance in later stretches of the road provide bits of cheer along the way.

Among the disease organisms isolated or discovered were the bacteria of leprosy by Armauer Hansen in 1871–1874; of gonorrhea by Albert Neisser in 1879; of typhoid fever by Carl Joseph Eberth in 1880; of glanders by Loeffler and Schutz in 1882; of diphtheria by Klebs and later Loeffler in 1882; of erysipelas by Friedrich Fehleisen in 1882. Gaffky obtained the first pure culture of the typhoid bacillus in 1884. Weichselbaum discovered the meningococcus in 1887, Kitasato the tetanus bacillus in 1889, Welch and Nuttall the gas bacillus in 1892; Ivanovski the first filterable virus, the agent causing tobacco mosaic, in 1892; Yersin and Kitasato simultaneously the plague bacillus in 1894; Shiga the dysentery bacillus in 1897; Schaudinn working with Hoffmann the *Spirochaeta pallida (Treponema pallidum)* of syphilis in 1905; and Bordet and Gengou the whooping cough bacillus in 1906.

As for research on the ways in which disease is transmitted, it is surmised in the Sanskrit *Susruta* that mosquitoes transmit malaria, but the theory was not proved until 1877 by Sir Patrick Manson. Flies as transmitters of disease are recognized in folklore, in the Bible, in early military medicine, but the proof that they transmit cholera awaited demonstration by Tizzoni and Cattani in 1886. Warnings are also given in the *Susruta* against rats that act strangely, evidently connecting them with plague, but the proof that the fleas of plague-ridden rats transmit the disease did not come until 1897 when Masaki Ogata found plague bacilli in them.

Laveran identified the malarial parasite in humans and Sir Ronald Ross in 1897 showed how the anopheles mosquito put it there. Mosquito control in the Canal Zone vanquished a disease that had been sapping the strength of the natives and would have made impossible the finishing and operating of the canal. Treatment with quinine and synthetic drugs developed during World War II, DDT, and other insecticides cleared Sardinia and Cyprus of the disease.

Yet with all the discoveries and applications, and the great progress in the war against communicable diseases, each advance seems to open up new territory to explore. Furthermore, the battles do not stay won. Bacteria acquire immunity. Control measures fail through carelessness or through catastrophes such as war, earthquakes, and floods. Cholera appears again in the Philippines, yellow fever somewhere else. With air travel, transportation of disease carriers is common.

Precautions have to be constant and stringent. The milestones can be buried and the wrong turn taken.

THE STRUGGLE AGAINST CHARLATANRY

Cato the Censor would today be called an obstructionist to medical progress. In common with most Romans of his day, who resented the intrusion of the Greek physicians, he favored superstitious rites and herbal remedies in treating disease and injury. In treating dislocations he mumbled the meaningless phrase, "Huat hanat ista pista domiabo damnaustra et luxato." He had great faith in the numeral "3" and administered herbal concoctions by using three leaves of the plant and continuing the dosage for three days. How much easier this was than to study the patient, study medical literature, and confer with other doctors! The first century A.D. Roman historian Pliny the Elder declared that for 600 years before the Greeks invaded their empire, his countrymen had got along without doctors. He reveals that the Greek physician was despised because he accepted fees for his services and was feared as a possible poisoner or assassin.

The strength of imagination in the cure of disease has always been obvious. Millingen[4] cites such "cures" as the relief of cramps by means of a ring made of the hinge of a coffin, also by a rusty old sword hung up by the bedside; toothache prevented by driving nails into an oak tree; headache cured by tying around the head a halter that had served in hanging a criminal and also by drying, pulverizing, and taking as a cephalic snuff the moss growing on a human skull; tumors of the glands cured by stroking the parts nine times with a dead man's hand; warts cured by stealing a piece of beef from the butcher and rubbing them with it, then interring the beef in any filth, the warts withering and falling when the beef rotted. He also says:

> Amongst the various and capricious experiments of Peter the Great, an edict is recorded ordering his sailors to give salt water to their male children, with a view of accustoming them to a beverage which might preclude the necessity of laying in large stocks of fresh water on board his ships! The result was obvious; this nursery of seamen perished in the experiment.

The tales of the quacks who flourished in the eighteenth and nineteenth centuries are read with either horror or amusement. Some of the concoctions prescribed contained antimony and arsenic. Others were harmless but foolish—like the famous Anodyne Necklace which was marketed by the Chamberlen family, notorious also for withholding description of the "secret" forceps invented by one of them. The necklace was supposed to speed up teething in children. The beads in it were claimed to have been made from the bones of St. Hugh, who when alive was said to have been able to cause infants' teeth to pop out after he had rubbed their gums nine times with a finger dipped in holy water. A Yale gradu-

[4] John Gideon Millingen: *Curiosities of Medical Experience.* Philadelphia, Haswell, Barrington, & Haswell, 1838, pp. 28–29, 174.

ate, Elisha Perkins, made a fortune in England and in America by marketing electrical tractors made of two metal rods which were supposed to relieve pain when rolled over the painful area. Even George Washington bought a pair. Perkins was exposed by a Yorkshire physician who proved that so-called cures could result from rollers made of wood and other substances.

Quackery is a long way from dead, however. All the legislation which has been passed through the years has had only temporary results. Knaves live in all periods and people are gullible. Continuous war must be waged against charlatans. Hospital personnel should participate in the educational campaigns. Currently in the United States the public pays more than a billion dollars a year for nostrums dispensed by quacks.

In the fall of 1961 under the sponsorship of the American Medical Association and the Food and Drug Administration of the Department of Health, Education and Welfare, the first National Congress on Medical Quackery was held in Washington. One of the speakers referred to three major kinds of quackery from the standpoint of protecting the public: device quackery, nutritional quackery, and drug and cosmetic quackery. Cancer and arthritis are the diseases on which quackery is especially flourishing because cures cannot yet be effected by the medical profession.

There is as much quackery in the promotion of foods as in drugs, and without regulation equally harmful effects on health are possible. It was late in the history of civilization before scientific experimentation began in connection with foods. About the first forward step was taken by the Scotch physician James Lind (1716–1794), surgeon in the Royal Navy, who in a ten weeks' voyage treated 350 cases of scurvy. A knowledge of naval history was useful to him in this emergency. He recalled that the Dutch had given the sailors lemon and orange juice in 1564 and that it had been used also in the voyages of Sir Richard Hawkins in 1593 and of Commodore James Lancaster in 1660. This led John Woodall to recommend it in *Surgeons' Mate,* published in 1636. Lind published a treatise in 1754 which revived the practice, and with the issuance of an admiralty order in 1795, scurvy disappeared entirely from the Navy as a result of the incorporation of lemon juice in the diet. Yet the reason for the preventive and curative powers of the citrus fruits and other foods was not learned until the late nineteenth and early twentieth centuries when vitamins were discovered and experiments with them began.

Periodically someone climbs to fame—and fortune—by advocating a back-to-nature diet. The use of their own common sense would save people a lot of money, but it is easier to buy a book, subscribe to a magazine, and patronize a "health food" store. Usually the diets recommended by faddists have no scientific basis, and frequently they are harmful because they exaggerate the virtues of certain foods and minimize or eliminate others which are essential for a balanced diet. Such books and articles, like others seeking to be best-sellers, sensationalize by playing up peculiar items to attract attention.

Nostrums and freak diets for weight-reducing are costing the public huge sums of money, when the fact should be clear to every scientifically educated person that reduction of food intake is the safest and most effective method.

Doctors and all personnel in the health field have an obligation to teach the facts about the lessening food needs for the more sedentary lives led by most persons today and the lower requirements with advancing age. It is a public service for them to get into this act because of their firsthand knowledge that overweight means the risk in surgery is greater; there is more likelihood of developing high blood pressure, diabetes, heart and kidney ailments, gallstones, etc.; and finally there is probability of an earlier death than would have occurred if weight had been properly controlled.

These facts were startlingly confirmed during World War II when in the occupied countries where food was scarce the death rate from coronary artery disease began dropping. Mainly this was because of reduction in consumption of fat; hence the current intensive experimenting with and theorizing about cholesterol.

The place of scientific investigation in the improvement of health and the progress of medicine cannot be overemphasized. Its importance keeps leading any discussion of medical and related affairs back to the laboratory.

PATHOLOGY

The great basic *medical* science, pathology, with its cohorts, bacteriology, epidemiology, and parasitology, is the root of all medical advance. It is the sum of all the basic natural sciences as they are related to disease. Like them, it is a part of the medical school curriculum. Also like them, every physician should keep abreast of and contribute to discoveries in this science if he is to give his patients the benefit of up-to-date knowledge. Why should the administrator of a medical service institution study it? As Dr. John Gorrell[5] says in an article, "The Administrator Has 'Arrived' ":

> Ours is the responsibility of cooperative leadership in all phases except the practice of medicine. Hence a knowledge of medicine is basic to us as it is to the doctor, but to a different degree and for different reasons.

The first physician whom Garrison calls a pathologist was Antonio Benevieni, a Florentine surgeon who died in 1502. Five years after Benevieni's death his 54-page *De Abditis Causis Morborum* was published. This was described by Malgaigne as "the only work on pathology which owes nothing to anyone." Benevieni pioneered in reporting postmortem sections, but was in advance of his time and was a Galenist. Another physician who is described as a pathologist was Girolamo Fracastoro (1484–1553), of Verona, who wrote a long poem in which was summed up the knowledge of his time on dietetics and the treatment of disease.

Pathology as a distinct field of study seems to have begun with the section

[5] *Mod. Hosp.*, April, 1952, p. 70.

"Pathologia" in the *Medicina* published in 1554 by Jean Fernel (1506–1588), of France, previously mentioned under physiology. In it each disease is considered with reference to its development.

Pathology was first made a true branch of modern medical science by Giovanni Battista Morgagni (1682–1771), professor at Padua, who late in life published five books of letters. In them were reported postmortem findings as related to clinical records, the first time this had been attempted. Many new forms of disease were described in these letters.

A much more ambitious attempt than Fernel's to treat pathology as a distinct study was made by Matthew Baillie (1761–1823), of Scotland, in his *Morbid Anatomy,* which appeared in 1793. The book was systematically arranged, describing the morbid appearances of each organ in succession, and the autopsies were correlated with complete case histories, following Morgagni's style.

A great modern pathologist was Richard Bright (1789–1858), of Bristol, England, who worked many hours each day in the wards and postmortem room at Guy's Hospital, eventually collecting his observations and records in his *Reports of Medical Cases,* published in 1827. In this work he made an epochal distinction between cardiac and renal dropsy. This was a result of having set aside two wards in the hospital connected by a consulting room and laboratory for the study of renal disease explicitly.

A lecturer on pathology and diagnosis is the next important figure. Thomas Addison (1793–1860), also of Guy's Hospital, described pernicious anemia, appendicitis, disease of the suprarenal capsules, and started study of diseases of the ductless glands. Addison's disease was named for him.

Another famous English pathologist was Thomas Hodgkin (1798–1866), a Quaker physician, who gave the first clear description of what is known as Hodgkin's disease, enlargement simultaneously of the spleen and lymphatic glands. He produced one of the earliest English works on pathology, *Lectures on the Morbid Anatomy of the Serous and Mucous Membranes.*

As in the basic sciences, illustrations are exceedingly important in enhancing the value of the pathology text. Sir Robert Carswell (1793–1857), of Scotland, medical graduate of Aberdeen, was a talented illustrator of gross pathology. Nine years after he became professor of pathology at University College, London, appeared his *Illustrations of the Elementary Forms of Disease* from a series of 2,000 of his water-color drawings of diseased structures, plated by himself.

Carl Rokitansky (1804–1878), of Bohemia, did great work in pathology. He is said to have had at his disposition some 1,500 to 1,800 cadavers a year and to have had more than 30,000 postmortem examinations. He first detected bacteria in the lesions of malignant endocarditis and contributed many other discoveries and new descriptions. Pathologists of today continue to learn from his writings.

A most important work on diseases of the thoracic organs was produced in 1826 by René-Theophile-Hyacinthe Laennec (1781–1826), of Brittany, physician successively to the hospitals Beaujon and Necker, Paris. This expert pathologist was called by Heise "the greatest of teachers on pulmonary tuberculosis."

The first chair of pathology in the Paris Faculty was held by Jean Cruveilhier (1791–1873), who first described disseminated sclerosis. In 1842 he published his well-illustrated atlases of pathology.

Rudolf Virchow (1821–1902), of Pomerania, professor of pathology at Würzburg and later at Berlin, has a top place in this field as the founder of cellular pathology. In 1847 he founded the *Archiv für pathologische Anatomie*.

At the request of the Prussian government, Virchow investigated and made recommendations for the control of an epidemic of typhus fever among the weavers of Upper Silesia. He was so moved by what he saw and the reform measures he advocated were so strong that the angry authorities removed him from his prosectorship at the Charité Hospital, but seven years later after having made a brilliant record at Würzburg he was invited to return and was made the director of the Pathological Institute which had been built for him.

Pioneering in experimental histology and pathology, Julius Cohnheim (1839–1884), Virchow's pupil and also a native of Pomerania, wrote his inaugural dissertation on the subject of inflammation of serous membranes and produced many other valuable papers. He was an army surgeon in the Prussian War and afterward served as professor of pathology at, successively, Kiel, Breslau, and Leipzig.

Investigations of the pathological anatomy of smallpox and Bright's disease were made by Carl Weigert (1845–1904), of Silesia, who was the first to employ the staining method for bacteria. That the amount of repair in an injured tissue is always greater than is needed was a law advanced by him.

An early assistant of Virchow's at Berlin and later professor of pathology at, successively, Bern, Würzburg, Prague, Zurich, and Rush Medical College at Chicago, was Edwin Klebs (1834–1913), of East Prussia. He not only was an anticipator with Pasteur in the bacterial theory of infection but was most influential in having the theory accepted by other pathologists.

In the United States the greatest pathologist of his period was Samuel David Gross (1805–1884), professor of surgery, successively, at Louisville and at Jefferson Medical College, Philadelphia. In 1839 he wrote the first exhaustive treatise on pathological anatomy in English.

The leading pathologist of Canada in his era was John George Adami (1862–1926), a native of Manchester, England. He had been a pupil of the eminent physiologist Sir Michael Foster, professor at Cambridge. He wrote notable works on cancer, classification of tumors, heredity, and pathology, the latter as textbooks.

One of the founders of experimental pathology was Friedrich Theodor von Frerichs (1819–1885), a graduate of Göttingen and ultimately professor of pathology at Berlin. He discovered leucin and tryosin in the urine of patients with acute yellow atrophy of the liver, made pathological studies of cirrhosis of the liver and of pernicious malarial fever, and published books on Bright's disease and diseases of the liver. His final monograph was on diabetes.

A leading authority in more recent pathology was Ludwig Aschoff, of Berlin, professor at Freiburg. Both systematic and philosophical, Aschoff tried to direct pathological thought along more reasonable lines than those into which it had drifted because of conflicting ideas and developments. He is especially noteworthy for having carried to Japan through his pupils the new spirit of this branch of medicine.

Other later prominent pathologists include Marchand of Leipzig, Chiari of Vienna, Foa of Italy, Ewing of Pittsburgh and New York, Mallory of Cleveland, Krumbhaar of Philadelphia, Winternitz of Baltimore and Yale, MacCallum and Klotz of Ontario, Hektoen and Anton Carlson of Chicago, the last-named of whom was described in Chapter 5 as a physiologist. Obviously all pathologists must be anatomists and physiologists first, but with their focus on abnormalities.

The way in which the pathologist serves through autopsies as an instructor to medical students and physicians is described by Dr. Edwin F. Hirsch, director of pathology and laboratories, Presbyterian–St. Luke's Hospital, in a lecture to Northwestern University students in hospital administration:

> The postmortem examination probably is the most enlightening and stimulating experience for all physicians participating. The pathologist, to whom is delegated the responsibility of making the examination and of interpreting the tissue changes, serves as an arbitrator. He demonstrates and describes to the others the changes caused by disease in the tissues and at the same time records his observations for the hospital files. Bacteriologic studies, microscopic and special examinations of the tissues, and photographs are supplementary tools. This material then becomes available for the conferences to be held later, at which the entire clinical history is reviewed and is compared with the results of the postmortem.
>
> To the pathologist the revelation of diseases, anomalies, and unusual conditions in postmortem examinations is a constant source of stimulation and fascinating interest. His curiosity is aroused to see in what manner the disease had expressed itself in the tissues, what are its phases, how can preventive measures be found and applied. . . . While the prime purpose in each postmortem is to establish the immediate cause of death so far as is possible, the pathologist is provided a much larger field of study. He is able to test the accuracy of his surgical tissue diagnoses (biopsies) which in a large hospital practice and in cancer control clinics occupy a considerable part of his time. The value of this discipline is again reflected to the advantage of the living clientele where accuracy in tissue diagnosis is highly important in determining the nature of a disease and thus indicating to the clinician the correct procedures for therapy.
>
> As arbitrator, the pathologist demonstrates to the clinicians the tissue changes revealed by the postmortem examination of their deceased patients and gives them a correlation of the tissue changes with the clinical symptoms. There is no question that the postmortem improves the quality of diagnoses, and as Dr. Alan Gregg has written, it is the terror of the casual guesser, but it is a reward to an eager and honest doctor even when it is a stark corrective; and it serves as a merciless incentive to the best we have in us as physicians. The frankness with which

clinicians discuss the results of these postmortem examinations reveals an honesty and sincerity of purpose which dispels any suspicion of fear about the disclosures of the examination. . . .

Dr. Hirsch gives the benefits of autopsies to the public as follows:

The benefits of the postmortem examination to the lay clientele are frequently omitted in discussions of the postmortem. The advantages are many in the improvement of medical practice, and in other ways, to the immediate family and friends. Great satisfaction is gained from knowing that the best medical attention and care were given to the deceased; that a disease not clearly diagnosed during life became factual knowledge later; that a communicable disease was disclosed against which suitable measures could be applied to protect other members of the family or exposed contacts; and that benefits, of an intangible character at the moment, can be realized later. The postmortem offers these and many other advantages not considered during the emotional stress at the time of the death of the relative or friend. It can be used constructively and not regarded as a violation of the sanctity of the human body.

The personal reminiscences of pathologists dramatize the story of the evolution of the hospital laboratory.[6] For example Dr. Samuel A. Goldberg who retired in 1962 after 31 years as director of the pathology laboratory in the Presbyterian Unit of the United Hospitals of Newark, New Jersey, looks back to that laboratory's start in one room staffed by himself and two technicians. In 1962 the personnel numbered 25, with an associate, two other medical doctors, and an accredited school of medical technology. In his last year as director he supervised more than 200,000 procedures, compared with 22,000 in 1931. He decreased the time to diagnose permanent paraffin-sectioned surgical specimens from a week to one day; instituted a system whereby with modern techniques and equipment frozen sections are diagnosed within five minutes, while the patient is still on the operating table; and discovered in 1935 that encephalitis could be treated by x-ray. For many years he regularly worked from early morning until midnight, and was called out during all hours of the night.

A famous New York pathologist, Dr. George N. Papanicolaou, died on February 19, 1962. He was known world-wide as the discoverer of the Papanicolaou smear test for the diagnosis of carcinoma of the uterus. Born in Greece in 1883, he received his M.D. degree from the University of Athens in 1904 and his Ph.D. from the University of Munich in 1910. He came to the United States late in 1913, almost immediately becoming assistant in the department of pathology of the New York Hospital, which became affiliated with Cornell University Medical College. He rose to the rank of professor of clinical anatomy in the college and was director of its research laboratory named after him. He was consultant to the Kate Depew Strang Prevention Clinic of the Sloan-Kettering Memorial Cancer Center. After accepting emeritus status at Cornell, he became director of the Papanicolaou Cancer Research Institute at Miami, Florida.

[6] A most excellent summary of the work of the hospital laboratory was published in the June, 1961, issue of *Memorial Baptist Scope*, Memorial Baptist Hospital, Houston, Texas.

BACTERIOLOGY, PARASITOLOGY, EPIDEMIOLOGY

In the first century B.C. Varro, of Rome, guessed that disease might be caused by invisible animals. Sixteen centuries later in the year 1546 Fracastorius advanced a theory of contagion involving infection by microorganisms.

No progress could be made on this theory which seemed pure imagination until the microscope was invented and developed by Jannsen and Galileo between 1590 and 1610, and even then it was not until 1658 that anybody actually reported having seen the animalcules supposed to be causing disease. A Jesuit priest and physician, Athanasius Kircher (1602–1680), of Italy, discovered "worms" in the blood of victims of the plague. His "worms" may have been only pus cells as critics claimed, his 32-power microscope perhaps not having enabled him to detect bacteria, but his theory of contagion which he deduced from what he saw was correct.

Robert Boyle (1627–1691), an Irish chemist who has been mentioned before, made a revealing statement in 1662 when he said: "He that . . . understands fermentation shall be . . . better able . . . to give a fair account of several diseases."

In 1668 by experiments with maggots Francesco Redi, of Italy, made the first onslaught on the theory of spontaneous generation.

In 1675 bacteria and protozoa were actually seen by van Leeuwenhoek (1632–1723), of Holland, a discovery confirmed by Robert Hooke in 1677.

The spontaneous generation theory bobbed up again in 1745 when John Turberville Needham (1713–1781), an English Catholic priest residing on the Continent, reported experiments showing that microorganisms appeared in boiled meat even when tightly sealed, but the Italian abbate Lazaro Spallanzani (1729–1799) proved by repeated experiments between 1756 and 1766 that the reason they appeared was that the technique was faulty.

In 1762 Marcus Anton von Plenciz, Sr., writing about scarlatina, developed a theory of causation of contagious diseases in man, animals, and plants by microscopic animalculae.

A valuable contribution to nutrition in this connection was that of Nicolas Appert, of France, who in 1810 patented a canning process for preserving food.

Transmission of rabies to dogs by injections of saliva of rabid man was effected in 1813 by Magendie and Bouchet.

In 1835 Agostino Bassi showed that microorganisms cause silkworm disease, and the next year Ernst Schulze proved that with chemically filtered air no spontaneous generation occurs. A year later Charles Cagniard-Latour announced that yeast cells were alive.

A great work on infusoria was published by Christian Gottfried Erenberg in 1838. An essay "On Miasms and Contagia" was written by Jacob Henle, of Germany, in 1840.

That tuberculosis may be transmitted by cow's milk was shown by Hermann Klencke, of Germany, in 1846.

The infectious nature of septicemia was an epochal discovery. An assistant in the first obstetric ward of the Allgemeines Krankenhaus at Vienna, Ignaz Semmelweis (1818–1865), shook the medical world in 1847 when he announced that lack of cleanliness was the cause of septicemia or childbed fever. By instituting rigorous rules for cleansing of attendants' hands, he reduced the mortality rate in the ward from 9.92 to 1.27 per cent. His discovery came from his noticing that students came to this particular ward directly from the dissecting room, often without taking time to wash their hands. In another ward where midwives were instructed, cleanliness was practiced and the mortality rate was lower.

Oliver Wendell Holmes in Massachusetts had started the same battle against the spread of infection five years earlier than Semmelweis, unknown to the latter, but had not recognized the nature of puerperal fever as a form of blood poisoning, his reasoning being more speculative in character.

A storm of opposition gathered around Semmelweis. The orthodox professors and obstetricians reviled him. Life became so miserable for him in Vienna that he suddenly fled to Budapest. In 1855 he was appointed professor of obstetrics at the university there. In 1861 he published his celebrated treatise, "The Cause, Concept, and Prophylaxis of Puerperal Fever," and also a scathing series of "Open Letters to Sundry Professors of Obstetrics." As a pre-Listerian recognition of the transmission of infection through carelessness in technique, Semmelweis' discovery is now accorded the highest tribute. For him personally the result of his persecution by ignorant contemporaries was insanity and early death.

Finally the event occurred which really started the science of bacteriology.

A chemist, Louis Pasteur (1822–1925) of France, sent a paper, "Lactic Acid Fermentation," to the Lille Scientific Society in 1857, which was the initial step in the development of antiseptic and aseptic surgery. The paper was the result of twenty years of experimentation with the spoiling of wine, and his discovery that partial heat sterilization (Pasteurization) could prevent this spoilage which was caused by microorganisms. He also worked on the defeat of a disease of silkworms which was bankrupting the silk industry, on microorganisms in beer, and on anthrax and chicken cholera. He defined a ferment as "a living form which originates from a germ."

The great Claude Bernard derided this theory, as did a few others, despite his demonstrations.

Although the doctrine of spontaneous generation had been proved to be fallacious as far back as 1671 by the Italian naturalist, Francesco Redi, as has been observed before, and bacteria had been discovered in 1675 by the microscopist van Leeuwenhoek, the germ theory of disease was first propounded by Pasteur. His other great discoveries were prevention of anthrax, of swine erysipelas, and of preventive vaccinations, particularly of hydrophobia. Edward Jenner, the English physician, had in 1796 given the first vaccination for smallpox. It remained for Pasteur to demonstrate how germs can be weakened and used as vaccines.

Pasteur's greatest triumph came in 1874 in the form of a letter from Joseph

Lister in which he acknowledged the value of his work in relation to antiseptic surgery. It was on learning of Pasteur's work, in fact, that Lister undertook his experiments.

In 1879 Pasteur proved the bacterial causation of puerperal fever, thus establishing the validity of the theories of contagion advanced by Holmes and Semmelweis. In 1881 he began studies on rabies and produced the disease in rabbits by inoculation of virus into the brain.

As a tribute to Pasteur, more than two and a half million francs were subscribed to build the Pasteur Institute at Paris, which was opened in 1888 for the scientific study of all infectious diseases.

The next great bacteriologist was Robert Koch (1843–1910), of Germany. Early in his medical career he was the chief medical officer of a military hospital during the Franco-Prussian War. Returning to practice as district physician at Wolstein, he began private microscopic studies which led to his working out the life history and sporulation of the anthrax bacillus. In 1876 he demonstrated his culture methods in the Botanical Institute at Breslau to the great interest of the celebrated botanist Ferdinand Cohn, who published his memoir on this series of studies. Two years later Koch described the bacteria of six different kinds of surgical infections in a memoir on the etiology of traumatic infectious disease.

In 1880 Koch was appointed to the staff of the Imperial Health Department, after which he made many other discoveries, including the famous one of the tubercle bacillus in 1882. For the experiments which preceded this discovery all of the hospitals of Berlin furnished material from the tissues of persons who had died of tuberculosis.

In 1881 Koch devised a plating method for obtaining pure cultures. In 1884 he isolated the cholera organism. In 1905 he received the Nobel prize.

Edwin Klebs (1834–1913) was also a pioneer in bacteriology. Later prominent names are Carl Flugge (1847–1923), of Hanover, and Emil von Behring (1854–1917), professor of hygiene first at Halle and then at Marburg.

Hans Zinsser (1878–1942), professor of bacteriology at Columbia University, produced excellent textbooks. His autobiography, *As I Remember Him,*[7] is a fascinating account of his experiences as an investigator and preventer of infectious disease. He helped to fight typhus in the devastating epidemic in Serbia in 1915. Later he spent two years with the American forces in France. His comments on the medical lessons learned in the first World War are illuminating. He insists that his is not a "doctor book"; nevertheless, it lets the reader in on medical affairs in a way that surpasses in impressiveness the ordinary textbook method. A quotation as illustration is from pages 313 and 314 where he tells about work with the French bacteriologist Charles Nicolle, with whom he began a friendship "that started in our heads and soon extended to our hearts":

[7] Boston, Little, Brown and Company, 1940, pp. 313–14.

North Africa is an eldorado for the student of infectious diseases. There are Malta fever, fièvre boutonneuse, relapsing fever, typhus, kalazar, leprosy, malaria, and odds and ends of tropical infection that come up from the oases in the south. There were many things to learn and much to discuss, and I was especially interested in trying to overcome some experimental difficulties by transmitting typhus to monkeys with human lice. Nicolle received me with open arms. He gave me a laboratory, a technician, and all the materials I needed—even to a supply of bearded Arabs, who furnished the insects. . . . Nicolle did relatively few and simple experiments. But every time he did one, it was the result of long hours of intellectual incubation during which all possible variants had been considered and were allowed for in the final tests. Then he went straight to the point, without wasted motion. That was the method of Pasteur, as it has been of all the really great men of our calling, whose simple, conclusive experiments are a joy to those able to appreciate them. For there is an "art" of experimentation which is as elusive of definition as the art of color, sound, or letters.

Parasitology is a phase of laboratory work which is increasing. Jet-age transportation is forcing it from what one pathologist calls a "now-and-then" department in the hospital to an acutely needed permanent everyday service. One of the pioneer laboratories was established in the New England Center Hospital at Boston, Massachusetts, in 1946, originating through the interest of a technician.

Employment of workers from tropical countries in hospital dietary departments is particularly responsible for the demand for routine parasitological examinations as a safety measure.

An intensive four-week course in parasitology is given to selected students at the Communicable Disease Center, conducted by the Department of Health, Education and Welfare, Public Health Service, at Chamblee, Georgia. The center also aids laboratory personnel in identifying and confirming parasites that are sent to it.

SURGERY

Surgery seems long, long ago to have attained high status as a skill, if not a science, and then to have lapsed with the rise and fall of civilizations. Writing currently, an Indian surgeon, Nabin Kishore Bidyadhar of Koraput, Orissa, sets 4720 B.C. as the approximate age in which Susruta of India flourished.

Susruta is no half-mythical figure like the Egyptian physician Im-ho-Tep, who is supposed to have lived around 2900 B.C. Susruta is real. He produced the world's first classical textbook on surgery. It shows that his predecessors also had possession of considerable anatomical knowledge, since in it surgery is based on anatomy. Susruta made his pupils do dissections.

This discovery of ancient Hindu medicine is fairly recent. Susruta and his book were known, but they were placed in a much later historical period. The curtain on the past was raised through the discoveries of Evans in Crete, of Sir Leonard Wooley at Ur, and of Sir John Marshal in Mohenjodaro and Taxilla.

Dr. Bidyadhar[8] quotes V. B. Green-Armytage, British surgeon, as saying:

To Susruta we owe the discovery of cataract-couching, skin-grafting and rhino-
plasty. From him we possess a precise knowledge of midwifery and learn the
position occupied by the foetus in utero. . . . He speaks of postmortem Caesarean
section. He writes of amputations and the necessity of artificial limbs made of
iron. Tumors are removed, ruptures reduced, and patients cut for stone. Still
more remarkable are the rules laid down for the operating room, for it is written
that it should be fumigated with sweet vapours, the surgeon is to keep his hair
and beard short, nails clean, and wear a sweet-smelling dress. It is not certain
what drug was used, but instructions are given that the patient was to inhale a
substance called "sommohini" (anesthetic) before operation. Over a hundred
steel instruments are depicted and their uses described.

Recent research, Green-Armytage goes on to say, has shown "that the genius
of the Greeks drew its sap from Phoenicia and Crete, from Babylon and Egypt,
and even farther afield from Sumeria and the dwellers in the Valley of the
Indus."

Although Susruta's treatise on surgery, *Susruta Samhita,* covers the fields of
general and special, major and minor, surgery, including the laying down of
rules for the practice of asepsis, he is especially known for his knowledge of eye
diseases and their treatment. Much of the teaching is still valid.

Crude surgery, of course, goes back far before Susruta. With new discoveries
and anthropological studies, the date of the earliest known operations is being
pushed back. "Shanidar Man" found in 1957 in Iraq lived in 43,000 B.C., according to T. Dale Stewart, curator of physical anthropology, Smithsonian Institution, and bone cases of his skeleton indicate amputation just above the elbow for
a withered arm. It is surmised that the operation was performed with flint instruments.

A summary of late nineteenth-century advances in surgery was given in his
address as retiring president of the American College of Surgeons in 1947 by the
late Dr. Irvin Abell, of Louisville:

The period between 1867 and 1881, during which the teaching of Lister was
spreading through Germany, America, and England, has been referred to as the
gestation period of modern surgery. Even before 1867 ovarian cysts had been
removed and colostomies had been performed, and during this period Billroth
began his pylorectomies. But before 1881 no appendix had been removed; no perforated ulcer had been successfully sutured; the functions, let alone the surgery,
of the thyroid were unknown; the surgery of the spinal cord and brain—apart
from depressed fracture—had not begun and renal surgery had hardly been
touched. It was about 1881 that surgeons first realized the possibilities opened up
by the prevention of wound infection and the period of 1800 to 1900—the childhood of modern surgery—saw great advances in all directions. Surgeons explored
every type of disease in which they thought relief might be brought by the new
surgery. The necessary process of trial and error was not always followed by
happy results but the net gain was so obvious and encouraging that by 1900,
when I had completed my postgraduate training, many of the main lines of
modern surgery had been laid down though they were by no means standardized.

[8] Editorial. *J. Internat. Coll. Surgeons,* August, 1960.

Important developments that reduced surgical mortality were the obligatory wearing by the surgeon of a sterile gown and mask—no more street clothes in the operating room—and the adoption of elaborate techniques for the cleanliness of the surgeon's hands. William Stewart Halsted (1852–1922), professor of surgery at Johns Hopkins University from 1889 to 1922, introduced rubber gloves in 1890. All of these precautions against infection plus improvements made in the surroundings and equipment contributed to the success of the many new surgical procedures that were devised by the brilliant surgeons of the late nineteenth and early twentieth centuries.

The strongest impetus for more and better hospitals came from advances in surgery. The new surgeon has to have a good operating room, in a good hospital in all respects, in order to assure the degree of success which the state of knowledge at the time makes possible in the proper environment.

The effect of advances in surgery and its accompanying procedures is nowhere more clearly shown than in the survival rate of aged patients compared with that of only a few years back. The science editor of the *Chicago Tribune,* Roy Gibbons, reported in the issue of August 6, 1961, that a review of operations performed on 400 patients between the ages of 75 and 98 at Evanston (Illinois) Hospital since 1957 showed a survival rate of 88 per cent. Almost all of these, the writer reported, would have been considered poor risks only a few years ago. A graphic step-by-step description of the preparation of a specific patient, the anesthetic and surgical procedures, and the aftercare were included in the article, with a comment with respect to aftercare that older patients, on an average, are kept a week longer in the hospital than younger ones, which brings up the cost. Of the geriatric surgical patients reported in the Evanston Hospital series, more than 63 per cent had organic heart disease and 106 of the 400 had various types of malignancies.

Among the advances for specific conditions has been the "blue baby" operation, first performed in 1946, which has saved the lives of thousands of children throughout the world. Perfected after extensive experiments on dogs at Northwestern University Medical School by Dr. Willis J. Potts and his associate, Dr. Sidney Smith, the procedure consists of making a connection between the aorta and the pulmonary artery so that extra blood can be brought to the lungs to absorb oxygen. The operation does not correct heart defects, nor assure normal life expectancy, and except in every young and very blue babies has been superseded by the open-heart operation in which the heart-lung machine can be used.

Microsurgery, which is one of the newest marvels in surgical technique, began as an idea in the mind of a surgeon who wondered why broader use could not be made of the principle of magnification in the Zeiss microscope which was developed around 1952 for use in ear surgery. Research, experimentation, observation, and invention combined to make possible the development of instruments to be used in the joining of blood vessels. The pioneering work was done by a team at the University of Vermont College of Medicine. The college's director of research told a reporter for *Hospital Topics* that for the future the new technique gave promise for "nerve reconstruction, for fertility problems that can be corrected with reconstruction of the Fallopian tubes, for all types of surgery where correction has been successful in only relatively large vessels . . . in brain surgery where it is now possible only to pinch off the offending aneurysm or swollen sac" and said it was "conceivable that a 'stroke' will become a surgical emergency in which the clot is removed from the cerebral vessels and these vessels joined together successfully. Such joining might also be employed in the surgical correction of angina pectoris."[9]

Transplantation of organs and tissues is a fascinating current surgical subject. Experimentation is world-wide. In 1960 the Soviet press reported that Dr. Maria Panova, of Moscow's Central Institute of Traumatology Orthopedics, had in 1958 successfully transplanted the thigh of a corpse into a young man. The thigh came from a young man killed in a traffic accident. The transplanted thigh was reported to be living normally. The patient was supposed to be ready in a short time to discard the light orthopedic apparatus he was using. Dr. Nikolai Priorov, the director of the Institute, was quoted as saying that human limbs and specially treated pieces of skin, cartilage, and sinews were regularly taken from corpses for transplanting in patients.

A warning was sounded by Dr. Joseph E. Murray, director of the Laboratory for Surgical Research, Harvard Medical School, Boston, speaking at the American Medical Association convention in 1960. He declared that transplantation of organs or tissues "probably will never become a fountain of youth for man," but he said that definite progress is being made. He said that for successful transplantation of vital organs like the kidney, lung, liver, and heart, "we must have survival of the cells themselves." He pointed out that the kidneys are specially adapted for transplantation because they are paired and "have large blood vessels which allow the surgical operation to be successful, and because patients can survive normally with only one kidney." The lungs, being also paired, might be transplanted. Perfection of methods of preservation of single organs like the heart and liver from deceased persons is necessary before transplantation can succeed. Dr. Murray said that although many "successes" had been reported for human transplantations of endocrine glands, there had not been any that were "completely" successful.

Of the many fantastic achievements in the history of medical science, extracorporeal circulation is one of the most fantastic, in the opinion of the Italian surgeon Dr. A. Mario Dogliotti,[10] of Turin. Within a few years it has passed from the experimental into the clinical stage, he declares, pointing out that its results have been particularly satisfactory in the treatment of several cardiac diseases by surgical operations on the bloodless heart. Many more possibilities can be seen in the near future, according to Dr. Dogliotti, who says that this discovery is

[9] Adapted from a news report in *Hosp. Topics*, May, 1962, pp. 75–77.
[10] *J. Internat. Coll. Surgeons*, February, 1961.

... the result of a synthesis of the work of numerous investigators of numberless problems, both primary and collateral. One of the first steps was certainly the study of blood transfusion, blood groups, the Rh factor, isotonic solutions, blood coagulation, and changes in the cells of plasma and blood. . . . The second substantial advance was made on the basis of research on the physical, chemical and biologic phenomena controlling oxygenation of the blood and the gaseous exchange between blood and tissue. Particularly interesting are the investigations that have been made of thermoregulation and the effect of hypothermia on the resistance of the various organs to hypoxia.

He adds that it was at a congress of the Société Internationale de Chirurgie in Paris in 1951 that the first successful use was announced of extracorporeal circulation in man, in an operation performed by himself in the Surgical Clinic of Turin on August 9, 1951. He foresees the possibility, with deep hypothermia, of performing difficult operations on the brain, the liver, the kidney, and the organs of the gastrointestinal tract.

The Blood

The subject of extracorporeal circulation leads into consideration of the blood, bloodletting, and blood transfusion as they figure in medical history and in current practice.

The soul was located in the blood, the ancients believed. As the vital force of the body its exhaustion was blamed for the infirmities of old age. For resuscitation and recuperation the Egyptians bathed in it. Epilepsy was frequently treated with it. Blood from animals was often used, and a historian tells of a woman selling the mixed blood of a turtle and a pigeon as a remedy. Pliny believed a man could cure himself of pain by rubbing his own blood on himself. Norwegians and Laplanders drank the blood of seals, whales, and reindeer as a remedy for epilepsy and scurvy.

In an attempt to save his life, blood transfusions were given to Pope Innocent VIII in 1492. He failed to recover, and the three boys who furnished the blood died.

After Harvey's announcement of his discovery of the circulation of the blood in 1613, many attempts were made to improve a patient's condition by transfusion, but these were gradually abandoned because of the danger. Among the experimenters was Robert Lower, who in 1665 transferred blood from the vertebral artery of one dog to the jugular vein of another. A contemporary, Jean Baptiste Denis, of France, physician to Louis XIV, is credited with performing in 1667 the first successful transfusion to a human being, using lamb's blood. In a later patient he had a failure which resulted in a lawsuit and the prohibition of further transfusions.

Fears arose that transfusions would result in acquiring characteristics of the donor. The use of cat's blood was supposed to result in cat behavior—actual cases were reported. As a result of the animosities, opposition, and alarm, the

Pope issued around 1675 a special edict against the procedure. For nearly 150 years thereafter no progress was made.

Bloodletting played a much larger part in early medicine than did blood-giving. It was not only employed as treatment of disease but also as a preventive measure. In the England of Samuel Johnson's time persons young and old went regularly to doctors or apothecaries to be bled. The wealthier folk had the doctors come to them, on which occasion every member of the household including the servants was bled. The custom had an economic advantage for the surgeons whose practice was naturally limited by the few surgical procedures that could then be safely attempted.

In America Dr. Benjamin Rush was a devotee of bloodletting, believing that overexcited tissues were relieved by the process. He employed it in every conceivable condition, including plague, not just once or in small quantities, but in series, taking as much as 12 ounces at a time.

Bloodletting is admitted to have had some benefits. It was less harmful, in moderation, than the violent purgings that were common medical practice, and it quieted the pulse and relieved pain in certain illnesses.

Leeches were also used in bleeding. Leeching was so common that the word "leech" came to mean a physician. Over 40 million of these sucking animals were imported into France alone in the year 1743.

Bloodletting or venesection is not by any means a discarded practice. It is used in the management of some stages of a few diseases such as erythremia and hemochromatosis. In erythroblastosis and in some cases of leukemia and hemophilia it is employed in conjunction with transfusion. It is used in the management of plethora in emergencies, until oxygen, digitalis, and diuretic therapy can be administered. Its main use is for emergency relief of high venous pressure. Dr. D. V. Holman[11] maintained that "controlled bleeding" improves not only the rate of regeneration but the quality of blood cells and plasma protein, and he expressed the hope that potential voluntary blood donors would be encouraged by knowledge of the beneficial effects of periodic bloodletting in addition to the concurrent increasing of blood supplies.

To return to the subject of transfusions, James Blundell, an English physician and obstetrician, was distressed by the deaths of many women from puerperal hemorrhage. He conducted experiments in the early nineteenth century which led him to conclude that only human blood was suitable for transfusion. He devised instruments which made it unnecessary to cannulate the donor's vein. He performed nine transfusions, five of which were successes, four failures. All were on patients in extremely poor condition. His revival of the procedure led other physicians to employ it also, but as a last resort. The differing reactions of patients led to many questions which stimulated research. Increasing interest caused a sort of boom around 1875, in which again transfusion was mistaken as the cure for everything. Research on the physiology of the blood subsequently

[11] *Bull. New York Acad. Med.*, September, 1955.

corrected some of the ideas and indicated what the reasons were for some of the failures.

The most important clue came in 1900 when Karl Landsteiner, an Austrian scientist and later Nobel prize winner, announced his discovery that all human blood is not alike, a discovery that in the same year was proved independently by Shattock. They divided it into three groups with respect to their agglutinating reactions; in 1902 a fourth group was added by Decastello and Sturli, supplemented by Jansky's working out and classification of the reactions. In 1907 Ludvig Hektoen, of Chicago, explained the significance of isoagglutinins in human blood and how the untoward reactions were related to them. In 1908 Ottenberg developed clinical methods for typing bloods. By preliminary tests, he discovered, accidents due to incompatibility of blood could be excluded. Finally, after much confusion about classification, the Landsteiner designation of blood groups as O, A, B, and AB was adopted.

In telling about one of the earliest known successful uses of blood transfusion which occurred in 1840, Dr. Carl W. Walter, director of the blood bank at Peter Bent Brigham Hospital, Boston, said: "It was fortunate that the kind-hearted neighbors unwittingly donated compatible blood." The surgeon Dr. Richard Oliver, of England, described the case as follows:

> Blanched by profuse hemorrhage, which no adequate means had been employed to suppress, but which had now ceased, she was lying on her back in a state of imperfect consciousness, with the pulse at her wrist barely perceptible. . . . deceitful promises of reaction were succeeded by progressive indications of sinking. . . . I was provided with the apparatus necessary for performing transfusion; and having obtained a willing supply of blood from three of the patient's kind-hearted neighbors, I opened a vein at the bend of the elbow. . . . we had the very perfect gratification of witnessing not only the complete restoration of the circulatory powers, but the return of consciousness.

In hemotherapy, or blood transfusion, pathologists and technical and clerical staff have an extraordinarily heavy responsibility, because a slight error may lead to disaster. The physician who prescribes the treatment has to depend upon laboratory procedures without any way of controlling or checking them, which is not the case with blood counts and bacteriological or chemical findings. Blood bank errors are rated very costly to hospitals in terms of malpractice suits as well as in terms of patient welfare.

In an introduction to an announcement of "Minimum Standards for Blood Transfusions" issued in 1955, members of a committee of the American College of Surgeons declared:

> All evidence suggests that the risk of administering a blood transfusion probably equals or exceeds that of performing an appendectomy. At the same time, the failure to administer blood when indicated probably carries a much greater risk. However, before the liberal use of blood can be encouraged, greater safety must be assured.

The hope was expressed that the recommendations be adopted as the basis for reports of surveys by the Joint Commission on Accreditation of Hospitals. This was done. In 1961 the Commission recommended that an educational program be conducted on the local hospital level to review blood transfusion practices, emphasizing that it should concern not only those physicians interested in blood banking but all those who prescribe the use of blood and blood products in transfusion therapy, and that the handling and use of blood should be studied and evaluated by the local hospital staff and a mechanism established to ensure continuous supervision and review.

One of the earliest blood banks was established by Dr. Bernard Fantus, of Chicago's Cook County Hospital, in 1937. Later that year the Red Cross chapter in Augusta, Georgia, started operation of the first Red Cross blood donor service in the United States. Impetus to the use of blood transfusion to alleviate shock came with World War II. Military hospitals first and civilian hospitals afterward established blood banks, although many of them were merely refrigerators for storage of blood.

The National Blood Program of the American Red Cross began with the activation of a blood collecting and processing center at Rochester, New York, on January 12, 1948, which became the focal point for a regional program in eleven counties. By 1960, 55 regional programs were in operation in 40 states, including an all-mobile unit service in Massachusetts. Each center has a medical director, an administrative director, and a local medical advisory committee. The Red Cross had had a blood collection program for the armed forces, collecting through 35 centers more than 13,000,000 pints for wartime use.

In 1947 the American Association of Blood Banks was formed by representatives of independent, hospital, and commercial blood banks. The object was to provide greater opportunity for interchange of ideas and experiences among pathologists and technologists. By 1961 the association had more than 600 institutional members.

In 1955 a Joint Blood Council was established by the Red Cross, the American Association of Blood Banks, the American Medical Association, and the American Society of Clinical Pathologists. In 1962 the council issued the third edition of "Standards for a Blood Transfusion Service." Late in the year the council was discontinued, having performed the function for which it was intended.

Beginning in 1963, any bank that wishes to participate in the American Association of Blood Bank's clearinghouse program will have to be inspected. The scope of blood transfusion activity is shown by the fact that in 1961 patients in hospitals in the United States were given 5,500,000 pints of blood.

Dried plasma, which can be stored at room temperature for six months or longer, whereas whole blood must be refrigerated and then can be kept only three or four weeks, was extensively used during the Korean War. In 1952 the use of pooled plasma was abandoned because more than 20 per cent of the recipients suffered attacks of homologous serum jaundice. Extensive research followed with the hope of developing suitable synthetic substitutes. These were found to have limited stand-by value in emergencies. Finally as a result of many studies, the use of pooled liquid plasma in the preparation of which certain well-defined precautions are taken, has been approved.

At the 1960 annual meeting of the American Association of Blood Banks a naval hospital technologist reported that waste could be reduced by incorporating frozen stored red cells into regular transfusions. These can safely be kept for three or four years, compared with three or four weeks for the whole blood. By a new process developed after long experimentation, blood itself can be frozen. This has made it possible for patients who face operations to make deposits of their own blood in advance. Chelsea Naval Hospital at Boston started this practice. Properly frozen blood is supposed to last for years.

In 1961 the Red Cross and the American Association of Blood Banks instituted reciprocal interchange of blood and blood credits on a nation-wide basis, following which the Joint Blood Council published the first comprehensive study of blood banking and its problems.[12] Before this there had been exchange through clearinghouse systems locally. At the time of the reciprocity agreement the two organizations were servicing 5,500 of the nation's 7000 general hospitals and were procuring, processing, and delivering about 80 per cent of the blood used every year.

In a dispatch from Strasbourg, France, on September 17, 1961, the Associated Press reported that nine European nations had set up an international blood bank providing for the free exchange of supplies of blood and blood plasma among members, according to the Council of Europe.

The use of blood as a sort of tonic in medical treatment and as a routine in connection with surgery is decried by many medical authorities who, while agreeing that it is a priceless boon in emergencies, point to the risks from hemolysis of the red blood cells, from infectious hepatitis, from air embolus, from bacterial contamination, and from cardiac overload, which make it necessary to use discrimination. This is not a new concept. Back in 1938 in his July 18 column for the Chicago Tribune–New York News Syndicate, Dr. Irving S. Cutter wrote:

> Perhaps we have now gone to the other extreme and are giving transfusions for too many ailments. . . . Unless vital fluid has been lost there is no advantage in transfusion, as a solution of gum acacia is fully as useful. Sometimes the situation may be combated merely by giving a large volume of water or weak tea by mouth.

The main point to remember, though, is that in 1 of every 20 transfusions a life would have been lost without this procedure.

Along with 2,214 blood banks and 1,565 blood-using facilities, the Joint Blood Council's *Directory of Blood Transfusion Facilities and Services* published in

---

[12] *The Nation's Blood Transfusion Facilities and Services.* Joint Blood Council, 1961.

1961 lists of 323 bone banks, 88 eye banks, 70 artery banks, 26 skin banks, and 18 mothers' milk banks.

The Mount Sinai Blood Center, Chicago, has a mobile unit operated by a team of 14 doctors and nurses that can set up a temporary blood bank anywhere in the city. The unit, which looks like a miniature hospital, went into service in October, 1960. It can handle 15 donors every 15 minutes. The Bloodmobile can be operating in 35 minutes. As reported in the *Chicago Daily News,* July 12, 1961, it can be sent to the prospective donor to save his time, either where he works or in the neighborhood of his home.[13] The unit is available without charge to any group of 65 or more donors. The donor and any member of his family can receive a blood transfusion without charge in any hospital in the United States during the year following his donation of blood. An individual donor has a four-year time limit for receipt of a pint of blood.

MEDICINE IN THE AMERICAS

Historians report that America was the most healthful of all the continents up to the time that Columbus arrived. There was no tuberculosis, no syphilis. Among the diseases brought over were measles, scarlet fever, diphtheria, chicken-pox, smallpox, typhus, typhoid, malaria, yellow fever, Malta fever, leprosy, trichinosis, tuberculosis, and venereal diseases.

The arthritic Columbus brought 90 persons on three ships from Palos and nearby towns. He left 40 in Hispaniola, who were all massacred, including two physicians. There was a surgeon on each ship. On his second voyage he had 17 small vessels, 1,500 men. The chief medical officer was Dr. Diego Alvarez Chanca, of Seville. On landing they founded Isabella. Within the first week they suffered from an epidemic, with 300 or 400 sick, many of whom died. This was the first recorded epidemic in the western hemisphere with its population of 30,000,000, chiefly red men, 1,000,000 of whom were north of the Rio Grande River.

The doctors' diagnosis was intestinal disease from change of diet, occupation, and climate. It was probably what was known as "famine pestilence," a result of the long voyage and deficient and limited food. The natives immediately became sickly also. Native slavery began in 1501. Sometimes half of them died in transfer to Spain from the slave markets. In 1492 the population of Hispaniola was 300,000; by 1548 it was down to 500. The same tragedy occurred in all the Spanish possessions.

On the third voyage Columbus had malaria. Many of the 330 persons with him died, as was true also of the 1,502 persons on the fourth voyage.

Medicine in the New World as the explorers reported it is not without its milestones. When Hernando Cortez reached the city of Temixtitlan (Mexico) in 1520 he found to his astonishment that the natives were exceedingly well

[13] *Chicago Daily News,* July 12, 1961.

equipped to treat disease and injury. He reported to the King of Spain that there was a street set apart for the sale of herbs, where could be found every sort of root and medicinal herb, and that there were houses like apothecary shops where prepared medicines were sold, as well as liquids, ointments, and plasters. He learned the names of more than 3,000 plants used in therapeutics and sent back to Europe a vast collection of remedies.

After the battle of Otumba, the wounded Cortez was attended by Aztec medical men. He was so impressed by their skill that he wrote the King that the New World did not need physicians from Spain.

James J. Walsh in his *History of Nursing* states that the first medical book printed on the American continent was Dr. Francisco Bravo's *Opera Medici Nalia,* published in Mexico City in 1570, and that the first medical school in the Americas was founded at the University of Mexico about 1578.

North of Mexico there were only Indian medicine men practicing primitive medicine under wilderness conditions. Little of their knowledge was of value to the new colonists.

A few medical men came with the early settlers, among them Dr. Robert Gifford, who settled in Quebec in 1627 and was the first attending surgeon of the oldest hospital north of Mexico, Hotel Dieu de Quebec, founded in 1639 by the Duchess d'Aguillon.

There was no physician in the Saint Joseph Hospital established at Montreal in 1641 by Mlle. Mance. Treatment was given by her, the priests, and the servants.

The *Mayflower* on its initial voyage in 1620 had a ship's doctor on board whose services appear to have been scorned by the Pilgrims. He was Giles Heale, who did not remain with the settlers but returned to London where he established a profitable practice.

The Pilgrims preferred the medical services, if they can be so called, of a member of their own group, Deacon Samuel Fuller, alluded to in their records as a "chirurgeon and physition." An enemy of Deacon Fuller's declared he had been "bred a butcher." Willison,[14] in *Saints and Strangers,* comments that the critic was probably "just being malicious." Anyway the Deacon cut and bled, violently physicked the patients, and used mysterious portions. Yet the verdict of his fellows in general was that he was a "man godly, and forward to doe good." The frightful mortality at Plymouth speaks not to well, however, for his skill. Of his ministrations in a neighboring settlement the same critic asserted that he "treated other ailing Saints, some forty in all, who had no complaints to make, for all went promptly to heaven."

In 1633 Deacon Fuller died of an "infectious fevoure" and the record says that he was "much missed." Willison adds: "For decades Plymouth was left without a doctor or anyone with even a smattering of medical lore."

The settlers in Virginia suffered the same kinds of afflictions as the Pilgrims.

[14] George F. Willison: *Saints and Strangers.* New York, Reynal & Hitchcock, 1945, pp. 85, 283.

George Percy[15] told about it in his account of the first summer, 1605, in Jamestown:

> Our men were destroyed with cruell diseases as Swellings, Flixes, Burning Fevers, and by Warres, and some departed suddenly, but for the most part they died of meere famine. . . . our food was but a small can of Barlie sod in water to five men a day, our drinke cold water taken out of the River, which was at a flood verie Salt, at a low tide full of slime and filth, which was the destruction of many of our men . . . some departing out of the World, many times three or foure in a night, in the mornings their bodies trailed out of their Cabines like Dogges to be buried: in this sort did I see the mortalitie of divers of our people.

A Peruvian surgeon, Dr. Guillermo Gastenete, of Lima, recounted for surgeons attending the third Inter-American Session of the American College of Surgeons in Lima, January 11, 1955, a little of the history of surgery in his country. In the Spanish galleons, he said, the first doctors arrived, along with the gold and silks of the nobility. Surgery was primitive and undeveloped during colonial times, however, its practice being confined to the lower social strata.

> Surgeons formed a bizarre, undefined group with barbers, the "syringers" and the "rubbers." It was not until the nineteenth century that the glorious figure of Don Hippolito Unanue appeared in the ranks of Peruvian doctors. It was then that the Medical College of San Fernando, later incorporated with the university, and the Anatomical Amphitheater were founded, initiating thus the true renaissance of surgery as an art and science, and the social rehabilitation of the Peruvian surgeon.

Dr. Gastenete, who at the time was honorary professor of surgery at the University National Mayor de San Marcos, continued with some personal reminiscences:

> I have lived in the epoch of the great discoveries: anesthesia, asepsis, antisepsis, x-ray, blood transfusion, applied chemistry, and antibiotics. I remember my teachers—Dr. Lino Alarco, professor of clinical surgery, skilled and elegant operator, and Dr. Nestor Corpancho, disciple of Dr. Jules Pean in Paris, one of the pioneers in abdominal surgery. They were actors in an heroic time when the principles for control of bacterial contamination did not prevail, for the discoveries of Lister were too recent. I remember also the kind appearance of Dr. Constantino T. Carvallo who, after painstaking studies in the universities of the Old World, came to us to spread the modern principles of aseptic surgery and the most advanced methods of gynecologic surgery.

In the colonies that were to form the United States, medical care was mainly in the hands of doctors who had been trained by apprenticeship only. Only a few had the advantage of training in European medical schools. Few names appear until the Revolution. Noteworthy in that struggle were the surgeons general John Morgan (1735–1789) and William Shippen, Jr. (1736–1808), both of whom were graduates of the medical school at Edinburgh, Scotland. Morgan had served as a surgeon in the French wars, returning to his home in

[15] *The Founding of Jamestown.* New York: P. P. Simmons, 1907, p. 7.

Philadelphia in 1765. His influence on medical education will be described in Chapter 8. Shippen was also a Philadelphian. After his military service he gave his entire time to teaching.

Benjamin Rush (1745–1813), of Pennsylvania, graduate of Princeton and of Edinburgh, was one of the signers of the Declaration of Independence. From 1799 to 1813 he was Treasurer of the United States Mint. During the war he was surgeon general for the middle department under Shippen. As a physician his treatment was rigorous—excessive bloodletting, large doses of calomel and jalap, cold sickrooms, low diet, hydrotherapy for both the inner and the outer man. He exhibited great courage in the yellow fever epidemic in Philadelphia and, when he thought he had contracted the disease, submitted to his own ideas of therapy. He had an inquiring mind and contributed to the medical literature.

Another graduate of Edinburgh, who is considered by some to be the Father of American Surgery, was Philip Syng Physick (1768–1837), of Philadelphia. John Warren (1753–1815) and his son, John Collins Warren (1778–1856), of Boston, are prominent figures in the history of medical education and are considered in Chapter 8, as is also Nathan Smith (1762–1829), of Rehoboth, Massachusetts, who studied in the Scotch and English schools. Valentine Mott (1785–1865), of Long Island, pupil of Sir Astley Cooper in London, was a great pioneer in vascular surgery. Oliver Wendell Holmes (1809–1894), of Boston, would be better known for his literary work than for his medical career were it not for his discovery, preceding Semmelweis, of the contagiousness of puerperal fever and its spread mainly through the physician and his assistants because of lack of personal cleanliness, especially of the hands. He encountered the same opposition from the profession as did Semmelweis, who, as mentioned, became insane and died because of it.

Daniel Drake (1785–1852), known as the greatest physician of the West, is an example of the log-cabin tradition of self-made men who conquer all obstacles in their rise to an illustrious career. He had to struggle for his education and for every step forward that he made. He obtained the first medical diploma to be issued west of the Alleghenies. His teacher was William Goforth, pioneer of Jennerian vaccination in the West. After a few years in practice, Drake completed his medical education in 1815 at the University of Pennsylvania. He was a restless, dissatisfied, combative type who constantly changed his location, but he holds a prominent place in medical education and literature as well as in the investigation of disease and in medical practice.

Daniel Brainerd (1812–1866) was the pioneer surgeon of the Middle West. A graduate of Jefferson Medical College, he went to Chicago in 1835. He performed the second major surgical operation in the city's history in 1838, when he amputated at the hip joint the leg of a laborer on the Illinois and Michigan Canal who had suffered a fracture of the femur, had the leg dressed, and had then walked several miles into the city, bringing on severe inflammation which necessitated drastic measures. Dr. Brainerd founded and headed the first medical college in the region—Rush, chartered by him in 1837; organized the first general hospital—100 beds in Tippecanoe Hall in 1847; became the city's first health officer and for more than twenty years its leading surgeon. He was professor of surgery and president of Rush Medical College up to his death from cholera in the epidemic of 1866, which claimed more than a thousand victims in Chicago.

An ovarian cyst was for the first time successfully removed surgically by Ephraim McDowell (1771–1830) in 1809. The patient, 47 years of age at the time, lived to the age of 78. McDowell had been a pupil of John Bell's, of Edinburgh, in 1793–1794 and had learned about these cases. Jane Crawford, the patient, went for her operation to Dr. McDowell's home in the village of Danville, Kentucky. Hers was the first of 13 similar operations, from which 8 of the patients recovered. He performed lithotomies 22 times in succession without losing a case. He and James Marion Sims (1813–1883) are considered to be the founders of operative gynecology. Sims was a graduate of Jefferson Medical College, practiced first in Alabama, and moved to New York in 1853 and established the State Hospital for Women (1855).

As a side light on the now common operation for ovarian cyst, surgeons report that many women still postpone their first seeking of medical attention until the cysts become tremendous in size. This happens even in large medical centers. Physicians at a Brooklyn hospital reported the admission in 1961 of a 48-year-old patient who had a greatly distended abdomen but no pain or discomfort other than interference with ambulation. The patient's weight was 175 pounds before surgery, 135 pounds on discharge 13 days later.[16]

One of America's greatest contributions to the progress of surgery was the introduction of ether anesthesia. Dr. Crawford Williamson Long (1815–1878), of Georgia, used it to remove a small tumor from the back of the neck of a patient in March, 1842, and afterward used it several times on other patients. He did not publish his results, however, so his work had no effect on medical practice in general. The tale shifts, therefore, to New England. A dentist of Hartford, Connecticut, Horace Wells (1815–1848) was using nitrous oxide in dentistry and told his former partner, William Green Morton (1819–1868) about it. Morton, of Charlton, Massachusetts, had been studying medicine with a chemist, Dr. Charles T. Jackson, who was using chloric ether in filling a tooth (1844). Morton learned next from Jackson about the properties of sulfuric ether and used it himself in extracting a tooth. Thereupon he persuaded Dr. John Collins Warren, of Massachusetts General Hospital, to let him try it in a surgical procedure. The patient from whom a tumor of the neck was dissected returned to consciousness with the assurance that he had felt no pain. Other operations under anesthesia followed, and on November 18, 1846, a paper about the discovery by Dr. Henry J. Bigelow was published in the *Boston Medical and Surgical Journal,* which led to the adoption of ether anesthesia all over the world. Oliver Wendell Holmes proposed the terms "anesthesia" and "anesthetic."

[16] Melvyn Berlind, M.D., and Mamoon Hemedan, M.D.: Ovarian Cyst. *J. Internat. Coll. Surgeons,* December, 1961, pp. 756–57.

An incident in the middle of the nineteenth century throws light on medical practices of the period.

A penniless boy named Peter White fell into the hold of a boat while he was on his way to Detroit in the 1840's from the upper peninsula copper country. His arm was fractured in the fall. When he reached Detroit, the arm was carefully examined at the hospital and the verdict was immediate amputation.

Peter was on the operating table and the surgeon was ready with his instruments when Dr. Zina Pitcher, a member of the staff, came in. Dr. Pitcher looked at the arm and advised delay. There was consternation on the part of the surgeon and attendants, but the case was turned over to him for management. The report that has gone down in history is that "though Peter carried his arm in splints for four months it was saved."

When Dr. Pitcher died in 1872, the then prosperous Peter White created a fund to cover the cost of planting flowers every year "on the grave of the good doctor who rescued me from lifelong disability as a cripple."

The story of Peter White is an uncommon one in the annals of early surgery in the United States. Sawing off mangled, broken, and shot-torn arms and legs was what a surgeon did mostly in hazardous pioneer days. Ways of treating wounds and fractures so that amputation is seldom required are relatively new. In fact, one good outcome of the World Wars has been the advance in this field growing out of the vast experience in treating injuries which surgeons had in military service.

Dr. Pitcher was ahead of his times in many ways, according to Sheldon A. Wood, of Detroit, commenting on him in the *Medical History of Michigan*[17] from recollections of his father's acquaintance with the physician:

> [He] strenuously opposed a popular practice of his day—bleeding (phlebotomy—venesection)—and denied any virtue in the practice. . . . although antisepsis and the activity of the microbe were then unknown, he showed in his practice that he had anticipated the discovery, for he insisted upon scrupulous personal cleanliness. Although beards were then in fashion, he was always clean-shaven. My mother says he washed his hands many times a day. He believed in the efficacy of common salt as a cleanser—recommended its use in catarrhal affections and in bathing. . . . His military services in the forties, while in Mexico and New Orleans, brought him in contact with yellow fever. In suspecting that the mosquito had some connection with yellow fever, he was some sixty years in advance of modern practice.

When Dr. Pitcher became a citizen of Detroit in 1836, after 14 years of army service, he immediately took part in the political and educational, as well as medical, interests of the city and the state. He has been termed the "father of free education in Detroit at public expense." The Pitcher School was named in his honor. He headed a petition for the creation of the office of city historiographer in 1842, and the office was created. He established, with Dr. E.

---

[17] Comp. and ed. by a committee, C. B. Burr, chairman. Minneapolis and St. Paul, Bruce Publishing Co., 1930. Vol. I, pp. 196–98.

Andrews, the *Peninsular Journal of Medicine* in 1853 and was for years one of the editors. He was a member of the first Board of Regents of the University of Michigan. He was one of the incorporators of the Detroit Savings Fund— out of which developed the Detroit Savings Bank—in 1849. He even ran for governor, having been the nominee of the Henry Clay party in 1844. Nor did he lack hobbies. He was a student of the lore of the Indian tribes, and so significant were his contributions to American botany that several plants and a number of fossils have the specific name "Pitcheri."

As a prelude to his illustrious career in medicine and civil life, what preparation had Dr. Pitcher? When, soon after graduation from Middlebury, Vermont, College Medical School in 1822, he was appointed assistant surgeon in the Army, he accepted the appointment "feeling all the embarrassment incident to the assumption of such grave responsibility" as his commission devolved upon him "without having received one lesson in clinical instruction."

The great American doctors who *had* received such instruction were, however, beginning to appear, and medicine in the western hemisphere was beginning to show a distinct character. Marti-Ibanez[18] comments on this as follows:

> American medicine was born on American soil; it is not as in Europe a continuation of previous autochthonous cultures. American medicine, like American culture and art, is of recent origin, for it is but a few centuries old. It was only in the sixteenth century that the first book on medicine in the Western hemisphere was printed and that was in Mexico by Spaniards. The importation into America of seventeenth-century European medical culture never succeeded in creating a medical "past" so solid as to bear upon the present with the force it still exerts in Europe. The result is that here it is easier to rebel and become emancipated from previous generations and their doctrines. Medicine in the United States has been optimistic from its beginning, perhaps because of its youth. Even some techniques to which the United States owes its spectacular progress were conceived in Europe largely during the eighteenth and nineteenth centuries, when this country was barely being born as a nation. In this great nation where everything is young, there has come about in medicine, as in everything else, a repristination or rejuvenation of ancient races, particularly of the European stock. There, in my opinion, we have the roots of one of the secrets of America's greatness—and also of one of its greater historical problems.

The "greatest American surgeon of his time" and the "greatest of the German-American physicians," according to Garrison,[19] was Samuel David Gross (1805–1884), of Easton, Pennsylvania, who first taught surgery at Louisville and later at Jefferson Medical College, Philadelphia. The "leading surgeon of New England during his lifetime" was Henry Jacob Bigelow (1816–1890), of Boston, professor of surgery in the Harvard Medical School. He was the first to excise the hip joint in America. The "leading American neurologist of his time" was Silas Weir Mitchell (1829–1914), of Philadelphia—well known also as poet and

---

[18] Felix Marti-Ibanez: *Centaur, Essays on the History of Medical Ideas.* New York, MD Publications, p. 311.

[19] *Op. cit.*, p. 599.

novelist. A "brilliant and skillful operator" was William Williams Keen (1837–1932), of Philadelphia, professor of surgery at Jefferson Medical College.

Then we come to "the greatest physician the modern world has ever known," so described by Dr. Otho Ball.[20] Born in Upper Canada, the son of a missionary from England, William Osler (1849–1919) received his medical education from McGill University, Montreal, graduating in 1872. For two years thereafter he studied in the clinics of London, Berlin, and Vienna. He returned to McGill to teach from 1874 to 1884, when he was appointed professor of clinical medicine at the University of Pennsylvania. Five years later he became professor of medicine at Johns Hopkins University, where he realized his wish to set up a clinic like those in Europe. In 1905 he was called to Oxford as regius professor of medicine, where he remained until his death from pneumonia in 1919. He was created a baronet in 1911 by King George V. In the foremost rank as a teacher of medicine, pathologist, investigator, writer on medical subjects, and medical editor, he had also a warm and vivid personality that made him a beloved physician.

Celebrated as a great bacteriologist and pathologist was William Henry Welch (1850–1934), of Norfolk, Connecticut, who after professorships at Bellevue Hospital Medical College and Johns Hopkins University became director of the School of Hygiene at the latter. Hans Zinsser[21] refers to Welch as "preeminent—the most potent individual force" in "shaping the course of American medicine." In 1926 he was appointed to the new chair of medical history at Johns Hopkins. On his eightieth birthday celebrations were held around the world in his honor, with the central function in Washington, D.C., where 1,600 of his friends gathered on April 8, 1930.

Known as the creator of the school of conservative surgery, William Stewart Halsted (1852–1922), professor of surgery, Johns Hopkins University, devised a number of operations; pioneered in anesthesia by cocaine (as a result of his experiments he fought addiction, it is believed, all his life and suffered a great change in personality as a result); used the strictest aseptic technique; and was so skillful and careful a surgeon that his patients seldom went into shock however long their ordeal. He was a slow operator, one of the first to change surgery from a display of showmanship and speed to an atmosphere of solemnity and caution.

Welch, Osler, and Halsted were part of the famous "Great Four" of Johns Hopkins, the fourth member of which was Howard Kelly (1858–1929), professor of gynecology, recognized as a leader of his field in America.

Looming high in later surgery are George Crile, the Mayos, and Harvey Cushing. Dr. Crile (1864–1943) was professor of clinical surgery at Western Reserve University. He is noted internationally for his experimental research on surgical shock, blood pressure in surgery, hemorrhage, and transfusion,

[20] *Mod. Hosp.*, November, 1950.
[21] From his autobiography, *As I Remember Him*, *op. cit.*, p. 130.

which led to his phenomenal success in certain types of operations which were previously hazardous. His first successful blood transfusion was in 1906. He first combined general and local anesthesia for the blocking of shock, known as anoci-association, which greatly reduced mortality. Cushing (1869–1939) is recognized as being at the very top of the list of neurosurgeons, especially in surgery of the pituitary body and the head. He came originally from Cleveland and was professor of surgery at Johns Hopkins, Harvard, and finally Yale. He was an autocrat in the operating room, tense and exacting as might be expected in one whose patients were on the brink of death; at first nearly every patient with brain tumor died, but by 1915 he had reduced his mortality to 8 per cent, and was generally conceded to be the leading neurological surgeon of the world.

The story of the Mayos was given in the section on group medicine in Chapter 3, for it is in the province of organized group effort in medicine that they have earned their distinctive acclaim.

War's Contribution to Medical Advances

Many a milestone was laid as a result of discoveries made and procedures developed in wartime. Treatment of disease and injury on a large scale and association of physicians on and near the battlefronts have spurred progress. The contrast between military medicine and surgery of the past and present is in itself a striking manifestation of medical progress.

The wars of history caused untold suffering. The conditions under which the fighting men lived, in crowded barracks, without sanitation, and many times poorly fed and clothed, furnished the optimum media for the occurrence, propagation, and dissemination of diseases. Through all the descriptions of the wars—from Biblical times up to and during the Crusades and the numerous European, Asiatic, and African wars, not excluding the American Revolution and the Civil War—there runs a monotonous repetition of accounts of leprosy, smallpox, scurvy, typhoid, typhus, scabies, syphilis, meningitis, measles, influenza, plague, malaria, cholera, and the dysenteries.

These diseases were not all accurately described, but from the writings about them there is justification for so classifying them. Doubtless many other diseases existed which have since died out. Rags, filth, famine, and ignorance made the wars incalculably greater risks from disease than from weapons.

The practice of segregation, with its evidence that the contagious nature of leprosy was suspected, first became widespread during the Crusades, when hundreds of lazarettos were established. Ambulances were first introduced by Baron Larrey. Navies began to learn something about scurvy and its prevention. Larrey, Paré, and Hunter stand out above the medical men of their times because they were able to benefit from their war experiences.

In the war between the United States and Mexico in 1846–1847, one in every three soldiers was lost to the Army through disease, and seven men died from disease to one who was killed in battle or who died of wounds.

In 1862 the Army Medical Museum was established in the United States, which is one indication of a more scientific attitude, but of about a million men continuously under arms during the War between the States, about 200,000 died of disease compared with about 100,000 of wounds.

The investigations of injuries to nerves by gunshot by S. Weir Mitchell, George R. Morehouse, and William W. Keen were among the outstanding surgical contributions, which have since become classical, of the Civil War period. The museum at the Jefferson Medical College, Philadelphia, still contains much of the material on which their studies were based. The effects of projectiles on human tissues were accurately studied for the first time.

In general, the war found the country little better prepared to care for the sick and wounded than had been the case during the Revolution of 1776. Hospitals were hastily improvised in hotels, schools, churches, warehouses, factories, and jails. The management was poor in the extreme; some of them were so badly administered that they "defied comparison with any other hospitals in the civilized world," in the words of George Worthington Adams.[22] The situation was quickly remedied under the leadership of a new surgeon general, W. A. Hammond, appointed early in 1862. With the help of the sanitary commissioners a hospital system was created which, again quoting Adams, "became one of the wonders of the medical world." He declares that during the four years of the war, the general hospitals cared for 1,057,523 soldiers with a mortality of only 8 per cent, "the lowest ever recorded for military hospitals and lower than in many civil institutions, and they far outdistanced the hospitals of Europe, those of the Prussians in 1870–1871 seeming dirty, badly organized, and twenty years behind in comparison."[23]

Adams concludes that failure to realize that the "medical and sanitary record of the Civil War was on the whole a good one" is "partly due to the fact that the Civil War took place at the very end of the medical 'middle ages'—immediately before bacteriology and aseptic surgery made some of the war generation's triumphs seem piddling or irrelevant."

In any case, medical and hospital progress in general was tremendously stimulated by the obvious advantages of teamwork learned through the war experience and from the knowledge gained by physicians and nurses in working with a great many patients in large, comparatively well-organized institutions. Doctors in fact organized and controlled most of the military hospitals and for most of them it was their initial experience in hospital management.

The public in general also learned through the war experience the value of public health measures and of good medical and hospital care.

The war with Spain was for the United States an introduction to tropical

[22] *Doctors in Blue: The Medical History of the Union Army in the Civil War,* New York, Henry Schuman, 1952.
[23] How this came about is a long story, well told in Adams' (*ibid.*) Chapter 8, "The General Hospitals"; also Chapter 9, "Nurses, Staffs and Convalescents"; and Chapter 6, "Wartime Surgery"; Chapter 7, "Operations and Infections"; and Chapter 11, "Diseases and Treatments,"

medicine. While the toll from disease was terrific, the war led to occupation of Cuba, Puerto Rico, and the Philippines, followed by the work of the Walter Reed Commission on yellow fever which made possible Gorgas' elimination of this disease and of malaria from Cuba and Panama. Gorgas' work was paralleled by that of Oswaldo Cruz in Rio de Janeiro. Ashford's work on hookworm in Puerto Rico and that of Stiles in the southern states were almost equally important.

Occupation of the Philippines led to the establishment of medical organizations and institutions, the importance of which has never been sufficiently recognized. First under military regime, and then under civil administration, an unparalleled program of sanitation and health education was undertaken and regulations drawn up and enforced. Modern hospitals, a medical school, and a medical research bureau were established, and from them the medical profession of the United States became conscious of the problems of tropical medicine and learned how to control many diseases. The literature emanating from the Bureau of Science, from the Bureau of Health, and from the University of the Philippines constitutes an epic in the control of smallpox, cholera, bubonic plague, beriberi, leprosy, malaria, the dysenteries, and other intestinal diseases.

The knowledge gained from these experiences was invaluable when the two World Wars came and members of the military services were assigned to duty in countries with greatly varying climatic conditions. The wars also produced the danger of the spread of disease to the civilian populations, a danger which carried over into the postwar periods with the speeding up of air transportation. The practitioner and the pathologist must be constantly on the alert for imported diseases. The parasites of most importance from the standpoint of human disease are included within the classes of the protozoa and the helminths, so familiarity with protozoology and helminthology is an essential part of the armamentarium of the physician, not only in the tropics but everywhere now that the jet has made "one world" a reality.

In the first World War the efficacy of preventive medicine as exemplified by the application of the principles of immunization was proved on a large scale. Typhoid and paratyphoid fevers were practically eliminated as war hazards. The method of control of typhus was definitely learned, and surgery received an enormous impetus. The treatment of wounds of soft parts and of fractures attracted more serious attention than ever before. Thoracic surgery may be said to have been born during the World War, which led to developments that made surgery upon the organs within the thorax so successful that operations unheard of a few years earlier became routine daily procedures in the larger clinics. Neurosurgery, including the surgery of the central nervous system as well as of the peripheral nerves, also profited greatly from the experiences of the first World War.

In the interval between the first and second World Wars, American medicine and surgery made great strides. Impoverishment of European schools forced extraordinary educational activity in the Americas. Important advances of the period, all of which were important to medical service in the second war, were increased knowledge of nutrition, including the vitamins; chemotherapy, including the sulfonamide compounds; better knowledge of the chemistry of the body, including water balance; improved results in the healing of wounds, especially burns; plastic surgery; better preparation of the patient for surgery to minimize shock; more knowledge of the blood and its various constituents and substitutes which could be used in transfusion; and improved techniques in anesthesia, radiology, and physical therapy.

It is all very well for politicians to decry organized medicine as a "medical trust." Let an emergency arise and they are eager enough to call upon the "trust" for help—help that could not be promptly mustered if it were not for good organization. It was because it was so well organized that the medical profession could cooperate so quickly and effectively with the military branches of the government by furnishing qualified medical personnel when the second World War struck. The American Medical Association compiled a complete roster of the members of the profession and with the aid of local committees evaluated the abilities of the individual members so that they might be placed where their particular training and experience would make them of the greatest service. This information accumulated by the association was placed freely at the disposal of various government agencies. The association also made an invaluable contribution through its numerous publications in carrying information to the medical profession concerning the innumerable problems of medical-military organization and of military medicine.

The American Medical Association, the American Hospital Association, and the American College of Surgeons placed information concerning the physical facilities and the medical, nursing, and technical personnel of hospitals at the disposition of the appropriate government agencies, so that the hospitals might render the greatest aid to the armed forces and to civilian defense. Of course, this threw a great burden on the medical profession and the hospitals, as with depleted staffs they had to continue to give the best medical and surgical care possible to the general civilian population. The experience gained and the good results achieved on both the military and civilian fronts in the crisis give security for equally prompt response in future emergencies.

The National Research Council appointed many medical and surgical committees which conducted research along lines which were of especial value in the efficient medical care of soldiers and sailors. Several manuals were published by these committees for the guidance of those in military medical service.

The medical schools of the country, also with depleted staffs, not only carried on their recruitment and teaching activities to keep the supply of doctors from falling, but many of them, as did the larger hospitals, formed special units which were placed at the disposition of the Surgeons General of the Army and the Navy for service in the theaters of war.

The problems of sustaining life at great heights and great speeds in the air and at great depths of the ocean in the submarine taxed the ingenuity of the physiologist, the medical scientist, and the engineer during the second great war, preparing them, so it now seems, for the demands of the space age. The wars not only precipitated global medicine, and furthered ordinary aviation medicine, but readied the doctor to protect astronauts and eventually perhaps everybody for journeys to the moon.

SOME PERSONAL MILESTONES

Along the way in medicine there are a goodly number of individuals whose lives are in themselves milestones, a number of whom have already been mentioned. In capsule form biographies of a few more of them follow:

Hippocrates (460–370 B.C.)

How satisfying it is to begin major medical biographies with a figure as eminent in every way as the Great Physician—the Father of Medicine.

Hippocrates was born on the island of Cos and died at Larissa in his ninetieth year. His father, Heraclides, was an Asclepiad, or physician. At Cos there was a medical school and not far away at Cnidus on the Asiatic coast of the Aegean Sea was another, with still others at Crotona, in Italy, on the island of Rhodes, at Cyrene in Africa, and at Athens, but only Cos lives forever in history—because of Hippocrates.

In *Minute Men of Life,* authors Samuel W. Lambert, M.D., and George M. Goodwin, M.D., began the chapter, "The Medicine of Greece," with this statement:[24]

> The traditions of medicine, the art of medicine, the science of medicine, the close and intimate relationship existing between individual physicians of whatever nationality are symbolized in the name of Hippocrates. The ideals and the rules of ethics of the profession are concentrated in the short code which is included in the written words attributed to Hippocrates and known as the Hippocratic Oath.

Increasing evidence shows that Hippocrates traveled widely. Especially from Hindu medicine he learned a great deal, visiting India and studying its medical records. He stands for what in his time was a new theory of disease—that not supernatural, but natural factors, are responsible for physical disorders. This is an idea that had many setbacks through the centuries that followed, and many a person still blames fate or the Deity for his illnesses.

Hippocrates was, as far as our knowledge goes, the first true diagnostician. He observed, analyzed, and, most important, recorded the symptoms of disease. Through his records others were able to study his findings. He figured out the

[24] New York, Grosset and Dunlap, 1929, p. 14.

general course that certain illnesses might be expected to run. He believed, as did everyone for two thousand years longer, that all disease arose from a common disturbance in the body, but he saw that different combinations of symptoms indicated that illnesses would run different courses. Also, observation led him to respect Nature's healing power.

His contemporaries greatly respected Hippocrates. His reputation and his writings show him to have been scholarly, serene, sympathetic, kind, and highly motivated.

Galen (A.D. 131–201)

After Hippocrates and his followers, the road of medicine took a circuitous course and many got lost on it. Medicine had come out into the light of reason only to be pushed back into the darkness of superstition. A bright figure, trying to head mankind in saner directions, appears now and then. Such a one was Galen, the first experimenter in medicine. He proved by experiment that the heart pumps blood, that the lungs draw in air when we breathe, that paralysis follows injury of nerves in the spinal cord. But as has been stated in the section on anatomy, Galen drew many false conclusions because his dissections were limited to hogs and apes, he assuming that their anatomy and physiology were the same as man's.

Garrison[25] calls Galen the greatest Greek physician after Hippocrates, and the founder of experimental physiology. Like Hippocrates he was born and grew up in a city with a temple of Aesculapius and a medical school. The city was Pergamus, whose school attracted brilliant teachers and students. Galen, too, traveled and broadened his knowledge by studying in Sicily, Phoenicia, Crete, Cyprus, and Palestine. He returned to Pergamus where for several years he was in charge of treatment of the injured athletes and gladiators. Later he practiced in Rome, where he did many dissections on animals, and continued to study and to write, eventually going back to Pergamus.

The writings of Galen were based in large part on Hippocratic teaching, elaborated upon by discoveries in the six centuries since Hippocrates and by his own findings. He was almost as skeptical as Hippocrates had been of cures by prayers and sacrificial offerings. He wrote with such convincing positiveness that his theories were hardly questioned for almost fourteen centuries. As a result medicine stagnated.

His own supreme self-assurance was undoubtedly an influence in his long reign as king of medicine. In a spirit of overweening egotism he said: "Never as yet have I gone astray, whether in treatment or in prognosis, as have so many other physicians of great reputation. If anyone wishes to gain fame all that he needs is to accept what I have been able to establish."

It will always be argued whether or not his was a good or a bad influence,

[25] *Op. cit.,* p. 112.

because those dark centuries were stagnant in nearly every aspect of life, and perhaps without an authority such as Galen to follow medicine would have been in an even worse state than his many errors and fantastic theories created.

At least there were some scientific facts in the system which he represented to be final and infallible. Doubtless lazy and gullible successors are more to be blamed than he for the throttling his teachings gave to medical progress. He rescued medicine from the philosophical doctrines which had smothered it after the time of Hippocrates, and he restored at least some of the Hippocratic approach to treatment.

Rhazes (A.D. 850–923)

The celebrated Persian physician, Rhazes, is known as the Arab Hippocrates. His real name was Abu Bakr Mohammed ibn Zakariya, and he was born at Raj in Khorassan. He was a Galenist. He was the first to describe smallpox correctly, distinguishing it from measles. Some ferment which invades the body was its cause, he believed. He described many new drugs and is credited with having introduced the use of mercurial ointment.

Cooling baths, cold compresses, and fruit juices were among the treatments used by Rhazes on patients with smallpox and other fevers. He did not believe in excessive bleeding as a therapeutic measure, although he used it in moderation.

Rhazes was a skillful surgeon. For suturing he used the intestines of sheep and is believed to have been the first to do this. He used alcohol to clean wounds.

When the Caliph el Muktadir wanted to build a hospital at Baghdad, he called upon Rhazes to choose the site. Rhazes at the time was the physician at a hospital in Rei near Teheran, and his fame had spread. Upon the completion of the great Hospital Marastin at Baghdad he was appointed its chief physician and attracted to it many medical students. He practiced also at Madrid and Alexandria.

Rhazes is especially famed for his great encyclopedia of medicine. It consists of 226 books, transcriptions and additions to the works of Galen, Aetius, Pliny, and Paul of Aegina. Garrison[26] says that the ninth book of Rhazes, which was revised by Vesalius and annotated by Gatinaria, "was the source of therapeutic knowledge until long after the Renaissance."

Avicenna (A.D. 980–1037)

Avicenna, otherwise known as Ibn Sina, was born at Afshena in Bokhara. This Arabian physician and philosopher was physician to several of the Samanide and Dilemite sovereigns. Also for a time he was vizier in Hamadan. After its enlargement and restoration by the Vizier Adud Addaula, he was physician

[26] *Ibid.*, p. 129.

in chief to the celebrated hospital at Baghdad, which in his time had a staff of 25 doctors.

Avicenna was called the "prince of physicians" because of his great popularity and sociability. It is reported that his death in the prime of life was probably the result of his overconviviality.

Apparently his gay life did not interfere with his work. He is said to have written more than a hundred treatises on different subjects. Most of these have been lost. He produced a gigantic canon of medical miscellany which was extremely popular in the Middle Ages. Like some other well-intentioned works, it has been judged to have had a bad effect because it discouraged firsthand investigation.

Another criticism of the canon is that it retarded the progress of surgery by portraying it as an inferior and separate branch of medicine.

Avicenna was a man of many interests. Geology was one of them. He produced a book on the formation of mountains. In consequence he is considered to be the Father of Geology. He wrote on literary subjects, in poetry as well as in prose, and many of his writings are philosophical in nature. At different times he held responsible political positions.

Guy de Chauliac (1300–1368)

The greatest surgeon of the Middle Ages, Guy de Chauliac, was born at Auvergne in France. With the help of friends he succeeded in becoming an ordained priest and in getting a medical education at Toulouse, Montpellier, and Paris. He also studied anatomy at Bologna.

By the force of his personality, his learning, and the success of his work, Guy restored surgery to the place in which it belonged in medical science. Decrees of the church against bloodletting had forced the withdrawal from surgery of the priest-physician, who represented about the only educated class of the medieval period. It was in this way that surgery came to be degraded to barber status. From the church's prohibition as concerned the priest grew a feeling that it was beneath any physician to operate.

Galen also, and Avicenna even more so, had something to do with creating this distinction between the practice of medicine and of surgery. Guy was a Galenist, but not a blind follower, advocating study of anatomy, direct observation, and experimentation.

For thirty years Guy served as personal physician and chaplain to three popes while the papal seat was located at Avignon. He personally performed in his practice at Lyons all of the operations which he described in his classic works on surgery. He was far ahead of his time except in one respect—he did not believe that a surgical wound could heal by first intention, and it has been said that this great error held surgery back for six hundred years. This physician, like Galen, was so greatly admired that his word was law for many generations after his death.

Paracelsus (1493–1541)

Not until the sixteenth century does there appear on a milestone the name of a doctor who dared to break completely from Galen and traditional ideas. This was Paracelsus, known as a rebel. His real name was Aureolus Theophrastus Bombastus von Hohenheim, and he was a native of Einsiedeln near Zurich in Switzerland. Garrison[27] says, "He was one of the few writers who ever advanced medicine by quarreling about it."

Paracelsus publicly burned the works of Galen and Avicenna in a bonfire. Some of his ideas were as unscientific and ridiculous as Galen's, but at least he arrived at them through his own powers of reasoning. He believed in weapon ointment for instance—applying the salve to the weapon to heal the wound—which, of course, does nobody any good but no harm either. His belief was not as foolish as it sounds because he had observed that wounds healed better when ointment was *not* applied to them. He did not know that the filthy, germ-laden ingredients in the ointment often aggravated the infection. He merely stumbled upon truth and evolved to account for it a fanciful theory of magnetism from the weapon.

Although he was the son of a learned physician and was well educated at Ferrara, besides having a knack of picking up knowledge from everyone he met, Paracelsus was a rough, uncouth character. He put his toughness to good use, however, in fighting for reforms. He is regarded as the first modern doctor —observant, practical, self-reliant, searching for truth, and generous to the poor.

Vesalius (1514–1564)

An illustrious name is that of Andreas Vesalius, born in Brussels in 1514 when Paracelsus was 21. Vesalius has been mentioned in the section on anatomy. He early determined to revive that science so that an understanding of the human body equal to that of the ancients could be obtained. Because of religious prejudices of the time, which continued long afterward, he had to obtain skeletons by stealth, but before long he had discovered enough to learn that Galen had never dissected human beings and that he already knew more than that particular ancient. But authorities said that the anatomy of men must have changed if it was different from that described by Galen.

Vesalius went to the University of Paris to study medicine, probably because of the reputation of the famous teacher Jacobus Sylvius, who had the unusual method in those days of occasionally dissecting a body to teach anatomy. However, to his dismay, Vesalius discovered that Sylvius taught Galen, not medicine. Hatred grew between the two in the conflict between tradition and an inquiring mind. Vesalius left to study first at Louvain and later in Venice, getting his degree in 1537 and a teaching appointment at the University of Padua.

[27] *Ibid.*, p. 204.

Besides teaching, he held public anatomies. Pupils flocked to him, which Sylvius resented.

The disclosure of the Galenic errors in 1541 and his *De Fabrica Humani Corporis,* published in 1543, brought violent opposition led by Sylvius. Although posterity, in the words of Garrison,[28] terms Vesalius "the most commanding figure in European medicine after Galen and before Harvey," who "by virtue of his strong and engaging personality made dissecting not only viable, but respectable," his personal story is an unhappy one. The persecution which followed his bold break with the past so embittered him that he left Padua to become court physician to Emperor Charles V at Madrid, giving up anatomy and burning his manuscripts for a book on medicine and pathology. In 1564 he was invited back to Padua to resume his old chair, but on his way to accept the invitation, while returning from a pilgrimage to Jerusalem, he became ill and died alone in the island of Zante.

Ambroise Paré (1510–1590)

Like Vesalius, at war with ignorance and superstition, was the French surgeon Ambroise Paré. He was born of parents who were poor in what is now part of the city of Laval in the province of Maine. He was apprenticed to a barber-surgeon, then studied for three years at the Hotel Dieu where he gained the broad and heart-rending experience supplied by the great old city hospital. In 1537 he went to war as the personal surgeon of a nobleman. He was free to help in caring for the wounded, without being actually in the army. He gained in experience and grew in compassion.

It was during this period that he secured his fame by discarding the Hippocratic doctrine that "diseases not curable by iron are curable by fire," which governed the treatment of gunshot wounds because they were considered to be poisoned burns. Consequently the first dressing was of boiling oil. Quite by accident Paré discovered that this barbarous treatment was wrong. He ran out of oil one night and found that the wounds not treated with oil healed faster than those on which it had been used. He immediately stopped the practice, and would have gone down in history as the pioneer of aseptic management of wounds had he not let tradition have a little sway by continuing to apply "fat of puppy-dogs."

After four or five years Paré left the army, returned to Paris, and took and passed examinations for a barber-surgery license. He went into practice and in 1545 produced his book on the treatment of gunshot wounds—in French because he had never learned Latin—which was everywhere acclaimed and adopted as standard. In 1549 he published the first handbook of anatomy in the French language. War duty claimed him again in 1552, and during this cam-

[28] *Ibid.,* p. 217.

paign he revived the Galenic use of the ligature and applied it to the stoppage of bleeding after amputation. This in itself was a milestone in medicine. It replaced the standard practice of stopping bleeding by burning the stump with hot irons or by applying boiling oil. Sometimes this had to be done more than once if the wound opened up.

When the new treatment was announced, the usual opposition to something different occurred, and all his life Paré had to defend the method.

Through his long years of service as an army surgeon and through his bravery and skill demonstrated in the wars, along with a popularity among all ranks of the military gained from his gentleness and spirit of mercy, Paré rose to such eminence that he became known as the best surgeon of his time and the greatest of army surgeons.

Thomas Sydenham (1624–1689)

A physician who more than any other is likened to Hippocrates in his methods of diagnosis and his attitude toward his patients is Thomas Sydenham. He was an observer and a practitioner, not a theorist or an experimenter. Educated at Oxford and Montpellier, he was indifferent to his contemporaries and predecessors in medicine except for Hippocrates, after whom he patterned himself. His pathology was the Hippocratic idea of the humors of the body. His treatment was based on what he saw at the bedside, coupled with what he had learned through practical experience.

Sydenham thought that cosmic or atmospheric influences were the cause of contagious diseases. He studied the geography and meteorology of epidemic diseases, noted their seasonal variations, and was impressed by their fairly regular cycles of recurrence. His deep interest in the subject and his descriptions of malarial fevers, scarlatina, measles, and dysentery earned him a place as one of the main founders of epidemiology. His most celebrated single production is his treatise on gout, a disease from which he himself suffered, as well as from stone. It is conjectured that his especially warm sympathy for patients was partly a result of his being a fellow sufferer.

The healing powers of nature were believed in by Sydenham, as shown by his insistence upon fresh air in the sickroom, an innovation in those times. He prescribed vegetable simples instead of the current obnoxious drugs. He was a bloodletter, but in moderation. He advised exercise. He saw that the body fought disease and that the symptoms were signs of the battle.

No remarkable scientific contributions can be credited to this Puritan physician of old England. He lives on among the great of all the ages by being an image of the ideal physician, an image he created by caring for his patients as one, as he put it, who was "answerable to God" for them.

William Hunter (1718–1783)
John Hunter (1728–1793)

The Hunter brothers have been mentioned in the preceding chapter as ardent anatomists. It is necessary also to include them among the great physicians. G. R. Mather in his book *Two Great Scotsmen,* published in Glasgow in 1893, said of John Hunter: "His career affords an illustrative example of great intellectual prowess triumphing over early defective training, and marching onward step by step, despite vast obstacles, to the highest pinnacle of human greatness."

Surgery at the time John Hunter entered it was not a prestige profession. He was in the forefront of those who raised it to its new rank, as was also his brother William. As evidence of William Hunter's vision, Dr. Otho Ball[29] cited the following statement by him:

> The more we know of our fabric, the more reason we have to believe that if our senses were more acute and our judgment more enlarged, we should be able to trace many springs of life which are now hidden from us; by the same sagacity we should discover the true causes and nature of diseases, and thereby be enabled to restore the health of many who are now, from our more confined knowledge, said to labor under incurable disorders. By such an intimate acquaintance with the economy of our bodies, we should discover even the seeds of disease, and destroy them before they had taken root in the constitution.

After completing his medical training at Glasgow and studying with William Smellie at London, William gave private lectures on dissecting and on operative surgery. His reputation grew until he was finally recognized as the leader in obstetrics in London.

John Hunter studied surgery under William Cheselden and Percival Pott, of London, and afterward combined his teaching and research with a large surgical practice. His renown as a surgeon stems from his scientific attitude, his insistence that surgery be grounded on physiology and pathology rather than being just a technical method of treatment. He devised a great many new surgical procedures. Garrison[30] says that "thousands of limbs and lives" have been saved by his "establishment of the principle that aneurysms due to arterial disease should be tied high up in the healthy tissues by a single ligature. . . . The novel feature was not the single ligature . . . but the sound pathologic reasoning upon which its use was based." He was "one of the three greatest surgeons of all times," Garrison declares, naming the others as Paré and Lister.

Edward Jenner (1749–1823)

The practice of vaccination was introduced long before the bacteriological theory of disease was formulated. The scientific basis for it was laid by Edward Jenner, the English country physician who as a medical apprentice pondered

[29] *Mod. Hosp.,* October, 1952.
[30] *Op. cit.,* p. 347.

over the belief of the Gloucestershire countryfolk that no one who had had the mild disease cowpox could get smallpox. His teachers scoffed at his theory, all except John Hunter, at whose house he lived while studying in London. Hunter urged, "But why think, why not try the experiment?" Jenner, however, was cautious. He kept thinking and observing. Not until 28 years after a patient who was a dairy maid had first given him the idea in 1768 did he vaccinate James Phipps with matter taken from a milkmaid who had cowpox. After he had accumulated 23 cases of immunization, he published his findings in 1798.

Jenner was rebuffed and rebuked by a number of prominent physicians and by the Royal Society. He was told that his theory was "incredible." Firm in his conviction that he had made a lifesaving discovery, he became a campaigner, and others in the Old World and the New joined him.

Smallpox was a scourge from the earliest times. It was distinguished from measles by the Arabian physicians. One in every five or six persons who contracted it died. Physicians such as Sydenham believed it to be a natural process through which everyone must pass. Inoculation against it was practiced sporadically from ancient times on through the centuries. Matter from the pustule of a mild case was injected into the skin of the patient to be protected. A famous instance occurred in 1718 when one of the children of Lady Mary Wortley Montagu was inoculated successfully in Turkey, and another later in England. Usually the person inoculated had a mild attack of the disease which gave him immunity thereafter, but not infrequently the attack was fatal, and in any case the disease could be spread by even the light cases. Persons vaccinated by Jenner's method did not infect others because their reaction was limited to the site of the vaccination.

Jealousy, superstition, quackery, and difficulty in obtaining the cowpox lymph delayed widespread employment of vaccination in England, whereas it was quickly adopted in other countries, being made compulsory in Denmark, Sweden, and parts of Prussia. Denmark released figures showing that 15,000 persons died from smallpox in 1779, compared with 6,000 in 1801 and only 37 in 1823, the year of Jenner's death.

Dominique-Jean Larrey (1766–1842)

Wars have precipitated many a medical advance through sheer necessity for improvisation in connection with mass injuries under stress of emergency. Military hospitals have been the first to show the benefits of these advances, although usually they have spread rapidly to civilian practice.

Known as the greatest military surgeon after Paré, Dominique-Jean Larrey taught as well as practiced military surgery and was a great hospital reformer. He established hospitals, administered them, worked in them. As surgeon-in-chief of Napoleon's grand army of 400,000 men which was to drive the Russians out of Europe but which was instead almost obliterated in the effort, he won adoration for being always courageous, humane, and good-natured. Napoleon willed 100,000 francs to him, characterized him as "the most virtuous man I have ever known," made him a baron, and said of him in 1816: "He is truly a worthy man, for to science he unites all the virtues of an effective philanthropist. All the wounded are his family. The chief object of his consideration has been to exert himself in his hospital, in which he has been so successful as to entitle him to both my esteem and my gratitude."

Larrey devised what were known as "flying ambulances" to get the wounded to the hospital in the shortest possible time. After one battle he performed 200 amputations in 24 hours. Following the war he was professor of the Ecole de Médicin Militaire at Val-de Grace.

As is the fate of all reformers, Larrey made enemies in his work to improve hospitals. He made six o'clock rounds each morning, gave clinical lectures, and continued his writing, weakened though he was by his wartime experiences. Between 1812 and 1817 he published his four-volume *Memoires de Medicine Militaire*. In his seventy-fifth year he died shortly after inspecting the military hospitals at Algiers.

Guillaume Dupuytren (1777–1835)

Seldom in medicine is a character of the type of Guillaume Dupuytren encountered, whose personal qualities should have consigned him to oblivion but who despite them must be recognized for his brilliant accomplishments. A contemporary of Larrey's, he seems unworthy to be mentioned with him. Baron Percy called him "the first of surgeons and the least of men." Lisfranc branded him "the brigand of the Hotel Dieu," of which he was chief surgeon. Unscrupulous, mean, vindictive, overbearing, scheming, he was universally hated. Yet he was a brilliant teacher, a shrewd diagnostician, and a surgeon unrivaled in his day. He died a success financially and professionally, a millionaire, a baron of the empire, and possessed of the largest practice in France in addition to his hospital work.

Dupuytren's failure as a person is attributed to the grinding poverty in which he was reared and possibly some embittering experiences in his youth. He had to fight his way up, and he did it without regard for those who stood in his way. He acquired a good scientific background and excelled as an experimental physiologist and pathologist. He devised a number of new surgical procedures, was the first to excise the lower jaw, and was especially expert in vascular surgery. His writings on surgical pathology entitle him to fame.

In 1803 Dupuytren founded the Anatomical Society of Paris and endowed the Dupuytren Museum at Paris, which had been founded by Orfila.

Dupuytren seems to negate Nothnagel's statement: "All knowledge attains its ethical value and its human significance only by the humane sense in which it is employed. Only a good man can be a great physician." Doubtless, however, had he been a better man, Dupuytren with his superior ability would have been in the very top rank of physicians—which he is not.

Thomas Wakley (1795–1862)

It should be a source of pride to the medical profession that one of its members was a leading figure in the great humanitarian movement that was the glory of England in the early half of the nineteenth century. Thomas Wakley began his career as a medical and hospital reformer but soon broadened his efforts by including other social welfare movements. Commenting on the role of the physician as a reformer, E. P. Scarlett[31] wrote:

> Physicians are seldom iconoclasts and for the most part they have been content to allow society to force the changes in medicine. Here was a man who brought the critical judgment of his time to bear on his profession and with something of the superb faith and fire of the greatest reformers of his race. Such men have been the salvation of the world in the past and are its hope in the future. With the prophets they may agree that "the heart is deceitful above all things and desperately wicked," but at the same time the vision of a new heaven and a new earth never fails them. In every age they have been wrong-headed in many things but with the shocks and explosions of their fireworks how magnificently do they light up the darkness of their generation! And always they fight consistently for social justice against narrow class privilege and personal selfishness. They constantly testify to the dignity of man. Thomas Wakley is an humble member in such ranks.

Dr. Scarlett declared that Wakley "has done as much as any other to bring into being high standards of medical education and practice and to increase the stability and dignity of medicine as a career" and deplored the fact that "he has been unaccountably slighted by history and—more surprisingly—by medical history."

Wakley's attacks on the administration of the London hospitals led to widespread and revolutionary reforms. His success may be attributed in part to the fact that reform was in the air and the public was easily aroused, but in his particular battle only the boldest and most determined of crusaders could have won. His preparation for a medical career, as told by Dr. Scarlett, gives insight into medical education in his day and especially the part which hospitals played in it:

> At fifteen he was apprenticed to a Taunton apothecary, then transferred as apprentice to his brother-in-law, Mr. Phelps, surgeon of Beaminster, and later as pupil to Mr. Coulson at Henley-on-Thames.
>
> In 1815 he went to London and entered as student the united schools of St. Thomas's and Guy's, known as the Borough Hospitals. He gained the most thorough part of his medical training at the private school of anatomy in Webb Street (the Grainger School), was a pupil in the joint anatomy classes of Henry Kline and Sir Astley Cooper at Thomas's, attended Sir Astley Cooper's lectures on the practice of surgery at Guy's where he did surgical dressings and ward work. . . .
>
> A very loose system of medical instruction, examination and licensing prevailed at the time. The requirements for the degree were five years' study

[31] *Historical Bulletin,* of the Calgary, Alberta, Associate Clinic, February, 1944. Dr. Scarlett's article is the basis for this account of Dr. Wakley's activities.

(including apprenticeship) which included two courses of anatomy lectures, two courses of dissecting and one year's practice in the wards of the city hospitals. Wakley took the course in his stride and in 1817, now twenty-two years of age, he passed his examination for membership in the Royal College of Surgeons.

When Wakley began to look around in London for an opportunity to practice medicine, he realized that there would be a hard struggle for one who did not belong to the "privileged classes." All hospital appointments were made from the Fellows of the Royal College of Physicians, to join which it was necessary to have a degree from Oxford or Cambridge. Also, the fellowship fees were high, and the applicant had to be a member of the Church of England. Personal influence carried great weight. As for appointments in surgery, these went to friends and relations of an influential group of Fellows of the Royal College of Surgeons. He also discovered that the men who received these appointments took the salaries and fees but farmed out the work to assistants. Ordinary licentiates of the Royal College of Physicians and members of the Royal College of Surgeons like himself had poor prospects. Bitter resentment followed his analysis of the situation.

With some financial assistance Wakley purchased a medical practice in 1819 and did quite well for six months. An unfortunate attack based on mistaken identity, an account of which is too long to give here, forced him to set up practice in another district where he was not too happy but hung on until 1823. He then became acquainted with the great reformer and political writer William Cobbett, through whom he met other social crusaders. Inspired by them he envisioned correction of the unfair methods of making hospital appointments, and he chose a most practical way of launching his campaign. He started a weekly newspaper to disseminate medical information and to bring to light the evils in medical and hospital practice. The journal which he founded was the now well-known *Lancet*, the first issue of which appeared on October 5, 1823. In this first number he openly stated his purposes to be to "declare war on the vested medical interests; to expose the family intrigues influencing appointments in metropolitan hospitals and medical corporations; to improve medical education; to disseminate medical information; to defend the rights and good of the general body of practitioners."

Ten libel actions were fought by Wakley in the first ten years of publication. Against 8,000 pounds claimed for damages, the courts awarded 155 pounds, but the costs were entirely met by public subscription.

Among the articles published in *Lancet* was a series of hospital reports of major operations in London hospitals. Comments on hospital routine were included. Indignation followed. Wakley was expelled from St. Thomas's Hospital. One surgeon sued him for 2,000 pounds but was awarded only 50 pounds. Asserting that hospitals as public institutions should have publicity, Wakley published reports on hospital cases, including some which involved malpractice. Other suits followed, but only small amounts were awarded, and at one time sympathizers held a public meeting at which damages and costs in full were paid through subscriptions. Dr. Scarlett[32] comments: "All of this time and for years to come Wakley was carrying on a pitched battle with the editors of the other three London medical journals, winning and losing several lawsuits."

Next Wakley took out after the Royal College of Surgeons, reported by Dr. Scarlett as follows:

> Since 1824 medical students were obliged to attend the lectures of the hospital surgeons. These same lecturers were heads of the College, charged large fees to the lowly students and were the self-elected body of examiners. This as Wakely saw it was a blow at the private schools. He assailed too the Constitution of the College which had been organized on an oligarchic basis. He now began an agitation to have the surgeons petition Parliament for a new constitution in which any official with the power to make by-laws should be appointed by a vote of all members. In this he had the support of the King's surgeon, James Wardrop, and tremendous support from the country surgeons.

After the usual storms of protest, with Wakley continuing his campaign, reforms in the college followed.

Recognizing that parliamentary action was needed to bring about medical and hospital reform, Wakley entered the political arena and was elected in 1835 for Finsbury, a great London constituency. His efforts there on behalf of justice won him more prestige. He supported the Poor Law amendments and other social welfare measures. The Medical Witness Bill, under which doctors were to be remunerated for court duties and for postmortem and inquest work, was passed through his influence. His chief parliamentary accomplishment was a "Bill for the Registration of Qualified Medical Practitioners and for amending the Law relating to the Practice of Medicine in Great Britain and Ireland." The Bill of 1858, now the legal basis for English medical practice, was the outcome of Wakley's bill.

Wakley's final contribution to improvement of medical care through exposure of evils was his service as coroner for West Middlesex, to which he was elected in 1839. He had preached in *Lancet* for years against the appointment of lay persons to the office of coroner, which made inquests a farce. Now came his opportunity for demonstration of the advantages of a medically trained coroner. Against the usual opposition, he increased the number of inquests; investigated all deaths in public institutions, asylums, prisons, and poorhouses; instructed the police about cases which must be referred to the coroner; insisted upon being notified of all women dying in labor or a few hours afterward; raised the tone of proceedings at inquests; and got himself involved in lawsuits because, as he said, he was determined to protect the public against incompetent medical practice, ignorant midwives, and enterprising quacks. A parliamentary investigation was forced by his enemies, but the report of the investigating committee upheld him. Charles Dickens, after serving in 1841 as member of a

[32] *Ibid.*

jury at an inquest over which Wakley presided, praised his management of the case and said that "as coroner he had shown how an official should behave to the poor."

The invaluable help of *Lancet* as a mouthpiece was a powerful factor in Wakley's success. Through this medium he launched many reforms. One example was an analysis of foods in 1851 which led to a parliamentary investigation and, in 1860, passage of the Adulteration Act. Many a charlatan was exposed and dethroned through the attacks in his columns.

Wakley's career and accomplishments merit close study because of the vision which he showed in relating medical and hospital reforms to the entire social background. He showed conclusively that major improvements in medical care administration can best be achieved by alignment with other forces working for social progress.

Rudolf Virchow (1821–1902)

Physicians and other hospital people do not always realize how the effectiveness of their work could be increased by their own participation in broad social, political, and economic activities. This is because their chief concern is of such a personal, individual nature. Humanity in the mass is a foreign concept. There have been physicians, however, who saw their whole duty as extending beyond even the health field. One of them, one of the greatest, was Rudolf Virchow.

Virchow was born in Schivelbein, Pomerania. In 1839, his eighteenth year, he entered the Friedrich Wilhelm Institute, founded for the education of medical officers for the Prussian Army. He graduated in 1843 and became assistant to the prosector to the pathological department at the Charité Hospital. In 1846 he was appointed prosector. His travels on government and other scientific missions which very early in his life broadened his knowledge and interests make fascinating reading in his accounts of his experiences. Particularly did they arouse his passion to help in whatever way he could to improve public welfare.

In his twenty-sixth year he said in a letter about the famine and epidemic in Silesia: "This distress is such a disgrace to the government that no manner of speech can change it in the least. Nothing can mitigate the scandal which is consummated by the death of thousands." The government sent him to help control the epidemic and care for the sick. He used as a propaganda piece a journal on pathological physiology which he had just started, attacking the government for centuries of neglect and corruption which were the foundation for the poverty and ignorance of the people. To strike at the root of the conditions which horrified him he started another journal, a weekly paper called "Medical Reform." It lasted only a year but gave him a mouthpiece. A typical extract follows:

> Physicians are the natural advocates of the poor and to a notable degree the social question falls within their jurisdiction. . . . The democratic state wills the

well-being of all the citizens, for it recognizes the equal rights of all. Meanwhile, in general, equal rights lead to self control. So the State has the right to hope that every man will obtain and establish within the limits of the law established by the people themselves a condition of well-being through his own work. However, the conditions of well-being are health and education, and the problem of the State is to the greatest possible extent to provide the means for the attainment and increase of health and education through the establishment of public health agencies and public education. . . . It is impossible to guarantee life or health— against the power of death there is no "medicamentum in hortis"—but it is possible to take such care that everyone may obtain the means without which life cannot be sustained, and that the possibility of existence shall not be actively withdrawn from any or passively withheld. . . .

In another issue he wrote:

Let gentlemen in winter remind themselves when they sit by the warm fire and distribute Christmas apples to their children that the sailors who brought the coal and the apples are dead of cholera. Yes, it is very sad that thousands must die in misery while things go well with some hundreds. . . . For the law, to each according to his need, appears nowhere so clear and pertinent as in the case of the public health. . . . If to anyone the necessary care cannot be given in his home he must be received into a public institution. Accordingly, to every patient who has such need, hospital care must be provided free, whether or not he has money, whether he is Jew or Gentile.

He continues with a blast at hospitals:

Especially in the system of providing for the poor, as well as in the management of hospitals, has it been the custom of one to shift his duties to another, and the bureau reports of the hospital have, unfortunately, deserved the evil reputation which they possess, because not Christian mercy, not social brotherliness, not natural right, but only a stiff formalism was in control . . .

While these statements were being written Virchow was one of the leaders of the revolutionaries in the uprising of 1848, explaining his position in a letter to his parents:

This Revolution is not simply political, but is essentially social. All that we are now doing in politics is only the mold in which social reform can be brought about, through which the conditions of society can be fundamentally changed. . . . I have the advantage that I am no half man, but one who is whole. My medical confession of faith merges into my political and social. . . .

The monarchy was restored, however, and Virchow was in high disfavor. In one letter he said: "The present director of medical affairs has a lively personal opposition to me." After a seven-year sort of exile as professor of pathological anatomy at the University of Würzburg, he returned to Berlin in 1856 to direct the department of pathology in the university, and the new Pathological Institute. He resumed his leadership in welfare activities with his election in 1859 to the Board of Aldermen in Berlin, serving continuously for 34 years. In an editorial notice at the time of his death in 1902 the *British Medical Journal* stated:

It is not too much to say that modern Berlin is a splendid monument of his zeal in the service of humanity. For three and forty years he was the consistent advocate of sanitary reform in that city; he was a member of the Municipal Council of which he was by far the most conspicuous figure. Water supply, disposal of sewage, hospitals and asylums all were remodeled at his instigation and under his watchful eye, and an unhealthy metropolis, standing upon an open sewer, has, thanks to his consistent energy, become one of the most salubrious cities in the world. The transformation of poor schools into parish schools, the municipal inspection of meat, the public disinfecting establishments, the municipal hospitals, asylums and sanatoria; last, not least, the drainage system, are due to Virchow's initiative and active cooperation.

Further evidence of this great doctor's public-spiritedness and courage was his long membership in the Parliament as one of a group opposed to Bismarck. So angry was Bismarck in 1865 over defeat of a government motion to create a German navy that he challenged Virchow to a duel. Virchow declined, saying his "life was too valuable to mankind to be put to the chance of a duel with a politician." He proved that this answer did not show lack of courage when a few years later he promptly went to the front with the medical corps at the breaking out of the Franco-Prussian war.

All of this effort on behalf of the public welfare was far from being a deterrent to Virchow's monumental work in medical and allied sciences. Out of the great mass of his scientific contributions, the particular achievement which places him high among the immortals in his exposition of the cell theory. Dr. James G. Carr[33] commented:

> The cell as an important factor in the processes of life had been recognized by Schwann and Muller. It remained for Virchow to demonstrate the cell as the basis of life—the ultimate vital structure of the human organism. Whatever else a physician may know or not know about Virchow, one is almost sure to find that the name of Virchow is associated with "Cellular Pathology." The cellular structure of living organisms had already been demonstrated; Virchow's particular contributions were to prove that one cell is derived only from another cell and not from any other substance, and further to present convincing proof that the state of the cell (or cells) conditions the health or disease of the body. . . .

Dr. Carr quotes Virchow as follows:

> No matter how we twist and turn, we finally come back to the cell. . . . The pathological essence is the diseased cell, and disease has no other unity than life, of which it is only an especial manifestation, particularly of the individual living cell. The life of the diseased cell and of the healthy are not differentiated thereby. . . . But if pathology is only physiology with alterations, the diseased life nothing except the healthy inhibited by various external and internal effects, so must pathology also be attributed to the cell. . . .

Archaeologist, anthropologist, brilliant teacher and research worker, voluminous writer on a broad range of subjects, the consensus on Virchow's contributions to civilization is epitomized in one word, "fabulous."

[33] *Bull. Northwestern Univ. Med. School,* January 31, 1938.

Joseph Lister (1827–1912)

It was an English surgeon who transformed the hospital operating room from an all-too-frequent setting for death to a place where fatalities seldom follow the surgical procedures. Joseph, later Lord, Lister graduated in medicine from the University of London. He then went to Edinburgh to study and practice surgery under James Syme, who was one of the first European surgeons to adopt ether anesthesia in 1847 and was the very first to seize upon the antiseptic method introduced in 1868 by his pupil Lister, who then was also his son-in-law. In 1860 Lister had been appointed professor of surgery at the University of Glasgow, and it was there that he pursued his research on antisepsis.

His experiences in hospitals led Lister to undertake this work. The high death rates from conditions following surgery, such as septicemia, pyemia, erysipelas, tetanus, and hospital gangrene, bewildered him. Nearly half of his own amputation cases died, notwithstanding strict cleanliness and frequent changes of dressings. He began to doubt the desirability of so-called laudable pus. Then he learned of the discovery by the chemist Pasteur that bacteria were living microorganisms and that they could be destroyed by heat and chemicals. Heat could not be directly used in surgery so he experimented with chemicals. He finally hit upon carbolic acid after watching workmen disinfecting and deodorizing sewage with this chemical.

Perhaps the best way to dramatize the Lister story is to use the account of a doctor who was present at the first demonstration of the antiseptic method in Chicago. The account has the added value of graphic firsthand description of the way in which surgery was conducted in the 1880's. The narrator is Dr. Franklin H. Martin, then a junior intern, who was later to found the American College of Surgeons.

The place is Mercy Hospital. The surgeon, newly appointed gynecologist on the hospital staff, is Professor Edward W. Jenks, who had come from Detroit to succeed Professor William H. Byford on the faculty of the Chicago Medical College. The operation is to be an ovariotomy, removal of a large tumor of the ovary, which in those days, 1881, was seldom attempted, even though Ephraim McDowell had successfully performed it 72 years earlier. The anesthetist is the narrator, Dr. Martin. There is a senior intern, Dr. Lorenzo T. Potter, as chief assistant; three Sisters of Mercy are the spongers and other assistants; two orderlies are there to "fetch and carry." Three professors of surgery and several other invited guests are present. The costumes of Professor Jenks and his chief assistant are light street clothes, with large aprons of oiled silk. The anesthetist and all others present are wearing ordinary street clothes. The operating room equipment consists of

> . . . sea sponges immersed in a basin of carbolic solution; two and a half per cent carbolic solution in a basin behind the operator and assistant operator; a table at

the right of the operator containing instruments in shallow pans, a large trocar with tube, and supply of silk ligatures in a small basin; a high table at the end of the room supporting the 'steam spray' which was manipulated by a nun.

The scene set, let Dr. Martin proceed with the story as related in his autobiography, *The Joy of Living*:[34]

The patient had been anesthetized for at least 30 minutes when the operator proceeded to wipe off the center of her abdomen with a sponge saturated with carbolic solution. He then selected his knife . . . and the incision was carefully extended from either end. It was the consensus that the *linea alba* had not been incised. However, the tense wall of the abdomen was thinned by the pressure of the tumor, and it was apparent that the peritoneum had been incised.

That blue something beneath the peritoneal opening must be the ovarian cyst. In those early operations, if the surgeon was not entirely sure of himself he would ask members of the audience for advisory comments, which were usually freely given. . . . Upon suggestion, the abdominal incision was extended slightly. There could be no mistake; the glistening mass that protruded must be a tumor. Should he explore with his hand to discover if it was non-adherent, or should he at once attack the protruding portion with the penetrating four-toothed trocar to secure the growth? It was suggested that the trocar with its rubber hose attachment would partially empty the tumor of its fluid, and thus facilitate exploration and delivery. This was attempted. The sides of the abdomen were pressed inward; the tumor, being very thin, burst; and the excessive pressure which spurted the fluid over the entire field of operation and sides of the abdomen, finally expelled the tumor with its undrained fluid.

Little sponging was necessary. A long pedicle with its blue blood vessels lay ready to ligate. With great force, the operator tied off the pedicle, using strong, braided silk ligatures. With trepidation the stalk was severed, and the mass—the empty tumor—with its dripping fluids was held high so that everyone present could see. . . . It was decided to close the wound with through-and-through sutures. The surface of the abdomen was again bathed with a carbolic solution, and elaborate dressings *a la Lister* were carefully applied. After a long hour and a half the anesthetist was ordered to "let up on the ether," and the patient was removed to her bed. Every member of the operating staff and the spectators—clothes, skin, hair, beards and all—was wet to saturation with the condensed carbolic spray. . . .

The operator, however, had covered himself with glory. The patient was alive, with a rapid but "good quality" pulse. "Good nursing" was the slogan that counted for or against recovery or death in these desperate cases, and it would complete the success. (When one in eight recovered, the attendants attributed it to "good nursing" and the surgeon to his skill.) . . . The patient awakened from her ether anesthetic. Strange that she was not nauseated. Strange that the first night she slept like a child. She was not disturbed by the constant taking of her pulse, the counting of the respiration, nor our feeling of her skin to note her temperature. The following morning she was brighter than any one of her attendants, or the surgeon-in-chief who had slept at home and continued to get reports at nine, at twelve, and at the dead hour—two o'clock.

The new thermometer was used to take her temperature, which indicated "normal" as it had the night before. This elicited considerable discussion. Should

[34] Vol. I. Garden City, New York, Doubleday, Doran & Co., 1933, pp. 209–14.

the wound be examined? Possibly the laudable, healthy pus was being suppressed. The consultants were reminded by someone who was more conversant with the recent literature than others that possibly the wound was healing "by first intention." But recent experience caused someone to say that although that was all right theoretically, it was something that didn't happen. The surgeon was uncomfortable about not seeing the wound, although Lister's injunction was "as long as there is no fever or hemorrhage, leave the dressing undisturbed." . . . The surgeon compromised by carefully raising the edges of the dressings and actually peeking under without bringing the carbolic spray to bear upon the wound. Nervously, the surgeon announced, "The wound is perfectly dry." . . .

The second day and the third day went by. . . . The patient's pulse beat was from 70 to 80 and her temperature was normal. This marvelous condition created much comment. . . . There was no chance for a crisis, because her temperature never went above the normal. . . . The third day dawned. No fever, and the strangest thing of all, the daily peeking at the wound had revealed not even "laudable pus." . . . At the end of ten days, according to instructions, the dressings were removed, the wound exposed under the spray, the surface sponged off with five per cent carbolic solution, and the stitches carefully removed, one by one. The wound was dry, no pus even on the silk sutures. It had *healed by first intention!* I doubt if any one of the senior and junior staff members of the hospital and the other witnesses to this wound exposure and stitch removal had ever before seen an abdominal wound that had actually healed without suppuration. . . .

The sad commentary on this account is that it took 13 years for Listerism to reach Chicago, and doubtless much longer in many other places. The penalty of the delay, the lag between discovery and application, was the loss of thousands of lives. Lister first used carbolic acid successfully on a patient in 1865. Discovering that undiluted carbolic acid was too strong, he experimented with ways of diluting it until he found a fairly satisfactory solution, but he kept on for years with attempts to find a better one. In 1868 he announced his discovery in an article in *Lancet.* London doctors were long skeptical, although others came from the Continent and from America seeking instruction. One great and immediate result was that hospitals improved sanitary conditions, which reduced the death toll a little. His invention of the spray for the spraying machine for the operating room came in 1870 and was a result of his overemphasis on polluted air. By 1887 he had realized this and discarded it. It is universally recognized that his was the work that opened the door to modern surgery, making possible the performing of many operations that had hitherto been avoided because of the extremely high mortality. Although asepsis has replaced antisepsis in the operating room, it was he who prepared the way for it, and it was Pasteur who gave him the clue, as he was to acknowledge gratefully to that scientist afterward.

CHAPTER 7

Major Health Problem Areas

A serious lag exists between the status of medical knowledge
and its application in the diagnosis, treatment, and prevention
of illness. While medical knowledge is striding forward in
seven-league boots, its application often trails far behind. . . .
The frontier of medical care lies within the walls of the
hospital as a medical center. The community hospital
represents common ground upon which patient, community,
and professional groups can meet to apply their knowledge.
Will the hospital be allowed to become a laggard and
hindering bottleneck to the application of medical science
or will it be expected, permitted, and encouraged to become
an expediter in the enlargement of the frontiers of this
applied science?
JAMES A. HAMILTON[1]

THE OVERVIEW that the administrator can cultivate, which gives
him insight into the possibilities of integration of medical services and of
interrelationships with community agencies, may enable him to exert great
influence in the future with the many problems that remain in major health
areas and the new problems that will be created.

Most of the problems are not new, although they have changed in many
respects. They have been with us for ages, as study of the writings of early
medical sages will show. In a talk at the American Hospital Association convention in 1935, Homer F. Sanger, then a member of the staff of the American
Medical Association's Council on Medical Education and Hospitals, referred

[1] *Hospital Trends and Developments 1940–1946*, Arthur C. Bachmeyer, M.D., and Gerhard Hartman, Ph.D. (eds.). New York, The Commonwealth Fund, 1948, pp. 48–49.

to topics mentioned in the proceedings of the first sessions of the A.M.A. in 1847. One of the big topics, he said, was maternity welfare, and a survey was initiated in that field. Another was care of the indigent. A third was the supply of qualified physicians, one delegate complaining that while riding five hundred miles on horseback, he "noticed so many doctors in cities and large towns and so few in rural districts."[2]

There is still an enormous lag in applying knowledge to practice in meeting these and many other problems of which 1847 physicians and administrators were well aware and in coping with new ones that have arisen since. A deep consciousness of the problems is needed by the administrator. His grounding in the basic sciences and in the development of medical science should be thorough enough to make him alert to the advances heralded in the news of the day. Fortunately for him the reporters of this era are skilled in translating into intelligible language for the layman the announcements that appear in the professional books and magazines and that are presented by lecturers at meetings of the learned societies. From the popular medical books and journals and from the public press he can glean good ideas of the significance of the new events and new thinking in medicine.

This chapter is no more than a meandering in the field of major health problems, in a way typical of the kind of meandering that an administrator will do. The subject of disease is vast and intricate; in restricted space only inklings of an infinitesimal part of it can be given. Medical dictionaries and medical terminology manuals should be on every administrator's desk; the American Medical Association published in 1962 the first edition of a paperback, pocket-size guide to the preferred medical terms of all important diseases. The handbook represents the first step in developing a system of correct medical terminology so that physicians from all parts of the world can understand each other. It contains a definition of each disease, the known or possible causes, and the most characteristic disturbance and findings. Frequent revision is the aim, so that it will keep up with expanding knowledge. This publication, *Current Medical Terminology,* has less than 500 pages, yet lists alphabetically 4,000 diseases and conditions, including psychological and neurological disorders. Frequent reference to such a guide will give the student in administration of medical services a grasp of the nomenclature of medicine and of the characteristics of each disease that will help him to understand the language of the introductory type of medical textbook that is the next step in his education.

MALIGNANT DISEASES

Victories are being won in the fight against cancer, though the great victory— a *known,* complete cure—is still elusive. Twenty-five years ago, 160,000 Americans were still alive were considered cured five years after their illness was

[2] *Bull. Am. Hosp. A.,* October, 1935, p. 26.

diagnosed as cancer. This year the number of five-year cures will exceed 1,100,000, according to the American Cancer Society.[3]

Guy de Chauliac, who practiced medicine at Avignon in the fourteenth century, used the knife to cut out cancer in the early stages and employed the cautery or hot iron to extirpate the fungous or spreading variety.

A Polish surgeon, von Mikulicz-Radecki, first treated cancer of the esophagus by resection and plastic transplantation and introduced lateral pharyngotomy in excising malignant tumors of the tonsillar region in 1886.

Jan Danysz in 1903 applied radium therapy to malignant tumors. Georg Perthes, of Germany, originated deep roentgen therapy in 1903.

A long succession of innovations and developments in surgical technique and of discoveries as a result of research followed these and many other attempts to learn more about and to treat cancer more successfully.

Always to be remembered yet frequently overlooked is the fact that cancer is not a single disease. This was highlighted by Dr. Michael B. Shimkin,[4] associate director for field studies, National Cancer Institute, who stated that: "Cancer is not an entity, but a great class of diseases with distinct etiologies, pathogenetic stages, and, probably, distinct intracellular and subcellular mechanisms and reactions." He further pointed out: "An important new concept of cancer is that many neoplasms are the end result of a long series of progressive changes and stages rather than being the effect of single mutation-like alterations endowing cells with immutable new characteristics."

Dr. Shimkin calls attention to a "rediscovery":

> An interesting series of problems has resulted from the rediscovery that tumor cells can be found in the blood of a small but significant proportion of patients with cancer. The presence of tumor cells in the blood is not necessarily indicative of metastasis, just as the recovery of tumor cells in the operative field does not indicate that a local recurrence is inevitable. This is a forceful demonstration of the systemic factors of resistance that must exist in some patients against some neoplasms, factors that it will be fruitful to define. Also, it is excellent evidence that cancer cells and the diseases we call cancer are not the same thing.

In the same paper, Dr. Shimkin made a plea for maintaining "a balance between the investments being made in virus research and in the studies of chemical and physical carcinogens, especially the complex carcinogenic environments that are being revealed and clarified by epidemiological research." He pointed out that "carcinogens are not limited to exotic industries, but exist in the air we breathe, the water we drink, the food we eat, and some habits we cherish."

He contended also that the distinction between fundamental and applied research is artificial, that "investigations on man can be as fundamental as investigations on fruit flies; and from another viewpoint, all research on cancer is applied research by definition."[5]

[3] Betty Coe Spicer: New Weapons Against Breast Cancer. *Ladies' Home Journal,* June, 1962, p. 46.
[4] Paper presented at the Fourth National Cancer Conference held at Minneapolis, September 13, 1960.
[5] Changing Concepts Concerning Cancer. *Pub. Health Rep.,* October, 1961, pp. 861–65.

Speaking of the many pioneers and leaders in experimental chemotherapy of cancer, Dr. Shimkin declared that the names of Sidney Farber, Alexander Haddow, Charles Huggins, and Cornelius Rhoads "tower above the rest."

Dr. Farber,[6] who is professor of pathology at Harvard Medical School and director of research, The Children's Cancer Research Foundation, Boston, speaking at the American Public Health Association meeting in 1960, said that the last twenty years have

> . . . seen the realization of the destruction of cancer in man by chemical substances introduced into the human body; the female sex hormone in the treatment of cancer of the prostate; testosterone in treatment of breast cancer; nitrogen mustard in patients with Hodgkin's disease; and the folic acid antagonist, aminopterin, the first antimetabolite, in acute leukemia in children. . . . Plant extracts have produced important temporary effects against choriocarcinoma which had become resistant to other forms of treatment and against acute monocytic leukemia, Hodgkin's disease, neuroblastoma, and other solid tumors in man.

He predicted use of bone marrow transfusion in the treatment of cancer and declared that the final goal of cancer chemotherapy is not the "mere amelioration of symptoms or simple increase in months or years of survival, but the control, prevention, and eventual eradication of the many diseases grouped under the word 'cancer.' "

Although medical scientists insist, as stated before, that there are many kinds of cancer, there is a "unifying concept," according to the seventh biennial report of the Sloan-Kettering Institute which summarizes research work at the institute from 1959 to 1961. The layman will not be much enlightened by this concept, but here it is in the words of Dr. Frank L. Horsfall, Jr.,[7] president and director of the Institute: "Cancer, no matter what the inducing agent, is ultimately the result of a change in the chromosomal nucleic acid (deoxyribonucleic acid or DNA) of the affected cells."

Improved technique, both surgical and roentgen, is credited by an Austrian surgeon as one of the causes of greater success in treating cancer of the cervix, although not perhaps the main one, which he considers to be decided improvement in diagnosis, making possible earlier discovery of the condition. Dr. Tassilo Antoine of Vienna, in a paper read at a meeting of the International College of Surgeons in November, 1961, expressed a conviction that the progress in treatment of cervical carcinoma is due to the fact that "the lesion can now be healed before it becomes invasive."

In other areas, results are less encouraging. Gastric carcinoma, for example, remains a condition in which life expectancy is low. Detection in the preinvasive phase is not easy. Cytological studies similar to those made in the Papanicolaou test for early carcinoma of the cervix are recommended by diagnosticians.

It is a strange but well-known fact that despite the same treatment, two

---

[6] Chemotherapy Aids Cancer Treatment. *Pub. Health Reports,* February, 1961, pp. 149, 150.
[7] *Fourfront,* publication of Memorial Hospital–Sloan-Kettering Institute–Strang Clinic–James Ewing Hospital, December, 1961, p. 1.

patients with similar cancers clinically and histologically will differ in their reactions, even to the extent that one may die and the other may be cured. Dr. Harry Rubin[8] of the University of California reported at a meeting on tumor immunity sponsored by the New York Academy of Sciences that some virus-caused cancers are fought and ultimately destroyed by defense cells called lymphocytes; the cancer cells are left incapable of manufacturing more of the viral particles that turned them into tumors in the first place. Dr. Rubin said that this discovery may ultimately be helpful in explaining how some sudden, unexplainable disappearances of cancers occur, and that thus a means for producing them artificially might be developed.

Evanston (Illinois) Hospital started using chemoinfusion, a technique for administering drugs to combat malignancy, in 1961 following extensive research. The method causes less toxicity than when chemical agents are given systemically.[9] In this method, which was developed by Dr. Edward F. Scanlon:

> . . . a drug to destroy the cancer is fed through a tube into an artery leading directly to the tumor at the same time that a drug to neutralize the effect of the toxic drug is fed through another tube into a vein leading from the tumor. The chemical is thus localized in the tumor in order to prevent healthy cells in other parts of the body being affected. A pump with four fingers which move in rotation regulates the flow of the drugs. The length of time a patient is infused may vary from a few days to 24 days. The infusion is continuous, night and day, from the time it starts until the treatment is concluded. A patient receiving this therapy is comfortable and can move around the room—but at no greater distance than the length of the tubes connected to the pump.

The hospital has three of these machines for chemoinfusion. The technique has been used both before and after surgery. In one such case there was a tumor whose primary site was in the hand, but which had spread to a secondary site in the lymph nodes of the armpit. The malignancy on the hand was first removed. Then the cancer-destroying drug was fed into the artery leading to the original cancer, and the lymph gland was removed after this treatment.

A not generally known fact is that cancer kills more children each year than any other disease. The most susceptible age is between 18 months and 4 years. The largest proportion, 30 per cent, are tumors of the central nervous system and lesions of the eye; next, accounting for 20 per cent, are lymphomas and leukemias; the remainder are flank tumors, 20 per cent, and miscellaneous tumors, 30 per cent.

Virtually unknown a half century ago, cancer of the lung now kills more than 36,000 Americans a year, hundreds of thousands throughout the world, and is increasing at what is termed an "epidemic rate." Evidence points heavily at irritants as the cause of the increase, especially smoking.

In a Reuters dispatch from London, dated March 7, 1962, it was reported that

[8] *Hosp. Topics,* April, 1962.
[9] *The Pilot,* April, 1962. (Publication of Evanston, Illinois, Hospital.)

on that day the Royal College of Physicians had indicted smoking—particularly of cigarettes—as a major cause of lung cancer and had urged decisive steps by the government to curb rising tobacco consumption. The report was by a nine-man research committee which suggested restriction of tobacco advertising; use of tax powers to discourage cigarette smoking in favor of less harmful pipes and cigars; and printing the tar and nicotine contents of each cigarette brand on its pack. Antismoking clinics were advocated. Besides cancer, bronchitis, it was said, could be caused by smoking, and it might contribute to the development of pulmonary tuberculosis. Coronary heart disease was also said to be a more frequent cause of death in smokers than in nonsmokers, a fact that was likewise established in a study of Seventh Day Adventists, who do not smoke, in the United States.

Research on Cancer

In 1890 in Germany a medical research worker gave way to despondency and ended his life because of the indifference of the profession and the public to his work on cancer. Arthur Hanau's pathetic story is only one of many in the annals of medical history. Its tragic undertone of individual frustration modulates the swelling notes of the symphony of medical progress. Toil and sacrifice and bitter disappointment—the constantly recurring cadence that interrupts the triumphant melody, whose poignancy is the sharper because so often to have waited a little would have been to have won the mead.

So it was with Hanau. First to make successful transplants of cancer in rodents, after long, arduous labor, he found no appreciation of the value of his accomplishment. Five years after Hanau's death Moran confirmed and followed up his work, and in the first two or three years after the turn of the century Leo Loeb and Jenson likewise confirmed his findings and pursued similar experiments. The latter carried cancer through some forty generations of mice. And Maud Slye after 1913 rendered valuable service and won wide fame through extended experiments with the ways of cancer in mice.

The American Cancer Society alone helped to support the research of some 1,300 key investigators in 1962. They were working in medical schools, hospitals, and research laboratories. Aiding them were thousands of technicians and research associates. Other research is supported by the federal government and by many private and public agencies.

Virology is one of the most promising fields of research, and it is rather new. The first person to suggest that cancer might be a viral disease was the French bacteriologist, Amedee Borrel, in 1903. It appears that he had no basis for the idea other than that he had failed to find a "microbe" of cancer. In 1908, according to Dr. John R. Heller[10] (director of the National Cancer Institute up to July 1, 1960, when he became president of the Memorial Sloan-Kettering Cancer

[10] Research on Cancer Viruses. *Pub. Health Rep.,* June, 1960.

Center, New York), the Danish scientists V. Ellerman and O. Bang "succeeded in transmitting leukemia from one chicken to another by injecting cell-free filtrates of blood and organ extracts." He adds that little attention was paid to their work because at that time leukemia was not generally considered a neoplastic disease. He states that two years later Dr. Peyton Rous, working at the Rockefeller Institute, New York, "transferred certain spontaneous tumors of chickens by cell-free filtrates. One of these was the source of the Rous sarcoma virus." This work, too, was discounted

> . . . because of the prevailing opposition to an infection theory, but subsequent work established beyond any doubt that these were true neoplasms and that there were no living tissue cells in the filtrate. Now we know that Rous' discovery marked an important stage in the history of experimental cancer research. The Rous sarcoma dramatically progresses in degree of malignancy through successive passages in the laboratory, either by cell transplants or tumor filtrates.

In the early thirties, Dr. Richard Shope, also at the Rockefeller Institute,

> . . . was studying rabbit tumors—in particular a papilloma occurring in certain wild cottontail rabbits. Using the same basic technique. . . . Shope extracted and filtered the papilloma tissue and injected the filtrate into domestic rabbits. . . . The Shope papilloma agent cannot be recovered from tumors in the domestic rabbit; the animal can be infected with a filtrate, but the papillomas that arise generally cannot be transmitted from one domestic rabbit to another. Nevertheless, the presence of a virus is signified by the appearance of antibodies in the blood as the tumor develops.

Further research described by Dr. Heller includes the transmission by a cell-free extract of kidney tumors in the leopard frog in 1934 by Dr. Balduin Lucké, of the University of Pennsylvania; work with inbred mouse strains by, among others, the geneticist Dr. John Bittner at the Roscoe B. Jackson Memorial Laboratory, Bar Harbor, Maine; and the successful transmission in 1951 by Dr. Ludwik Gross, of the Bronx Veterans Administration Hospital, of mouse leukemia with filtered extracts by injecting newborn mice of a susceptible strain. This study "marked the beginning of a new, active period; before that virus-cancer research was considered to result only in 'isolated laboratory curiosities.' "

In 1960 a new method of cancer treatment—exposing cancer patients to x-rays in an atmosphere of highly concentrated oxygen—was made available after long research and experiment at Columbia-Presbyterian Hospital, New York. The equipment is similar to that installed in 1959 at St. Thomas' Hospital, London, England. The unit includes a pressure chamber in the form of an eight-foot cylinder in which the anesthetized patient lies. The cylinder is pressurized until the patient is breathing up to twenty times the amount of oxygen he would normally receive from the air. The highly concentrated oxygen sensitizes normally resistant cancer cells to the radiation, and good results are reported.

Experiments are being conducted in Sweden, financed by two of the country's largest life insurance firms, on the use of a new vaccine against cancer, utilizing fractions of dead cancer cells. Volunteers, all relatively old people, are being used for the experiments, with expansion of the initial 120 healthy persons if success is shown by the tests.

A group from the Mayo Clinic published in 1961 a report of a study in which ultrasonic energy was used to kill experimental osteogenic sarcoma in the thigh of the dog. In a report at the annual meeting of the American Academy of Orthopedic Surgeons, January 27 to February 1, 1962, they showed that it was also possible to destroy the blood supply to the tumor, thus preventing its spread by the blood stream. The studies, however, also showed that excessively high doses of ultrasound were dangerous to bone.

Another promising development, which was reported at the 1962 meeting of the American Medical Association, is the use of an atomic reactor in treating solid tumors. Experiments are being conducted at Brookhaven National Laboratory, Upton, New York. This boron-neutron treatment can be used after maximum doses of other radiation have been tried and have failed. The treatment is reported not to damage normal tissues, destroying only the tumor cells.

A new chemical drug, uracil mustard, was reported in 1962 to have brought improvement in 31 of 47 patients with adult lymphatic leukemia and malignant lymphoma in tests at the University of Minnesota. The compound is given in capsule form, by mouth, whereas nitrogen mustard, used for the past 15 years to treat widespread lymphomas, is given intravenously and the patient must be immobilized for four to six days. The new preparation is still under study.

A United Press dispatch on May 30, 1961, carried a statement by Surgeon General Luther Terry of the United States Public Health Service that "the government was confident it had found the first drug ever to cure a cancer." He referred to the chemical methotrexate, which in tests cured or arrested nearly 50 per cent of the cases of a rare form of cancer which develops in the womb of pregnant women, spreads rapidly to the rest of the body, and is almost always fatal. It was also said to have prolonged the lives of some victims of leukemia. The announcement was made with the usual warning that this is not effective in all types of cancer, that only a portion of cures are obtained even in the types on which good results have been shown, and that whether a real "cure" or only an arrest has been achieved will not be known until a reasonably long period of time has elapsed without recurrence. There are also rather severe side effects.

Another drug on which research is being conducted in the cancer battle is vincaleukoblastine, derived from the periwinkle.

Manufacturers submit some 50,000 substances a year to the National Cancer Institute for tests of possible anticancer properties. Around 200 have been accepted for tests on human beings.

Organized Effort Against Cancer

Organization has been a powerful force in the battle against cancer. One of the leading influences has been the formation of cancer clinics in hospitals, combining as they do the advantages of research, group consultation, pooling of knowledge, and critical review concentrated on a particular classification of diseases. A summarized description of their origin and purpose follows:[11]

> In 1927 the American Society for the Control of Cancer appointed a committee to report on the best method of improving service to the cancer patient. In 1929 that committee reported on the medical service available in the United States and made suggestions for its improvement, among which was a more widespread organization of cancer clinics in general hospitals. With the approval and at the request of the directors of the Society, the American College of Surgeons in 1930 formulated a Minimum Standard for Cancer Clinics in general hospitals, and through correspondence and personal communications with interested individuals in hospitals throughout Canada and the United States, recommended the formation of cancer clinics. Existing facilities were surveyed beginning in 1931, and in 1933 the College published the first list of 140 cancer clinics to which it was able to give approval on the basis of compliance with the Standard. . . .
> Approval is based on personal surveys by trained representatives. The College has detailed reports of personal surveys of facilities for the management of cancer cases in practically all of the institutions in the United States and Canada which have introduced the cancer clinic method of approach to the cancer problem. There has been formed on this continent a network of cancer clinics in which patients may be reasonably assured of complete examination, accurate diagnosis, group opinion, accurate records, and the best treatment that is offered in the community.

There are now some 900 cancer programs in the United States and Canada which are approved in accordance with the minimum requirements published in the *Manual for Cancer Programs, 1961*. A new minimum standard became effective June 1, 1961, in which only two major categories of cancer activities are recognized: the clinical activities program which is conducted in the cancer hospital or general hospital, and the cancer registry which is conducted in the general hospital.[12]

In its activities in the cancer field the American College of Surgeons receives financial aid and consultive support from the American Cancer Society and the National Cancer Institute to supplement funds and advice derived from its own resources.

The American Cancer Society is concerned with the *total* cancer problem, social, economic, educational, and psychological, as well as scientific aspects. It is noteworthy that its beginning was almost simultaneous with that of the American College of Surgeons and that a number of surgeons were active in its promotion and development. Its first meeting, as the American Society for the Control of Cancer, was on May 22, 1913, and it was attended by ten physicians and five laymen at the Harvard Club in New York City. The impetus came in November, 1912, when the program of the Clinical Congress of Surgeons of

---

[11] Laura G. Jackson: Hospital, Surgical and Related Standards. *Standards World,* summer, 1949, pp. 73–74.
[12] Cancer Programs Approved by the College in 1961. *Bull. Am. Coll. Surgeons,* September–October, 1961, p. 223.

North America (later to merge with the American College of Surgeons) was devoted entirely to cancer. One of the presentations was that of Dr. Thomas S. Cullen of Baltimore who advocated education of the public. As a result a cancer campaign committee was appointed with him as chairman.

One of Dr. Cullen's first acts was to induce the *Ladies' Home Journal* to publish an article on cancer. Samuel Hopkins Adams was assigned to write it, and his production, "What Can We Do About Cancer?" was one of the very first articles to disclose the plain facts about cancer in the public press. It was Dr. Cullen and the American Gynecological Society which arranged the May conference in New York. The members of the cancer campaign committee of the Clinical Congress of Surgeons of North America were made members of the executive committee of the new society, to start whose work the 15 persons present raised $10,000 among themselves.

The American College of Surgeons, which had come officially into existence on May 5, 1913, 17 days before the Cancer Society, conducted at the Clinical Congress in Chicago on November 13, 1913, the first symposium on cancer to be held in the United States. In the same month the American Medical Association appointed a cancer committee made up of the members of the college's cancer committee. The College of Surgeons' committee was reorganized in 1922 as the Committee on the Treatment of Malignant Diseases with Radium and X-ray, renamed in 1929 the Committee on Treatment of Malignant Diseases, and in 1939, the Committee on Cancer.

Although the activities of these committees have been of a scientific and organizational (cancer clinic) nature in the main, the original purpose of public education has always been an important one. To accomplish this they need only publicize their own activities and collaborate with the American Cancer Society and other organizations. Early diagnosis of cancer offers the best probability of cure. All doctors agree about this. The great necessity therefore is to educate the public to the wisdom of periodic physical examinations and prompt seeking of medical advice when suspicious symptoms appear.

The college for many years collected records of five-year cures of cancer and publicized them to both the profession and the laity. Especially outstanding as public educational devices were the "Cancer Is Curable" symposia featured at the 1932, 1933, 1934, and several subsequent congresses. So-called detection or prevention centers which were established beginning in 1946 were included in the approval program of the college at the request of the American Cancer Society, giving further ammunition for publicity, although the approval program was discontinued in 1953 because of the great variation between the different projects.

The Eighth International Cancer Congress was held in Moscow, U.S.S.R., July 22 to 28, 1962, under the sponsorship of the International Union Against Cancer.

Fraudulent Cancer "Cures"

Deplorable exploitation of cancer victims is carried on by quacks. Treatment by diet, starvation, by "wonder" salves and ointments, by serums and injections, by "ozone generators," "color lamps" and other devices, is a complete waste of time, effort, and money—but convictions of the crooks are hard to get. The American Cancer Society estimates that $100 million a year is spent by Americans on treatment that does them no good and often dangerously delays proper care.

Held up for derision are the concoctions prescribed by the doctors of old, but there is no ground for the public to be happy about the situation today, when it accepts and pays heavily for worthless treatments by quacks and besieges regular physicians for drugs it does not need but must have to satisfy some psychological demand for "something to take." Some of the public education in which the administrator participates should be concerned with warnings about fake practitioners and remedies.

CARDIOVASCULAR DISEASES

The treatment of coronary insufficiency may be medical, surgical or a combination of the two. Each case must be treated on the basis of the individual pathologic picture, as no one treatment can serve all types. . . . Fears and obsessions of the patient must be banished, and a psychiatrist should be called in before and after treatment is carried out. . . . Coronary heart disease is a grim battle for survival, between the relentless occlusive process on the one hand and a compensating collateral circulation on the other. The victim is in an extremely precarious stage of his life. . . . There is need of a review, conducted locally and nationally, and a more energetic effort toward prevention, early diagnosis and treatment of a kind that will benefit the patient and lower the mortality rate of coronary insufficiency and infarction. Too many comparatively young men are dying from an otherwise frequently preventable cause. In no field of circulation have professional views changed more frequently than in the interpretation of the coronary circulation.[13]

The number one health problem is the cardiovascular diseases. In the United States they cause over one-half of the deaths each year, and the ratio is growing. Most of them are a result of arteriosclerotic heart disease, including coronary disease. The hypertensive diseases and vascular lesions affecting the central nervous system come next in deadliness. More than ten million people in the United States have some form of cardiovascular disease, and about half of them have heart disease.

Dr. Whiteside,[14] of Victoria, British Columbia, Canada, says that progress in cardiac surgery was held up for 25 years "because of the teaching of a single

[13] W. Carleton Whiteside: A New Era in the Treatment of Coronary Insufficiency. *J. Internat. Coll. Surgeons,* May, 1960.
[14] *Ibid.*

physician 'authority,' " whom he identifies as Sir James Mackenzie. A London surgeon, Mr. Souttar, performed a mitral commissurotomy for mitral stenosis in 1925, but Sir James "denounced this 'interference' with the physicians' 'sacred' organ," and the field was static for a quarter of a century.

Dr. James B. Herrick (1861–1954), of Chicago, was the first physician to describe coronary thrombosis in a human being. It was in 1912 after long study that he clarified the symptoms and its manifestations as a distinct disease entity. Caused by an obstruction of one of the arteries which furnish nourishment to the heart, it had previously been diagnosed only at autopsy. Its origin had been supposed to be in the gastrointestinal tract. With his paper on the condition before the Association of American Physicians in 1912, Dr. Herrick aroused little interest at first. He contended that with proper treatment the victim could live for years afterward. He installed in his office a forerunner of the electrocardiograph—the Einthoven string galvanometer, which had just been invented—and he experimented on laboratory animals. He presented another paper in 1919, which this time was enthusiastically received, and in 1922 when he addressed a meeting he was given an ovation.

On June 16, 1947, Dr. Claude S. Beck, of Cleveland, Ohio, performed the first defibrillation in medical history when a young boy went into convulsion on the operating table. The convulsion was stopped by a strong electric shock applied to the surface of the heart. In June, 1955, another Cleveland doctor, who had been a student of Dr. Beck's, revived a doctor who had fallen over dead in the hospital lobby, by opening the chest and pumping the heart by hand, while Dr. Beck "shocked the heart out of fibrillation," getting oxygen into the lungs. The doctor completely recovered.[15] These results followed many years of research and experimentation on dogs. Some of it done by early workers was unnoticed and forgotten until records were unearthed years later. Drs. Crile and Dolley revived, with perfusion or massage, the asphyxiated hearts of dogs and published their work in 1906. Dr. Crile pointed out that restoring the heart beat was secondary to getting oxygen to the brain. The immediacy factor in resuscitation is extremely important, as is shown by the fact that the brain cannot be without oxygen for more than five minutes.

Closed-chest heart massage, developed by a Johns Hopkins electrical engineer, W. B. Kouwenhoven, Ph.D., with the help of staff members of the Johns Hopkins University School of Medicine, Baltimore, is saving many lives of persons whose hearts stop suddenly. Its great advantage is that properly trained laymen can practice it. Accompanied by mouth-to-mouth breathing by a second person, which prevents brain damage from lack of oxygen, the victim can sometimes be revived in a few minutes, although it may take several hours. The doctors experimented with the technique on dogs for two years before attempting it on human beings. In the operating room it is proving to be a lifesaving technique

[15] Adapted from Ellen L. Davis: Hearts "Too Good to Die" Are Given a Dramatic Second Chance to Beat Again. *Hosp. Topics,* July, 1961, p. 75.

with better results and less damage to the patient than opening the heart for massage. If the emergency occurs outside of the hospital, the procedure must be continued until professional medical aid comes, preferably in a hospital. The fire department ambulance service staff in Baltimore have been taught the technique and used it to revive one of their own firemen whose heart stopped after he was overcome by smoke while fighting a fire. The technique is strenuous, especially when there is only one person to perform it. Therefore further experiments have been made and a closed heart-lung machine has been developed by Dr. Claude Beck, working with J. H. Rand. This administers oxygen and mechanically pumps the heart. Early experiments on dogs were successful, encouraging further development of a portable machine which can be placed in many strategic places.[16]

Louis Rehn of Frankfort, Germany, was the first surgeon to suture successfully a lacerated heart. This was in 1896—an important milestone. Alexis Carrel popularized the technique for vascular suturing and predicted the development of grafting of vessels.

Dilation of the aortic valve of a human patient with aortic stenosis was accomplished by Tuffier in 1913 by finger invagination of the aortic wall.

Cardiac arrest is a major cause of operating room deaths, and it is increasing. Some of the increase is because more patients of advanced age are undergoing major surgery than was the case only a few years back. Also, because of advances in surgical technique, more patients whose general state of health would have prohibited consideration for surgery in the past are now given the chance of life-saving surgical procedures, and among them the mortality rate would be expected to be high. Cardiac arrest is as great a problem in obstetrical as in surgical patients.

Open-heart surgery for congenital and other heart defects is saving many lives, especially of children and young adults. The equipment includes a pump oxygenator which virtually replaces the heart and lungs during the operation, enabling the surgeons to work freely in the area of the heart.

As for the causes of heart disease, these are many and include the commonly recognized ones—overexertion, emotional states, and infections—but Whiteside gives the greatest offenders as diet, alcohol, and tobacco. Albany Medical College, in two studies reported at the end of 1961, found that the risks of heart attacks and death from coronary heart diseases and from all causes were more than twice as great for cigarette smokers as compared with others and that for the heaviest smokers the risks were three times as great.

The American Heart Association is publicizing the role of the public in lowering the death rate from heart disease, saying: "Today some forms of heart disease can be prevented and a few can be cured. Almost all cases can be helped by proper treatment, especially if started at an early stage."

[16] Adapted from a condensation in *Reader's Digest*, November, 1960, pp. 96–99, of an article published in *Today's Health*, American Medical Association, November, 1960.

This is the same kind of appeal that the American Cancer Society is making in its field. Medicine, in order to capitalize on its progress, requires a cooperative, educated public which will seek its aid "early."

Hypertension

Hypertension is generally believed to be closely linked with emotional disturbances. There is also a clear hereditary connection. In a few cases it is caused by specific organic trouble. Surgery is frequently effective in lowering blood pressure when organic disease exists such as a tumor of the adrenal glands or narrowing of one of the kidney blood vessels.

The low-salt diet advocated in treatment of hypertension is a hardship for many persons. The introduction of the compound chlorothiazide makes it possible to liberalize somewhat the consumption of salt. Drugs used are rauwolfia, or Indian snakeroot. Reserpine, one of its derivatives, acts as a tranquilizer, reducing tension and indirectly the blood pressure. Other drugs are used to dilate blood vessels, to shut off excess nerve impulses, and to block the action of an enzyme which is believed to play some part in the condition.

What is known as malignant hypertension was always, and quickly, fatal thirty years ago; now if treated early enough life can be prolonged for many years, almost to normal length.

For stroke patients, the outlook is improving. From what one authority calls a "hopeless" attitude in 1954, the medical profession changed to an energetic attack approach within five years. Success with the use of anticoagulants in the treatment of thrombosis was one impetus to the almost frenzied research that is now being conducted. One heart specialist estimates that in the United States two million persons who have suffered strokes are alive today. The question is, what is their condition? How active are they? Discussion of these questions appears in the section in this chapter on rehabilitation.

INJURIES

In general, accident prevention has achieved the greatest success where society has been able to organize its efforts. Safety regulations are stringently enforced in industry, railroads, scheduled air transport, public beaches, and similar environments, with gratifying results. On the other hand, where the individual himself must assume most of the responsibility for his own safety and in many instances for that of others (such as in the home or while in a motor vehicle) safety progress has been slower. Although some accidents are often beyond human control, a large element of carelessness and irresponsibility is involved in others. Perhaps the most direct solution to the accident problem lies in intensified public educational activities designed to spread safety consciousness.[17]

[17] *Progress in Health Services,* Health Information Foundation, March–April, 1962.

Accidents rank fourth among the leading causes of death in the United States. There are more than 90,000 fatal accidents a year, and 9.5 million disabling injuries. The cost is estimated to be about $13.5 billion a year in medical care, loss of wages, and frequently permanent unemployability and dependency, besides the sorrow and suffering.

It is estimated that about one-third of the 2.5 million occupational accidents that occur each year involve the hand and forearm. Not until a hand is injured or its use affected by disease is its full value realized by its possessor. Fortunately there are surgeons who specialize in this field and accomplish marvels in restoring function.

Burns are one of the serious injuries upon which research is constantly being focused for improved methods of treatment. As in many other conditions, frequently chance produces useful findings. For example, a British physician, Dr. Frederick Willington of Devon, reported that a woman who had scalded herself severely plunged her injured hand into the only handy cold liquid. It was milk. She kept her hand in it for 30 minutes. No blistering and only slight reddening resulted. The physician used the treatment afterward on several hundred burn victims, with excellent results if it was used immediately and compresses kept over the burn for 24 hours. The efficacy of moist cold applications is well known in reducing the heat from burns and alleviating pain. Milk has a colloidal quality which makes it adhere to flesh without pressure. Also, it contains protein similar to that in human tissue.

Even burns that are almost always fatal are being stripped of their terror by newer medical, surgical, and nursing techniques. A five-year-old who had been "helping" with the cooking, and whose dress caught fire, suffered burns over 80 per cent of her body, 65 per cent in the third degree. For three months her life was at stake. From February until the end of July she was on the critical list, having to be fed intravenously. After ten months in which she had 18 operations, including skin grafts and removal of keloids, numerous plasma and whole blood transfusions, and intensive physical therapy, she was able to go home, although additional skin grafts and continued physical therapy were still needed.

All too many accidents occur right within the medical environment. Explosions in operating rooms are spectacular examples. The precautions are outlined in detail in the literature but are too often ignored through complacency or lack of training on the part of personnel. The National Fire Protection Association has a special committee on hospital operating rooms which has established functional standards that should reduce the explosion hazard to minimum.

The injury problem for doctors and hospitals has to be faced by preparedness for any kind of event, whether it be a crash involving only one automobile, a wreck of a 300-passenger train, a flood inundating a city, or, to speculate on the worst possible disaster, nuclear warfare. To further this complete preparedness ideal, organized effort is essential.

The National Safety Council, the American College of Surgeons, and the American Association for the Surgery of Trauma inaugurated in 1958 a joint action program aimed at preventing accidents and improving care of the victims of accidents. The program includes (1) public education in accident prevention and handling of the injured; (2) employment of joint state and local committees of the American College of Surgeons and the National Safety Council, together with other interested surgeons, safety engineers, and public officials to formulate safety plans for local communities; (3) possible registration of unusual cases of injury; (4) proposed investigations of emergency care of traffic injuries; (5) model legislation to require adequate training in first aid and transportation of the injured for ambulance attendants, policemen, and firemen; (6) cooperation in the production and improvement of training materials and instructional aids dealing with problems in handling of the injured.

In 1922 the American College of Surgeons formed a committee on the Treatment of Fractures. In 1939 it was combined with the Committee on Industrial Medicine and Traumatic Surgery as the Committee on Fractures and Other Trauma. In 1949 the name was shortened to Committee on Trauma. About 15 per cent of the membership of the college are members of the committee, which has more than 200 regional committees. Despite the tremendous educational efforts directed both to the profession and the laity over these many years, the standards for the treatment of trauma are conceded to be lower than in any other branch of surgery. "Integration of the basic sciences with the problems of trauma, or coordination of instruction between the clinical divisions of surgery" is lacking in medical education, one surgical authority declares, adding that another obstruction is "the fantasy that certain conditions of trauma must be treated by one type of surgeon, and may not be treated by another, regardless of the competence of either." He urges the exercise of American College of Surgeons' leadership to develop uniformly acceptable standards of training and of practice in this field.[18]

In 1960 under a $146,275 grant received from the John A. Hartford Foundation the American College of Surgeons inaugurated a new program to improve medical management of the surgical and injured patient. It was stated that with this grant the college could enlarge its activities in the field of trauma, that its national committee on trauma and the 241 state and local trauma committees could work more effectively in a concentrated effort to determine patterns of care for the injured patient and to inaugurate improvements in this care, and that pilot projects could be established in selected cities. Envisioned also are employment of a field staff to provide personal guidance to the public as well as to the profession and initiation of an evaluation program.

Reported in the November-December, 1962, issue of the college *Bulletin* was a training program for ambulance attendants conducted by the North Carolina regional committee on trauma; also the inauguration of an independent ambulance service by physicians in Missoula, Montana, because it had been found difficult to dictate to attendants employed by morticians how accidents should

[18] Harrison L. McLaughlin: Education in Trauma. *Bull. Am. Coll. Surgeons,* June–July, 1957, pp. 41, 70.

be handled at the scene. Reports were also published of the studies by members of the central committee of the ways in which the injured in two railroad wrecks were handled—one near Missoula, Montana, on June 10, 1962, the other near Harrisburg, Pennsylvania, on July 28, 1962. Lack of coordination was the chief criticism, also lack of centralized direction at the scene, but in both cases the doctors and hospitals showed striking evidence of the value of disaster planning and drills within their institutions. Many lessons were learned during these disasters, but that is a hard time in which to have to learn them. In both cases one particularly outstanding error was failure to distribute the patients among the hospitals, taxing the resources of one while the others were insufficiently utilized.

Doctors and hospitals are cooperating in the general campaign, spearheaded by the Public Health Service and the American Medical Association, to safeguard the public against poison. The P.H.S. division of accident prevention directs a national clearinghouse for poison control centers with which local centers may affiliate. Some 500 of them are in operation in the United States, the Panama Canal Zone, the Virgin Islands, and Guam. The clearinghouse provides local centers, many of which are in hospitals, with information on ingredients and antidotes for new products. More than 200 major manufacturers of drugs and household products supply the data. The centers in turn give the information to physicians by telephone, day and night. First-aid instructions and suggestions to call their doctor are given parents who call the centers.

Each year an estimated 600,000 children swallow household aids left within their reach, and about 350 die. Altogether, around 1,500 persons in the United States die each year from accidental overexposure to packaged chemicals. The American Medical Association estimates nonfatal poisonings to be 100 to 150 times the number of fatalities.

The American Medical Association first formally registered the need for precautionary labeling of chemical products in 1884 with adoption of a resolution urging that Congress and the several state legislatures be called on to enact legislation requiring lye to be sold as a poison, under a poison label. In 1910 and 1918 resolutions were adopted urging precautionary labeling of caustic poisons. Through the efforts of three doctors a Federal Caustic Poison Act was enacted in 1927, since which time state laws uniform with or parallel to this federal law have been enacted. Bringing the accidental poisoning problem right into the hospital was death in 1962 of six babies in a New York hospital from salt instead of sugar being placed in the formula-room sugar canister, which emphasizes the fact that products not poisonous in nature can kill when wrongly used.

APPENDICITIS

During my early years in the practice of medicine, acute appendicitis was confusedly recorded as a form of incurable peritonitis. In 1886, Fitz conclusively demonstrated the pathology of perforating inflammation of the vermiform appendix, and in 1889, John B. Murphy of Chicago, and Charles McBurney of Roxbury, Massachusetts, added greatly to knowledge of a disease to which so many people were subject. This added another important chapter to the history of medicine.[19]

Hippocrates died of appendicitis some two thousand years before the organ was identified in the year A.D. 1522 by an Italian professor of surgery, Berengarius Carpus. Scientifically, however, little was known about appendicitis until the early 1890's. The dawn of the new day in treatment of the disease came as a result of quick judgment and impulsive action.

On the morning of March 2, 1889, a young laborer with a broken leg, in the County Hospital in Chicago, complained to the intern that he had a severe pain in his abdomen. In making his rounds that day Dr. John B. Murphy stopped beside laborer Monahan's cot and asked him how he felt. "Not good at all," said Monahan, and described his pain, which had now left him, but had been replaced by an extreme sensation of nausea.

Murphy examined the youth's abdominal wall. He noted the sensitiveness of the midsection to deep pressure, especially between the navel and the crest of the ilium, where there was a slight muscle rigidity. He asked the intern about the patient's temperature, which the former said was 100°. Murphy told the intern to keep the patient quiet, saying that he would be back as soon as he finished his rounds.

Murphy was excited. He had lately read an article by Reginald Fitz in which he urged early surgical intervention when certain symptoms indicated infection of the appendix. Operations performed after the appendix had ruptured, Fitz pointed out and experience had proved, were usually too late to save life.

Two hours later when Murphy returned, his patient was vomiting and his temperature had risen to 101°. He could not stand the least touch over the lower right side of the abdomen. Murphy's decision was quickly made. He told the youth he would die if his appendix was not immediately removed. The patient nodded assent. Murphy operated and found a typical red appendix with pus in it, but not yet the inflammation of the connective tissue leading to dangerous abscess.

An obscure laborer had undergone that day, and the soon-to-be famous surgeon had performed, the first operation for appendicitis before a large, hard mass of pus had formed—the operation having been consciously performed on the theory that the primary lesion was an infection of the appendix.

Did other surgeons quickly accept the idea and follow the same procedure to save lives? Not without a battle more stirring, and in a sense more momentous, than Waterloo or Verdun. Dr. Loyal Davis[20] describes it in his biography of Dr. Murphy:

[19] Franklin H. Martin: *The Joy of Living,* Vol. I. Garden City, New York, Doubleday, Doran & Co., 1933, p. 381.
[20] *J. B. Murphy—Stormy Petrel of Surgery.* New York, G. P. Putnam's Sons, 1938, pp. 128–39.

Hot on the trail of what might prove a great boon to the human race, J. B. carried the subject with him wherever he went, to whatever he did. He ate, slept, and hurried through the days with that little wormlike sac on his mind. . . . The skepticism of his associates whetted his anger, aroused in him an overwhelming desire to make them agree with him. . . . He accepted every invitation to speak at medical meetings, and wherever he went he made strong arguments against conservatism in treating this disease. The appendicitis question became a bitter battle from one end of the country to the other, centering in the Middle West, where feeling ran highest, where expressions of opinion were couched in stronger language. There were times when Murphy seemed drowned in the bedlam of objections, but on he went. Within four years he had collected over 250 cases, and 14 years after his first appearance before the Chicago Medical Society he was back again. This time he spoke authoritatively, with 2,000 cases of appendicitis to his credit, and there was not a man in the crowded hall to dispute him.

Murphy himself, as quoted by Dr. Davis, said of the battle:

There is no procedure in surgery where the battle was so fierce and so continuous and where the statements of the uninformed were so personal, so galling, and so unjust as in the contest for and against early operation in acute infective appendicitis. Looking backward one can scarcely comprehend how a so-called intelligent profession was so slow in accepting the overwhelming force of numbers and facts, which could not be altered by theory or speculation. Practitioners whose cases recovered from the attack insisted that they were catarrhal inflammatory processes and recovered without the formation of pus, notwithstanding the evidence produced by every operator of that time that pus was present in all of the acute infective cases operated in the early stages—now a recognized fact. Everyone recalls how reluctantly the advocate of the soothing death lullaby of the opium treatment vacated his position and how equally persistent and belligerent was the advocate of the death-groaning calomel and castor oil participant; the still unconquered, nine-lived procrastinator has not yet capitulated, each and every one of these standing out against the most convincing presentation of pathological phenomena.

Dr. Davis adds the comment: "Murphy set out to make the public and the profession appendicitis conscious. How completely he accomplished this the world knows."

The world needs to know, nevertheless, more than it does know about appendicitis. Thousands and thousands of lives have been saved because of Dr. Murphy's victorious battle against procrastination in operating for appendicitis. Appendectomies performed in time are practically 100 per cent safe. Yet some 6,000 persons continue to die of appendicitis and its complications in the United States each year when there should be none. It has been said that only one person out of seven who has taken a laxative during an appendicitis attack has a chance to live. Attempts at self-treatment balk the lifesaving efforts of the surgeon.

COMMUNICABLE DISEASES

It is well known that in the Old Testament the existence of contagion is referred to as irrefutable. For example, in the Second Book of Kings appears "The leprosy therefore of Naaman shall cleave to thee, and unto thy seed forever."

Particular precautions were taken against gonorrhea; persons with that disease were isolated. Another quotation from the Old Testament reads: "And the Lord spake unto Moses, saying 'Command the children of Israel that they put out of the camp every leper, and everyone that hath an issue, and whosoever is defiled by the dead: Both male and female shall ye put them out, that they defile not their camps, in the midst of which I dwell.'" . . . Inscriptions on Babylonian plaques reveal that in this ancient nation contagion was attributed to very small insects. This belief prevailed to such an extent that the Babylonians gave the god who symbolized the plagues the form of an insect. The Egyptians, in embalming their dead, became aware that the bowels of the deceased were infectious, whereas the Greeks, among them Hippocrates and later Galen, defined a miasma as composed of infinitely small material organic elements derived exclusively from putrefaction. . . . The geniuses of the nineteenth century, who receive and deserve all admiration for giving the final impetus toward modern knowledge of infection, its causes and its prevention, were nevertheless heirs to a considerable body of soundly rooted knowledge bequeathed them by their predecessors over the generations.[21]

Great as the victories over infectious diseases have been, these diseases have by no means been vanquished. Deaths for which infections are given as the underlying cause still number more than 100,000 a year in the United States alone. Like ghosts of the past, some of those that were assumed to be practically dead are reappearing.

Deaths from septicemia and pyemia tripled between 1949 and 1959, according to *Public Health Reports* for April, 1959; the rate per million population increased from 3.8 to 10.5. Deaths from infections in infants under one month of age increased 30 per cent between 1955 and 1959. Pneumonia was the leading cause, increasing from 2,966 deaths in 1949 and 3,108 in 1955 to 3,918 in 1958. All deaths from influenza and pneumonia increased from 44,640 in 1949 to 57,300 in 1959 and deaths from infections of the kidney more than doubled.

Commenting on these and other figures Dr. Carl C. Dauer[22] said: "The number of deaths in which infection is a contributing cause is several times larger than the number of those in which infections are certified as the underlying cause."

Consider hepatitis, generally accepted as of two types: infectious (virus A) and serum (virus B). A record high year was 1954, when 50,093 cases were reported by the Public Health Service, but in 1961 that figure had been exceeded in the first eight months, with 52,826 cases reported, and the final all-time high for the year was 73,000 cases. Most of the increase is in the first type, which is transmitted by contaminated food or water; close personal contact with an infected person or with a carrier; and contaminated blood, syringes, or other equipment used parenterally. The serum type is believed to be transmitted only through the last media. The two are similar in clinical features and management. The most elaborate precautions are necessary in hospitals to prevent the spread of the disease to personnel and to other patients.

[21] N. C. Louros: Theories of Contagion Through the Centuries. *J. Internat. Coll. Surgeons,* February, 1962, pp. 196–205. The third I. C. Rubin Memorial Lecture.
[22] Mortality from Infection. *Pub. Health Rep.,* February, 1961, pp. 159–65.

Although the disease has long been recognized and epidemics occurred from time to time in the past, its inclusion as a nationally reportable disease came only in 1952, and the Public Health Service believes that cases reported constitute only a small part of those that exist. In mild cases diagnosis may not be made properly because there may be no evidence of jaundice. The viral strains have been isolated and identified and an experimental vaccine developed in the battle against this dangerous and frequently fatal disease. Gamma globulin is a protection against it for persons like doctors and nurses who are exposed and for family and other contacts.

Smallpox reappeared alarmingly in 1959, with serious epidemics in India and Pakistan. There was an outbreak in Britain late in December, 1961. A nine-year-old girl from Pakistan flew to London, took a train to Bedford, became ill, and was taken to a hospital. Malarial parasites were found before her death, but neither the pathologist nor the attending physician suspected smallpox. Two weeks later ten persons—hospital personnel, patients, and visitors—became severely ill with smallpox. Four of them died: a nurse, a hospital cook, the pathologist, and a patient.

The incident pinpoints the danger of misdiagnoses in connection with diseases like smallpox and typhoid fever that have become rare in most countries. Not since 1946, when there were 65 cases and 20 deaths in Seattle, Washington, has smallpox claimed more than one or two victims. Doctors do not suspect it. Its special danger is that there is no known treatment for it. The only weapon against it is immunization.

Among the widespread infectious diseases about which the public is not very well aware is snail fever, called a "world scourge" in an article in *Army,* August, 1961, by James Poling. It is common in Puerto Rico, much of tropical South America, Africa, the Middle East, Japan, China, and the Philippines. Other names for it are schistosomiasis and bilharziasis. The disease is being spread by the irrigation projects being constructed in underdeveloped areas. Dr. Claude Barlow in Egypt was so disturbed about the spread of the disease that he placed 224 of the blood flukes, of which the snail is a carrier, on his own abdomen, counting the stings, and then despite the ensuing misery, studied himself with a microscope. For a cure he had injections of tartar emetic, which adds immeasurably to the misery, but no more effective drug is known. Nor has there been any great success in experiments with poison to kill the snails. Puerto Rican immigrants in particular are spreading it to America. So are servicemen and other travelers.

Influenzal meningitis is a menace which takes heroic measures to combat. Treatment with antibiotics is the usual procedure but is not always effective, even when accompanied by the use of oxygen, digitalis, cortisone, intravenous fluids and blood. Evanston (Illinois) Hospital in 1959 had a two-year-old patient who was not responding to the new methods. Someone recalled a serum formerly used for meningitis. Extensive inquiries led to the discovery of a small supply in New Jersey. Police relays, an Air Force jet plane, and finally a helicopter were employed to bring it to the hospital, accompanied by publicity which aroused nation-wide sympathy. The result—four weeks after his admission to the hospital, after battling a combination of meningitis, bacteremic shock, cardiac failure, and pulmonary edema, the child was well enough to go home. Even in this day of medical miracles, such incidents are breath-taking, because the equipment and the techniques are so obviously secondary to the human brains, skills, and devotion concentrated day and night on a single small patient. This high degree of pooled intelligence and skills, together with the technological aids, is the hospital's contribution to medical progress.

The outbreak of encephalitis, or sleeping sickness, in Florida in 1962 focused attention upon the battle being waged in Africa against the tsetse flies which transmit the disease. Corridors are being cleared in the woodlands to form barriers to their advance; controlling the game which provides their food and using a wide range of insecticides are other devices.

Swarms of the kind of mosquitoes that can transmit yellow fever have been discovered in several of the southern states of the United States. The disease exists in Central America and is appearing in Mexico. A mosquito that had bitten a victim could transmit the disease anywhere.

Now that both the Salk and the Sabin oral vaccines are available to fight poliomyelitis, the disease can be conquered if they are utilized by susceptible members of the population.

International eradication of malaria is the goal of the World Health Organization. Malaria-free areas are being created. Sixty-six countries are involved in this program, the expense of which is heavily supported by the United States.

Amebiasis is estimated to have a 4 per cent incidence for the United States as a whole. It can be prevented by control of migratory populations, food handlers, sewage disposal, and sanitary measures in order to eliminate insect carriers, supplemented by an educational program to emphasize the importance of personal hygiene and good sanitation.

The danger of relaxation in the war on communicable disease was cited by Thorstein Guthe, M.D., chief medical officer for feveral disease and treponematoses, World Health Organization, at the World Forum on Syphilis and Other Treponematoses in Washington on September 8, 1962. He said that a premature victory was celebrated a few years ago when syphilis reached a low ebb that coincided with the world-wide use of penicillin as a treatment; reports from 106 nations showed that the sharp decline in the disease gave way to an increase in the mid-1950's.

The death toll from measles is not high, ranging from 300 to 600 a year, but it "weakens its victims, making them prey to more serious illness: pneumonia, strep infections, ear troubles, tuberculosis." How it may flare into death-dealing violence was related by J. D. Ratcliff,[23] who said that for 65 years the Faroe

[23] *Parents' Magazine,* January, 1962.

Islands, between England and Iceland, hadn't a single outbreak of the disease, natural immunity dwindling to zero. In 1846 it returned—and destroyed a quarter of the population. Later, it struck Fiji, killing 40,000 of a population of 150,-000. In 1952 it hit Greenland's Eskimos. It is one of rural Africa's most pressing disease problems. To combat measles a new vaccine has been developed by Dr. John F. Enders, 1954 Nobel prize winner from Harvard Medical School. The *Journal of the American Medical Association* appraised this vaccine as "one of the great accomplishments in the history of public health."

On July 26, 1962, the Public Health Service announced discovery of the virus which causes German measles, saying that this development is an essential step toward making a vaccine against the disease. The discovery was made by two medical research teams working independently, one at the Harvard School of Public Health, the other at the Walter Reed Army Institute of Research, Washington.[24] The disease, which is also called rubella, can cause deafness, blindness, and heart disease in infants when it occurs in expectant mothers.

Respiratory Infections

In 1900 the leading cause of death was influenza and pneumonia—202.2 per 100,000, 11.8 per cent of deaths. In 1960 they were the sixth cause—36.6 per 100,-000, 3.9 per cent of deaths. This was more than an 80 per cent decline. Yet this is still a major health problem, far from controlled, causing 65,000 deaths in the United States in 1960. There still exists, also, the specter of epidemics—like the one in 1918 which brought the death rate soaring to 584.5 per 100,000 from this cause alone. The sulfonamides came along in 1940 to cut the toll, and penicillin entered the scene after World War II. Immunization is now possible, with 60 to 75 per cent effectiveness.

Pneumonia is linked with influenza in statistics because the onset is similar and because pneumonia often follows an attack of influenza. Most of the deaths, however, are ascribed to pneumonia.

The Communicable Disease Center of the Public Health Service at Atlanta, Georgia, has an Influenza Surveillance Unit which collects and analyzes data from many sources on the prevalence of the disease.

Tuberculosis, long termed the "Captain of the Men of Death," no longer has such status, yet about 60,000 new active cases can be anticipated yearly in the United States, and the reservoir of cases because of activity, relapse, or pulmonary insufficiency may be 200,000 to 300,000. In many other parts of the world it continues to be a vicious killer.

Phthisis is mentioned in the medical writings of Greece, Alexandria, and Rome, but with very confused ideas of its causes and how to treat it. One of the remedies mentioned by Pliny the Elder was the liver of a wolf. There was some appreciation in early times of the fact that it was contagious, but later this was

[24] *Proc. Soc. Exper. Biol. & Med.,* October, 1962.

overlooked or not believed. Some investigators died of the disease—Stark, Baillie, Bayle, and Laennec for example. The two latter performed many autopsies and concluded that it was a distinct disease. The more common conclusion that it was not contagious grew from a theory that it was just a final stage of other diseases of the chest. Even Virchow believed this. Koch's discovery of the tubercle bacillus in 1882 settled that argument. Yet in Spain and in Italy in the sixteenth century, laws required that all cases be reported and that the victim's effects be burned, the public seeming to have more knowledge in this respect than the doctors.

The battle against tuberculosis represents one of the first widespread, highly organized efforts by laymen to help in controlling disease. The original ideas for the mass attack, however, came from doctors. Three consulting pathologists to the Department of Health of New York City—Drs. Biggs, Prudden, and Loomis—made an official report and issued a leaflet on tuberculosis for the public in 1889. The idea for the organization of a voluntary group came also from a physician, Dr. Lawrence F. Flick, who with associates organized in 1892 the Pennsylvania Society for the Prevention of Tuberculosis. So in advance of the times was this action that it was not until nine years later that the second state society was inaugurated in Ohio. New York was the third state to enter the fight with organization in 1902 of the Committee for the Prevention of Tuberculosis of the Charity Organization Society of New York. By 1904 when the National Association for the Study and Prevention of Tuberculosis was organized in Atlantic City (name changed in 1918 to National Tuberculosis Association), there were in existence 23 state or local associations. Now practically every city, county, and state has an active organization.

Referring to the National Tuberculosis Association Charles-Edward A. Winslow[25] said: "For nearly a quarter of a century it has been the leading and the stabilizing force in the development of a sound and progressive program for the control of tuberculosis in the United States; and, by opening our vision to the possibilities of mobilizing popular support for the public health program as a whole, it has transformed that program throughout the world."

Long concerned with education, prevention, and care programs, the societies are readily taking the further step of joining forces with those who are conducting research. Diseases change. As new treatments are devised to destroy the germ, the germ acquires resistance and changes too. Research continues on immunization. Investigations must tie in with those in allied fields—for example, lung cancer, especially in tuberculous patients.

Tuberculosis is not licked. In a tuberculin testing program in Chicago schools in 1960, 16 per cent of some 14,000 students were reactors. Relapses and reactivations occur after "cures" in all too many cases. One authority[26] declares:

[25] *Life of Hermann M. Biggs.* Philadelphia, Lea and Febiger, 1929.
[26] From remarks by Dr. Edward A. Piszczek, field director, Suburban Cook County Tuberculosis District: TB Round-Up. *The Challenge,* The Tuberculosis Institute of Chicago and Cook County, December, 1960, p. 8.

People who have ever been diagnosed as tuberculous should have medical attention as long as they live. In many instances a chest x-ray once or twice a year is enough, and they may get this free of charge at a mobile unit in their home neighborhood or possibly at the place where they work. Some old cases should have more frequent x-rays, periodic sputum studies or a course of treatment with the new drugs, as recommended by their physicians. . . . Last year 30 per cent of the 509 patients treated in our sanitarium (Suburban Cook County) had been in a tuberculosis hospital previously, and of that group ten had been inactive for more than ten years.

As an event in the history of tuberculosis, the closing of the Trudeau Sanatorium at Saranac Lake, New York, on December 1, 1954, was an occasion for rejoicing rather than mourning. The average occupancy of less than 70 patients, as compared with its capacity of 180, did not justify continued operation. When the sanatorium was founded in 1884 by a tuberculosis victim, Dr. Edward L. Trudeau, the only known treatment was a "rest cure" with some medical supervision. The hospital was initially a one-room cottage. The fee was five dollars a week including medical care. It grew to 51 buildings on a 100-acre tract, so great was the demand. Not only that, it spurred the opening of hundreds of similar institutions, many of them of the cottage colony type, when "fresh air" was supposed to be the cure-all for all types of the disease and victims slept through the coldest winters on open porches.

The son of the founder,[27] in speaking of the closing, said:

My father would look on the closing of Trudeau Sanatorium as a victory and would be happy to know that new drugs and surgical methods seem to have outmoded the type of care which Trudeau Sanatorium supplied. He would be proud to know that his institution has had some part in helping to reduce the death rate from tuberculosis in America from 158 per 100,000 in 1910 to approximately 12 per 100,000 today.

The director of the Trudeau-Saranac Institute, which operated the sanatorium, Dr. Gordon Meade, said that the institute would continue its research programs in tuberculosis and other lung diseases. He attributed the declining numbers of patients to the discovery of new drugs and surgical methods, the decline in relapse and reinfection rates, increase in public education resulting in earlier detection, and increase in the number of state, federal, and voluntary institutions providing care.

Emphysema is said to be more common than tuberculosis and lung cancer combined; upward of a million persons have it. The apparent causes are infection, tumors, asthma, smoking. The minute air sacs in the lungs become distended and lose their elasticity. Instead of collapsing and forcing air out after each breath, they permit it to stagnate. Labored and painful breathing is the result. If there is infection, treatment is with antibiotics; if asthma is the cause, hormones are used; removal of the involved portion of the lung may be necessary in serious cases. There is no real cure; the breathlessness has to be fought

[27] From a dispatch from Saranac Lake: *Mod. Hosp.,* December, 1954, p. 181.

the rest of the victim's life, but there are some aids to living with it, such as bronchodilating drugs which cause relaxation of the bronchial muscle and special detergents developed to liquefy the accumulated secretions. Most good hospitals also have intermittent positive pressure breathing apparatus which breathes for the patient mechanically. Oxygen therapy is also used but it must be carefully regulated. Physiatrists, however, point out that no apparatus will serve as well as the patient's own muscular activity and that he should be encouraged to keep active, to inhale deeply while walking, and to exercise daily and cultivate good breathing habits and posture. These are also preventive measures. In *Today's Health* for September, 1961, it was reported that the nation's first mobile emphysema testing project was under way in Alabama, financed by 24 of the state's county tuberculosis associations and the national associations, with the hope of identifying early breathing abnormalities that might lead to emphysema.

Emphysema may be on the way to losing its reputation as "our most neglected disease"—sometimes diagnosed as bronchitis, sometimes asthma, sometimes as a symptom of aging—most often just passed off as the shortness-of-breath ailment.

Immunization Problems Continue

Vigilance against plague cannot be relaxed. The booming population of California is blamed for sporadic cases of bubonic plague contracted from wild rodents. Other small animals also can transmit the disease through exchange of fleas. Vaccines have been developed against plague, but immunity is not achieved with a single injection. The sulfa drugs and the antibiotics are used in treatment with some success.

In an article, "The Future of Immunization," Dr. Geoffrey Edsall[28] said in part:

> The fact is that there are still great deficiencies in our knowledge of both the principles and the application of immunization. . . . Many unsolved difficulties in disease control revolve around what appear to be basic deficiencies in the antigenic response to the disease, and others are complicated by the multiplicity of antigens concerned. Certainly no single line of research promises success, for on the one hand the patterns of immunity in nature differ tremendously from disease to disease, and on the other hand the specific immunizing antigens in various diseases differ greatly in chemical composition, stability, ease of extraction and purification, and, indeed, in antigenicity. Finally, the various diseases which concern us differ among themselves in their basic antigenic stability.

All discussion of infectious diseases and their treatment should include mention of the antibiotics, with some emphasis on caution in their use. They are generally effective against streptococcic throats, tonsillitis, and bacterial pneumonia. Cautious physicians delay antibiotic medication, knowing that it may

[28] Superintendent, Institute of Laboratories, Massachusetts Department of Health, and Professor of Applied Microbiology, Harvard School of Public Health: *Pub. Health Rep.*, September, 1961.

evoke allergic reactions ranging from hives to sudden death in about one of every ten patients. Sometimes the reaction does not occur until after a number of treatments. Penicillin is the worst; to it can be traced an appalling number of deaths. An enzyme that is useful in counteracting acute reactions, penicillinase, must be administered with equal caution because it, in turn, has resulted in severe allergic shock reactions. Synthetic penicillins may overcome this problem of allergy.

New Concepts

Host susceptibility is a factor in infectious disease that has been slow in attracting study, according to the authors of "An Epidemiologic Approach to Inherited Disease Susceptibility."[29] They state:

> Epidemiologists are now concerned with a broad array of diseases in which a specific invading parasite or toxic substance cannot be identified as of etiological importance. In some, long periods of latent abnormal metabolism or even frank tissue pathology precede manifest disease. Diabetes, rheumatoid arthritis, atherosclerosis, ischemic heart disease, and allergic phenomena, as well as many other diseases, fall into this category. In studying these conditions the epidemiologist is challenged by the tasks of identifying the susceptible individual, determining the basic defect, and then assessing the factors or stresses which break through the reserve of the susceptible individual and cause disease. To achieve this goal it is necessary to seek new clues to disease susceptibility and to find new ways to identify, prior to the appearance of manifest disease, those individuals who are subject to an increased risk.

This upsets the notion that infectious diseases, at least, have a specific cause that can be treated by specific measures. It brings the epidemiologist back to basic science and the strong conviction by the medical geneticist that "genes may influence the occurrence of disease in a variety of ways" and that "some diseases are under direct genetic control." Why some persons die and others recover from the same kind of infectious disease, and why others, despite close contact, do not contract it at all, are questions being subjected to continuing investigation.

World-wide Coordinated Action

A dispatch from Urbana, Illinois, on November 30, 1960, disclosed the organization from headquarters at the University of Illinois of the world's newest scientific organization, International Federation of Parasitologists, as a step to coordinate efforts toward world health.

The scope of the organization's objective is its distinguishing feature. It is "to unite scientists concerned with age-old scourges of mankind, making information available and combining in common attack on parasite problems which

[29] Thomas D. Durbin, M.D., Dr. P. H., and Baruch S. Blumberg, M.D., Ph.D.: *Pub. Health Rep.*, June, 1961, pp. 499–505.

affect public health, livestock and fishing industries, wildlife conservation, and control of insects and other pests."

Workers in medical, veterinary, and biological fields are included in the federation, which consists of affiliated societies and individuals and extends throughout the world, including scientists of both Eastern and Western countries. It works through the World Health Organization, serving as an international study group. It supports international conferences and communications in its field.

Maternal and Infant Welfare

The decrease in infant mortality which took place during the eighteenth century may be attributed to the renewed favor found for maternal breast-feeding and to the improvements in child-care; in London, between 1730 and 1749, three out of every four children died before the age of five; between 1790 and 1809, the proportion had declined to one in two. Robert Watt, a professor at Glasgow University, estimated at the beginning of the nineteenth century that more than half the human race died before the age of ten, and that more than a third of these deaths were due to smallpox.[30]

The area of maternal and infant welfare is one of warm social appeal. It was with schemes for the assistance of poor mothers and their babies that social welfare began in the eighteenth century. Its bearing on the future of society gives this area further appeal from a practical standpoint. Working with the medical profession and public health services to improve maternal and child care are many voluntary organizations which contribute a great deal of support. Prominent among them is the American Committee on Maternal and Infant Welfare, founded in 1919 by Dr. Fred L. Adair. A committee of this organization headed by Dr. Luella E. Nadelhoffer developed a teaching outline for programs in hospital administration, the objectives of which were:

1. To appreciate the historical background, and understand the aims of a maternal welfare program
2. To know the federal, state, and local agencies (voluntary and official) interested in maternal welfare and to be familiar with what these programs offer
3. To become aware of standards necessary for adequate maternity care insofar as the hospital is concerned
4. To realize that cooperation with other community agencies in the field is important
5. To glimpse present trends and problems

The aims of a maternal welfare program were stated to be:

For the protection of the health of mothers and their offspring before and during pregnancy and labor and after confinement to the end that the conditions which menace and interfere with the health or life of the mother or infant may be improved or prevented, disease and disorder corrected, health promoted and

[30] René Sand: *The Advance to Social Medicine*. London, Staples Press, 1952, p. 165.

lives saved; to teach the principles and practices of general and personal hygiene and health to parents and to improve and generalize the standards and methods of training physicians, nurses and others dealing with the problems of maternity.

In the following outline pertinent facts in the history of maternal welfare in the United States were listed:

1912—Establishment of U.S. Children's Bureau, with birth registration areas established in 1915
1919—Formation of Joint Committee on Maternal Welfare, which in 1934 became the American Committee on Maternal Welfare, Inc. (later changed to American Association for Maternal and Infant Health), by agencies interested in maternal and infant welfare:

    1. American Child Health Association (no longer in existence)
    2. American Gynecological Society
    3. American Association of Obstetricians, Gynecologists, and Abdominal Surgeons
    4. Central Association of Obstetricians and Gynecologists
    5. New England Obstetrical and Gynecological Society
    6. Section on Obstetrics and Gynecology of the American Medical Association

1921—The Sheppard Towner Act—important because as a result, bureaus of maternal and infant welfare in states were begun
1930—White House Conference on Child Health and Protection called by President Herbert Hoover. Dr. Fred L. Adair appointed chairman of the Committee on Prenatal and Maternal Care

These events were followed by formation of maternal mortality committees, prominent among them those of the New York Academy of Medicine and the Philadelphia County Medical Society, and the development of teaching centers.

Historically, the statistics on maternal and infant welfare give a bright picture of the advance of care in this field. It was not only poverty-stricken mothers who in former times died early and whose children preceded them in death. Queen Anne of England, who died in 1749 at the age of 49, had 17 children. Sixteen died in infancy; the other at the age of 11 years.

Nowadays in the United States around 1,400 mothers die annually as a result of pregnancy and childbirth. This figure represents a decline of about 56 per cent from the 1950 rate. Credited for the reduction are prenatal care and improved obstetrical service.

For prematures under two pounds, there is a better than 25 per cent chance to live as compared with little chance twenty years ago. The urgent problem is to keep them warm. Incubators at Babies Hospital, New York, utilize infrared heat, developed by a doctor in the hospital's department of anatomy in cooperation with a manufacturer. Prematurity is the chief cause of infant deaths, almost 50 per cent, and frequently is due to little or no prenatal care.

The United Hospitals of Newark, New Jersey, established in 1962 a special treatment center for birth defects, one of less than ten similar units in the United

States. Dramatic episodes in hospitals are created by the desperate attempts to correct such defects. An example[31] was that of Randy Wilson, born with hardly more than stubs of his esophagus. There was a fistula growing between his esophagus and trachea. Through it, stomach secretions had backed into his lungs. On his second day of life this fistula was closed off by cutting and suturing. But saliva had been sucked down his windpipe, causing pneumonia; the surgeon made an opening in his neck and drew the end of his upper esophagus through it, opening the end so that the saliva which went into his esophagus would then drain out through the new opening. But the air admitted by chest surgery caused a partial collapse of his right lung; a tube was inserted into this lung to suction out air and fluid, the outside end being attached to a chest suction apparatus. The tube remained in his lung four days until it was back to normal, at which time he was taken back to surgery for his second operation, consisting of making an opening into his stomach and inserting a feeding tube which protrudes from his side. Previously he had been fed intravenously. The tube is now coiled up and taped to his body with the opening clamped shut between feedings. He can have no solid food. He must have another operation later, involving removal of a piece of his large intestine which will be sutured to each end of his esophagus, making it complete. When his progress and physical condition permit, he will have this third operation, sometime between his first and fifth year. After that he will have to learn how to swallow, eat, and drink.

One of Randy's doctors made an illuminating comment on the difference between pediatric and other surgery. "Operating on a baby," he said, "is like playing dolls. Everything in his body is so tiny—his stomach, for instance, is little bigger than a pecan—that you have to use surgical instruments scaled down to extremely small sizes."

A somewhat similar birth defect occurred in a baby born on November 30, 1959, in Sherman Hospital, Elgin, Illinois.[32] At his first feeding it was discovered that he could not swallow. Examination, followed by x-ray, showed that the upper part of the esophagus was closed and that the lower portion was attached to the windpipe, preventing food and saliva from passing normally to the stomach and resulting in regurgitation which occasionally passed into the windpipe and thence to the lungs, causing strangulation or pneumonia. A three-hour operation was performed successfully when the baby was three days old; the chest was opened, both ends of the esophagus were freed from surrounding tissue, the abnormal opening into the windpipe was disconnected and closed, and the two ends of the esophagus were joined. The baby was discharged from the hospital 17 days later with a normal weight of six pounds.

Of course, the thalidomide tragedies have attracted international attention to the problem of birth defects of all kinds, and they have made physicians more

[31] *Scope*, September, 1962. (Published by Memorial Baptist Hospital, Houston.)
[32] Rare Operation Saves Life of Baby. *The Sherman R*, January, 1960.

cautious about prescribing drugs, especially for pregnant women. Developed by German scientists, the drug was introduced into Britain in 1958. Manufacturers withdrew it from sale in November, 1961, after reports that mothers who had taken it were giving birth to babies with shortened arms, legs, and other deformities. Specialists estimate that about 1,400 such babies were born in Britain. Prompt withdrawal of the drug from sale in the United States minimized the danger. Much more rigid controls over drugs are likely to result in all countries in consequence, and the plight of the deformed child from any cause is being given renewed attention by child welfare organizations.

MENTAL ILLNESS

It is surely beyond doubt today that modern psychiatry is able to help people who could not previously be helped; anyone who has seen the transformation it can bring about in a painfully disordered child is apt to be impatient with the chronic scoffers. It has emphasized the role of love in normal development and has produced a new awareness of the importance of childhood, a greater generosity of spirit toward the needs of the child. It has provided man with ways and means of deepening his understanding of himself and of his basic problems as a culture-building animal. In sum, it represents, perhaps, a crucial break-through in man's pursuit of self-knowledge and self-realization.[33]

When a magazine of the nature and stature of *The Atlantic* publishes a special supplement, as it did in July, 1961, devoting 49 of its pages to contributions by 14 writers on the subject of psychiatry in American life, the time has arrived when mental illness has achieved the importance it deserves among the great health problem areas.

A long, dismal history of heroic but sporadic effort forms the background of the study of mental disease. Because the insane were supposed to be possessed of evil spirits, the ancients treated them cruelly to drive these spirits out, shutting them up, chaining, starving, and beating them. Medieval Christians tortured them also, believing that they were possessed of the devil. The exceptions to this treatment are notable. Asclepiades, a Greek physician who practiced in Rome in the first century B.C., advocated humane treatment, occupation, teaching, and music and wine to calm them. Caelus Aurelianus in the fourth century and Paul of Aegina in the seventh argued against restraint, privation, and punishment in their treatment. Gentle and considerate treatment was the rule in Mohammedan countries.

Not until the sixteenth century was action taken in western Europe to use psychotherapy and humane methods in treating mental patients. The instigator of the change was Felix Plater, anatomist and municipal physician at Basel in the 1570's. Plater also began the work of classifying mental disorders. Elsewhere conditions did not improve. In Paris at the Hotel Dieu the unmanageable pa-

[33] Charles J. Rolo, Editor of the Special Supplement. *The Atlantic,* July, 1961, pp. 62–111.

tients were first subjected to fasting, purging, bleeding, and douching; but if they did not respond to this treatment, they were transferred to underground cells elsewhere where they were quickly stricken with typhus, dysentery and tuberculosis because of the sanitary conditions, cruelty, and deprivation of air and proper food.

In the early years of the nineteenth century the mental specialist Jean-Etienne-Dominique Esquirol established a nursing home at Paris in which the patients were well treated. Philippe Pinel in 1798 struck off the chains of the insane at Bicetre in Paris and put them under sympathetic physicians in hospitals. He founded the "open-door" school of psychiatry, but had no followers for a long time. In most places the mentally ill were still chained in dungeons.

The Quakers founded a model asylum in 1792 at York, England—the York Retreat—whose medical superintendent in 1842, Daniel Hack Tuke, founded the Society for Improving the Condition of the Insane, with Lord Shaftesbury as president. During the same period Dorothea Lynde Dix in the United States was waging a campaign for reform of prisons and lunatic asylums in both her country and Europe. It is to be noted that the psychiatrists had no great influence until the public became aroused by reformers. One psychiatrist, Johann Heinroth, even as uneducated people do today, regarded insanity as divine punishment for personal guilt, as shown in his books which appeared between 1818 and 1834.

Wilhelm Griesinger (1817–1868), of Stuttgart, did away, so Garrison[34] states, "with much of the mysticism of the past, gave clear and unmistakable clinical pictures based upon rational psychological analysis, aimed to connect the subject with pathological anatomy, and advocated the open door and the psychiatric clinic." The pioneer of experimental psychiatry was Emil Kraepelin (1856–1927), professor of psychiatry at Munich. Again to quote Garrison, he was "the great systematist of psychiatry, in which he brought order out of chaos."

A history of American psychiatry was written in 1916 by Henry Mills Hurd (1843–1927), professor of psychiatry and superintendent of the Johns Hopkins Hospital from 1889 to 1911, which is included in *The Institutional Care of the Insane in the United States and Canada,* which he edited. Adolf Meyer of Switzerland joined the faculty of the same university in 1910 and brought the new concept of "psychobiology" into American psychiatry. This idea of fusing physiology and psychology had some similarity to the reasoning of Sigmund Freud, professor of neurology at Vienna, who stressed the effect of the mind upon the body, along with the great influence of the individual's past history, especially in childhood, upon his neurosis. Alfred Adler of Vienna, one of Freud's pupils, advanced in 1907 the idea of the inferiority complex, organic inferiority of some kind, as one of the chief causes of neurosis.

The new psychiatry is enmeshed with the biological sciences and the social sciences to such a degree that there is no clear pattern. Yet a distinct change

[34] *Op. cit.,* p. 647.

appears in the approach to mental illness. Just as nobody is perfect physically, so nobody is perfect mentally, and this truism has penetrated public consciousness to the point where the woman next door says, "I have an appointment with my psychiatrist," as casually as she would if it were a dental or medical interview. The psychiatrist is included in consultations concerning patients whose physical condition creates emotional disturbance but who are not mentally ill, and he is asked to talk with others who are about to undergo or who have just undergone major surgery or some other rather frightening procedure. The acceptance that is beginning to be given psychological along with physical direction holds promise of prevention of mental illness that is the most encouraging element in the mental problem area.

Offsetting this is the discouraging fact that too little of this attitude is penetrating the public institutions for the mentally ill. There are many patients in these institutions who with the newer drugs and psychotherapy could be safely released, but there are not enough psychiatrists on their staffs to devote sufficient time to individual diagnosis and direction. Also, the fact cannot be escaped that a large number cannot be helped by any treatment, yet can live out their lives more comfortably if they receive more understanding care, for which there are not now enough personnel. Like long-term patients who have physical disabilities, they are frustrating to those who care for them because the door of hope is closed; but there remains the incentive to do all that can be done to ease their lives. Some of the mental patients, it is true, are so unmanageable and unresponsive that caring for them becomes most disagreeable. This is the unique final problem of mental illness for which there is no solution.

For those who can pay and for whom there is hope of improvement, the psychiatric departments that many general hospitals are establishing are a most promising development, as are also the psychiatric day clinics that are appearing in many places. Out of this linkage with the general hospital will come more appreciation of the contribution that psychiatry can make to recovery from physical illness. This is territory long since discovered but far from thoroughly explored.

Dr. Mortimer Ostow,[35] a practicing psychoanalyst associated with New York's Montefiore Hospital, in discussing "the new drugs," concluded his article with the statement: "Drug therapy has provided the first new tool of major significance for the treatment and understanding of mental illness in several decades. I would find it difficult to overestimate its role in psychiatric and psychoanalytic practice and theory in the years to come." His conclusion is preceded by warning of the limitations, chief among which is "its inapplicability to most patients with neurotic disorders." He asserts: "When the neurosis is treated psychotherapeutically and dynamic changes invoke energetic perturbations, drugs are virtually useless. The spontaneous deviations are so small and the equilibrium so fluid that even a small pharmaceutic push easily causes an

[35] *The Atlantic, op. cit.*

inordinate swing from which a second set of symptoms evolves and replaces those symptoms that have been relieved."

The caution expressed in an article by Dr. Howard D. Sabing,[36] of Cincin-nati, also indicates that solution of the mental illness problem is not in sight, notwithstanding the spectacular advances:

> Is the millennium just around the corner? Are the mental hospitals to be emptied out soon, and will the new drugs produce in us the serene peace of mind and tranquility that the followers of Epicurus searched for in their philosophy? Let's not kid ourselves about these things. There are many chronic neurological and psychiatric diseases, and although we talk a great deal about their etiology, we know practically nothing about the cause of many of these conditions which fill half our hospital beds. Rational therapy will come after we gain this knowledge. Furthermore, as we empty a few beds occupied by these psychotics who are young, we fill them up immediately with the aged. The geriatric problem is a monstrous one. . . . We have almost exhausted ourselves striving for a big thing we call "security" during the last quarter century, and we seem no closer to it than when we started. Let us not add another unattainable goal of dubious values, i. e., "serenity," pills or no pills.

Alcoholism and Narcotic Addiction

Nearly five million Americans are suffering from a disease of their own creation—a form of mental disease really—alcoholism. The disease has its own scientific publication, *Journal for Studies of Alcohol,* and scientific society, the National Council of Alcoholism. Both are contributing enormously to knowledge of the disease, its causes, its treatment, its effects—social, psychological, and economic, as well as physical.

As the nation's fourth greatest health problem, alcoholism is of the greatest concern to doctors and hospitals. Its uncontrollability by such specific means as surgery and miracle drugs makes it a baffling problem. It is not only incapacitating; it makes its victims more susceptible to other diseases.

Brain deterioration is related to chronic alcoholism or an associated nutritional defect, according to the results of a study reported in the December, 1959, issue of the American Medical Association's *Archives of Neurology.* The study was made by doctors in Massachusetts General Hospital and the Harvard Medical School. The persons studied lacked muscular coordination of gait and of the legs.

There is a new drug, chlordiazepoxide, which has some effect against delirium tremens and alcoholic hangovers. When injected into the veins of victims it is said to make them calm enough to be interviewed within a few seconds. Hospitalization with special treatment including psychological is effecting some cures (see Chap. 21).

In 1953 the American Medical Association appointed a subcommittee on

[36] Whence the Millenium. *American Professional Pharmacist,* May, 1956.

alcoholism to function under the Committee on Mental Health, its main aim to be development of community programs coordinated with public and private hospitals, public health and education departments, and other interested agencies.

Drug addiction is an even more melancholy problem than alcoholism. According to a Columbia University study, more patients recover from cancer than from narcotic addiction. Withdrawal produces devastating symptoms which are ameliorated only by a return to the drug, whereas the withdrawal symptoms of alcohol are mainly psychic, since the body does not acquire physical dependence on the presence of alcohol in the tissues.

There are some 50,000 addicts in the United States, 44 per cent of them in New York, 14 per cent in Illinois, 13 per cent in California. Heroin accounts for 92 per cent of the addiction. Drug addiction among members of the medical and allied professions is a hundred times greater than among the general population, the study showed, pointing out the emotional drain on the life of the doctor. Often alcohol and barbiturates take the place of a vacation. The drugs are near and are available.

Subsequent to the study, the National Association for the Prevention of Addiction to Narcotics announced[37] a campaign for funds to establish projects at an East Coast and a West Coast medical center to experiment with outpatient treatment of narcotics addiction.

Drugs are costly, which is why so many addicts turn to crime to finance the habit. Women comprise only 20 per cent of addicts.

Forced hospitalization has been tried in New York and other places. "Cures" are usually so brief that the results are most discouraging.

RHEUMATIC DISEASES

It is of vital importance that those who come in contact with the child who has a chronic illness such as rheumatoid arthritis are geared in their thinking to a program of comprehensive care. It is of equal importance that they be warm, giving, mature persons aware of the far-reaching effects of hospitalization as evidenced by the child's behavior. Chronic illness affects countless numbers of children. It is a challenging task to help a child learn to live with his illness so that he can develop those inner strengths and resources which will enable him to live comfortably with others. It is a task which requires not only the cooperation of the parents, but also the assistance of a closely allied medical team. Our team consists of internists, pediatrician, orthopedists, psychiatrist, nurse, physical therapist, occupational therapist, psychologist, medical social worker, and many others who help to bridge the gap between home and hospital.[38]

Rheumatic disease causes disability so severe that 320,000 persons in the United States each year cannot be employed. Some 12 million persons are

---

[37] New York Times–Chicago Tribune Service, October 1, 1963.
[38] Lucille A. McMahon and Mary Norma O'Hara: Care of Arthritic Child Calls for Multidiscipline Approach. *Hosp. Topics,* September, 1962, p. 79. Miss McMahon is a medical social worker in the Arthritis Clinical Study Section, and Miss O'Hara is Assistant Professor of Nursing, Pediatrics, at the University of Rochester School of Medicine and Dentistry, New York.

suffering from this group of diseases. About the cause only the most vague statements can be made, such as emotional and physical stress and strain, fatigue, injury, shock.

Arthritis is one of the most disabling diseases. Research has developed treatment which relieves some kinds of conditions in some patients. Synthetic cortisone-type hormones were at first hailed as offering bright prospects, but dangerous side effects darkened the picture. Continued research by experimentation has resulted in the development of new synthetic hormones that are effective and also safe if the right dosage is used. The new products are being administered to more than a million patients, giving them considerable relief, although severe cases which require long-continued treatment still suffer side effects. So the experiments go on, and the old and the new hormones are tried in different combinations, and the still more potent steroids are being employed with watchfulness and caution. In the arthritis center at Rochester, New York, cortisone therapy is avoided because of its medical complications; steroids are also not generally used in treating a child with rheumatoid arthritis, because of the problem of gradual withdrawal which is accompanied by swings of mood.

Yet Evanston (Illinois) Hospital reports that most of the children under treatment in its juvenile rheumatoid arthritis clinic show improvement through the use of cortisone, ACTH, and similar drugs, along with physical therapy and surgery. The clinic was established in 1950 in cooperation with the Division of Services for Crippled Children of the State of Illinois.

A film[39] outlining the latest developments in the treatment of arthritis was produced by the Canadian Arthritis and Rheumatism Society. In the film it is pointed out that there is good initial response to some of the drugs being used but there are also side effects. Emphasized is the fact that although conservative therapy is slow and unspectacular, there are many techniques and procedures which bring relief and a measure of improvement.

The Arthritis and Rheumatism Foundation has stated that crippling can be prevented in about 70 per cent of cases if proper treatment is started early.

As in cancer, arthritis, a disease for which medical science has not found the cause or cure, is a boon to quacks who promise all sorts of virtues for many kinds of concoctions, wasting the victim's time and money on self-medication and delaying proper medical treatment to prevent needless crippling. Ordinary sea water, condensed, was one such "treatment," selling at $3.00 a pint. High-priced pills are marketed which are nothing more than disguised aspirin. An "electro" bracelet was until lately being sold to treat muscle pains, contusions, arthritis, rheumatism, sprains, etc., at a price of $7.50.

Muscular dystrophy is estimated to have 200,000 victims in the United States alone, half of them children. This hereditary disease is progressive and, while not usually fatal in itself, causes death because the weakened muscles cannot combat the complications brought on by other diseases. Treatment brought

[39] *Canad. Hosp.*, April, 1962.

little or no results until vigorous research was instigated in 1950 by the Muscular Dystrophy Associations of America. Animal experimentation has given some prospect of success with drugs. A blood test has been devised for infants which shows whether they are likely to have the disease, which permits starting physical therapy earlier and delaying the helpless stage.

The evidence collected seems to be pointing toward the idea that muscular dystrophy is a generalized disease, and investigators are working on the theory that some substance is missing in the blood which possibly might be replaced by a synthetic product. Other investigators cling to the idea that it is a disease of the muscles alone and does not involve the tissues generally.

CHRONIC ILLNESS

The long duration of a chronic illness is the reason for its emptying the pocketbook for all but the wealthy citizen, and the reason the financial problem in the community is so great is that these patients are uninteresting to philanthropists as well as to doctors. The acute patient can be restored quickly to economic usefulness; the chronic patient does not represent as good an investment.[40]

The problem and the attitude have changed a little since Dr. Bluestone made that comment in 1935. His belief that the chronic patient should be a challenge to the scientific physician is shared by a few more members of the medical profession than it was then. One of the reasons is that there has been progress in the alleviation of a number of so-called chronic diseases, and even cures in some cases.

Dr. Bluestone deplored the removal of chronically ill patients to a custodial type of hospital, thus taking them away from the benefit of the specialty groups and diminishing their chance of improvement. He contended that chronic diseases, like injuries, cross the lines of medical specialties. Transfers were made, he said, at the time when the patient "most needs scientific and humanitarian care." The chronic patient should be "kept before their eyes" and "not isolated."

The current crusading over care of the aged, among whom there are an especially great proportion of chronically ill, has opened the eyes of physicians and physiologists to the barbarity of "dumping" the chronically ill into custodial institutions in which scientific medical treatment is virtually nonexistent. Agreement is increasing with Dr. Bluestone's conviction that the patient who is in the hospital for a longer period is a subject for study of the "remote results" of treatment, which in the short term can only be guessed. Besides, the chronic patient is susceptible to "complicating or intercurrent acute disease" for which he needs good care.

These ideas are beginning to percolate. The doctor is starting to recognize that the general hospital has advantages for all types of patients. The cost pro-

[40] E. M. Bluestone: *Bull. Am. Hosp. A.,* July, 1935. Dr. Bluestone was then director of Montefiore Hospital, New York.

hibits complete integration, but affiliated units or separate but administratively connected facilities are increasing in number.

A great many diseases result in chronic illness. Besides those which have been discussed, there are such crippling ones as *multiple sclerosis,* the initial signs of which are so like those of other afflictions that diagnosis in the early stages may be missed. The cause is not known, but observation has seemed to establish that the most frequent victims are neurotics. Infection is also given as a possible cause. There is no satisfactory treatment but the victims have unaccountable periods of remission which prolong their lives. *Parkinson's disease,* the "shaking palsy," is also disabling, although the crippling effects of the symptoms may be reduced by treatment. Lasting relief is promised by bloodless surgery of the brain achieved through hypothermia or intense cold, as first employed in this disease by Dr. Irving S. Cooper, of St. Barnabas Hospital, New York, in 1962. He previously had used injections of a special kind of alcohol in surgery for this and similar neurological conditions on more than 2,000 patients. Some hope is therefore extended to the 300,000 victims of Parkinson's disease. *Cerebral palsy* is another affliction that does not yield to treatment, as yet, but whose victims can be helped to lead fairly normal lives through education, training, and physical therapy.

Diabetes is a chronic disease which is under control, thanks to Banting and Best's isolation of insulin from the animal pancreas more than forty years ago and their treatment of patients with it the following year. There are estimated to be around a million diabetics in the United States, but there may be more because so many persons do not know they have it until the symptoms are too disturbing or it is discovered in a precautionary test before surgery. An especially serious complication of untreated diabetes is diabetic retinopathy.

There are types of *thyroid disease* which cause chronic illness, sometimes only to the point of constant fatigue both physically and mentally. Partial hypothyroidism is one condition which can be diagnosed by analysis of the blood and can be treated by thyroid medication. For hyperthyroidism surgery remains the most effective treatment, although the value of radioactive iodine is also acknowledged when used in conjunction with it.

Asthma is a widespread chronic illness. The term appears early in medical literature. Hippocrates mentioned it in four of his aphorisms. Symptoms were recognized and methods of treatment recommended by many later physicians. That the condition had a nervous origin was first suggested by Thomas Willis (1621–1675), and he recognized a pneumonic and a convulsive type. In 1698 a physician who suffered from asthma himself, Sir John Floyer, wrote a book, *Treatise of the Asthma.* He observed that different odors and foods affected sufferers differently. He especially noted that some had attacks caused by London fogs and smoke.

With Auenbrugger's invention of percussion, Laennec's invention of the stethoscope, and Roentgen's discovery of x-rays, more understanding of the disease and its management was possible. Another doctor who had asthma himself, Henry Hyde Salter, of London, published in 1860 the best nineteenth-century book on the subject, *Asthma: Its Pathology and Treatment*. Cats were his main object of attack.

Hay fever (wrongly named because hay does not produce it, and anyway there is no measurable fever) was first ascribed to pollen by John Elliotson (1786–1868), who suffered from it. This as a cause was proved beyond doubt through experimentation by another victim, Charles Harrison Blackley (1820–1900), of Manchester, England. By one of his experiments he proved that pollen is high up in the air as well as near the ground.

The diseases including eczema and other skin conditions, which like asthma and hay fever are related to allergies in causation, have been the subject through the years of a great many studies, and there remain many unknowns and considerable confusion and disagreement. Nobody knows why some persons are allergic, others not. Skin tests have proved useful in detecting causes, but they must be accompanied by and correlated with clinical observations. Hereditary influences are recognized, which has made preventive measures possible when the history of the patient is known. Avoidance of certain occupations is often indicated. Injections are useful in treatment. Inhalants and sprays using epinephrine, or Adrenalin, and certain newer products are effective. The antihistamines and ACTH may bring relief. Allergy to drugs opens a whole new field for exploration.

The American Foundation for Allergy, recently formed, is doing educational work in prevention and is supporting treatment centers. Both in the Americas and in Europe homes are being established for asthmatic children.

A crippling bone disease, *Paget's disease,* has been considered incurable for a century, but recent experiments with large doses of aspirin have shown lessening of pain and of other symptoms.

Hemophilia is a disease against which the only weapon is preparedness for instant action when bleeding occurs. One in every 10,000 white males suffers from it. The disease is transmitted through the female, but only males inherit it. Before the era of transfusions, the life span of the hemophiliac was usually short. Failure to get admitted to a hospital promptly on one occasion when internal bleeding occurred led Frank Schnabel to organize a Montreal chapter of the National Hemophilia Foundation, which had previously been set up in the United States, to campaign for a center for treatment, and to help to set up a research program on hemophilia at McGill University.[41]

Except in certain crises, chronic disease victims are not hospitalized until the late stages. Rehabilitation, discussed in the section which follows, is a promising way of deferring or even preventing, in some instances, these advanced conditions.

[41] Robert Littell: Bearer Is a Hemophiliac. *Liberty*, February, 1959.

REHABILITATION

None of us is wise enough to predict accurately the forces for good or evil which will dominate the international scene in the years to come, but it is a safe guess that the measure of success with which the democratic forms of government and ways of life meet the test of human dignity and individual rights in all lands will lie, to some extent at least, in the initiative and understanding with which adequate programs for the complete rehabilitation of the world's disabled people are encouraged and developed. . . . The appeal to human welfare is far stronger than political ideology, social theory, or economic assistance. Used wisely and sincerely, medical care and better rehabilitation could form a potent force for international security and mutual trust, with insistence that disability should not mean inability, that misfortune should not remove opportunity.[42]

Although it shows the overoptimism of youth in its ideal of "complete re-habilitation of the world's disabled people," the above statement expresses well the international scope and possibilities of the movement. It also shows the influence of the enthusiastic teacher upon the thinking of the student.

The creed in rehabilitation is simply and forcefully expressed, over and over in every talk he makes, every paper he writes, every discussion he leads, by Dr. Louis B. Newman, of Chicago, professor of physical medicine and rehabilitation, Northwestern University Medical School, and chief of the Physical Medicine and Rehabilitation Service, Veterans Administration Research Hospital. The creed is this:

Life is being prolonged, but it should also be enriched.

Dr. Newman advocates more rehabilitation facilities and trained personnel in hospitals in order to assure early measures against disability; he deplores the lack of physical medicine and rehabilitation services in many general hospitals which is responsible for failure to institute prompt measures to prevent disability following injuries, strokes, heart attacks, and other misfortunes. Of the heart patient he says:[43]

Most patients with heart disorders can be rehabilitated back to useful, productive living. Physical medicine and rehabilitation activities integrated with the medical program result in improved mental and physical performance, alleviate anxiety and frustration, and eliminate other psychological complications. The total rehabilitative program must be medically directed and supervised, for the over-all medical status of the patient governs the type, amount, and timing of rehabilitative procedures. Patients who cannot return to their former employment need vocational rehabilitation. Periodic reviews of medical status and occupational environment are essential.

[42] Concluding statement of the thesis submitted by Kenzo Kiikuni in 1960 to Northwestern University for his master's degree in hospital administration. Mr. Kiikuni now heads the management consulting department of the Institute of Hospital Administration, Ministry of Welfare, Tokyo, Japan.
[43] Total Rehabilitation in Heart Disease. *J. A. M. A.*, April 15, 1961.

He adds that the earlier medically prescribed rehabilitation procedures are instituted, "the greater the prospect of aiding the patient during the trying period when he first learns that he has a 'heart disorder.'"

Physiatrists and the members of their teams work to prevent complications even when there is little that can be done for the primary disability. Invalidism spells deterioration. The challenge to keep going, to progress to at least the self-care stage, promotes general health which is so very important in achieving the degree of recovery which is maximal in the particular case, whether it be a physical or a mental disability.

The rehabilitation movement is a coordinated attack within and without the institution upon invalidism. It was long felt that much of the effort was wasted on the aged who were on the downgrade anyway. What is changing this notion is experience in trying to rehabilitate elderly patients. Success, just as among younger persons, is found to be generally in the individual's determination not to give up. In a custodial setting he does give up, and sometimes is encouraged to do so because he is easier to take care of when bedridden. In the home also, the family is inclined to be overprotective and to urge the patient to rest when exertion is what he needs for recovery or improvement. Prostheses may be cast aside, even though the patient has been thoroughly trained in their use and has been functioning very well with them at the time of leaving the rehabilitation hospital. Follow-up is the great need, but in few places is there sufficient staff to practice it with every discharged patient.

Lagging in the advance against disability is the treatment of stroke patients. One of the reasons is the persistence of mistaken notions that little can be done. Another is the fact that most of them are well up in years, and it is therefore taken for granted that comeback is unlikely. These assumptions are no longer valid, studies show.

> Aged stroke victims are walking out of D. C. General Hospital in Washington, D. C., capable of complete self-care. Of 3,000 stroke victims admitted to the hospital in the last eight years, 90 per cent responded to vigorous restorative treatment. Their stay in the hospital has been cut in half with treatment and, when released, they remain active in their homes. The patients who retrogressed after leaving the hospital were found to be in homes of well-meaning but ill-informed relatives who insist that the stroke victim return to bed.[44]

Stroke is a major rehabilitation problem. The Public Health Service estimates that about 250,000 cases occur yearly in the United States and that some two and a quarter million persons have been disabled from this cause. Although sometimes quickly fatal, frequently the paralyzed victim lives for many years in misery if he does not receive proper care.

There remain insufficient facilities and extreme shortages of skilled personnel for the care of patients who would benefit by rehabilitation. Cerebral hemorrhage with residual paralysis is the reason for the presence of 18.3 per cent

[44] *Pub. Health Rep.*, August, 1959.

of the total number of patients in long-term care institutions in the Chicago area, but only 11.6 per cent of the patients referred to the Rehabilitation Institute of Chicago in the same year (1960) were there as a result of this condition. How many there were who were not in institutions is open to conjecture. Few hospitals do any follow-up after discharge. Home care programs, which have proved to be effective from economic and social as well as physical standpoints, are available in very few communities.

Dr. Edward E. Gordon,[45] director of the department of physical medicine, Michael Reese Medical Center, Chicago, declares: "Medicine and nursing have many rewarding moments; none ranks higher than giving substance and meaning to the last miles of the journey of life."

---

[45] Immediate Rehabilitation Measures Protect Hemiplegic Patient's Abilities. *Hosp. Topics,* November, 1961, pp. 40–43.

CHAPTER 8

Medical Education, Research, Literature, Audit

To the art of medicine all owe allegiance. Medical education to be complete must embrace instruction in the philosophy as well as the mechanics of medicine. It should arouse in the student the laudable desire to be associated, even in a small way, with the brilliant procession of physicians stretching back into dim antiquity who have enriched science and served humanity. . . . Medicine is the most ancient of professions. . . . Its best work is done in the light which beats on its throne, not in the arena of politics encouraged by the cheers of thousands, not in the seclusion of the cloister sustained by the hope of eternal joy, but in the storm and wind swept country, in the streets of the village, in the boulevards of the city, on the desolate field of battle, where pain and pestilence, illness and misery are combated often with none but God to see it.

IRVIN ABELL, M.D.[1]

MEDICAL EDUCATORS and hospital administrators have mutual interests which are being promoted in new ways. It was a somewhat epochal event when the Association of American Medical Colleges invited into membership in 1958 the administrators of university hospitals and faculty members of schools of hospital administration. The alliance holds promise of improved educational standards for interns and residents; of perhaps more supervision of clerkship, intern, residency, and postgraduate programs by medical faculties; of better cooperation in use of each other's facilities and personnel; and, altogether, of more teamwork in all educational and research endeavors.

[1] The Goal of Medical Education, *J. A. M. A.*, March 30, 1940, pp. 1146, 1147.

MEDICAL EDUCATION

The ancient Hindus had a way of beginning the teaching of surgery that has recently been revived in some respects. The student started his practice with plants. He punctured and lanced the hollow stalks of water lilies or the veins of large leaves, as well as the blood vessels of dead animals. Thus he acquired dexterity and rapidity necessary in performing operations without anesthesia. He also was made to tap or incise gourds, cucumbers, and other soft vegetables and fruits, or leather bags filled with water, in order to help him when he began to deal with hydrocele or other disorders of a hollow cavity. Amputations and the plastic operations were practiced upon dead animals. Flexible models were used for bandaging. When he was ready for actual practice, he followed a carefully supervised system of apprenticeship. The Hindus pioneered in clever teaching methods.

Among the earliest known medical schools were those in the temples at Cos and Cnidus in Greece and at Alexandria. The case method of teaching, a comparatively recent innovation in schools of business, is at least 24 centuries old in medicine. Hippocrates employed it at Cos in the fourth century B.C. Familiar with the educational theories of his contemporaries, Socrates and Plato, he went beyond them in fitting methods to specific objectives. "To him," says Garrison,[2] "medicine owes the art of clinical inspection and observation, and he is, above all, the exemplar of that flexible, well-poised attitude of mind, ever on the lookout for sources of error, which is the very essence of the scientific spirit."

If succeeding generations of teachers had followed the lead of Hippocrates, the history of medical education would be a joy to read and medical progress would have been infinitely speeded. But the way of the original thinker and investigator is thorny. Popularity is more easily won by high-sounding verbiage and mouthing of doctrine. Only Plato's pupil Aristotle made a major contribution to medical education for the next several centuries. By dissection of animals and the use of diagrams he taught anatomy and biology as they actually appeared, rather than as abstractions about which to speculate. Spasmodically a teacher appeared who followed similar methods of observation, and even of experimentation, but on the whole theorizing supplanted firsthand study and interpretation up to the seventeenth century, with the most pernicious influence that of Galen in the second century. Although a great physician and an eminent scientist, as has been mentioned in a previous chapter, he wrote with such facility and authority that for fourteen centuries European medicine was static because his theories were accepted as ultimate and unimpeachable.

So it was that plausible but false doctrines, aided by the concurrent general decline in learning and the rise of superstition, made medical education for centuries virtually an exercise in the memorizing of the voluminous writings

[2] "Greek Medicine," in *An Introduction to the History of Medicine,* 4th ed. p. 94. Philadelphia, W. B. Saunders Co., 1929.

of Galen. Medical science partook of the same paralysis of the spirit that afflicted all mental activity during the decline and eventual downfall of the Western Roman Empire. Notwithstanding the founding of hospitals and the chartering of universities by popes and emperors during the medieval period, progress was thwarted by the ban against free thinking and the uncritical acceptance of old theories and practices.

Longfellow in *The Golden Legend* represents physicians and medical students of the Middle Ages as, in the words of Garrison,[3] "frittering away their time in endless discussions about the nature of universals, the relation between the idea and matter, and other dialectic subtleties."

A bright spot appears here and there. The School of Salerno in Italy is an example. This was the first medical school independent of the ecclesiastical authorities. It was opened in the ninth century. Neuburger[4] says that during the eleventh and twelfth centuries it "aroused the healing art from the decrepitude of half a millenium, infused new life into things, and guarded as a Palladium the best traditions of ancient practice." He observes that the Salernitan masters were the first medieval physicians to cultivate medicine as an independent branch of science. How this school came into being is unknown. There is a legend that it was founded by "Four Masters," a Greek, a Latin, a Jew, and a Saracen. Along about the second quarter of the thirteenth century, Salerno began to decline, after it was sacked by Henry VI in 1194.

Arabic medical doctrine was emphasized at Salerno following the arrival of Constantinus Africanus in 1072. It was as a result of his influence that Mohammedan culture pervaded western European medicine for some five centuries, equally as static an effect as that of Galen. In one respect, however, it offers a precedent, long forgotten, that current medical education is just beginning to revive. This was the medical student's comprehensive cultural training; he was taught theology, law, philosophy, astronomy, astrology, music, chess-playing, and other arts and sciences as well as medicine. Likewise nonmedical students were taught some medicine along with their other subjects. What is so new about this furor today over the need for a "liberal" education?

Contributing to the decline of Salerno was the rise of rival schools at Naples, Palermo, and Montpellier. Other famous schools were founded at Bologna, Toulouse, Paris and Padua. Salerno had periods of rise and fall until it was abolished in 1811 by Napoleon.

It was the personal element, the teachers, in all of these schools that brought them fame. At Salerno, Roger of Palermo and Roland of Parma, the latter a pupil of the former, reveal in their writings considerable knowledge and originality. At Montpellier were at different times de Mondeville and Guy; at Bologna, Saliceto, Mundinus, and Malpighi; at Paris, Albertus Magnus and Sylvius; and at Padua, Peter of Abano, Vesalius, and Sanctorius.

[3] *Ibid.,* p. 143.
[4] Max Neuburger: *History of Medicine.* Trans. by Ernest Playfair. London, H. Frowde, 1910–25, 2 vols. Quoted by Garrison, *ibid.,* p. 147.

A dynasty of surgeons ruled the medical school at Edinburgh, founded in 1700 by John Monro, who was succeeded as professor of anatomy by his son and grandsons, all three named Alexander, their total years of service amounting to 126. Later it blazed into glory with Lister.

Leyden and Paris were the other great centers of anatomical teaching in the seventeenth, eighteenth, and early nineteenth centuries. Boerhaave introduced clinical instruction at Leyden in 1714. It was at Leyden that Sylvius established a little infirmary of 12 beds that was one of the first attempts at ward instruction in medical education.

Medical Education in America

The oldest university in the Americas is the Universidad Mayor de San Marcos, founded by royal decree of Emperor Charles V of Spain in May, 1531, in Lima, Peru, with a medical faculty from Salamanca. The first chair of medicine in the New World was established at the University of Mexico in 1580.

An instigator of medical schools in the colonies was John Morgan (1735–1789), who in 1765 published his *Discourse upon the Institution of Medical Schools in America,* commemorating the organization of the medical department of the University of Pennsylvania, which he, with William Shippen, started at the College of Philadelphia which had been founded in 1740. Morgan held the first chair of practice of medicine at the new medical school.

Two years later, in 1767 in New York, Dr. Samuel Bard and five other physicians established a medical school in conjunction with King's College. As a result of Dr. Bard's address at the first medical graduation in 1769 a subscription for a hospital was immediately commenced by the governor of the province, Sir Henry Moore. Often quoted are these words of Dr. Bard:[5] "Chemistry requires a laboratory, botany a garden; and anatomy a theatre and subjects, and, above all, the nature of diseases and the practice of medicine cannot be taught but in a hospital."

Construction of the hospital was started in 1773, but when nearly completed it was almost entirely destroyed by fire in 1775—and then came the Revolution. The hospital, now known as the New York Hospital, was not opened for patients until 1791.

What medical education in the provinces was like is described as follows by John E. Ranson:[6]

> Unless a young man who planned to become a physician had sufficient money with which to go abroad to study in one of the English or continental schools, he studied with some local practitioner until he thought he had acquired enough knowledge to enable him to begin practicing; he then hung out his shingle and began. There was no hospital in which he could take an internship. He did not need a license to practice, for none was available. The first act to regulate the

[5] John G. Coffin: A Dissertation on Medical Education and on the Medical Profession, *Communications,* 4: 16, 1822–1829. (Published by the Massachusetts Medical Society.)
[6] *Hosps.,* January, 1942.

practice of medicine and surgery was a local ordinance of New York City, enacted in 1760; New Jersey followed with a similar regulation in 1772. He could not use a medical library, for there was none until in 1762, when one was established in the Pennsylvania Hospital. He did not read medical journals, nor belong to a medical society—there were none.

If he had forethought and industry he probably planted a garden of medicinal herbs and from them prepared many of the medicines he used. When he became sufficiently well known and successful to attract apprentice students he used their time in the early stages of their training to compound the drugs and medicines which he used and perhaps sent them to the woods and fields to gather Jimpson weed for his asthmatic patients, poke berries for the treatment of chronic sores, sour dock for the itch, blackberry roots, dogwood bark, elderberries and goldenrod for dysentery, juniper berries, not for bathtub gin, but for worms (we now call them intestinal parasites), boneset for ague and consumption and the roots, bark, leaves and fruit of many other plants. He used his medicines very liberally on the assumption that if a little was good, a lot was better. It was only as homeopathy later became a rival school of medical theory and practice that the overdosing of patients began to abate.

The War of the Revolution changed this setting and these practices. Suddenly large numbers of wounded and ill soldiers had to be cared for en masse. In 1780 an army hospital was established at Boston with Dr. John Warren as surgeon. He had the idea of combining the clinical material with the teaching of anatomy, and gave a series of lectures to students who were interested in studying medicine. The lectures were received with great favor. Authorities of Harvard University, which had been established in 1636, invited him to lecture at Cambridge and to aid them in establishing a medical school. In 1782 his plan was approved and he was appointed professor of anatomy and surgery. Dr. Aaron Dexter was appointed professor of chemistry and materia medica, and Dr. Benjamin Waterhouse, professor of the theory and practice of medicine.

Dr. John Warren had a son, John Collins Warren (1778–1856), who was studying surgery around 1798 under Astley Cooper at St. Thomas' and Guy's hospitals, London, and under Dupuytren, surgeon-in-chief at Hotel Dieu, Paris. He kept writing to his father about his conviction that without hospitals, no really scientific investigation of the nature of disease was possible. Leonard K. Eaton[7] expresses the gist of the son's letters:

> Basic to the training which Warren (John Collins Warren) had received were the great hospital systems of London and Paris, and no one was more aware of this fact than he. Without these establishments . . . the doctor could not isolate a large number of cases which presented the same clinical picture, and thus determine the best mode of treatment. In addition, the hospital was an indispensable training school for young physicians; a connection with it in a teaching capacity added greatly to the prestige of aspiring practitioners. All of these considerations were in Warren's mind when he wrote his father about the possibility of founding a hospital in Boston . . . the story of Sir Astley Cooper and Guy's was, after all, familiar to both of them. His father replied morosely

[7] *New England Hospitals.* Ann Arbor, The University of Michigan Press, 1957, p. 14.

that there was no hospital in Boston, nor was it probable that there soon would be—little thinking that he would live to see the chartering of exactly such a one as they both wished.

Eventually the hospital was built, receiving its first patients in 1821, and being opened for teaching purposes to students from the Harvard Medical School. Previously their clinical instruction had been limited to the almshouse, and even there only since 1811 on petition of three of the professors.

The eastern seaboard cities soon began to establish more medical schools and hospitals which, in a most informal way, depending upon the progressive spirit of individual physicians, began some interchange of scientific knowledge. Actually, perhaps, in these early years more advances occurred through information brought back by Americans who had studied in European schools than by communication among American institutions.

Dartmouth was the third college to start a medical department (1797), with Nathan Smith, a medical graduate of Harvard, as chief organizer and professor of anatomy, surgery, chemistry, and practice. In 1810 he was asked to organize the department at Yale. In 1820 he organized a department for Bowdoin College and later for the University of Vermont. Samuel Bard, Valentine Mott, and other physicians organized the College of Physicians and Surgeons of New York in 1810. Samuel Henry Dickson founded the Medical College of South Carolina at Charleston in 1824; Nathan Smith's name again appears as one of the organizers of the Jefferson Medical College at Philadelphia in 1825.

The Medical Faculty of McGill University at Montreal, Canada, was organized in 1829, an outgrowth of a course in teaching in a hospital, the Montreal General.

The East was not as far ahead of the hinterland as might be expected, thanks to some pioneer physicians with courage and vision. Daniel Drake (1785–1852), mentioned in Chapter 6, founded the Medical College of Ohio at Cincinnati in 1819 and immediately began to promote the establishment of a hospital, one of the main objects being to provide clinical instruction for the students. The Commercial Hospital and Lunatic Asylum of Ohio, later to be known as the Cincinnati Hospital, and since 1915 as Cincinnati General Hospital, was opened for patients in 1823—only two years after Boston's Massachusetts General. Drake, with Benjamin Dudley, had also founded medical teaching at Transylvania University, Louisville, in 1817, which was affiliated with a new hospital. These were the first hospitals in the Ohio and upper Mississippi valleys and west of the Allegheny Mountains, and both were "under municipal control and affiliated with the only municipal universities which conduct schools of medicine."[8]

Daniel Brainerd's founding of Rush Medical College at Chicago in 1837, the opening of which was delayed until 1843 by financial and other obstacles, was mentioned in Chapter 6.

Following the Civil War, as can readily be imagined from the recent postwar

[8] *Hospital Care in the United States.* New York, The Commonwealth Fund, 1947, pp. 445, 446.

experiences, there was an aftermath of disability from injuries and disease which drew public attention to medical and hospital care. Occurring simultaneously were some epochal discoveries in medicine. Communication with other countries had been improved through technical developments, and there soon ceased to be an isolated American medical theater. Some delay occurred in adopting the improved educational methods introduced overseas, and at first not much was contributed by the New World. The most progressive members of the medical profession continued to seek a major part of their education overseas. By the end of the century, however, a two-way flow of knowledge had been established. European physicians began to cross the seas to see what went on in American medicine.

One of the rebels against didactic medical teaching who followed up his dissatisfaction with action was Theodore A. McGraw, of Detroit. In 1861, when he was 22, McGraw left the University of Bonn where he had switched from law to medicine for two semesters, influenced to change his career by a friend who was professor of anatomy there, to go to Berlin to continue his medical studies. In 1862 he returned home because of the outbreak of the war. Wishing to continue in medicine, he entered the College of Physicians and Surgeons at New York. What he found there is an enlightening glimpse of medical education in that period:[9]

> I found to my amazement that admission to the college, as regards medical qualification, was nearly free to all comers. In the graduating class were men who had spent their first two years of study in a preceptor's office. Everyone was obliged to take two courses of lectures, but as each course was only four months long, the two could be taken in one year. There were no obligatory laboratory courses except anatomy and all instruction was given by didactic lectures. There was no division of the classes and the man who spent three years in a medical school was obliged to listen three times to the same talk.

War service, giving him excellent clinical training, took his energies for a while before he returned to Detroit, where in 1864 there was no medical school. He with some other physicians started one in Harper Hospital in the summer of that year. This met with success, so in 1869 it was developed into a regular medical college, the Detroit College of Medicine. Nineteen years before that the medical school had been started at the University of Michigan, this having been a pioneer state in medical education. However, lectures, quizzes, and a short course in anatomy were all that the student received in the way of medical education, and for 25 years there was no hospital connected with it offering clinical facilities for study. The school in Detroit had the advantage of such facilities that were lacking in Ann Arbor. At Harper Hospital the government had erected special buildings for caring for wounded soldiers.

[9] Frederick A. Coller's article in *Medical History of Michigan,* compiled by a committee, C. B. Burr, chairman. Minneapolis and St. Paul, Bruce Publishing Co., 1930. Vol. 1, pp. 561–70.

Two years after founding the Detroit College of Medicine, Dr. McGraw was invited to occupy the chair of surgery at the state university. Of his experience there he wrote:[10]

> I entered upon many discussions with my colleagues about possibilities of improvement. The faculty were all anxious to change the conditions. Ann Arbor was at that time a small village. . . . The clinics were small and very unsatisfactory. I had, as surgeon, enough material for a weekly clinic, but had no proper place to treat patients after operation. . . . It is hard for those who are acquainted with the great University of Michigan as it is today to realize what time, labor and education it required to make the people understand that it was impossible to carry on a great institution of learning without money. I discussed the matter with legislators. The stereotyped reply was, why should people be taxed to educate doctors?

Insight into the philosophy of this Michigan surgeon-teacher is given in a statement he made in a commencement address in 1879: "Gentlemen, I cannot believe that that physician does his whole duty who allows himself to despair of his patient."

Johns Hopkins Medical School

It is possible to single out one school which became a model—Johns Hopkins. The university, with a department of medicine, was established at Baltimore in 1876. Brilliant medical educators were attracted to it from the beginning. The plans for Johns Hopkins Hospital were drawn up simultaneously with those of the university, although it was not until 14 years later that the hospital was opened. In John S. Billings' (1838–1913) original recommendations for the hospital in 1875 he introduced the idea of medical education by saying: "Not only the care of the sick poor, but the graded accommodation of pay and private patients in rooms or suites of rooms, proper education of physicians and nurses, and, above all, the promotion of discoveries in the science and art of medicine, and to make these known for the general good." He insisted that clinical instruction should be given mostly in the wards and outpatient department and not in an amphitheater, except in the surgical unit; that medical cases should not be brought from beds to an amphitheater; that there should be two pharmacies and a training school for nurses; and that a perfect system of records, financial, historical, and clinical, should be kept.

Billings was a great reformer in medical education. He fought to change the conditions under which he was taught when he attended Western Reserve University from 1857 to 1860. Of those days he said: "They taught us medicine as you teach boys to swim, by throwing them into the water." He was one of the organizers of the Johns Hopkins Medical School when it was changed from a department of the university in 1893. The new school had, or was to attract,

[10] *Ibid.*, p. 569.

such star educators as Welch, Halsted, Osler, Mall, Howell, and Abel. It was to be the only medical school in the United States that was designated as "worthy of the name" in the celebrated Flexner report in 1910, which was the result of a study made at the request of the American Medical Association Council on Medical Education and the Association of American Medical Colleges, and financed by the Carnegie Foundation for the Advancement of Teaching.

The Flexner Report

A chaotic situation had developed in medical education toward the end of the nineteenth and the early years of the twentieth centuries. In 1904 there were 160 schools in the United States, more than the combined total of medical colleges in all other parts of the world. Most of the schools were conducted for profit and had low admission requirements, as is shown by the high total of 28,142 medical students (by 1919 this had dropped to 12,137). The quality of teaching was almost universally poor.

Dr. N. P. Colwell, the first secretary of the A.M.A. council, accompanied Abraham Flexner (who was not a physician) of the Carnegie Foundation on many of his inspections, which included every medical school in the nation. The report, which was well documented, was widely publicized and shocked both the profession and the public into action for reform. Hans Zinsser's comment[11] reflects the reaction:

> Oh, Abraham Flexner! We have fought with you on minor points, have alternately admired and disliked you, have applauded you for wisdom and detested you for opinionatedness. But in just retrospect—layman as you are—we hail you as the father—or, better, the uncle—of modern medical education in America. You did, on occasion, hit below the belt, yet in the spirit in which the Christian knights slashed off the infidels' heads while shouting "Kyrie Eleison!" It was your report—uncompromising, cruelly objective, courageous and incisive —which opened the eyes of the medical profession to the state of their training schools, aroused public opinion to the need of better education of the guardians of health, and set the floodgates of the golden streams of philanthropy in medical directions.

The first edition of an important document in medical education "Essentials of an Acceptable Medical School," was published by the American Medical Association the same year as the Flexner report, 1910.

Immediately after the release of the Flexner report, schools began closing or merging. In those that remained, standards were raised as financial help became available. Flexner, afterward supported by the resources of the Rockefeller Foundation, figured prominently in the campaign to found laboratories in the schools, to attract trained and enthusiastic faculty to them, and to establish research institutes in or affiliated with them.

[11] *As I Remember Him.* Little, Brown and Co., Boston, 1940, p. 131.

The fiftieth anniversary of the publication of the Flexner report was observed at the 56th annual Congress on Medical Education and Licensure of the American Medical Association held in Chicago in February, 1960. One of the sessions was dedicated to the author of the study, who died in 1961 at the age of 92.

It has been estimated that between 1913 and 1930, capital funds totaling at least $200 million were contributed by foundations, individual philanthropists, and state legislatures to medical education in the United States.

Trends in Medical Education

Of the 444 medical schools established in the United States since the first one came into being in 1765, only 87, or 20 per cent, exist today. Just since 1900, 45 of 77 organized after that year have closed. Economic factors were responsible for many of the closings, besides the impact of the work of reformers.

The Council on Medical Education and Hospitals and the Association of American Medical Colleges jointly conduct an approval program. The list of approved schools is published in the annual "Education Number" of the *Journal of the American Medical Association* in November. The 1963 list showed 83 approved medical schools and 4 approved schools of the basic medical sciences. In line with a recognized need for more physicians than are being graduated from the present schools, expansion programs and the establishment of several new schools are in the planning or developmental stage. There are 12 approved medical schools in Canada, which had 834 graduates in 1962. Graduates from schools in the United States in the same year totaled 6,994.

Of the 87 approved schools in the United States, 39 are public and 48 private. The four largest medical schools in the United States, according to number of graduates, are the University of Illinois College of Medicine, the University of Michigan Medical School, Jefferson Medical College of Philadelphia, and the University of Tennessee College of Medicine, which ranged from 167 to 177 graduating. The largest schools in Canada are the University of Toronto Faculty of Medicine, McGill University Faculty of Medicine, University of Montreal Faculty of Medicine, and Laval University Faculty of Medicine, which ranged from 103 to 143 graduating.

Among the trends generally reported by the schools are efforts toward increasing the proportion of full-time faculty; relaxing the medical curriculum to permit more time for elective work; devising ways to accelerate the program; experimenting with changes in the educational program; arranging for integration with master's and D.Sc. or Ph.D. programs; liberalizing the curriculum to give the student broader background; planning more correlation with hospitals in both undergraduate and postgraduate education; and expanding research activities.

Full-time faculty increased by 6 per cent in 1961 and 7 per cent in 1962. The main obstacle is financing, the rewards for clinical work being in general far in excess of those that can be set up in a university budget.

The time for more elective work by the student is being accomplished by lengthening the school year, either throughout the period in school, or in some instances only in the senior year.

Acceleration is made possible by using elective and vacation periods for course credit or by offering to selected students opportunity to combine their college and medical school work in such a way that the entire program is shortened by a year or more. Johns Hopkins admits students who have completed their second or third year of college to a joint program of study under the faculties of philosophy and medicine. Boston University admits students directly from high school into a six-year program which utilizes five summer sessions in addition to the regular school terms. Northwestern admits honors students from high school who spend the first two years in the College of Liberal Arts with specially redesigned science courses as half, and arts, humanities, and behavioral sciences as the other half, of their programs. They enter the regular medical program in the third year.

Changes in the educational program include less compartmentalization of subject matter, lessening of repetition, improved sequence, and more use of the seminar as opposed to the lecture method of presentation.

Integration with master's and doctorate programs mostly involves lengthening of the student's program, in some cases by permitting withdrawal from the medical school for a period of special study and research, in others by incorporating more opportunity for basic science study in the medical school curriculum.

Liberalizing the curriculum is being accomplished by introducing social science study, sometimes through noncredit seminars at which attendance is required, and by overcoming through a different approach the narrowing effect of choosing specialties too soon and concentrating upon them too much. Including a world-wide viewpoint and emphasizing prevention along with treatment are other directions in which the curriculum is being enriched. Study of organization and administration is also beginning to be accepted as an area in which the medical student should at least have some orientation.

Better correlation with hospitals is being furthered by bringing the student into the hospital earlier in his program and increasing communication between the administrative staff and the student, intern, and resident in the hospital. The persistent, almost overwhelming demand for postgraduate courses of every imaginable nature has also brought the schools and hospitals together in efforts to satisfy the demands. The consensus is that the desire to keep up with the latest knowledge should be encouraged. Beginning in 1954, the American Medical Association has published annually a list of such courses under some forty classifications. Among the especially noteworthy medical school–hospital cooperative offerings are the "circuit courses" conducted in several hospitals by the University of Mississippi Medical Center, by the University of Michigan Medical School, and by the University of Kansas Medical Center.

The expansion of research activities in medical schools is a response to the growing appreciation in all graduate education of the necessity for continuous reanalysis and investigation. Learning from the lecture and the textbook is outmoded. Not only the faculty but the student must get into the detective mood and act. Memory is a false guide nowadays when facts change from day to day with new discoveries. A good memory is essential but alert minds will constantly check before using the knowledge which it contains.

Specific project research as contrasted with general basic science research is, some authorities believe, getting a little out of bounds in medical schools, notwithstanding the desirable climate it creates for whetting the student's appetite for investigation. Dr. Grayson L. Kirk,[12] president of Columbia University, expressed this view in an address at the Clinical Congress of the American College of Surgeons on October 31, 1955, saying:

> Today, foundation assistance is doled out almost entirely for the support of research projects, and the medical administrators are left to their own devices to find operating funds. I am by no means convinced that current foundation policy is in the best interests of the future of American medical education.

Six years later the same objection was voiced by Dr. Dominick F. Maurillo,[13] of New York, in a symposium, "Ways of Meeting the Physician Shortage," during a congress of the North American Federation, International College of Surgeons, in May, 1961:

> In 1935 the medical colleges and other agencies doing medical research spent about $1,000,000; in 1960, approximately $730,000,000. . . . I doubt that the entire cost of undergraduate medical education in 85 medical colleges is more than $125,000,000 a year. . . . Should there be such a great discrepancy? . . . I am not opposed to research work . . . but let us be reasonable! We should not spend such a large amount for research without first producing doctors.

These objections are beginning to percolate, and grants from the federal government and other sources are occasionally being awarded for construction and modernization of facilities and other operating rather than research purposes.

Association Activities

Besides the help that the American Medical Association and other organizations of physicians are giving to improve medical education, the schools have their own organization, the Association of American Medical Colleges, to which in 1962 the Carnegie Corporation of New York awarded a grant of $300,000 for a five-year period to establish a Division of Education. The over-all objective is to improve medical education at all levels through services and studies designed to stimulate medical faculty research in medical teaching and learning.

[12] *Bull. Am. Coll. Surgeons*, March–April, 1956, p. 54.
[13] *J. Internat. Coll. Surgeons*, September, 1961, p. 409.

Progress on an international scale is being made through the World Medical Association and the World Health Organization. The first World Conference on Medical Education was held in London in 1953 under the sponsorship of W.M.A. with the collaboration of W.H.O., the Council for International Organization of Medical Sciences, and the International Association of Universities. Universities represented totaled 127; participants came from 62 countries. A second conference was held in Chicago in 1959.

The American Medical Association in the fall of 1962 announced establishment of a citizens' committee to study graduate medical education. The report of this committee will be for the consideration of the many "organizations and individuals who share with the medical profession a responsibility for maintaining educational standards at a level which will assure the public of a quality of medical care that is limited only by the boundaries of existing knowledge." Dr. John S. Mills, president, Western Reserve University, is serving as chairman of the commission. Dr. Leland S. McKittrick,[14] chairman of the A.M.A.'s Council on Medical Education and Hospitals, has stated that the report could well be the most important development in medical education since the Flexner report in 1910.

Selection of Students

In professions such as medicine and administration of medical services which require a high degree of dedication, it is well when selecting students to give special consideration to some who were late in getting motivated. The current insistence upon high college grades for admission is doubtless excluding some students who would surpass the others in their final record of achievement. Examples of such students who became brilliant successes abound in all fields. Dr. William Stewart Halsted was a playboy until his final year in college, distinguished only by his prowess at football and his biting wit. Not until his last year did he decide that he wanted to be a doctor and suddenly buckled down to study and work. His scholastic record at Andover and Yale would doubtless have barred from acceptance in a present-day medical school a doctor who is celebrated as a teacher, as the crystallizer of the conservative surgery idea, and as the originator of procedures that are still in use for certain basic operations. Individualization remains an important factor in the selection of students. Grades are not always the best indication of intelligence. Geniuses are often rebels against what they consider overformalized, restricted educational programs.

Forty-six medical schools require four years of college or indicate that preference is given to such applicants. The minimum requirement for approval of a school is a three-year college background. Only about 15 per cent of the students being accepted have not earned baccalaureate or advanced degrees.

[14] *This Month at the American Hospital Association,* No. 161, November, 1962.

National Intern Matching Program

Both hospitals and interns have benefited by the National Intern Matching Program, which was inaugurated in 1951 under the name National Interassociation Committee on Internships. It is a nonprofit corporation financed by fees received from students and hospitals. The members of the board of directors are a senior student representing the Student American Medical Association, a senior student chosen by the Matching Program, and representatives of the American Hospital Association, the American Medical Association, the American Protestant Hospital Association, the Catholic Hospital Association, and the Association of American Medical Colleges. There is liaison representation from the federal agencies which offer internships—Army, Navy, Air Force, Veterans Administration, and the Public Health Service.

The student seeking an internship signs a "student agreement" and sends with it a two-dollar fee. He then applies to the hospitals of his choice without limitation as to number or type. He makes out a preference list of the positions for which he has applied and files it before February 1 with the matching program. At the same time the hospitals make out ranking lists of their student applicants. The student gets back a confirmation of his list, sending it back for correction if needed. He is "matched" to the highest hospital on his list that has an opening for him.

The student ranking list in combination with the hospital list is the entire basis for matching decisions. If the hospital of his first choice is interested in him he gets that appointment—in any event he gets the highest choice on his list that wants him. If none of the hospitals wants a particular student, he goes unmatched and makes his own arrangements among the positions that remain unfilled after the matching. The matching service is speedy in action, March 16 being the date on which prospective interns are notified of their fate.

Prior to the introduction of the matching plan, pressure for appointments began back in the junior and sophomore years in medical school; both hospitals and interns broke contracts when either had a chance for what they considered a better match; and the whole process was chaotic and unfair.

There were 7,180 participants in the twelfth National Intern Matching Program. Results showed 6,954 of these matched—6,753 from United States medical schools, 88 from Canadian, 105 from foreign schools, and 8 unclassified graduates. There were 12,456 internships to be filled through the plan. Unfilled internships totaled 5,502. Hospitals participating totaled 799.

Inasmuch as the internship and residency programs are conducted in hospitals, without medical school supervision, discussion of this aspect of medical education, as well as the foreign intern problem, is deferred to Chapter 17. However, protests are being made that hospitals alone cannot cope with the foreign medical graduate problem. The basic science background of many of these physicians is deficient. A few medical schools, such as Tulane and Cornell, are offering basic science review courses to precede house officer appointments in their affiliated hospitals. Hospitals need tie-ins with medical schools to help them with the orientation of the foreign intern, resident, and house physician.

Visual Aids in Medical Education

Television has made a major contribution to medical education at all levels. At the postgraduate level, it has, for example, enabled the American College of Surgeons to depart from its long-cherished ideal of learning by seeing the surgeon at first hand, operating in his own hospital, to the far less hazardous (to the patient) method of viewing him on television through a closed circuit to a meeting room in the convention hotel. The opportunity to go to clinics, which was one of the reasons for the formation of the college, is no longer a lure to attend congresses. Everybody gets a close-up view now, which was denied those on the fringes of the surgical amphitheater audience. Now meetings can be held at resorts and surgical procedures can be televised and relayed, supplementing the medical motion pictures which were an innovation also not too long ago.

The acceptability of telecasts as educational media depends upon good planning and programming. At first crowds were attracted because of the novelty. That was back in 1947. After a while interest waned until techniques were improved, especially the use of color. To hold the attention of students and to obtain the best teaching results, educators who use this method must acquire skill in educational methods as well as in television techniques. Most of the larger hospitals have installed or plan to install color, closed-circuit television systems, and showings are frequently open to medical students and postgraduate groups as well as to members of their own staffs.

An example of the professional skill that is employed in the production of educational motion pictures is the 28-minute film *Innovations in Transfusion Therapy,* which was shown for the first time at the Clinical Congress of the American College of Surgeons in 1962.[15] The film was sponsored by the College's Committee of Pre- and Postoperative Care, authored by Dr. Carl W. Walter, of Boston, produced by Robert B. Churchill, Los Angeles, and financed by Fenwal Laboratories, Morton Grove, Illinois. The leading role is that of Dr. Richard Oliver of Carlisle, Scotland, who in 1840 administered the first successful transfusion by a physician who intended to replace the blood loss and re-establish the circulatory power. The patient was "the wife of John Cook, a weaver, living at Eden Place." Dr. Oliver described the event in the *Edinburgh Medical and Surgical Journal* of 1840. The film also features studies of the microcirculation in hamsters' cheek pouches conducted at Boston University and clinical scenes at the Los Angeles County Hospital and the Orthopaedic

---

[15] *Bull. Am. Coll. Surgeons,* January-February, 1963, pp. 35–36.

Hospital, Los Angeles. The film was carefully documented with the aid of three libraries and a museum, the weaver's cottage where the transfusion took place is duplicated from illustrations furnished by the town clerk of Carlisle, and some of the props such as the transfusion apparatus are from museum collections. Dr. Oliver's achievement was mentioned in the previous chapter with Dr. Carl Walter's comment on blood types.

RESEARCH

In an address given at the Health Congress, Blackpool, England, on April 24, 1961, Dr. M. G. Candau,[16] director-general of the World Health Organization, stated that W.H.O. now lays just as much emphasis upon medical research and the education and training of professional and auxiliary personnel as it does on measures for control of disease, the strengthening of national health services, and the coordination of health activities with the social and economic activities of other agencies. He pointed out the "interdependence of diverse activities," saying:

> A review of the roles of education and training on the one hand, and research on the other, bears testimony to the universality of the problems of health and disease, and compels us to recognize in practice, as in theory, the essential unity of the basic sciences, medicine and administration—the triad upon which the effective solution of health problems depends.

The basic research scientist is a special kind of individual who needs special understanding from administration. Dr. Hans Selye,[17] himself a basic scientist, director of the Institute of Experimental Medicine and Surgery at the University of Montreal, gave a clue in stating:

> . . . the scientist must have a peculiar kind of intuition. Perhaps his most important characteristic is a negative one. He must lack prejudice to a degree where he can look at the most "self-evident" facts or concepts without necessarily accepting them, and, conversely, allow his imagination to play with the most unlikely possibilities. In the process he requires serendipity, the gift of finding unsought treasure. . . . He must have the power of abstract thinking. . . . The basic researcher must also be able to dream and have faith in his dreams. . . .

The impulse for a great deal of specific research comes from the fact that a physician or a member of his family is a sufferer from a certain disease. The founder of the nonprofit National Cystic Fibrosis Research Foundation in 1955, Dr. Wynne Sharples, of Philadelphia, has a son and daughter of her own who have the disease, the cause of which is blocked pancreatic ducts. The foundation has more than fifty chapters in the United States which are raising money for research. The lives of some 6,000 babies are threatened by it each year. Although early doctors noted that the pancreatic juice sometimes thickened

[16] *J. Roy. Soc. Health*, July-August, 1961.
[17] *Saturday Evening Post*, January 24, 1959.

and affected digestion, the disease was not formally diagnosed until 1936, when Dr. Guido Fanconi of Switzerland described three cases. The discovery was not publicized; however, in 1938 a pathologist at Columbia-Presbyterian Babies Hospital, New York, studied autopsies of infants assumed to have died of pulmonary disease and found an alarming number of blocked pancreatic ducts. Her discovery led to the development of methods of treatment to forestall infection and suffocation, although prevention and cure are still a challenge for the future.[18]

Many discoveries are the result of what the American Medical Association calls "happy accidents." Among them are Fleming's discovery of penicillin when he left a Petri dish uncovered; van Leeuwenhoek's discovery of bacteria when he focused a magnifying glass on a drop of water instead of on a fly's leg; Dr. Winston H. Price's discovery of a common cold vaccine when he was working on isolating influenza viruses; Rene Theophile Laennec's development of the stethoscope after he saw children tapping messages to each other along opposite ends of a discarded plank; the discovery of saccharine when a chemist forgot to wash his hands before lunch, wondered about the sugary taste of his roast beef sandwich, and related it to the strange chemical with which he had been working.

Time and time again research workers have first tested their discoveries on themselves. Dr. Herald Cox, of Lederle Laboratories, took the first dose himself in 1950 of the oral vaccine for poliomyelitis developed under his leadership—a preparation not made available to the public until some 700,000 persons had taken almost 2,000,000 single strain doses. Many of the tests were made during epidemics in several countries, with impressive immunization results.

Bright hopes are held out by medical scientists for treatment with enzymes—large protein molecules, termed nature's chemists. All living things have them and they play a supreme role. There are some 700 known kinds. They perform all different kinds of functions. Many of them are already being used in medicine. One of the most effective uses is in dissolving blood clots. Prospects grow for their efficacy in the treatment of cancer. The possibility is even suggested of using them some day to delay the aging process.

DNA, deoxyribonucleic acid—the chemical compound that makes up the genes, discovered in 1952 by Dr. Maurice Wilkins, of King's College, London, and diagrammed in 1953 by Drs. James D. Watson and Francis H. C. Crick, of Cambridge University—has research scientists frantically working for clues to its role in health and disease.

A fine example of the way in which medical research may lessen the need for surgery is the "re-education in perception" concept at Boston University School of Medicine in restoring normal vision to cross-eyed and wall-eyed patients. This new technique, called synoptics, by imparting a sense of move-

[18] Adapted from a report by James C. G. Conniff: *New York World–Telegram and Sun*, March 29, 1958.

ment, touch, and ground position of an object to the "lazy" eye, produces reorientation in the cerebral cortex of the brain, allowing improvement of vision. In many cases normal and eventual fusion of images from both eyes results in patients considered hopeless by former standard techniques.

The National Society for Medical Research, which was founded by Anton J. Carlson, wages a continuous battle against the propaganda and other activities of groups such as the Humane Society of the United States and the National Antivivisection Society which seek to prevent by legislation and other means scientific experimentation with animals.

The use of animals in research has led to the need for specially trained personnel to care for them. At the tenth annual meeting of the Animal Care Panel in 1959 in Washington, D.C., a certifying board for animal technicians was created to correlate the plans and activities of the numerous training courses for animal technicians and supervisors. The board is modeled in part after the Animal Technicians Association of Great Britain, which has offered training programs for twelve years. Three ranks of caretakers are recognized: animal technician, senior animal technician, and animal quarters supervisor.

Research on Highway Accidents

Extensive new research is needed to reduce highway accidents. One of the needs is collection of exhaustive details on the circumstances of the accident and the injuries which resulted. Then the data should be given deep and imaginative study to reconstruct the different kinds of causes of the accidents and to figure out ways of preventing them. Changes in the design of cars will be one of the means of prevention. Laboratory research will be involved. The changes would be tested by statistics on the reduction of accidents. Manufacturers, legislators, the public, safety experts, and medical and hospital personnel are being urged to cooperate. Viewed as a kind of epidemic, whose toll in the United States alone has been around 185,000 lives in the last five years, the obligation of persons working in the health field to help in control measures is clear. An example of the plan of attack is given by the Cornell Automotive Crash Injury Research Program, which is based on state troopers' reports, photographs, and medical reports. These are processed, checked, analyzed, and the conclusions recorded on punch cards.

Research on Cancer

In every medical school, in practically every hospital, and in many other laboratories and centers, research on the causes and treatment of cancer goes on, supported by funds from government and private sources. The American Cancer Society alone had almost $17 million in grants outstanding on March 1, 1962, most of them long-term in nature. Research in progress included human leukemia, basic biochemistry, genetics, chemicals which promote cancer, carcinogenic hydrocarbons which cause lung cancer, the effect on the glands of the stomach of cancer-causing chemicals, immunity to cancer in mice, abnormal enzymes in the serum of cancer patients, anticancer compounds, endocrine abnormalities, uterine cervix abnormalities, hormonal control of human cancer, viruses and cancer, surgery for lung cancer. A new grant category was added known as "Postdoctoral Residency Scholarships" aimed at preparing young physicians and doctors of philosophy for careers in the clinical investigation of cancer.[19]

In 1953 the American College of Surgeons transferred its Registry of Bone Sarcoma to the Armed Forces Institute of Pathology. This important research project was initiated by Dr. Ernest Amory Codman in 1922. He transferred it to the college in 1928, where it was conducted under the direction of Dr. Bowman C. Crowell, former associate director of the college in charge of clinical research. By 1939 there were more than 2,200 cases in the registry, and 2,045 cases were circulated to 37 consultants or investigators for opinion or for study that year. The registry aided greatly in systematizing nomenclature, histological and roentgenographic diagnosis, and management of bone sarcoma. Many contributions to the literature have resulted from study of the cases in the registry.

The college, to further research on cancer, has organized its cancer program into 14 geographic sections, 12 in the United States, 2 in Canada, each under a chief who is a member of the Committee on Cancer. The aim is to mobilize forces at the local level. In devising the plan four recommendations were made: (1) that interested fellows who are learned and motivated in cancer-control programs at the state level be appointed to serve in a liaison capacity among their respective communities, other cancer-control agencies, and the Committee on Cancer; (2) that an organization of tumor clinic directors be established in each state or province; (3) that an executive director of the regionalization program be employed by the college to act as a consultant to local tumor clinics, to provide continuity to the program, and to prepare an annual report of regional cancer activities; (4) that cancer registry workshops be conducted in conjunction with selected local, state, and sectional medical meetings. Following up the third proposal, the college has added to its staff a full-time registry consultant and a biostatistician under contract to the Public Health Service. The fourth recommendation has been activated by conducting a number of workshops. The American Cancer Society and the Public Health Service assist with the meetings.

In his thesis submitted in 1957 to Northwestern University on "The Impact of Cancer—Can We Help?" Harold V. King, now administrator of Columbia View Manor Rehabilitation Center, Vancouver, Washington, urged that cancer patients be informed of the intensive research that is being conducted by many agencies and institutions, of the public contribution to this research through do-

[19] From *Cancer News,* American Cancer Society, Illinois Division, summer, 1962.

nations to such agencies as the American Cancer Society, and of the prospect that is becoming brighter all the time for eventual conquering of the disease, thanks to discoveries of procedures and drugs that offer promise of control. Mr. King said:

> One outstanding service that we in hospitals can give is to keep abreast of cancer control progress. When dealing with these patients for whom the future may indeed be stormy, our advice concerning quacks (if need be), home remedies, and the like may save them much heartache. . . . A naive cancer patient cannot possibly judge objectively. . . . Our knowledge of the exploiting done by quacks and our lists of facilities and services offered in our state and community may be as valuable to him as insulin to a diabetic or thorazine to the mentally ill.

A comprehensive cancer research and treatment center was established in Los Angeles in 1960 through amalgamation of the facilities of the California Hospital with those of the Southern California Cancer Center to form a complete cancer diagnostic, treatment, and research operation. The facility will include a tissue culture laboratory which will grow human cancer tissues in an artificial medium to be subjected to chemotherapeutic and radiological agents.[20]

Federal Government Research and Aid to Research

Projected federal grants for medical research will amount to $500 million by 1970, a figure which will be equaled by philanthropic and industrial grants, according to a report issued in 1958, "The Advancement of Medical Research and Education through the Department of Health, Education and Welfare."[21] The report was prepared by a committee under the chairmanship of Dr. Stanhope Bayne-Jones, president of the Joint Administrative Board of New York Hospital-Cornell Medical Center and formerly dean of Yale University School of Medicine. Among the recommendations were:

> 1. That the planning of both governmental and private agencies be based upon a volume of medical research expenditures requiring a continuing intensive effort to recruit and train medical scientists; and to provide the facilities in which they can work productively.
> 2. That every significant governmental activity relating to medical research and education have the counsel of a group of highly competent advisers from private life.
> 3. That the Public Health Service review comprehensively its functions, organization, and staffing relating to research bearing on all aspects of medical care, financing of medical care, and medical resources, with a view to establishing a total research program appropriately divided between grant supported and direct research.
> 4. That research and training be further developed as a part of the activities of the Bureau of State Services, particularly in relation to development of public

---

[20] *Hosp. Forum,* November, 1960, p. 10.
[21] Final Report of the Secretary's Consultants on Medical Research and Education, U. S. Government Printing Office, June 27, 1958.

health programs: (a) substantial increase of research and training activities of the Communicable Disease Center; (b) substantial increase of funds for research and training at Robert A. Taft Sanitary Engineering Center; (c) moderate increase of funds for research at Occupational Health Field Station pending acquisition of improved facilities and development of staff; (d) consideration of further development of research and training in connection with the Arctic Health Research Center; (e) carefully considered extension of research programs concerned with radiation injury, accidents, air and water pollution; (f) a budget be provided adequate to support medical care of high quality in PHS hospitals; (g) an expanded program of research related to the health of American Indians and Alaska natives; (h) extension of the Office of Vocational Rehabilitation grant program; (i) expansion of the research programs of the Food and Drug Administration and the Children's Bureau.

The billion-dollar figure by 1970 predicted in the 1958 report was reached only three years later. Joseph S. Murtaugh, Chief, Office of Program Planning, National Institutes of Health, brought out this fact at a meeting of the joint councils of the American Hospital Association on October 25, 1962. His prediction was that this expenditure for medical research would be $3 billion by 1970 and that the 1962 medical research manpower of 39,700 would be doubled by that time.

In January, 1963, the United States Public Health Service and the Hospital Research and Educational Trust of the American Hospital Association held a conference to evaluate recent research and to discuss areas in which research should be conducted.

The National Institutes of Health at Bethesda, Maryland, is the largest group of medical research laboratories in the world and represents an investment of nearly $300 million.

Research in Progress

The Health Information Foundation has published each year since 1952 *An Inventory of Social and Economic Research in Health.* The listings, with descriptions, are in three categories: "Studies Related to Health Levels"; "Studies Related to Behavioral Aspects of Health"; and "Studies Related to Health Resources and Economic Aspects of Health." Beginning with the 1961 edition, only those projects which were initiated in the current year are listed, a change which was made necessary by the increasing number of projects. Even with this limitation, the 1961 edition was 144 pages in length and listed 361 projects. Sixty-eight of the projects were being conducted by colleges, some of them in cooperation with hospitals and other agencies. The financial sponsors totaled 226. The aims of the inventory are to describe current research, to stimulate new research, and to help to avert duplication of effort and assist in the application of knowledge.

Vital Statistics

The very word "statistics" causes a mental block in many persons, yet through statistics it is possible to measure progress, to determine where we were, where we are, and whither we are heading in the battle for health.

> Demography is concerned with the growth, development and movement of human populations as aggregates. Its raw material ranges from the statistics of heights and weights or of blood pressure in men, to the distribution of the rents they pay for their housing accommodations or to the classes of education they give their children. As a science it impinges on the imagination of all who are at any time concerned with the survival of nations. . . . The "counting of heads" is an essential preliminary of democratic government itself. Whether we speak of demography or of vital statistics we are dealing with an intensely utilitarian science, because the very organization of society depends upon it.[22]

The student who is not too fond of mathematics will be attracted by the statement that this book[23] "neither assumes nor provides any knowledge of mathematics or of statistical theory," although the author received his Ph.D. in medical statistics at the University of London and is chief statistician to the General Register Office of Great Britain.[24]

The very first book on vital statistics is credited to English medicine. Published in 1662 at London, the *National and Political Observations upon the Bills of Mortality,* by John Graunt, disclosed that more boys are born than girls and that from an accurate death rate the population can be estimated. It was pointed out that current statistics were relatively valueless. They were gathered through the practice started in 1581 of having the parish clerk direct the work of women searchers for data in their neighborhoods.

Hailed as the virtual founder of vital statistics is an English astronomer, Edmund Halley, of Halley's comet fame, who in 1693 compiled the Breslau Table of births and funerals. By means of it he purported to show "the proportion of men able to bear arms in any multitude," to "ascertain the price of annuities upon lives," and to estimate mortality rates.

A German army chaplain, Johann Peter Sussmilch, made the next important contribution by publishing in 1742 *The Divine Order,* in which all kinds of data were included on public hygiene, life insurance, and national polity. He introduced into statistics the idea that they are significant not just for material reasons but, more important, for disclosing the health, energy, and general morale of the populace to the end that steps might be taken to improve them.

Medical statistics virtually began with the French physician Pierre-Charles-Alexandre Louis (1787–1872). He believed, as has since many times been proved,

---

[22] Bernard Benjamin: *Elements of Vital Statistics.* Chicago, Quadrangle Books, 1959, Chap. 1.

[23] *Ibid.,* advertisement.

[24] *Ibid.* Chapter 15 is "Hospital Statistics" and other chapters related to specific health subjects are on death rates and causes, environmental factors affecting morbidity, infectious diseases, tuberculosis, maternity and child welfare, public health, cancer, mental health, and general practitioners.

that statistics sometimes give insight into what is happening when experimental methods seem to fail to point to definite conclusions. To him, and to others who later recognized the value of his ideas, the positiveness of facts and figures had a strong appeal over the fruitless theorizing of many physicians and other scientists of the past.

In 1798 appeared the widely acclaimed *Essay on the Principles of Population* by Thomas Robert Malthus, of England. Arithmetic and geometric ratios are used to substantiate his theory that poverty is the inevitable outcome of increased population because of limited food supply. Authorities believed that the publicizing of this theory caused the widespread postponement of marriage and the decreased size of families in several countries almost down to the present. The influence of the theory has evidently waned in the past few years. Perhaps because of the development of synthetic foods? Whatever the cause, the population explosion is viewed by many with deep concern.

Vital statistics began really to be used in the cause of health by Sir Edwin Chadwick (1800–1890), who employed the census and bills of mortality as means of diagnosing the ills of the populace. Between 1834 and 1855 he issued famous reports to the Poor Law commissioners, recommending many reforms. He was followed by Sir John Simon (1816–1904) in his celebrated *English Sanitary Institutions* in 1890 in which extensive use was made of statistics.

The first strong warning against the fallacies of statistics used alone was voiced by Henry Wyldbore Rumsey in 1875.

The greatest of all medical statisticians, William Farr, was active in this period, estimating among other things that the shortage of doctors was such that if all the sick people in London had sought the help of physicians, each one would have had 1,200 patients to look after each day. In 1839 Farr asserted that the English mortality rate could be reduced by one-tenth through improvements in hygiene. (A modest guess; a century later it had been reduced by 65 per cent.)

Farr declared that the average expectation of life at birth in England throughout the eighteenth century never passed the nineteen years mark. One of his often quoted remarks was: "Diseases are the iron index of misery." As a physician he viewed statistics as a medical tool, their function being to serve the common good.

In the United States, Lemuel Shattuck, of Boston, was influenced by Chadwick's report and work. He became interested in community health while writing a history of the town of Colcord, as a result of which he put through in 1842 a bill for compulsory registration of births, marriages, and deaths in Massachusetts. He was instrumental in making the census much more comprehensive, starting in 1845. In the report which he wrote in 1850 as president of a commission to survey sanitary conditions in his state, he included among his recommendations the compilation of demographic statistics.

Many others in all continents have worked to develop statistics as a medical and social tool for progress. There is no room for complacency, however. The defects in the processes and in the results are numerous. Having led the way,

England has the broadest and most complete statistics on variations in mortality rates by occupation and socioeconomic status. According to Harold F. Dorn,[25] Ph.D., chief of the Office of Biometry, National Institutes of Health, Public Health Service, the United States "does not have a series of analyses of mortality statistics comparable to those of England and Wales." Among the shortcomings he includes the publication of very little concerning geographic variations in mortality rates; no tabulation of mortality data by economic subregions; except for one study (tuberculosis), no analysis of mortality differences among occupational or socioeconomic groups based upon official death statistics (although one was under way); and no comprehensive data concerning morbidity for the entire population of the United States.

Sickness surveys were started in 1915 by the Metropolitan Life Insurance Company. The following year the Public Health Service began this kind of activity, limited to certain areas or groups. One undertaken in 1935–1936 included 2,800,000 persons in 800,000 families in some 83 towns and 23 rural districts. Similar restricted surveys have been conducted in other countries.

New methods are constantly being developed in statistics, and many not so new are being improved. Notable early ideas now flourishing are the theory of probabilities, the formulation of which the physician Cardan, of Italy, is reported to have improved in 1539; further contributions to the same theory by Blaise Pascal, of France, in 1654; adaptations of the theory to medical statistics by Jules Dominique Gavarret, of France, in 1840. Correlation was introduced by Sir Francis Galton in 1885 and partial correlation by Karl Pearson in 1897.

The rapidity with which computing equipment is being installed portends a multiplication of statistics with which it will indeed be difficult to keep pace but also assures greatly increased efficiency of the individual statistician.

MEDICAL LITERATURE

Medical literature is a sea in which keeping afloat, even for the physician, requires extraordinary resistance to temptation to explore the depths and to drift out to the purple waters that beckon on the horizon. In no other science or art is there such a vast accumulation from the past or such constant pouring in of new material. The flood has gained momentum with the growing interest of the public. Everybody wants to plunge into this ocean which offers exciting revelations to the amateur as well as to the expert swimmer. Not only does medical literature help man to understand himself, physically, emotionally, and mentally, but it has a curious appeal to his morbid fancies. It unfolds tales of horrors as well as of marvels. Both villains and heroes play leading roles. The psychological effect on the public is one of the diseases of the times, for some people are drowning in imaginary symptoms and need rescuing.

[25] Some Problems for Research in Mortality and Morbidity. *Pub. Health Rep.*, January, 1956, pp. 1–5.

The student of administration needs to dip into this sea with discrimination or he, too, will drown, not just because of the hypochondria that may result, but because of the overwhelming volume of fascinating reading material. Again it should be reiterated that the administrator should cultivate balance, and medical literature—and hospital, too, for that matter—should be selected with a sense of proportion to other branches of reporting with which he also needs to keep up.

Reference works and guides of many kinds are available to help in the selection process. Bearing in mind that every year some 3,000 medical journals are published, and about as many books and pamphlets, the administrator will see the futility of attempting to gain very much from unguided reading. Yet in order to cooperate with his medical staff and medical librarian he has to have a general idea of the main publications.

Medical History

Henry E. Sigerist[26] tells a story that shows why medical schools, medical societies, hospitals, and individuals are giving so much time to study of medical history.

"A boy is reading an old book on electricity," relates Sigerist. "An observer says, 'Why do you read such old stuff?' The boy snaps: 'I want to become an engineer. If I can't understand what they knew 150 years ago, how can I ever hope to understand what we must know today?' "

The librarian of the American College of Surgeons in 1959, L. Margueriete Prime,[27] traced briefly, as follows, the growth of the interest by associations in medical history:

> The International Congresses of the History of Medicine began in 1920 and have been held at intervals since that time. The twelfth Congress occurred under the auspices of the International Society of the History of Medicine at Amsterdam in 1950. Later Congresses have been held at Nice, Cannes, Monaco, 1952; at Rome and Salerno, 1954; at Madrid in 1956; and at Montpellier, France, in 1958. The American Association of the History of Medicine functions as the American and Canadian section of the International Association and meets annually. European countries have similar divisions. There is an International Academy of the History of Pharmacy founded in 1952 with its seat at The Hague, and an American Academy of the History of Dentistry. The Welch Institute of the History of Medicine at Johns Hopkins University, inaugurated in 1929, with supplementary funds from the General Education Board appropriated in 1930, has made an outstanding contribution through the efforts of William H. Welch (1927–1930), Fielding H. Garrison (1930–1932), Henry E. Sigerist (1932–1947) and Richard H. Shryock from 1949 on. There are innumerable local history of medicine societies either established for and by medical students in an individual school or by local medical men who wish to encourage study, publication, and discussion of medical history.

[26] Editorial. *Bull. History of Med.*, June, 1944.
[27] *Bull. Am. Coll. Surgeons,* May-June, 1959.

Miss Prime went on to list a few current publications which have to do with medical history, including *Medical Books in Print* (1958–1959); *Current Work in the History of Medicine: an International Bibliography,* published quarterly since January, 1954, by F.N.L. Poynter of Wellcome Historical Medical Library, London; the "Bibliography of the History of Medicine of the United States and Canada," appearing annually in the *Bulletin of the History of Medicine; Annals of Medical History,* 1928 to 1942, when it was discontinued; *Bulletin of the History of Medicine,* organ of the American Association of the History of Medicine and Johns Hopkins University Institute of the History of Medicine, 1933 to date; *Journal of the History of Medicine and Allied Sciences,* 1946 to date; and *Medical History* (British), 1957 to date. A *Bulletin of Polish Medical History and Science* began publication in Chicago in 1956. Pharmaceutical houses publish well-illustrated, authentic historical material. A particularly good example was the series of the *Ciba Symposia* which appeared from April, 1939, to the fall of 1951.

Herodotus, the "Father of History," included much medical information in his chronicles, especially about Egyptian and early Greek medicine. Homer gives a great deal of insight into ancient medicine. So do a number of other early writers, among them Terence, Lucretius, Ovid, Horace, Vergil, and Juvenal. The first great name as a medical historian is that of Celsus, a Roman of the early first century who was not a physician but a writer of great skill. He came to be called the "medical Cicero." In his work, *De re medicina,* he tells of some 72 medical authors and their writings, all of which have been lost except those of Hippocrates. In the eight books of his masterpiece authorities agree there is much that was translated from other authors, but the great achievement is the preservation of so much knowledge of the past. In 1478 his work was printed, one of the first medical books in that form, and it passed through many editions.

Pliny, later on in the same century, wrote a sort of encyclopedia of all scientific knowledge, his *Natural History;* medicine is the subject of twelve of the books. It also went through many editions after the invention of printing. Not so much historical in nature as a reservoir of information, it nevertheless has historical significance because of the light it sheds on medicine in that period. Like the works of Galen it had some bad effects in that for centuries it was taken as the final revelation of truth, despite the pointing out of errors by courageous individuals from time to time.

Guy de Chauliac (1300–1368) was the next important historian, followed in the late fifteenth and early sixteenth centuries by Symphorian Champier of Lyons (1472–1539). Daniel Leclerc (1652–1728) wrote the first large history of medicine in 1696, and this is still a good reference book. Albrecht von Haller (1708–1777), the great physiologist of Leyden and Bern, wrote not only history but poems and historic novels and has a high place in literature.

The more recent group of prominent medical historians begins with Sir Thomas Clifford Allbutt (1836–1925), of the University of Cambridge, England,

and includes such later writers as Sir William Osler, Karl Sudhoff, Max Neu-burger, Henry E. Sigerist, Arturo Castiglioni, Felix Marti-Ibanez, and Fielding Garrison.

F. R. Packard published in 1901 a *History of Medicine in the United States,* and J. G. Mumford in 1903 *A Narrative of Medicine in America.*

Journals and Pamphlets

Garrison[28] says, "There is no modern science or group of sciences which has so many current periodicals as medicine." This is a comparatively new state of af-fairs; medicine was slow in developing this type of literature. Now there are "too many," the historian goes on to say, and anyone who scans the list will agree. The urge to communicate his knowledge and his discoveries has led the physi-cian to inundate the market to the despair of those who try to keep up with the new knowledge.

A not uncommon instance is that of a professor of urology at the National University of Athens, Dr. Zannis A. Kairis (1897–1962), from whose obituary[29] it may be learned that he left more than 230 works—textbooks, monographs, and articles published in both Greek and other journals—despite his busy life as chief of a 130-bed urological clinic at the Evangelismos Hospital.

Among the more than 3,000 medical periodicals, the administrator and poten-tial administrator will be able to get acquainted with only a few. Among these should be: *Journal of the American Medical Association; British Medical Jour-nal; Lancet; Canadian Doctor; Canadian Medical Association Journal; Journal of Medical Education; Modern Medicine; Medical Economics; Proceedings of the Royal Society of Medicine; Today's Health* (A.M.A.); and *World Medical Journal.*

Fortunately there are aids for the busy reader—digests, summaries, news notes. Among them are *Medical-Hospital Research Digest; Current Medical Digest; Science News Letter,* a publication aimed at the student of science from high school up; and *Medical Tribune,* a weekly tabloid type news medium. The hos-pital journals also include digests of medical news, *Hospital Topics* in particular carrying fairly thorough coverage of the main national medical conventions.

This great outpouring of periodical literaure began in 1679 when Nicolas de Blegny (1652–1722) founded the first medical journal, *Nouvelles découvertes sur toutes les parties de la médecine,* published in Paris for two years. It was trans-lated into German and Latin. The first journal of psychiatry was founded by Johann Christian Reil (1795–1815) in 1805. Christian Wilhelm Hufeland (1762–1836) edited *Hufeland's Journal* in 82 volumes between 1795 and 1836, as well as three other periodicals. The *British Medical Journal* was founded in 1857, preceded by periodicals under two different names, the first of which began in 1840, succeeded by the second in 1853.

[28] *Op. cit.,* p. 785.
[29] Nicolas C. Louros: *J. Internat. Coll. Surgeons,* October, 1962, p. 44.

In the United States the first medical periodical was the *Medical Repository,* published in New York from 1797 to 1824; Mexico had an earlier one, started in 1772. Others sprung up, most of which were short-lived, until in 1827 the *American Journal of the Medical Sciences,* successor to the *Philadelphia Journal of the Medical and Physical Sciences* (1820–1827), both founded by Nathaniel Chapman, began its long career. The weekly *Boston Medical Journal* celebrated its hundredth year in 1928.

One of the newest ways to bring to a larger audience than was able to attend the discussions presented at medical meetings is the issuance beginning in 1961 of the *Voice of Medicine* by the Excerpta Medica Foundation. This journal contains recordings of talks and interviews taken during national and international medical congresses, clinical-pathological conferences, world health assemblies, medical meetings and symposia. The foundation is a nonprofit international organization, founded in 1946 to abstract and disseminate the medical literature of the world.

An abstract service, started in the fall of 1963, is a biweekly journal published by the American Society of Hospital Pharmacists. At the beginning, 339 world magazines were listed for abstracting and ultimately all of the world's pharmaceutical literature will be surveyed.

Medical Libraries

In the February, 1962, issue of *Public Health Reports* appeared this announcement, which was preceded by years and years of crusading by physicians, medical organizations, and friends of medicine:

> The new quarters of the National Library of Medicine on the grounds of the National Institutes of Health in Bethesda, Maryland, will house the world's greatest collection of medical literature. The $7 million structure, designed by the firm of O'Connor & Kilham of New York City, has space for about 1 1/4 million bound volumes on its five floors, three below ground. The library's collections at 7th and Independence, SW, Washington, D.C., and its historical and rare book collections, now in Cleveland, Ohio, will be transferred to Bethesda in the spring of 1962. The National Library of Medicine celebrated its 125th anniversary in 1961.
>
> Among the speakers at the dedication ceremonies, held December 14–15, 1961, were Senator Lister Hill of Alabama, co-author with the then Senator John F. Kennedy of the National Library of Medicine Act of 1956, which authorized construction of the new building, and Abraham Ribicoff, Secretary of Health, Education, and Welfare.
>
> A gift to the library, presented by Alexis L. Liatis, Ambassador of the Government of Greece, was a cutting from an Oriental plane tree on the island of Cos under which Hippocrates is reported to have taught his pupils. The tree will be planted on the library's 11-acre grounds this spring.

A new division of the library will be concerned entirely with medical history.

Aristotle had a library. He left it to his pupil Theophrastus of Eresos. There was a great library in Alexandria. It was destroyed by the Arabs in the seventh century A.D. In other wars, other collections of books were destroyed. Had it not been for the careful collection of medical books by priests and monks, there would be no "past" in medical literature. The medieval universities began to collect small libraries. Yet in 1733 there were only 32 books in the library of the Faculty of Medicine of Paris. In that year 2,273 volumes were added by a single donor, and the library was to become the largest in the medical world.

The first medical library in the United States was founded in 1762 in the Pennsylvania Hospital. Other hospitals and medical schools followed the example as circumstances permitted. A library was established in the Surgeon General's department, but it contained only about a thousand volumes up to the time of the Civil War. John Shaw Billings built it up to internationally pre-eminent proportions.

In 1898 the Medical Library Association of the United States and Canada was founded. The rise of the profession of medical librarianship was discussed in Chapter 4.

Medical Bibliography

Bibliographies are available which disclose the areas in which scientists are working and publishing their findings. Noteworthy among them is the *Scientific Directory and Annual Bibliography,* published each year by the National Institutes of Health of the United States Department of Health, Education and Welfare, and available from the Superintendent of Documents. This volume "presents the broad outlines of the NIH structure, names the professional staff, and lists those scientific and technical publications which derive from the program of direct research—laboratory and clinical—at Bethesda, Maryland, and in the field."

Foremost among bibliographies is the *Index Catalogue* of the Library of the Surgeon General's Office at Washington, the first volume of which was issued in 1880 by John Shaw Billings, with the aid of Robert Fletcher, of Bristol, England. The monthly *Index Medicus* was issued by Billings and Fletcher from 1879 to 1899. It was revived from 1903 to 1927 by the Carnegie Institute of Washington, Fletcher continuing as editor-in-chief. It was succeeded by the *Quarterly Cumulative Index Medicus* which was replaced in 1960 by the annual *Cumulative Index Medicus,* published by the American Medical Association. This index is coordinated with the National Library of Medicine's *Index Medicus.*

Although preceded by a few bibliographers, such as Otho Brunfels, of Mainz (1464–1534), who published one of the first lists of physicians and their writings, and Conrad Gesner of Zurich (1516–1565), who produced twenty volumes of his *Bibliotheca universalis* (medical part uncompleted), Albrecht von Haller (1708–1777) is generally hailed as the founder of medical and scientific bibliography. His work covered the fields of botany, anatomy, surgery, and medical practice.

One of Sir William Osler's last achievements was a catalogue of his vast collection of historical texts, *Bibliotheca Prima.*

As an example of the work that may be involved in cataloguing the writings of a single author, J. Schwalbe's compilation in 1902 of a bibliography of the works of Rudolph Virchow took 118 pages averaging 18 titles to the page.

CASE REPORTS, OR MEDICAL RECORDS[30]

The foundation of all medical literature is the case report. Medical records of the earliest periods consisted for the most part of carvings on the hillsides; graven plates; potsherds; tracings burned into the clay tablets of Nineveh and Babylon; hieroglyphics on the papyri, tombs, and temples of Egypt; lettering on the parchment rolls of ancient Rome; polychrome murals on the walls of the caves of the Old Stone Age; and drawings on the walls of the paleolithic caverns in Spain. All these crude efforts of early man served the same purpose as medical records serve the physicians of today.

The earliest authentic date of reports on the care and treatment given patients goes back to 4500 B.C. when Thot, an Egyptian, wrote a series of books, six of which were primarily treatises of a medical nature. We have reports of operations dating back to 3000 B.C. found on medical papyri and pictures engraved on the door posts of a tomb which show circumcisions and surgery of the neck and extremities.

As early as 1600 B.C. an Egyptian papyrus—known as the Edwin Smith Papyrus, in honor of one of the early students of Egyptology during the nineteenth century—consists of a discussion of 48 cases of clinical surgery, all of which follow a systematic pattern of discussion, namely, a title, examination, diagnosis, and treatment. The original of this manuscript perhaps dates back to the days of the pyramids (3000–2500 B.C.).

Another early medical account is known as the Papyrus Ebers, written about 1500 B.C. This manuscript shows a careful and critical observation of disease and an intelligent application of remedies. Its size is monumental as compared with present conceptions of size—100 feet long and 12 inches wide, and it is rolled in a scroll.

Another interesting side light of the early ages are the temples, so-called Aesculapia, in honor of the Greek god of medicine, the columns of which are engraved with the names of patients, brief histories, and comments on the cases.

The Golden Age of ancient Greece is dominated in the field of medicine by the works of Hippocrates. The medical histories of his patients as he wrote them are models even by today's standards. He was not the first to observe critically the symptoms of disease, but he was the first to systematically record them. So the modern record of today was born the child of a great intellect, 2,400 years ago, after a long historical gestation. Hippocrates kept detailed records of his

[30] The historical part of this section is adapted from a paper presented to Alpha Delta Mu Fraternity, Northwestern University, by Josue Pagan-Carlo, of Puerto Rico, who received his master's degree in hospital administration in 1949, has since graduated in medicine and served a residency in radiology, and is now associate radiologist, Touro Infirmary, New Orleans.

patients and instructed his sons Thesalus, Dracon, and Dexippus in the art of recording clinical findings.

For the sake of interest, one of his cases is quoted, a case of puerperal fever as translated from the original Greek by Francis Adams in 1846:

> In Thasus, the wife of Philinus, having been delivered of a daughter, the lochial discharge being natural, and matters going mildly, on the 14th day after delivery she was seized with fever attended by rigor; was pained at first in the cardiac region of the stomach and right hypochondrium; pain in the genital organs; lochial discharge ceased. Upon application of a pessary all these symptoms alleviated; pains of the head, neck and loins remained; no sleep; extremities cold; thirst, bowels in a hot state; stools scanty; urine thin and colorless at first. On the 6th towards night, senses much disordered, but again were restored. On the 7th thirsty and the evacuations bilious and high colored. On the 8th had a rigor; acute fever; much spasm with pain; talked much, incoherently; upon application of suppository, rose to stool, and passed copious dejections with a bilious flux; no sleep. On the 9th spasms. On the 10th slightly recollected. On the 11th, slept; had perfect recollection, but again immediately wandered; passed a large quantity of urine with spasm (the attendants seldom putting her in mind) it was thick, white, like urine which had been shaken after it had stood for a considerable time until it had subsided, but it had no sediment; in color and consistence, the urine resembled that of cattle, as far as I observed. About the 14th day, startings over the whole body; talked much; slightly collected; but presently became again delirious. About the 17th day became speechless, and on the 20th died.

One man of towering intellect, Galen, dominated the Greco-Roman period from 156 B.C. to A.D. 476. In his teaching he took his pupils on his medical rounds, and one of his writings depicts an illustration of the taking of a medical history at the bedside. He was the first to recognize the function of the arteries, which he proved to be filled with blood instead of air as was a current belief. In one of his written cases he describes the symptoms of an attack of gallstones as a pain radiating from the upper abdomen into the right shoulder, said symptom being used today consistently for diagnostic purposes.

With the rise of Islam and the Dark Ages medical records, in fact medicine itself, consisted mostly of the study of the past masters like Hippocrates and Galen. However, the famed surgeon Avicenna added some remarkable reports to the literature as a result of his observations during his numerous trips through the Moslem Empire.

An interesting point in this period is the fact that St. Jerome, who conducted a hospital about A.D. 300, in his medical writings was the first to use the word "hospital," derived from the Latin word "hospes," meaning host or guest.

With the decline of the Greek and Roman civilization from 476 to 1438, very little progress was made in recording and preserving medical records. Emaciated monks in the seclusion of their punitive cells, within the cold and massive walls of the monasteries, copied and translated the classics; medical literature became the scholastic tool of a few erudites. The flame was not extinguished completely; with the establishment of St. Bartholomew's Hospital at London by Rahere in the twelfth century, medical records were kept for all patients. The *Book of the Foundation,* published by the Early English Text Society and edited from the original manuscript by Sir Norman Moore, contains about 28 original case histories.

With the Renaissance beginning about the middle of the fifteenth century, and the reign of King Henry VIII (1509-1547), conditions in St. Bartholomew's Hospital were improved and rules were drawn for its government, "The Ordres and Ordinances for the Better Government of the Hospital of Bartholomew the Lesse." Among the rules was "an ordre for the saufe kepying of the evidences and writings apperteining to the Hospitall." Another part reads:

> . . . and in the ende ye shall manifestly declare the names and sirnames of so many diseased personnes, as that yeare have bene cured and delivered out of this house . . . and also the names and surnames of so many that year have died in the house . . . the names and sirnames also of as many as then shal remain sycke and diseased in thys house with the names of the shier wherein eche was borne, and their faculties, exercise and ocupaciones.

Vesalius, credited with making the first contributions to the study of anatomy, realized the importance of recording his findings, as shown in his *Fabrica,* published in 1543. In 1622 Dr. Nicholas Tulp was elected prelator of the Surgeons Guild of Amsterdam and wrote his *Medical Observations,* which contains hundreds of interesting case histories. At this time the guild began public dissections for teaching purposes and kept records of them. Thus the surgeons of that day felt the responsibility for recording their own cases and findings so that they might be available for reference and study.

That it was made the responsibility of the doctors to write their own orders as early as the beginning of the seventeenth century is shown by the charge given Dr. William Harvey when he was made physician to St. Bartholomew's Hospital in 1609:

> . . . that you endeavor yourself to the best of your knowledge in the profession of Physic to the poor then present, or any of the poor at any time of the week which shall be sent home to you by the Hospitaller or Matron for your counsel, writing in a book appointed for that purpose such medicines with their compounds and necessaries as appertaineth to the Apothecary of this house to be provided and made ready for to be administered unto the poor, everyone in particular, according to his disease.

For the first fifty years the only medical records kept in the Pennsylvania Hospital which was established at Philadelphia in 1752 were those in the register, in which was recorded the patient's name, address, disorder, the dates of admission and discharge, with results on discharge, and the patient's security. In 1803 it was ordered that a detailed record be kept of the interesting cases and many of these are found to be illustrated with pen and ink sketches. In 1873 the hospital began to keep histories with no interruption since. The first patients' index was started in 1873 but was not kept on cards until 1906.

Many of the histories dating from about 1808 at the New York Hospital, which was opened in 1771, follow a definite routine similar to that followed today, stating diagnosis, age, date of admission, occupation, appearance, illness, and treatment together with progress notes.

The Massachusetts General Hospital, which was opened in 1821, has the distinction of having a complete file of clinical records, with all cases catalogued, dating from the opening date. Before the end of 1897 a librarian had been appointed, and the care of medical records including their cataloguing became part of her work. The terminology of those early days seems strange now. Among the diagnoses recorded are: "squeezed head," "whistle in the esophagus," "wild animals in the blood."

Aside from the case report itself, which is the subject of this historical summary, all medical scientific literature depends to a large extent upon the individual case record for explanation, illustration, and interest.

For an objective, medically oriented viewpoint of the whole subject of medical records, there can be no better qualified authority than the representative of the Joint Commission on Accreditation of Hospitals, who is out in the field as a surveyor. He has a unique opportunity for drawing comparisons of policies, practices, and philosophies of different institutions.

It was while serving in this capacity that Dr. Frederick N. Elliott wrote the following meditations on medical records as part of a thesis submitted in 1960 for his master's degree in hospital administration from Northwestern University. Dr. Elliott is assistant to the director of the American Hospital Association. Other quotations from the same paper were given in Chapter 1.

Medical Records and Hospital Accreditation

FREDERICK N. ELLIOTT, M.D.

In considering the matter of medical records, we must do so first by evaluating their potential contribution to patient care.

While in most instances there is an acceptance of the necessity for a recorded physical examination and for the appearance on the chart of the results of such special examinations as radiography, electrocardiography, and various clinical tests, there is less widespread endorsement of some of the elements of the complete chart acceptable to accreditation standards. This is attested to by their frequent absence or disposition as "negative," "noncontributory," or even "irrelevent." A few may be mentioned.

Provisional Diagnosis. This is frequently absent. A natural and human reluctance to commit oneself to an early judgment may account for this reticence. However, the requirement for this is indeed in the interest of the new patient and of those already in the hospital. It is only with this information that the hospital may admit a patient with safety to others and at the same time assign him so that he may receive optimum type of accommodation, nursing, and ancillary care appropriate to his condition. The acquaintance of all with the difficulties of early diagnosis should effectively remove the fear of humiliation as a revision becomes necessary.

The Complaint. It seems important to me that the physician and the hospital should avoid an important source of public misunderstanding and loss of confidence resulting from failure to treat the patient's complaint. It is, of course, not intended to depreciate the immensely valuable work done in the early detection and eradication of potentially serious disease. Yet it is not unusual to find the removal of a radiologically refractory gallbladder or the extirpation of some sagging organ following the admission of a patient who entered the hospital complaining of some unrelated condition which excited less respect and enthusiasm on the part of the physician, and with which he goes home, untreated, only to have it again obtrude itself on his mind when the drama and experience of the diversionary treatment have abated.

Past History and Family History. These, while not so frequently omitted, are often accorded less attention than their potential contribution to diagnosis and treatment would appear to warrant. Certainly there is acknowledgment of the necessity, emphasized by therapeutic disasters, for careful inquiry concerning allergic and hypersensitivity reactions. Yet many other indications suggest themselves which are not uncommonly overlooked. It is still a common practice to obtain bleeding and clotting times on patients for surgery, particularly tonsillectomy, though it is now generally conceded that there is extremely poor correlation between the results of these tests and the cases presenting hemorrhagic complications. On the other hand, cases complicated by hemorrhage are seldom found to have been anticipated by the careful past and family history which would have indicated the likelihood of a deficiency too occult for detection by the crude laboratory procedures still generally in use. Many other examples suggest themselves, such as the association between bearing large infants and the predisposition to diabetes mellitus, the familial patterns of specific malignancies, and the predisposition to diseases not overtly hereditary, all of which offer contributions to diagnosis and indications to treatment and to its possible hazards.

The consideration of these particular and more commonly neglected elements of the complete chart, together with those usually recorded, must lead us to the acknowledgment that the medical record is properly to be regarded as a clinical instrument in the treatment of the patient, providing the basis for diagnosis, the indications for, and record of treatment, and the critical assessment of observed response to treatment, in the form of progress notes.

These days, few endeavors are approached without a recorded evaluation of the situation, a plan and specification for action, and an accounting of results.

This applies from organizational activities to the simplest piece of construction. Even the politician, jealous and wary of his maneuverability, is constrained to first record what he must say in order to guard himself from extemporaneous omission or, worse, committal. How much more justifiable it is to demand that the undertaking of medical treatment, where the penalty of oversight may endanger even the life committed to the physician's care, be supported by a record of the evidence on which it is based. How easily we assume knowledge which, when faced with critical inquiry or the need for action, we find is incomplete! Only the necessity for recording the evidence in factual terms will reveal the hiatus where it exists to humiliate the physician and engulf the patient. In seeking a diagnosis, it is essential that all the elements of the history be presented and all the evidence be sifted and arranged for logical consideration. To do this requires a record. In a pursuit as complicated as medical practice, beclouded by so many human factors, burdened by the mass of what is known and has to be remembered, and handicapped by the vast as yet unknowns, to act without an inventory and assessment of indications is to offer the patient something less than the best.

Another key to the increasing importance of the medical record in the care of the patient is to be found in the changing pattern of medical practice.

It has been said that the advances in medicine of the past half century exceed in volume and scope all those of previously recorded history.

In time well within the memory of many physicians still practicing, the doctor carried on his own shoulders the sole responsibility for the diagnosis and treatment of disease. Fortunately, in many cases, the history of the patient was known to him, and often it included the family and social history and a good deal on the patient's psychological background. This, a physical examination, and, if he was scientifically zealous, a urinalysis and hemoglobin estimation told the physician all he could learn about the patient! With this a diagnosis was made, and with the physician's knowledge, acquired skills, and art, the patient was treated. The hospital provided the care necessary for those rendered helpless by disease or treatment or with the injunction to stay in bed. This consisted of a clean bed, bedpan service, and a diet cooked for people without teeth. In admitting his patient to the modern hospital, the physician faces a totally different set of circumstances. Though still burdened with the final responsibility for the decisions which must be made, and while still his skills are of crucial importance in the care of the patient, the physician must utilize, order, and direct in the hospital many ancillary services participating in treatment.

The diagnostic methods of radiology, clinical and anatomical pathology, and many other specialized procedures performed by others must be utilized by him. The treatment facilities of nursing care of a complexity undreamed of a few years ago, scientific diet therapy, physical medicine, therapeutic radiology, medical social service, and others provided by the modern hospital must be integrated into the plan of treatment and made complementary to the physician's efforts. All these must be utilized to their fullest potential. This requires that all those who now share in the treatment of the patient must be sufficiently informed that they do so without inflicting harm. To provide the information necessary for all who contribute to the care of the patient to do so safely becomes the function of the medical record. The injunction *primum non nocere* can be ensured in no other way.

In addition to the growth of ancillary services in the hospital is another development in medical practice giving new emphasis to the importance of the medical record. Less and less are doctors working alone. The development of specialization and the growth of the "clinic" concept of medical practice both mean that the patient often receives attention from several physicians at one time and also from different physicians at different times. It then becomes vital that none of the physicians contributing to the care of the patient be called upon to do so without the background and assistance of all the facts available. For a physician to be faced with the treatment of a patient doing badly after surgery, while the findings and procedures at operation remain an unrecorded secret, is to seriously restrict his ability to give timely and intelligent aid.

Finally there is the value of the medical record to the patient in subsequent treatment. As a legacy of the good old days when the record was unimportant, and frequently nonexistent, many patients today have essential treatment delayed and compromised by the lack of information on previous treatment. We have, then, in the preparation of a precise but comprehensive record, an instrument of present care, and the opportunity to serve the patient again in the future, when we may not be there.

The Medical Record and the Physician. While there are no considerations which equal in value those of the care of the patient, yet it need not detract from these to consider also the personal advantages and security which may accrue to the physician by the preparation of adequate medical records. While it may be presently unfashionable to proclaim it, and good physicians too self-conscious to admit it, there remains the fact of the intangible but only lasting reward of work well done. And one may say categorically that there is no consistently good clinical work done without the keeping of complete and detailed records. Without these, it is impossible to think exactly about the present case. Bacon summarized it when he wrote that "reading maketh a full man, conference a ready man, and writing an exact man." Without records it is impossible to undertake the review and comparison necessary if progress is to be made and the significance of events eventually comprehended. This is amply substantiated in a review of all the significant contributions to medical progress, and those who made them. From Hippocrates, Harvey, and Hunter to the great men of present-day medicine, there are as many personalities, separate, distinct, and unique, but they all had one characteristic in common which comes readily to mind. They all kept notes of their observations and experiences, detailed and honest. Nor did they shrink from recording that which was at variance with their cherished beliefs, when it occurred. For the physician who would know the satisfaction of continued growth in clinical knowledge and achievement, the way is clear.

A more pragmatic value of the medical record to the physician is its bearing on the legal aspects of the practice of medicine. As much as it is to be deplored, and as much as it is the result of correctable situations which tempt further discussion, we face the fact of the growing volume of litigation arising out of medical practice. The physician is concerned primarily with tort actions alleging negligence or the more recently popular allegation of assault. In defending such actions, the physician has no better advocate than an adequate medical record of the case. It is, of course, essential that the record be made concurrent with the events it describes, and before events have occurred which would render it self-serving, or merely a post hoc deposition. A complete and concurrent record merits credence beyond the power of adversary experts to detract or discredit. Certainly it would appear that such a record, indicating careful observation, thoughtful differential diagnosis, accepted treatment, and alert evaluation of its effects, should be a potent refutation of negligence, almost mutually exclusive, and something for which the beleagured physician may be devoutly thankful.

The Medical Record and the Medical Staff. A given and accepted function of the organized medical staff of the hospital is to provide for the education of its members. There are many ways in which medical groups can do this. Programs offering motion pictures, demonstrations, symposia, lectures by acknowledged or temporary authorities, and journal clubs are some of these. However, none of these alone meet the requirements of the Joint Commission on Accreditation of Hospitals. There is one educational possibility unique to the hospital which accreditation standards require to be used. This is, of course, the utilization of the clinical material provided by the hospital. The presentation of selected cases from patients in the hospital, or recently discharged, provides at once a contribution to the education and clinical experience of the staff, while proceeding with the necessary review of the clinical work of the hospital. To do this effectively, it is essential that the medical record be adequate not only to support the diagnosis and treatment given, but to provide answers to questions inspired by other clinical points of view. In the absence of such a record, much of the value of presentation is lost and the quality of discussion necessarily reduced.

The Medical Record and the Hospital. Though areas of misunderstanding and, based on it, in some cases resistance still exist, it is now generally accepted that in the hospital, ultimate authority must rest with those bearing ultimate responsibility. In most cases this places authority in the hands of a board of trustees who are responsible for all that goes on. In order to discharge responsibility in areas in which it is not, nor need be, competent, various degrees of responsibility and authority are delegated to those trained and adjudged competent by the board, which, of course, retains the right of approval. Thus it is that physicians granted the privilege of practice within the hospital are required to become participating members of the organized medical staff. Among the responsibilities assigned to this group are the investigation and recommendation of applicants for staff membership and the recommendation of clinical privileges, and their modification from time to time, based on evidence of training, experience, skill, clinical judgment, and ethical standards. These are required and described by the Joint Commission on Accreditation of Hospitals as credential committee functions.

Another responsibility assigned of necessity to the staff, and described as a tissue committee function, calls for review and evaluation of the standards of surgical practice in the hospital, using tissue submitted to pathological examination as a guide. Now that medical progress has armed the internist with medicines as potent for good or ill as the surgeon's scalpel, it is being encouraged that the medical practice in the hospital be appraised, case by case, as in the practice of surgery.

In order for the medical staff to discharge these responsibilities assigned to it, it is delegated with the authority to instruct its members, as functionaries of its appropriate committees, and only in that capacity, to scrutinize records and appraise performance on the evidence there presented. In order to maintain the records at a satisfactory standard for the diagnosis and treatment of the patient, the protection of the physician, and the functions of medical staff control, a medical records committee is established to encourage these standards and to act against observed deficiencies and delinquencies, for the protection of patient, physician, and hospital.

With the implication of the record explained as an instrumentality in the treatment of the patient, an incorruptible witness for the prudent physician, and the only tangible evidence available to the medical staff in discharging its heavy responsibilities to the hospital, we must have a fresh viewpoint and a positive approach toward this activity. It must be accepted that the concurrent preparation of the medical record is an integral part of the treatment of the patient.

Failure to have enough time may as well be applied as a reason for leaving sponges or instruments behind at operation. Failure to contribute good records to the necessary auditing procedure of the medical staff is parallel with the cashier handling a large volume of cash who fails to keep books for lack of time.

On the records depends the assurance to the trustees and to the public that the hospital is achieving the aspirations held for it and is meriting the confidence of the patient and those who are dear to him.

Supplementary Remarks on Medical Records

Strong emphasis on the value of medical records is shared by all great authorities on medical service. Here is one quotation:[31]

---

[31] Dr. Haven Emerson on "How Hospital Records Can Contribute to Health Protection" at the 1921 annual meeting of the American Hospital Association, West Baden, Indiana, a talk reproduced in a volume of his *Selected Papers,* published by the W. K. Kellogg Foundation on the occasion of his seventy-fifth birthday, October 19, 1949.

Facts upon which improvements in hospital procedure and management can be based, by which policies and the principles of administration can be tested, require an analysis of the experiences with disease which the bedside and laboratory service offer. Health, human salvage, relief from pain, from disability, from fever, and from anxiety, and postponement of death—these are the hospital's output. How success is attained or failure results, because of or in spite of our knowledge or our ignorance; what is myth and mystery; what is superstition and sentiment—to answer any such queries, we turn to the record . . . the truth *as* we see it, *when* we see it, the fact as our faltering and unskilled senses take note of it, on the spot, in the presence of suffering humanity, at the autopsy table, while the reaction in test tube or the tissue fragment under the microscope are knocking at our consciousness.

This is the spirit of the medical record as expressed more than forty years ago by one who fully appreciated its possibilities long before they were generally understood. The greatest impetus to its program of hospital standardization begun in 1918 by the American College of Surgeons was the fact that hospitals were furnishing such poor records of operations that they could not be used as gauges of the competency of surgeons applying for fellowship, as originally intended. Some hospitals could furnish no records at all. So it was just for a piece of paper—but how important a one—that a great reform movement began.

Dr. Haven Emerson expressed complete accord with that clause of the Minimum Standard for Hospitals, newly proposed by the American College of Surgeons, which had to do with medical records and heartily endorsed the recommendations of the college in regard to the periodic analysis of clinical records. "Science advances," he declared,[32] "on the back of accumulated facts," commenting that up to that moment "with rare and individual exceptions, the information given out from hospitals has been dry and valueless and may be called the dead ashes of the great repair shops of humanity." Fortunately thousands have labored so that this can no longer be said, among them the medical record librarian, whose role was described in Chapter 4, and certainly the hospital administrator, whose interest and cooperation are essential.

THE MEDICAL AUDIT

The development of good medical record systems has made possible the evaluation of medical care known as the medical audit—an appraisal of the work of the individual physician as well as of that of the medical staff as a whole. It serves, somewhat like the grading system in schools, as a spur to improvement. It introduces an element of wholesome competition for excellence, not only within the institution, but among institutions, for if conducted according to a uniform pattern useful comparisons can be drawn if certain distinctive features are taken into consideration. The whole standard of medical care can be uplifted by scrupulous study of why one hospital's results in treatment of a specific disease are superior to another's.

[32] *Ibid.,* p. 119.

Woman's Hospital, New York, is credited with having conducted in 1918 the first medical audit. The initiator was Dr. George Gray Ward. It has been carried on continuously ever since in that hospital. Ten years later Dr. Thomas R. Ponton devised what he called a professional accounting system.[33]

On September 17, 1960, the Board of Commissioners of the Joint Commission on Accreditation of Hospitals voted to recommend to its member organizations —the American College of Physicians, the American College of Surgeons, the American Hospital Association, and the American Medical Association—that they *encourage* physicians and hospitals to use on a trial basis a method of internal appraisal of medical care similar to the Medical Care Appraisal Plan of the American College of Physicians or the medical audit method of the Commission on Professional and Hospital Activities, in addition to the present devices such as the tissue committee, medical record committee, or a combination audit committee. The commission expressed the belief "that all hospitals should employ an adequate method of appraisal of medical care of which these two are examples and that the application of such methods will lead to improvement in the care of the patient."

The commission is a charitable, scientific and educational institution which provides statistical services to the medical profession and hospitals. In 1962 approximately 235 hospitals in 32 states, Puerto Rico, the District of Columbia, and three Canadian provinces were subscribing to its services. These hospitals discharge more than two million patients annually. The commission is sponsored by the American College of Physicians, American College of Surgeons, American Hospital Association, and the Southwestern Michigan Hospital Council. The audit method employed was developed by the American College of Surgeons. It was transferred by the college to the commission after successful use of the method had been demonstrated.

The college started the research project, which led to the development of the new method, in July, 1953, aided by a grant from the W. K. Kellogg Foundation. Already in operation at the time was a method devised by the Southwestern Michigan Hospital Council, also under a Kellogg grant. What the college mainly added was the factor of medical judgment. When the college and the council started to collaborate, the great difficulty that they encountered was the lack of uniform basic data, and with this problem the commission continues to labor.

Explanation of the manner in which the program operates was given in an article in the June, 1957, issue of *The Modern Hospital,* adapted and brought up to date by the authors, Drs. Robert S. Myers and Vergil N. Slee, in a reprint dated March, 1958:

> In actual practice the College's medical audit method works this way: All hospitals participating in the audit program audit a basic core of clinical records.

[33] This and later developments are described in Chapter VIII, pp. 167–215, of Ponton's *The Medical Staff in the Hospital,* as revised in 1953 by Dr. Malcolm T. MacEachern. Chicago, Physicians' Record Co., 1953 (1st ed. 1939).

This is done in accordance with a schedule developed with the assistance of an advisory audit committee of physicians from the medical staffs of participating hospitals. In 1957, for example, the schedule required auditing of all deaths on a current basis. The auditing also included: during the first quarter, review of a representative series of primary appendectomies; during the second quarter, premature infants; in the third quarter, diabetes patients; and in the fourth quarter, complicated deliveries. In addition, more detailed studies of two groups of patients, coronary occlusions and hysterectomies, were carried out.

For the current year, 1958, all deaths remain in the schedule, while the number of audits on medical categories has been reduced from six to four. Bleeding duodenal ulcer cases are being covered in the first quarter and "Inguinal Hemiorrhaphy and Antibacterials" will be the topic for the second quarter. An internal medicine topic and a pediatric topic will be selected for the other two quarters. For each of these specific evaluations, pertinent clinical questions are printed on the reverse side of the basic code sheet. The additional medical details recorded here by the audit committee are also analyzed by the Commission.

The total patients embraced by this schedule will ordinarily represent between 7 and 8 per cent of all the hospital's discharge and will not exceed 10 per cent. Medical staffs are, of course, given the privilege of auditing additional cases as dictated by local interest or needs. The Commission services of tabulation and analysis are available for all of the auditing a staff wishes to do.

At the commission's offices in Ann Arbor, punch cards are made and the data are processed by business machines. Two types of reports are prepared and returned to the participating hospitals. One is a summary of the hospital's own audit findings, prepared by the tabulating machines in such a manner that the medical staff can see the scope of its medical auditing activity and the strengths and weaknesses of its medical practice as judged by its own audit committee; the other is one in which the auditing experiences of the group of participating hospitals (whose identities are concealed from one another) are assembled so that each medical staff may see how its auditing activity and evaluations compare with those of other hospitals in the program.

It takes about five minutes per clinical record for case abstracting in the Professional Activities Study (P.A.S.). This is done in the hospital's medical record department from the regular clinical record and consists of key data for most classes of patients.

The machines at the commission's headquarters organize the abstracts for easy reference and analysis—by diagnosis, operation, and physician—and can rearrange them on other bases such as age, sex, and clinical service. They can summarize the number of patients transfused, given antibiotics, having blood pressure taken, given consultation, and autopsied.

More than seven million case abstracts have accumulated in the commission offices, an invaluable mine of material for research and reference purposes.

The commission itself cautions that its method has some limitations in its usefulness because of its statistical nature; the findings for one hospital are relative to those for other hospitals. Therefore it cannot replace such end-result methods as those employed by tissue committees and other medical audit procedures within the individual hospital. In internal medicine, however, there is no such clue to error as the removal of healthy tissue provides in surgery. The American College of Physicians conducted an intensive study to try to set up criteria for evaluating results in treating different diseases. The results were on the whole negative. The variable factors were too many and too complicated. In this area the statistical approach is for the present the most hopeful way of bringing about improvement through a desire of the staff in the low-ranking hospital to emulate the achievements of those with higher recovery showings.

Of the medical record librarian's role in the medical audit, Dr. Paul A. Lembcke,[34] professor of preventive medicine and public health, School of Medicine and School of Public Health, University of California, Los Angeles, says:

> Without a medical record librarian to lay the groundwork, medical auditing is virtually impossible. One of the main areas of responsibility is, of course, in assisting members of the medical staff to make useful records. Physicians should be assisted in preparing medical records that are legible, by being provided with dictation and transcription service; in preparing records that are complete, by a system of checking them for completeness and by working with the medical staff committees concerned with records of professional activities; and in completing records promptly, by a system of reminders. The preparation of statistics on admissions, discharges, births, deaths, occupancy, length of stay, and such epidemiological characteristics of patients as age, sex, residence, economic and insured status, is the responsibility of the medical record librarian, who must also maintain standard indexes of diseases, operations and deaths. . . .

And of the administrator's part in the process he states:

> The hospital administrator is in a position to influence the governing board, the medical staff, and others, to understand and to welcome medical auditing. He should keep the governing board up to date on the quality of medical care that is provided by leading hospitals, and through a joint medical liaison committee he can keep the leaders of both board and medical staff posted on developments in medical auditing as he learns of them through hospital journals and meetings. He should not, however, initiate a medical audit independently. When an audit is decided upon, the hospital administrator should be the coordinator. He should advise on the general methodology and scope of the audit, and the selection of an individual or agency to carry it out. He should coordinate the roles of the auditor, governing board, medical staff, pathology and clinical laboratory departments, and the medical record librarian. He should be able to understand a medical audit report at least as well as he can read a financial balance sheet or a statement of income and expense, and should be able to explain the general procedure and the specific findings to individual members of the medical staff or governing board, if necessary; but if a formal presentation and interpretation of a medical audit report is to be made to the entire staff or board, the administrator should delegate this task to the medical auditor.

This quotation from a talk by a medical educator is an eloquent and convincing answer to those who would restrict the administrative function to the business management of the hospital.

[34] From an address, Medical Auditing, presented at the Educational Institute, California Association of Medical Record Librarians, Santa Barbara, April 20, 1959. *J. Am. A. Med. Rec. Librarians,* December, 1959, pp. 324–27, 346.

MEDICAL ETHICS

Documentary evidence of concern for medical ethics begins with the Hippocratic Oath:

> I swear by Apollo the physician, and Aesculapius, and Health, and All-heal, and all the gods and goddesses, that, according to my ability and judgment, I will keep this Oath and this stipulation—to reckon him who taught me this Art equally dear to me as my parents, to share my substance with him, and relieve his necessities if required; to look upon his offspring in the same footing as my own brothers, and to teach them this Art, if they shall wish to learn it, without fee or stipulation; and that by precept, lecture, and every other mode of instruction, I will impart a knowledge of the Art to my own sons, and those of my teachers, and to disciples bound by a stipulation and oath according to the law of medicine, but to none others.
>
> I will follow that system of regimen which, according to my ability and judgment, I consider for the benefit of my patients, and abstain from whatever is deleterious and mischievous. I will give no deadly medicine to any one if asked, nor suggest any such counsel; and in like manner I will not give to a woman a pessary to produce abortion. With purity and with holiness I will pass my life and practice my Art.
>
> I will not cut persons laboring under the stone, but will leave this to be done by men who are practitioners of this work. Into whatever houses I enter, I will go into them for the benefit of the sick, and will abstain from every voluntary act of mischief and corruption; and, further, from the seduction of females or males, of freemen and slaves.
>
> Whatever, in connection with my professional practice or not in connection with it, I see or hear, in the life of men, which ought not to be spoken of abroad, I will not divulge, as reckoning that all such should be kept secret. While I continue to keep this Oath unviolated, may it be granted to me to enjoy life and the practice of the Art, respected by all men, in all times! But should I trespass and violate this Oath, may the reverse be my lot.

Adaptations of this oath to fit the times have served as the guiding philosophy of physicians through the centuries. A set of rules for medical ethics and medical etiquette introduced in the fifth century A.D. is the *Formula comitis archiatrorum* of Theodoric. An early example of a local code of ethics is the bilingual "Statutes" of the Royal College of Physicians of England. As early as 1452 the Paris faculty had similar statutes.

In the seventeenth century medical ethics became sort of personalized in Thomas Sydenham as a result of his attitude toward patients, an interest in the individual which went beyond a scientific approach to the disease. Toward the end of the century Percival's code of medical ethics was privately printed; it was published in 1803.

With due regard for these early, general codes, each medical and related organization has drawn up one of its own, and it behooves the medical service administrator to have some knowledge of them, especially the main ones.

The American Medical Association has revised the Principles of Medical Ethics which it adopted at its inception, the latest revision having been the radically changed one adopted by the House of Delegates in June, 1957. The revision reduced the Principles from a document of more than 8,000 words to one of less than 500 words. It was stated that "much of the wordiness and ambiguity which made ready explanation difficult" were eliminated but that "every basic principle had been preserved." The ten sections of the Principles as revised are:

1. The principal objective of the medical profession is to render service to humanity with full respect for the dignity of man. Physicians should merit the confidence of patients entrusted to their care, rendering to each a full measure of service and devotion.

2. Physicians should strive continually to improve medical knowledge and skill, and should make available to their patients and colleagues the benefits of their professional attainments.

3. A physician should practice a method of healing founded on a scientific basis; and he should not voluntarily associate professionally with anyone who violates this principle.

4. The medical profession should safeguard the public and itself against physicians deficient in moral character or professional competence. Physicians should observe all laws, uphold the dignity and honor of the profession and accept its self-imposed disciplines. They should expose, without hesitation, illegal or unethical conduct of fellow members of the profession.

5. A physician may choose whom he will serve. In an emergency, however, he should render service to the best of his ability. Having undertaken the care of a patient, he may not neglect him; and unless he has been discharged he may discontinue his services only after giving adequate notice. He should not solicit patients.

6. A physician should not dispose of his services under terms or conditions which tend to interfere with or impair the free and complete exercise of his medical judgment and skill, or tend to cause a deterioration of the quality of medical care.

7. In the practice of medicine a physician should limit the source of his professional income to medical services actually rendered by him, or under his supervision, to his patients. His fee should be commensurate with the services rendered and the patient's ability to pay. He should neither pay nor receive a commission for referral of patients. Drugs, remedies or appliances may be dispensed or supplied by the physician provided it is in the best interests of the patient.

8. A physician should seek consultation upon request; in doubtful or difficult cases; or whenever it appears that the quality of medical service may be enhanced thereby.

9. A physician may not reveal the confidences entrusted to him in the course of medical attendance, or the deficiencies he may observe in the character of patients, unless he is required to do so by law or unless it becomes necessary in order to protect the welfare of the individual or of the community.

10. The honored ideals of the medical profession imply that the responsibilities of the physician extend not only to the individual, but also to society where these responsibilities deserve his interest and participation in activities which have the purpose of improving both the health and the well being of the individual and the community.

Local medical societies are provided with a manual annotating decisions of the A.M.A. Judicial Council on ethical problems, since interpretation and enforcement of the Principles must be carried out by local medical societies. It is important for the hospital administrator to know what regulations of its own the local medical society may have adopted, particularly those concerned with the use of physicians' names in publicity.

The American College of Surgeons disclaims having a code of ethics of its own, expecting its members like those of all medical organizations in the United States to adhere to the Principles of medical ethics of the American Medical Association. Before admission to fellowship, however, every candidate takes this fellowship pledge:

> Recognizing that the American College of Surgeons seeks to develop, exemplify, and enforce the highest traditions of our calling, I hereby pledge myself, as a condition of Fellowship in the College, to live in strict accordance with all its principles, declarations, and regulations. In particular, I pledge myself to pursue the practice of surgery with thorough self-restraint and to place the welfare of my patients above all else; to advance constantly in knowledge by the study of surgical literature, the instruction of eminent teachers, interchange of opinion among associates, and attendance on the important societies and clinics; to regard scrupulously the interests of my professional brothers and seek their counsel when in doubt of my own judgment; to render willing help to my colleagues and to give freely my services to the needy. Moreover, I pledge myself, so far as I am able, to avoid the sins of selfishness; to shun unwarranted publicity, dishonest money-seeking, and commercialism as disgraceful to our profession; to refuse utterly all money trades with consultants, practitioners, makers of surgical appliances and optical instruments, or others; to teach the patient his financial duty to the physician and to expect the practitioner to obtain his compensation directly from the patient; to make my fees commensurate with the service rendered and with the patient's rights; and to avoid discrediting my associates by taking unwarranted compensation. Finally, I pledge myself to cooperate in advancing and extending, by every lawful means within my power, the influence of the American College of Surgeons.

In addition the candidate signs a declaration that he will not practice the division of fees. This unethical practice the college has fought since its founding in 1913. In its Principles of Financial Relations in the Professional Care of the Patient and in further definition of these principles in a resolution adopted in 1952, the objections to fee-splitting, ghost surgery, and certain other practices are forcefully expressed along with the threat of punitive action against a fellow of the college who is known to be guilty of any of them. The college has on several occasions taken such action. It has also in some instances required fellows to submit to financial audits to prove they do not split fees and, if they refuse, has asked for their resignations.

Hospitals have been powerful allies in helping the medical organizations with their efforts to maintain high ethical standards. Every staff appointee in an accredited hospital, for example, takes an oath that he will not split fees.

Medical ethics are subject to certain religious beliefs which affect procedures. These are especially sharply defined by the Roman Catholic Church.[35]

---

[35] Rev. Edwin F. Healy, S.J., was author of a book entitled *Medical Ethics* (Chicago, Loyola Univ. Press, 1956) which should be a good source of reference for hospital personnel as well as physicians.

Part three

THE TECHNOLOGICAL
AND
BUSINESS COMMUNITY

CHAPTER 9

Buildings and Builders

We must seriously study the shape and size of our new hospitals. There is something favorable to be said for direct observation of patients in an intensive-care unit built circular and there is something to be said against a circular general nursing floor with a large number of rooms. . . . All new hospital construction must now consider patient care first and this will lead naturally into the study of automation in the general hospital.

GEORGE RADCLIFFE[1]

"Space Medicine Is Coming Down to Earth" was the title of an article in the November, 1959, issue of *The Reader's Digest* by Dr. Hugh C. MacGuire with Allen Rankin. Dr. MacGuire is a pediatric surgeon in Montgomery, Alabama, who, as the footnote to the article relates, has been "a national leader in persuading science, industry and medicine to combine their resources and bring 'moon-going medicine' down to this planet; he is the organizer of Atomedics, Inc., a nonprofit organization which aspires to build a pilot-model 'automated' hospital and research center which will use extensively the techniques described in this article."

Since the article was written, the first of four prototype Atomedic hospitals has been opened in Montgomery and a second one built to serve as the official emergency hospital of the New York World's Fair in 1964.

The Atomedics Research Center was moved from Montgomery to Tuskegee in 1961 because of more space being available there. The prototype hospitals are

[1] Mr. Radcliffe is director of development, Columbus Hospital, Newark, New Jersey. The quotation is from an address presented before the Congress of the International College of Surgeons, Chicago, May 16, 1961.

305

entirely electronic and with all the electronic equipment are planned to be built at a cost of around $120,000 each. The materials used for construction are lightweight and flexible. Prefabrication is employed and mass production is visualized. The units are small, accommodating 33 beds. The original model was built by Beauchamp Nolin, who operates a refrigeration engineering plant at Montgomery. As research progressed, and as new developments in electronics occurred, changes were made in the design. Especially enacted for Atomedics is an Alabama state law exempting the center from meeting the construction requirements for hospital facilities. The prototype hospital is circular, is about 100 feet in diameter, has a large working area in the center and the patients' rooms in individual units around the periphery. There are heating elements in the walls. The units are expandable and could in emergencies accommodate four patients. The hospital is equipped with electronic transducers for recording blood pressure, pulse rate, and other measures automatically, the information going to a central computing center.

To the hospital administrator these atomic age developments in hospitals mean that he must be cognizant of the thinking that is going on around him about innovations that seem in the realm of fantasy. Serious, practical-minded architects, industrialists, electronics engineers, physicists, and chemists are working with the physicians in the Atomedics Center, and many of the startling new ideas are already incorporated in the operation as well as in the plans of several hospitals in different parts of the country. The Atomedics Center's progress is something he must study. On the 2,200-acre site, which is that of the former Tuskegee Army Air Base, eventual plans call for an international medical university and a fabricating plant, besides the research center, the prototype hospitals, and living quarters.[2]

It is easy to go overboard from enthusiasm over new ideas in planning, and it is well to remember that millions of dollars have been wasted on building ideas that have either never materialized or have proved to be impractical. In 1961 in an architectural exhibit at the Illinois Institute of Technology entitled "Visionary Architecture," plans were included for monumental domes and arches of colored glass to decorate the Alps, the idea of Bruno Taut, a German; underwater apartments to relieve crowding in Japan, planned as an entire off-shore city by architect Kiyonori Kitukake; a road 14 miles long to be built on top of a 14-story building of that length, suggested by Le Corbusier of France; and Frank Lloyd Wright's mile-high, 528-story building to accommodate 130,-000 persons with transportation by 56 atomic-powered elevators.

[2] Among the articles published describing the project are "Dr. Hugh C. MacGuire Inspires Inter-Industry Crowd" in the November, 1960, issue of the American Surgical Trades Association *Journal*, pp. 40–41, and September, 1960, pp. 41–42 and 88–92; "Construction of Atomedic 'Dream' Hospital to Begin Next Year" in the December, 1960, issue of *Hospital Topics;* and Jane Barton's "Electronics Is Changing the Structure of Hospitals and Medical Care" in the June, 1960, issue, pp. 81–87 and 168, and "Atomedics Moves Hospitals into Electronics Era" in the November, 1961, issue, pp. 92–95 and 156–58, of *The Modern Hospital.*

Some of the new hospital planning smacks of these extravagances. A sense of humor helps in deciding what is not likely to succeed and what is. Prefacing his remarks by the statement, "There is a fair chance that the hospital as we know it will disappear entirely within a generation," architect E. Todd Wheeler told an audience on May 8, 1960, at the opening of the hospital exhibit at the International College of Surgeons' Hall of Fame, that carried to their logical conclusion some of the advances in medical science forebode strange effects upon hospital planning and operation. One of his examples was anesthesiology, of which he said:[3]

If the use of anesthetics permits painful surgery to be endured without the patient experiencing pain, why not extend these benefits to all patients and anesthetize each one upon admission to the hospital, keeping him comatose until he is discharged? The patient would be relieved of many of the irritations of hospital life, not the least of which is worry over his future; and his system, thus freed of all attendant burdens, could devote its full natural resources to fighting the disease. Why not lighten the burden of normal body functions for all patients?

The hospital to be derived from such a scientific innovation we call the "Gas House." Its elements will include patient rooms, but they will not be bed rooms. Each patient, happily asleep, will occupy a wheel chair equipped with pneumatic pads on the seat, back, arms and foot rests activated rhythmically to stimulate peristalsis and tilted back at intervals to elevate the feet. His room will consist of a completely air conditioned chamber 3 feet wide, 4 feet deep and 5 feet high. Contrast this compact space of 60 cubic feet with our present wasteful bed rooms of not less than 1,200 cubic feet—a twenty to one difference! Attached to the patient will be electrical devices to measure pulse, respiration, temperature, evaporation, skin color, brain waves, cardiactivity, and probably many other qualities which will be the diagnostic material of the future.

It will be necessary to develop an objective pain recorder, since the anesthesia precludes use of that subjective symptom. Feeding of the patient will be intravenously or by stomach tube, of either a prescribed menu or one selected in advance of admission. It is possible that the fluid intake can be limited to no more than can be expelled in respiration and evaporated from the skin, and solid intake may be replaced by chemicals, thus eliminating evacuation both liquid and solid. What a boon to the patient, not to mention the nurse!

Complete control of the patient's immediate environment will permit therapy by humidity, temperature, infrared or ultraviolet radiation, oxygen or other special gases, even vibration and sound if they be found therapeutic. An aseptic environment can easily be maintained. If psychotherapy is indicated, hypnotism can be used for induction instead of anesthetic gases. . . . And the patient enters the hospital sick, goes to sleep, and wakes up well. No bother, no worry, no food complaints, no noise, no glare, no odors, no incompatible roommates, no visitors, complete privacy and complete concentration on getting well. What could be more ideal?

Mr. Wheeler was not being facetious, however, when he said: "We can be certain that the hospital will change in many respects and our problem is to anticipate those changes where we can and to provide methods to adapt to the

[3] Hospital of the Future, Sec. II. *J. Internat. Coll. Surgeons,* September, 1960, pp. 19–31.

unpredictable when it comes. This is what the architect seeks to do when he makes a long range plan for a hospital." He went on to say that the conscientious hospital architect when he looks ahead tries to visualize how developments will affect the patient, medical science, hospital architecture, and hospital functions. Waxing facetious again, he wound up his talk with the following six possibilities for the day *after* tomorrow:

1. The hospital will disappear entirely because medical science will treat all diseases in the home.

2. The hospital will remain the center of treatment but will be used wholly for ambulant patients.

3. All health services will be rendered by the state at a series of ten or twelve central points to which patients will be sent, anesthetized, through pneumatic tubes.

4. Mechanical and electronic scanners will assemble and record each patient's symptoms, an IBM machine will diagnose the ailment and prescribe the treatment, and an automatic therapy machine will give treatment to the patient, comfortably relaxed on a continuous conveyor belt.

5. At the other extreme, psychotherapy may develop to such a point that all treatment will be given through that medium and the hospital, if it exists at all, will become a club.

6. And, finally, the most ominous portent of all is that hospitals will eventually be planned without architects and operated without doctors.

The extreme preoccupation with hospital planning, made necessary by scientific and technological developments for which provision must be made in the structure, and by rising costs of care which demand full utilization of such developments for the sake of economy as well as for improved patient care, is forcing educators in hospital administration to devote considerable time to the subject. A subcommittee of the American Institute of Architects a few years ago prepared a suggested outline on "What the Hospital Administrator Should Know about Hospital Planning and Architectural Service." It is assumed in this outline that the administrator will usually be (1) the important agent in drawing up the hospital program; (2) the liaison man between the hospital board and the architect; (3) the source of much detailed information as to hospital procedures, special service equipment, relation and relative importance of various hospital departments.

Consultation with department heads in planning construction or remodeling is essential, but the architects' outline conveys this warning: "The administrator must be in a position to veto demands for excessive space or equipment by individual departments which would throw such departments out of scale with the institution as a whole." Obviously the administrator must himself know enough about every operation, in general as well as in his own institution or proposed institution, to be able to balance the needs fairly and judge them sensibly.

Surveys of community needs for hospitalization, selection of building site, and probably employment of a hospital consultant precede preparation of preliminary plans and selection of an architect.

The Joint Commission on Accreditation of Hospitals, in its *Bulletin* of August, 1961, which was devoted almost entirely to discussion of the physical plant, stated that it has established no standards on types of construction for hospitals; does not approve architectural plans or endorse building materials (as a rule, state or local building codes for hospitals take care of this adequately); and evaluates the physical plant on the basis of its functional qualities. The standards do state that the physical plant must be constructed and arranged to ensure the safety of the patient, and in order to do this, according to the *Bulletin,* the commission believes that the physical plant should provide facilities for the segregation of patients, for isolation, for adequate space per bed, for emergency lighting, and for emergency gas or water supply. The commission considers fire hazards "so serious that no matter how excellent the medical care, a hospital that is a fire trap will not be accredited." The danger of explosions is pointed out. Maintenance is also emphasized in the standards and in the special *Bulletin* as a factor in ensuring the safety of patients.

Planning should proceed in stages: First are the preliminary studies in which all concerned take part, differences of opinion are adjusted, general agreement is reached with respect to patient capacity, interior layout, and approximate costs. Second, after all studies are completed, working drawings and specifications are commenced and carried to completion by the architect, assisted by engineers and consultant. Third, estimates are received, contracts let to responsible contractors, and actual building operations commenced. Equipment and furnishing should proceed along with the planning, separate schedules and specifications being drawn up for each class of equipment. The outside relationships involved in the whole process of building, equipping, and maintaining a hospital demand understanding and skill on the part of the administrator to achieve the best results.

Planning the building for administrative efficiency is a concept that has developed very slowly. In the section, "The Development of Hospital Architecture in the United States," in the *Yale Studies of Hospital Function and Design*[4] it is stated that "the erroneous assumption that disease is caused by miasmas generated by organic filth" caused a "great sanitary awakening" about 1860 "marked by the medical discovery that disease is influenced by the environment, and therefore a controlled environment is necessary for health." In consequence of this assumption, "the first products of the collaboration between medicine and architecture had then one guiding purpose—to produce a sanitary environment for the sick." The report continues:

All other considerations were relatively unimportant: hygiene was indeed the chief goal of these hospital planners. The successful accomplishment of this guiding purpose, coupled with the discovery of anesthesia and the later development of asepsis, revolutionized not only the architecture of the hospital, but also

[4] Study conducted under Public Health Service Grant W 53. First section representing studies completed during the first three years released in 1960.

the character of the hospital itself. . . . Hospitals were built before 1860, and in some instances the designers expressed concern for environmental cleanliness, but such concern was overridden by other considerations, many of which have a familiar sound. Dr. John Jones, one of the founders of New York Hospital, in 1776 emphasized "how necessary pure air is to the cure of disease in general" and went on to protest against a too-utilitarian approach to hospital building. . . .

The most common types of hospital plans before 1860 in the United States were classified by Wylie as the "Old Conglomerate Plan" and the "Block Plan." The former was really a planless hospital that evolved from a building not originally intended for a hospital, such as a prison, an almshouse, or a private home. The "Block Plan" may be illustrated by the original building of the General Hospital Society of Connecticut, now the Grace-New Haven Community Hospital. The architect, Itheil Town, had been instructed by the Society to erect in 1832 a hospital "of three stories to be built after the manner of the Episcopal chapel in this city." Mr. Town objected to these instructions and instead proposed that the hospital be constructed after the manner of the New State House, and his suggestion was accepted. A single building, two stories high, with a basement and a "Grecian portico" was constructed for less than $13,000.

The report quotes Sir Henry C. Burdett,[5] of England, as stating, "The great aim up to within almost recent times appears to have been to aggregate together under one roof as many sick as possible and the end was attained by adding ward to ward and story to story."

Florence Nightingale, Lord Lister, Sir Douglas Dalton, and Sir Henry Burdett wielded great influence in the promotion of sanitation of hospitals. In the United States truly thoughful planning was exemplified in the Johns Hopkins Hospital at Baltimore, designed by John Shaw Billings, which, in accordance with the then primary consideration of the necessity for "pure air," was planned first of all to assure maximum ventilation. The hospital was opened in 1889. It was not until the 1890's that the germ theory and, a little later, efficiency began to transform hospital design. The idea of efficiency led to reconsideration of the advantages of the pavilion plan, which is still the favored one in Europe.

The present situation as far as horizontal *versus* vertical plans are concerned is complicated by the growing multipurpose concept of the general hospital, which is in some respects at variance with the single huge building of many stories in height. Plans for the new Columbus Hospital in Newark, New Jersey, call for eight buildings: a 170-bed acute-care building; a diagnostic building with about 20 beds; a 40-bed obstetrical building; an administration building; a 15-bed psychiatric building; a 20-bed chronic-care building; a 15-bed physical medicine buildings; and a 100-bed nursing home. All buildings will be connected, both above and below ground, so that patients can be readily transferred from one to another and the staff will have easy access to all parts of the complex.

Not to be forgotten in designing hospitals are some important changes in ideas about patient care. A. Querido[6] lists greater concern for aesthetics in the

---

[5] *Hospitals and Asylums of the World*. London, J. A. Churchill, 1893, vol. 4, p. 33.
[6] The Changing Role of the Hospital in a Changing World. *Hospitals*, January 1, 1962.

patient area, need for more out-of-bed space for patients because of early ambulation, increasing concern for the psychiatric aspects of illness which have led to experiments in rooming-in for other conditions besides obstetrics and the new born, growing responsibility for rehabilitation, and the impact of patient monitoring, communication systems, and other mechanical aids.

The average construction cost per bed in 1961 for Hill-Burton projects, ranging from 25 to 150 beds mainly, was $18,290. The cost per square foot was $24 for buildings and fixed equipment only. A 300-bed Ohio hospital cost $27,471 per bed and $28.80 per square foot, with total cost including buildings, fixed and movable equipment, architect's fee, supervision, site survey, and soil investigation coming to $29.64 per square foot.[7]

A research project on planning is being conducted jointly by the American Hospital Association and the American Institute of Architects. With the aid of computers the data accumulated will be organized in a way, it is hoped, that will be of factual assistance in guiding planners.

The A.H.A. lists individual, experienced architects who are registered by their states and who have carried a major responsibility for at least three hospitals, one of which must be completed and in operation; two may be in the process of design or construction. Additions to existing hospitals are acceptable only if they contain the major elements of the hospital structure to an extent that clearly indicates the architect's familiarity with hospital requirements. Listing is a requirement for personal membership. Once an architect is listed, the association invites the firm he represents to become an associate member.

The American Hospital Association, the Association of American Medical Colleges, the American Medical Association, and the Public Health Service are jointly sponsoring the development by a committee of more information dealing with architectural requirements of the university teaching hospital. The committee held its first meeting in Washington, D. C., November 15–16, 1962.

Aesthetic Considerations

In an era when even factories are competing in the beautification of their premises, hospitals are obliged, as service institutions supported usually by their communities, to earn the favor of patients and the public by making their buildings and grounds as attractive as possible. They have the additional incentive of the therapeutic value of pleasant surroundings.

Starting with the design of the hospital, through the landscaping, interior decorating, and furnishing stages, the administrator should consult with experts in order to achieve the best results from standpoints of both utility and appearance.

---

[7] A useful book produced in 1961 by the editors of *Architectural Record* and published by Dodge Books is the 265-page *Hospitals, Clinics and Health Centers*, illustrated by 700 photographs, plans, and diagrams.

Color is a recognized vital element in beauty. It should be employed with taste and discrimination to suit the purposes of the area and to harmonize with the surroundings.

The artist plays an important role in the beautifying of hospitals. Pictures, panels, murals, and art objects of many kinds contribute to the creation of an atmosphere conducive to allaying fears and quieting distress. Interesting wall coverings, color combinations and tones, and ornamentation give the patient something to take his mind off his woes.

Lighting is one of the media that combine practical and aesthetic elements. It is a study in itself. Lighting engineers should be consulted before any installations are definitely planned. Visits to other hospitals should be made to see how new ideas look and work in practice. Lighting for the operating room deserves particular study with the aid of specialists.

PATIENT CARE UNITS

The disadvantages as well as the advantages of classifying patients and setting up separate units for the various classes are becoming apparent. The pendulum of specialization may have swung too far. Occupancy is affected. There are waiting lists for some units; vacant beds in others. Vacant beds are costly. Planners should take heed.

Segregation by age is desirable in theory. However, too large a ratio of vacant beds in pediatrics, teen-age, or geriatric units points to a need for greater flexibility or else arrangements with other hospitals in the community so that the diversification will not be so great in any one institution. The same principle holds with respect to segregation by disease or type of treatment. Every hospital in a community need not maintain obstetric or psychiatric units.

Progressive patient care has introduced occupancy and staffing problems in the different stages. The intensive care unit has in general strong support. Whether it should combine services for the patient recovering from surgery and for the severely ill medical patient is debatable. Usually they are separated. The progression to a limited-care area and then to a self-help unit has unquestionable benefits, economic and social as well as physical, for the patient but complicates administration and helps to create fluctuations in occupancy.

The full implications of the theories of early ambulation and of rehabilitation through activity seem to have been slow in penetrating the thinking of planners. Now the light is dawning that patients can and will benefit by doing more for themselves and that herein lies one of the solutions to the problem of shortages of nurses and other personnel. So there arrives on the scene the roomette, compact like the Pullman version but containing also a built-in dresser and bedside cabinet, the latter including a small refrigerator, cupboard, ice-water compartment, telephone, and even a toaster and coffeepot. Trial installation of such units at Porter Sanitarium and Hospital, Denver, and Boulder Sanitarium and Hospital, Boulder, Colorado, was reported in 1957.[8] The space-saving potentialities as well as the incentive to the patient to self-help are obvious.

The Laboratory

The "most plaguing" problem in hospitals today is inadequate laboratory space, according to Dr. George Z. Williams,[9] of the National Institutes of Health, Washington, D.C. Dr. Williams said that government standards for laboratory construction are unrealistic, being based on needs of many years ago, and that laboratories are being built too small and without provision for expansion. Another participant agreed, saying, "There is nothing in the classic standards which helps."

The same conclusion was reached by a Northwestern University student, David W. Stickney, during his administrative residency at Children's Memorial Hospital, Chicago. It led him to choose as the subject for his thesis, submitted in June, 1960, "Changing Patterns of Hospital Clinical Laboratories." Mr. Stickney is now associate director of the Illinois Hospital Association. Extracts from his paper follow:

> Hospital pathologists and their technical assistants are handicapped by insufficient clinical laboratory capacity to handle the expanding volume and complexity of tests being prescribed by physicians. . . . Current plans for modernizing and expanding hospitals, old and new, invariably include enlarged quarters for the over-taxed laboratory. In the meantime, many institutions are finding stop-gap relief through recourse to the services of independent outside laboratories for tests which should be made quickly and under the supervision of the staff pathologist; the Joint Commission on Accreditation of Hospitals on occasion has criticized the quality of control under this practice.
>
> Inadequate laboratory capacity, especially when it develops without increased patient census, dramatizes the needs of planners, consultants and architects for critical review of the conventional guides which experience is proving deficient and for more dependable guides to future construction.
>
> Planners' concerns range from the cubic footage of building space and the selection and arrangement of fixtures and equipment to the complement of staffing personnel. Of these, the most inflexible decisions are the physical space which is to be cast into the concrete of the structure and the orientation of that space into the operational system of the hospital plant. Awareness of these physical rigidities reinforces the planners' pressing needs for better guides in order to avert early and costly obsolescence.
>
> Adequacy of the area and facilities is an element not only of the anticipated volume of work, but also of the types of laboratory determinations and the quality of control. In turn, these factors themselves affect patient care in so far as it is related to the diagnostic and therapeutic support of dependable laboratory tests.

[8] H. E. Rice: Self-Help Is No Problem in This Unit. *Mod. Hosp.*, August, 1957, pp. 66–67.
[9] In a paper read for him at the October, 1960, annual joint meeting in Seattle of the American Society of Clinical Pathologists and the College of American Pathologists.

This situation led me, in 1958, to search the literature for guides used by hospitals in planning their clinical laboratories. I sought to ascertain the volume of tests, quantitatively and by type, that hospitals were told they should anticipate per admission, per patient day and per clinic visit. Nothing was found, so letters were directed to authoritative sources. Two responded, but said they were aware of no such data. . . . The most relevant finding was the 1952 recommendation of the laboratory consultant of the Division of Hospital and Medical Facilities, Public Health Service: "4.5 square feet per hospital bed will provide an estimate for the minimum areas required in general hospitals up to 500 beds."

This was restatement of the old standard which had been incorporated six years earlier in the original 1946 edition of *Elements of the General Hospital,* the basic guide for administration of Hill-Burton construction funds. Although the *Elements* have been revised from time to time, the section dealing with laboratories has remained without change. The value of this standard has been further clouded by personal experience visiting hospital laboratories with inadequate space and capacity although their areas were several times the ratio of 4 1/2 square feet per bed. . . .

In the spring of 1959, after statistics had been gathered and were being analyzed on actual clinical practice, new and relevant data began to appear in the hospital literature. Dr. Louis Block, then Senior Scientist of the Division of Hospital and Medical Facilities of the Public Health Service, began up-dating his 1953 *Prototype Studies* of typical general hospitals with 25, 50, 100, 200, 400 and 600 beds. . . .

Growth of hospital laboratories may be measured by the gross increase of their product: the number of tests performed each year. . . . Important generalizations (from the author's research) are: (1) Laboratory test volume has expanded greatly in most general hospitals; (2) Growth rates have been remarkably parallel in most hospitals regardless of size, location or type of medical education program; (3) Since 1930, the gross volume of tests performed in the average general hospital has increased about five times; (4) . . . The growth rate may be expected to continue into the future. . . .

The growth of hospital laboratory activity has been accompanied by extensive redistribution of the work among divisions of the laboratory. . . . The most significant conclusions . . . are: (1) Hematology tests have expanded spectacularly, 11 1/2 times since 1930; (2) Chemistries and tissue examinations have not kept pace with the total growth (former tripled, latter not quite quadrupled). . . .

These generalizations [from statistics shown in tables in the original manuscript] are clear: (1) The hematology laboratory performs half of the tests being prescribed by physicians, and the chemistry division about 30 per cent. Together these two departments perform 80 per cent of all tests; (2) The patterns of distribution of the expanding volume of tests among the various laboratory divisions has been stable since 1950 with one exception—the bacteriology-parasitology division has doubled its share of the expansion, from 5 to 10 per cent. . . .

Space needs for the future depend not only upon implications of present trends, but also on the unknown "break-throughs" of the next decade, and the evolutionary changes in a hospital and its community. . . .

Dr. Karl S. Klicka (then Director, Hospital Planning Council for Metropolitan Chicago) appears to be the only man who has published a judgment on future space needs of the laboratory. Posing as a reporter of the hospital scene in 1965, he writes historically of "Hospital Care—1965" (*Hospital Management,*

January, 1959, 87:77): "In 1959 it was common for hospital laboratories to occupy 10 to 15 net square feet per bed. In 1965 this figure has risen to between 75 and 100 feet, and in those hospitals that do research the figure approaches 200 square feet per bed." . . .

Taken altogether, consulted authorities feel that clinical laboratories of the future will be considerably larger, although none was able to accept completely the concept of 200 square feet per bed.

Mr. Stickney then presents a table in which he estimates future gross square feet needs per bed as 150 for teaching hospitals, 40 for small teaching hospitals, and 25 for nonteaching hospitals.

CENTRAL SERVICE

Modern Hospital in its March, 1961, issue devoted an entire section, 24 pages, to a special report, "Planning Central Service," prefacing it with these comments:

Central sterile supply, or central service, might be considered the heart of the modern hospital, pumping vital material into organs such as the operating room and the nursing floor, then receiving it back, as the heart receives venous blood, for processing and recirculation. As an ailing heart makes a man falter, poor central service may make a hospital sick. The disease may be congenital, as when the department is badly planned, or functional, when it is inadequately staffed or badly managed. In either case, the result can be critical. . . .

Architects divide on the question of whether central service should be near the operating rooms or whether convenient transportation to the nursing floors is the more important consideration. Planners and central service supervisors also choose sides in favor of either dumb-waiters or carts, fixed or movable work-tables, open or closed shelving, stainless steel or less durable, and less expensive, material, and many other variables. Some authorities even told reporters that the increasing use of disposable supplies will eventually make the central service department as obsolete as the leech, but this is a minority view. The sterilizer seems as permanent a part of the hospital as the surgeon and nurse, and, in fact, a prevacuum sterilizer is scheduled to appear soon that will drastically cut down sterilizing time and speed up central service operations, possibly eliminating a shift in many hospitals—a result that would gladden the hearts of cost-laden administrators.

NURSING UNIT

The nursing unit is one area in which there has been little change over the past few decades. Nobody has come up with any clearly defined and generally acceptable ideas for major improvements. True, it has gone circular in some hospitals, but that has made no great change in its essential characteristics, although advocates of the circular plan seem to show some advantages in efficiency.

Believing that improvements are possible if a sustained study project could be attempted, Dr. Mark S. Blumberg,[10] senior health economist at the Stanford Research Institute, Menlo Park, California, suggests the establishment of a center for advanced design of nursing units at which designs of interest could be tried out on an experimental basis.

For the present, hospital planners must study existing nursing units to help them to reach a decision as to what shape, size, and arrangement the unit should have in their institutions.

PHARMACY

The Public Health Service has developed plans, revised from time to time, for hospital pharmacies as well as for other departments in the hospital. The pharmacy plans have been prepared with the assistance of the Division of Hospital Pharmacy of the American Pharmaceutical Association and the American Society of Hospital Pharmacists.

Like most other services, pharmacy has greatly increased in scope and complexity, and increasing space is needed for efficient operation.

The main divisions of the pharmacy include the parenteral solution laboratory, the compounding and dispensing laboratory, the manufacturing laboratory, an alcohol vault, an active storeroom, an office, and a pharmacy library.

FACILITIES FOR SURGERY

Typical of the type of information architects must have in order to draw up good plans are the items one of them[11] poses with respect to the surgical suite: number of operations performed (or anticipated) within a given time; types of operations and number of each; number of personnel per shift required to staff the suite during the same periods of time with their capacities; average daily or weekly list of supplies required from central supply and central stores; average time required for operations of various types including set-up and clean-up time; whether a separate induction room is desired; whether provisions are to be made for heart surgery; what provisions are to be made for observation if it is a teaching hospital; any special room or space requirements; any variations from the normal with respect to room sizes; service and storage space requirements; what the traffic patterns will be so that space relationships may be determined; and the requirements for fixed equipment to the extent that they affect preliminary design.

In Britain a group of doctors, architects, and lighting engineers has designed a model of a new operating room that is supposed to be infection-proof. It has a domed ceiling. Its roof and walls contain more than a hundred portholes through which come purified air and lighting.

[10] *Mod. Hosp.*, November, 1962, pp. 12–14.
[11] Joseph M. Moore, Jr., R.A.: *Hosp. Topics,* June, 1962, pp. 101–103.

X-RAY

The manufacturers of x-ray equipment have acquired a great deal of experience through observation of the operation of a large number of departments in a great many hospitals. In their efforts to improve equipment to meet the growing needs they have learned also the advantages and disadvantages of different department arrangements. They know how much space should be allocated for certain equipment and how it should be placed for the most convenient and effective use. They can furnish plans and supply trained personnel to consult with the architect, the radiologist, the administrator, and other persons concerned in planning. The plans are complete, from the reception area to the cobalt room. There are provisions for space for high isotopes, low isotopes, fluoroscope rooms, radiographic rooms, chest x-ray, angiographic x-ray room, cystoscopy, head and neck x-ray, light therapy, deep therapy, darkroom, drying room, film files, and various working areas—the plans give an idea of the scope of activity that goes on in this department and indicate how carefully it should be designed.

Although the radiology department because of its complexity is an outstanding example of the wisdom of including manufacturers' representatives in certain planning conferences, other departments also offer opportunity for taking advantage of advice from suppliers of materials and equipment who have had experience in installations in a number of hospitals.

KITCHENS AND THE LAUNDRY

In such departments as dietary and laundry the planner is confronted with rather new problems such as the use of outside services. Such an arrangement affects space requirements, especially in the laundry. Another development is cooperative service. In 1963 a group of six voluntary general hospitals in Baltimore, Maryland, became the owners and operators of a new laundry plant capable of processing 12 million pounds of linen per year. The plant is valued at $1.6 million. This cooperative arrangement was decided upon because several of the hospitals had obsolete or worn-out equipment which needed replacement, and space that needed remodeling. A similar project is under way by five hospitals in Boston. State hospitals in Maryland are planning cooperative laundry service.[12]

As for commercial laundry service, the editor of the *American Laundry Digest,* referring to advertising planned by the Linen Supply Association of America, wrote in a column headed "Don't Sell Hospitals" in the September 15, 1959 issue, "The laundry has become an integral part of a hospital's

[12] Walter F. Perkins: Cooperative Laundry Will Serve Six Hospitals. *Hospitals,* September 16, 1962, pp. 119–20.

operation. . . . It seems to us that advertising which attempts to sell hospitals on closing their plants and using linen supply service would be a waste of money."

Outside food service contracting is working well in many places. The practice was started mainly because it is hard to get competent administrative dietitians especially in small hospitals. Outside service leaves the dietitian free for teaching nutrition to patients and staff and handling therapeutic diets.

ELECTRICAL AND MECHANICAL SYSTEMS

Electrical and mechanical systems use up at least 40 per cent of the hospital's budget for construction, according to Moreland Griffith Smith, president of Sherlock, Smith & Adams, Inc., of Montgomery, Alabama.[13]

Mr. Smith says the administrator is justifiably apprehensive about this area of planning since

> the effective functioning of his entire operation will be pretty well paralyzed by failure of any of them. . . . He is alarmed about the future—concerned about saddling himself with expensive apparatus that will be obsolete or inadequate within a few years. He feels technically incompetent when this kind of equipment is involved, and he knows that there will be more headaches from bugs in the electrical and plumbing systems than from the bacterial variety on the nursing units.

Equal anxieties are felt by the architect and engineer, Mr. Smith admits, "for they must assume responsibility for solving problems that the administrator does not even realize he has." He says that the electrical system has been called the nervous system of the hospital and suggests that the mechanical system be considered its circulatory system.

Central piping systems for oxygen and other gases; air conditioning that includes heating, cooling, and humidity control; horizontal and vertical transportation; power including stand-by facilities; telephones, radio, and television; elevators; lighting; refrigeration; plumbing; water supply and heating; a master control center for automated equipment—there is no end to the multiplication of facilities that come under the management of the hospital engineer.

Air Conditioning—Heating and Cooling

Air conditioning, great contributor to the comfort and frequently the recovery of hospital patients, began to be used in such institutions only about forty years ago, although its inception came in 1902. Its first purpose was to cool machines, not people. Willis H. Carrier, an engineer, devised it to curb problems which high temperatures created in a printing plant. That the employees benefited was a side issue. Humidity changes made color printing difficult in a Brooklyn

---

[13] In the first article in a series of nine in the 50-page section on these systems in the 1962 "Planning and Construction Issue" of *Hospitals,* March 1, 1962. The article is entitled "Defining the Ultimate Objectives."

lithographing plant. When he was called in for help, only a year after he grad-uated from college, he assembled a device that moved air over rows of chilled pipes and took the moisture from it. Other factories quickly adopted the system, particularly textile, pharmaceutical, tobacco, and food plants. Then, along in the 1920's, motion picture theaters installed the innovation which is now utilized to cool every kind of building including nearly seven million homes.

Even in colder climates like that of Canada, year-around air conditioning throughout the building is becoming common in hospitals. The head of a Cana-dian consulting engineering firm comments that patients are less able to resist high temperatures, unclean air, low or high humidity levels, than healthy per-sons, and that in addition there are more heat- and odor-producing sources in hospitals than in other types of buildings because of steam sterilizers and cook-ing facilities. He states:[14]

> Temperature and humidity control are generally recognized to have definite. . therapeutic value in the treatment of such clinical conditions as head injuries, or operations which affect the heat regulatory center of the brain; cardiac con-ditions, which may be adversely affected by the strain of increased blood circula-tion; hemorrhagic conditions, which reduce the quantity of blood in circulation; severe burn conditions, where large skin areas are damaged; diseases of liver and kidneys and many diseases associated with fever; and certain allergies.

With reference to the design of hospital facilities, he points out that the very low temperatures in the operating room required in the use of hypothermia make it necessary to consider this fact when planning hospitals.

Constant controlled temperature is achieved at Milwaukee Children's Hos-pital with the use of radiant heat. Hot water circulates through the coils in the ceiling in cold weather and chilled water flows through them in warm weather. The system is so designed that one zone can be cooled while other zones are still heating.[15] Many installations of radiant heating equipment in hospitals, however, do not provide this dual heating-cooling possibility.

The late Charles F. Neergaard,[16] a former hospital consultant, declares that although radiant heating is still rarely used in hospitals, it provides fuel savings and comfort that in the long run can offset any increased cost of installation.

The dilemma confronting the air conditioning engineer is how he may simul-taneously design for (1) control of electrostatic hazards, (2) efficient removal of flammable anesthetic vapors and odors, (3) physical comfort of the operating room occupants, and (4) maximum air quality within the operating room from a bacteriological point of view, according to an article, "Trends in Air Conditioning," by Donald L. Snow and Richard P. Gaulin.[17] The authors are members of the Committee on Hospital Facilities, American Public Health Asso-ciation, investigating health-related principles in operating room air condition

[14] D. L. Angus: Indoor Climate Control. *Canad. Hosp.,* May, 1962, pp. 61–62.
[15] *Mod. Hosp.,* April, 1960, p. 176.
[16] *Ibid.,* Radiant Heating Is Not Just Hot Air, pp. 172–76.
[17] *Hospitals,* March 16, 1960, pp. 59–60.

design and maintenance practices. They indicate that "the chief factor in reducing air-borne contamination by means of the ventilating system is the dilution effect due to the air change rate, and the crux of the air conditioning designer's problem is how any increase in the air change rate, over and above those based on computed thermal loads, can be justified."

Communication Systems

A survey[18] of 267 hospitals in 1962 disclosed that "administrators want hospital communication systems that, above all else, are simple, dependable and private," that are easy to maintain, that include paging facilities, that perform swiftly, and that are not too costly. Eleven hospitals in the survey had installed a radio system with audible receivers carried by doctors and 25 others mentioned this as the system they would install if their existing installation were replaced. Internal dial telephone systems were used by 202 hospitals and dictating machines for doctors by 264 hospitals. A central stenographic pool with provision for machine dictation was considered desirable by most hospitals, but 156 did not have it.

In the report of the survey it was recommended that "during the basic planning period, the specialized knowledge of manufacturers' experts can help in reaching early decisions as to what type of equipment will meet the particular needs of each section of the hospital."

FALL-OUT SHELTERS

Along with Robert C. Ruark, who in his newspaper column a while back said, "The day I go underground will be the day somebody tamps me down neatly with a spade," most of us shudder at the thought of the underground shelter. Nevertheless, hospitals, as places of refuge and treatment in times of catastrophe, have to include in their planning protection from fall-out.

The Public Health Service's Division of Hospital and Medical Facilities, Architectural and Engineering Branch, is prepared to give information about the design of new hospitals and additions to existing hospitals with radiation protection.

The Public Health Service indicates that little additional space and equipment are required solely for protective purposes, because a hospital is well supplied with mechanical and electrical equipment that is readily convertible for shelter use. The cost of protection is therefore estimated not to increase the cost by more than 5 per cent.

By locating many of their services below ground, hospitals are providing the basic elements of fall-out shelters. The new Saint Barnabas Medical Center in Livingston, New Jersey, for example, has been planned with its functioning

---

[18] *Mod. Hosp.,* March, 1962, pp. 111–20.

nucleus—all the professional and other essential services including the dietary department—in two stories below ground. In planning such facilities the dual purpose of serving as a fall-out shelter and as a disaster hospital in the event of flood, hurricane, tornado, or earthquake should be considered.

MOBILE HOSPITALS

A portable hospital for casualties in the Crimea was designed by Isambard Kingdom Brunel in 1855. It consisted of units having two 24-bed wards, each with nurses' rooms, lavatories, and showers. The units could be joined by covered passages. Kitchens and laundry were separate. Building materials, furnishings, and supplies were assembled and shipped, and skilled workers in each trade were sent with them to supervise the construction of the buildings in the Crimea.

Preparations for civil defense and for disasters are reviving this concept of the mobile or transportable hospital, which has heretofore been thought of as a wartime expedient. When Hurricane Audrey struck the Louisiana coast in July, 1957, the 200-bed civil defense hospital unit directed by the Louisiana Hospital Association was loaded on six army amphibious trucks at Lake Charles and sent southward to the devastated area. There, since no suitable building remained standing, the hospital was set upon a high spot in the center of the road surrounded by water. Ordinarily the hospital would have been transported on a special truck-trailer van provided for it, but the impassable roads prevented use of the van. Army vehicles with nurses and physicians were sent from this emergency base hospital to various points to collect and give first aid to patients before their evacuation by helicopter to hospitals. The story was told by Joseph W. Hinsley,[19] administrator, Lake Charles Memorial Hospital.

The Michigan Epilepsy Center and Association has a mobile unit for epileptic patients which carries an electroencephalograph to help determine the degree and type of epilepsy a person has. Local physicians refer their patients for EEG readings and neurological investigation.

Mobile units are in use in programs dealing with chest x-rays, hearing and speech disorders, blood donation, and diabetes detection. Mobile operating rooms were advocated by Drs. Claude S. Beck and David S. Leighninger,[20] who said that they would be particularly lifesaving for heart victims. Moving the operating room to the victim instead of the victim being moved to the operating room would make possible restoration of the heart to a normal rhythm and the opening and closing of the chest at the scene of the emergency. The unit should be manned by trained personnel who can give artificial respiration.

Ambulances can be made into mobile hospitals. Examples are those in use

[19] *Mod. Hosp.*, August, 1957.
[20] *J. A. M. A.*, September 10, 1960, pp. 133–35.

by the Milwaukee County Institutions and Departments, Milwaukee, Wisconsin. Ten of them have the "necessary modern equipment and expert personnel to provide the maximum medical services possible in a moving motor vehicle." They answer some 20,000 calls a year and handle some 25,000 patients. In the training course there is strong emphasis on oxygen therapy and handling of fractures, plus the usual first aid rescue work.

Mobile hospitals use the airways. The Saskatchewan Air Ambulance Service, for example, was founded in 1946. The planes are equipped for emergency treatment and have a specially trained flight nurse on duty. A number of hospitals are building heliports, some of them on their roofs, to accommodate the helicopter ambulance services which are being organized.

The German Red Cross has developed a motorized surgical ambulance. It generates its own electricity. It is independent of local water supply in case of emergency. Included in the equipment are an operating table, an x-ray machine, surgical instruments, and a supply of anesthetics. The equipment is all in duplicate so that a second operating room can be set up in a sheltered place in disaster areas.

Nursing Homes and Homes for the Aging

The planning and construction of nursing homes, whether they are separate institutions or operated by a general hospital as an integral part of its service, demand special study. Edna Nicholson,[21] executive director of The Institute of Medicine of Chicago's Central Service for the Chronically Ill, has this to say about selection of the architect:

> If possible, an architect should be chosen who has already had successful experience in designing buildings for this particular use. Emphasis might be placed here upon the word *successful*. In recent years many buildings have been constructed for use as homes for the aged and nursing homes and have been found subsequently to be far from ideal. It is well for the owner or the building committee of the governing board to inspect other buildings designed by the architect under consideration and, particularly, to ask the administrators and department heads responsible for operation of these buildings how well they are functioning in actual use. . . . Regardless of his competence and experience, the architect should not be expected to work alone, and, by some miracle, produce a building well suited to all of the needs in the particular case. Only after he knows specifically what those needs are can he design a structure to meet them. . . .

Miss Nicholson states that "good programming," which consists of "listing the use to be made of the building, all the activities that must be carried on within it, the relationships among them, and the approximate amount of space required for each," should precede the drawing up of preliminary plans for buildings. She makes a noteworthy comment with respect to selection of the site:

[21] *Planning New Institutional Facilities for Long-Term Care.* New York, G. P. Putnam's Sons, 1956, pp. 170–72.

The healthy, active person who is leading a busy life usually longs for the peace and quiet of the country as a respite from too much bustle and excitement in his ordinary existence. He may assume, for this reason, that such peace and quiet are highly desirable to everyone. This is far from the truth. Every human being needs and wants the challenge and stimulation of some contact with an active life. The peace, beauty, and quiet of the country, desirable as they may be to the person who has too much activity, can be filled with deadly boredom when there is nothing else to see or hear day after day.[22]

Miss Nicholson quotes one experienced administrator of an institution for long-term care as asserting that there should be a law prohibiting the establishment of any facilities of this kind more than three blocks away from a ten-cent store. "This is one way of pointing out," she comments, "the importance of keeping people in need of long-term care as close as possible to the center of active living. Even though the patient may not be able to leave the building, he may find stimulation, entertainment and great satisfaction in being able to see and hear activity." She adds that the patients are likely to be visited more often if the institution is near a shopping area. Nevertheless, it "should not be located in a neighborhood already so crowded that the addition of another building will create excessive problems for the institution or for the residents already in the area in the form of congestion, noise, traffic, and parking difficulties," and there should be "sufficient open areas surrounding it to provide reasonable light, ventilation, and sunshine."[23]

GROUP MEDICAL CENTERS

Group medical practice has resulted in special problems of planning and design for the buildings in which it is conducted.

Recognition of the particular needs and how to meet them may be found in an article[24] by Alonzo S. Yerby, M.D., consultant on medical center planning, Health Insurance Plan of Greater New York, and Basil Yurchenco, New York City architect.

[22] *Ibid.*, pp. 179, 180.
[23] *Ibid.*, p. 181.
[24] Blueprint for Group Medical Centers. *Mod. Hosp.*, December, 1954, pp. 88–96.

CHAPTER 10

Equipment; Suppliers; Automation

One day in Dayton I had lunch with some doctors. I said, "You fellows have the same problem I have: how to keep up with research and at the same time earn a living." They agreed. The problem seemed so important to me for the welfare of my home town that I decided to set up an endowment to pay a first-class medical research man to keep up with what was going on in medicine and explain it to the Dayton doctors in weekly meetings. A great many things came out of that. For one thing, we got together and developed an artificial fever machine. Fever used to be considered a disease. Now we know it is nature's remedy for disease. This machine can give a temperature of 106° for five hours. At first, a patient had to spend three days in a hospital after treatment. Everybody said that was natural weakness resulting from the fever. But we kept hunting around and found it was not "natural weakness." It was because the patient sweated all the salt out of his body. So we gave the patient salt water next time. After the treatment he got into his car and drove home.

CHARLES F. KETTERING[1]

HISTORICAL RECORDS are replete with expressions by famous men, even famous inventors, to the effect that the ultimate had been achieved (some thought by themselves) and that no further progress was possible in that direction. It is doubtful that present and future records will betray so much naïveté or conceit. Spectacular as the technology of the atomic and space age is,

[1] Then vice-president of General Motors and director of research. From an article, The World Has Just Begun, *The American Magazine*, December, 1937, condensed in *The Reader's Digest*, January, 1938, pp. 8–11.

it seems to leave inventors, users, and the public certain that it is only in the embryo stage. Complacency has been knocked over by the rapidity of "impossible" and generally incomprehensible developments. Almost everybody believes, rightly, that anything can happen tomorrow to completely change living—and medical—conditions through new scientific findings and the technological apparatus that accompanies them. Consequently change, of itself, cannot be as hard to accept and to visualize as it once was.

Science and industry have been brought closer together through the new ideas. A great many industries depend upon doctors and hospitals for their existence. Many more depend upon them for a large share of their markets. While these industries have made tremendous contributions to medical progress, usually the idea for the instrument or the apparatus has come from the physician, the medical research scientist, or members of the professions allied to medicine, including administrators.

Wise manufacturers keep close watch on experimental medicine and clinical research, engaging in laboratory research themselves to develop new products when they sense the direction in which progress is moving. Conversely, wise physicians and administrators of medical services watch the technologists in industry for developments that may be adapted to their needs.

In this connection, Robert Shampaine, then president of the Shampaine Company, made the following remarks about developing operating room and obstetrical equipment in a lecture to a class of students in hospital administration at Northwestern University:

> From a development, as well as manufacturing standpoint, most pieces of equipment used in an operating room represent production and engineering problems which run the entire gamut of engineering. In other words, an operating table involves almost every engineering and production process which is required in the development and manufacturing of an automobile. Every conceivable type of material is used, every type of precision machining is involved. It is difficult for a small industry to maintain a research staff, and yet for effective operation it must be done, and there must be a well defined research program. This means that it must have personnel in its organization who are not only versed in engineering, but are also familiar with or trained in medicine and surgery. This research staff serves as liaison between the engineering department and the medical profession. *Needless to say, most of our ideas in their primary or fundamental form are obtained from surgeons, nurses, dentists,* etc., and are then translated into mechanics by the engineering department.

Impressive as the equipment is in the modern hospital, tempting the observer to feel that this is what has made progress possible, the important thing really is the mind that felt the need and saw the vision, which were translated into the bronchoscope or the heart-lung machine, and that after they were developed knew how to apply them in practice to the best advantage. Medicine and industry can work together on technical improvements to their mutual benefit for the ultimate advantage of the patient. The hospital is one of the world's greatest resources for the conception, birth, and nurture of ideas for technical improvements.

An interesting industrial-medical cooperative effort of a voluntary nature is "SAVE" (Service Activities of Volunteer Engineers). In Illinois about forty Bell Telephone Company engineers belong to it with the object of helping to devise medical instruments in their spare time. A company publication, *Tele-briefs,* which is enclosed with telephone bills, reported in the August, 1961, issue that these men had developed a new device that reads a person's pulse rate instantaneously to help researchers in heart disease. It is known as an instantaneous Pulse Rate Monitor. It shows any change in the pulse rate immediately. The rate of the last two pulse beats is carried to a dial from two electrodes fastened to the patient's chest. This tells instantly when a drug or process has taken its first effect on the heart beat. Such split-second information could not be obtained before. The monitor's transistorized workings make it light enough to be easily portable for use in operating rooms. An auxiliary jack will let a surgeon hear a pulse beat through an amplified speaker. A paper on the new device, one of several produced by SAVE, was presented at the International Conference on Medical Electronics in New York in the summer of 1961.

Another invention of the group, which was reported in the January, 1960, issue of the same publication, is a pushbutton "teacher" which is used to help train medical students at the Chicago Lying-in Hospital to recognize cancer cells. The device lets a student record his diagnosis of a specimen by pressing a series of buttons. Pushing another button allows the student to score himself. All data on a punched card is shown when still another button is pressed. The process is repeated until the correct discriminations are memorized. Use of the machine permits a doctor to devote more time to patients while still training students to become diagnosticians.

THE LAG IN UTILIZATION OF INVENTIONS

Although Zacharias Janssen, of Holland, is believed to have made the first microscope around 1590, and the Jesuit priest and physician Athanasius Kircher, of Fulda, seems to have been the first to use it in investigating the causes of disease toward the middle of the seventeenth century, closely followed by Robert Hooke, Jan Swammerdam, Anton van Leeuwenhoek, Marcello Malpighi, and Francesco Redi, it was neglected throughout the whole eighteenth century. Had there been in those days manufacturers seeking markets and salesmen wanting customers, would this instrument have been so sadly neglected? Perhaps so, because the truth is that the need for it became acute only when the theory of infection was propounded. Then its value in identifying pathogenic microorganisms became evident.

Charles Sedgwick Minot used to quote to his classes at Harvard Medical

School an old Dutch proverb, "Of what use can light and lenses be, if owlets look and will not see."

The hundred and more years of virtual rest for the microscope came to an end in 1830 when Joseph Jackson Lister, father of Lord Lister, improved the achromatic lenses of the instrument and thus became the father of modern microscopy. The elder Lister was a London wine merchant whose interest outside of his business was optical problems. The son early showed a kindred interest in microscopy when after his graduation in medicine he wrote several papers on the histology of muscle.

General use of the microscope in medical practice had to wait for the establishment of laboratories in hospitals, which did not occur until late in the nineteenth century. Up to that time the microscope was more of a curiosity than a practical tool.

A similar story can be told about that indispensable instrument, the thermometer. Galileo invented one around 1595. Sanctorius described, in a book published in 1625, a clinical thermometer which he had invented. Apparently, nobody thought any more about the instrument for nearly a hundred years. James Currie in the late eighteenth century used it in studying typhoid in Scotland and French clinicians used it around the middle of the nineteenth century, but it was not until Wunderlich's publication in 1868 of his treatise on the relations of animal heat in disease that a science of clinical thermometry was founded. It then became a recognized feature in clinical diagnosis. By 1870 thermometers were in general use in English hospitals. Yet it is said that in the largest Union Army hospitals throughout the Civil War, there were probably not a half dozen clinical thermometers employed. Interns in a leading hospital in Chicago in 1880 called the clinical thermometer a "newfangled affair." It took a long time to adopt and generally to accept what now seems a simple invention.

The stethoscope suffered the same fate. The famous French internist René Laennec won immortality by inventing it in 1819, along with his treatise describing its use. Older physicians scorned the device. Not until the issue of 1868–1869 did the Harvard Medical School catalogue even deign to mention it.

Discontinuity occurs in technologocial as well as in scientific history. The *Susruta,* according to Garrison,[2] "describes about 121 different surgical instruments, including scalpels, lancets, saws, scissors, needles, hooks, probes, directors, sounds, forceps, trocars, catheters, syringes, bougies, and a rectal speculum. These were properly handled and jointed, the blade instruments sharp enough to cut a hair and kept clean by wrapping in flannel in a box."

Galen ridiculed some of the Roman surgeons for carrying with them so many instruments. Among these, he inferred, were many that were of precious metals highly polished, meant more to impress patients than for real use. In the ruins of Pompeii and Herculaneum many of these instruments have been found.

[2] *An Introduction to the History of Medicine,* 4th ed., *op. cit.* p. 72.

The fact that medieval hospitals were little more than lodging places for the sick is shown by the fact that in the year 1500 the stock of surgical instruments possessed by the famous hospital at Lyons, France, Hotel Dieu, founded by Childebert the First in 542, comprised the following items: one 13-part trephine (crown saw); one uterine speculum; one ear speculum; one mouth-plug with which to keep the jaws separated; and one elevatorium (a kind of instrument for lifting a depressed part or for removing roots of a tooth). And only one medical man who did not live in the building was around to care for the surgical cases in this hospital which accommodated 550 patients.

During the American Revolution, when Dr. Binney of the military hospital was sent to Philadelphia in 1776 to purchase some urgently needed surgical instruments, he reported that there were no instruments to be purchased at any cost and that the only workmen in the city who could make surgeons' instruments were manufacturing arms by order of Congress and could not be diverted from that task for a long time to come.

On August 22, 1776, four days before the battle of Long Island, Dr. John Morgan wrote Dr. John Warren, surgeon of the General Hospital at Long Island, that he was sending him a surgeon and four surgeons' mates, with 500 bandages and 12 fracture boxes, but he feared they had no scalpels and was therefore sending two; should more scalpels be wanted he suggested using a razor for an incising knife.

INSTRUMENT MANUFACTURING

Vinzenz Mueller[3] states that records do not seem to exist showing that the making of surgical instruments was a special profession until the beginning of the seventeenth century. "Before that time," he continues, "the surgeons had to depend for their equipment on the one time famous armourers, the makers of weapons of every type of warfare. Later on, at the beginning of the eighteenth century, the surgeons' instruments were made for him by the cutlers." In Germany, France, Holland, and England the cutlers were the main producers of surgical instruments, and some of the cutlers in those countries are still said to be making them. Mr. Mueller believes that the House of Windler, founded in 1819 in Berlin, was one of the earliest strictly surgical instrument houses on the European continent.

In tracing the history of surgical equipment and instruments in the United States for students in hospital administration at Northwestern University, Robert Shampaine said:

> There were, undoubtedly, some types of surgical equipment and instruments manufactured in this country prior to the Civil War, but for all practical purposes as a commercial industry I do not believe that this industry became consequential until the Civil War emphasized the need for producing them in

[3] President of V. Mueller & Co., Chicago. From reprint of an article, Surgical Instruments, in the *A.S.T.A. Journal,* official organ of the American Surgical Trade Association, reprint not dated.

substantial quantities to cope with the deterioration and dissipation of such materials during wartime conditions. There were several manufacturers of surgical equipment and instruments in the eastern part of the country who flourished during the latter part of the nineteenth century, but unfortunately for this industry the removal of protective tariffs permitted European competition, especially from Germany, to enter the commercial scene so that by the turn of the century our small, but what had nonetheless been a promising, industry was on its way out. It was impossible for the domestic industry to compete with the German system whereby parts for instruments and equipment were made in the homes at ridiculously low cost, and finally assembled in the so-called "factories" producing and exporting them.

Then in the early part of the twentieth century an urgent demand arose for domestic production of surgical equipment. One of the reasons for the demand was the industrial development in the Pacific Coast region. Imports from Europe were being brought by ship around the bottom of South America, there being no Panama Canal at that time. Sometimes need for surgical supplies was urgent, and the long period needed for their shipment was disastrous. Small repair and manufacturing shops were opened to meet emergency requirements, but they could not produce supplies in large enough quantities to meet the competition from abroad.

Then came World War I. Shipments from Germany ceased. Suddenly there was extreme necessity for domestic production. Imports continued from Japan, but at that time the Japanese instruments were inferior. Surgical instrument and equipment manufacturing began in earnest and flourished for a time. Not being too firmly established by the time of the depression in the late twenties, many of them succumbed because of financial problems. World War II brought encouragement from the military, and several new firms were added to those that had survived the depression.

Mr. Shampaine relates:

> From 1941 until 1950 this country began to dominate the *export* market in surgical instruments and equipment with some strong competition from England and some lesser competition from France, Sweden, and Switzerland. Since 1950, however, the German surgical instrument and equipment industry has again begun to come to life, and that country is exporting surgical supplies in larger quantities although it still has a long way to go in order to redeem the dominant position which it enjoyed prior to World War II.

Germany, as well as Sweden and Japan, is now producing surgical instruments in fairly large quantities, and all three are increasing their exports. Again the low tariff is operating to the disadvantage of American firms. Since labor cost in this industry is 90 per cent of the total, it would take an extremely high tariff, not politically feasible, to compete with European manufacturers, whose labor costs are much lower.

John H. Hayes,[4] hospital consultant and former hospital administrator, states:

[4] Surgical Instruments: Serious Gap in National Defense. Reprint in *Trustee,* February 1, 1959, pp. 12–18, of an article published in *Hospitals,* January 1, 1958.

In February, 1958, the Office of Defense Mobilization published a list of items which would be required to sustain the civilian population after a nuclear attack. The first items on the list are health supplies and equipment, including surgical instruments. In connection with stockpiling it is well to remember that surgical instruments undergo a constant change and new instruments are being constantly developed. Therefore, such stockpiling is not like storing wheat or copper. . . . There are today in the United States only a handful of surgical instrument makers and an alarmingly few skilled artisans in this field. As these men die or seek other employment, the time will soon arrive when there will be scarcely any left—perhaps not even enough to make repairs. . . . Quality being equal, it is only natural that hospital purchasing agents will buy at lower prices. They would be severely criticized if they were to do otherwise. In so doing, however, we are unconsciously hastening the death of an industry; an industry of tremendous importance, in peace or at war.

Mr. Hayes can offer no answer to the problem except that an instrument and equipment committee of professional people be appointed in each hospital to assist the purchasing department in securing the best possible prices and services from manufacturers and dealers, with the idea in mind at all times of "the need to support as far as possible the United States manufacturers and make sure that a dependence on foreign manufacturers does not threaten supplies in the event of another emergency."

The situation seems to be a good example of the need for understanding of external factors, in this case the life of an industry, by the hospital administrator.

INSTRUMENTS AS SYMBOLS

Instruments are often regarded as symbols of certain professions or of specialties within a profession. This may lead to false or exaggerated impressions.

The surgeon deplores the fact that the knife is considered the symbol of surgery. In an address before the graduating class of the Naval Medical School several years ago, included in a book of his writings, Dr. Hubert Ashley Royster, of Raleigh, North Carolina, said:

> The knife—that most dreaded of all instruments—is chosen to typify the whole surgical art, and such expressions as "going under the knife," "nothing but the knife will do," or the "horror of the knife," are frequently heard both from the laity and from medical men.
>
> The truth is that the knife, while, of course, one of the most important instruments, is really used less than are many other instruments. A being of stern visage brandishing the scalpel would not be a true picture of the surgeon; rather should he be represented as one of calm countenance with a handful of hemostats or a needle and thread—instruments far less gruesome, but more widely employed and requiring greater ingenuity in their use.
>
> Besides, there are many operations done wholly without the knife. The singling out of this alarming implement as the popular embodiment of surgery is but a sign of the fascination for most minds of the terrifying and the dramatic. It smacks of the old days of the barber surgeon.

MATERIALS

Research goes on constantly to develop improved materials for use in hospitals.

A petroleum company in Oklahoma has developed a surgical mesh known as Marlex, made of high-density polyethylene, which has been used successfully in the repair of tissue defects of the chest and abdominal wall.

A surgical dressing has been developed for hemophiliacs which halts bleeding, then melts away into the body. It is made of a specially treated cellulose and has an affinity for hemoglobin. It is also used on nonhemophiliac patients to stifle bleeding in accident cases; it can halt blood seepage in wounds of the kidney, liver, and spleen.

A synthetic fiber was developed by a manufacturer for use in pads to prevent and cure decubitus ulcers. The material was tested by a group at the Milwaukee County (Wisconsin) Mental Health Center, South Division, and found to be surprisingly effective.

A soft percale, in color, is furnished by a manufacturer to Lenox Hill Hospital, New York, in gowns for patients that are an agreeable substitute for the old, scratchy, tied-on gowns.

Sherman Hospital, Elgin, Illinois, replaced its traditional tie-back gowns with colored broadcloth pajamas.

An adhesive tape has proved successful in closing wounds and incisions usually requiring stitches.

A first aid dressing combines nonadhesion to wounds with absorbency that prevents accumulation of secretions and resulting maceration. They keep the wound in a semidry condition.

Two Northwestern University surgeons reported finding Dacron to be the most satisfactory material for suturing so far developed.

A heavy vinyl with a backing, which comes in rolls instead of in tiles, is being used for floors. Plastic materials are being used for wall covering. Mattress ticking is impregnated with plastic, tufting being on the inside, to make the mattress waterproof and bacteria-resistant. Nylon has widespread use as an upholstery fabric.

AIDS TO PLANNING EQUIPMENT

One of the most useful aids to equipment planning is the *Hospital Equipment Planning Guide* published annually by the Public Health Service, Division of Hospital and Medical Facilities, since 1950. In it are suggested equipment lists for 50-, 100-, and 200-bed general hospitals under the headings of administration, laboratory, radiographic, x-ray therapy, occupational therapy, pharmacy, nursing service, nursery, surgical, central sterilizing and supply, obstetrical, emergency, dietary, housekeeping, laundry, maintenance, outpatient, and dental. Two charts show, respectively, equipment costs for general hospitals and departmental equipment costs for general hospitals.

The *Hospital Purchasing File* published by the Modern Hospital Publishing Company, Inc., is another valuable reference source. It contains a list of manufacturers and distributors of hospital equipment. This is also issued annually.

A monthly "reference directory and review of hospital products" is *Hospital Handbook,* published by Associated Product Publications, North Hollywood, California.

SIMPLIFICATION AND STANDARDIZATION

If the situation with respect to hospital furnishings, supplies, and equipment appears to be a dense jungle to the administrator, he would find it to be an almost impenetrable one if it were not for the work of a number of outside agencies in trying to achieve some measure of simplification and standardization. A so-called certification plan was developed in 1927 by the Bureau of Standards of the United States Department of Commerce in cooperation with a Committee on Simplification and Standardization of the American Hospital Association, other associations, universities, manufacturers, and government agencies including the Public Health Service. In a letter dated August 29, 1927, which accompanied a pamphlet describing the plan, the director of the Bureau of Standards stated:[5]

> In carrying out this plan there are compiled lists of manufacturers who have expressed their desire to supply material in accordance with certain selected specifications and willing to certify to the purchaser upon request that the material thus supplied is guaranteed to comply with the requirements and tests of the specifications.

The director further stated that the plan had already been applied to 75 specifications, and 75 separate lists of "willing-to-certify manufacturers" had been compiled by the Bureau of Standards.

Charles F. Neergaard, former New York architect, was the A.H.A. representative on this early committee, in which attention was concentrated mainly on "metal doors and bucks, hardware, plumbing fixtures, metal cabinets used for kitchen, pantry and general storage, blankets and solution warmers, instrument cabinets, cubicle partitions, sterilizers, food trucks, laundry trucks, dressing carriages and baked enamel ware utensils." Sizes of textiles for adult beds, cribs and bassinets were recommended by the Division of Simplified Practice of the Department of Commerce as a result of joint meetings, the recommendations going into effect on October 1, 1927, with provision for annual revision. Under the auspices of the division a preliminary conference on surgical dressings was

[5] *Bull. Am. Hosp. A.,* December, 1927, pp. 113–20.

held on April 20, 1927, following which the manufacturers of these dressings began studies of the "various weaves of gauze and crinoline and the widths and lengths of bandages, with the object of eliminating the unnecessary varieties of weaves and sizes." The American Hospital Association was asked to co-operate in this study.

In 1922 the American Hospital Association adopted a "Professional Standing Order" on clinical and scientific equipment and work which was revised in 1927 by a committee headed by Dr. Lewis A. Sexton, who became president of the association in 1931. One of the interesting recommendations in the report of the committee was:[6]

> If these orders are to do the greatest amount of good for the largest number of hospitals, we believe that all temperature readings should be recorded by the Fahrenheit scale instead of the Centigrade, or both, which should be indicated in each instance. It is a well established fact that a large majority of the hospitals represented in the Association use a Fahrenheit scale.

The American College of Surgeons also played a leading part in the standardization of surgical dressings. For several years it also conducted an evaluation and approval program for medical, surgical, and hospital equipment, issuing annual approved lists with names of the manufacturers. The American Medical Association has also been active in the simplification and standardization endeavor.

The National Bureau of Standards of the U.S. Department of Commerce continues to be exceedingly active in its work of upholding high standards of quality for medical equipment and supplies.

The American Standards Association, Inc., has headquarters in New York, and the Canadian Standards Association is in Ottawa.

Each hospital should have a standardization committee on which the medical staff is represented to avoid as much confusion and duplication as possible in the purchasing of equipment. Such a committee, however, would have little effectiveness in the individual hospital if it were not for the efforts of the American Hospital Association, the American Medical Association, and the Bureau of Standards in establishing guides and standards.

An example of the confusion that still exists is the practice permitted in some hospitals of having surgeons supply their own instruments if they insist on doing so. This is an old practice which should long since have been forbidden. Frances Ginsberg,[7] consultant on operating room nursing and hospital aseptic techniques and a member of the Bingham Associates Program at New England Center Hospital, Boston, declares:

> When each surgeon either brings his own instruments to the hospital or has them stored for his exclusive use at the hospital, hospital personnel must be

[6] *Ibid.,* p. 120.
[7] Hospitals, Not Surgeons, Should Provide All Surgical Instruments. *Mod. Hosp.,* December, 1961, p. 118.

responsible not only for their sterilization, but also for their separation, intact storage, and full inventory. Separating the instruments, seeing that they are in good condition, and then storing them require, in addition to time and space, the constant concern that they are neither lost nor mixed with another surgeon's set. Time and space cost money. Mistakes often result in tensions, anxieties and bad relationships. . . . As if these facts are not enough argument against this practice, it is obvious that few surgeons can or will continue to provide themselves with a sufficient quantity of instruments of the quality and variety which modern surgical technics demand.

AUTOMATION

A protest against excessive automation was voiced by astronaut John Glenn. Commenting on taking over the controls himself when the attitude-control system failed to work properly, thus proving that man can "fly" a capsule through space, he said: "Now we can get rid of some of that automatic equipment and let man take over."

In a hospital, in particular, "automation can never supplant individuals in providing care," as is aptly stated in an editorial in the October, 1960, issue of the Evanston Hospital (Illinois) *Pilot*. The editorial continues:

For hospital care is a personalized service. An automatic counter may record the white or red blood cells—but skilled, especially trained persons must interpret the findings, if the patient is to benefit. The nurse intercom is of value only because the patient can be in close contact with a person who is prepared to give the nursing care required. The pneumatic tube system can never take the place of any member of the nursing team but, because of its use, this same personnel has more time to spend on other patient services. The benefits which automation brings are to be measured in increased services. It can never take the place of physicians, nurses, resident, interns, technologists, dietitians, therapists and the many others who provide the personal service which is a requisite for good patient care.

Just listing a few of the devices which produce these benefits is to open the doors to insight into what a labor leader recently called the "tornado of technological change." The items are listed with the warning that day after tomorrow, if not tomorrow, they will be so improved or superseded as to be ready for discard.

A portable operating enclosure made of plexiglas in which temperature down to $-10\,^{\circ}$C. and humidity 40 to 80 per cent R.H. are automatically controlled. The enclosure has openings for the admission of oxygen and other gases.

An automatic dry cleaner which not only cleans but disinfects hospital blankets.

Radioisotope measuring instrument.

Automatic muscle stimulator.

Automatically controlled ultra-superspeed refrigerated centrifuge.

Respiratory gas analyzer.

Automatically regulated food pump for tube feeding.

An electronic, transistorized telephone unit which leaves the hands free, has a loud-speaking system, and permits group discussion with an outside caller. Manufactured in France.

A heat exchanger for cooling or warming patients, developed by the Harrison Radiator Division of General Motors in 1956 at the request of Dr. Ivan W. Brown, Jr., of Duke University Medical School.

Special-purpose computer tentatively named the Hospital Indicator for Physicians' Orders proposed by the staff at the Stanford Research Institute. (See *Hospitals,* August 1, 1961, pp. 43, 99.)

The Psychomet, an instrument for use in the early detection of disease and for evaluating a person's psychomotor ability. Designed and constructed at the Public Health Service's National Institute of Mental Health, Bethesda, Maryland. Used by the Federal Aviation Agency in studying the aging process in civil air pilots and air traffic controllers.

Body Function Recorder developed by Minneapolis-Honeywell's Heiland division in cooperation with medical authorities and technical experts at the Mayo Clinic.

Computer system for use in applying data processing techniques to the study of radiation in diagnosing and treating cancer patients at Memorial Sloan-Kettering Cancer Center.

A 21-inch, eight-channel cathode ray oscilloscope mounted from the ceiling of the operating room theater at St. Barnabas Hospital, New York, which monitors the responses of the patient during surgery, acts as the anesthesiologist's facility supply panel, and gives the surgical team instant visualization of physiological measurements on the patient's electromyograms, blood pressure, pulse waves, breathing characteristics, nerve impulses, and other vital signs. The kymograph screen is located on one wall of the operating room.

An endoradiosonde—an instrument that is sensitive to pressure and permits measurement of intraluminal pressure, temperature, acidity, and other characteristics of the intestinal tract.

A portable instrument for emergency treatment in congestive heart failure which weighs only 16 pounds. Acts as an automatic alternating tourniquet.

The heart-lung machine, which, during the bypass of the heart, takes over its pumping action and also supplies needed oxygen, removes harmful carbon dioxide, and returns the blood to the patient by a temporary route which leaves the heart free of blood.

A Pulmoanalyzer and a Pulmotest, made in Holland, which measure respiratory effort and record results on graph paper, called a spirogram.

A serum protein meter which provides accurate protein analyses in about a tenth of the time required by chemical methods.

An electronic stethoscope which amplifies sounds up to 100 times greater than the usual stethoscope.

Refrigerators which maintain temperatures at $-120°$ F., used for storing blood vessels, skin, bone, and dura, the covering of the brain.

A portable electronic nerve finder.

An echo-sounder pen developed in Sweden which aids heart diagnosis; it emits ultrasound waves.

Anesthalung—aids the anesthesiologist in controlling the rate and volume of a patient's breathing.

An ultrasound device which relieves muscular pain.

A brain wave synchronizer which aids the induction of hypnosis.

Sterilization by radiation with the use of isotopes. It is not believed, however, that this will ever replace steam sterilization of instruments in the hospital. The equipment is too costly. Its use is likely to be confined to sterilizing foodstuffs in large quantities and other industrial applications.

At the Columbia-Presbyterian Medical Center, New York, a stethescope that can be swallowed by the patient permits recordings of the sound of blood flow in the aorta.

Automatic and semiautomatic instruments that stitch blood vessels together, developed in Russia by the Research Institute for Experimental Surgical Equipment, obtainable through V. Mueller and Company, Chicago. Instruments are also designed for joining nerves, bronchial tubes, bones, and soft tissues; for stitching the intestines and for joining intestines to the stomach; for stitching the base and tissues of the lungs; and for other suturing following surgery.

Presbyterian–St. Luke's Hospital, Chicago, is planning a laboratory for the development of artificial heart valves.

Electrohydraulically controlled operating table with five movable sections—head, spinal, pelvic, femoral, and lower leg.

The American Optometric Association at its 65th annual Congress, held in Chicago, July, 1962, gave awards to Drs. Elwin Marg and R. Stuart Mackay, of the University of California School of Optometry, for developing the electronic tonometer. This instrument is a diagnostic device which employs an electronically powered probe to detect the presence of glaucoma. It measures fluid pressures within the eye without use of an anesthetic. It is about the size of a portable radio and costs $1,865. It is an adaptation of the tonometer which Dr. Hjalmar Schiotz, of Norway, invented in 1906, in the use of which anesthetization is employed. When the diagnosis is glaucoma, treatment is instituted with a drug developed in 1950 known as Diamox. A peculiar fact about this drug is that a pharmaceutical manufacturer developed it to prevent congestive heart failure. It saves lives by causing expulsion of excess fluids through the kidneys, thus relieving overburdened hearts. An ophthalmologist who studied its action began experiments with it in 1953 on patients with glaucoma.

Cybernetic Medicine

With the organization in 1958 of the International Society of Cybernetic Medicine and the holding of the first general assembly of that body in November, 1959, medicine plunged headlong into automation. In 1960 the society held at Naples an International Symposium of Cybernetic Medicine in which the founder of cybernetics, Professor Norbert Wiener, participated. The first president of the society was Professor Aldo Masturzo, of Naples University, and the office of the secretary general is in Naples.

Disposables

Contributing substantially to automation through labor-saving are the disposable items which are being produced in ever-increasing variety and quantity by manufacturers.

On the whole, disposables are supposed to reduce infection hazards, and in general they do. Authorities point out, however, that federal or other controls are not adequate to meet the critical standards of hospital personnel, and that labeling an item "nontoxic and sterile" is not a sufficient guarantee to the hospital user. Care must be exercised, therefore, in testing disposables, and reactions to them must be studied and measures taken to prevent them.

Disposables for use in the operating room include plastic scalpels, plastic gloves, exchange transfusion trays, plastic anoscopes, plastic isolator through which the surgeon operates, surgical masks, needles, syringes, lancets, tongue depressors, dressings, surgical drape sheets, surgical lubricant tubes, plastic bags to replace glass jars previously used to send pathological specimens to the laboratory, forceps, kidney basins, caps, gowns, and slippers. A few of the others used in medical diagnosis and treatment are stomach irrigation tubes, Levine tubes, oxygen catheters, injection sets, urinary drainage containers, enema administration units, oxygen masks, urine specimen testing systems, suture cutters, colostomy and ileostomy appliances, blood bags for transfusions, and so on.

For general use there are paper water pitchers, soluble laundry bags, drinking cups, denture and sputum cups, patient gowns, laboratory coats, pillow covers, drapes, cuspidors, toothbrushes, blanket protectors, bedpan covers, paper food service in infectious disease units—the list is endless.

The chief consideration in the use of disposables is, as **Dr. Carl R. Trask**[8] expressed it, "the effect on the patient." Dr. Trask asked:

> Does the disposable product make it easier for the patient? Does it prevent him from being infected? How would you feel if you were a patient in a hospital? Would you want the nurse to use a new hypodermic needle and throw it away, or would you rather hope the central supply staff was as careful as you had been told? . . . Can a hospital afford to expose its patients to pyrogens, hepatitis, blood transfusion reactions and infections, if these can be avoided even at greater cost? Since the disposable needle is so much sharper that it hurts the patient less, should hospitals not use them to give less painful injections?

X-ray Department

Among the most spectacular applications of technology to the diagnosis and treatment of disease are the machines to be seen in the radiology department. A regular x-ray machine costs around $12,000, and a large hospital has several of them. A special type takes pictures at different levels of depth called laminograms. Serialographs are used to take arteriograms, aortograms, and angiocardiograms.

A therapeutic x-ray machine costs around $19,000. An X-Omat processor, which develops, fixes, washes, and dries film in six minutes, costs $25,000 (it used to take an hour by hand developing methods).

[8] In a paper presented at an institute sponsored by the Maritime Hospital Association, Moncton, New Brunswick, Canada, in April, 1962. *Canad. Hosp.*, October, 1962, pp. 114–26.

Portable units are necessary for use in the emergency room, in surgery, and in patients' rooms.

Other apparatus includes view boxes, intravenous injection trays for dyes, fluoroscopy and x-ray films, and scintiscanners, which with the aid of radioactive isotopes "paint" pictures of organs and glands (mainly used in thyroid gland diagnosis).

A cesium unit used in radiation of cancer was installed in 1960 at Montefiore Hospital, New York. It can serve as a supplement to the cobalt unit and has the advantage of being small enough to fit into a filing cabinet drawer.

Cineradiography units are being used in heart stations. They have radiographic equipment to do all kinds of work plus several features of a motion picture camera which will make up to 60 frames a second; an image amplifier to reduce radiation to the patient and make viewing easier; and a rapid film changer.

General Electric has introduced a system which makes fully remote-controlled teleroentgen diagnosis a practical reality. The radiologist is not exposed to radiation. The patient is not in the dark. Fluoroscope viewing is via a high-brightness closed-circuit television monitor. The system incorporates remote-controlled spot filming and cinefluorography.

A new fluoroscopic device designed to help doctors see their patients from more than one angle has been introduced by Westinghouse. Known as "Panavision" the apparatus makes it possible for the physician to fluoroscope body parts from a continuous succession of different angles without moving the patient. An x-ray tube installed in the table of the unit is not fixed in a stationary position as in the conventional unit, but is built to swing through an arc of 40 degrees.

The x-ray stereoscope, a device for three-dimensional viewing of x-rays, was invented by a physician, Dr. Fred W. Borden.

Laboratory and Pharmacy

Automation is strikingly obvious in the laboratory. There are clot timers, automatic electrobalances, recorders, meters, temperature controllers, interchangeable thermistor probes, telethermometers, ultramicroanalyzers, spectrophotometers, among many other devices, and there are disposables from reaction cups to mouse cages.

The big automatic development in pharmacy is the Brewer system which is designed to provide pharmacy packaged, labeled, and controlled drugs; validated requisitions for drugs or other supplies; 24-hour-a-day pharmacy service; reduction of medical errors; and substantial savings of the nursing time required for medication rounds. It is supposed to eliminate nurses having to write charge slips; the pharmacy having to price charge slips; much of the business office sorting and posting of charge slips; nurses having to inventory, to requisition, or to be responsible for the shelf-life of floor stock drugs; and the waste of valuable floor space.

One of the hospitals in which the system was tested is Lankenau Hospital, Philadelphia. R. F. Hosford,[9] then director, now vice president of the hospital, described the installation and answered some questions about its operation. Some weaknesses were observed which the manufacturer took steps to correct. Mr. Hosford's conclusion: "It is our opinion at this time that this automatic drug dispenser system will prove a valuable addition to the hospital field in its continuing efforts for improved service and reduced operating costs."

Food Service

The most conspicuous development in automated food service is the coin-operated vending machine. Probably the outstanding 1962 installation was the opening in Chicago of the largest fully automatic public restaurant in the United States. This is called the Brass Rail Automatic Restaurant and is located in the Wrigley Building, Chicago. It has an area of more than 6,700 square feet, will seat 250 persons, and offers a complete menu through a bank of 20 vending machines.

To introduce a historical note, a United Press dispatch of July 19, 1962, stated that 2,000 years ago Hero of Alexandria, a Greek inventor and philosopher, illustrated and described a coin-operated device used for vending sacrificial water in Egyptian temples. This was in 215 B.C. The dispatch continues:

> Vending in the United States got under way in 1888 when a workable slot machine for dispensing chewing gum was installed in New York City's elevated railroad system. The business jogged along for about fifty years, then started to pick up momentum after World War II. Sales have quadrupled since 1946, reaching 205 billion dollars by 1960, and are expected to climb to about four billions by 1965. The industry consists of about a hundred companies that manufacture equipment. Most of the machines are sold outright to some six thousand operating companies, servicing an estimated four million machines. New machines are being invented constantly, including one that will accept and change bills.

For the hospital which must be staffed 24 hours a day, seven days a week, this innovation has obvious advantages along with some disadvantages, such as impersonality, mechanical breakdowns, pilferage possibilities, and problems of sanitation and variety and appealing appearance of goods. What other hospitals are doing and what the developments are in the field as a whole must be carefully and constantly studied.

Freeze-dried foods are another innovation. According to Professor Lendal H. Kotschevar,[10] "Probably no food processing method since Appert invented canning, and thereby won the gratitude of Napoleon and 2,000 francs, holds as

[9] *Hospitals,* January 16, 1963, pp. 96–104.
[10] *Hospitals,* September 16, 1962, p. 83.

much potential for changing our methods of preserving, marketing and using foods as does the freeze-drying method."

This is the same method which is being used to preserve blood plasma, hormones, and delicate drugs.

The armed forces are pushing the development of the freeze-drying process, being especially interested in the very light weight of food products handled in this way. The product is used as any fresh product would be after it is hydrated.

Microwave cooking is providing high-speed food preparation, but the electronic stoves have limitations in the kinds of food that they can handle, and cooks require training in their operation.

Prepackaging and precooking are drastically reducing the labor in the hospital kitchen—in fact some authorities predict the kitchen is on the way out. The Kaiser Foundation Hospital opened in 1962 in Panorama City, California, for example, uses only food preprepared, precooked, and prepackaged outside the hospital. Food preparation in the hospital, according to Jane Barton,[11] of *The Modern Hospital* editorial staff, "is a matter of thawing the frozen foods, portioning them, assembling the trays, putting hot dishes into electronic ovens for final heating, and distributing the trays to patients on hot and cold food trucks."

Dishwashers of the 1960's scrape the dishes, dispense the detergent in accurate amounts and keep it at a constant predetermined level, and air-dry the dishes. Ultrasonic equipment is also being introduced. Vibration which loosens the dirt or soil from the dishes, silver, or glassware is produced by high-frequency sound waves sent through the water.

Ranges and deck ovens are equipped with casters and brakes; in fact almost all of the equipment in the kitchen is now mobile.

Kitchens on every floor are included in the design of one new hospital whose architect states that complete units to store food and reheat it and enough utilities for future electronic equipment are being placed on every patient floor.

Housekeeping and Maintenance

Automated cleaning equipment—power scrubbers, central vacuum systems, power waxers—reduces the number of personnel needed and attracts a better class of workers. Vacuum pickup of scrub water, for example, is said to result in a 50 per cent saving of time compared with mopping floors dry after scrubbing.

In the Industrial Sanitation Counselors' booth at the American Hospital Association's convention in Chicago in September, 1962, a computer was available to analyze electronically housekeeping programs in hospitals. The specially programmed computer calculated the per cent efficiency of the present program and compared this figure with the productivity of a standardized housekeeping program. The computer programming was based upon the I.S.C.'s accumulated research files, said to cover more than 25 years' experience in over 53 million

---

[11] Microwaves Take Cooking Out of the Kitchen. *Mod. Hosp.*, November, 1962, pp. 134–42.

square feet of buildings. Survey forms were supplied which were either mailed in advance or brought to the exhibit; these were run through the Monorobot during the convention and mailed back the following week.

A big problem in the maintenance department can be solved electronically—telephone answering when the engineer, houseman, or housekeeper was out on service duties. Bert Stajich,[12] assistant administrator, Columbia Hospital, Milwaukee, Wisconsin, told how "a small electronic box, an automatic answering service, has been a great time saver and has improved interdepartmental relations." The foot-square box contains a

> . . . tape recording instrument that automatically cuts into the telephone system after a single ring of the telephone. It begins to function with this message: "This is the maintenance man's automatic answering service. After two beeps will you please leave your message? Thank you." Within a few seconds there are two electronic beeps and the equipment is ready to receive a message of 30 seconds duration. When the caller hangs up, the circuit is disconnected and the machine stops operating. As many as 20 messages of 30 seconds duration can be taped on the machine.

Mr. Stajich adds, "The automatic answering service has saved many extra calls to the switchboard in a vain effort to locate a maintenance man or a houseman."

Laundry

The laundry has been mechanized for a long time. It has been proved that costs can be reduced by further automation, especially in larger hospitals. Laundry equipment manufacturers have been particularly helpful in making adaptations to hospital use. Some washers can be unloaded automatically. Some combine washing and extracting. Other installations use overhead hoist rails for transfer from washer to extractor. In the full-automatic control type no attention from the operator is needed throughout the entire wash-rinse cycle. There is equipment for continuous conditioning of flatwork, for delivering conditioned pieces directly to ironer, and for automatic folding and stacking.

The American Laundry Machinery Industries and the Canadian Laundry Machinery Company, Ltd., maintain laundry planning services and furnish booklets showing typical laundry layouts for various size hospitals.

Furniture—Beds

Beds[13] have developed through a long evolutionary process. They seem gradually to have become higher. The hospital bed was standardized in 1924 at 27 inches from the floor to the top of the springs. The thickness of the mattress

---

[12] *Hospitals,* June 16, 1959, pp. 48–49.
[13] An interesting article, "A History of the Hospital Bed," by Dorothy M. Gailani, Harold E. Smalley, Ph.D., Albert J. Dinnerstein, Ph.D., and Richard A. Dudek, Ph.D., who were engaged in a "bed project" which was the first phase of an "Investigation of the Hospital Patient Unit" conducted at the University of Pittsburgh, was published in the October 16, 1958 (pp. 38–42), issue of *Hospitals.*

and the use of casters affected the actual height, bringing it generally to about 32 inches where it has remained.

The adjustable bed was made desirable mostly because of early ambulation, the lowering being necessary for the patient to get in and out without accident, and the raising being desirable for the convenience of personnel who are working on the patient.

The position-adjustable spring, a major development, was conceived by an Indiana surgeon, Dr. W. D. Gatch, after whom it is named, who had the help of an engineer in working out the mechanics.

Hospital beds have become elaborate "machines" through electrical operation for lowering and raising for position adjustment, and, a few of them, for rocking. They may be connected to plumbing and have toilet and lavatory facilities incorporated in them. They may have a self-contained stretcher and permanently affixed bed rails.

Dr. Mark S. Blumberg[14] says mechanization is not enough; "electrical control of each patient's thermal environment is desirable." Electric blankets would be too hazardous for several reasons. He advocates a light tentlike cover for the body with segmental controls to permit selective warming of the patient's lower extremities and other areas and "a thermostat mechanism coupled to a thermistor which records skin or internal temperatures." Then he thinks it would be nice also to have a small and portable air cooler which could probably use the same cover as the warming system.

Communications

The wireless communications systems which permit doctors to report on the progress of patients as they make rounds, to record procedures as they operate with the microphone hung around their necks, and to receive and send messages up to half a mile away are coming into general use. Also beginning to be installed are two-way radio systems between vehicles and base stations. In some communities hospitals form a radio network with one of them usually designated as the primary control point. All radio transmitters must be operated under and in accordance with proper station authorizations granted by the Federal Communications Commission.

Closed-circuit television installations keep the nurse in audiovisual communication with the patient. Furthermore they can be adapted at little cost to direct audiovisual communication between a doctor in his office and his hospital patients on exclusive medical channels when the time comes for realization of this possibility.

In the teaching hospital, a medical color television installation pays high dividends in help to the learner, whether he is a medical student, a resident, or a physician far advanced in his career who must keep up with advances. The first

[14] We're a Long Way from the Perfect Bed. *Mod. Hosp.*, September, 1962, p. 14.

effective experiments in televising surgery in black-and-white were made at Johns Hopkins Hospital, Baltimore, early in 1947. Surgery televised in color was first officially shown at the 1949 convention of the American Medical Association in Atlantic City, the telecasts originating in Philadelphia at the University of Pennsylvania Hospital. Smith, Kline and French sponsored the early demonstrations, the equipment being designed and operated by Columbia Broadcasting System personnel.

With all the new and dramatic developments in communications, one of the very earliest, and for a long time to come still a high-ranking one, is likely to be overlooked. Printed material, from pamphlets to books, is a most important means of communication. The printer who designs forms and other literature specially for hospital use is, or should be, a frequently called in consultant. His products, too are changing with the times, and ideas are needed for their revision.

Medical Statistics and Records

Automation in medical records was the subject of an address at the 1961 annual meeting of the American Association of Medical Record Librarians by Robert S. Lindley, president, National Biomedical Research Foundation, Silver Spring, Maryland.

Mr. Lindley discussed the purpose of electronic data processing and the advantages of an integrated system relative to the use of CO-BOL, which is a computer system to be utilized by individuals who are not necessarily skilled in programming. He stated that the future will see the establishment of a national health computer network with strategically located computer centers to which information will flow from hospitals supplying valuable information for solving the nation's health problems. He declared:[15]

> The use of an electronic computer is a virtual necessity for fulfilling the complicated processing requirements for medical information today. The medical research done in the past ten years—which is more than has ever been done before in the history of mankind—has resulted in increased demands on hospital personnel, and increased complexity in hospital records. The computer can ease these demands, and cope with the complexity on both the non-medical and medical levels.

"Machines Make Light Work of Medical Data" is the subject of an article[16] by L. R. Jordan and Robert G. Hoffmann, Ph.D. of the University of Florida, and they describe how it is done, stating,[16] "For data sorting and classifying problems of this kind, there is only one satisfactory method for handling the problem: Let machines do most of the work."

The American Medical Association recently announced that it had made

[15] *J. Am. A. Med. Rec. Librarians*, December. 1961, p. 252.
[16] *Mod. Hosp.*, December, 1960, pp. 67–71.

use of an electronic brain to help in bringing out its 345-page book entitled *Current Medical Terminology*. The book gives each disease a code number. This enables a doctor to designate a disease or symptom by referring to its code identification. A second somewhat larger edition appeared in December, 1963.

Devices to Help the Disabled Patient

Electronic Artificial Larynx. The development of an electronic artificial larynx for persons who have lost the power of speech because of paralysis or surgical removal of the larynx is described as follows:[17]

> When the instrument is held against the side of the throat, the sound waves it generates pass into the throat cavity and are formed into speech by the lips and tongue. The electronically produced sound waves thus replace those normally produced by air passing over the vocal cords. The pocket-sized instrument uses transistors and is powered by self-contained mercury batteries. It is available with a high pitch for women and a low pitch for men. The pitch may be varied to produce inflections over a half octave by depressing a switch. Speech volume is equivalent to that of a normal talker speaking at a conversational level.

The device was developed and is being sold at manufacturing cost by the Bell Telephone System.

All-transistor Hearing Screener. Ten seconds per individual is the average testing time required to determine the presence or absence of hearing impairment with the aid of a new transistorized device. It was designed for use by the military, schools, and industry, and has proved to be of value to otologists and other physicians. Power is provided by a single mercury battery.

Headphones for Quadriplegics. According to Illinois Bell Telephone Company's *Telebriefs*, specially designed headphones bring telephone privacy to quadriplegics at the Veterans Administration Hospital at Hines, Illinois. The telephones are wheeled to the bedside on carts. Formerly when the patient made or received a call, someone had to hold the instrument to his head. The new headphones muffle loud noises, amplify faint ones.

Aural Reading Machine for Blind. The Veterans Administration has developed a device by means of which the blind can read ordinary printed material, such as books and magazines. The unit is portable. It produces sounds that resemble patterns of musical tones similar to chords played on an organ. Trained users by interpreting these tones can ultimately attain a reading speed of from 15 to 30 words per minute. This machine enables the blind to read current material, including correspondence, which is not and cannot be made available in Braille.

Glass Leg. An orthopedist of Nice, France, Georges Lebre, was awarded the 1958 L'Herminier Prize[18] for promoting the manufacture of artificial limbs made of polyester fiber and glass wool.

[17] *Pub. Health Rep.,* November, 1961.
[18] A report in the November, 1959, issue of *Canadian Hospital,* republished from *World Veteran,* relates that the prize, set up to reward French orthopedists for developing new appliances for the

Electric Arms and Hands. Back in 1952, ancient history in the annals of electronics, 2,000 doctors attending the assembly of the International College of Surgeons in Madrid saw a one-legged man who had been fitted with an artificial leg and taught to use it by Dr. Henry H. Kessler of Newark, New Jersey, cutting intricate figures on roller skates around a stone paved rink. Dr. Kessler, as reported in *Time,* June 2, 1952, described to the delegates an electric arm which was made by International Business Machines Corporation, the switches of which are operated by pressure of the toes. Power to bend and extend the elbow and wrist, to rotate the lifelike, plastic hand, and to open and close the fingers and thumb is supplied by electric motors. In another model the switches were shifted from the toes to the stump at the shoulder.

An electronically equipped cane was developed in 1953 at the Franklin Institute, Philadelphia. A vibrator in the handle silently signals the user when its tip is passed over a curb, a stepdown, or a hole.

Automatic Data Processing

Automatic data processing was the subject of a thesis submitted by Patrick H. Wade, Jr., as the final requirement for his degree of Master of Science in Hospital Administration from Northwestern University in June, 1959. Mr. Wade is administrator of Northwestern University Medical School Clinics. Extracts from his thesis follow.

The basic principle of "office automation" is not new. Simply stated it is the avoidance of repetition of work. It is a means of freeing people from routine drudgery, and it thereby results in the performance of more work in less time. By slow stages automation has been taking place for many years. The typist using carbon paper to produce second and subsequent copies of a patient's admission record is making use of this principle. Adding machines, bookkeeping machines, calculators, duplicators, and typewriters have all contributed to increased efficiency in the office. Automation includes all these devices, but each of these machines, functioning as a separate unit, has its limitations. Business transactions, data, progressing from one to the other, have to be recorded and checked. Each copying and checking causes delays, builds up clerical costs, and introduces errors despite checking. Machines are now in use which do some of this copying and processing of data automatically.

Every new machine is labeled with an impressive name and is accompanied by a multisyllable vocabulary of its own. The terminology lends an air of mystery to the device and often creates misunderstanding about its use. The executive views automation as the panacea for all his office problems; the office worker sees the machines as monsters which will replace her and thousands of other workers—victims of technological unemployment. The truth lies somewhere between.

The greatest benefit to the executive from the automated systems now in use has come from their ability to provide better, more accurate, and more timely information about the operation of his business. Mechanical processing of data has

---

disabled, was first established in 1957 as a memorial to Commander Jean L'Herminier, a French naval officer and war hero. The award consists of $600 cash, proceeds of royalties from L'Herminier's book, *Casabianca,* which the author bequeathed to the French government.

not yet produced "substantial office work savings that were expected," reports *Office Management* in the January, 1959, issue, page 113. The machines have replaced low-skilled clerical workers in performing the monotonous repetitious office jobs, but they have created a greater demand for skilled office workers and accountants. This has upgraded the status and salary of the office worker to the extent that labor costs are generally higher in the automated office.

Three general classes of data processing equipment are available:

Punched card machines have been in use longer, and the punched card is a basic feature of the newer system.

The electronic data processing machine or *computer* has been referred to as an electronic "brain." This equipment was originally designed for the one-time operations; that is, the solving of complex scientific problems which would normally require years to solve manually. The development of the transistor in 1948 made it possible to begin converting this original monster into a unit which had the flexibility to be adapted to business operations. During the fifties the development of this equipment was phenomenal. Many manufacturers are now engaged in the production of computers. New improvements are being introduced daily. The machines which make up a computer can be contained within a compact unit which is no longer than two or three regular-size office desks. Small units for limited application can be used on the desk. The computer, or a machine which will evolve from the computer, is the equipment which will ultimately "automate" the processing of hospital records.

Integrated data processing machines, or I.D.P., are the most recent automatic office machines to gain popularity. They are attachments to the conventional office machines such as electric typewriters, calculators, and bookkeeping machines. In business operations information is handled by many types of machines. Each time the information is handled in a conventional office, it must be translated by a manual operation. This requires much copying and recopying. Each time the records are processed in this way there is the possibility of error, which requires checking at each point. Integrated data processing makes possible transfer of information from one machine to another by means of a "machine language." The "language" used is one that has successfully been employed for some time with wire transmission equipment such as the teletype machine—the punched paper tape. A typist working with a punched tape system uses the typewriter in a conventional way, but as she does so, the machine she is using produces a punched tape, or more recently a punched card, as a by-product of her work. The accountant using a calculator or bookkeeping machine, in the same manner, can produce a record in a tape or card. This information without other manual reproduction can be introduced into the computer for producing reports. The typist or the accountant can be in one city, the computer in another city across the country. Many industrial firms have adopted this system as a means of attaining centralized recordkeeping. This system can be used by hospitals participating in a group data processing system and will probably be adopted as a method of partial automation by small hospitals.

Probably more than 50 per cent of the automation job is procedure analysis. This involves collecting forms currently in use; charting the paper-work flow; showing all calculations, sorting, writing, and other handling; preparing job descriptions; determining the frequency of transactions, the schedule requirements, and the cost of operations. These are terms with which every administrator is familiar, but about which most administrators are doing little. If a hospital executive believes that going into the use of electronic equipment will take the place of a good, honest look at his problem, he is heading for a very disappointing experience and an irate board. Some administrators and comptrollers may decide to concentrate on developing the new system without attempting to improve the old. This plan may succeed, but it is not a sound basis for installing expensive equipment. Information gathered in studying the present system, will in most instances enhance the efficiency of any new system selected.

Hospital executives do not need to be experts on the details of the data processing system, but they must have a basic understanding of the principles of office automation.

The hospital industry is big business, *collectively;* but even the largest *individual* hospital is small business by comparison with the industrial firms which use automation. A complete installation is probably not economically justified in less than a 500-bed hospital. The use of automation for most hospitals lies in the use of a modified system, within the hospital, integrated with a central service supplying data to several small hospitals.

Since this thesis was written, some interesting developments have occurred, such as the holding of institutes by the American Hospital Association. The first state-wide hospital data processing program was installed in 1961 by the Connecticut Hospital Association. The United Hospitals of Newark automated their bookkeeping records by using high-speed data processing without any capital investment in equipment or any immediate need for building and equipment expansion—accomplished through the Service Bureau Corporation, East Orange, New Jersey.

At the beginning of 1964, only 7 per cent of hospitals were using ADP, according to the report of a survey,[19] but indications were that usage was growing rapidly.

---

[19] Raymond H. Geisler: How Many Hospitals Use Automatic Data Processing Equipment? One of 13 articles in the special issue on ADP in *Hospitals*, January 1, 1964.

CHAPTER 11

The World of Business and Businessmen

Four phases or chapters can be discerned in the history of the large American industrial enterprise: the initial expansion and accumulation of resources; the rationalization of the use of resources; the expansion into new markets and lines to help assure the continuing full use of resources; and finally the development of a new structure to make possible continuing effective mobilization of resources to meet both changing short-term market demands and long-term market trends.

ALFRED D. CHANDLER, JR.[1]

AMERICAN INDUSTRY has a totally different kind of historical background from that of Europe. Starting in an untamed wilderness, it developed swiftly in a rough, bold way suited to the environment which it was helping to shape. Whatever ideas some of its leaders brought over from Old World business practices were quickly changed to go along with the opportunism that was creating a new civilization with little thought for what future generations might think of their methods or concern for the future of their own enterprises. Grab what you can today, plan what to do with it tomorrow, was the way the "tycoons" operated. Perhaps it was the best way to meet the needs. It got the population spread out over a vast territory in a hurry.

Big business is, however, only the most obvious part of American industrial

---

[1] *Strategy and Structure: Chapters in the History of the Industrial Enterprise.* Cambridge, Massachusetts, The M.I.T. Press, Massachusetts Institute of Technology, 1962, p. 385.

history. Craftsmen who had learned their arts and trades in Europe brought to the new land many skills that they practiced and taught. It was not as if new tribes of barbarians were arriving to drive back and submerge the American Indian. These invaders were civilized. Other countries through their emigrants gave America far-advanced knowledge, culture, and training. They gave traditions, beliefs, ideals. America, North and South, was not so much to be the beginning of a new civilization as a welding of many old civilizations in new surroundings. The roots are in the Old World. Americans, however many generations back their ancestors may have been born on this side of the ocean, have a feeling of going "home" to countries on the other continents. Some of them with mixed ancestry can claim several such homes, and everyone feels a cultural kinship with countries whose writers, painters and composers have produced works for all to enjoy, and whose architects and artisans have built cathedrals worthy of traveling far to see.

Commerce, like medical science, flourished at different times in different countries and languished in between. No steady line of progress can possibly be drawn anywhere. Lack of communication was, of course, one of the main reasons for geographic differences and for interruptions and up and down movements with the times.

Why was the shopping center idea forgotten for fourteen hundred years? They dug up one the other day in Sardis, Turkey, the ancient capital of the Lydian empire of King Croesus. The archaeological team from Harvard University said it was not unlike the modern-day counterpart used by American housewives, although it was first laid out around A.D. 200 and rebuilt in the fifth century. There is an "avenue 50 feet wide with marble pavement and sidewalks flanked by mosaic colonnades where the people could shop or chat out of the sun or rain." Dating back to the actual time of Croesus, the sixth century B.C., are remnants of a Lydian bazaar showing the floors of shops and workshops and bronze objects, including cups, plates, and jugs.[2]

Manufacturing was not always done in the home in olden times, as is commonly believed. There were factories in some places at some periods. When the Mohammedan princes, called the "Great Moguls," were ruling parts of India beginning in the early sixteenth century, stimulating culture and commerce, factories were established throughout the Mogul Empire by European trading companies. Without power or machinery, they nevertheless were quite large and employed many workers. Physicians, most of them from Venice, settled in the area.

Long before that, in the middle of the thirteenth century, the Polo brothers went on a merchandising expedition to Peking from Venice. On a second journey Marco Polo, the son of one of them, went along and returned after twenty years to tell his fabulous tale of the wonders he had seen, especially the spice markets of the Moluccas and of Ceylon. Trade was spurred by the tale. The

[2] From a United Press dispatch, October 21, 1961.

Crusades stimulated trade between western and eastern Europe. By the fifteenth century the spirit of exploration was beginning to make shipping a major industry, and manufacturing and merchandising were furnishing it with goods, all unorganized and uncorrelated. In fact, establishment by the Portuguese of direct shipping to and from India, with trading stations, put the Mohammedan spice merchants out of business along with those in the Italian towns, especially Venice, who had previously received and relayed the spices.

It was in search of another way to the East Indies and their spices that Columbus set out on his voyages which led to America. Here we have a good example of the changes in human wants that lead to the decline of certain businesses. Who would go venturing into unknown seas in sailboats nowadays to find a better way to reach the places from which spices come? Then, spices masked the bad taste of spoiled food that there was no known way to keep from spoiling. With the advent of canning the exorbitant demand for spices disappeared.

Up to the present era of fast transportation, industry could flourish only in large towns. In the early Middle Ages there were no such towns in western Europe, hence no industry to speak of. The invasions and the resultant confusion led to decreasing size of most Roman towns and the disappearance of others. The pattern of life was mostly the great feudal castle with its lord and the village below or near it in which dwelt the serfs. Production was limited to their own needs. Little came in from outside except farm products. At fairs there was a little trading, which whetted an appetite for more. At length there were insurrections which finally led to the granting of charters to the towns.

With this change, trading increased. Manufacturing and merchandising were combined in the same operation. Craft guilds were formed to protect the special interests of each shop. The statutes of the guild of candle makers, the oldest in Paris, date back to 1061. There were guilds of armorers, sword makers, bakers, butchers, goldsmiths, etc., each one of which established its own standards of training and kept from practicing the trade those who did not meet them.

Wholesale trade was almost impossible in most places because of the requirement that the manufacturer keep a shop and sell only to consumers. There was fear that any "middle man" would buy up all the stocks of a commodity, sort of cornering the market, and raise the price, a fear that subsequent history has shown not to be too naïve!

Scarcity of money and the belief that moneylending for profit was wicked were other deterrents to the growth of business. Because they were not Christians, and therefore were not supposed to be bound by the same code of ethics, only the Jews were permitted to collect interest. The Jews were excluded from the guilds, which practically forced them into the moneylending business.

A kind of banking business began in Italy in the thirteenth century. Bills of exchange were employed. Although no interest was charged, there were damages for delays in repayment.

On the highways, bridges, and fords, tolls and duties were charged by the barons and monks through whose domains the merchant traveled, and sometimes a part of the merchandise was confiscated. On the seas there were pirates, some of them men of high rank out for adventure. Ships were lured to shore by false signals and plundered by the wreckers.

Out of the perils came the stimulus to organize for defense. Seventy German cities united to form the Hanseatic League. The league became powerful. Through treaties and influence it practically monopolized the trade on the Baltic and North Seas. It bought and managed settlements in London, Bergen, and Novgorod in Russia. Its ships traveled in fleets guarded by a battleship. After three centuries of great activity it gradually declined, passing out of existence in the middle of the seventeenth century.

Through the whole late medieval period—the thirteenth, fourteenth, and fifteenth centuries—nations as such had no commercial importance, nor did individuals, all trade being regulated by towns and conducted by towns and the merchant and craft guilds. All cooperative effort through unions such as the Hanseatic League was between towns, not countries.

With the lessening of prejudice against the wholesaler or dealer, the merchants began to flourish, to grow wealthy, and to wield considerable influence in town governments. A business class gradually gained some of the rights, privileges, and power theretofore reserved for the nobility and the clergy. Its money was needed for war and for other government affairs. The money of the bankers and the merchants was, along with political changes, quite a factor in the merging of towns into nations. In fact, trade accounts for more national spirit and for more progress of all kinds than most historians give it credit for.

Presages of the Industrial Revolution

During this period the "germs," as Mumford[3] calls them, of modern technology were being generated. Clocks were among the important devices, the first modern one appearing in 1370, credited to Heinrich von Wyck, although the ancients had water clocks. Around 1500 Peter Henlein, of Nuremberg, invented the watch operated by springs. In 1657 Huygens produced the first pendulum clock. Leonardo da Vinci left designs of submarines, helicopters, and airplanes and, more important when it was brought to light two hundred years later in the eighteenth century, a drawing of a mechanical spindle. John Kay's flying shuttle invented in 1733 cut human labor for weaving in half. James Hargreaves invented a carding machine in 1760 and the spinning jenny about 1764; four years later his fellow spinners broke into his house and destroyed his machine for fear of its effect on their jobs. The next year, however, Richard Arkwright patented the water-powered spinning frame; and ten years later, in 1779, Samuel Crompton, a spinner, combined the water frame and the spinning jenny in a hybrid mule. The power loom was invented by Edmund Cartwright, a clergyman, in 1785.

[3] Lewis Mumford: *Technics and Civilization*. New York, Harcourt Brace & Co., 1934, p. 65.

A mob destroyed the factory of Barthelemy Thimonnier in France in which uniforms were being made for the army through use of a sewing machine which he had produced in 1830. The first real competitor for hand labor, however, was the sewing machine invented by Elias Howe in 1846.

The steam engine was invented by Hero in the third century, but not until his writings were published in 1575 in Europe was the principle studied and its possibilities for application to manufacture on a large scale visualized. A steam engine that could be used for pumping was developed by Edward Somerset, Marquis of Worcester, in 1630. An atmospheric engine which pushed a piston by expanding steam in a cylinder, and forced it back after cooling the cylinder, was produced by Denis Papin of France around 1690. Thomas Savery made some improvements in 1698, and Thomas Newcomen used the ideas of both around 1705 to build an engine which could be used in pumping water out of the mines. James Watt, with a partner who was a manufacturer, Matthew Boulton, worked beginning in 1765 on engines which could drive machinery, finally equipping a spinning factory with their first engine in 1785—an epochal date in the history of industry because it was the same year in which Cartwright invented the power loom. By 1822 this loom was perfected sufficiently to market, Oliver Evans in the meantime having developed a high-pressure engine.

THE INDUSTRIAL REVOLUTION

The mechanical revolution which created the factory system beginning about 1760 was now well on its way, accompanied by the industrial revolution which brought about the radical changes in living conditions to meet the new demands for workers in the rapidly expanding industrial centers. Simultaneous political changes were uniting the towns and regions into powerful countries. The upheaval and its effect upon the mass of the people are being studied with new concern in the present day when automation is proceeding so far that factories can be run almost without people. These are considerations, however, for the chapters on economics and on sociology, although the impact of the human element, both workers and consumers, is strongly affecting the new trends in business. The workers have learned that destroying the machines cannot stop the technological advance, but have found other ways to assert their cause that affect hospitals as well as factories.

Hence the need for executives of medical service institutions to study the ways of business with men, as well as with machines—not to copy them but rather to excel in them, as is logically to be expected of service organizations whose purpose is to improve people, not just to sell them some product or service. In this learning process governmental influences and controls upon business must be included. The twentieth century is known as the age of business but the signs are clear that government is advancing toward an equally important part in the lives of the populace, to the dismay of business leaders.

Why this is happening is also clear from a study of business history. When the acquisition of expensive machinery became necessary to mine coal and iron and to produce cloth and kettles, a capitalist class arose which thought of nothing but profit from their investment and had no concern for the misery of the miners and factory hands and their families. Vicious competition almost forced this state of affairs to meet the sudden vast demands for goods, mainly from the new colonies, whose raw materials were sent to the home countries for processing. It was only through appeals for government regulation, some of them originating with factory owners, that general improvement of the workers' lot could be accomplished.

In the American colonies, at first the situation was different. There were no machines, and even when they came there was not the same overcrowding in factory towns as in Europe because there was plenty of land. America, however, grew on capital from the home countries on which the investors expected a return. It was not an independent growth. The Virginia Company, a commercial venture, sent the colonists to Jamestown from England; the London Company financed the Pilgrims with the understanding that industry should be carried out in common for seven years; the Dorchester Company established settlements around Massachusetts Bay to promote fishing; a Dutch trading company established in 1613 a post called New Amsterdam, now New York, and in 1621 the Dutch West India Company was given the right to colonize territory adjoining the post. Even the grants made by monarchs, such as Maryland to George Calvert by King James and Pennsylvania to William Penn by King James II, had trade as a primary motive. Ships carried tobacco and cotton from the colonies in the south, fish and grain from those in the north, and brought back tools, clothing, glass, paper, and many other manufactured products. This was not to last. Samuel Slater imported Arkwright's machine into Rhode Island in 1790, and cotton mills began in the United States. In 1813 Francis C. Lowell introduced the power loom into his factories in Waltham, Massachusetts. By 1830 there were nearly 800 cotton textile plants in the United States. Of course, Eli Whitney's invention of the cotton gin in 1794, which greatly speeded cotton production, was a significant factor in keeping up with the increased demands of the mills for raw material.

Shipping and shipbuilding became major industries. Stephen Girard, who went from his native France to Philadelphia to engage in trade, and who became a very wealthy merchant and banker, owned and operated forty sailing ships from 1780 to 1790 to carry on his trade with the West Indies and other parts of the world.

Protests against exploitation of labor took place in the New World as well as in the Old. In 1786 printers in Philadelphia walked out to enforce their demand for a six-dollar minimum weekly wage. This was the earliest known strike for higher wages. In 1835 the unions in the same city succeeded in the establishment of a ten-hour working day.

THE "ROBBER BARONS"

The story of the "robber barons" is well known. Heilbroner points out that they ruled in the United States as they could not have in Britain because of social tradition in the Old World which made the newly rich remain inferior to and often imitative of the hereditary ruling class. The Old World insisted on "a modicum of punctilio." Sometimes when an outstanding achievement seemed to merit the act, an inventor, merchant, or manufacturer was knighted—the barber's apprentice, Richard Arkwright, became Sir Richard after he had made a fortune with his spinning jenny. Somehow this elevation to a higher social position created a greater sense of social responsibility and interdicted the cutthroat competitive tactics that were practiced for a while in America, the land of self-made and self-absorbed men who strove for the power that wealth alone could give in the new land. Heilbroner states:[4]

> The successful European money-maker might be rich as Croesus, but the savor of his riches was a trifle dulled by the recognition that this was only one— and not the final—step up the social ladder. All this was vastly different in America. Not only had this country been founded by men who were deeply opposed to gradations of name and birth, but the spirit of individual independence and individual achievement had sunk deep into the national folklore. In America a man was as good as he proved himself, and his success needed no validation from a genealogist. Hence, while there was not too much to differentiate the dark and sweated mills of New England from the gloomy mills of old England, when one looked into the manners and behavior of their masters, the resemblance lessened. For while the European capitalist was still caught in the shadow of a feudal past, the American money-maker basked in the sun—there were no inhibitions on his drive to power or in the exuberant enjoyment of his wealth. In the bubbling last half of the nineteenth century, money was the stepping stone to social recognition in the United States, and having acquired a passport of suitable wealth, the American millionaire needed no further visa for his entree into the upper classes.
>
> And so the game of money-making in the New World was a rougher and less gentlemanly affair than the competitive struggle abroad. The stakes were higher and the chances for success were greater. The sportsmanship, accordingly, was somewhat less.

Heilbroner then quotes a letter sent by the genius of shipping and commerce, Cornelius Vanderbilt, in the 1860's, to his own business associates whom he suspected were threatening his interests: "Gentlemen: You have undertaken to ruin me. I will not sue you, for law takes too long. I will ruin you." Which he proceeded to do. The rest of Heilbroner's Chapter VIII, "The Savage World of Thorstein Veblen," should be read for more examples of the ruthless, dishonest, and devious maneuvering for wealth and power that victimized associates, competitors, investors, employees, and the public. All this was taken with equanimity

---

[4] Robert L. Heilbroner: *The Worldly Philosophers,* New York, Simon and Schuster, Inc., 1953, pp. 200–201.

and glossed over by the *laissez-faire* economists of the time—until Thorstein Veblen came along. Government officials were, many of them, deliberately blind because they were personally caught up in the fever of speculation, and their own interests would have been endangered by repressive measures. Giant corporations had their beginning in this period—E. I. du Pont de Nemours Powder Company, 1802; American Fur Company, John Jacob Astor's creation, 1811; New York Central Railroad under Cornelius Vanderbilt's control, 1867; Pullman Palace Car Company organized by George M. Pullman around 1865; Armour and Company around 1860; Marshall Field and Company, 1881; the Carnegie Steel Company, a consolidation of other steelworks, in 1899, merged in 1901 in the United States Steel Corporation, by Andrew Carnegie; the Northern Pacific Railroad started by Henry Villard in 1883; J. P. Morgan and Company, 1873, successor to Drexel, Morgan & Company, founded 1871; Great Northern Railway by James J. Hill, 1888; Standard Oil Company by John D. Rockefeller, 1870; McCormick Reaper Company, predecessor of International Harvester Company, by Cyrus McCormick, 1847; Southern Pacific Railway by Edward Henry Harriman around 1880; Woolworth's, 1879; Ford Motor Company, 1903; Montgomery Ward & Company, 1872; Sears, Roebuck and Company, of which Julius Rosenwald became president, in 1895; American Tobacco Company by James B. Duke through consolidations in 1890; and General Motors Corporation, the world's largest industrial organization, founded by William C. Durant as a holding company for other motor companies, in 1908. Overexpanding, Durant lost control and management to banking interests in the 1910 business recession. He came back as president in 1916 and Pierre S. du Pont became chairman of the board, signaling the controlling interest in General Motors which the Du Pont Company was to have in the 1920 reorganization involving the merger of some 60 automobile companies. With another recession in that year, Durant was replaced by du Pont as president, and Alfred P. Sloan, who had joined the organization in 1899 when it purchased his roller bearing company, and who had developed the reorganization plan, became operating vice-president and later president. On January 28, 1963, General Motors announced that it "made more money in 1962 than any other business ever cleared in a year's time"—the net earnings were $1,459,000,000. Its United States and foreign taxes exceeded its net earnings, amounting to an estimated $1,475,000,000, and its world-wide payrolls were reported to have reached $3,900,000,000. Sales totaled $14,600,000,000.

American Telephone and Telegraph Company, with net income of around $1,430,000,000 in 1962, was next largest, and in the previous year was $432,000,000 ahead of General Motors.

Standard Oil of New Jersey, with net annual income of around $760,000,000, appears to be next largest, followed by Du Pont's $452,000,000, Texaco's $430,000,000, Ford's $410,000,000, Standard Oil of California's $294,000,000, General Electric Company's $242,500,000, Creole Petroleum's $241,000,000, Sears Roebuck's $220,000,000, International Business Machines' $207,000,000, and U. S. Steel's $190,000,000.

GROWTH OF CORPORATIONS

These and some two hundred other concerns are industrial giants, and the trend toward increasing size is viewed with concern in many quarters, although no one knows how to check it except by legislation against monopolies.

The reasons for the growth of corporations are interesting and understandable. One of them is to promote efficiency by owning and controlling the sources of supply of raw materials and/or parts and services. Another extremely important one, becoming more so every day, is fortification against technological changes which will destroy the market for present products or services. Diversification is becoming a necessity. That it has always been desirable ever since manufacture began is shown by the effect changes have on the industries of a whole city, as exemplified by Birmingham, England. One writer says:[5]

> Long ago 20,000 buckle-makers in the city were unemployed when somebody invented shoe-laces; they petitioned the Court and the Prince of Wales ordered all nobility to discard the "effeminate shoe-string" to aid them. But the march of progress was inexorable and the buckle had gone for good. Soon, however, buttons became popular and the 20,000 found themselves busy again, especially on pearl buttons. . . . But with buttons, as with many other trades, the Midlands has felt keen world competition and the flourishing state of its industries today is not due to the continuity of a few standard trades but to the remarkable elasticity which caused manufacturers suddenly facing ruin in one line to branch into another with even greater success. The pearl button trade, for instance, was captured by the Japanese and the ivory button trade by the Italians—so Birmingham switched to linen buttons and retained a world monopoly in them, whilst those makers who were bolder started making electric light switches. Belgium's iron imports hit Staffordshire; Czecho-Slovakia almost killed the glass trade; Norway nearly made a success of wiping out the fish-hook business. Then the advent of vacuum-cleaners and a sudden change in women's hair style seriously affected the Midland brush industry. But, owing largely to the huge pool of skilled labour always available in the area, plus the original individuality of traders, springing from the fact that Birmingham had always attracted "refugees" and dissenters during the days when it was not a corporate town and had not the strict regulations of older communities, the turning to new products or variations of the old invariably prevented the area feeling the slumps (later called "trade-recessions") which caused such distress to other cities devoted almost wholly to particular trades, such as coal, shipping, or cotton.

The risks involved in starting a business and in maintaining it on a profitable level despite changes in the market demand in the men who assume them a spirit of enterprise that inescapably requires a boldness that borders on ruthlessness. It is quite unlike the kind of spirit that motivates the director of a nonprofit organization, notwithstanding the fact that competition of a kind confronts the latter also. Without the entrepreneur's daring, business would stagnate. He must

[5] John Booth: The Midlands, in *Great Britain: England, Scotland and Wales*, Doré Ogrizek (ed.). New York, McGraw-Hill Book Co., Inc., 1956, pp. 266–68.

be accorded freedom to innovate. So the argument goes, up and down, how much freedom, how much regulation over business, are best for society.

There came a time around the turn of the century when freedom had been stretched so far that society rebelled. Veblen has been mentioned as an influence, but far more effective than an economist's analyses of the evils were the revelations made to the public through books and articles by social reformers, prominent among whom were the so-called muck-rakers—David Graham Phillips, Lincoln Steffens, Ida Tarbell, and Upton Sinclair. Ida Tarbell wrote a blistering *History of the Standard Oil Company*. Sinclair took out after the packing industry in *The Jungle,* as a result of which new laws were drafted and passed establishing food standards and sanitation requirements. An aroused public blasted the profiteers whose wealth was piled up by exploiting both workers and consumers. In 1934 Matthew Josephson used the title *The Robber Barons* for a book published by Harcourt, Brace and Company, New York.

What was known as "whitewashing" followed, led by Standard Oil with its employment of Ivy Lee to institute propaganda favorable to industry—the beginning of a new profession, public relations. A leading approach was an attempt to humanize industry by publicity about its leaders, such as the emphasis on John D. Rockefeller's beneficences. Somehow in the process of setting up a favorable image, the attributes of the image began to be adopted. Industry tried to live up to the picture created by its propagandists, in fact had to for survival. And it has done so ever since, in tardy recognition of the social complex in which it operates.

Naturally there were numerous exceptions to the "robber baron" type. In Britain there was Robert Owen, who at New Lanark in Scotland around 1800 established a community for his workers which became world-famous for its neatness, educational and recreational facilities, and general attractiveness, while in the mills hours were shorter, wages were higher, and practices fairer than elsewhere, yet the business was profitable. Provision was even made for hearing objections to rules and regulations. Owen became afterward the launcher of a nation-wide trade union. He was an idealist and a fanatic, but his beliefs in opportunity for all were a tremendous spur to improvement.

The crusade for ten-hour working-day legislation in England was financed largely by the great cotton mill owner, John Wood.

Peter Cooper, owner of an ironworks at Baltimore, builder after his own designs of the first locomotive engine made in America, established in 1854 an institution for the instruction of working people—Cooper Union, New York—not by bequest (he lived until 1883), but while he was active in industry.

Few persons in Philadelphia were more solicitous for the relief of yellow fever victims and gave more generously to aid them than Stephen Girard, the city's leading merchant-banker.

Henry Ford's comparatively high wage scale and establishment of a profit-sharing plan for employees, at the same time that he sold automobiles at a lower price than his competitors, heralded the then new concept that the market could be expanded by making it possible for labor to buy the goods it was producing. Implicit in this concept, of course, was the basic one of mass production—the assembly line.

Always, there are two sides; and the student should study them both. As Edgar Johnson[6] says:

> Two opposing limitations have afflicted the biographies of the industrialists and financiers. In one group, the biographer has been blinded by admiration for these efficient freebooters. By means of the discreet arts of omission, soft-pedaling, and extenuation, he has portrayed them with gilt and a halo, arrayed in the shining luminosity of public-spirited citizens, art-lovers, and philanthropists. The brutalities of the Homestead strike all forgotten, Carnegie becomes the peace-lover, endower of libraries, and dispenser of medals to men who jump off wharves to rescue little girls from drowning. The Goulds, James J. Hill, Collis P. Huntington, the great railway pirates, all become similarly saintlified. Seen with the trusting gaze of Mrs. Fremont Older, William Randolph Hearst is a Bayard crusading for the welfare of a democracy he loves.
>
> Or else, emulating the reek raised by Ida Tarbell's *History of Standard Oil,* in the days of the muckrakers, all is damnification. *God's Gold* leaves John D. Rockefeller unsilvered of the shining dimes with which Ivy Lee exorcised the earlier taint; the Mellons, the Morgans, the Du Ponts, have been portrayed simply as obscene accumulations, sources of exploitation and corruption. Matthew Josephson's *The Robber Barons* sees the new weapons of finance capitalism devoted to perpetuating a predatory feudalism; it does not show how these very exploiters were channels of the new. Their technical role in building up large-scale industrial units, in elaborating the economic life of modern society has been almost ignored.

Heilbroner[7] sums it up in a telling sentence: "Make no mistake about it, capitalism has performed exceedingly well in the United States and it holds every promise of being able to surpass its own performance."

It is with discrimination that business and businessmen must be viewed in the endeavor to fit the hospital into its proper niche in those phases of its operation which ally it to business. Strong forces are at work to make business more social-minded, just as they are in trying to make science more appreciative of economics and its influence on all living.

Ethics in a Business Society is the interesting title of a book by Marquis W. Childs and Douglass Cater[8] with the explanation in the foreword, "These studies are an inquiry into the relationship between religion and economics, into the department of the spirit and the department of getting and spending; into the easy assumptions that all will be for the best in the best possible of worlds if only each man digs and delves to the best of his own ability." The studies were financed by a grant from the Rockefeller Foundation. The titles of the ten chapters show their scope:

[6] *One Mighty Torrent: The Drama of Biography.* New York, The Macmillan Company, 1955, p. 535.

[7] *Op. cit.,* p. 283.

[8] Published by Harper & Brothers in 1954 and later, with a third printing in May, 1959, as a Mentor Book.

I. The Age of Certitude
II. The Circle Is Shattered
III. The Contending Forces
IV. Modern Man and Modern Dogma
V. The Businessman's Dilemma
VI. Free Enterprise—Fact and Fancy
VII. Government and Business—the Uneasy Balance
VIII. The Church and the Kingdom
IX. Technology, Creator and Destroyer
X. End or Beginning

Another book which presents the case for due consideration of human values in the industrial organization is James C. Worthy's *Big Business and Free Men*.[9] In the preface the author, vice-president of Sears, Roebuck and Company and president of the Sears, Roebuck Foundation, states that primarily "the book seeks to explore the role of business in modern American life, the means for preserving the essentials of human freedom within the structure of large-scale organization, and the emerging responsibilities of business within a democratic social order."

A third significant book is *Social Science Research on Business: Product and Potential* by Robert A. Dahl, Mason Haire, and Paul F. Lazarsfeld.[10] The essays in the book constitute the final phase of a multiphase program sponsored by the Ford Foundation "to stimulate increased interest in the world of business as a subject for research by social scientists, and to encourage a greater appreciation on the part of faculty members in business administration of the potential contribution these underlying disciplines offer." In the three sections of the book the views of the political scientist, the psychologist, and the sociologist are presented.

THE MANAGERIAL REVOLUTION

A radical change in the control of industry occurred with the passing from the scene of the early entrepeneurs in America. A number of these men were more interested in the building of industrial empires than in running them. Some of them were lacking in organization and management skills and employed managers. In a minority of instances, sons and other relatives succeeded to the control, as in the case of the Du Pont Company, the Ford Company, and the Dillingham interests in Hawaii; but in general, ownership became diffused through outside investors, and professional managers became the controlling power.

This was a gradual change, not fully understood or appreciated perhaps until James Burnham's book *The Managerial Revolution*[11] appeared in 1941.

The professional manager is no more free from attack than were the former

---

[9] New York, Harper & Bros., 1959.
[10] New York, Columbia University Press, 1959.
[11] New York, John Day Co.

owner-operators. The *Attack on Big Business* by John D. Glover,[12] published in 1954, tells the story.

In 1962 Vance Packard's *The Pyramid Climbers*[13] raised some questions about the initiative and perspective of the new leaders in the exaggerated type of attack he had used in his previous books, *The Hidden Persuaders, The Status Seekers,* and *The Waste Makers.*

Of the more than three million business firms in the United States, 95 per cent are small. They have a big problem of competition with big business and there are many failures, but they remain a symbol at least of the "free competition" that is a prized attribute of business in a democracy.

Defenders of the present system of business control frequently point to the wide distribution of ownership through the 15 million or so shareholders, one out of eight adults, including 1.3 million members of labor unions, but the "control" aspect is really a myth, as the ordinary shareholder has no voice in the conduct of the company despite the proxy that he is asked to send in and the invitation that he receives to the annual meeting.

A rather new light on the management of American business was shed by Cameron Hawley in a paper delivered at a personnel conference of the American Management Association in February, 1960.[14] Speaking of the common charge that labor costs are much higher in America than in Europe, causing some manufacturers to transfer part of their operations to other countries, he told of comparisons made by the president of one company. In hourly workers, in the same sized plant, the overseas factory employed a few more, and the payroll was a little less but not much. The great difference was in *salaried employees,* who were four times as many in the plant in the United States as they were in the overseas organization, a ratio of 912 to 221, compared with 1,300 to 1,200 hourly workers. "Here in the United States we have the most expensive industrial management on earth," declares Mr. Hawley. In Europe much more than in America they still run their businesses as practically "one-man shows," and the difference in cost of operation should make hospital administrators cautious of following the example of business too far in proliferating management. The process divides responsibility but it is expensive.

Sylvia Porter in her column in the *Chicago Daily News,* November 1, 1962, quoted figures to show that at least toward the bottom of the white-collar group a change is already occurring. She says that according to a survey by *Factory,* automation is less responsible than are improved business methods for eliminating jobs. The survey showed that there was less probability of displaced office workers being transferred to other jobs than there was for factory workers and that new equipment accounted for only 5 per cent of the white-collar and 16 per cent of the blue-shirt jobs eliminated.

[12] Boston, Harvard University Bureau of Business Research.
[13] New York, McGraw-Hill Book Co., Inc.
[14] *Personnel,* May–June, 1960. The Hawley article, which is entitled, "Needed: More Tough-Minded Leaders in Business," may be read in adapted form in *The Reader's Digest,* February, 1961, pp. 55–59.

Strikes are one of the influences that are causing management to install more and more automated machinery and to institute improved methods. Supervisory employees can in emergencies take over much of the operation of an increasing number of industries and prevent complete shutdowns. Mallinckrodt Chemical Works, St. Louis, reported in the fall of 1962 when a short strike occurred that its 200 supervisory personnel who operated critical processes and shipped crucial items in the emergency proved fully equal to the need; and the Shell Oil Company around the same time declared that its supervisory personnel who were working in its Wood River, Illinois, refinery, "had more know-how than the striking workers whom they replaced."

The power of the labor unions and the way in which it is being wielded pose baffling problems for management. It has been demonstrated that the powerful labor czar can be as unscrupulous a profiteer with the union's money as any old-fashioned robber baron was with that of the public, and that the laborer is just as much the victim.

The labor unions are accumulating capital, which brings up another strange trend of the times. They are becoming capitalists, not just through investing in stocks and bonds, but through establishing and controlling their own projects—Marina City, the 896-apartment office-business-recreation-cultural center on the north bank of the Chicago River, the creation of the Building Service Employees International Union and its affiliates, is a conspicuous example. This is a luxury project with high rentals, not something intended to relieve the housing shortage for workers.

CYBERNETICS

One of the noteworthy differences between the industrial revolution and the cybernetics one is the type of worker affected. The sufferer from the first was the craftsman, who worked with his hands. In this new revolution the manual laborer continues to be involved, but also a new class, those who work with their heads. Ever since commerce and industry became organized, a steady demand has grown for office workers. For account-keeping, for correspondence, for compiling reports of operations, for the endless detail work necessary in holding large organizations together, people who could use their brains as well as their hands were in constant demand. Replacing the handwritten with the typewritten document only increased the need, and the calculating machine only served to offset somewhat the shortage in supply of workers.

The computer puts the bookkeeper on the list of unemployed. Clerical workers of all kinds are losing or are in fear of losing their jobs. The rank and file executive is in danger. The computer thinks—after the programmer gives it something to think about. Of course, there is a demand for programmers, a key job in the new era, and workers are needed to build and service the computers, but these are not functions which the unemployed clerical worker can fill except in isolated instances. The robot which controls the automatic manufacturing operation displaces men who exercised these controls with their own brains—and there are few new jobs to which they can adjust without training.

Looking out at this new phenomenon in industry, at the concern for the unemployment which it is causing, the administrator of the medical service institution has a chance to study the changes, the problems, the solutions suggested and put into effect, before conditions become too acute in his own setting. For once he can be glad that hospitals lag a little. On industry, as one writer puts it, "The new age of automation bears down on us with the speed of a rocket" while "it took the old industrial revolution some 150 years to unfold." He says, "Name a human chore, and chances are there is already an intelligent machine that does it." He declares that at one New York bank 700 human bookkeepers have been replaced by 90 programmers, maintenance men and others servicing the check-reader and computer.[15]

The Labor Department's new Office of Automation and Manpower can so far offer only one solution—education and retraining. To industry the shortage of the kind of workers they now need is appalling. Mechanical engineers, computer-maintenance engineers, technologists, data-systems analysts, programmers, the new kind of executive who knows how to direct the new types of operations—for these there is an overwhelming demand. As the rise of democracy forced universal elementary education so that people could understand the issues and vote, and the industrial revolution forced secondary education so that people would acquire new wants and buy products, so cybernetics may force heretofore unknown higher education standards in order to supply the human brains to operate the mechanical ones. In any case it would seem to be a period in which hospitals can share in the impetus for education by expanding their training programs for personnel in fields allied to medicine. With clerical opportunities diminishing, more young persons should be attracted to nursing, physical and occupational therapy, medical technology, and other careers in which the shortage is acute.

INVENTION

The inventor is a pivotal figure in the progress of business as it becomes increasingly dependent upon technological developments. This is the reason for the rapid expansion of research departments in industrial firms, even medium-sized ones. The inventor of the past was frequently a person without too much scientific background but with an alert mind for new ideas. Technology has now reached a stage at which there is little likelihood of the average person stumbling upon an idea for a major new mechanical device, although he may very well be able to suggest improvements in existing devices. On the whole, invention has moved into the realm of the research specialist, and teams rather than individuals are making the discoveries that lead to revolutionary changes in equipment and techniques.

[15] L. Velie: Automation—Friend or Foe? *The Reader's Digest,* October, 1962, pp. 101–6.

Because of the inevitable effects of industrial research and invention upon the medical service institution, it is incumbent upon its administrator to follow closely what is happening in the functioning of all of the major industries.

Consider that spectacular instrument, the laser, which, of course, has great significance for medicine. Visualized are the possibilities of operating on a cell and of changing the structure of a protein molecule with laser knives. One of these knives has already been used to destroy a small tumor in a patient's retina. Laser research projects are being conducted by more than 400 firms and universities. General Electric Company research engineers produced in 1962 a laser which emits "visible light in the red region of the spectrum," and they "hope to build lasers which will convert ordinary electric current into white light with a high degree of efficiency," opening up the prospect that the "lamp of the future may be a speck of metal the size of a pencil-point which will be practically indestructible, will never burn out, and will convert at least ten times as much current into light as does today's bulb."[16]

The obvious comment is that industry in the sixties is so research- and innovation-minded that it has no fear of inventing new devices that will kill the demand for present products. This was certainly not true of even the recent past. Howard Vincent O'Brien in his column, "All Things Considered," in a 1940 issue of the *Chicago Daily News,* told of his experiences around 1910 when he was a press agent for the telephone company:

> That great and austere corporation was deeply troubled. Invention had reared its horrid head, and a company had actually been formed to market what was conceded, by all sound and right-thinking men, to be a diabolical violation of 100 per cent Americanism and the sanctity of the home, not to speak of its definite aspersions on the virtue and the nobility of American womanhood.
>
> This viper, gnawing at the vitals of everything that had made this country what it was, and in particular, the telephone company, was nothing less than an instrument which operated without benefit of operators—namely, the *automatic.*
>
> That awe-inspiring phase, technological unemployment, had not yet been coined; but its spectre was all too plain. The automatic telephone not only jeopardized the investment of all who had staked their all on the eternal invention of Alexander Graham Bell, it would put thousands of earnest, hard-working young women, the sole support of countless widowed mothers, into breadlines.
>
> The system of free enterprise was faced by nothing less than a crisis; and in its desperation no aid was too lowly to be spurned. So it was that I found employment writing articles about the peril that lurked beneath the dial of an automatic telephone. Incredible, as I look back upon it, was the bilge I perpetrated—and got paid for. One masterpiece, printed in Sunday newspapers with lurid illustrations well splashed with red ink, was a story about a fire in the stockyards, with special emphasis on the heroic girls who stuck to their switchboards, warning the nation of its peril. Not too subtly, I pointed out that no automatic machine could be expected to act with such courage and resourcefulness. I gave the impression, if I did not say it, that once the automatic telephone wormed its way into the hearts of men, the peril of fire would be enormously increased.

[16] Harland Manchester: Light of Hope—or Terror? *The Reader's Digest,* February, 1963, pp. 97–100.

Great and small, shoulder to shoulder in the cause of sound economics, I and the telephone company labored to scotch this heresy before it left the world in smoking ruins. Early and late we hammered home to a lethargic people what would happen to them if they ever yielded to the blandishments of the automatic telephone. There were no communists then, but if there had been I am sure we would have connected the mechanical telephone operator with Moscow and disbelief in religion. It was a brave fight, but, as this sleek instrument at my elbow testifies, a futile one. Our heads bloody but unbowed, the telephone company and I had to retreat to positions previously prepared in the rear. . . . It is rather frightening to drag out these buried bones. It makes one wonder what new heresies may be battering at our gates now, what new defeats the conservatives have yet to swallow; but swallowed they must be—there is no end to progress.

Mr. O'Brien did not live to see the advent of Centrex, which would have inspired him to write a piece about this "new heresy," one which the telephone company itself is gleefully introducing to practically do away with the industrial and institutional switchboards and release more "heroic girls" to look for other jobs.

Wars and preparedness for other wars should they come have sparked the development of a considerable proportion of the new inventions, so that the activities of the military in initiating and employing them merit study. The Minutemen missile project was presented to the Air Force in 1958 by Bethlehem Steel Company and Paul Hardeman, Inc., after the idea had been conceived and the initial research completed by them and after hundreds of private firms had participated in and continued to work on its development. The development of electronically operated computers has been speeded by military and other governmental needs for rapid data processing and for guiding ballistics missiles.

Reversing the usual order of application of an industrial invention to medicine, Dr. Charles S. Gibson of Guy's Hospital, London, through his research work on gold compounds for the treatment of arthritis, discovered a way of coating fabrics, china, or glass with a thin film of pure gold at a low cost, thus making possible inexpensive cloth of gold and gold dinner services.

It is common practice to call in industrial geniuses for help with medical problems. The electronics expert, Percy Spencer, senior vice-president of the Raytheon Manufacturing Company, invented microwave diathermy equipment with the cooperation of the Mayo Clinic. Transistor medical-recording devices have been made so small that they can be swallowed. Adaptations are occurring constantly, by luck and by design.

Hospitals benefit indirectly by numerous industrial inventions. For example, patients in Memorial Hospital, New York, were not disturbed by the crane used in the construction of the new 12-story Sloan-Kettering Institute Laboratory in 1963. Instead of being diesel-powered and noisy like most cranes, this one, made in Sweden, is powered by electricity, and it operates inside the building itself instead of out on the sidewalk or road.

The institution's heating *and* refrigeration systems may be transformed by developments of the thermoelectric engine. Heat *or* cold can be put into a thermo-electric panel. Without motor, compressor, or other moving parts, and in complete silence, a refrigerator can be operated. Among the firms that are working on thermoelectric devices are Westinghouse, General Electric, Bell Telephone, and the Minnesota Mining and Manufacturing Company. Also active in the research is the Massachusetts Institute of Technology.

Doubtless the crowning achievement of American inventors in the early sixties is the Bell Telephone Laboratories' Telstar, first launched in 1962 at Bell System expense by the National Aeronautics and Space Administration for experiments in relaying telephone calls and television internationally. Six basic components were contributed by the private communications industry to make practical the eventual development of a world-wide satellite communications system—the transistor, the solar battery, the traveling wave tube, ruby masers, the wave guide, and new antennas for the ground stations with innovations in circuitry—all of which, according to a Bell advertisement, are "direct outgrowths of Bell System research and development." What tons of equipment are being and will be made obsolete by these technological advances!

It is well to realize that keeping up with the progress of invention takes study on an international scale. Telstar receiving stations have been built in England, France, Italy, and West Germany. Numerous developments have come out of industrial, governmental, and institutional research laboratories in every leading country. As Waldemar Kaempffert,[17] science editor of the *New York Times,* pointed out, "about 30 steamers, more or less successful, had been built" before Robert Fulton's *Clermont* "plowed the Hudson in 1807," William Symington in England having launched a paddle-wheel boat in 1787. Isaac de Rivas, a Swiss, patented a gas-driven car in France in 1807, and Lenoir of France built one in 1860; whereas George Selden in America secured his patents in 1879, four years after Siegfried Marcus began operating his gas-driven car in Vienna. Kaempffert states that of the numberless improvements in engineering since those of Daimler and Benz in Germany between 1883 and 1885, "very few can be credited to Americans." Four-wheel brakes, he says, are English, invented in 1904; "knee action came from the Frenchman Dubonnet (about 1932), though Lancia was using a similar principle ten years earlier"; the "straight-eight cylinder engine was introduced by Isotta-Fraschini in Italy and the V-type descends from that developed in France by De Dion and Bouton in 1913." Kaempffert adds that the "American car is American because of mass production methods and not because it is American in mechanical conception." He continues with many other examples, among them the invention by Thimonnier, of France, of the sewing machine "so good that, about 1830, Parisian workers broke it up," more than fifteen years before Elias Howe. The Scotch reaper antedated by 39 years Cyrus McCormick's reaper in America; Philip Reis of Germany sent music over a wire in 1861, 15 years before Bell; von Soemmering of Germany was telegraphing

[17] *The Readers' Digest,* December, 1936, pp. 45–48.

electrically in 1809, whereas Samuel F. B. Morse's invention did not appear until about 1837. The photoelectric cell was invented by two German physicists, Elster and Geitel; the Autogiro by the Spaniard, Cierva; the Diesel engine by the German, Rudolf Diesel.

The progress of invention is accompanied for most people by a feeling of nostalgia for at least some aspects of the past, well expressed by the following:[18]

> Within five to ten years, say Canadian officials, the lighthouse keeper may vanish from the scene along the coast of Nova Scotia.
>
> Automatic devices are taking over the traditionally romantic task of maintaining the beacons, whose shafts of light stab deep into the fog and dark of night to guide the sailor around the rocks and bars.
>
> Gone then, too, will be the joke, hoary with age, about the advertisement for light housekeeping.
>
> More than 200 lights dot the Nova Scotia coast line from the northern tip of Cape Breton southward to Barrington passage. Somehow it seems it could never be the same, without a human presence there beneath the flashing eye, which science cannot teach to care.

For a final note on the fantastic possibilities of automation in the future, there is the prediction by some traffic experts that electronic devices in the road and the automobile could take over the driving, making accidents impossible.

Skepticism about any invention is fading in the light of the unbelievable ones that are coming into practical use almost every day. Edison in 1906 brushed off the idea of wireless telegraphy just a few months before Lee DeForest's test of his first radio telephone was heard by wireless operators on ships near the Atlantic Coast. The airplane became a reality notwithstanding the proof offered by Lord Kelvin that it was an impossibility by the laws of physics.

SERVICE BUSINESSES

A wide variety of outside services are available to the hospital administrator who goes exploring. When staff is hard to get and to retain, when labor problems seem insurmountable, when space for certain operations is inadequate, when equipment becomes obsolete, and for several other reasons, these services may be a valuable resource.

Food service is probably the most obvious area to cover by this means. It may be taken over completely except for the therapeutic dietetic service, or it may be limited to certain functions such as purchasing or management. There are concerns which will conduct surveys, train the kitchen personnel, and make recommendations for improvement without taking over any part of the operation except perhaps temporarily as a demonstration. Dispensing services are also to be considered, from coffee and other drinks, toasted sandwiches, and desserts, to hot plate dinners. Generally the latter type of service is confined to personnel and visitors.

[18] Editorial in a 1962 issue of the *Decatur* (Illinois) *Herald* headed "Nobody Keeping the Lighthouse."

Housekeeping and maintenance services are contracted for by many hospitals. A few of the concerns in this business go outside the regular housekeeping and maintenance services and take over such functions as operating elevators, gardening, exterminating, and guard duty. Some of them furnish all of the personnel; others train and supervise personnel who are employees of the institution.

Laundering is another area in which the possibility exists of contracting for service, even to the extent of linen supply.

Certain concerns will come in and take over—or take out—the office procedures, the degree of delegation varying with the wishes and needs of the client. Small business firms have the same problem as small hospitals in deciding how much automation they can afford. Computer service centers seem to offer the best solution for both. Some of these centers are equipped to take over the entire data-processing function for a client.

Leasing of equipment, instruments, and furnishings is another service which industrial concerns are offering medical service institutions. They list as advantages the conservation of working capital, the preservation of existing credit, the overcoming of budget limitations, the avoidance of obsolescence, acquisition of equipment a hospital needs but could not afford to purchase, and additional income.

So closely is the hospital tied in with all industry that almost any manufacturer and supplier can be considered to have a service value if the administrator will study the business world around him and learn how to capitalize on the resources offered.

In a 1963 advertisement directed especially to the hospital field, the Bell Telephone System, picturing a man carrying a briefcase, urges: "Add this specialist to your staff—but not to your payroll" and continues:

> In his bag are remedies for hospital management problems: improving patient care, controlling costs, streamlining the practices of your administrative staff and the medical team.
>
> He's a Bell System Communications Consultant who can put greater efficiency and economy into all phases of your communications . . . internal and external . . . voice, data or written.
>
> He can show you that many hospital problems are really communications problems. And he can offer practical solutions.
>
> Let him start by studying your needs. Just call your Bell Telephone Business Office and ask for your Communications Consultant.

A manufacturer of parenteral solutions, which were first commercially prepared in 1928, prior to which all hospitals made their own and some still do, advertises in 1963:

> Our roots go back to men who pioneered ideas. We, too, will pioneer ideas. We will be innovators. Our lifeblood . . . and yours . . . lies in improved products and methods for better patient care, in technological advance . . . Products, however, are only part of the McGraw system. Service to you is another vital part.

From an advertisement in *Canadian Hospital*:

Your Onan man will work with you—without obligation—to help determine *how much* standby power is really needed. And don't be surprised if he recommends less than you had thought necessary. He'll recommend the best fuel and best cooling system for your particular building. He'll work with you to find the ideal location in the building for the installation. . . . He'll be there at start-up, back for run-in checks. But more important, your Onan distributor will always be only a phone call away, whenever your installation needs service.

The Linde Company, Division of Union Carbide Corporation, advertises:

We're ready to advise you at any time on your intensive care facility—its planning, alteration, installation, or operation. And Linde advice is unexcelled because of our long experience in matters pertaining to oxygen therapy.

The hospital administrator cannot keep up with advances in and possibilities of hospital equipment and supplies, but he can learn which industrial organizations stand back of their products and give reliable advice and service. Many companies and their representatives derive the same satisfaction that members of hospital staffs do in feeling that they are making important contributions to patient welfare and medical progress. This spirit in industry should be encouraged by considering them as a vital part of the hospital team.

BUSINESS ASSOCIATIONS

Among the business associations that are closely related to hospitals are the American Surgical Trade Association, the Manufacturers Surgical Trade Association, the European Surgical Trade Association, and the Hospital Industries' Association.

The American Surgical Trade Association was organized in 1902. There were only a very few surgical supply dealers before that time. In the 1960's there are nearly 350 members in the United States, Canada, and Puerto Rico. There is also one European member, the Lameris Instrument Company of Utrecht, The Netherlands. The members of the association employ some 3,500 salesmen. The association publishes a *Manufacturers' Directory* in which are listed 1,500 companies which sell their products mainly through hospital supply dealers. The dealers cite as advantages to the customer the convenience of local contact with salesmen who are trained technicians and with their service departments and servicemen. Another publication of the association is *The A.S.T.A. Journal*.

The European Surgical Trade Association was formed in 1960 by a group of European surgical supply dealers. One of the founding members was D. C. Lameris, Sr., president of the Lameris Instrument Company of Utrecht, the only European member of the American Surgical Trade Association. Mr. Lameris died at the age of 82 in 1961. He founded the company fifty years earlier.

The Manufacturers Surgical Trade Association adopted in 1962 a product quality pledge to give hospitals "as close to product quality perfection as possible."

The work of the National Better Business Bureau should be studied. This is a nonprofit organization created by business to protect itself and its customers from advertising and selling practices which are fraudulent, misleading or unfair. Its chief objectives are (1) to discourage and eliminate from the buyer-seller relationship practices which cause legitimate consumer complaints; and (2) to strive for better consumer satisfaction by encouraging accurate representation of products, securities, and services. Local complaints are handled by local bureaus, or, in communities which do not have them, by chambers of commerce. Financing is through membership subscriptions of business firms and organizations.

HEALTH SERVICE IN INDUSTRY

A two-way relationship of primary importance may be built up between hospitals and businesses, to the advantage of both, by cooperation in promoting the health of executives and workers. This involves more than arrangements for hospitalization and outpatient services in emergencies. It embraces such activities as health education talks to executive and labor groups, research on health hazards in industry as revealed in medical treatment of employees, aid in setting up medical departments, promotion of community projects that contribute to health, joint action in cooperating with public health authorities to combat air and water pollution and to enforce pure food laws—the list of possibilities is endless.

The health of the worker has been a concern of industry for a long time. Besides the humanitarian aspects, it came to be realized that health affected labor turnover, absenteeism, accidents, initiative, efficiency, and attitude, and that in order to have good workmen the employer needed to maintain a healthy environment not only in his establishment but in the community insofar as he was able to wield an influence.

The use of statistics was one of the first devices to arouse interest in the health of the worker. In 1842 Edwin Chadwick, lawyer-secretary to the Poor Law Commissioners, presented to the Secretary of State for the Home Department his famous *Survey into the Sanitary Condition of the Labouring Classes of Great Britain*. His survey had been preceded by John Howard's prison report in 1777 and later reports by Drs. Arnott, Kay, Southwood Smith, and Kay-Shuttleworth, but he gave statistical proof of the conditions which the others had described. His figures showed that the death rate fell when surface pollution of well water was prevented and when drainage was installed. They also showed that in the dark and stuffy workshops in London, tailors died ten years earlier than those who worked in better lighted and ventilated workrooms in small towns, although wages were lower in those towns. And they showed that half of the children of the laborer and servant class died before the age of 5, whereas the gentry lost only one-fifth of their children before that age. In the pleasant city of Carlisle the average life expectancy was 38, while in the crowded dock and manufacturing city of Liverpool it was only 17.

In the United States a number of industries established hospitals for their employees. Most of these were railroads. A few of them are still in existence. The Southern Pacific General Hospital in San Francisco, established in 1869, now has 450 beds. In general, however, industries have confined their medical services to health departments and have established affiliations with community hospitals.

Dr. Malcolm T. MacEachern[19] gave the following account of the relationship between the railroads and the American College of Surgeons with respect to hospital standardization:

In the year 1920 the American Railway Association formed a medical and surgical section made up of medical and surgical chiefs of the various member railroads. One of the first actions of that section was to appoint a Committee on Hospital Standardization. This was done because the railroads felt that it was imperative that their employees injured in service get the best possible care and treatment. Through its chairman, Dr. A. F. Jonas, of the Union Pacific Railroad, the Committee on Hospital Standardization made the following recommendation:

"The Medical and Surgical Section Committee on Hospital Standardization had a meeting at Chicago on April 6, 1921, in accordance with its understanding of its purpose. The Committee has adopted the Minimum Standard of the American College of Surgeons as the basic recommendations for the railroads of the Association."

The recommendation of the committee was accepted. It was submitted to the various members of the sections, unanimously approved, submitted on November 16 at the annual sessions of the American Railway Association, and approved as a practical policy to be followed by the member railroads.

At the time this action was taken, Dr. Daniel Z. Dunott of Baltimore was chairman of the Medical and Surgical Section of the Association. In interpreting its significance at the 1921 Clinical Congress of the American College of Surgeons at Philadelphia, he said:

"This will mean that railroads through their surgical service will take the position that they will have their men treated in hospitals that meet the Minimum Standard of the American College of Surgeons. You appreciate, as well as I, that a large amount of our work is of an emergency character and that, therefore, we cannot always be choosey. There will be times when we shall have to put men in a hospital that has not adopted the Minimum Standard for Hospitals, but it is our intention, wherever it is practicable, to remove those patients from such hospitals and put them in a hospital having the Minimum Standard just as soon as consistent with the safety of the patient. I do not know but that it is a pretty good thing to follow that up even a little bit closer than that. I am sure that in a number of instances the transportation of a man seriously injured—crushed leg, we shall say—for a greater distance to a better hospital would be giving that man a greater opportunity for recovery than putting him in a hospital that was not up to the Standard in its work."

You will see from this quotation how enthusiastic the doctors . . . were over the idea of standardized hospitals. The action of the American Railway Associa-

[19] *The Railroad Journal*, August, 1944, pp. 39–40, 67–69.

tion, of course, helped to promote Hospital Standardization because, as Dr. Dunott said, there were in the railroads about 13,000 doctors serving as physicians and surgeons, and about 2,750 or 2,800 of them were members of the surgical staffs of hospitals. At that time the Baltimore and Ohio Railroad was using about 310 hospitals; the Pennsylvania Railroad, about 277; and the Union Pacific, about 123. It was Dr. Dunott's estimate that altogether the railroads were using in greater or less degree four fifths of the hospitals of the country. Some of these hospitals were directly under their control and these were immediately brought up to standard in those cases in which there were deficiencies. With other hospitals the railroads had contracts and these also were requested to comply with the requirements. The remainder received a tremendous incentive to improve their service through the position taken by the Railway Association recommending the use of approved hospitals.

Growing out of this relationship with the railroads was an approval program for all medical services in industry, which the college began in 1928 at the suggestion of the Dr. Dunott mentioned in the quotation. The program was preceded by a two-year study of the need for better organization and service in caring for the ill and injured in industry and for elimination or control of industrial health hazards. The study was made by a committee on industrial medicine and traumatic surgery consisting of representatives of the college, of medical departments of insurance carriers, and of other industrial organizations. The committee formulated a Minimum Standard for Medical Service in Industry, acceptance and maintenance of which was entirely voluntary, and published for the guidance of industrial organizations a manual, *Medical Services in Industry and Workmen's Compensation Laws.*

The approval program, which has since been discontinued, implanted the idea of high standards in the organization and operation of a medical service. On the medical side this purpose is being furthered through the activities of the Council on Occupational Health of the American Medical Association, the American Academy of Occupational Medicine, the American Board of Preventive Medicine, the Industrial Medical Association, the American Association of Railway Surgeons, the American Industrial Hygiene Association, the American Association of Industrial Nurses, the American Association of Industrial Dentists, the Occupational Health Branch of the Public Health Service, and others.

This has become, as the list shows, a highly organized field. The medical specialty of occupational medicine was started by a woman physician early in the twentieth century. Dr. Alice Hamilton studied and publicized the dangers of carbon monoxide in steel mills; mercurial fixes in hat factories; fumes in a paint factory; aniline dyes; and TNT. Laws and labor-management regulations were results of her findings.

Sixty-five million persons compose the industrial population of the United States. More than 5,000 full-time and 20,000 part-time physicians, and many thousands of nurses, technicians, and other aides, are on the staffs of medical services in industry. The preventive aspects of their work in particular have far-reaching effects upon families and communities. Of companies that employ 5,000 or more workers, nine out of ten have medical departments, and almost every large concern makes some provision for referral service if it does not have its own department.

Mental Health of the Worker

Intense activity is going on in the prevention of mental disease in industry. The very existence of medical service in a plant is believed to have considerable influence in checking mental breakdowns. Employees, including executives, will unburden their emotional problems to a doctor or nurse when they would never confide in a superior officer. The release of tension which follows just talking about problems to someone who is understanding may result in cure, and sometimes the interviewer can have something done to remove the cause of the worker's frustration. A less monotonous job may be found for one who chafes at too repetitive a task. A change in departments may be possible for one whose personality clashes with that of his foreman or department head.

Hospital administrators may well take note of the following statements made by Dr. Ralph T. Collins,[20] psychiatric consultant, Eastman Kodak Company, in opening a discussion of mental health in the industrial setting at the National Health Forum held in Chicago in March, 1959:

> Emotional illnesses cause more absenteeism from work than any other illness except the common cold.
>
> Eighty to ninety per cent of dismissals today are attributed to social incompetence, the inability to get along with people. Ten to twenty per cent of dismissals are defined as technical incompetence.
>
> One of four workers, or 16 million of 65 million, manifest personality disturbances through absenteeism, accidents, alcoholism, illness, job dissatisfactions, or trouble with co-workers and supervisors.
>
> Off-the-job stresses loom large in the causation of on-the-job dissatisfactions, ineffectiveness, poor work habits, ineffectual relations, and faulty attitudes.
>
> The cost to industry of the disruption resulting from emotional disturbances among workers, supervisors, and executives runs into hundreds of millions of dollars annually.
>
> Leadership in the office and factory is a vital force in the promotion and preservation of mental health in the environment of the worker at any level.
>
> If he is to be a good leader, the health of the executive must be conserved, and yet today there are many pressures, frustrations, fears, and feelings of insecurity in his life. Consider the titles of some recent articles in business and popular magazines relating to the hazards of being an executive, such as "Slow Up or Blow Up," "Your Next Promotion Can Kill You," and "Must Executives Die Young?"

A business corporation has contracted with a psychiatric unit at Mount Sinai Hospital, New York, at an annual fee, for psychiatric services to emotionally

---

[20] *Pub. Health Rep.*, August, 1959, p. 703.

disturbed employees. The project is being used for research purposes to determine the possibility of including psychiatric services in the Health Insurance Plan of Greater New York.

The Chicago Association of Commerce and Industry and the Chicago Committee on Alcoholism sponsor an annual "Alcoholism in Industry" conference with the cooperation of the Central States Society of Industrial Medicine and Surgery and some ten other organizations. In the announcement stating the reasons for industry's concern with the alcoholism problem these statements are made:

> An estimated half of the 5,000,000 alcoholic men and women in the United States are currently employed in business and industry.
> Total cost of alcoholism in industry runs to over a billion dollars a year, largely hidden from view at present.
> Alcoholic employees are found at all levels: executives, engineers, production line workers and office employees.

Accidents and Disasters

In United States industry each year there are some four million accidental injuries, about 2,000 of them resulting in death. Although these figures sound large, they represent a better than 30 per cent decline since 1940. A 46 per cent decline in industrial injuries and diseases and nearly 50 per cent reduction in workmen's compensation and other insurance payments were achieved in the same period by companies which had health programs. And the factory is safer than the home!

In establishing the National Safety Council in 1913, industry made a tremendous contribution to the prevention of accidents. Its services are available to everybody, including, of course, hospitals. Using statistics as one of its weapons, it stimulates precautionary measures to cut down the accident toll. Its educational activities are likewise most effective. Every major field of industry is represented by a section, all of them meeting together in the great annual National Safety Congress, which throws the limelight for the public on safe practices.

Information and assistance with safety programs are also available from insurance companies, the National Fire Protection Association, Underwriters Laboratories, the National Board of Fire Underwriters, Factory Mutual Laboratories, the American Standards Association, state industrial commissions and trade associations. The National Board of Fire Underwriters is an association of capital stock fire insurance companies. Among its publications are two which are especially for hospitals, *Hospital Operating Rooms* and *Fire Safe Hospitals*. The latter covers new hospital construction, improving existing buildings, fire hazards and their safeguards in new and existing buildings, fire protection facilities in new and existing hospitals, fire drills, and rules for safety in case of fire. The American Hospital Association has published a manual on fire emergency programs. The National Fire Protection Association has a committee on hospitals and prepares standards concerning fire safety in hospitals, including the use of flammable anesthetics in operating rooms and emergency electrical systems.

The Committee on Trauma of the American College of Surgeons through a subcommittee on industrial relations, on which the Congress of Industrial Organizations, the American Federation of Labor, and the United Mine Workers are represented, formulated "Principles for Rehabilitation of the Injured Worker," clause 5 of which reads in part:

> Rehabilitation and restoration to gainful employment of the injured worker must begin with first aid and continue through the period of disability. . . . The physician must bring to bear on these problems all the skills and disciplines that science and society can offer, and utilize all community resources which can assist him in the accomplishment of these objectives.

Industry is assuming its share in preparation for disaster and civil defense. The American Medical Association's Council on Occupational Health published in 1961 a guide, in the form of a questionnaire along with certain information, to aid medical departments of industries in developing disaster plans.

Rehabilitation in Industry

Injuries and illness frequently leave disabilities. Industry is furnishing some rehabilitation services and is helping to support others.

The Liberty Mutual Insurance Company, which writes a substantial volume of workmen's compensation, operates rehabilitation centers. This activity began in the 1940's when the company established a pilot clinic in Boston with the aim of restoring the worker whenever possible to a working status. Experience in this clinic disclosed the tragedy of starting rehabilitation too late. Hospitals were urged to establish rehabilitation services. Many of them have done so in rendering physical therapy and in some cases occupational therapy service, but full service in vocational rehabilitation is difficult for most hospitals to give and is provided mostly in separate centers. The Veterans Administration hospitals are an exception. In them complete rehabilitation service has been established with most encouraging results.

Many patients continue to seek or be referred to rehabilitation services too late to be greatly improved by the treatment. This is an area in which hospitals owe industry much more cooperation than most of them are giving.

In Toronto, Canada, the Workmen's Compensation Board of Ontario operates a hospital and rehabilitation center, including a vocational rehabilitation department, which constitute a total rehabilitation facility. The hospital section accommodates 180 beds for convalescent patients and has a clinic treatment area for physical and occupational therapy and remedial gymnastics. The clinic area has dormitory accommodation for 340 patients and locker accommodation for 60 outpatients. No major surgery is performed. Most patients come for treatment of injuries although a few are admitted for industrial diseases and medical conditions.

Placement of the handicapped is a problem that cannot be separated from that of the treatment of the injured workman. Frequently he cannot do the work required in his old job, and there may be no other place for him in his former company. A few industries have been formed for the specific purpose of employing the handicapped. They have demonstrated that the handicapped worker is usually efficient and thoroughly reliable and that a business that employs such workers can prosper. Other firms are discovering the same thing, and some are adopting a deliberate policy of employing a certain proportion of handicapped workers.

The President's Committee on Employment of the Physically Handicapped, established in 1947 by President Roosevelt, conducts an intensive educational campaign which has been a large factor in the success of the movement. Laws have had an effect also. Originally workmen's compensation laws made employers responsible for the total disabilities of workers who had had prior handicaps. Laws are now being passed by many of the states under which a "second injury fund" is set up to limit the employer's liability to injuries suffered while in his employ.

The Office of Vocational Rehabilitation of the Department of Health, Education and Welfare has also been a potent force in arousing interest in employment of the rehabilitated worker.

Labor Unions and the Worker's Health

The International Ladies' Garment Workers' Union established in 1913 a health center for its members. It was thirty years before another union established a similar project, and this has since been discontinued.

In 1942 the War Labor Board ruled, at a time when wages were frozen, that a welfare plan agreed upon by the employer and union would not be considered a wage increase if the cost did not exceed 5 per cent of the payroll. Since that time fringe benefits have become as important as wages in negotiations between labor and management, and the unions have been quite active in promoting health insurance and health services for their members.

The United Mine Workers of America pays physicians and hospitals directly for services rendered its members and their families. The United Automobile Workers,[21] which established the second union health center in 1943, later closed it and adopted the policy of paying for services through a local hospital. Local units of the International Ladies' Garment Workers' Union have health

[21] Name changed in 1962 to United Automobile, Aerospace and Agricultural Workers of America.

centers in some dozen cities, one of which, in Harrisburg, Pennsylvania, provides diagnostic services by means of a mobile unit.

Through collective bargaining agreements, employers contribute to the health centers.

New Hazards

The atomic age is creating new hazards for employees in industries and in hospitals. Hospitals have a dual concern—dangers to their own staff and treatment of patients referred by industry.

The Public Health Service is actively investigating such hazards as radioactive contamination in uranium mines, bronchogenic carcinoma being one of the causes of an excessive number of deaths. The New York Institute of Industrial Medicine is emphasizing chemical and radiological toxicological problems that are encountered in many phases of the atomic energy industry. In agriculture and medicine as well as in industry, the use of radioactive materials necessitates profound study of the effects upon the personnel who work with them. Protective clothing is one of the essential elements in protecting the worker.

The problems are summarized in different ways by two authorities. First, Dr. Harold J. Magnuson,[22] chief of the Occupational Health Branch of the Public Health Service, states:

> Because of its growing influence, automation deserves serious scrutiny from the standpoint of worker health. One of the most immediate problems coming to our attention is, in some instances, that of greater exposure to noise, resulting from the greater use of electrical motors and equipment in the factory. More nervous strain may also be expected from the character of automatic operations. The effect of errors is more serious, the responsibility of the maintenance worker is higher, and machines are more complex. Eye attention is also intensified by the concentration and close work and the focus on control dials, lights, and panels. As the need lessens for physical effort by workers tending automatic machines, a growth of the health problems associated with the sedentary worker may be expected. We may also expect psychological hazards to the worker from isolation, boredom, and even from increased leisure. . . . Figures reflecting the growth of the chemical industry stagger the imagination. Consider, for example, that there are 500,000 distinct chemical compounds in use in industrial production, all but a few hundred of them unknown on this earth 20 years ago. . . . Continuous study and vigilance are required to determine their health effects and develop means for their control.

Dr. Robert A. Kehoe,[23] director of the Kettering Laboratory, Department of Preventive Medicine and Industrial Health, College of Medicine, University of Cincinnati, declares:

> The threats visited upon our working population and upon our industrial society generally by the technological revolution are serious, are increasing in

[22] Anticipating Safety and Health Needs. *Pub. Health Rep.,* January, 1960, pp. 69–70.
[23] Occupational Medicine and Public Health. *Pub. Health Rep.,* July, 1961, p. 647.

number and type, and are unfathomed and currently unfathomable by the available medical and hygienic resources that are brought to bear upon them. This is not to indulge in harsh criticism, or to suggest that physicians, medical investigators, and medical educators have been idle or irresponsible. On the contrary, the achievements of our contemporary medical leaders and colleagues have been notable. But it must be recorded and granted that their attention has been directed toward the further understanding of the older and more familiar as well as the more baffling forms of human disease and toward their therapy, rather than toward the recognition, elucidation, and control of the new threats which have been multiplied around us in our places of work and elsewhere by the inventive genius of our intensely curious, industrious, and venturesome technologists.

CHAPTER 12

The Place of the Hospital in the Business World

Business and industry have largely replaced the individual
benefactors in the matter of hospital finance. Unfortunately,
business and industry have too often been used only as a
source of funds, a pocketbook, a means to fill the hospital
coffers; but seldom have they been chosen as partners to help
plan, to extend to the hospital their resources of organization
and management techniques. . . . Business and industry
have at least three broad and deep concerns in the hospital
field: (1) Assurance of good facilities for employees; (2) The
desire that these services be provided as inexpensively as
possible; (3) A desire for economy in expansion programs,
since they are often called upon to meet the major portion of
the expenditure. . . . Business is not only prepared to invest
a priceless asset in the future hospital care of its community
by virtue of participation in planning, but wants to become
a part of, and not apart from, the movement.
NATHAN J. STARK[1]

HERE WE have a sharp expression of the need for the administrator to
appreciate that while he has an obligation to project himself and his institution
into the life of the community, he has also an obligation to bring the community in—"a part of, and not apart from" the actual *planning,* something far
beyond giving them tours and the opportunity to look around. This is a difficult

[1] Industry Wants to Help Plan As Well As To Pay. *Trustee,* December, 1956, pp. 11–15. Mr.
Stark is a member of the Board of Directors of the Kansas City Area Hospital Association and vice-
president of the Rival Manufacturing Company, Kansas City.

assignment. It is likely to bring interference along with cooperation. The businessman in particular is critical of hospitals. He thinks he could run them much better than whoever is running them now. In some respects he probably could, and that fact needs to be accepted and capitalized upon. The future of hospitals may even depend upon administration's use of the businessman's know-how and the development of its own business acumen. That future also depends, however, upon administration's success in showing the industrialist, by patient teaching, the differences between the methods that best achieve high production of manufactured goods and those that best promote the recovery of sick and injured people.

Applying time study to nursing—well, let Janet M. Geister,[2] in a letter to the editor of *Hospitals,* explode in well-justified wrath:

> According to the *National Observer* (Aug. 13, 1962), efficiency engineers studying methods in a California hospital have learned that a good back rub can be given in three minutes. As a nurse who practiced in the old days when our only stopwatch was the patient's comfort and safety, I would like to know:
>
> 1. How many seconds are allowed to get the patient into position for his rub: (a) the man who's just had abdominal surgery, (b) the one with a broken leg, (c) the 225 pounder?
>
> 2. What areas are included in the good back rub? The tired elbows? The aching buttocks? The tight neck? Or just the straight up and down?
>
> 3. What technique is best? The fast to-and-fro sloshing on of a lotion? Or is there time for a little massage that gets at the deep-down weariness?
>
> 4. How many seconds are allowed to get the patient back into a comfortable position? To puff up his pillows? To tighten the draw-sheet? To fix the shade and find his glasses? To answer a question or two? Or does another worker come in to take care of these things?

Here it must be interposed that the efficiency engineers are not running business yet, any more than they are hospitals. Theirs has been a magnificent contribution to methods improvement, but some have gone too far in applying the principles of Taylor and his successors, and business managers have learned to use judgment in implementing their recommendations. Studies tend to show that the heads of business who are succeeding the entrepreneurs in the "managerial revolution" have come up mostly through the sales and personnel branches. The inference is that in business as in hospitals, skills in human relations are the ones that speed men to the top and keep them there. Nevertheless, there must be full consciousness of the fact that this is an age of automation, that the designers of machines are its stars, and that engineering skills, both mechanical and efficiency, are vital elements in the successful operation of every business and institution.

A hospital is not a business unless it is operated for profit. It belongs in the business world because to be operated effectively it must employ many of the methods of business. In some instances it extracts no fees for service and operates

[2] October 16, 1962, p. 34.

purely as a consumer, from a business point of view. Industry recognizes the importance of medical service institutions as buyers—*Dun's Review and Modern Industry* recently published an article on "How to Sell the $30 Billion Health Market." Hospitals alone expend nearly a third of this amount, including nearly $7 billion for wages. Approximately 1,763,000 persons are employed in hospitals, and an incalculable number are engaged in supplying them services and products. Total assets were $19,980,000 in 1962. Admissions increased from 15,675,000 reported by 6,125 hospitals in 1946 to 26,531,000 reported by 7,028 hospitals in 1962. Births reported by the same hospitals increased from 2,135,327 to 3,857,626.[3]

These figures are often interpreted to place hospitals in the realm of big business, because in the aggregate they pose a gigantic problem of management. In the singular, especially down at the bottom of the scale in size—the 62.9 per cent which have less than 100 beds and which give 20 per cent of the total patient days of care—they present undoubtedly one of the most perplexing of all management situations. Unlike the small business, the small hospital does not represent simplification; ways must be devised to give its patients as nearly as possible the same variety and quality of care that the large hospital provides. People cannot be classified down to homogenous units. They present the same physical and mental complexities wherever they may be.

Financial transactions with patients are quite unlike any dealings with customers and patrons by commercial concerns and service industries. The business department here becomes involved in the nonbusiness aspects of the hospital, its primary scientific and social objectives. The hospital bill seems to be one which people most dislike to pay. Unless some dramatic improvement in health has resulted, they feel that they have nothing to show for their money. The hospital experience is related in their minds usually to pain, distress, and loss of income. They do not understand the intricacies of the behind-the-scenes activities which figured in their treatment. A special kind of human relations skill is needed for the delicate task of keeping the good will of the patient while persuading him to settle his account.

Another difference concerned with the business aspects of patient care is the fact that if a hospital should show a substantial surplus of income from patients over expenditures in an annual statement, even in the case of a private for-profit institution, this would be tantamount to admitting that insufficient consideration was given to improvements and projects for the benefit of the patient. If the ledger shows a balance on the black side, the nonprofit hospital must utilize it for research, education, and improvements. Using a surplus presents no problem! The advances in medical science and in technology must be translated quickly into practice, and the changes involved in doing so are expensive. Their cost cannot be offset by increased or streamlined production as in a factory. A few, such as office machines, will lower labor costs, but most of them seem to be steps in an ever more expensive array of equipment necessary

[3] Statistics from the 1963 "Guide Issue," p. 448.

to give the patient the benefit of the latest means of promoting his recovery and delaying to the utmost possible limit his death.

Of course, the basic, baffling difference between hospitals and industry is their individualism, their lack of coordination. The costs of the services which in the aggregate hospitals provide are comparable in dollar volume with those of service industries—railroads, airlines, telephone, electric or gas companies. What is not comparable is control over operations, income, and expenditures. The transportation, communications, and power industries consist of huge, superbly organized systems coordinated to a high degree of efficiency and economy. But there is no hospital system. Hospitals compete to a degree no longer tolerated in commercial service organizations. Arrangements for exchange of costly equipment or for transfer of patients when a given hospital lacks certain therapeutic facilities are rare; each, with a pride of ownership, wants its own. Businessmen in general cannot understand this, although when they become members of hospital boards they sometimes are the greatest promoters of making *their* hospital the *best*. Tradition is the cause of this. It must go, like other outworn policies and practices. There is a remedy—regional planning with teeth in it—as will be discussed in a later chapter. Such planning must also include voluntary and public health organizations of all kinds, whose duplicating and overlapping operations are tragically wasteful, in view of other woefully under-met needs.

Adapting to New Developments

Among the many new business developments that hospitals should study is the rise of the shopping center. They numbered around 100 in 1953 compared with 5,000 ten years later, with a business volume of around $60 billion, about a fourth of the total retail sales in the United States. Some include medical centers; more are likely to do so. At Northland, near Detroit, medical diagnostic service, eye examinations, and dental work can be combined with the shopping tour. At Old Orchard near Chicago is a doctors' office building, and a short distance away a new hospital has been built.

The shopping center industry is organized too; there is an International Council of Shopping Centers, Inc. Canada, Australia, England, Sweden, Argentina, are among the nations that are building large shopping complexes. The large, attractive center at Rotterdam, in The Netherlands, has arisen on part of the area that was destroyed by German bombers at the end of the war.

New ideas in banking service need to be watched. An example is payroll processing which enables an organization to handle its payroll with a single check, the bank then crediting the accounts of the employees with the amounts due them. Several large banks furnish such a service, and an increasing number of companies are using it with certain variations to suit their own needs. The

American Banking Association declares that firms benefit by reducing payroll processing costs, saving time in distributing checks or money, lessening holdup risks as well as burglary and forgery, and improving employee relations.

Automation and methods improvement demand judgment in their application to hospitals—a kind of decision making that is somewhat different from that which the industrial manager would employ. The title of an article by the architect E. Todd Wheeler[4] gives the keynote: "Base Line for Evaluating Automatic Equipment—Is It Good for the Patient?" The industrialist seldom has to think of the customer when he installs machines to increase his production and cut his costs. Mr. Wheeler avers that there are two sides to the automation question, because

> ... our machines, whether electrical or mechanical, are in all respects still far inferior to the human mind. We must take care not to be awed by what appears to be the amazing complexity in a machine, when in fact it is relatively crude. The most complicated computer we have yet devised is a technical idiot compared to the mind of a child, and its best work is far inferior in complexity to what goes on subconsciously in the child's mind each time he finds his mouth with a spoonful of breakfast food. This point is important in helping us to avoid the temptation of relinquishing to the machine those processes that human beings can do better. Being lazy, we will want to do just that at the first opportunity. Instead, we should use the machine for what it can do better than we, which is much, and let automation sharpen our minds rather than dull them. . . . The best psychotherapy in the world continues to be that contact between individuals which involves forces of the spirit, whether within or without man, in the interests of healing. Thus far we have produced no machine or automatic system endowed with that unfathomable quality we call spirit.

Operations research is another industrial activity which hospitals need to adopt selectively. It is not a new concept but it is rather new in name and in the zeal with which it is being pushed. The name and the development began in the United Kingdom during World War II. The definition, as given by G. W. Churchman, R. L. Ackoff, and E. L. Arnoff,[5] is: "Operations research is the application of scientific methods, techniques, and tools to problems involving the operations of a system so as to provide those in control of the system with optimum solutions to problems."

The phases of operations research as given in their text are (1) formulating the problem; (2) construction of the mathematical model; (3) deriving a solution from the model; (4) testing the model and solution; (5) establishing controls over the solution; (6) putting the solution to work. The processes to which they are applicable are given as (1) inventory processes; (2) allocation processes; (3) waiting-time processes; (4) replacement processes; (5) competitive processes (to which the game theory is applied); and (6) combined processes, usually solved in sequence. In waiting-time processes queuing theory, sequencing theory,

[4] *Hospitals,* September 16, 1962.
[5] *Introduction to Operations Research.* New York, John Wiley and Sons, Inc., 1957.

and line-balancing theory are applied. That applications have not been limited to industry is shown by the literature.[6]

Operations research is conducted by teams of scientists, the members representing scientific and engineering disciplines.

Fund Raising

The problems of financing hospitals are quite different from those of financing businesses. The latter rely on banks and investment houses for loans and for floating stock and bond issues. Hospitals occasionally make loans and sell bonds, but most of their support comes from donors, and it takes special techniques to raise funds. When major financing is needed for new construction or modernization, usually professional fund-raising concerns are employed. Costs of a fund-raising campaign range between 4 and 9 per cent, including the fixed fee of professional counsel.

Fund raisers emphasize that to be successful, campaigns must be preceded by a record of good service, good personnel relations, high-caliber medical staff, high-quality board of trustees, and a continuous public relations program through which the work of the hospital has been made known to the community. Campaigns cannot stand alone. The hospital should be able to show that methods improvement is practiced, that waste is controlled, and that operation in general is efficient and economical. The ground must be paved before the campaign is started, and timing must be determined by circumstances in the particular community so as not to conflict with other fund drives or to be hampered by poor business conditions. Opinion surveys through house-to-house visits and questionnaires are generally used to test the climate for a campaign and to try to correct in advance any misunderstandings.

Although usually four-fifths of the total funds come from 8 per cent who give $1,000 or more, the most effort is expended on the 92 per cent who give small sums. It is generally agreed that the reward in personal interest and good will more than justifies the effort and that the fact must not be lost sight of that the small giver today may have more to give tomorrow.

At a conference at the University of Chicago sponsored in 1957 by the National Fund for Medical Education in cooperation with the International Harvester and United States Steel Foundations, Raymond Perry, vice-president of International Telephone and Telegraph Company, raised a question about an industry's right to make philanthropic donations out of stockholders' funds, however worthy and important the cause. The Hon. James B. Conant, former president of Harvard, then United States Ambassador to West Germany, replied that many industries justified substantial contributions to hospitals and medical

---

[6] *Modern Hospital* published in March, 1960, an article entitled, "How Queuing Theory Works in a Hospital," and there have been several other articles in hospital magazines. In 1962 Oxford University Press published for the Nuffield Provincial Hospitals Trust a volume by J. O. F. Davies *et al.*, entitled: *Toward a Measure of Patient Care: Operational Research in the Health Services.*

schools as an investment in the future health and stability of the community's population, including industry's customers and working force. "Your stockholders," he said, "have to pay the costs of these institutions either through industry or in taxes—the United States is the only country in which such institutions are supported substantially by nongovernment sources."

At the same meeting someone remarked that industries wanted to know that "the expansion program is not just institutional egotism," and Dr. W. Homer Turner, executive director of the United States Steel Foundation, said that hospitals bungle appeals for industry support. His criticisms, based on more than 100 appeals received from hospitals in the preceding six months with an average request of $500,000, were that the "appeals were usually phrased in vague, theoretical language; glittering generalizations about the hospital's teaching or research functions, and poorly organized presentations." He suggested sending able representatives prepared to discuss the facts.[7]

Certainly the impression upon the public, including industry, is good when those who work in the hospital contribute substantially to the fund. In the $4 million joint campaign of Research and Saint Joseph hospitals in Kansas City, Missouri, started in 1958, the physicians at Research were responsible for raising more than $375,000. With a goal of $68,000, employees of Baptist Memorial Hospital, Memphis, Tennessee, gave $94,400 in 1954. Similar examples are numerous.

By far the most exciting and pleasant event in hospital financing history occurred on December 11, 1955, when 3,500 privately supported tax-exempt hospitals received the following telegram:

> The trustees of the Ford Foundation have authorized a program of grants to assist the nation's voluntary non-profit hospitals in improving and extending their services to their respective communities. An announcement of the program will be released to the press at six P.M. Monday, December twelfth. I am pleased to inform you that we believe your hospital is among those eligible to receive a grant in the tentative amount of _____ under this program. Please make no (repeat no) public statement until after our announcement. A letter with full details will go forward to you shortly.

The amount of the grant was computed on the basis of the number of patient days total which does not reflect days of care to newborn infants, although recognition for this important hospital service was considered essential. A liberal range of possibilities was given for use of the funds, with the main restriction that they be used to improve or expand the hospital's services to its community rather than to finance day-to-day operations. The total gift was $200,000,000. Using its grant as a starting stimulus, a southern hospital launched a half-million dollar fund drive; a North Carolina hospital developed a nursing course in cooperation with a college; hospitals bought new equipment, installed automatic sprinkler systems, added new boiler rooms, established classroom facilities— countless improvements not provided for in the annual budget.

[7] *Mod. Hosp.*, April, 1957, p. 52.

Of course, trust funds must be administered wisely, invested for the highest safe return, and protected in every possible way, generally by agreement with the trust departments of banks. Provision must be made for continuity of investment policy despite changes in the personnel of the governing board. Frequently real estate is given to hospitals which is included in the trust agreement, and the bank with the advice and approval of the hospital renews leases and conducts other necessary transactions.

Besides donors, sources of income for hospitals consist of receipts from paying patients and from prepayment plans, payments from public and voluntary agencies for care of the indigent or clients, participation in community chest funds, and to a limited degree revenue from gift shops, coffee shops, and rental of offices to physicians in hospital-owned space or buildings. The last practice is increasing at a rapid pace as doctors and patients come to appreciate the convenience of the nearby or integrated location. The $5 million Professional Building of Memorial Hospital, Houston, Texas, completed in 1958, is an outstanding example of this trend which was started in 1928 by the Baptist Memorial Hospital, Memphis, when it erected the adjoining "P & S" Building to provide office space for 54 doctors under the hospital roof. In 1958 the Baptist Medical Building was added to provide offices for 58 more doctors. Some 1,000 hospitals now have similar buildings or have converted to offices existing space either inside the hospital or nearby.

Business concerns are quick to resent what they consider competition from hospitals in this kind of activity, but when benefits to the patient can be proved there can be no serious objection. The situation needs diplomatic handling, however. The dispensing of prescriptions to outpatients by hospital pharmacies has been labeled unfair competition by the American Pharmaceutical Association. Yet the convenience for the ailing patient should be justification of the practice.

A new way of financing hospital construction was made possible in Ohio by a law signed by the governor in 1955. It permits construction of new facilities by counties which then lease them to existing hospital boards for operation. The law stipulates that the lay boards will be responsible for full maintenance of the hospital and for its administration. The plans for new buildings or additions are to be submitted by the hospitals to a county commission which evaluates them from the standpoint of need and approves or hires the architects. The method was described by Delbert L. Pugh,[8] executive director, Columbus Hospital Federation.

Accounting and Statistics; Costs; Charges

Under the title "Sound Accounting: Master Key to Cost Control," Henry Amicarella,[9] administrator of Longmont, Colorado, Community Hospital, states:

[8] *Hospitals,* September 16, 1956; *Trustee,* September, 1956, pp. 23–26.
[9] Lead article. *Hospitals,* July 1, 1962.

In the absence of accurate and complete accounting practices, the administrator cannot exercise adequate control and direction. Accounting reports are invaluable management tools and, as such, are basic to internal control, cost analysis and financial forecasting. Costs must be known by the administrator if he is to effectively and adequately control and direct hospital function. Rising hospital costs, the greater interest now being shown by the general public, the trend in prepayment plans and cost formulas have made hospital boards and administrators aware of the inadequacy of individual accounting procedures and of the need for establishing a systematic program of accounting in conformity with accepted accounting principles and procedures. . . . Uniform accounting procedures are as important to smaller as to larger hospitals and must be given proper attention as an essential of good administrative control.

Uniform accounting has been preached and pushed by the American Hospital Association for many years. It first published a manual on accounting in 1922. Revisions and amplifications followed. In 1950 *Section 1 Handbook on Accounting, Statistics and Business Office Procedures for Hospitals* was published, superseded in 1959 by *Uniform Chart of Accounts and Definitions for Hospitals*. According to the preface to this manual, it is intended to serve as the basis for all accounting manuals published by the association, and publications such as *Bookkeeping Procedures and Business Practices for Small Hospitals* and *Cost Finding for Hospitals* "develop the recommended statistics and classification of accounts into systems and procedures for further use by hospitals."

In late 1962 came the announcement:[10] "The centralized accounting program of Hospital Administrative Services has been expanded nationally. At present, the program, which is affiliated with the American Hospital Association, is functioning in eight states as a project of the Hospital Research and Educational Trust." The announcement continues:

> Under the system, hospitals submit raw statistical information to H.A.S. which then prepares statements for individual hospitals and comparative reports for groups of hospitals.
> The expanded program was made possible by the grant from the W. K. Kellogg Foundation to the Hospital Research and Educational Trust (see Chapter 23).
> In addition to the expansion, a concentrated study in cost allocation will be made in Michigan during the three years of the grant. Its aim is to provide technics for centralized cost finding, budgeting and other accounting improvements. The Michigan Hospital Association and the Michigan Hospital Service (Blue Cross) will join the Kellogg Foundation in supporting the work in that state.
> Following the period of the grant, the program will become an A.H.A. service.

Despite the strong support which the association has given uniform accounting systems, and the impetus to comparative studies provided by such projects as this new one, there remains a deplorable lag in putting uniform accounting into practice. This is handicapping the entire field, not only the hospitals which

[10] *Hospitals,* October, 1962, p. 169.

do not conform. How can comparative costs be studied, how can actual costs be determined, if different hospitals use different classifications of accounts, different recording of similar transactions, and different application of accounting principles which are generally accepted, using the accrual basis? The need for uniformity has been brought to the fore by pressures from government agencies in connection with reimbursement for care of the indigent and from third-party payment agencies.

The hospital administrator must be sufficiently grounded in the principles of accounting and must be familiar enough with the outside resources available to help him so that he may be sure that his accounting system gives a true picture of his financial operations which enables him to make trustworthy comparisons with those of other hospitals.

Commercial insurance companies have made claim forms available. The Health Insurance Council in cooperation with the American Hospital Association developed in 1952 a group hospital admission form and an individual hospital insurance form.

With varying charges for varying services, the accountant is called upon to exercise judgment, and frequently his work with figures gives him insight into uneconomical practices which can be remedied. As the author of the article on "Accounting and Financial Management" stated in the Annual Administrative Reviews in *Hospitals,* April 16, 1962:

> Accountants ... are emerging from positions as pencil pushers to one of top importance on management's team. In this new role, the controller is the hospital's financial diagnostician as well as an adviser to the administrator and his board of directors. By means of the budget, the accountant is in a position to spot weak points, analyze their course, and report them in capsule form to top management for disposition. By means of cost analysis, accounting can supply management with the vital managerial tools.[11]

Perhaps hospitals may profitably adopt the new concept called "value control" that is replacing the conventional "cost control" idea in the thinking of many American companies. It goes beyond mere determination of costs of service or production and involves analysis of all of the facts that enter into the cost, consideration of specific problems, methods improvement, and recommendations for economies. Under value control the man who works with figures seeks meaning behind them and interprets that meaning to management.

Costs

"Sick Hospitals" was the title of an article by John S. Cooper.[12] Mr. Cooper cited the 1953 cost of $21.09 per patient day. A decade later costs had risen to

[11] C. Henry Hottum, quoting from E. C. Laetz: Accounting's Contribution to Administration. *Hospital Accounting,* February, 1961.
[12] Staff reporter, *Wall Street Journal,* September 23, 1954 (reprinted in *Trustee* in December of that year).

more than $35.00 a day and are predicted to rise to nearly $55.00 by 1970. A figure of $53.70 for that year, cited by Richard L. Johnson, then assistant director, American Hospital Association, at a meeting of the Indiana Hospital Association in November, 1962, is based on estimated annual cost increases of 7 per cent through 1965 and 3.5 per cent annually from 1966 through 1970. The spiraling costs and the resulting deficits are the major problems of a business nature that face hospitals and others who are concerned about the economic burden of illness and injury.

Reimbursement for care of the indigent seldom covers the entire cost, and losses from this source can be disastrous. Constant negotiating with the agencies involved is required to try to close this gap. For example, Cook County, Illinois, officials refused in 1962 to pay private hospitals anything at all for care of patients who are medically indigent but who are not on the relief rolls and therefore not paid for by the Illinois Public Aid Commission and the Cook County Public Aid Department.

The author of an article in *Hospitals*[13] endorses the "billings" method of reimbursement to hospitals by third party payers over the average per diem cost formula. Both are recognized in the "Principles of Payment for Hospital Care" approved by the American Hospital Association. Dr. Hale[14] indicates that the cost formula method does not reimburse the hospital for all of its expense.

In another article[15] the authors likewise object to the cost per day formula, asserting:

> Although the cost per patient day statistic is easily understood, easily computed, and generally accepted, a close examination of its construction indicates that it is a gross and unrealistic measure. Cost per patient day as an over-all figure is usually computed by dividing total operating expense by total adult and pediatric patient days of service. The derived figure, however, does not adequately describe over-all hospital operations.

The alternative suggested is "cost per unit of service."

Charges

A study of charges from hospital to hospital discloses startling differences, which certainly add to the confusion of the public and frequently to ill will. This is an area in which the hospital should function as a business concern would. Geographic and class-of-trade differences occur in the prices of commercial products and services, to be sure, but never with the wide range found in hospitals.

[13] Thomas Hale, M.D., director, Albany (New York) Medical Center Hospital. Is the Cost Formula Outmoded? *Hospitals,* August, 1962.

[14] *Ibid.,* pp. 41–46.

[15] Donald E. Saathoff, M.H.A., and Richard A. Kurtz, Ph.D., associate director and director respectively of Hospital Research Project, Nebraska State Department of Health: Cost Per Day Comparisons Don't Do the Job. *Mod. Hosp.,* October, 1962.

Reporting on a survey in Mississippi, Ewell D. Singleton,[16] now administrator of Glenwood Hospital, West Monroe, Louisiana, stated

> It would be hard for the public to understand why one hospital can get, for example, $3.00 for 100,000 units of penicillin, while another gets 50 cents for the same item. We can understand why one hospital can charge $6.00 for a bed and another charge $22.00 for a bed, because the hospital with the low-priced bed is charging the patient heavy ancillary charges; but it is difficult to understand why an item such as penicillin can cost the patient six times as much in one hospital as in another. It is also hard to understand why a complete spinal x-ray should run from a low of $15.00 to a high of $60.00. . . . In Mississippi the hospitals with the low room rates are charging heavy ancillary rates.
>
> Fifteen years ago the cost of 100,000 units of penicillin was about 70 cents and the patient was charged about $1.00 for each 100,000 units given to him. Today a hospital pays roughly 4 cents for that same 100,000 units. Do we pass the saving on to the patient? We still on the average charge him the same that we did several years ago. . . . Naturally the reason for much of this is that salaries and food costs have gone up and to cover this added expense the original charge for the drug has been maintained. . . . In Mississippi certain charges were far below cost—delivery room, operating room, nurseries, and room and board; others, on the average, were above—x-ray, laboratory, pharmacy.

Following are a few figures from the Mississippi survey:

	Low	High
Room Rates (total of 1,603 beds in hospitals replying)		
Private	$ 6	$22
Semi-private	5	15
Ward	5	11
Operating Room		
Major procedures, 32 hospitals reporting	12	55 (flat rate)
Minor procedures, 33 hospitals reporting	5	30
Eye, Ear, Nose, and Throat		
Two hospitals reporting	20	25
Miscellaneous Surgery		
Six hospitals reporting	5	20
Operating Room, Major		
Time basis ½ hour, 15 hospitals	5	30
1 " 17 "	10	45
2 " 7 "	15	55
Anesthesia, general major, 26 hospitals	10	55

Obviously a great deal more uniformity is needed in the setting of rates. The Oklahoma Hospital Association appointed a special committee to study and compare charges. Tremendous variation in charges was discovered.[17] As a result, principles were formulated.

Few, however, dispute the fact that no matter how unjustifiable the prorating of charges may be, the total bill fairly well reflects the actual cost of service.

[16] In his thesis submitted in 1961 to Northwestern University as the final requirement for his master's degree in hospital administration.

[17] Benny Carlisle: Relating Charges to Cost. *South. Hosp.,* December, 1959.

The point is that it should be itemized to show this, as is the practice of some hospitals. This should be done whether or not a third-party payer is involved, in order that the patient and the public may know exactly what is being received for their money or insurance benefit. Furthermore, somehow the fact should be made known through literature accompanying the bill that it does not cover the full cost—that the average patient pays around two dollars a day less than the cost—because of unpaid bills by medically indigent and other patients, expense of training and educating professional personnel, clinical research, and other costs which must be met by gifts and grants.

In an article, Jack A. L. Hahn,[18] executive director of the Methodist Hospital of Indianapolis, Indiana, traced the developments, including the abandonment of the "all-inclusive rate," which led to the adoption by the American Hospital Association in 1960 of the "Guiding Policy for Hospitals in Pricing Their Service to the Public." In conclusion he states that this policy

> . . . can best be implemented by hospitals on an over-all community basis with gradual installation. Adoption of the policy on a national and in many instances a state basis will help in the local implementation, but action at the grass roots is where its meaning will truly be felt. Pricing is another area where sound business practices must be used if hospital service and hospital economics are to be understood, appreciated and accepted by the public.

PURCHASING

The purchasing function in hospitals is not unlike that in industry. Both are confronted by one probably paramount problem—increasing costs—and both are trying to find ways to solve it. There is advantage to the medical service institution in studying the purchasing methods of industry, as well as in utilizing the aids which hospital supply firms furnish to buyers.

LeRoy F. Riley[19] says: "Hospitals are not facing the problem of increasing purchasing costs alone. . . . Industry is grappling with it too. What is industry doing about it? One Texas company, for example, is using 'annual contracts wherever possible' to reduce total paper work."

Concerning the hospital supplier, Riley[20] says:

> Hospital supply houses by and large have reputable, conscientious representatives. Many of them are highly and technically trained to serve the hospital and the purchasing agent. They need the purchasing agent as much as he needs them. They form a cooperative team. In most instances, these houses represent a multitude of produce sources and so assist both these sources and hospitals in holding down costs. For if each production source had to have its own salesmen on the road, prices would soar. Good relations between supply house representatives,

[18] *Hospitals,* June 16, 1952.

[19] "Purchasing," in the Annual Administrative Reviews section of the April 16, 1962, issue of *Hospitals.* Statement based on an article in *Purchasing,* March, 1961, by F. Wodrich.

[20] *Ibid.* Using as a reference an article by Frank M. Rhatigan, executive secretary of the American Surgical Trade Association, "How the Surgical Supply Dealer Serves the Hospital," in the March, 1961, issue of the *A.S.T.A. Journal.*

the administrator and the purchasing agent are of extreme importance if hospitals are to get the full benefit from these advisor-consultants. It is only as purchasing agents view problems of effective and conservative purchasing against the backdrop of producer-supplier representatives that they will be able to solve these problems effectively and economically.

The hospital, of course, has equipment problems that industry never dreams of, certain kinds of sterilization for example. One item[21] tells about the purchase of a new heart pump, the performance of which was satisfactory, "but it could not be cleaned. The hospital had to rebuild the pump so that all parts could be readily disassembled for cleaning sterilization. In this instance, the manufacturer violated a cardinal principle of not providing a means for cleaning the equipment." Another instance cited in the same item is purchase of an ultrasonic washer to strip soil from instruments prior to autoclaving. "This washer could perform limited cleaning operations under controlled conditions. These limitations were not known to the hospital at the time of purchase. This, plus the important fact that the design did not take into account that the unit itself had to be cleaned." Then, the item goes on, there is the problem of wheels.

> Every hospital uses portable equipment, yet no one in the hospital pays any attention to the cleanliness of the wheels. There is a definite reason why this is so, namely, most of the wheels cannot be cleaned. Just think of how much dirt is rolled into all areas of the hospital just because steps have not been taken to correct this relatively simple problem. Is it not time that cleanable wheels were made mandatory on all portable equipment?

Industry is trying to meet these problems and is seeking help. In February, 1961, Becton, Dickinson and Company sponsored a symposium[22] on the subject, "Changing Standards, Controls and Responsibility for Sterility and Materials of Disposable Medical Supplies." The panelists included a surgeon, an operating room supervisor, a hospital pharmacist, a purchasing agent, an administrator, a research director in industry, a research director in government, and a representative of the Food and Drug Administration.

Group Purchasing

A controversial subject in that it works in some places and areas and not in others, is group purchasing. A noteworthy expression of the viewpoint in favor of it was that of John J. Brennan, Jr., D.C.S., budget director, Electronics Corporation of America, Cambridge, Massachusetts. The salient points in his 1956 address were:[23]

---

[21] "Built-in Problems" is the headline of the introduction to the N.A.H.P.A. (National Association of Hospital Purchasing Agents) section in *Hospital Management,* February, 1963.

[22] A transcript of the discussion was published in the May, 1961, issue of *Conference* published by the Science Information Bureau.

[23] In an address, "A Businessman's Analysis of Group Purchasing for Hospitals" at the annual meeting of the Hospital Bureau of Standards and Supplies, Inc., February 23, 1956. Dr. Brennan, in obtaining his doctor's degree in commercial science from the Harvard Business School, used as the topic for his thesis, "Purchasing for Hospitals," which was based on detailed study and analysis

Group purchasing intrinsically of value to hospital administration and management.

Should be little difference between industrial and hospital procurement.

Should be partnership between hospital and group buying managements.

Burden of proof on hospital management to show why industrial procurement principles should not apply to hospital procurement and administration.

Hospitals are big business, hence sociological approach must be related to financial aspect. These two must be balanced.

Hospital deficits too readily accepted as the normal thing.

Set up effective cost control through area of purchasing since salaries are more uncontrollable.

Dr. Brennan listed as the "duties of a good hospital buyer:

1. Coordinate all hospital purchases.
2. Know product specifications in terms of permissible substitutions.
3. Control the use-rate of the item.
4. Buy appropriate quality, service and price.
5. Coordinate inventory control and purchases.
6. Interview salesmen to keep abreast of current market conditions, products and prices.
7. Analyze market conditions and prices.
8. Standardize supplies.
9. Educate hospital management on importance of purchasing as an administrative function.
10. Make an unbiased and thorough investigation of hospital group purchasing program.
11. Check constantly value of his membership in group buying association.
12. Evaluate the efficiency of the purchasing performance in terms of cost of specific supplies, quantities used, etc.

Only one of these is being done in most hospitals—order placing—according to Dr. Brennan,[24] who declares that this is the fault of hospital administration.

On the other side, a hospital administrator, Robert M. Jones, of Waukesha (Wisconsin) Memorial Hospital, spoke on "Anything a Cooperative Group Can Do, the Hospital With a Good Purchasing Program Can Do Better." He gives cogent reasons, among them: "We sometimes have enough difficulty getting our own staff doctors to standardize on items, without trying to get all the doctors on all hospital staffs in an area to agree!"

Jones' remarks[25] were made at a session on "What Are the Facts About Group Purchasing?" held during the 1956 Tri-State Hospital Assembly. Another speaker at the same session, Frank M. Rhatigan, executive secretary, American Surgical Trade Association, said that the director of the Hospital Bureau of

---

of the purchasing practices of a number of hospitals of various sizes and types in the eastern United States and of five of the major hospital group-purchasing agencies from the standpoint of the procurement principles used in industry. Afterward he was for seven years chairman of the Industrial Management Department of Boston College and for seven more years was an industrial consultant, primarily in the fields of procurement and business policy.

[24] The full text of Dr. Brennan's address, which includes the objections to group purchasing with answers to them, may be obtained from the Hospital Bureau of Standards and Supplies, Inc., 247 Park Avenue, New York 17.

[25] *Mod. Hosp.*, April, 1957.

Standards and Supplies, Inc., New York, the oldest and largest cooperative buying group, stated at an A.S.T.A. meeting in 1953 that there are "definite savings to be made in cooperative buying of such supplies as fuel, food, cleaning powders, detergents and some other supplies" but that the bureau had tried to buy medical supplies for its members in the past and that it "proved to be too costly."

Rhatigan said, "Nowhere in the picture of cooperative buying is there any mention of quality, service and delivery," and "If in an effort to effect a saving in your relatively small percentage of expenditure for medical and hospital supplies, your service to the patient is in any sense jeopardized, then cooperative buying is neither economical nor fundamentally wise."

In his lectures on purchasing to students in hospital administration at Northwestern University, Everett W. Jones, now a hospital consultant, then vice-president of The Modern Hospital Publishing Company, listed as follows the advantages and disadvantages of cooperative purchasing:

Advantages
Savings through quantity buying.
Yardstick for hospitals in comparing prices.
Bulletins containing information about commodities and market trends.
Advantages particularly for small hospitals to obtain benefit of quantity discounts.
Quality testing of merchandise.

Disadvantages
Individual choice is reduced.
Claims against vendor—indirect and not as effective.
Difficulty with local sources if staples are bought from cooperative group.
Cooperative group may be primarily interested in selling a product.
Buyer forgets about simplification or substitutions.
Purchasing agent may get into a rut and poor service may be rendered.
No service in form of "use economy surveys."

Purchasing Problem in Canada

The devalued dollar is creating special purchasing problems in Canada. One solution proposed is to encourage Canadian manufacturers to enlarge their lines of products. Another is to induce American and other foreign manufacturers to package or assemble in Canada, as some of them are already doing.

The situation is forcing re-examination of resources in Canada for making commodities which heretofore were imported, and redoubling of efforts to standardize supplies, to simplify purchasing procedures, and to economize.

PERSONNEL MANAGEMENT

Sixty per cent at least of the hospital's budget goes into payroll. Personnel management consequently may be considered one of the chief elements in its functioning as a business. The problems are essentially the same, with doubtless a little weighting in favor of the hospital with respect to motivation. The warfare with the unions, however, shows that motivation cannot be capitalized upon too far. Nowadays hospitals compete with industry for labor, and wages and salaries must be equalized, also fringe benefits and other advantages.

Apparently the progressive thinkers in business and industry are agreeing that something more than the recently popular "human relations" approach is needed in order to gain the full cooperation of personnel. The new approach has for some time been used in what is known as "executive development." Now it is going right down through the ranks. Displacement as a result of methods improvement and automation has something to do with it. It is a tougher concept than "human relations" in a way, yet far more promising in its effect upon the individual. Under the human relations type of management, the worker was supposed to flourish in an atmosphere of benignancy and concern for his welfare, with encouragement of his efforts by a well-liked boss acting as the spur to maximum effort.

The new approach is more like a human development than a human relations concept. It is realistic. Life is hard, work is hard, business is hard to get, customers (and patients) are hard to suit—let's all face it together—that is the tune! By facing it together, each doing his part to the best of his "developed" ability, with full understanding by both labor and management of each other's problems, maybe we can win out and make a success of our joint venture in this troubled world—that is the philosophy!

This is the hardest kind of leadership that has yet been proposed for the director of an organization. Few will be able to rise to the full possibilities. The idea is bound to take hold, and it unquestionably holds high hope for the future. When the improvement of man is linked to the improvement of methods, management is assuming the sociological responsibilities which it has long shirked. The trouble is that methods improvement can be demonstrated in statistics, improvement in men cannot, and the techniques are infinitely harder to learn and to employ successfully. Ways must be devised of evaluating the capabilities and potentialities of each and every worker through new channels of information more complete than the application form, the job classification, and the job rating sheet. Using educators as consultants would seem to be one good way and would bring about a most desirable liaison between the educational and the business worlds.

The logic behind human development is that it is as much needed by business as by labor. Automation is displacing the "common" unskilled worker. Business needs him in a more demanding category. Likewise the artisan skilled in one job needs evaluation for training in another that industry wants somebody to fill. There is also the incentive to higher production and efficiency that real participation in a project gives. The suggestion system has proved that workers have good ideas; they need the stimulation for still better ones that frequent discussion gives.

In general, the search for jobs and assignments to jobs is haphazard. Vocational guidance in school has helped; guidance afterward is equally important. The first choice, perhaps guided only by chance, may well be the wrong one for both employer and employee.

Human development is a tough undertaking because it brooks no compromise with laziness or indifference or incompetence. It envisages a firm hand on the controls. It implies better performance as opportunities for education and training are provided along with promotion to a better, more responsible position. Here the hospital is unfortunately somewhat handicapped by the rigidity of its professional departments, interchangeability of personnel being practically impossible in the higher brackets. To the extent that it is possible, however, the development of personnel to take higher posts should be pursued.

The Standard Oil Company (Indiana) has formulated an "Employee Relations Policy Statement—Appraisal and Development of Personnel," in which the concept of opportunity for the employee to develop is incorporated. The policy statement reads:

It is the Company's policy, working through all levels of supervision, to provide the following for each individual employee:

1. An adequate understanding between the individual and his supervisor as to what is expected of him on the job he occupies.
2. An objective appraisal of his work performance at least once a year, followed by discussion with his supervisor wherein he is advised how he is getting along on the job and receives specific suggestions for improvement.
3. Encouragement to develop his work performance to maximum capacity, together with an opportunity to discuss with his supervisor a plan of action for his personal growth and development.
4. Adequate counseling and on-the-job coaching by his supervisor and others, supplemented by other developmental activities appropriate to his individual needs, both to improve performance on his present job and to indicate his ability to perform successfully on higher positions.
5. Assurance that, on the basis of an objective evaluation of his qualifications and potential, he will receive full consideration in the selection of men for higher positions. Whenever it can be done consistent with good business practice, each employee will be given opportunities to demonstrate his ability to handle greater responsibilities successfully.

Besides the policy statement, the company has issued manuals in three parts (I) The Appraisal Process; (II) Counseling for Improved Job Performance; (III) Developmental Opportunities for the Individual; a Guide for Evaluating Management Potential; a Guide for Appraisal of Management Personnel; and forms including a "Personal Data" sheet. E. W. Ahern, manager, personnel development, described the program at a 1960 Preceptors' Conference sponsored by the American College of Hospital Administrators in Chicago. He also told about the conferences conducted for supervisors during the company's formalized program of supervisory training.

The Double Hierarchy of Authority in Hospitals

Alexander Cloner[26] calls attention to a distinct problem in hospitals—the double hierarchy of authority:

> In almost every organizational entity there exists a *single* administrative structure with a complex set of arrangements of authority and control, of delegation, coordination and administrative supervision. We in the hospital field have doubled the problem. We have two. We have the administrative hierarchy under the non-medical administrator, and we have the professional staff hierarchy composed of our attending staff members. In our hospital management culture we must learn to work with a minimum of tension with these two administrative bodies, take orders from and correlate the needs and desires of these two separate authority structures, and try to harmonize their desires, orders, and goals in order to have a single functioning institution. As a group, the nursing personnel are perhaps more exposed to this kind of situation, and the personnel officer must learn how to function within this kind of framework.

The Morale Survey

Study of personnel practices in industry will disclose many concepts that medical care institutions can adopt to improve employee relations. Among these is the morale survey. A Northwestern University student in hospital administration, Virginia Jones, gave her views on this in a talk at a meeting of the Alpha Delta Mu Fraternity in 1960:

> The most common method of measuring morale is a well-designed questionnaire which employees and executives fill out on an anonymous basis. The questionnaire contains a number of statements with which employees may agree or disagree and reflects the kinds of things important to employees. Generally space is also provided for employees' written comments.
>
> While the questionnaire is an important and necessary tool, the most adequate program is a "full scale" or complete survey which provides employees with an opportunity to fill out a questionnaire and to express their attitudes in an interview with trained interviewers on any subject pertaining to the work situation. The questionnaire tells management how employees feel but it does not explain why. A special type of non-directive interviewing is employed for this purpose.

Miss Jones believes that a large hospital, like a large business, should set up its own survey program. A small organization can employ consultants such as the Industrial Relations Center at the University of Chicago, Science Research Associates, and Social Research, Inc. She thinks that an administrative resident who is objective, being new to the institution, might be a good person to conduct it. Another way would be to employ trained interviewers for just that part of the program. Sometimes a board member whose firm has had morale surveys can be recruited as an adviser or might even have trained personnel in his company assist with the project. Hospital councils could be another source of help.

[26] Ph.D., director, Civic Center Campus, University of Southern California, formerly director of personnel and management relations at Cedars of Lebanon Hospital, Los Angeles. *Hosp. Forum,* September, 1962.

Credit Unions

Donald A. Lacey, speaking at an Alpha Delta Mu meeting at Northwestern University in 1960, cited the following benefits which can be obtained by having a credit union in a hospital: employees are taught not to overborrow but to calculate both the benefits and the cost of borrowing; thrift is encouraged through regular payroll savings; efficiency and productivity are promoted by relieving employees from financial worry; training and education in business methods, corporate procedures, self-government, and mutual helpfulness are furthered. To start a credit union, the Credit Union National Association should be contacted. A representative will aid in the initial planning. He will set up a charter meeting, acting as temporary chairman, setting up the necessary charter as well as filling out the forms needed in organizing the credit union. After completing the forms a petition for the right to operate must be approved, signed generally by seven citizens (in no state more than twenty) at the time the bylaws are submitted. If the petition is granted, the organizing group perfects its organization by electing officers who must be chosen from the members but not necessarily from the originating members. Prior to the filing of this petition the various state laws covering credit unions should be fully investigated so that the bylaws will comply with the provisions.

Labor Unions and Hospitals

One of the reasons that unions are trying so hard to enroll hospital workers is that union growth has come to a halt and in some areas is even declining. Their main hope is to get more members from service fields and among white-collar workers. Automation is a serious threat in reducing the number of potential members in manufacturing in particular. What the unions are driving for is more dues to keep up their budgets.

Unionization drives on hospitals were outlined by Jack Owen,[27] then with the American Hospital Association, in a talk at the American Protestant Hospital Association meeting in Kansas City, Missouri, in 1961, as follows:

> In 1936, Local 250 of AFL successfully organized three San Francisco hospitals and soon after ten others were organized. As a result of these agreements the San Francisco Conference was formed, and negotiations were handled on a conference wide basis. . . .
>
> In 1939, the Minnesota legislature passed the Minnesota Labor Relations Act. This legislation opened up the possibility of hospitals being unionized. In 1941, the BSIEU began organizing hospitals in the Twin City area. Not only do these hospitals have contracts with non-professional employees, they also have contracts with the Minnesota Nurses Association and the Licensed Practical Nurses Association.
>
> In 1956, after a strike at Mercy Hospital, Toledo, Ohio, the AFL-CIO and teamsters signed an agreement with the administration of the Toledo hospitals.

[27] *Am. Protestant Hosp. A. Bull.,* July, 1961.

This is now known as the Toledo Plan, and it was hoped would be the basis for future labor relations settlements with hospitals. (Six members—2 hospital, 2 union, 2 elected).

In 1958, an 84-day strike took place at Swedish Hospital, Seattle, Washington. . . . This was eventually settled by adoption of the Toledo Plan after the union felt it could not win.

Unionization drives have gained tremendous momentum with the inception of the drive on New York City hospitals. Since the New York outbreak, practically every city has had a drive for union organization. . . . It has not been restricted to the large cities. In a recent survey by AHA we have found 205 contracts with unions, 156 contracts with nursing associations, and 53 partial contracts. As large as this seems it still only represents 2.9 per cent of the total voluntary hospitals. Hospitals today probably face the greatest union threat in the Economic Security Program of the A.H.A. This platform asks for collective bargaining and seeks it through all the techniques of any union activity.

Unions moving into the hospital field present a far different approach from the average industrial union. The industrial union is usually a large union operating in a specific manner either by tradition or by their charter. Because they are a large union it is easy to study their tactics and cope with them as they move from one organization to another. Unions attempting to organize the hospital field are mostly small locals. . . .

Part four

THE SOCIOECONOMIC, POLITICAL, AND RELIGIOUS COMMUNITIES

CHAPTER 13

Social Science Backgrounds; Medical Sociology; Philanthropy

The principal task of sociology is to obtain and interpret the facts regarding human association, not to solve social problems. Its ultimate aim, however, is to improve man's adjustment to life by developing objective knowledge concerning social phenomena which can be used to deal effectively with social problems. In this respect sociology bears the same relation to the solution of social problems as, say, biology and bacteriology bear to medicine, or mathematics and physics to engineering. Without the research done in the theoretical and experimental sciences, modern techniques for curing disease or those for bridge-building would be impossible. Similarly, without the investigations carried on by sociology and the other social sciences, no really effective social planning or lasting solutions to social problems would be possible. In this sense, theory can be the most practical thing in the world.
S MUEL KOENIG[1]

WITH DUE recognition of the truth of the distinction between sociology as a basic science, and social problems as practical matters to which sociological theory can be applied, the student whose goal is administration in the health field would do well to minimize the distinction and to weld principles and application together in his thinking about how the social sciences are related to medical

[1] Associate Professor of Sociology and Anthropology, Brooklyn College, New York. From *Man and Society: The Basic Teachings of Sociology.* New York, Barnes & Noble, Inc., 1957. p. 1.

service. Elton Mayo,[2] in *The Social Problems of an Industrial Civilization,* deplores the separation of the academic or theoretical side from everyday living,
saying that although the graduate's standard of intellectual achievement is high,
his knowledge of acquaintance of actual human situations is exceedingly low,
and he is ill equipped for the task of bringing order into social chaos.

The gap is being bridged gradually both by social scientists and by men of affairs. Nearly thirty years ago a sociologist, James H. S. Bossard, professor of
sociology at the Wharton School of Finance and Commerce, University of
Pennsylvania, devoted Parts V and VI of his eight-part book, *Social Change and
Social Problems,*[3] to physical and mental health and throughout his discussion of
other social problems took cognizance of the impact of physical and mental abnormalities upon them. In his introduction to the chapter, "The Socio-Health
Movement," he said:

> While it is true that selected phases of health work must, by their very nature,
> be carried on by such technically trained persons as physicians, surgeons, nurses,
> and the like, it is equally true that the development of their services, their mode
> and point of attack, the direction and emphasis of their work, are essentially
> problems of social policy, social understanding and social organization. Just as
> the expert and technician in business and in public life are subject to the con-
> sideration of larger matters of policy, so the work of our medically trained per-
> sonnel must be considered in the light of the larger phases of social policy and
> welfare.

Sociology, which is defined in one dictionary as "the science of the constitution, evolution, and phenomena of human society," is the primary social science
for study by those aspiring to leadership in the health field. Concern about care
of the sick began and still exists in the most primitive societies as one of the main
evidences of a sense of brotherhood and mutual responsibility among men. The
organization of this concern on an institutional plane is one of the early manifestations of civilization.

There is no distinct sociology for the health field. The sociology texts must be
studied and the interrelationships of social institutions understood before it is
sensible to try to fit in the doctor and the public health service or the hospital.
The whole is much more important than the sum of its parts. Each social activity
not only affects the others but has the potential of increasing their individual and
combined effectiveness.

Herbert Spencer tells a story of a Frenchman who, having been three weeks in
the British Isles, "proposed to write a book on England; who, after three months,
found that he was not quite ready; and who, after three years, concluded that he
knew nothing about it." Durant[4] summarizes Spencer's comments: "Such a man
was ripe to *begin* the study of sociology. Men prepare themselves with life-long

---

[2] Then Professor of Industrial Research, Graduate School of Business Administration, Harvard
University. Published by the university, printed at Andover, Massachusetts, The Andover Press, 1945,
p. 21.
[3] Harper & Brothers, New York, rev. ed., 1938, p. 412.
[4] Will Durant: *The Story of Philosophy.* New York, Garden City Publishing Co., 1927, p. 409.

study before becoming authorities in physics or chemistry or biology; but in the field of social and political affairs every grocer's boy is an expert, knows the solution, and demands to be heard."

One has only to dip into the vast literature that is accumulating in the social sciences to recognize that a little knowledge in this field can be dangerously misleading. It is necessary to dig deeply. What one author produces as facts is discounted by another. There is no clear progression in theory as knowledge increases. Rather the trend is for new authorities to throw overboard the conclusions of their predecessors. This is a science in which speculation often runs riot and in which there are few certainties. Nevertheless new flashes of insight are constantly being added by students and research workers.

Study of Comte, Herbert Spencer, Hobbes, Locke, Malthus, Marshall, Pareto, Durkheim, Weber, Dewey, and later theorists is essential even though it leads to confusion. Part of the reason for the confusion, of course, is that sociology cannot stand alone as a science. Before men functioning as a group can be understood, men functioning as individuals must be studied. Hence the underlying science is psychology. Its principles, which also are not really fundamental but change somewhat with each new thinker, need to be grasped as a preliminary to a venture into the morass of sociology. Universities combine them to some extent in courses called "social psychology." Anthropology, the "science of man," also has an important place.

Then there is philosophy. That is a "must" study too because most of the sociologists consider themselves philosophers, and propound philosophical theories along with their social ideas. None of these is a distinct discipline. Neither, in truth, are political science and economics, though in certain respects they do lend themselves better than the others to separate treatment.

Bearing in mind, therefore, the essential unity of the social sciences, the student must nevertheless risk some division or he will flounder in fathomless depths. Talcott Parsons, in *The Structure of Social Action,* published in 1937,[5] stated the case thus:

> There is a great deal of current protest against attempts to set up boundaries between the sciences, to divide them into neat compartments. We are told that all knowledge is one, that the way of progress is to break down divisions, not to set them up. It is possible to sympathize generally with the spirit of this protest. For concrete empirical research it is clearly impossible to adhere to any neatly separated fields. The empirical scholar will follow his problems wherever they may lead and refuse to be deterred by any signs which read "foreign territory." Indeed this study by demonstrating the extent to which different conceptual schemes must be called upon to unravel the complexities of the same empirical field, has given a direct justification to the advocacy of such scientific "wanderlust." But at the same time such an attitude pushed to the extreme of refusing even to discuss the problems of systematic relationship of theoretical systems involved in classifications of the sciences, becomes a case of the kind of empiricist

[5] Reprinted 1949. Free Press of Glencoe, Illinois, p. 759.

evasion of political problems which has been shown again and again to be scientifically disastrous. It is an excellent thing to travel in many countries, but unless he knows the peculiarities and customs of the countries he visits he is likely to get into trouble. Many a traveler has lost his life through sheer ignorance of these things.

A sobering fact is the extreme slowness of social progress. With a certain amount of justification, some claim that there has been no measurable advance and that there has even been retrogression in some aspects of the social scene.

Robert Morss Lovett,[6] writing about Chicago's Century of Progress in 1934, praised the exhibits which portrayed the development of the basic sciences, but asked where "was the evidence of the larger life for mankind, or even the promise of it" which was the theme of the exposition. He cited a diorama showing "a family gathering singing hymns versus a nearly empty church in which a servant of God addressed the microphone" and another showing outdoor games versus a motion picture audience, and wondered where anybody saw progress in these, to him, cynical portrayals of supposed progress.

Lovett admitted that the "subject matter of technology lends itself to exhibition in concrete form, while social progress can often be revealed only by symbols, charts, and statistics," but he complained that even with this reservation the exhibits offered in the names of religion and social systems "suggested a troubling doubt as to the meaning, reality and future of progress toward a larger life for mankind."

Three decades have not changed the grounds for Lovett's disappointment. A new Century of Progress could show few more evidences of a larger life than the first one did. Yet we know they exist. Especially are we certain of them in the health field. They simply do not lend themselves to outward show.

To take a material object as an example, it is not the appearance of the jet contrasted with that of the stagecoach that matters; it is the inner ecstasy that sailing through the ethereal blue at the speed of sound gives compared with the discomfort of jogging down a bumpy road; and it is the exhilarating prospect of world-wide cultural and social interchange that the compression of distances assures, in place of the virtual isolation from even the next village. These material advances in transportation do bring "a larger life" to many more people, exactly as do better operating room equipment and new, more effective drugs, and they have overwhelming social implications.

All is not gain, to be sure. Almost everybody has times when retreat to pastoral living, however primitive, has a powerful appeal. Doubts assail about the worthwhileness of the social whirl, industrial competition, and political strife. Yet there are challenge and opportunity for personal growth in trying to solve the ever more complicated problems. Contentment somehow does not seem to be what we want, or what is good for us, in the twentieth century—except occasionally, on holiday. The anxiety state, despite its emotional repercussions, seems to have compensations.

[6] *Current History*, January, 1934.

In hospitals, would we really like to go back? Certainly not to the frightful institutions of medieval times and even those of a single century ago. True, there is a kind of nostalgia when one thinks about those "cottage" hospitals in England and even about the earliest ones in America which were often established in doctors' or clergymen's homes and had a home atmosphere. Always more friendliness, more personal attention, can be counted on in small places. One look at the mortality rates in the old days, however, and the nostalgia vanishes.

Dr. Anthony J. J. Rourke, consultant to hospitals, with long experience in hospital administration, places at the very top of the list of attributes needed for success in this career, that the administrator "should have the broad concept of the social scientist." There should therefore be no skimming of the subject in the student's preparation. He needs to be familiar with the various theories: utilitarian, positivistic, empirical, individualistic, voluntaristic, objective, intuitive; also with the men who propounded them, the ideologies upon which they are based, the degrees and shades of difference in each theory by individual proponents, and the criticisms that have been made of them and by whom. It is exceedingly important that the student be acquainted with the leaders of thought and of action. Personification intensifies interest and promotes understanding. A "social" science in particular needs to be associated with people.

Social movements and their leaders have shown some cognizance, but not much, of the relationship of health and medical care to social welfare. While hospitals have lagged behind social theory because of isolationism and blindness to the fact that changes must inevitably affect them, sociologists have been partly to blame for insufficient awareness of the impact of health on their own field. In order to remedy this neglect of each other's sphere, a new kind of sociologist is appearing on the scene, the medical sociologist, and a new branch of the science is emerging, medical sociology. Professor Bossard, mentioned earlier in this chapter, may be credited with having been among those who led the way to its development.

MEDICAL SOCIOLOGY

René Sand, in a remarkable book by virtue of its scope, penetrating analysis, and vision, ties together medicine and sociology in the most enlightening way throughout the entire volume. His term "social medicine" must not be confused with America's distasteful "socialized medicine"—he means simply the linked social and medical milieu as shown in the following quotation:[7]

> The social functions of medicine go back . . . to the very origins of the profession, while industrial medicine and social welfare services were instituted in the eighteenth century. The conception, even the name *social medicine,* dates back a hundred years, and it has developed side by side with the other sciences of man. Socio-medical demography evolves from statistics demonstrating the

[7] René Sand was head of the Institute of Hygiene and Social Medicine, Brussels, Belgium, and, before the second World War, secretary of the International Hospital Association. Quotation from *The Advance to Social Medicine.* London and New York, Staples Press, English edition, pp. 3–4.

inequality of the classes in face of illness and death, socio-medical anthropometry from records which reveal the same inequalities in the physical and intellectual characteristics of these classes. Socio-medical pathology comes into the picture when the joint observations of doctors and social workers begin to elucidate the part played by the various social factors in the origin and progress of disease. Genetics (the study of heredity), gerontology (the science of old age and old people), and geriatrics (the branch of medicine concerned with their treatment), the science of population, psychology, social sciences and social service all make their contribution to the establishment of a new medical sociology or sociological medicine. . . .

Medicine has always subsisted on methods and data borrowed from other sciences; from physics, chemistry, mathematics to start with, and later from biology, parasitology and bacteriology. In adding to these objective psychology and the social sciences, including working and living conditions among the factors governing health and sickness, social medicine carries out the intention of Hippocrates and bestows on the art of medicine its full breadth, its full efficacy, its full nobility.

Sand cites as developments which contributed to the growth at the turn of the century of medical sociology as a recognized branch of science, "the improvement of hospitals, the raising of the status of the nursing profession, the spread of hygiene, the establishment of social services and social insurance, fresh progress in industrial and social legislation, the rise of industrial medicine, the development of the social sciences, and the prevailing economic conditions themselves." He continues:[8]

From this point, social medicine joins forces with the school of thought, taking shape at the same period, which aims at rationalizing not only production but all human activities. Material elements are not forgotten, but it is man who is placed in the forefront as being not only unique in the spiritual field but also the prime economic factor. He holds this place by virtue of his physical strength, which depends on good health; his mental capacity, which depends on healthy formative influences; and his goodwill, which depends on respect of his individuality.

Up to the present day, provision for the needs of all was a Utopian ideal; the technique of production was inadequate. But today, having fertilized the soil, subjugated the elements, overcome the more devastating diseases and opened up great sources of wealth, man can cut out at the roots the evils which have held him enslaved.

Naked before his destiny, his spiritual value was continually threatened, his material worth as yet negligible; but the more his health and his skill can be developed, the more wealth will his productive capacity represent. It is in order to protect man, to cultivate his mental and spiritual gifts, to encourage that expansion of his personality on which individual happiness and social equilibrium alike depend, that medicine joins forces with this "human economics," adopts its point of view and embraces man as a whole—in the cradle, at school, at work, and in the home.

Social medicine is the final flowering of the preventive and curative art. It satisfies at once man's material interests, his reason, his sense of communal responsibility and that unconquerable aspiration towards a better lot on which his hopes are nourished.

[8] *Ibid.*, pp. 4–5.

The concept as set forth by Sand is clear, indisputable, enticing in its vision of the possibilities although the science is in its infancy.

"Clearly," says M. Allen Pond,[9] "poverty and disease are bedfellows, yet the precise relationship of one to the other continues to be unknown. Does poverty spawn disease? Or are people impoverished because they are sickly?" Pond's concluding summarization[10] is:

> There is a need for continuing and expanding our efforts to raise the standard of living and to improve educational opportunities. These are the sinews of better health. Without them, no society can be healthy. Poverty and disease go hand in hand, and removing the burden of poverty from the shoulders of the less fortunate will contribute to the health of all.

So it is that articles like "The Plight of the Hill People"[11] cannot be ignored by medical and hospital people as depicting somebody else's responsibility. The one-twentieth of the nation "that lives on unproductive land and is dismally, chronically poor" constitute a health problem for the medical sociologist. Furthermore, it is from among these poorly educated, socially behind-the-times people that the cities are drawing families that go on the relief rolls and stay there because there is no work for the unskilled fathers and sons.

That there has been advance in medical sociological thinking is shown by an extract from an article published in the *Chicago Medical Journal and Examiner* in 1879 that no reputable publication would permit in its pages today:

> It is frequently stated that the poor should be protected by the government against the causes of disease which are said to infest the habitation of the lower classes. . . . It is the lazy people and their sentimental friends who are always calling for government aid. If now you undertake to protect this fraction of the community, you have to protect it against the consequences of idleness, luxury, intemperance and vice—thus interfering with the operation of the wholesome monitory laws of nature; and you do it at the expense of the meritorious classes of society. Having accustomed such worthless people to rely upon government for protection against smallpox, and scarlet fever, and syphilis, and diphtheria, and sewer-gas, and scabies, it will not need the passage of many generations before they will demand protection by the government against the cold and hunger and nakedness for which they should themselves make provision.[12]

This is not as out-of-date as it might seem, though, for in 1949 it was stated in an article:[13]

> Any experienced general practitioner will agree that what keeps the great majority of people well is the fact that they can't afford to be ill. That is a harsh,

[9] Interrelationship of Poverty and Disease. *Pub. Health Rep.*, November, 1961, p. 967.
[10] *Ibid.*, p. 973.
[11] Jerome Ellison. *Saturday Evening Post*, June 4, 1960, pp. 45–49.
[12] Editorial. *Chicago Med. J. and Examiner*, 39:319, 1879. Quoted by George Rosen, M.D., in Provision of Medical Care: History, Sociology, Innovation, *Pub. Health Rep.*, March, 1959, p. 203.
[13] Editorial. License for Illness. *New York J. Med.*, September 15, 1949. Quoted by Dr. Rosen in same article as above.

stern dictum and we readily admit that under it a certain number of cases of early tuberculosis and cancer, for example, may go undetected. Is it not better that a few such should perish rather than that the majority of the population should be encouraged on every occasion to run snivelling to the doctor? That in order to get their money's worth they should be sick at every available opportunity? They will find out in time that the services they think they get for nothing—but which the whole people of the United States would pay for—are also worth nothing.

Unbelievable in the light of present-day thinking—but verifiable in cold print.

Some sixty years ago, Patrick Geddes wrote: "Slum, semi-slum, super-slum, to this has come the evolution of our Cities." He should see what we have now, despite the host of slum-clearance projects. The older suburbs deteriorate into slums, and some of the newer ones are already on the way because of the lack of planning in their development. The medical sociologist views with concern the equally unplanned mushroom growths of hospitals and other medical facilities in the new subdivisions, and their decay along with their surroundings in the old neighborhoods. The districts in which public housing projects are situated are not attracting physicians and dentists, so that even in the hearts of the cities the ratio of physicians to the population is disturbingly low. Along with the regional planning of health facilities which looks so promising at the moment, there needs to be more linkage with general community planning for any real improvement to result in health service to all classes of people.

A hospital that has gone so far as to rejuvenate its surroundings instead of moving away when they became intolerable is Michael Reese Hospital, Chicago. Its board engaged a planning team in 1945 to develop a long-range plan for a great medical center in a reconstructed neighborhood. A seven-square-mile area was included in the plan, extending from 12th Street on the north to 47th Street on the south, and Lake Michigan on the east to the Pennsylvania Railroad tracks on the west. Institutions and industries in the area, seeing advantages for themselves in remaining, readily cooperated. A South Side Development Association was formed. Housing projects were built by the hospital, the Chicago Housing Authority, insurance companies and other investors, and the Illinois Institute of Technology. The latter already had under way a $17 million expansion program for its 16-block campus.

There is still a long way to complete the entire plan, but the outlook from the hospital campus is startlingly different from that of two decades ago. High-rising apartment buildings and well-kept lawns have replaced the ugly, dilapidated dwellings and littered yards. Upon completion of a $2.8 million surgical wing in 1962, the medical center became a $21 million development, with plans under way for further projects totaling $7 million. After that, according to an announcement by the board, it is anticipated that expansion and improvements will continue at the rate of $3 million a year. Started inside the medical center 80-acre area in 1960 was a privately financed $350,000 shopping center.

Health Records and Examinations

A medical sociological aid if it is generally adopted is a health recording service available to the public. The service was started in 1961 by Health History, Inc., Chicago, which offers what it describes as "the first complete health recording service available to the public." For a yearly fee, it will assemble and maintain a complete individual health record in strictest confidence for each subscriber. It will, at no additional charge, make the information available for medical purposes to doctors, hospitals, clinics, schools, and various agencies, immediately upon proper request of the subscriber or his authorized representative. The subscriber is given a wallet-size identification card designed to contain his blood type, recent illnesses, allergies, doctor's name and telephone, next of kin, and other special conditions related to a medical emergency. When conditions require immediate action, the card serves as a guard against improper treatment and administration of medicine to which a patient may be sensitive.

The record is obtained on self-addressed, postage-free physician's report forms which are given to the subscriber to give to his doctor. By means of these forms the doctor and the subscriber notify the firm of the important changes and developments to be recorded in the permanent form. Attached to the form is an authorization, to be signed by the subscriber, requesting his doctor to fill out the form with the necessary information regarding an illness or medical incident, and then send it to the firm.

The catch is, of course, where are doctors going to get the time to fill out so many forms, swamped as they already are with many types of insurance forms and other records? Notwithstanding the additional chore, a California surgeon, Dr. J. Theron Hunter, of Solana Beach, provides his patients with records and has distributed a brochure advocating the adoption of permanent and continuing health records for every person. He states:[14]

> An acceptable health record should require little or no longhand writing by physicians. Necessary entries can be made by his assistants, and much of the data is in the form of carbon copies. Certain possible events of a medical history have no place in a health record for civilians, i.e., venereal disease, criminal abortion, alcoholism, and drug addiction. . . .

He points to the advantage of having technical information unknown to or not usually understood by the patient, such as laboratory and x-ray findings, blood pressure and other technical information, readily available to a doctor, an especially important reason for the lifetime record being the migrating population and the rapid passing of the family physician who carried the medical histories of the community in his memory.

Another socially important contribution that medicine should make is the

[14] *Bull. Am. Coll. Surgeons*, March-April, 1959, p. 172. See also *Lifetime Health Record* by David D. Rutstein, Cambridge, Harvard University Press, 1958.

encouragement of voluntary periodic health examinations. The fact that an astoundingly high proportion of apparently healthy persons have disease of some kind in its early stages has been borne out in several experimental programs. In a study of 10,709 apparently healthy persons given over-all examinations at Tulane University School of Medicine, New Orleans, 92 per cent were found to have "disease or abnormalities of varying significance." Much of the disease was in the early stages. Less than one per cent had malignancies, or serious disease. The patients in this study over a 12-year period represented all socioeconomic levels and many occupations. In a second study conducted at the University of Pennsylvania Diagnostic Clinic from 1949 to 1958, the examinees were 1,513 business executives. Previously unrecognized diseases were found in 40 per cent, and the newly found disease was believed capable of resulting, if unchecked, in death or major disability in over one-half of this group, disability in one-third, and was judged insignificant in the remaining 9 per cent. These studies and results were reported in a news release from the American Medical Association, January 1, 1960.

Like all problems, this one of medicine in its social aspects has its other side—the danger of talking about disease and disease prevention so much that a large number of persons become hypochondriacs. This is in itself a serious health problem and a burden to society. In an interview[15] by Donald McDonald with Herbert Ratner, M.D., Public Health Director, Oak Park, Illinois, and associate professor of preventive medicine and public health at Loyola University, Dr. Ratner said:

> It is generally recognized that America is the most overmedicated, most over-operated, and most overinoculated country in the world. It is also the most anxiety-ridden with regard to health. We make health an end in itself. We have forgotten that health is really a means that enables a person to do his work and do it well. . . . As actionists who feel more comfortable doing something and having something done to us, we impose life-saving drugs and technics intended for serious ailments on minor, even trivial, illnesses—illnesses that are self-limited and that, except for occasional symptomatic relief, do better without interference from the physician. . . . Americans look upon health as something that can be bought rather than a state to be sought through an accommodation to the norms of nature. We have become increasingly a paying animal, as if health were solely a commodity of the market-place.

It should be remembered that the medical sociological section of the American Sociological Society was not created until 1959 and that it has less than 400 members. There has not been time for very deep penetration of sociological philosophy into the consciousness of the medical profession in general.

Problems that are looming larger than ever before, such as chronic diseases and mental illness, are forcing the medical-social viewpoint to the forefront because the sufferers from these conditions have more obvious social maladjust-

---

[15] A condensation from *Medicine*, a publication of the Center for the Study of Democratic Institutions, Santa Barbara, California. *Hosp. Topics*, November, 1962.

ments than the acutely ill. The public eye is focused on all aspects of living, for the aged in particular, and medical care cannot be separated from the comprehensive social needs.

SOCIAL STRUCTURE OF THE HOSPITAL

One aspect of medical sociology is the social structure within the hospital. It is a fermenting, status-seeking situation, by personnel who were once placidly subservient to the top authority, the physician. With scientific advances complicating and elevating the functions of other professional personnel, and machines taking over the manual labor of many of the nonprofessional workers, the position of the individual employee has been upgraded, and he demands and should have recognition for his improved status. As Perry Jones, now administrative assistant at Louis A. Weiss Memorial Hospital, Chicago, then a student in hospital administration at Northwestern University, remarked in a talk in 1960 at an Alpha Delta Mu meeting, the fellows from the teamsters' union have been telling the garbage man that "he must better himself; after all, the doctors and the administrator are only men like himself, so why should they be so much better off." The union movement has unquestionably had a great deal to do with unrest in the hospital, for its gospel is improvement of the worker's lot, and who can deny the social justification of that goal?

Jones pointed out in his talk that throughout the hospital, more than in other organizations, there are overlapping of roles and confusion in demarcation of responsibilities, but that sociologists are studying the situation and may come up with helpful suggestions.

An outstanding study[16] was the one initiated by the American Hospital Association and conducted by a team of research workers from the New York State School of Industrial and Labor Relations of Cornell University. The book includes a great many quotations of remarks by employees to the interviewers which illustrate status consciousness. For example, a maintenance worker said:[17]

> You can't help but get sore at some of the nurses. Every once in awhile you run into one who tries to show her authority over you. Actually they have no authority at all. I don't know whether they think they are better than you are just because they have that white cap on their heads or what it is, but they sure like to push people around. What do we do? Nothing in particular, just keep them waiting.

A maid whose comment typified that of others said:[18] "Some nurses are very nice to you and others aren't. Some of them wouldn't get friendly with you if they knew you for a million years. Same thing with doctors."

Each profession and occupation in the hospital is being built up in prestige

[16] Temple Burling, Edith M. Lentz, and Robert N. Wilson: *The Give and Take in Hospitals: A Study of Human Organization.* New York, G. P. Putnam's Sons, 1956.
[17] *Ibid.*, p. 177.
[18] *Ibid.*, p. 191.

through the organizations and journals which it has established. They play upon the theme of the importance and prestige of the particular field, whatever it may be. This is good. It is one of the ways in which progress is promoted. It arouses and stimulates the worker to excel for the advancement of his group. It is not peculiar to hospitals, only more noticeable because of the many classifications of personnel. All society is permeated with it. It is as much a problem of the atomic age as is automation, in fact part of the same process. Vance Packard has highlighted it in *The Status Seekers*.[19] "Our occupational rank," he says, "looms as a powerful factor in fixing our status in the public's mind."

Patient Relationship

Important as the personnel factor is in consideration of the hospital as a social institution, a more important one is the patient relationship. Sociologists are studying this, too. Ernest Dichter, Ph.D., studied the doctor-patient relationship, his findings having been published by the California Medical Association in 1950; then delved into the hospital-patient relationship.[20] Dr. Dichter is a consulting psychologist who has made studies for the American Medical Association and other professional and industrial groups.

Suicide is one of the social problems with which the hospital is confronted, both from an inpatient standpoint and from caring for patients whose attempts have not been successful.[21]

Another medical sociological problem of the first order is grimly portrayed in Aldous Huxley's *Brave New World Revisited*.[22] Conquest of disease and the rising birth rate are overpopulating the world and creating more poverty and misery, in underdeveloped lands especially, than ever before. Even in America, the relief rolls are high, and being on relief is far from a pleasant way of life. Meeting the health and welfare problems of sharecroppers and of migratory workers is another discouraging task in an otherwise prosperous period.

Segregation of patients and discrimination in employment because of race are acute problems for hospitals. The United States Commission on Civil Rights in the summer of 1963 sent questionnaires about racial problems to 400 hospitals.

SOCIAL RESEARCH

Statistical social research had its beginning on a large scale in the 17-volume work of Charles Booth, *Life and Labour of the People in London*,[23] published between 1892 and 1902, an exposition of misery with statistical proof. Booth was

---

[19] Philadelphia, David McKay Co.; condensed in *Med. Economics,* December 7, 1959.

[20] *Mod. Hosp.,* September and December, 1954.

[21] *Clues to Suicide* edited by Edwin S. Schneidman, Ph.D., and Norman R. Farberow, Ph.D. (McGraw-Hill Book Co., New York, 1957) includes a chapter on suicide in a general hospital.

[22] New York, Harper and Brothers, 1958; condensed in Death Knell of Democracy. *Med. Economics,* December 21, 1959.

[23] London, The Macmillan Company, 1892–1902.

a shipowner and merchant. He poured his own money and years of work into the investigations of social conditions from which he drew the material for his books, which won for him wide recognition and honors. He was a member of the Royal Commission of 1905–1909, which was formed to revise English Poor Law policy adopted in 1834. Booth's investigations as reported in his books showed that one-fourth of the people in East London were living in poverty, which was a shock to many complacent citizens in view of a century of industrial progress. Old-age pensions were one of his proposals.

An earlier account, *London Labour and the London Poor,* the work of Henry Mayhew, published between 1851 and 1864, was also based on surveys, but only in part, and was not a really scientific study.

Toward the end of the eighteenth century, before the impact of industrialization had affected society to any great extent, two significant research projects were conducted. One was the collection and distribution of reports on social problems, with plans for their solution, by The Society for Bettering the Conditions and Increasing the Comforts of the Poor, founded with associates by Sir Thomas Bernard, another philanthropist who chose to try to help the poor instead of continuing in business to make more money. The other project was a survey by means of questionnaires, followed up by personal interviews and field work, by Sir Frederick Morton Eden which resulted in the publication in 1797 of his *State of the Poor*[24] in three quarto volumes. The author was one of the founders of the Globe Insurance Company.

These were the forerunners of the social research in England that led to many reforms and were to culminate in the *Report on Social Insurance and Allied Services* submitted by Lord Beveridge to the government in November, 1942, followed by a second report in October, 1944, suggesting how full employment in a free society could be achieved, and a third report published in 1948 under the title *Voluntary Action: A Report on Methods of Social Advance.*[25] In the last, after detailed analysis of the "friendly societies" whose mutual benefit objectives were virtually assumed by the government under social insurance, Lord Beveridge stated his conviction that many needs remain for the societies to meet over and beyond those that can be covered by the National Health Service and other government agencies. He saw richer than ever opportunity for voluntary activities and for private philanthropy, asserting:

> The capacity of voluntary action inspired by philanthropy to do new things is beyond question. Voluntary action is needed to do things which the State should not do, in the giving of advice, or in organizing the use of leisure. It is needed to do things which the State is most unlikely to do. It is needed to pioneer ahead of the State and make experiments. It is needed to get services rendered which cannot be got by paying for them.

[24] Full title, *The State of the Poor, a History of the Labouring Classes in England, with Parochial Reports,* 1797. Re-edited by A. G. L. Rogers, London, Routledge, 1928.
[25] London, George Allen & Unwin, Ltd.

Social research in America has lagged far behind that in Great Britain, but the current great need for it is spurring study of the methods used in other countries and development of new ones. As Dr. Henry T. Heald, president of the Ford Foundation, told delegates to the annual National Electronics Conference in 1962, "Scientific and technological progress has outstripped social research and development to an alarming degree."

One example of organized social research effort is the Institute for Social Research established in 1947 at the University of Michigan. In 1948 the Research Center for Group Dynamics moved from the Massachusetts Institute of Technology to merge with the Institute. There is also a Foundation for Research on Human Behavior.

Literature on social research as it is related to specific fields is becoming prolific.[26]

Within the hospital, social research takes many forms. Questionnaires to patients about service are one way, to selected segments of the community another. To produce the information wanted, the questions must be carefully thought out and worded. After the answers are obtained they must be organized and analyzed in a scientific manner by persons who are familiar with opinion survey techniques and recognize how much or how little weight to give the easily satisfied and the chronically critical persons who respond.

Social research on health need not be on a large scale. Problems can be uncovered through recruiting interest in the small, rural communities, just as well as in metropolitan areas, and they sometimes turn out to be more surprising in their revelation of unmet needs. Doctors and hospital administrators can quietly start the needling which leads to such projects. Albert Q. Maisel[27] told how a health council in Clinton County, Ohio, drew up a one-page questionnaire, organized subcommittees of canvassers in every township and village in the county, and sent them out on interviews. They interviewed 5,450 families, more than 90 per cent of the entire population, and came up with these shocking facts:

One pregnancy in every six ended in the death of the baby.
A majority of pre-school children had received no inoculations against diphtheria, lockjaw, whooping cough, or smallpox.
Forty per cent of all the school-age children had no protection against smallpox or diphtheria.
Seventy per cent of the rural folk and 14 per cent of the town dwellers were drinking unpasteurized milk.
More than half the population was drawing its water from easily contaminated wells.
The old-fashioned surface privy, a constant invitation to disease, was still used by 45 per cent of all rural families and even by many of the families living in towns.

[26] An example in the business area is *Social Science Research on Business: Product and Potential,* by Robert A. Dahl, Mason Haire, and Paul F. Lazarsfeld, published by Columbia University Press, New York, 1959.
[27] *Public Affairs Pamphlet,* No. 180, published by the Public Affairs Committee, Inc., revised edition, May,1960.

Undulant fever, usually caused by the use of infected, unpasteurized milk, had
stricken more than 500 persons among the families interviewed.

Thousands of persons had never been reached by the free chest x-ray service of
the local tuberculosis association.

With these statistics and facts, almost any county would do what Clinton
County did, use them as spurs to better health services and more utilization of
them.

Social Work

In a two-volume, 1,435-page study of *American Medicine,* compiled and published in 1937 by the American Foundation, less than one page was devoted to
medical social work. In only two or three other places in the report is there any
mention of social service, and in these instances it is merely included with other
community welfare projects. The discussion of medical social work that is presented is rather unfavorable in tone; in fact it is introduced by a subhead, "The
Social Worker Arraigned as an Element of Confusion."[28]

This study was based on letters of inquiry directed to "a representative list of
medical men and women who have been in practice for twenty years or more."
Therefore the attitude expressed on medical social service may be regarded as
representative of that of the doctor in general in the period in which the book
was written. The attitude, which in a quarter of a century has changed disturbingly little, is summarized by the editors as follows:[29]

> On behalf of the social worker, it should be said that the need of effective social
> service work connected with hospitals and dispensaries is considered, in this cor-
> respondence, a primary need. But the calibre of the people who do the work has
> not given general satisfaction. The social worker, it is pointed out, is often re-
> sponsible for really defeating the ends of the institution so far as the indigent are
> concerned. They are, the charge is, more intent on showing how many persons
> need medical care (and therefore how important it is for their own positions as
> "intake" workers to be continued) than on weeding out those that do not deserve
> free care.

The doctor and the social worker are, or should be, co-workers. Not to be
lightly dismissed, therefore, is censure or lack of appreciation of social service by
the medical profession. One way to establish medical social work on a more
sound basis is apparently to analyze the doctors' criticisms and attempt to overcome them. In doing this, it will be noticed that it is not the medical social work
idea that is arraigned as much as the type of medical social worker. The discussion in *American Medicine* is concluded with this statement:[30] "The recommendation of the writers would be to improve the social service work, broadening
its present base and substituting for meticulous workers of small calibre with

---

[28] *American Medicine—Expert Testimony Out of Court.* New York, The American Foundation,
Inc., 1937, pp. 169–70.

[29] *Ibid.,* p. 190.

[30] *Ibid.,* p. 170.

competent people who understand both the world around them and the institution's aims and capacities."

That phrase, "meticulous workers of small calibre," should bring social workers up with a start. It is used as if it were so generally applicable to them. However, in evaluating any criticism of one profession by another, it is not an idle pastime to see whether the shoe may not fit the other foot. Certainly in the eyes of the general public today the doctor is surrounded by no halo of great understanding of the world around him. Rather, it is felt, and the feeling is often expressed, that the demands of his own field of work are too exacting for him ordinarily to develop much perspective outside of that field; hence his slowness to appreciate the value of social work in supplementing medical care. Those who have recognized its worth have been members of the medical profession who were not themselves of "small calibre" but who understood "the world around them."

The trouble with the conduct of every activity on earth, from the directing of the destinies of governments to healing people and trying to keep them healed, is that too many people of "small calibre" are engaged in them. Any arraignment of social workers which is based on this general aspersion falls by virtue of its universal applicability to all types of laborers in the vineyard of human affairs. Nonetheless, the social service profession is obliged to ask: Is our percentage of competent, understanding people lower than that in other fields? Do we have the broad vision needed for playing a significant part in the whole movement to advance the social welfare of people?

The only way to have high-calibre workers is to set high standards. If the medical social service profession has done this, it will follow that agencies employing social workers can protect themselves from small-calibre people by recognizing the standard. Such a standard has been set by the American Association of Medical Social Workers for eligibility for membership, and the standard is revised upward from time to time as circumstances dictate.

Dr. Malcolm T. MacEachern[31] recommended that the

> . . . hospital administrator and the director of social service look for more than academic qualifications in applicants. If these two individuals themselves have the social viewpoint, they will have little difficulty in sensing it in others. . . . There are graduates from good schools of social work who have not and will never acquire the proper personality. The social worker's personality must be a combination of sympathy and hard-headed intelligence. These qualities, although innate, can and will be developed by a proper course in social service. But none can be entirely acquired even after years of experience if it did not originally exist in embryo.

In the foregoing we have a clear statement of the general qualifications for medical social work plus the idea of consideration of individual characteristics furnished by Dr. MacEachern. The responsibility for having the right type of

[31] *Hospital Organization and Management,* 2nd ed. Chicago, Physicians' Record Co., 1935, pp. 537–63.

worker is therefore placed squarely on the shoulders of those who select and employ her. It may justifiably be assumed that there has not been as intelligent exercise of discrimination in employing medical social workers as there has been in selecting personnel for better-understood types of activity.

The entire problem hinges on understanding. If doctors understood the aims of medical social work, there could not have been so much indifference displayed toward it in the American Foundation's report. We only ignore and depreciate work we do not understand. Quickest to depreciate a new idea is a person who has no ideas of his own on the subject; and it must be admitted that the medical profession, considered as a unit, which of course it is not, has had few ideas to present on how to improve the adaptation of medical service to the needs of the people. On this point the sociologist has some ideas. The medical social service worker can act as a link between the two, fusing the ideas of both and finding for them practical outlets. But first her aims must be understood.

Dr. MacEachern[32] states the purpose of medical social work in the hospital to be:

> To obtain and apply such understanding of the patient as will enable the institution, the physician, and other agencies concerned to comprehend and treat his illness more effectively. . . . The principal idea which should be conveyed by the term "medical social work" is that whereas all or nearly all others who deal with the patient are concerned with rendering him some particular service, hospital social service is concerned with anything that the patient may need to further his recovery. In other words, it is service to the total personality of the patient in so far as this service is needed to promote health and welfare. The social worker is the general practitioner among a group of specialists.

Alden B. Mills, then managing editor of *The Modern Hospital,* in a book, *Hospital Public Relations,*[33] had this to say about medical social service:

> For patients who have serious economic and social problems, a good medical social service department in the hospital is an essential, at least in a large city. The prime function of this department is to aid the doctor in treating the patient by providing him with as clear an understanding of the mental and emotional processes at work on the patient as he has of the physical handicaps under which the patient is suffering. The doctor and the social worker must often work out a social therapy just as carefully as the doctor and his medical colleagues work out a physical course of treatment. Another hospital responsibility which the social service department may assume under the direction of the medical staff and administration is the systematic follow-up of discharged patients to determine the end-results of in-patient and outpatient care. Only by such a follow-up service can the hospital accurately judge the effectiveness of its work.

The purposes as stated by Dr. MacEachern and by Mr. Mills express a scope in medical social service which is not even indicated in *American Medicine.* The latter recognizes this service only in connection with the charity patient—puts it entirely on an economic basis. The social service worker is to protect the hospital

[32] *Op. cit.,* pp. 537–63
[33] Physicians' Record Co., 1939.

from patients "who do not deserve free care." One doctor says bluntly, "Many social workers, in order to expand their activity, encourage the use of free facilities by people able to pay some or all of the cost of their medical care."

If social workers really had as their primary aim "to expand their activity," why would they have to encourage people to use the free facilities? Why not expand their activities into the parts of the hospital in which people paid for their care?

Dr. Richard C. Cabot commented that the following statement by Elsie Wulkop in *The Social Worker in a Hospital Ward*[34] is "very much to the point": "The need of medical-social work is not conditioned by the social or economic status of the patient; it is not peculiar to those who obtain the requisite medical treatment at clinic and dispensary rather than in the private office of their own physicians."

Dr. Cabot added: "I know that physicians are frequently in need of just such aid as these cases (previously described by Miss Wulkop) exemplify, for the aid of their private patients. But they are not used to the idea and nothing reminds them of the possibility of getting such aid. In hospitals, they are sometimes reminded of it by their interns or by seeing the social worker in the ward."

Dr. MacEachern[35] said that hospitals and the medical profession in general were slow to accept the idea of medical social service after Dr. Cabot introduced such a department in the Massachusetts General Hospital in Boston in 1905; that as late as 1915 there were

> . . . scarcely more than a dozen hospitals having a department of social service, and even in these few the work was limited exclusively to service among free patients. . . . The social problems in illness are not limited to the indigent. Attention has been directed in recent years to the unfortunate position of the man of moderate means when illness comes to his family, and the social worker has realized that he is as deserving of assistance as is the indigent and needs it almost as badly. The medical social worker has found that if help is tactfully offered it is accepted and appreciated. Thus, social work has developed from a benevolent administration of charity in the middle ages, through an effort to prevent the abuse of that charity in the nineteenth century, to become in the twentieth century a source of help to the poor and also to the moderately well to do. In addition, it has proved to be an aid to both physician and hospital in caring for the indigent and the man in moderate circumstances. . . . In the future the medical social worker will be as valuable in supplementing the work of the specialist practicing exclusively among the wealthy as she has been and is to physicians caring for the sick who are financially less fortunate. In the field of scientific medicine her place will be more definitely defined and established. She will follow the discharged patient who might otherwise not return, thereby insuring a continuation of treatment and enabling the physician to determine end-results, so necessary in appraising the value of any form of therapy.

It is a disturbing contradiction that in a book such as *Hospital Organization and Management,* the "bible" of the hospital world, the statement is made: "The

[34] Houghton Mifflin Co., 1926.
[35] *Op. cit.*, pp. 538–39.

medical social worker has become an assistant to the physician in diagnosis and treatment; . . . her opportunity for service is unlimited," whereas in an "exhaustive" study of *American Medicine* she is arraigned by the physician en masse as an "element of confusion." However, progress was never achieved without a struggle, and in any struggle there must be an element of confusion. May it not follow that the medical social worker, by adding confusion to the strained situation in which hidebound medicine finds itself, may help to force consideration of all of the different factors, particularly the social ones, which enter into our current medical problems?

The medical social worker can be the doctor's best ally. Why he is so slow to see this is hard to comprehend. Traditionalism is probably the leading cause. The old family doctor combined the viewpoints of physician and social worker. The modern doctor is unable to do that, because so seldom has he any contact with the homes of his patients. Yet the background is all-important. Dr. Cabot said that the modern doctor is afflicted with "blindness to backgrounds." In *Social Service and the Art of Healing*[36] he declared:

> I see a case of phthisis in a sad-eyed Irishman, but I cannot see, as he does, his children at home, the coldness of his employer when he asks if his job can be kept for him, the dreariness of this great hospital with its suggestion of nameless horrors behind doors which open for a moment and are swiftly closed again. The self that is pushing painfully through these experiences I fail to see, though it is all written in the stoop of his shoulders, the fear in his eyes, and the swift snatches of hesitating speech as he questions me about his lungs.

So Dr. Cabot enlists the aid of the social worker in "seeing." "What's missing here of the essentials of a human life?" he wants the social worker to ask, to supplement his concentrated attention on just a part of a human being. He declared:

> In a hospital patient, the missing necessities may be food and clothes, rest, work, decency, hope, self-respect, a bath, a crutch, or a confidant—to make him wholesome the social worker looks steadfastly to the man's whole needs and tries to fill in wherever the need is greatest. He is the synthesizer, and he must stand beside the analyzing specialist always, if hospital work is to be worth the enormous sum it costs. . . . Without hygiene most of medicine is useless, and without skillful fitting to the individual's needs, hygiene rules are simply old junk. . . . Better health means more money, usually; in consumption, heart disease, neurasthenia, somebody has got to hustle for some money if the doctor's orders are to be carried out.

The hospital is losing by its "blindness to backgrounds," Dr. Cabot insisted, for "the same ailments in the same patients are treated again and again, with a wisdom equal to that of the sage who dipped up water with a sieve." To illustrate he cited taking into the wards a baby whose digestion was upset, giving it free treatment, which cost the hospital $20, sending it out again without any inquiry into the way the mother fed it or the air it breathed or the clothes it wore;

[36] New York, Dodd, Mead & Co., 1931.

a month later it was back again, as sick as before, and the hospital spent another $20 in getting it well, and so on; until a chance follow-up established that the mother was ignorant of the first principles of feeding a baby and caring for it, though capable of being taught.

Obviously medical social service must use educational methods in its struggle to gain a better-defined place in hospital service. Many, many doctors of broad vision are completely sold, as were Dr. Cabot and Dr. MacEachern, on its merits. They give ground for hope that an increased number of others may be convinced that the social worker has much more to offer than merely investigate applicants for admission to clinics and determine who can pay and who can not.

No matter how well the worker functions, no one, least of all the attending physician, can appreciate the value of her services unless they are reported, and the profession cannot advance unless they are *ably* reported, with skillful interpretation of the full implications in each case. It was partly with this purpose in mind that case records competitions were conducted by the American Association of Hospital Social Workers several years ago. The prize records were published in 1928, preceded by an introduction by Sophonisba P. Breckinridge in which she said: "The medical social case-worker is only one of an increasing number of workers whose services are conditioned by their association with another highly developed professional group. . . . The competition was resorted to in order to develop interest in recording."[37]

In the grading of the five case reports published, all were adjudged verbose, yet none was considered complete. It is interesting to note that in the proposed scale for the next contest, the factor of vividness of presentation was to be considered in the score. Integration of medical and social work was in the main rated high, showing due appreciation by the social worker of the necessity of working closely with the doctor.

There is no easy road to better mutual understanding between doctor and social worker. The latter must duly consider all criticisms. Overzealousness defeats its own ends and creates misunderstanding. There is need for a balanced viewpoint and sound judgment if medical social service is to bring about a better order in the application of medical science to human welfare. Injection of any new element in the doctor-patient relationship may be expected to bring confusion, but the new element is obligated to try to minimize the disturbance so far as this can be done without sacrificing the mutual aim—better service to the patient.

An interesting and promising development is the establishment of teaching programs on medical social service for medical students. In 1933 the Massachusetts General Hospital, birthplace of the profession, began teaching medical students the social interpretation of clinical findings and broadened its social work instruction to include theological students, nurses, dietitians, volunteers, and

[37] Social Service Monograph No. 3. *Medical Social Case Records.* Chicago, University of Chicago Press, 1928.

others, teaching them to include in their services an appreciation of social, financial, and racial complications. In 1948 the medical social service group published a pamphlet, "Widening Horizons in Medical Education." An especially effective effort to establish social teaching in medical schools has been conducted by workers in the field of psychiatry, operating through a specially appointed National Committee on Social Work Teaching in Medical Schools of the American Association of Psychiatric Social Workers. Quite a number of medical schools have given faculty appointments to medical social workers.

The Health and Welfare Jungle

In the laudable effort to help poor and afflicted people, social reformers on a large and small scale have started projects which have grown into organizations vying with one another and multiplying beyond all reason. Hospitals are no more examples of sensible planning than are the agencies in other fields. Someone who had money or could attract it sensed a need, rallied others to the cause, and soon there was an institution or an organization which from the time of its birth became in itself a focus for loyalty without much thought of intermeshing with other agencies in the meeting of total needs. The overwhelming problem is that human beings are not segmented into the classifications represented by the different agencies. The cancer patient may be mentally ill, crippled, and poor at the same time; the insane may have tuberculosis and diabetes; the blind person may have heart disease. Afflictions oftentimes come in numbers, attacking the victim from all sides—physical, mental, social, and economic.

Naturally in the beginning the meeting of social problems had to be approached more or less singly. The fight against tuberculosis would not have gotten far if it had been welded into a total health program campaign. Dr. Lawrence F. Flick and associates organized the first voluntary drive in 1892—the Pennsylvania Society for the Prevention of Tuberculosis. Ohio was the next state to organize a society, in 1901, and New York followed the next year with the Committee for the Prevention of Tuberculosis of the Charity Organization Society of New York. Twenty-three associations in other states and cities had been founded by 1904 when the National Tuberculosis Association was organized.

Voluntary effort in venereal disease control was launched in 1914 as the American Social Hygiene Association, which represented a consolidation of several prior small organizations. The chief leader in the movement was Dr. Prince A. Morrow.

Dr. Thomas S. Cullen, of Baltimore, spearheaded the fight against cancer by presenting a plan for public education about cancer at a meeting of the American Gynaecological Society. The society appointed committees to study the plan, and the outcome was the formation of the American Society for the Control of Cancer on May 22, 1913. The name has since been simplified to the American Cancer Society. Lay members were admitted from the beginning, and the society had from the first the avowed purpose of public education. In 1961 the Eleanor Roosevelt Cancer Foundation became affiliated with the American Cancer Society to strengthen the cancer program and to reduce the number of organizations in the field.

The American Heart Association was founded in 1916 as the Association for the Prevention and Relief of Heart Disease. Dr. Haven Emerson and Dr. Lewis I. Conner were the leaders in the movement, which at first consisted mainly in developing standards for cardiac clinics and research work on the causes, prevention, and cure of diseases of the heart and arteries. The association had only professional members until 1948 when it was reorganized and lay members were admitted.

Follow-up care and relief of victims of poliomyelitis was begun by the National Society for Crippled Children and by service clubs such as Rotary, Shriners, Kiwanis, and Elks. Separate organization came in 1938 with the founding by President Franklin D. Roosevelt of the National Foundation for Infantile Paralysis. When the original purpose began to recede with the development of the Salk and the Sabin vaccines, the name was changed to the National Foundation and the program changed to include medical research, patient care, and education of the health professions in birth defects and arthritis, as well as in poliomyelitis.

Among the other national organizations whose activities are restricted to a single disease or group of diseases are the United Cerebral Palsy Associations, the Leukemia Society, the Multiple Sclerosis Society, the Muscular Dystrophy Associations of America, and the American Epilepsy Society.

In 1915 conservation of vision became the goal of an organization now known as the National Society for the Prevention of Blindness. Conservation of hearing was undertaken by the American Society for the Hard of Hearing in 1919, now the American Hearing Society. Dental health is promoted through public education by the National Dental Hygiene Association established in 1940.

The victims of crippling, from whatever cause, are the concern of a number of organizations, including service clubs. The National Society for Crippled Children and Adults was organized in 1921. Visible evidences of the scope of their work abound in such institutions as the Shriners' hospitals for crippled children and the rehabilitation centers which are trying to restore to normal living as many as possible of the disabled.

Maternal and infant welfare provides one of the most urgent appeals, and a great number of organizations are engaged in meeting them. The American Association for Maternal and Infant Health is prominent in research and public educational activities.

Greatly accelerated activity is being exerted by organizations in the field of mental health as increasingly the concept is being accepted by the public that mental abnormalities are as natural as physical ones and can in most instances be cured or alleviated just as physical illness can. Clifford W. Beers, author in

1908 of his autobiography, *A Mind That Found Itself,* started the new concept, and promoted it through forming the Connecticut Society for Mental Hygiene, which was soon followed by a national organization, now the National Association for Mental Health.

In disaster planning and work, hospitals, besides cooperating with public agencies, tie in with the American National Red Cross and the Salvation Army. The American Hospital Association has drawn up official agreements with both organizations in which the respective responsibilities are defined.

The Red Cross differs from other voluntary agencies in that it is quasi-governmental, as the following legal opinion rendered by the Honorable John W. Davis when he was Solicitor General sets forth:[38]

> When any question arises as to the scope and activities of the American Red Cross, it must always be remembered that its Charter is not only a grant of power but an imposition of duties. The American Red Cross is a quasi-governmental organization, operating under Congressional Charter, officered in part, at least, by governmental appointment, disbursing its funds under the security of a governmental audit, and designated by Presidential order for the fulfillment of certain treaty obligations into which the Government has entered. It owes, therefore, to the Government which it serves the distinct duty of discharging all those functions for which it was created. Not only is it constrained by those considerations growing out of its organic character, but there is also a moral obligation resting upon it to its membership and to the American people, who have so freely and generously contributed to its support.

The purposes referred to, as stated in its Congressional Charter, are: "To continue and carry on a system of national and international relief in time of peace and to apply the same in mitigating the sufferings caused by pestilence, famine, fire, floods, and other great national calamities, and to devise and carry on measures for preventing the same."[39]

Through the board of governors, comprising fifty members, some of whom are appointed by the President and others elected by the 3,700 local chapters, the general rules and regulations of the Red Cross are decided. One of these regulations is that the American National Red Cross does not recognize a disaster as catastrophic in nature unless five or more families are involved, feeling that the local community can care for the needs of less than five families. Help is given on an individual casework basis and not on a mass or community-wide basis, except for mass feeding and mass shelter provided during the initial period following a catastrophe.

Freeman E. May, now administrator of Baptist Hospital, Alexandria, Louisiana, then a student in hospital administration at Northwestern University, gave the following explanation in a talk to Alpha Delta Mu of the way in which Red Cross and hospitals interrelate in times of disaster:[40]

[38] *Family Service—Authority and Policies,* Washington, D.C., American National Red Cross, p. 57.
[39] *Ibid.,* pp. 57–58.
[40] Based upon "Cooperative Understanding Between the American Hospital Association and the American Red Cross on Hospitalization of Disaster Sufferers," Washington, D.C., The American National Red Cross.

If the local hospital equipment is inadequate to meet the need and it is agreed between the chairman of the medical and nursing aid sub-committee of the Chapter disaster preparedness committee and the local medical authorities that supplementation is needed, then the Red Cross will supplement the local facility. If this supplementation takes the form of establishing emergency facilities beyond that within the hospital buildings, Red Cross would pay the cost. The extra personnel needed could be volunteers or paid by Red Cross. The Red Cross assumes this position in payment of disaster patients' hospital bills. The normal relationship between doctor, hospital and patient exists. The Red Cross will pay the bill for disaster victims who apply for assistance and when it is proven on a casework basis that the family needs help in meeting the hospital bills incurred. However, no automatic guarantee to pay bills is ever given by the Red Cross just because the person or persons were involved in a disaster. The amount of payment depends on the policy of the hospital concerned; however, excessive charges would be refused. The Red Cross expects some consideration in view of the kind of work which it does, but it will not beg favors. . . .

The agreement between the American Hospital Association and the American National Red Cross . . . should be studied by the hospital administrator and by the local Red Cross Chapter. Further, some understanding should be reached between the two regarding what can be expected of each other as each locality will have its own peculiar problems to be worked out. In this pre-disaster planning for the cooperative utilization of the personnel and facilities, much loss of time and confusion could be avoided if the local hospitals, the Red Cross, the public health services, and the local safety forces could agree on the responsibilities of each as there will be little time for judicial planning after the injured and their families and friends concentrate on the hospital immediately after a disaster.

To prevent duplication, confusion, and to provide for maximum coordination of all community resources for the time when disaster may strike, definite plans should be worked out in advance. It is not the job of any one organization to carry the burden of the disaster. There are always willing hands to help, but without organization too much confusion results, thereby losing time that should be put to the direct relief of the sufferer.

When great numbers of injured are being brought in, the hospital may want to utilize Red Cross personnel and should feel free to ask for any of the following: physicians, nurses, first aiders, family caseworkers, utility personnel, messengers, canteen workers, motor corps, nurses' aides and staff aides. The hospital, if it cannot supply the need, may also ask for cots, blankets and linens, drugs, dressings, biologics, and storerooms. The administrator would also have a plan in the hospital so that when a disaster hits in the vicinity the following personnel may be alerted: information, house staff, visiting staff, nursing department, anesthesia department, business office, record department, laboratory and x-ray departments.

In accordance with its Charter responsibility, the American Red Cross provides supplementary assistance and rehabilitation of disaster victims. This requires the establishment of a central registration through which can be definitely determined the number, name, and location of persons ill, injured and dead, as well as those who are homeless or lost from relatives and friends. To do this it is necessary for Red Cross workers to visit the hospital to obtain this information at the earliest posible time. The hospital staff and authorities should cooperate in providing this information, while at the same time the Red Cross should limit their hospital contacts to a minimum to avoid disturbing hospital routine any more than necessary. In all visits proper clearance with the administrator and with the physicians in attendance should be made. A reciprocal exchange of pertinent home and family information is most helpful to Red Cross and the hospital.

Pre-planning by the American Red Cross and the hospitals of a community can and will solve many problems before they arise and leave each free to do a better community job when and if the disaster strikes.

The "Statement of Understanding"[41] between the American Hospital Association and the Salvation Army was approved by the board of trustees of the Association in May, 1960. It is quite similar in its general aspects to the agreement with the Red Cross.

Practically all these voluntary organizations have counterparts in Canada and other countries. They and many others are performing services as important in raising the general level of health and welfare as those of scientific and government organizations. The voluntary agency has a distinct disadvantage compared with the public agency in that the latter has the power of government behind it to implement its program. The former, however, has balancing advantages. It has more flexibility, can respond more quickly to a new need, and is free to change its objectives when it seems desirable to do so. It is not bound by the rigid regulations that necessarily hamper the public agency, and this is as true of the voluntary hospital as of any other welfare organization or institution.

The voluntary agency can, and frequently does, pave the way for government action. It can pioneer. It can serve as a needling instrument. It was voluntary action through little societies and unions that brought about in Britain such reforms as shortening of the working day, age limits for the employment of children, and workmen's compensation laws. The same thing happened in America and in other countries. Sometimes the purpose of an organization is realized and its work is done when other, more powerful agencies such as the government take on its program. An example of this is the American Child Health Association, pioneer, after merger with earlier associations, in nutrition and other factors contributing to child welfare. The United States Children's Bureau which was formed in 1912, state and local divisions of maternal and child health, and other public and voluntary agencies were by 1935 carrying out the program which it had mapped, and so it dissolved.

Dissolution is uncommon in this field, however. Agencies go on and on, grimly holding on to their programs despite duplication and overlapping of effort. Haphazard in origin, many of them are equally haphazard in operation, and some are fraudulent, collecting funds for the collectors' own enrichment. As far back as 1913 businessmen and others were concerned about the situation. A conference "to discuss the possibilities of mutual cooperation and proper division of the field with the view of eliminating unnecessary organizations and

[41] *Hospitals,* October 16, 1960.

the coordination of existing activities"[42] was called by Dr. Frederick R. Green, secretary of the Council on Health and Public Instruction of the American Medical Association, in April, 1913. In the following years criticism came from many sources, and after the war the air was full of demands for action toward some unification. Finally ten voluntary national health agencies formed the National Health Council. It began its operations January 1, 1921. The United States Public Health Service was an advisory member. The ten founding agencies were the American Public Health Association, American National Red Cross, American Social Hygiene Association, American Cancer Society, Conference of State and Provincial Health Authorities of North America, Council on Health and Public Instruction of the American Medical Association, National Child Health Council, National Committee for Mental Hygiene, National Organization for Public Health Nursing, and National Tuberculosis Association.

Generous contributions came from foundations. Many joint services were instituted with the object of economy. A number of the agencies were housed in the same building. The "joint planning" idea did not materialize, as a survey in 1935 by Professor Ira C. Hiscock showed; and despite the addition of new members and constant lip service to the coordinated effort theme, each organization has in general gone along on its own separate way. The remaining benefits are the providing of joint services to some of the members and probably also considerable psychological satisfaction in the fact that a coordinating council exists. This is an illusion, some say, since there is no coordination. The difficulties in the way of real unification, such as unwieldiness and administrative headaches, are apparent. The possibility of lessening the total constructive accomplishment is real.

As the director of a social agency himself, the hospital administrator is an actor, not a bystander, in the chaotic world of human welfare effort. Hospitals are contributors to the chaos. Loosely coordinated if at all, they are offenders along with the rest in duplicating and overlapping of services. The separate fund drives of the many separate agencies are being loudly criticized, but it is a rarity to hear of "united" fund-raising campaigns by the hospitals in any community. They are lone operators too for the most part, so cannot be overcritical of the same characteristic in other agencies. Yet this is exactly where change must come if new challenges are to be met. All are in trouble together because they are not working together.

Strenuous efforts to combine fund-raising campaigns on the local level have been made by communities and have been fought equally strenuously by several national agencies. The Community Chest idea has been warmly welcomed by the public but not by some of those who should be participants in it. The separate drives continue. The result is almost a social problem in itself.

The most successful of the endeavors to interrelate activities and to prevent

[42] Selskar M. Gunn and Philip S. Platt: *Voluntary Health Agencies: An Interpretive Study*. The Ronald Press Company, New York, 1945, p. 182.

overlapping is that of the councils of social agencies which operate under different names in different places—in Chicago as the Welfare Council of Metropolitan Chicago, in Cincinnati as the Public Health Federation of Cincinnati and Hamilton County, in Cleveland as the Cleveland Health Council. Their reservoirs of information about the activities of the various agencies are a great boon to administrators and medical social workers who need cooperation in the referral of patients and other problems. In a study of the voluntary health agencies of the United States—of which there were then over 20,000—in 1945, under the auspices of the National Health Council, the following statement on the importance of local councils was made:[43]

> The health council is potentially one of the most valuable and powerful health forces in a community. It can cultivate the public's understanding of its health problems and help the official health department to attain higher levels of effectiveness and more adequate range of services. Occasionally, the health council is actually a stronger leader than the health department. Even the strong health department needs the assistance of the health council and the wise public health official will assiduously encourage its development.

PHILANTHROPY AND SOCIAL REFORM

Giving of fortune and of self to make the world a better place in which to live has been practiced through the ages. Few studies are more agreeable than tracing the lives of the great benefactors of humanity. Particularly are they fascinating when the donors are the kind who throw the weight of their own energies behind their gifts of substance. A redeeming quality of mankind is concern for the welfare of others. Finding evidences of it lifts the pall from too many disclosures of struggles merely to get rich or to become powerful.

The need for large charitable projects was not acute in the Middle Ages. The lords of the manor usually looked out for their serfs in sickness and in old age. The clergy in the monasteries ministered to wayfarers and the poor. Good deeds on earth were supposed to pave the way to rewards in heaven, so the Christian impulse was to relieve suffering. Probably much more personal beneficence was practiced than is realized. There was a kind of security for the mass of the people that disappeared with the end of feudalism. For the freed serfs life became more uncertain. As industrialization progressed and they crowded into the towns that gave them employment, their poverty and misery presented a more concentrated picture than before to the observer who was welfare-minded.

The so-called Ragged Schools, Sunday schools for children from the slums whose tattered clothes kept them from attending regular Sunday schools, were started around 1790 and developed by a crippled cobbler, John Pounds (1766–1839); the proprietor of a tailor shop, Thomas Cranfield (1766–1838); and a

[43] *Ibid.*, p. 127.

lawyer and carriage manufacturer, Samuel Robert Starey (1820–1904). The last, with three associates, in 1844 organized the twenty schools then existing into a "Ragged School Union." Through a small advertisement in a London newspaper asking for support, Lord Ashley, later Lord Shaftesbury, was attracted to the movement, into which he plunged heart and soul, his biographer, Edwin Hodder,[44] saying that "for many years the ragged children of London were rarely out of his thoughts, waking or sleeping."

Lord Shaftesbury (1801–1885) was not wealthy, but he had wealthy friends who gave generously to the many charitable movements which he promoted. His name heads the list of nineteenth-century philanthropists and social reformers. At the memorial service to him held in Westminster Abbey on October 8, 1885, 200 religious and philanthropic institutions were represented.

An early interest was better housing for the poor, a result of his own observation of conditions in the slums. He threw his support behind the Society for Improving the Conditions of the Labouring Classes, working mainly on the housing problem. He was president for fifty years of the Indigent Blind Visiting Society. The London City Mission was one of his other major interests. His power as an aristocrat and as a member of Parliament was used to promote legislation on behalf of the working classes. His first public speech was concerned with the mentally ill, and he was chairman of the Lunacy Commissioners for 57 years. He pushed through the Factory Acts and legislation for the protection of chimney sweeps and for safety in coal mines.

In connection with the Factory Acts, Beatrice Webb,[45] commenting in 1901 on opposition which was "blocking all progress in the effective application of the acts to other industries," said:

> What we have to do is to detach the great employer, whose profits are too large to feel the immediate pressure of regulation and who stands to gain by the increased efficiency of the factors of production, from the ruck of employers or stupid ones. What seems clear is that we shall get no further installments of reform unless we gain the consent of an influential minority of the threatened interest.

The savings bank originated as a social reform. Henry Duncan, a minister, started one in Scotland in 1810 to encourage saving by the poorer classes. In 1819 he was instrumental in having a bill passed in Scotland for the establishment of savings banks without their registration as friendly societies.

Relieving the lot of the working classes was the purpose of the Congregational minister Henry Solly (1813–1903) in forming workingmen's clubs and helping Frederick Denison Maurice (1805–1872), a minister of the Church of England, in the starting and conduct of workingmen's colleges, with evening as well as day classes. Solly was also one of the promoters, with Charles Stewart Loch, of the Charity Organization Society, which was concerned with the relief of

---

[44] *The Life and Work of the Seventh Earl of Shaftesbury, K.G.*, London, Cassell & Company, 1886.

[45] *Our Partnership*, London, Longmans, Green and Co., 1948, p. 205.

distress among people who were even worse off than the working class, the disorganized, the unemployed, the disabled, and the sick. He proposed in 1884 "industrial villages" which were to be self-sufficient communities.

The Young Men's Christian Association was started in 1884 by George Williams, who afterward made a fortune in the drapery business. Its interdenominational religious aim was fundamental, but it quickly branched out into educational, social, and welfare activities.

The British and Foreign Blind Association for Promoting the Education of the Blind was founded in 1868 by a surgeon who had lost his sight, Thomas Rhodes Armitage. The executive committee of this association selected Braille from several methods as the best for making books for the blind. The name of the association was later changed to the National Institute for the Blind. Armitage's fortune and his knowledge and experience in medicine were contributed completely to this cause.

Profit-sharing schemes, housing, and a new type of friendly society were among the activities of a successful manufacturer of clothing, George Holloway (1825–1892).

The Salvation Army with its philanthropic as well as religious purposes was founded by William Booth in 1865 as an independent Christian Mission in Whitechapel, the present name having been selected in 1878. Among its activities in the latter part of the century was the Hadleigh Farm Colony, where occupation and subsistence were provided for the unemployed and unemployable. Comparing it with the Hollesley Bay Colony, one of the philanthropic projects of Joseph Fels, who made his millions in Fels-Naptha soap, Beatrice Webb[46] wrote following an inspection:

A more mixed lot of men—ex-convicts, ex-tramps, workhouse-able-bodied and men picked up in shelters, far more human wreckage, but, on the other hand, less the ordinary ruck of casual labourers. Here they are, I think, more successful in getting the men to work, there is less foul talk, perhaps less discontent and jeering. The self-devotion of the officers counts for something in raising the tone of the colonists. On the other hand, there is tremendous religious pressure—far more than I had realized.

Of the Hollesley colony she said:

... the impression of the place was mournfully tragic—half educated, half disciplined humans, who felt themselves to have been trampled on by their kind, were sore and angry, every man of them in favour of every kind of protection, protection against machinery, protection against female, boy and foreign labour, protection against Irish, Scotch and country men, protection against foreign commodities, protection against all or anything that had succeeded whilst they had failed. There was a growing assumption in their minds that they had the *right* to 30s. a week—in London the rate for borough council work, though this assumption was, as yet, tall talk to most of them. They were a faint-hearted, nerveless set of men, their manner sometimes servile, sometimes sullen, never easy and independent.

[46] *Ibid.,* pp. 398–401.

Obviously Mrs. Webb had serious doubts about the wisdom of colonization as a means of social reform or as a way of accomplishing very much in relieving the distress of the unemployed.

Modern housing management was the activity in which Octavia Hill pioneered in 1864. She was a granddaughter of the sanitarian Dr. Thomas Southwood Smith. Miss Hill was also a pillar in the Charity Organization Society and not only was a philanthropist in her own right, her father having been a corn merchant and banker, but was successful in obtaining support from others for her projects. Emma Cons worked with Miss Hill on housing reform and also started hostels for girls.

Juvenile missions and boys' homes were the creations of a physician, Thomas John Barnardo (1845-1905). He was also superintendent of a Ragged School. The boys' homes, known by his name, spread throughout England.

The Boy Scouts and, with his sister, the Girl Guides, were the invention of Robert Baden-Powell, an army career man who retired in 1910 to start the activity for which he had prepared the way by three books, published in 1884, 1899, and 1908, the last of which in particular, aroused wide interest.

Political action rather than voluntary was in the main the objective of the Webbs, Sidney (1859-1947) and Beatrice (1858-1943), who devoted their entire lives to battles for legislation to promote public welfare. Necessarily this activity brought them in contact with, and enlisted their support of, all kinds of voluntary philanthropic and reform movements. They conceived and founded the London School of Economics and Political Science. Although they were Socialists, they chose the directors of the school without regard to party and it was not a Socialist institution. Beatrice Webb was a member of the 1905-1909 Royal Poor Law Commission, and she made an interesting comment about a question that she brought up for discussion—"the relation of poor law medical treatment to public health":[47]

> In listening to the evidence brought by the Charity Organization Society members in favour of restricting medical relief to the technically destitute, it suddenly flashed across my mind that what we had to do was to adopt the exactly contrary attitude, and make medical inspection and medical treatment compulsory on all sick persons—to treat illness, in fact, as a public nuisance to be suppressed in the interests of the community.

The philanthropic organization mentioned as the Charity Organization Society through which so many individual philanthropists worked was founded in 1869 as the Society for Organizing Charitable Relief and Repressing Mendicity; in 1944 its name was again changed to the Family Welfare Association. A historical statement in one of its recent publications gives the following as the original purpose:[48]

[47] *Ibid.*, p. 348.
[48] Quoted by Lord Beveridge in *Voluntary Action,* pp. 143-44. London, Unwin Brothers, Ltd., 1948.

The founders of the Association had in view the reduction of the beggary and the pauperism then rife in London. There was much unemployment; of the many families evicted from their homes by the construction of the railways, only twenty thousand had been rehoused, and it was estimated that over a hundred thousand children were homeless. Inadequate out-relief was supplemented by coal and bread funds, free dormitories, soup kitchens, free refuges, etc., but these only relieved the immediate distress. Boards of Guardians gave inadequate relief because they knew it would be supplemented by indiscriminate charity; the charities gave because the Guardians' relief was inadequate.

From the first the Association held that gifts of food and money, however necessary, were by themselves insufficient and that people in distress could only be helped constructively through the careful study of each individual problem.

Groups of people organized for mutual help are an important type of philanthropy. United by some common interest such as a craft, an industry, a geographic location, or a specific purpose, they can serve a social as well as an economic or insurance function. The members of medieval guilds were protected against unemployment and other disasters by funds raised among themselves. Trade unions in Belgium were among the first to pay their members when work was not to be had. In 1897 the local trade unions were subsidized for this purpose by the city of Liege and in 1902 by the city of Ghent, after which the Belgian government began to make grants for unemployment relief to the trade unions.

In Britain almost a unique development occurred—the friendly societies. Some of them were on the order of the guilds elsewhere, composed of workers in a single craft, such as the Goldsmiths' Friendly Society established in 1712 in Clerkenwell, and the oldest known one, the Incorporation of Carters in Leith, said to date back to 1555. Huguenot refugees established in 1703 the Norman Society and later several others. A few were organized like lodges or fraternal societies and have spread to America, such as the Oddfellows and the Ancient Order of Foresters. Among the general or specific purposes of the different societies, to be met from funds accumulated to be disbursed in case of need, are relief to the aged, the sick, the disabled, widows, and orphans. Other purposes were the provision of annuities and funds to pay the expenses of burial. There were "building societies" from whose treasury members drew funds to build homes. The names of a number of them give insight into the spirit in which they were founded—the Old Amicable Society of Grantham, the Hearts of Oak Benefit Society, and the Grand Independent Order of Loyal Caledonian Corks Friendly Sick and Dividend Society, which had in 1948 some 200 branches and 20,000 members. The Hearts of Oak also developed into a large society with many branches, but the typical friendly society was local, small, and met in the village tavern. The past tense has to be used because so many of them are disappearing with the taking over of their functions by the welfare state, notwithstanding Lord Beveridge's plea that they develop objectives beyond those the government can meet.[49]

[49] *Ibid.*, pp. 21–62.

Another development in Britain that Lord Beveridge said represents "one of the most remarkable growths of mutual aid in modern times" is the Hospital Contributory Scheme. Most of these schemes were not registered as friendly societies but were incorporated under the Companies Acts as companies limited by guarantee—in other words, nonprofit. These organizations are a combination of insurance with charitable and community support. They conduct campaigns for the support of hospitals. Lord Beveridge was very partial to these contributory plans and did not include voluntary hospitals or hospitalization in the recommendations in his report for unification of all social insurances under a single plan. Louis Pink[50] comments:

> He is evidently torn between carrying out his principle of including all social services under a common centralized government scheme and preserving the voluntary hospitals which are so important in promoting and protecting the health of Britain. He therefore makes no decision, but remarks that if the state takes over, "there will be little or nothing left for which people can be asked to contribute voluntarily, and an important financial resource of the voluntary hospitals will come to an end."

After the extension of social insurance in 1946, Lord Beveridge[51] changed his position somewhat, stating that the hospital contributory schemes

> . . . show the vitality of voluntary action on the lines of mutual aid, in meeting newly recognized needs even after the beginning of social insurance in 1911. Even after the extension of social insurance in 1946, many urgent needs of many citizens will remain, and . . . can be met only or best by voluntary action. The original financial purpose which called the hospital contributory schemes into being will presumably come to an end within the next few years. It may be that the organizations which launched these schemes or some of them will be able to undertake new tasks of meeting human needs by citizen cooperation. It is certain that the spirit of mutual aid among all classes which inspired these schemes must continue in one form or another, if the Britain of the future is to be worthy of the past.

It is essential for the hospital executive and student to delve deeply into British philanthropic history, so briefly highlighted in the foregoing pages, in order that he may gain an understanding of the effect upon society as a whole, not only hospitals, of the taking over by the federal government, actual and threatened, of responsibilities now assumed by voluntary agencies. Conditions in the United States are different in many ways from those in the United Kingdom, but enough similarities exist to make studies and comparisons profitable.

Philanthropy in America

A great deal of the friendly society spirit, if not the name, exists in America. Alexis de Tocqueville of France noticed it when he toured the country in 1830, observing:

[50] *Freedom from Fear*. New York and London, Harper & Brothers, 1944, pp. 73–74.
[51] *Voluntary Action*, p. 116.

Americans are the most peculiar people in the world. In a local community a citizen may conceive of some need which is not being met. He goes across the street and discusses it with his neighbor. A committee begins to function in behalf of that need, and you won't believe this but it's true: all of this is done without reference to any bureaucrat, by the private citizens on their own initiative.

True, and besides, judging by the multitude of "committees" that exist, once they are formed they go on forever; when one need is met they find another to keep them busy.

An overview of individual American philanthropy might well begin with George Peabody (1795–1869), since he divided his beneficences between the New World and the Old. Born in Massachusetts, spending twenty years in the dry goods business in Baltimore, he went to London in 1843 to become a merchant and broker. He accumulated a large fortune. In 1852 he sent a substantial donation to found an educational institution and library in his native town, South Danvers, now Peabody, Masachusetts. Then he gave to the city of Baltimore $1.4 million for an institute of science, literature, and fine arts. Next he established the Peabody Education Fund for promotion of education in the southern states—this was the first of the American educational foundations. His gifts to education amounted to some $7 million. To the city of London he gave $2.5 million for the construction of lodginghouses. These were magnificent and unheard of benefactions for the times, and Peabody was honored in both countries. In 1900 he was elected to the American Hall of Fame.

Dr. Samuel Gridley Howe (1801–1876), a graduate of Harvard Medical College and the husband of Julia Ward Howe, had an unusual career as a philanthropist. He organized the medical staff for the Greek army during 1824–1827, then came back to the United States to get donations for the starving people. He returned with supplies and formed a colony on the isthmus of Corinth. Later, after studying methods of educating the blind in France, he founded schools for the blind and for idiots in Massachusetts. Not forgetting his friends in Greece, he made another journey in 1867 bringing supplies for the Cretans. His career culminated with his founding of the Massachusetts State Board of Charities, which he served as chairman from 1865 to 1874.

Clara Barton (1821–1912) devoted her life to good works. In the Civil War she did relief work on the battlefields and was especially active in organizing search for missing men. During the Franco-Prussian War she helped to found hospitals. In 1881 through her efforts the American Red Cross was founded, and she served as its president until 1904. The relief work of the Red Cross during disasters was initiated by her. Wherever there was need for relief of suffering in America or elsewhere she was quick to respond, superintending among many others the rescue and aid work during the Johnstown flood in 1889, the famine in Russia in 1892, and the massacres in Armenia in 1896.

As a fourth example among the numerous individual philanthropists, Margaret Olivia Slocum Sage (1828–1918) is a logical choice because her generosity lives on in the Russell Sage Foundation, which she established with a gift of ten million dollars in 1907. Russell Sage began life as an errand boy and clerk in a grocery store. In 1874 he purchased a seat on the New York Stock Exchange and became associated with Jay Gould in his railway operations. He bequeathed his large fortune to his wife who devoted it to educational and religious purposes. The Russell Sage Foundation cooperates with social agencies for the administration of charities and other social enterprises. It has been especially active in education.

John D. Rockefeller endowed the General Education Board with a gift of $130 million in 1902. Fifty years later it was terminated after having spent in its final year the last $5 million of the total expenditures of $326 million. Rockefeller also established with a gift of $39 million the Rockefeller Institute for Medical Research; the Rockefeller Foundation (mainly devoted to development of medical education) with $180 million; and the Laura Spelman Rockefeller Memorial with $73 million. The last was consolidated in 1929 with the foundation. Despite having spent several times the original endowment, the foundation has a larger fund on hand than when it was established. John D. Rockefeller, Jr. (1874–1960), has been quoted as saying: "My father created an organization for the making of wealth. I regard it as my responsibility to see that the vast amount of money he accumulated is used for the good of humanity." His contributions in his own name to New York's Memorial Hospital alone totaled more than $9 million.

Andrew Carnegie (1835–1919) established in 1902 the Carnegie Institute for promoting scientific research and publishing the results, and in 1905 the Carnegie Foundation for the Advancement of Teaching. He also established and endowed a technical school at Pittsburgh and libraries all over the country and in Britain. The Carnegie Corporation, as it now operates, dispenses large funds for any worthy educational or charitable purpose. It was the Carnegie Foundation for the Advancement of Teaching that financed with a grant of $40,000 the study by Abraham Flexner of American medical schools in 1909–1910. In 1953 a $5 million center was dedicated in New York for the Carnegie Endowment for International Peace.

Mrs. Stephen V. Harkness founded the Commonwealth Fund in 1918. Its purpose is to promote health through grants for medical education, research, and other means.

James B. Duke, the tobacco king, founded the Duke Endowment in 1924. Its purpose is to assist philanthropic institutions in North and South Carolina, including hospitals, orphanages, universities, and the Methodist Church.

W. K. Kellogg, whose fortune was made in the cereal business, established in 1930 a fund of about $50 million for the establishment of the W. K. Kellogg Foundation, with the stipulation that it was to be used for the promotion of the health, education, and welfare of mankind but principally of children and youth, directly or indirectly.

Henry and Edsel Ford established the Ford Foundation in 1936. Its object is to advance human welfare by identifying problems of national importance and granting funds for efforts toward their solution, primarily through educational means. In 1953 five divisions were established: behavioral sciences, establishment of peace, strengthening of democracy, strengthening of the economy, and advancement of education. The Ford Foundation is the largest philanthropic foundation in the world with assets of nearly two billion dollars.

Henry Roy Cullen (1878–1957), Texas oil millionaire, was the greatest individual benefactor of hospitals in recent years. He set up in 1947 the Cullen Foundation, endowed with oil properties which will ultimately yield an estimated $160 million. During his lifetime he gave away some $200 million. Irrespective of denomination he distributed millions among the hospitals of Houston, once donating in a single week more than $4 million to four hospitals.

A different kind of philanthropic institution from these individually endowed ones is exemplified by the Cleveland Foundation, established in 1914 by F. H. Goff, president of the Cleveland Trust Company. In his handling of estates Mr. Goff had discovered that many philanthropically inclined persons had difficulty in selecting a satisfactory cause to which to contribute. He conceived the idea of a community trust, the funds to be used for any worthy social undertaking, especially in the city of Cleveland, the board to consist partly of public officials, partly of citizens. This plan has been copied by many other communities in the United States and Canada. The largest one, the New York City Community Trust, has the same general pattern. A National Council on Community Foundations has been organized.

All in all, there are some 4,000 foundations which have a principal fund, most of them small and limited in their objectives.

The millions given by wealthy individual donors and by foundations should not obscure the millions given, in total, by countless philanthropists of small means who give what they can in response to appeals of the needy. Typical is a hospital "that pennies built" in the north woods of Wisconsin, all the result of a television program in 1954. On the program, "This Is Your Life," the story of Dr. Kate Newcomb's struggle to raise funds to build a hospital in the remote area was told. Participants on the show described the local high school's "Penny Parade" campaign that brought in enough money to start the hospital but not to complete it. As a result of the show, pennies poured in from television viewers to the total of $102,000. The hospital was finished and is serving well the needs of the inhabitants including Indians who are scattered over the hundreds of square miles surrounding it.[52]

[52] Abstracted from an article by Helen D. Behnke: The Hospital That Pennies Built—Five Years Later. *Hospitals*, June, 1959, pp. 43–44.

World-wide Philanthropic Projects

Project HOPE (Health Opportunities for People Everywhere) is an example of the lengths to which Americans are going in helping others. Dr. William Walsh, an internist of Washington, D.C., conceived the idea. The government made available the old Navy hospital ship, the S.S. *Consolation.* The ship was renamed the *Hope* and it is the first privately sponsored large hospital ship in the world. Financing for equipping it and for the first year's voyage and work amounted to about four million dollars. The funds came through donations from the public, from business, from labor, from private groups. A small permanent professional staff was recruited, along with a large staff of volunteer physicians who rotated for about two months each during the first year's trip to countries in southeast Asia in 1960–1961. In 1962–1963 a similar program was being followed in South America, mainly in Peru. Besides giving medical and surgical care, the purpose is education—education of medical students, doctors, nurses, and the people in the countries visited. The *Hope* has a heavy future schedule to respond to the invitations of the many countries which are wanting visits to their shores, including "come back" requests from those visited before.

Another world-wide project was organized in 1960 by the American Surgical Trade Association—the Surgical Trade Foundation with Dr. Albert Schweitzer as honorary sponsor. The aim of the project is "to bring better medical care to millions of people in underprivileged areas of the world." The association through this project is helping to distribute surplus medical equipment and supplies to foreign health and medical missions on a charitable basis with the aid of the entire surgical industry, both manufacturers and distributors. Before the first year of operation was completed the value of goods donated had exceeded $100,000.

CARE, to which thousands of Americans are contributing for the relief of the poverty-stricken in underdeveloped countries, merged in 1962 with MED-ICO. The latter is now operating as a service of the former. The consolidation was effected in order to reduce administration costs, to eliminate duplicate facilities, and to lessen the number of appeals for funds.

The importance of the individual is demonstrated again and again in important philanthropic projects that were conceived and put into operation by one person. World Medical Relief, Inc., for example, was founded and is directed by the wife of a retired Detroit businessman. Mrs. Lester Auberlin "has collected and shipped to 64 countries more than 750 tons of medical supplies valued at thirty million dollars."[53] Her motivation came from watching a televised documentary about Korean orphans. After considerable collecting on her own of sample and excess drugs, outmoded but still serviceable equipment, and other surplus supplies, she organized a board of businessmen and doctors and incor-

[53] *Christian Century,* March, 1962.

porated the venture. Involved in the operation of the project, which is housed in a five-story building at low rental, are nearly 150 volunteers who sort, bottle, and package the drugs. Volunteer chemists and registered pharmacists check the procedures and supplies.

Corporate Giving

In 1951 the Tennessee Coal, Iron and Railroad Company, Birmingham, Alabama, a subsidiary of the United States Steel Corporation, presented to a foundation for the benefit of people of the western section of Jefferson County, the 350-bed Lloyd Noland Hospital at Fairfield, Alabama, plus a sum of $750,000 to erect and equip a new outpatient clinic building to be operated in connection with the hospital. All of the hospital properties, equipment, and facilities were included in the gift. Thus was transferred to the community a hospital established in 1919 by an industry for the care of its employees. The transfer is an example of one of the changes in industrial health service policy as well as a way of corporate giving.

Another steel company, the Algoma Steel Corporation of Sault Ste. Marie, Ontario, donated in 1961 all of the structural steel used in building the addition to the Chippewa County War Memorial Hospital in Sault Ste. Marie, Michigan, a spokesman for the company explaining: "Although there is a river between us, there is a common bond."

The Sears-Roebuck Foundation and the Student American Medical Association Foundation announced in 1963 sponsorship of a preceptorship program to acquaint medical students with general practice in small communities. The students selected are to spend two consecutive months with physicians in communities which have built clinics under the Sears Foundation's medical assistance program.

The Mead Johnson Laboratories of Evansville, Indiana, has a "Service to Medicine Program" designed to "help physicians help their patients." Among the projects are awards for postgraduate training in hospital administration.

The Kresge Foundation has given $200,000 for a school of nursing on the upper campus of the University of Western Ontario.

The Smith, Kline and French Foundation makes grants for educational purposes to combat mental illness, for public charities and improvements, for the purchase of scientific and educational equipment, and for awards in basic research in medicine and related sciences.

The John A. Hartford Foundation, established by George L. Hartford and his brother, who headed the Great Atlantic and Pacific Tea Company, has given millions to "reduce the time lag that exists between medical research findings and their clinical use." Open-heart surgery research in hospitals, including grants for the purchase of equipment, is one of the projects sponsored. Another is aid to the American College of Surgeons in its program for improving the medical management of the injured.

Harold Dillingham, president of the family holding company established by the Dillinghams of Hawaii, builders of the $23-million Honolulu shopping center and many other commercial and industrial projects, developed the Kauikeolani Children's Hospital, Honolulu, as a first-class institution.

The Ford Foundation's $200 million surprise grants to 3,464 voluntary hospitals in the United States in December, 1955, were spent for a great variety of improvements. Among them were installations of heliports, blood banks, occupational therapy departments; expansion of geriatric, psychiatric, rehabilitation, emergency, premature, pediatrics, outpatient, diagnostic, pharmacy, dental, medical library, research, education, and many other services; acquisition of equipment; and as the base for construction of new buildings and modernization of existing ones.

These are just a few of the examples of corporate giving which accounts for a good share of the support for medical and hospital service. Occasionally shareholders question the right of corporation managers to give money for charitable purposes. To one of these who objected that the company was "not an eleemosynary institution," that shareholders are "certainly entitled to choose their own beneficiaries," and that the company was "supposed to be run solely for the stockholders' benefit," the president of the Standard Oil Company of New Jersey answered:[54]

> We in the Jersey Company believe in being good corporate citizens. We think the principle of corporate giving is well established. It is encouraged by our tax laws; it has been upheld in our courts; and the public has come to expect it of corporations. Perhaps this was not so, say, some 25 years ago, but it is today. In our judgment these contributions are extremely important if Jersey is to merit the good will of the public, which is essential to the prosperity of your company.
>
> When you're a good corporate citizen, it is often necessary to give support to private institutions from which you expect no direct dollar-and-cents benefit—hospitals, community service organizations, the Red Cross, colleges, universities, and so on. If good citizens, corporate and individual alike, did not support these institutions, they would have to turn to the government for support—and that, certainly, is not the way to advance the cause of free enterprise.
>
> As to the merits of giving to one institution, or one type of institution, over another, the possibilities for discussion are infinite. As we normally do in such a situation, we call upon a competent staff to gather information, to study the various facets of the problem, to appraise and analyze the facts, to evaluate the direct and indirect benefit to the company and its shareholders, and to make recommendations to the board. Your directors are then in a position to make a sound decision, and I assure you that in every instance the shareholders' interests are paramount.

In 1952 several stockholders objected to a contribution of $1,500 to the 1951 "Annual Giving" of Princeton University by the A. P. Smith Manufacturing

[54] *79th Annual Meeting Report,* Standard Oil Company of New Jersey, May 24, 1961, p. 15.

Company of East Orange, New Jersey, saying that the corporation charter did not permit such contributions. The company asked the Superior Court of New Jersey for a declaratory judgment recognizing the right of the corporation to make such a contribution. The company president and officials of other companies testified at the trial in favor of corporate giving. The action and contention of the corporation were upheld in the opinion by both the Superior Court and the Supreme Court of New Jersey, the latter saying, in part:[55]

> With the transfer of most of the wealth to corporate hands and the imposition of heavy burdens of individual taxation, individuals have been unable to keep pace with increased philanthropic needs. They have, therefore, with justification turned to corporations to assume the modern obligations of good citizenship in the same manner as humans do. Congress and state legislatures have enacted laws which encourage corporate contributions, and much has recently been written to indicate the crying need and adequate legal basis therefor. . . . Modern conditions require that corporations acknowledge and discharge social as well as private responsibilities as members of the communities within which they operate. Within this broad concept there is no difficulty in sustaining, as incidental to their proper objects and in aid of the public welfare, the power of corporations to contribute corporate funds within reasonable limits in support of [charitable] institutions.

Giving, as a regular management function along with manufacturing, marketing or research, was discussed in an article by John A. Pollard.[56]

Philanthropy Not Diminishing

According to the American Association of Fund-Raising Council's 1962 figures in *A Compilation of Facts Related to American Philanthropy,* contributions to health, education and welfare are not going down, contrary to the general belief. Private giving totaled an estimated $8.7 billion in 1961, an increase of $500 million over 1960. Gifts to hospitals reached an estimated $742 million in 1961.

CIVIC SERVICE CLUBS AND FRATERNAL ORGANIZATIONS

The hospital administrator in order to enter into the life of the community as fully as possible must have familiarity with all of its activities, not the least of which in influence are the civic service clubs and fraternal organizations. Roy C. House, now administrator and executive vice president of Wesley Hospital and School of Nursing, Wichita, Kansas, used these organizations as the subject of a talk at a meeting of Alpha Delta Mu when he was a student in hospital administration at Northwestern University a few years ago. The following is a condensation of his remarks:

[55] M. J. Foster: Corporate Gifts to Charities. *Trustee,* November, 1954, pp. 2–3.
[56] Emerging Pattern in Corporate Giving. *Harvard Business Review,* May–June, 1960.

Civic Service Clubs

Generally speaking the major service club organizations have similar purposes, organizations, and requirements for membership. These clubs are organized with outstanding businessmen and community leaders as the backbone and membership, and usually limit this membership, sometimes rather clannishly, by various devices. Invariably the purposes have to do with community service, either as a body or as individuals. It can safely be stated that these clubs channel a tremendous amount of home-town leadership in community betterment, and frequently there is engendered among the various service clubs in a community a goodly amount of friendly rivalry. Values accrue to the individual through new friendships and opportunities for expression.

Rotary International is the granddaddy of all the service clubs. This group more or less paved the way for the similar organizations founded in later years. Rotary is a "world fellowship of business and professional executives who accept the Ideal of Service as the basis for success and happiness in business and community life." Since its founding in 1905 by a young Chicago lawyer named Paul Harris, Rotary has spread to many cities and to other lands. The first club organized outside the United States was in Winnipeg, Canada, in 1910; in the following year the first club outside the hemisphere was organized in Dublin, Ireland. There are some 6,500 clubs in 80 countries and geographical regions. More than 300,000 business and professional executives are members. Membership is selected on the basis of one active member from each recognized business and profession in the community. The member must be an adult male of good character and business reputation engaged as a proprietor, partner, corporate officer, or manager of a worthy and recognized business or be in an executive capacity in such business, or engaged in a worthy profession. The motto is "Service Above Self." Once membership is granted, there are annual dues which contribute to the support of the national and international offices and also the activities of the local club. Included with the annual dues is a subscription to the monthly magazine, *The Rotarian*. The program of the international organization is to encourage and foster this "Ideal of Service" and to encourage and foster:

1. The development of acquaintance as an opportunity for service.
2. High ethical standards in business and professions; the recognition and worthiness of all useful occupations; and the dignifying by each Rotarian of his occupation as an opportunity to serve society.
3. The application of the "Ideal of Service" by every Rotarian to his personal, business, and community life.
4. The advancement of international understanding, good will, and peace through a world fellowship of business and professional men united in t.e "Ideal of Service."

Kiwanis International had its beginnings in Detroit in 1914 when Allan Browne, a fraternal organizer, and Joseph G. Prance, a Detroit businessman, formed a club. After a time the name "kee-wanis"—an Indian word meaning "to make one's self known"—was selected, and the spelling modified to its present form. The organization received its charter in January, 1915, the official founding date. International growth has been confined largely to the United States, its possessions, and Canada. Two representatives are permitted membership simultaneously from the same line of activity, contrasted with the limitation by Rotary to only one. Executive or professional requirements are about the same as in Rotary. Kiwanis embraces about 2,700 clubs with a total membership of around 180,000. The clubs are usually noted for their activities and their vitality, accomplishing much that is worthwhile in their local areas. In this respect it might be appropriate to point out that in some areas Rotary is known as "the old men's club" by the Kiwanians, whereas the Rotarians have been known to refer to the Kiwanians as the "rah-rah boys" and "eager beavers." In other localities the reverse would undoubtedly hold true. The objects as expressed in the constitution are:

To give primacy to the human and the spiritual, rather than the material values of life.

To encourage the daily living of the Golden Rule in all human relationships.

To promote the adoption and application of higher social, business, and professional standards.

To develop, by precept and example, a more intelligent, aggressive, and serviceable citizenship.

To provide, through Kiwanis clubs, a practical means to form enduring friendships, to render altruistic service, and to build better communities.

To cooperate in creating and maintaining that sound public opinion and high idealism which make possible the increase of righteousness, justice, patriotism, and good will.

The International Association of Lions Clubs was formally founded in 1917 and was made up of about 50 independent clubs, some of which dated back to about 1914. By 1920 the organization had spread to Canada, and by 1927 to Mexico and China. Presently there are nearly 7,000 Lions Clubs in some twenty countries on four continents wtih a total membership of around 360,000. It is therefore the largest service club organization in the world. Organization is similar to that of Rotary. The community activities program is outlined under eight headings. Lions are proud of the completeness of their coverage of community activities. A monthly magazine, *The Lion,* is published. The stated objects of the organization are:

To create and foster a spirit of generous consideration among the peoples of the world.

To promote the theory and practice of the principles of good government and good citizenship.

To take an active interest in the civic, commercial, social and moral welfare of the community.

To unite the members in the bonds of friendship, good fellowship, and mutual understanding.

To provide a forum for the full and free discussion of all matters of public interest, partisan politics and sectarian religion alone excepted.

To encourage efficiency and promote high ethical standards in business and professions. No club shall hold as one of its objects financial benefits to its members.

Numerous other service clubs have been founded upon the same general principles and ideals of the "big three." Among these are Exchange, Civitan, and Optimists, probably the most prominent. The Optimist Creed, the guide posts of this pleasantly named group, is a beautiful statement which all of us might do well to heed:

Promise yourself—
To be so strong that nothing can disturb your peace of mind.
To talk health, happiness, and prosperity to every person you meet.
To make all your friends feel there is something in them.
To look at the sunny side of everything and make your optimism come true.
To think only of the best, to work only for the best, and to expect only the best.
To be just as enthusiastic about the success of others as you are about your own.
To forget the mistakes of the past and press on to greater achievements of the future.
To wear a cheerful countenance at all times and give every living creature you meet a smile.
To give so much time to the improvement of yourself that you have no time to criticize others.
To be too large for worry, too noble for anger, too strong for fear, and too happy to permit the presence of trouble.

Functions of such organizations as chambers of commerce, junior chambers of commerce, and similar associations which approach the category of trade or strictly business associations are widely known. However, it might be well to point out that in most communities the Junior Chamber of Commerce is in reality a junior service club in scope and activities, composed of men under the age of 35.

For the hospital administrator I cannot emphasize too strongly the desirability of affiliation with a service club. It is a "must" for you as an individual and for the institution you represent. Personally you will benefit from the intangibles of friendship and acquaintance and service to your fellow man. You will get a thrill out of visiting your club in far-off cities as you travel, meeting and greeting people on a friendly basis whom otherwise you would never meet. It is not expected that one profit financially from membership, or that business affairs enter into the life of the club at any time. Nevertheless it is obvious that some values may be realized to your hospital by, for example, being on a friendly basis with the editor of your local paper, whom you call by his first name, and whom you may have met in the service club.

Fraternal Organizations

The largest fraternal organizations, the Masons and the Knights of Columbus, are omitted from this discussion because everyone is familiar with them. The Eagles, Elks, and Moose all seem to have had their origins as "aid" groups, the primary reason for forming being to assist their members in weathering times of crises by providing such things as nominal death benefits. Generally their charters were for fraternal benefit associations of one type or another. Many have enlarged the purposes and activities, and the general statement can be made that they attempt to provide social outlets now for the member and usually for each member of his family.

The Fraternal Order of Eagles, or F.O.E., as the neon sign is likely to read outside the "Aerie," was founded in 1898. The original purpose was to provide a weekly sick benefit for members when needed, a nominal death benefit, and the service of an Aerie physician. The Eagles have been very active politically and socially, and claim considerable credit for Social Security laws and Workmen's Compensation. Membership has grown to around 1,500,000 in 1,600 Aeries in the United States and Canada. They call themselves the "fighting fraternity with more than a million members."

The B.P.O.E., or Benevolent and Protective Order of Elks, was established in 1868. The name chosen was thought to characterize a number of the attributes thought typical of those desired for membership. The order is rather ritualistic and prides itself on its charitable activities. It places great emphasis on patriotism and Americanism and is noted for response and assistance in times of calamity. In 1902 a national home for indigent and aged Elks was established at Bedford, Virginia. The Elks have a beautiful memorial in Chicago which serves as the national headquarters. Membership is about half a million.

The Loyal Order of Moose, founded in 1888 in Louisville by Dr. J. H. Wilson, has high ideals and principles and is ritualistic in procedures. There are some 1,500 Moose lodges on the North American continent with a membership of more than half a million. The order is rightfully proud of its world-famous Mooseheart, not far from Chicago, which is a school-city for children of deceased members of Moose. Moosehaven in Florida is maintained as a refuge for the aged.

The Independent Order of Odd Fellows, a fraternal, beneficiary society, draws heavily upon moralistic teachings in its rituals. There are nearly 1,500,000 members. It was formed in the early eighteenth century in England as the Order of Odd Fellows, the "Independent" designation having been added in 1843 when the Manchester lodge withdrew from the parent organization in London. The American order, founded in 1819, in turn declared its independence from the Manchester lodge after a few years.

The lodges, or aeries, or "nests," etc., differ in nature from one community to the next, but the total importance of the many fraternal orders in their effect upon the well-being of the community cannot be overestimated. The administrator at some time or other will undoubtedly be confronted with an invitation or an opportunity to affiliate. "Joiners" in some communities will belong to three or even four of these groups. Of course, there is the thought that advantage to the hospital can accrue through such activity, but the administrator is cautioned to check the character and reputation of the group in which he is considering membership. There should be no hurry in affiliating when you go into a new community. It will depend upon you as an individual to decide whether or not you join, remembering always that your activities cannot be divorced entirely from your institution.

Veterans' organizations such as the American Legion and the Veterans of Foreign Wars must be included as civic, and national, service organizations which respond quickly to calls for their help in times of crisis and for cooperation in all projects directed toward betterment of the community.

TRUSTEES, AUXILIARY MEMBERS, AND VOLUNTEERS

Most sociologists and some psychologists have difficulty explaining in scientific terms how and why certain people are motivated to service that frequently is a kind of martyrdom so far as personal comfort and advancement are concerned. Utilitarians and materialists have reckoned little with the spiritual aspects of human nature, yet a substantial part of the structure that makes society as advanced as it is was built on a service motive. Hospitals owe their very existence to these people.

What trustees, auxiliary members, and volunteers do, and how they are organized within the hospital, are topics apart from the purposes of this study. Here the concern is with the fact that they are links with the community in a different way from the professional staff and employed personnel. They are the community, coming in to help of their own free will, with no personal economic motive.

Trustees

In the question period at a public meeting the trustee who had been the speaker was asked, "Are the trustees paid?" The hour was late and he was weary, so he answered "Yes, we're paid amply—with gripes!" That drew a laugh. Thinking it over some time afterward, he said his more mature and honest reply would be:

> Yes, we're paid. We're paid with the knowledge that we have contributed of ourselves to the service of our neighbor. We're paid by knowing that in the brick and mortar of the hospital there is a bit of each of us. We're paid over and

over again with the knowledge of a life saved in our hospital. We're paid with the thanks from the medical staff and employees for our part in making their task easier. Yes, we trustees are paid. And it's a darn good salary.[57]

Tol Terrell, during his term of presidency of the American Hospital Association in 1957–1958, was asked to comment on trusteeship in small hospitals. He said that no matter how small the hospital is, its board of trustees should be formally organized as defined in the Association's *Model Constitution and Bylaws for a Voluntary Hospital;* that as in all hospitals there should be wide spread of interests, vocations and abilities; that there should be no more than ten members; that tenure should not be limited when the trustee "continues in health and in the acceptance and discharge of his responsibilities"; and that there is necessarily a closer relationship with the administrator which might make more difficult the delegation of authority to him and which gives special importance to his keeping his trustees well informed. He added that study of the subject helped him to formulate the following philosophy of a good trustee:[58]

Most good trustees are conservative. The true conservative is one who distrusts change just for the sake of change. He wants to examine new ideas carefully, weigh them, and determine their effect upon the intricate fabric of our society before adopting them. He doesn't believe in trying to make people do what someone else judges to be good for them.

He does what he does voluntarily and without compensation; thus, he is idealistic. He lives by high ideals and is moved by a vision of service. To bring to his work more than just a regard for the balance sheet, the increasing professionalism of administration needs the balancing influence of a truly conservative trustee. It has been this blend of scientific skill and moral idealism that has given America its marvelous system of health care. This teamwork of two great forces is our strongest defense against socialized medicine and collective control.

The trustee gives his time because of faith in what the hospital is doing. The organizational, financial, personnel, property and public relations duties are undertaken by him to help further the work of the hospital. If the program responsibility of the board is neglected or reduced, his job will become most unsatisfying, resulting in a routine instead of a challenge. The program plans of a hospital are sounder and more realistic if they blend the dreams of the experts and the reality of the community through the trustees. The board member knows better than the administrator what the community wants and what the community will accept. The administrator and staff are actually technical advisors. The trustees must take the responsibility before the public for acceptance of the hospital program.

Dr. John R. McGibony[59] points out that there are two principal methods of appointing the governing board:

[57] Edwin A. Hinds, vice president, First National Bank of Boston and trustee, South Shore Hospital, South Weymouth, Massachusetts: Trustees Are Paid Unusually Well. *Trustee,* May, 1953, pp. 21–23.

[58] Your President Reports. *Hospitals,* December 1, 1957, p. 59.

[59] *Principles of Hospital Administration.* New York, G. P. Putnam's Sons, 1952, pp. 139–40.

The governing board itself may become the corporation and thus be self-perpetuating, selecting its membership without reference to any other organized body; or it may maintain at least a semblance of a corporation which periodically elects such members of the governing board as are needed to preserve the required membership. . . . Members should not be selected solely on the basis of their financial contributions to the hospital, their prominence in the community or their social standing. Selection should also be based on what they can and will add to the strength of the governing board in its trusteeship of one of the community's most important public welfare agencies. . . . The more varied the backgrounds of the members, the stronger the character of the board.

Other considerations besides direct gain to the institution through ability to give or influence giving of funds or to get publicity in the newspaper should govern the selection of trustees. A businessman who has ideas that can improve the business functioning of the hospital and who can enlist the moral support of the business community may be more valuable than one who is merely wealthy. The editor has an over-all familiarity with the community that can make him the best possible source of knowledge of needs that the hospital should meet. His interpretation of the community to the hospital can be more important than his interpretation of the hospital to the community. Ideas and vision are what keep an organization moving forward. They must precede the seeking of funds.[60]

Auxiliary Members

Although men and women have always worked as volunteers in hospitals and related institutions, organization as auxiliaries is only about a hundred years old. Probably the first one in North America was the Hospital Aid Society organized in 1865 in Ontario, Canada. This society was founded not to help any hospital, because there was none, but to stir up interest in establishing one. They went from house to house collecting money, linens, cooking utensils, and anything else that could be used for or in a hospital. Then they rented a house and turned it into a hospital which they operated until 1873 when a hospital and nurses' training school were built, after which they continued to function as an "aid" society.

The big aim of most auxiliaries is to raise money for the hospital from the community, and many are the ways devised to get it. The projects in themselves, fairs, carnivals, benefit shows, gift shops, cake sales, have publicity value.

Recruitment of members is an activity that the administrator should help to stimulate. As Dr. Arnold L. Swanson[61] says:

This job is never done. . . . Today our population is on the move. New people are constantly arriving in our towns and cities, while others leave. Most hospitals

[60] For excellent coverage of the role of the trustee see *Hospital Trusteeship* by Charles U. Letourneau, M.D., published by Starling Publications, Chicago, 1959.

[61] *Canad. Hosp.*, February, 1963. Dr. Swanson is executive director, University Hospital, Saskatoon, Saskatchewan, Canada.

are growing larger and are in need of more help than ever before despite better financing by governments. Recruitment means recruiting the *right* person or group for the job. Likewise, people change. They get bored. They age. They have changes in interest. The lady who headed up the transportation committee so well for the last five years may now do a better job working for the patient library or the gift shop. Recruitment means bringing in new people with new ideas; enlarging the membership to keep up with demand; and recruiting from within the organization to take over new jobs and to maintain interest. It is a job for every member.

In larger hospitals the auxiliary members and the volunteers are separately organized. In general the former organization is more stable and is more formally organized. There is considerable overlapping, auxiliary members performing many services as volunteers. In some smaller hospitals all volunteer service is rendered by auxiliary members, except perhaps for that given by teen-agers like the Candy Stripers.

The importance that rests upon the auxiliary as a public relations agency was summarized by Sister Gregory, administrator of Resurrection Hospital, Chicago, in her thesis for her master's degree from Northwestern University in 1960:

1. A combination sounding board and intelligence service regarding community attitudes.
2. A bridge between the hospital and the community.
3. One of the most influential publics which operates for the hospital's benefit.
4. A help when properly informed in keeping the community acquainted with what really happens within the walls of the hospital, cultivating the trust and confidence of the people in the community which in time becomes a genuine therapeutic tool in the psychology of future patients.

Volunteers

It is estimated that more than half of the adults in the United States serve in some way as volunteers in social agencies. Hospitals are the center of the most highly developed forms of volunteer activity. Frequently the workers in hospitals represent groups, such as the American Legion Auxiliary, service clubs, and fraternal organizations. Home care programs, besides supplying nursing service, can utilize these volunteers. Volunteers spring to the rescue in time of catastrophe, take over any duty they can when hospital employees go on strike, as occasionally happens. "Private agencies would wither and die" if the 25 to 35 million volunteers went on strike, according to the late Dr. Edward C. Lindeman,[62] professor of social philosophy at the New York School of Social Work, adding, "The health of a democratic society may be measured in terms of the quality of services rendered by citizens who act in 'obedience to the unenforceable.' "

[62] Quoted by Mrs. Robert D. Steefel: Our Indispensable Volunteers. *Trustee,* January, 1955, p. 5.

Volunteers man ambulance squads. Trained in first aid work, they save many lives. Volunteers administer volunteer blood donor services. Psychiatric departments and hospitals are attracting volunteers as the war against mental illness progresses. Nursing homes, rehabilitation centers, clinics—all are depending upon volunteers to give the extra services and attention to patients for which the busy employed staff has no time.

From the teen-ager to the retired person hospitals are drawing volunteers to perform countless tasks that would not get done without them. They take back to the community knowledge and understanding that give them high rank as ambassadors of good will—besides those teen-agers can grow up to be nurses, technicians, administrators and doctors.

CHAPTER 14

Economic Backgrounds; Health Economics

> In the past when economics was only an aggregative, mass
> process, the great economists could stand aside from the flow
> of events, and shed their light on history purely as
> commentators, as analysts, or as disinterested prophets.
> In the present, as economics becomes entangled in the
> political decision-making process, that aloofness is no longer
> possible. There is no longer only one possible conclusion
> for the economic drama, but many, and the economists must
> not only describe for us the course on which we are sailing
> but point out other courses, other destinations to which
> we may, if we wish, direct ourselves.
> ROBERT L. HEILBRONER[1]

ON THE jacket and in the table of contents of the book in which Heilbroner describes the lives and doctrines of "The Worldly Philosophers" appear these differentiations of their worlds:

The wonderful world of Adam Smith.
The gloomy world of Parson Malthus and David Ricardo.
The beautiful world of the Utopian Socialists, John Stuart Mill, Charles
    Fourier, Saint-Simon, Robert Owen.
The inexorable world of Karl Marx.
The Victorian world and the underworld of economics, Henry George.
The savage world of Thorstein Veblen.
The sick world of John Maynard Keynes.
The modern world of Joseph Schumpeter.

[1] *The Worldly Philosophers: The Lives, Times and Ideas of the Great Economic Thinkers.* New York, Simon and Schuster, 1953, p. 314.

449

The dismal science has a relatively short history and these are the leaders in it. Before Adam Smith, as Heilbroner graphically delineates, there was no economy and therefore there could be no economics or economists. Acceptance of the market system had to come first, he declares, pointing out that markets were centuries old but did not constitute a market system. Before the system stage arrived "the idea of the propriety (not to say the necessity) of a system organized on the basis of *personal gain* had not yet taken root" and "a separate, self-contained economic world had not yet lifted itself from its social context." Elaborating on this, he states:[2]

> It may strike us as odd that the idea of gain is a relatively modern one; we are schooled to believe that man is essentially an acquisitive creature and that left to himself he will behave as any self-respecting businessman would. The profit motive, we are constantly being told, is as old as man himself.
> Nothing could be further from the truth. Not only is the notion of gain for gain's sake foreign to a large portion of the world's population today, but it has been conspicuous by its absence over most of recorded history.

Incidentally, economics can be very dull reading, but treated as biography with illuminating description of the life and times of each subject, by a skilled author, it becomes what Heilbroner has made it, a fascinating study.

Before Adam Smith, there were philosophers who included ideas about economics in their writings. In France there was a court physician, Francois Quesnay (1694–1774), who formed a sort of economic school of thought known as physiocracy, based on the idea that true wealth was produced only by the agricultural classes, the others merely manipulating it. Smith knew him and accepted some of his ideas. Most of those of the earlier philosopher John Locke (1632–1704) he opposed. David Hume (1711–1776) was his good friend and had some influence on his thinking. In his *Inquiry into the Nature and Causes of the Wealth of Nations,* which appeared in 1776, Smith mentions some hundred authors, but as Heilbroner comments, "Where others had fished here and there, Smith spread his net wide; where others had clarified this and that issue, Smith illuminated the entire landscape. The *Wealth of Nations* may not be an original book, but it is unquestionably a masterpiece."[3]

On this, the first systematic work on economics, the science is founded. As propounded by Smith, the theory was a comfortable one—for those on top. "All systems either of preference or restraint being taken away," he wrote, "the obvious and simple system of natural liberty establishes itself of its own accord." And, "It is not from the benevolence of the butcher, the brewer, or the baker that we expect our dinner, but from their regard to their self-interest. We address ourselves, not to their humanity, but to their self-love, and never talk to them of our necessities, but of their advantages." Competition, he theorizes, prevents pushing the profit motive too far and promotes social harmony. The same theory

[2] *Ibid.,* p. 15.
[3] *Ibid.,* p. 42.

applies to wages. Smith was fully cognizant of the greed and scheming for power of the merchants and the manufacturers, and of the sorry lot of the workers, but figured that if trade and government regulations were removed, production would soar and redound to the benefit of everybody. The capitalists seized upon the idea to fight factory legislation and other social reforms. And thus a laissez faire society came about.

James Bryce found it in the United States on his visit in 1888, saying in his *American Commonwealth*:[4]

> One half of the capitalists are occupied in preaching *laissez faire* as regards railroads, the other half in resisting it in railroad matters, in order to have their goods carried more cheaply, and in tariff matters in order to protect industries threatened with foreign competition. Yet they manage to hold well together. Their practical talent does not necessarily imply political insight, any more than moral elevation, nor have they generally the taste or leisure to think seriously about the needs of the state. In no country does one find so many men of eminent capacity for business, shrewd, forcible, and daring, who are so uninteresting, so intellectually barren, outside the sphere of their business knowledge.
>
> But the wealthy have many ways of influencing opinion and the course of events. Some of them own, others find means of inspiring, newspapers. Presidents of great corporations have armies of officials under their orders, who cannot indeed be intimidated, for public opinion would resent that, yet may be suffered to know what their superior thinks and expects. Cities, districts of country, even States or territories, have much to hope or fear from the management of a railway, and good reason to conciliate its president. Moreover, as the finance of the country is in the hands of these men and every trader is affected by financial changes, as they control enormous joint-stock enterprises whose shares are held and speculated in by hosts of private persons of all ranks, their policy and utterances are watched with anxious curiosity, and the line they take determines the conduct of thousands not directly connected with them. A word from several of the great financiers would go a long way with leading statesmen. They are for the most part a steadying influence in politics, being opposed to sudden changes which might disturb the money market or depress trade, and especially opposed to complications with foreign States.

These impressions are followed by remarks on the influence of the professional classes, with the conclusion that the "lawyers best deserve to be called the leading class," and the dismissal of the "physicians as neither bringing any distinctive element into politics, nor often taking an active interest therein."[5]

Back and forth ever since the publication of *The Wealth of Nations* the pendulum has swung between letting the economy alone and regulating it, with new ideas contributed by every economist and changing conditions operating to disclose their truth or error. The division of labor in a ten-man factory used as an example by Smith has ballooned to thousands of men on an assembly line making automobiles; capital has multiplied far beyond the imagination

---

[4] Reflections on American Institutions: Selections, with an Introduction by Henry Steele Commager, from *The American Commonwealth* by James Bryce. Greenwich, Connecticut, Fawcett Publications, Inc., 1961, pp. 40–41.

[5] *Ibid.*, pp. 41–42.

of the man who first realized the significance of its accumulation in terms of the wealth of the entire nation. The science has expanded through inescapable overlapping with other sciences. The scope is indicated by the following chapter headings from Allen M. Sievers' *General Economics: An Introduction:*[6]

The Automobile
A Loaf of Bread and the History of Technology
The Money-Market-Machine Economy: Its Nature and History
Resources: Natural, Technological, and Human
Financial Organization
Business Organization
Government As Producer and Spender
National Income and National Product
International Trade, Accounting, and Finance
Economic Systems and Economics: Some Definitions
Society, Law, Liberty, and the Economy
Economic Theories and Social Movements
Capitalism
Sovietism
Fascism
Postwar Great Britain and the British Labour Party
Comparative Economic Systems: A Summary
The Meaning of Economic Analysis
Tools of Analysis: Mathematics, Statistics, and the Equilibrium Concept
Consumption and Demand
Production, Cost and Supply
Equilibrium in the Competitive Market
Distribution, Allocation, and General Equilibrium
Equilibrium in Imperfect Competition
The Keynesian System: Heresy, Macroeconomics, and Dynamics
The Business Cycle
Monetary Theory and Monetary-Fiscal Policy
Wealth and Weal
Farmers and the Farm Problem
The Labor Movement
Labor Protection and Social Security
Waste and Conservation
Social Control of Business
A War-Oriented Economy
Progress or Regress?

Trends are indicated in these headings also, trends that show the injection of social welfare ideals. Under "Wealth and Weal" the statement is made:

Since wealth is inseparable from weal, the analysis of the wealth activities of society cannot be divorced from the analysis of all other dimensions of social well-being. In short, economics analyzes the forces which contribute by means of wealth-seeking activities to the common weal of the commonwealth, and it seeks to determine the limits beyond which wealth-seeking injures the common weal.[7]

[6] New York, J. B. Lippincott Co., 1952.
[7] *Ibid.,* pp. 607–8.

As Heilbroner[8] expresses it in his chapter, "Beyond the Economic Revolution":

It is not that economic motives are dead: far from it. If the principle of "buy cheap and sell dear" did not still organize our otherwise undirected economy, we should face chaos on the market place tomorrow. If the drive to amass wealth did not still impel people to shift from job to job, to change the direction of their business efforts, to expand or contract their business operations, we should have a sluggish, inert, changeless economy instead of an active, fluid, and dynamic one. The economic motive is still present and still vitally important. And therefore society still displays purely economic trends. Indeed, the forecasts of the modern economists are nothing but the projections of the consequences of the purely economic characteristics of our market society. But society no longer obeys its economic impulse *alone*.

HEALTH ECONOMICS

Adam Smith recognized health as an element in economics, and so to a limited extent have later economists. Mostly it was considered in its negative aspects, the abnormalities, as a drain on charity and therefore on capital. Disease and injury as causes of absenteeism and of poor work were matters of concern because they interfered with production. These remain not an unimportant part of the economic view of health, for economics is a cold science.

However, the concern has moved up the social ladder. As advances in medical science have opened up more and more prospects for the prevention, control, and cure of disease, and for rehabilitation after injury, the concept of positive health, for everybody, has become an economic as well as a social goal. It is an economic loss when a brilliant engineer, or manager, or financier is cut off in his prime. It is an economic loss when a merchant or manufacturer or inventor is debilitated by disease and cannot function to his full capacity. The contributions to the cancer society, the heart association, the arthritis foundation, the hospital, are not the kind of philanthropy that we had of old, for the benefit of the poor exclusively. The benefits go to all, rich and poor. The millionaire goes to the hospital too, and if he had not helped to build it he would have no place to go, speaking in general. The poor man who gives a few dollars to the building campaign is playing philanthropist to the rich, to everybody, not merely his own class from an economic standpoint.

Few purely charitable organizations remain in our mixed society. The fruits of giving are shared by the givers. The research that is going on everywhere is one of the reasons for the spread. Whether the project is an educational institution, a scientific laboratory, a medical investigation, a library, or a hospital, something is learned and everyone benefits. Only the donor who waits until death to make his gift is left out.

The not-for-profit organizations are therefore more important in the economic weal than they ever were before. They have more to give to keep the

[8] *Op. cit.,* p. 308.

economy stable than they ever did when they were outlets only for charity. With the positive function of keeping everybody living and working as long and as effectively as possible, hospitals are no more like their nosocomium predecessors than the jet plane is like the ox cart.

Granted that they have a long way to go in meeting the needs of special types of illness, such as chronic and psychiatric, the relief that hospitals give as repair shops for the ill and injured, as conservers of the labor force by making it unnecessary for workers to stay home to care for the sick, as educational and research facilities for the professions, and as proving grounds for scientific discoveries makes them vital forces in the economy. The administrator needs to study them against the entire economic background with this conception of their position in it. They are not drains upon the economy; they are among its leading safeguards. They fit into it in many ways besides their main purpose, service to patients.

For the best comprehensive picture of current conditions and problems in health economics, the two-volume report of the Michigan study *Hospital and Medical Economics: A Study of Population, Services, Costs, Methods of Operations, and Controls* should be consulted. The report, by Walter J. McNerney and study staff, was published in 1962 by the Hospital Research and Educational Trust, Chicago. The study came about through a request in 1955 by the Michigan Hospital Service, the Blue Cross Plan of Michigan, for a 23 per cent increase in rates. Investigation of hospital costs and prepayment was demanded by both labor and government. The president of Michigan Hospital Service then recommended to the governor that a study be made. Accordingly Governor G. Mennen Williams in February, 1956, appointed the Governor's Study Commission in Prepaid Hospital and Medical Care Plans. The commission asked the University of Michigan to do the research. The university's Bureau of Hospital Administration, supported by the W. K. Kellogg Foundation's grants of more than $380,000, conducted the study.[9] The facts and conclusions of the study were to be used by the governor's commission in developing its recommendations.

The factors which have altered and continue to alter the hospital from a socioeconomic standpoint are population growth (estimated to reach 220 million by 1975); greater utilization as a result of advances in medical science, education of the public to the advantages of hospital care, and prepayment for hospital and medical service; increase in the size of families; geographic shifts of population; higher accident rates; apartment and small home living; increase in working wives; increase in the life span; and more expensive equipment and techniques—all contributing to higher costs and need for unprecedented capital expansion.

A way of exploring old-age needs in a community was used in the Blooming-

[9] A summary of the report was published in the August 1, 1961, issue of *Hospitals,* pp. 17–24, and a review in the December 16, 1962, issue, pp. 92, 106.

ton-Normal survey in Illinois in 1960 and 1961, under the direction of Vernon C. Pohlman, Ph.D. An unrestricted random sampling technique was employed with direct interview of persons 65 years of age or older. A 10 per cent sampling was the goal. The blocks surveyed within the two cities were selected at random. The report showed that only half as many of the local older citizens received Old-Age Assistance as statistics gave for the country as a whole; that 40 per cent had hospital insurance compared with 26 per cent; and that they had more years of schooling than like groups in the country at large.

These findings establish the need for exploration of needs on the local level because communities vary so greatly. The Bloomington-Normal report disclosed severe social, economic, and health limitations, as a result of which the community and especially the physicians have been aroused to action.

The Hospital in a Capitalistic Economy

The nonprofit medical service institution might be considered as a drain on capital because funds are poured into it and no marketable goods come out. In this respect, though, it is no different from the public utility. The railroads and the steamships haul materials but do not make them. The telephone, telegraph, electric and gas companies produce something that nobody can see and only they can sell. Insurance companies and banks, garages and hotels, manufacture no products.

A slight inclination exists to class hospitals as public utilities since, like them, they are service institutions. The intention would be to submit them to a similar kind of government regulation. The comparison is completely fallacious. Public utilities are systems, most of them vast and interconnected. Hospitals are sadly unsystematized, common though it is to refer to a hospital system. Each stands virtually alone, a remnant, agreeable in a way, of periods when the economy was not as highly organized as it is now.

Hospitals have a large stake in the capitalistic system. They have endowments, many of them substantial, and the funds are invested, the returns in interest and dividends being plowed back into the operation or added to the endowment capital. Eleemosynary institutions differ in their investment practices only in being obliged to be ultraconservative in their selections. The trustees of the institutions in cooperation with the trust departments of banks govern this part of the operations. Bond issues for new construction are another way in which these institutions participate in the realm of finance.

Private hospitals are, of course, similar to any other business that is conducted for profit and are capitalistic enterprises.

Since land represents capital, and hospitals and related institutions own and occupy in the aggregate a large amount of real estate, their property gives them a part in the capitalistic economy even though much of it was donated. This landed interest involves them in community affairs that affect the values, for frequently they are given or acquire property that proves not to be feasible to occupy and they may wish to sell or to lease it. The economic advantage to the hospital of being free from taxation if it is a nonprofit facility is naturally accompanied by an obligation to repay the community by giving it the best possible service.

As a consumer of goods and services, the medical service institution is not only a market for all kinds of supplies, from food to cobalt, but is a stimulator of improvements and innovations as a result of its scientific nature. Industry furnished hospitals listed by the American Hospital Association in the United States in 1962 goods and services costing more than $3 billion.[10] The estimated $47 billion in 1962 and $53 billion in 1963 (F. W. Dodge Corporation) expenditures for building hospitals and institutions indicate the additional impact upon building and related industries.

Financing hospital care is a constant, unrelenting struggle, with little similarity to the financing of a commercial enterprise. Medical advances come fast, outstripping the ability of the budget to keep up with them, and operational deficits result. Services for the indigent and the medically indigent are seldom completely reimbursed by outside agencies, so the deficits mount. The only effective way to reduce costs is to lower quality of service, and this is unthinkable in a life-and-death situation. Philanthropy must be appealed to because of fear of public rebellion against rates high enough to meet actual all-inclusive costs.

Understanding of the situation was shown in the Ford Foundation's report[11] at the time the $200-million grant was made to hospitals:

> It is easy to see why most voluntary hospitals are afflicted with an institutional ailment known among trustees and administrators as "chronic under-financing." The symptoms do not always show up in red ink; in fact, most voluntary hospitals manage to balance their books. Usually, though, hospital income from payments and gifts is barely enough to meet current operating expenses, and there is no money for adding or replacing facilities. The result is a deficit in hospital services.
>
> How large and how significant has the deficit been?
>
> A study of 1,400 nonprofit community hospitals by an independent citizens' commission, operating under American Hospital Association auspices, reported in 1954 a serious lack of facilities: fewer than half of all short-term, nonprofit hospitals provided more than ten of nineteen selected services. . . . The point is not that a hospital must offer all nineteen services or be rated inadequate. The survey simply revealed, rather impressively, but not surprisingly, that facilities frequently fall short of the ideal.
>
> There isn't a hospital administrator in the country who doesn't have in his desk drawer a list of urgently needed equipment and personnel. . . .

The report referred to in this statement was that of the Commission on Financing of Hospital Care, in which the investigation showed urgent need for eliminating duplication of facilities, gaps in health services, and excessive utiliza-

[10] 1963 A.H.A. "Guide Issue," p. 441.
[11] Quoted in *Hospitals*, October 16, 1958, p. 35.

tion, along with expanding outpatient services and increasing bed occupancy by reducing bed complement.

Sources of income vary widely in different areas. Report of a survey conducted in 1960 by the Hospital Council of Greater New York showed income of short-term hospitals in 15 cities was 3.4 per cent from philanthropy, 17.5 per cent from tax funds, and 79.1 per cent from private payments. These percentages compared with New York City's 7.6 per cent from philanthropy, 33 per cent from tax funds, and only 56.5 per cent from private payments.

Looming unhealthily on the horizon is profiteering in hospital care. Eight per cent interest was offered to purchasers of first mortgage bonds in a "nonprofit hospital corporation" which was constructing a hospital in a southwestern state. Ninety days' interest was offered in advance in order to lure quick money. How new hospitals could pay this high rate of interest and render high-quality service is, of course, the enigma. Mortgage financing is legitimate and is resorted to on occasion by many hospitals, but there are limits to its economic feasibility.

Proprietary for-profit hospitals and nursing homes are meeting special needs in regions or in areas of care in which voluntary hospitals may not have had time to provide service. The good ones are handicapped by the gouging practices of those that are out to make money with little regard for patient and public welfare. The educational and research activities of the typical voluntary hospital are seldom a part of the proprietary hospital operation, nor is care of the indigent provided, unless fully reimbursed by government, so these institutions do not offer valid cost comparisons with the nonprofit group. Some of them are properly motivated and fully appreciate their responsibilities to their communities. The administrator of a proprietary hospital in California warns: "It is important . . . to fit our hospitals into community plans, area plans, and statewide plans. . . . We are running a business, yes—but the nature of the business is such that we cannot ignore the community responsibility that goes with it." He recommends that proprietary hospitals limit profits, contribute to medical research, help finance teaching programs, and

> . . . provide only superior service . . . comply fully with not only the words but the intent of *Guiding Principles*,[12] the program for establishing hospital charges. . . . If there is a division between voluntary hospitals in the future, it will not be between "profit" and "nonprofit" but between those that abide by the *Guiding Principles* and those that do not.[13]

One-fourth of the short-term general hospitals in California, nonfederal, are proprietary. For the country as a whole, however, the percentage in the nonfederal classification decreased from 17.5 in 1946 to 12.3 in 1962, and the percentage of admissions decreased from 8.9 in 1946 to 6.3 in 1962.[14]

[12] Formulated by the Hospital Council of Southern California.

[13] George J. Badenhausen, administrator, Harriman Jones Clinic and Hospital, Long Beach, California: Free Enterprise and the Proprietary Hospital. *Hosp. Forum,* January, 1962, p. 33.

[14] A.H.A. "Guide Issue," 1963, pp. 436, 472.

Hospital Costs and the Economy

With visualization of costs (and charges) of $50 a day and higher in the not too distant future, the prospect for the average citizen's being able to pay even with prepayment insurance is dim. Insurance is limited generally in its coverage, especially for long-term catastrophic illness and injury. Major medical insurance is costly, and also limited. Is the result going to be an increase in the medically indigent? What can hospitals do to prevent this? What is the outlook for government aid?

Overutilization of hospital service is receiving some blame for the increase in hospital costs. It is contended that prepayment causes abuse by subscribers who want to get their money's worth, and more, by hospitalization when it is unnecessary. This sends premiums higher. Doctors are accused of contributing to overutilization by hospitalizing patients for their own convenience and as a concession to the patient's wishes. The situation is difficult to analyze.

In a Columbia University study of beneficiaries hospitalized under Teamster Welfare Fund programs, reported on in 1962, one-fifth of hospital admissions were judged unnecessary. Another finding was the incidence of unnecessarily prolonged hospitalization. The teamsters are insured under Blue Cross and other forms of hospital and medical insurance.

In Pennsylvania overutilization was accused as a leading factor in high costs by Insurance Commissioner Francis R. Smith in a 1958 adjudication, which has led hospitals all over the United States to institute utilization committees. Their functions are to study indications for admission, average lengths of stay, and diagnostic procedures needed for different conditions and to educate medical staff members in the economic necessity for control.

Ray Brown[15] declares:

> How much hospital care is enough has never been determined. One can suspect that a thorough medical examination of a sufficient sample of the population would disclose that most people do not go to the doctor as often as they should, and there are a great many people who could utilize hospital care to the profit of their physical condition but who never go to the hospital. It is highly doubtful that many members of the population go to the hospital because they have prepayment, but rather that they purchase prepayment because they want to be assured of the necessary financial resources when they do have to go to the hospital. This is in part demonstrated by the findings of a study by Health Information Foundation. This study showed that, sure enough, individuals with insurance go to the hospital quicker than those without such insurance. But it also showed that those individuals with insurance also paid out of their own pockets medical expenditures two times larger than the expenditures made by those without insurance. In other words, while the population utilizes their prepayment, they are at the same time quite willing to pay out their own personal funds for medical and hospital care.

[15] What Do We Mean by Hospital Costs? *Hosp. Forum*, May, 1961, pp. 17–23.

The largest single factor in controlling costs to the patient is reduction in the number of days of stay, an accomplishment which has nearly equalized charges for similar conditions compared with those of a quarter century ago. Among the new discoveries has been the fallacy of long rest in bed after surgery; early ambulation is now the rule in all possible cases including obstetrics. It has therapeutic benefits and gets the patient back home sooner. It is problematical, however, whether average length of stay can be further reduced from the present figure of around seven and a half days in short-term voluntary hospitals. About the only way of doing this seems to be the practice of some hospitals of stepping up to practically full activity on Saturdays and Sundays.

A study[16] conducted at Thayer Hospital, Waterville, Maine, in 1960 showed that the average length of stay of private patients was from 5 to 7 days, while the service or indigent patient had an average stay of 13.1 days. Partly accountable for the latter were previous neglect or social or nutritional problems, but the doctor's convenience and the patient's desire to stay were also responsible. Discovered also was the practice of some doctors of trying to keep a patient longer in order to hold the bed to bargain with the admitting office for a new prospective patient.

In the Thayer study, as in others, it was indicated that length of stay can be shortened by use of outpatient facilities, social service, psychiatric counseling, and patient and family education or training in activities of daily living, home care, and homemaker service.

Economies in operation are important in controlling costs but are limited in their extent by the nature of hospital care. The automation potential is relatively low and cannot offset the rise in wage scales and fringe benefits for employees. Patients need personal care. With 66 per cent of the total operating cost represented by people, machines can replace the work of an insignificant number of them. This is a radical difference from industry.

Overbuilding is a danger in some areas. Vacant beds are economic waste. Again the hospital differs from industry in having to provide some leverage in beds and equipment for emergencies of catastrophic scope. Regional planning is the best answer to controlling underoccupancy.

Grants for construction have been one answer by government to the needs. Another is reimbursement for the care of those who cannot pay. The latter fluctuates in different localities and is nowhere sufficient to cover the full costs. Fifty-one Philadelphia area hospitals reported a loss of nearly $15,000,000 for care to charity patients during 1961. This loss was over and above the $3,685,803 paid to these hospitals by the state. The metropolitan Philadelphia area hospitals in the Delaware Valley Hospital Council spent an average of $26 per day for ward care for indigent and medically indigent inpatients and were reimbursed by the state at a maximum rate of $10 a day for patients under 65 years of age. University Hospital, Ann Arbor, Michigan, a self-supporting unit of the University of

---

[16] Frederick T. Hill, M.D. and Joseph R. Mailloux: How a Small Hospital Checks on Utilization. *Mod. Hosp.*, November, 1962, pp. 107–8.

Michigan Medical Center, refused in 1959 to accept patients from state institutions except in emergencies because over the preceding ten years it had lost $895,000 through actual services rendered to the Michigan Crippled Children's Commission alone. Detroit Children's Hospital took the same action in the same year.

Separate charges are advocated as one way of making the hospital bill more clear and maybe more digestible. Nursing service, meals, and every other item could be shown on the bill instead of the per-day rate. Whatever changes are made, and they must be made, the public—and government—needs to be educated to realize that, to use a simple example, there were 25 items on the Chicago Medical Society's schedule of medical fees in 1900; current Blue Shield manuals list around 1,400 items for possible medical charges. The past offers no solutions for cost problems of the 1960's.

But the criticisms stand out and the appreciations seldom get into print. When they do they are heart-warming. George E. Sokolsky,[17] columnist for King Features, commenting on writers who harp on the high cost of medicine, the excessive utilization of hospitals, and the unnecessary reference to specialists, cites his experience as a patient:

> During the past two or three years an exceptional proportion of my income has gone to doctors and hospitals, but the alternative would undoubtedly have been no income and beyond any doubt, a tombstone which would have cost more than my hospital bill. In fact, half a century ago, nobody survived who had my combination of illnesses, and as the cost of burials has gone up with inflation, I figure that the doctors who kept me alive and fighting, did it at a very fair price.
>
> How much is a life worth? I don't know, but I like to be alive. I enjoy every moment of it and if I must pay to stay alive, no price is too high. During all the illnesses I lost not more than three columns. True, some of them were written under unbelievable circumstances. But today nothing is unbelievable. . . .
>
> Hospitals are the place to go for the best medical attention. The theory that folks go to hospitals for no good reason is, generally speaking, nonsense.

"Miracles cost money," says a writer in an article in the *Reader's Digest*,[18] presented in the public interest by the Blue Cross Association. Walter F. Perkins, president of the board of trustees of Johns Hopkins Hospital, continues:

> Working miracles on order demands specialized new equipment. It's complicated and it's expensive. Just a "blood pump" and a sterilizer, for example, cost more than an 8-room house. Machines are supposed to cut down manpower. In industry, they do. But not in hospitals. Here they boost it, call for more help— for specially trained technicians.

Hospitals as Users of Manpower

Hospitals listed by the American Hospital Association in the United States employed 1,762,957 persons in 1962 and paid them $6,734,877,000. Payrolls accounted for nearly two-thirds of the operating cost.

---

[17] What Is a Fair Price for Life? Reprinted from the *Rochester Times Union* and King Features Syndicate by *Trustee,* June, 1959, pp. 5–6.

[18] Advertisement. June, 1961, p. 181.

From an economic point of view hospitals as employers have a strange history. When they were simply custodial refuges for the poor, the poor, as soon as they could be put to work, performed the menial tasks in return for subsistence, a workhouse type of operation. Any paid workers were those who could not get employment elsewhere, hence were paid the lowest possible wage and were in general the dregs of society. This situation changed when Florence Nightingale and others introduced the idea that training was needed for rendering good nursing care. A much higher type of person was attracted, but the wage scale remained on the bare subsistence level because these persons were supposed to be, and usually were, dedicated to the service of humanity. This applied not only to nursing but to all occupations in the hospital which, with the progress of science and technology, began to demand more skill.

The service motive is not dead. If it were, hospitals could not attract personnel to most jobs even if compensation was equal to that in industry, because hospital work puts more strain on the emotions and often demands more giving of self than does office or factory work. Competition and pressure from labor unions have forced wages up until they are in general comparable with those paid elsewhere. Soaring operating costs are the inevitable result.

At the end of this chapter is a discussion of hospital wage and salary administration by O. K. Stephens.

Hospitals have a peculiar economic conflict with respect to physicians who are employed on a salary basis, such as radiologists, pathologists, and anesthesiologists. Extremists in the medical profession consider it unethical and demoralizing, practically, for any physician to work on other than a fee-for-service basis. The issue has become involved in litigation several times with the doctors accusing hospitals of practicing "corporate medicine." Said Dr. Albert W. Snoke,[19] then president-elect of the American Hospital Association:

> County medical societies and state medical associations which pass resolutions condemning the full-time practice of medicine, experiments in group practice, prepayment insurance and the financial participation of employed physicians in medical insurance payments are failing to recognize the trend of the times. A number of medical societies have also condemned the use of fees paid by medical and surgical insurance plans to help defray the maintenance cost and the salaries of hospital resident staffs. It is paradoxical that the physicians who object to such practice are often the ones who are dependent upon the hospital's resident staff for assistance in caring for their patients.

Not every physician, by any means, is wedded to the idea that there is something disgraceful about being a salaried doctor. Said Dr. Bertram M. Bernheim,[20] referring to surgeons:

> They and the work they do are never going to be in proper perspective until every one of them is taken out of private practice and attached to the hospital as a salaried man. Good salary and for life, with opportunity to do research and to develop according to ability and wishes. With insurance and proper pension. . . .

[19] *Trustee*, February, 1955.
[20] *Mod. Hosp.*, April, 1956.

If you take note of the fast developing full-time system in nonteaching as well as teaching hospitals, if you will note the increase of clinics of the Mayo and Lahey types, to say nothing of private groups, you will see clearly that the idea is not too far-fetched. I would not for a moment take the doctor's personal freedom of action and thought away from him. But I would modernize the system of which he is a part and in which he works. It is antiquated, wasteful and fails to fulfill its purpose of distributing medical care to society.

Dr. Bernheim is associate professor emeritus of surgery, Johns Hopkins Medical School, and surgeon to Johns Hopkins Hospital, Baltimore. In a footnote to his article appears this cautious statement: "The opinions and views here expressed are those of the author and do not necessarily represent those of his one-time colleagues."

The *American Medical Directory* for 1958 disclosed that of 228,300 doctors of medicine in the United States, there were 13,600 employed full-time in hospitals as specialists or administrators. Additional thousands, according to a report of a pilot study on contractual physicians in general hospitals, are engaged in

> . . . government agencies (14,800) and "health plans" (7,200); many of these work in hospitals; if one excludes from consideration retired physicians (11,200), as well as those still in hospital training periods (24,400), and if one estimates that about two-thirds of government and health plan physicians are essentially in hospital service, it is found that about 15 per cent of American practicing physicians are in some form of full-time hospital employment.[21]

Dr. Robert S. Myers[22] comments that "the splendid care given through the years by professors who have been paid by medical schools, by salaried staff members of distinguished clinics, and by physician employees of Veterans Administration hospitals is proof that employment on a salary does not affect adversely the quality of care" and concludes:

> Since this conflict between specialists and hospitals is concerned primarily with economics, rather than ethics, and since the economics of medical practice varies greatly between communities, the solution should be left to each hospital and its specialists to work out at the local level according to the patients' interests and the community's needs.

HEALTH INSURANCE

Medical and hospital economics in the 1960's focuses on a movement that more than any other single factor saved the voluntary hospitals following the depression of 1929 and the 1930's. It is now hoped that it will save them, and medicine, from compulsory health insurance—the specter of socialized medicine. This is voluntary health insurance, the main bulwark against the rising cost of medical and hospital care.

[21] Milton I. Roemer, M.D. and Max Shain: *Hospitals,* May 1, 1960, p. 39.

[22] Dr. Myers is assistant executive director of the American College of Surgeons. Hospital-Specialist Conflict Is Primarily a Matter of Economics. *Mod. Hosp.,* May, 1961, p. 118.

Historic dates in health insurance in the United States are listed as follows in the *Source Book of Health Insurance Data 1962* published by the Health Insurance Institute:

1798   U.S. Marine Hospital Service established by U.S. Congress. Compulsory deductions for hospital service were made from seamen's wages.

1847   Organization of Massachusetts Health Insurance Company of Boston. First U.S. company organized to issue insurance against the costs of medical care.

1850   Franklin Health Assurance Company of Massachusetts organized; first insurance company authorized to issue accident insurance in the United States.

1863   Founding of Travelers Insurance Company of Hartford. The company offered accident insurance for railway mishaps; then all forms of accident protection. It was the first company to issue accident insurance on a basis resembling its present form.

1880   Iowa State Travelers Mutual Association established; oldest fraternal group to issue accident insurance.

1890   Introduction of individual insurance policies offering disability income protection from certain specified diseases.

1891   Meeting of the Accident Section of the Association of Mutual Life Insurance Companies; first recorded meeting of accident-insurance men.

1891   Formation of International Association of Accident Underwriters. It later evolved into the Bureau of Personal Accident and Health Underwriters.

1902   Organization of the Detroit Conference, an association of insurance companies issuing accident insurance.

1903   Limited surgical benefits included in some individual disability income policies.

1905   Hospital expense benefits first offered in some individual disability income policies in the form of a benefit increase while the disabled insured person was hospitalized.

1907   First non-cancellable and guaranteed renewable disability income policy offered in the U.S.

1910   Benefits for medical treatment first introduced in some individual disability income policies.

1910   First group accident and sickness policy issued.

1912   Uniform Standard Provisions Law promulgated by the National Association of Insurance Commissioners.

1914   Organization of the Health and Accident Underwriters Conference, an outgrowth of the Detroit Conference.

1920   Weekly indemnity benefits for disability due to sickness or non-occupational accident first offered on a group insurance basis.

1921   Pioneer Mutual Life Insurance Company becomes first fraternal benefit society to issue accident and health insurance.

1921   First non-cancellable and guaranteed renewable disability policy issued to contain a stated maximum indemnity period for total disability due to sickness with no aggregate limit.

1928   Hospital and surgical benefits first offered on a group insurance basis.

1929   Baylor University, Dallas, Texas, introduces first group hospitalization plan for local teachers' society; predecessor of Blue Cross movement in the U.S. Hospitalization prepayment groups began to develop.

1932   First city-wide Blue Cross plan tried out with a group of hospitals in Sacramento, California.

1937   Organization of Health Service Plan Commission (Blue Cross Commission).

1939   Establishment of the California Physicians' Service, the first Blue Shield–type plan formed.

1940   Medical expense benefits made available with insurance company group insurance contracts.

1942   Kaiser Health Plan set up by Kaiser Foundation in California to provide medical care for employees of Kaiser shipyards and other interests.

1945   Public Law 15 (McCarran Act) passed by Congress. It affirmed state regulation of insurance and declared that Federal anti-trust laws would be applicable to the business of insurance only "to the extent that such business is not regulated by state law."

1946   Organization of Blue Shield Medical Care Plans, Inc. (Blue Shield Commission).

1946   Formation of the Health Insurance Council, a federation of eight insurance associations organized to give technical and practical assistance on health insurance to the providers of medical care.

1947   Health Insurance Plan of Greater New York organized, providing a group practice medical plan for New York City employees.

1948   First non-cancellable and guaranteed renewable hospital-surgical-medical policy issued providing protection to age 65.

1949   First major medical group insurance contract issued. Liberty Mutual Insurance Company issued this contract to the Elfun Society—management personnel of General Electric Company.

1950   Uniform Individual Accident and Sickness Policy Provisions Law promulgated by National Association of Insurance Commissioners.

1950   Federal Trade Commission sets down trade practice rules governing the advertising and promotion of mail order insurance.

1951   First small group hospital and surgical policy introduced which covered groups of five employees or more.

1952   First guaranteed renewable hospital and surgical policy offered on an individual basis.

1955   Advertising code for health insurers promulgated by National Association of Insurance Commissioners.

1955   First guaranteed renewable hospital-surgical policy issued becoming fully paid-up at age 65.

1955   First comprehensive major medical group insurance, as it is known today, offered.

1955   First guaranteed renewable lifetime hospital-surgical policy designed for older age people.

1956   Federal Trade Commission promulgates fair trade practice advertising rules for health insurers.

1956   Organization of the Health Insurance Association of America, representing insurance companies in the health insurance business. It replaced the Bureau of Accident and Health Underwriters and the Health and Accident Underwriters Conference.

1957   First senior citizen hospital-surgical policy issued using a group insurance principle.

1958   First comprehensive major medical individual insurance policy issued.

To this list of historic dates should be added the formation in February, 1961, of the Joint Commission for the Promotion of Voluntary Nonprofit Prepayment Health Plans, incorporating the American Hospital Association, the American Medical Association, Blue Cross Association and the National Association of Blue Shield Plans. This action was preceded in August, 1960, by the creation of a single, national Blue Cross organization, the Blue Cross Association, which is responsible for the functions previously divided between the Blue Cross Commission and the old Blue Cross Association.

Growth of Health Insurance

By 1940, 12 per cent of the population, or 12,312,000 persons, were insured under voluntary plans. Two years earlier the National Health Conference had concluded, "Voluntary sickness insurance without subsidy or other encouragement through official action . . . has nowhere shown the possibility of reaching more than a small fraction of those who need its protection." However, by the end of 1962, 75 per cent of the civilian population of the United States, some 140,000,000 persons, had some form of health insurance, according to figures announced by the Health Insurance Institute. This was an increase of 3,500,000 over the record figure of 136,522,000 reached at the end of 1961.

The institute also estimated that health insurance benefit payments during 1962 totaled $7,100,000,000, an increase of 11.5 per cent over the record $6,397,-000,000 paid out in 1961.

The estimated 1962 year-end coverage for each of the five major types of health insurance, said the institute, was 140,000,000 persons protected by hospital expense insurance; 130,000,000 covered by surgical expense insurance; 97,000,000 with regular medical expense insurance; 38,000,000 protected by major medical expense insurance; and 43,500,000 covered by loss-of-income insurance.

The American people received the coverage and the benefits from some 1,800 voluntary insuring organizations, including 839 insurance companies, 77 Blue Cross plans, 69 Blue Shield plans, and nearly 800 other independent health plans.

The $7,100,000,000 total paid in health insurance benefits by all insurers in 1962 compares with $2,083,000,000 paid in 1952.

Blue Cross

In lectures to students in hospital administration Richard M. Jones, former director of the Blue Cross Commission of the American Hospital Association, and after its merger with the Blue Cross Association, director of the A.H.A. Division of Hospital–Blue Cross Relations (and since July, 1963, executive director, Hospital Planning Council for the Metropolitan Portland Area, Oregon), gave the following account of Blue Cross origin and development:

The schoolteachers of Dallas were hard hit by the influenza epidemic of 1918–20, suffering both from loss of income due to absence and from the costs of illness itself. Justin Ford Kimball, Ph.D., then superintendent of Dallas schools, worked out a mutual group assessment scheme for the teachers under which each contributed $1 a month into a common fund and from which a teacher would draw $6 a day for each day's absence, after being absent for one week.

In June, 1929, Dr. Kimball was named executive vice president of Baylor University in charge of the Dallas Scientific Units: a medical school, dental college, school of nursing, school of pharmacy, and Baylor University Hospital. All of the Dallas units were losing money, but the largest and most difficult financial problem was a continuing hospital deficit. A review of the hospital's accounts receivable disclosed the names of many schoolteachers who owed amounts of from less than $100 to more than $1,000. Dr. Kimball knew that most of the teachers could never repay obligations from their modest savings, so he decided to explore the possibilities of solving this mutual problem through a means similar to the previously established sick benefit fund. Accordingly, he obtained permission to study the records of the latter funds with respect to the incidence and cost of illness among the teachers' group.

Upon completing his study of the sick benefit fund records, Dr. Kimball offered the Dallas teachers prepayment of the services of Baylor Hospital for 50 cents a month, provided that at least 75 per cent of them enrolled. Response to the offer resulted in more than the 75 per cent enrolling and the Dallas teachers became eligible for prepayment of hospital care at Baylor Hospital on December 20, 1929.

The teachers' group was followed by the employees of the Dallas *Morning News* and then a large Dallas bank enrolled its personnel.

C. Rufus Rorem, Ph.D., then with the Rosenwald Foundation and later the first director of the Blue Cross Commission, visited Dallas early in 1930 and gave national publicity to the Dallas experiment. Dr. E. H. Cary, then president of the American Medical Association and until his death president of the Texas Blue Cross and Blue Shield Plans, rendered invaluable service to the beginnings of the Texas prepayment organization by allaying medical suspicion through his own support and professional prestige.

Word of the Baylor venture into prepayment spread widely. Here was a new idea that worked, not only to assure hospital income, but also to solve the abiding social problem of paying for the cost of personal hospital care. Men of social purpose came to Dallas to study this phenomenon and took it to California, New Jersey, Minnesota, Louisiana, North Carolina, West Virginia—and they made the idea work there as it had in Texas. . . .

An innovation in applying the Baylor idea elsewhere was that the programs embraced all of the voluntary hospitals in the community instead of being limited to one. This was timely, for financing of hospital care in the early '30s was an acute problem. Deep depression had settled over much of the national economy. The typical community hospital continued to serve all elements of its community even though an increasing number of patients could not pay for its services. At the very time that individual incomes were being reduced, the kinds of services provided by hospitals were being increased through the advent of new and improved professional techniques. Although the public was aware of these advances, it did not appreciate the fact that new equipment and more highly trained personnel had forced hospital operating expenses upward.

The American Hospital Association demonstrated its understanding of the growing significance of the non-profit prepayment movement in 1933 by undertaking a study of it with the intent of developing standards to guide its evolution. The Association's Council on Community Relations and Administrative Practice issued a brochure entitled "Essentials of an Acceptable Plan for Group Hospitalization" which listed the following requirements:

1. Stress public welfare.
2. Be limited to hospital charges.
3. Enlist professional and public interest.
4. Provide free choice of physician and hospital.
5. Be maintained as a non-profit organization.
6. Be maintained on a sound economic basis.
7. Be promoted in cooperative spirit and dignified manner.

These "Essentials" were the basis of the Blue Cross approval program of the American Hospital Association whose standards Blue Cross Plans had to meet annually in qualifying for approval. In 1937 the Association issued its first approvals to local non-profit hospital service associations and the Commission on Hospital Service, changed in 1946 to the Blue Cross Commission, was established at Association headquarters.

By 1937 Blue Cross had a million members. Enrollment doubled in both 1938 and 1939. Beginning in 1940 and through 1948, enrollment doubled every three-year period. Starting with 1944, annual growth exceeded 3,000,000 members; more than 5,000,000 were added in 1946, more than 4,300,000 in 1950. The rate of increase declined in 1951 but rose again in 1953. Total enrollment at the close of 1953 was 46,140,816; at the end of 1961 it was 56,489,259, more than two-fifths of the total enrolled by all voluntary health insurers. An additional 3,322,873 were enrolled in Canadian Blue Cross Plans.

The early plans covered only persons who were employed and provided no maternity benefits. A few ventures for family coverage on a percentage basis were made. By 1936 the New York City Plan was providing coverage for dependents on the same basis as the employed subscriber.

The purpose of the Blue Cross Commission, which was established by the American Hospital Association in 1936 with the aid of a grant from the Julius Rosenwald Fund, was to advise and inform those hospitals and communities which were considering the establishment of voluntary, nonprofit hospital care insurance plans, to serve as a clearinghouse of information for executives of existing hospital service associations, and to study related problems of hospital administration and finance. The commission adopted as its symbol of recognition the blue cross, and the local plans approved by it became known as Blue Cross Plans. On March 1, 1954, the plans conveyed in trust to the American Hospital Association their local rights in the Blue Cross words and service mark. According to Jones, although the words and Blue Cross symbol were registered with the United States Patent Office in 1947 under the new Lanham Act, assurance of protection against the infringement of the Blue Cross service mark had not been as strong as it should have been until the adoption of the license agreement of 1954.

The patent attorney is constantly investigating and acting upon cases of apparent infringement.

The difference between Blue Cross and other voluntary health plans is described as follows:[23]

> In contrast to other forms of health insurance, particularly that offered by commercial insurance companies and certain industrial companies which usually provide dollar indemnities and cover employed persons only, Blue Cross plans offer service benefits (benefits in kind) and cover family groups. In 1938, 60 per cent of the subscribers were employed individuals and 40 per cent were members of family groups; today (1947) the situation is almost reversed. Enrollment in Blue Cross plans is accomplished through employers on a group basis and, in most instances, subscriptions are collected by the employer through payroll deductions. This method of collection is relatively inexpensive, since it reduces the volume of bookkeeping and billing and is an important factor in keeping Blue Cross administrative costs at a low figure. In communities where it is not practicable to effect enrollment through the employer or in sections where groups do not meet the required size for participation, community organizations such as lodges, church societies, and professional groups are sometimes used instead. In some areas membership is made available to individuals who are self-employed or otherwise not identified with a group. All Blue Cross organizations are being encouraged to extend membership on a much wider scale to such persons.

A number of organizational changes occurred through the years, among them the creation in 1949 of Health Services, Inc., a stock insurance company, controlled by Blue Cross Plans through the Blue Cross Association, a parent company whose governing board was identical with that of the Blue Cross Commission, thus assuring its not-for-profit operation. The company is empowered to contract with national firms for the provision of Blue Cross benefits. These contracts provide uniform rates, benefits, enrollment and billing procedures on any national account. Also in 1949, the Inter-Plan Service Benefit Bank was established to assist reciprocal agreements between different Blue Cross Plans. The bank constitutes a reciprocal program for providing service benefits to subscribers of one participating plan when they are hospitalized in a member hospital located in an area served by another participating plan.

The "Vital Partnership" which Frank S. Groner, then president of the American Hospital Association, used as the subject for a report,[24] was a result of changes finally approved on August 29, 1960, which made it possible for the first time for Blue Cross "to formulate a national prepayment plan." Reorganization, which began on October 1, created a single, national Blue Cross organization and did away with the division between the Blue Cross Commission and the old Blue Cross Association. The American Hospital Association and the new Blue Cross Association have representatives on each other's boards of trustees. At the same time the American Hospital Association created a Council on Blue Cross Prepayment and Financing to promote its duties concerning Blue

[23] *Hospital Care in the United States,* Commission on Hospital Care, New York, The Commonwealth Fund, 1947, p. 576.
[24] *Hospitals,* October 1, 1960.

Cross. The local authority of the plans is not affected, but the new system is regarded as greatly strengthening Blue Cross. Earlier in the same year the American Hospital Association approved a National Program for Hospitals' Community Services, the impetus for which was chiefly growing criticism of higher Blue Cross rates and of increased government appropriations to pay for the medical and hospital care required by public assistance recipients.[25]

Organization developments culminated with the formation in February, 1961, of the Joint Commission for the Promotion of Voluntary Nonprofit Prepayment Health Plans. Through the coordination thus effected, organizationally speaking, it is hoped, in the words of Walter J. McNerney,[26] president of the Blue Cross Association, to face such considerations as "the proper relationships between Blue Shield and Blue Cross Plans and hospitals, between physicians and hospitals, between Blue Shield Plans and physicians," and to answer such questions as "Do the nonprofit prepayment plans deserve special support by physicians and hospitals? How can this be expressed? Is the salvation of the voluntary movement in service benefits and professional controls worked out and administered by physicians, hospitals and prepayment?"

Chairmanship of the joint commission is for one year and alternates between the American Medical Association and the American Hospital Association.

Blue Shield

Through the joint commission mentioned in the preceding section better correlation between Blue Cross and Blue Shield is expected as each acquires more understanding of the viewpoints and problems of the other.

The first Blue Shield Plan was formed in 1939 by the California Physicians' Service. A year later Michigan Medical Service started its plan. Like the Blue Cross Plans, the medical insurance plans came to life in depression years when patients could not pay their doctors' bills and physicians' income was low. Enrollment was slow at first, then grew rapidly. Methods of operation, rates, ways of reimbursing physicians, varied widely among the separately incorporated plans. Lack of experience caused gross errors in the figuring of risks, and reorganization of plans occurred frequently. Sponsorship was by local medical societies mainly, and there was slight governmental supervision.

In recognition of the need for coordination and centralization, the Blue Shield Commission was organized in 1946. Local control continues to be strong. Through the years overlap with Blue Cross has increased, and more often than not the two are combined in one package in group contracts. Expansion of coverage is proceeding gradually in the direction of inclusion of ambulatory care, home care, and follow-up care.

[25] See *Hospitals*, October 1, 1960, p. 52.
[26] The New Commission Promoting Voluntary Prepayment—Why Is It Important? What Are Its Objectives? How Does It Function? *Hospitals*, July 16, 1962, p. 52.

The National Association of Blue Shield Plans reported that on January 1, 1962, enrollment totaled 49,122,164. Of this total, 2,037,176 were enrolled in the Canadian Blue Shield Plans in British Columbia, Manitoba, the Maritime Provinces, Ontario, and Saskatchewan. During 1961 Blue Shield paid $816,012,231 to physicians for care of members. Blue Shield Plans provide benefits in the form of service or cash indemnities, depending upon the income of the subscriber.

To a greater degree even than Blue Cross, Blue Shield Plans are under fire from the regulatory bodies, the public, and their own groups. Just as hospitals have objections to some of the methods used by Blue Cross, physicians are critical of their own creation, Blue Shield. The American College of Radiology asked the Blue Cross Association in 1962 to exclude from proposed contracts for the aged payments for medical services such as radiology, pathology, and anesthesiology, an issue which has been fought out many times and which in practice is unchanged since the American Hospital Association established "Principles of Relationships Between Hospitals and Radiologists, Anesthetists, and Pathologists." (Some Blue Cross Plans include these services, others do not.) Blue Shield was the object of severe criticism in the Trussell–van Dyke report released late in 1962 which aroused the ire of the New York State Medical Society and several county societies.

Former governor W. Averell Harriman of New York State initiated the study in 1958 following hearings on Blue Cross premium rates. It was conducted by Columbia University's School of Public Health and Administrative Medicine. In a review of the report[27] are the following comments:

> Particularly critical of Blue Shield Plans, which were originally set up by the medical societies, the study report says they do not provide full coverage and that this has encouraged extra fees and unnecessary surgery by unqualified physicians. The report details such recommendations as greater representation of health plans by labor, management and the public; enforcement of the exemption from additional physicians' charges for Blue Shield members whose income is under a specified limit, especially in New York City where, the report said, "the overcharging problem appears to be worst," and sanctions by medical societies against unwilling or unqualified physicians as a means of maintaining the quality of medical care.

Particular exception was made in the report to the hospitalization in unaccredited hospitals of subscribers who consulted physicians who were not qualified surgeons. The further statement was made that the proportion of surgical procedures performed by qualified surgeons ranged from 50 to 70 per cent in the upstate plans and from 60 to 80 per cent in New York City. The director of the study, Dr. Ray E. Trussell, in a talk before the Connecticut Hospital Association in October, 1962, said that in some of the small, unaccredited proprietary hospitals included in the surgical study the proportion of major operations performed by qualified surgeons was as low as 5 per cent.[28]

[27] *Hospitals,* November 16, 1962, p. 20.
[28] N. Y. Prepayment Report Shows Need for Expanded Effort to Improve Medical Care. *Mod. Hosp.,* November, 1962, pp. 79–80.

In an article entitled, "Tighten the Link with 'Great Medicine,' " Dr. Russell A. Nelson,[29] then president of the American Hospital Association, commented as follows on the differences between Blue Cross and Blue Shield methods:

> The success of Blue Cross in meeting the need for hospital services of Great Medicine led to increasing demand for protection against medical and surgical costs for the hospitalized patients. Blue Shield, in attempting to meet this need on a service basis, has run into serious conflict with the traditional "charge according to means" economics (called by some "Robin Hood economics") of medical practice. Disputes have also risen among the specialists' groups and great efforts are made to remove x-ray and pathology services from hospital coverage and place them in Blue Shield. In some places, charges are made that physicians use Blue Shield coverage as a mechanism of increasing their usual fees. In general Blue Cross has maintained its service principle and cost of reduced charge method of paying hospitals; Blue Shield tends more to indemnity, rising fee schedules—and to exclusion of hospital-physician services. These differing approaches by Blue Cross and Blue Shield limit severely the ability of the non-profit voluntary insurance to expand in coverage. . . . Blue Cross has been a prominent factor in the growth of hospitals and has been one of the major effectuating mechanisms in making possible the growth of specialization through popularization of the diagnostic and special therapeutic facilities. As the result of the increased public usage of hospitals, there are greater needs for 24-hour medical coverage and for the services of experienced residents. But Blue Cross and Blue Shield have tended strongly to set up forces that put more and more patients in the hands of personal physicians and surgeons, leaving serious problems regarding the number of patients available for teaching in the residency system.

Dr. Nelson urges that both Blue Cross and Blue Shield do more research into their own activities, saying that we need statistical studies of utilization and comparative studies of patterns of care and costs in various regions and under the different benefits, contracts, and administrative mechanisms.

In June, 1961, Blue Shield announced approval of a composite benefit index as a major step toward development of a uniform nation-wide program. The index uses the allowance for an appendectomy as the base figure, set at 35 units, and allows for local determination of the dollar value given to each relative-value unit under each national contract. The uniform program does not interfere with local plan operations.

Insurance Companies

The Health Insurance Institute estimated that insurance companies paid more than $3.8 billion of the 1962 benefits to subscribers in health plans. This was more than three times the benefits paid by insurance companies during 1952. Payments for hospital expenses formed the largest single portion of health insurance benefits distributed by insurance companies. In 1962 they amounted to an estimated $1.5 billion of the more than $3.8 billion paid to insured persons by insurance companies in the United States. Other payments during the same year were

---

[29] *Hospitals*, November 1, 1960, pp. 37–41.

estimated to be $496 million for surgical and $137 million for regular medical expenses. An additional amount of benefits for hospital-surgical-medical costs came out of the $684 million paid to persons insured under major medical expense policies.

More than $1 billion in benefits were paid to help replace income lost due to off-the-job illness or injury, this figure including accidental death and dismemberment benefit payments.

In 1961, 19 per cent more insurance companies were issuing health insurance than in 1958, and 63 per cent more companies than in 1953. Between 1958 and 1961, insurance companies making group health insurance programs available increased by 130.

Premiums of the 839 insurance companies from health insurance policies reached $5 billion in 1961, a 62 per cent increase over 1956 and more than three times the amount of premiums written in 1951.[30]

Independent Health Insurers

The "independent" plans are sponsored by industrial, community, private clinic, and college health groups. These plans number around 800.

Independent plans have a long history, and the manner in which they collect and disburse funds is as varied as their own organization and purposes. The aid to the sick given by the early societies was not commercially motivated nor did it entail regular contributions or fixed payments as a rule. Daniel Defoe back in 1697 advocated insurance for sailors, guaranteeing them medical attention in case of injury, a pension for loss of an eye or limb and for disablement or old age. He even went so far as to outline a system of mutual insurance for all against every kind of risk including sickness, saying that insurance "might be improved into methods that should prevent the general misery and poverty of mankind, and at once secure us against beggars, parish poor, almshouses and hospitals and by which not a creature so miserable or so poor but should claim subsistence as their due, and not ask it of charity."[31]

A scheme for mutual insurance against sickness was proposed by the French philanthropist Piarron de Chamousset, in a publication, *Views of a Citizen,* published in Paris in 1757. Employers were to pay the contributions for their employees. John Acland of Devon, England, advocated in 1786 a plan for subscriptions from wage earners which would provide, among other things, sick benefits. For the benefit of ex-seamen, France, through Jean-Baptiste Colbert, had established a fund against sickness and disability by deductions from pay. This was in 1693. Some of the benefit societies were subsidized by governments in the second half of the nineteenth century.

In the United States workmen's compensation laws led to contracts between

---

[30] *Source Book of Health Insurance Data 1962,* Health Insurance Institute, New York.
[31] Daniel Defoe: *Essay upon Projects,* London, Cassell, reprinted 1887.

hospitals and industries for the care of injury or work-connected illness. Out of this arrangement came plans liberalizing the scope of coverage through an insurance plan financed at least in part by deductions from salaries. The mining and lumber industries were conspicuous in developing these plans, usually through contract arrangements with specific hospitals. The Northern Pacific Beneficial Association was formed by the Northern Pacific Railway Company to provide for the medical, surgical and hospital care of its members through salary deductions, the care being limited except in emergency to the association's doctors and hospitals. Other railroads make similar provisions for their employees. The Endicott Johnson Corporation in New York State contracts with voluntary hospitals for the care of its employees and members of their families.

Complete and comprehensive medical service for employees in the plants of Henry J. Kaiser is provided through the medical and hospital service plan developed by the Permanente Foundation in 1942. This plan uses its own hospitals.

The Health Insurance Plan of Greater New York began operation in 1947. The following description is taken from an article by Paul M. Densen, Sam Shapiro, Ellen W. Jones, and Irving Baldinger:[32]

> The principal features of the plan are comprehensive medical service rendered through the group practice of medicine, with capitation as the basis of payment to groups of physicians. Enrollees in the plan and their covered dependents choose a medical group in the area in which they live, and within that group make a choice of family physician. Available to the enrollee, through the group practice mechanism, are services from family physicians and board certified or board eligible specialists in each of 12 major medical specialties. In addition to general and specialist medical care, benefits available to enrollees are periodic health examinations, immunizations, laboratory and x-ray services, physical therapy, administration of blood and plasma, psychiatric consultations, visiting nurse services and ambulance services. Physicians see patients in the patients' homes, in physicians' private offices, in the medical group center, or in the hospital. For these services, patients receive no bills, the entire cost being met by the premium (with the exception of a possible $2 charge for a night call to the home between 10 p.m. and 7 a.m.). Physicians are paid by the medical groups with which they are associated, and the groups are paid on a per capita basis for each individual enrolled, regardless of volume of service requested by the enrollees.
>
> *All enrollees carry Blue Cross or other insurance against the costs of hospitalization* so that financial provision is available for HIP patients to be hospitalized.

The "self-insurance situation" with which the authors compare H.I.P. is the plan administered by District 65 Retail, Wholesale and Department Store Unions, affiliated with the A.F.L.-C.I.O. This labor union administers an alternate plan to H.I.P. in the form of a fee-for-service plan for payment of medical costs, and also its own hospital insurance program. The authors state:[33]

> Since September, 1955, District 65 union members have registered annually their choice of plan for medical coverage, the alternatives being H.I.P. and the

---

[32] Comparison of a Group Practice and a Self-Insurance Situation. *Hospitals,* November 16, 1962.
[33] *Hospitals,* November 16, 1962, p. 63.

union's own fee-for-service plan. . . . Under the union's plan, enrollees obtain medical care from any physician and are reimbursed according to a set schedule of fees. Regardless of source of medical insurance coverage, all members have hospital insurance coverage by the union-administered plan.

The comparative study showed that the annual hospital admission rates for the two groups of enrollees were almost identical. In most of the broad diagnostic categories, the rates were similar for H.I.P. and the union plan. Duration of hospital stay showed no significant differences between the groups, 8.3 for H.I.P. and 8.4 for fee-for-service. Examination of the rate of utilization of physician services outside the hospital indicated that the two study groups were very similar.

In 1959 the Group Health Federation of America and the American Labor Health Association merged to form the Group Health Association of America. The federation consisted of consumer-sponsored medical care plans, the Labor Health Association of labor health clinics.

In 1961 representatives of the New York Medical College–Flower and Fifth Avenue Hospitals, the New York Hotel Trades Council (A.F.L.–C.I.O.), and the Hotel Association of New York City signed a five-year agreement for comprehensive medical care for employees of the hotel industry and their families. The program is financed by the Union Family Medical Fund of the Hotel Industry of New York City, a joint labor-management body. Initially 9,000 employees and dependents were covered, with an eventual coverage in a city-wide program of 80,000 persons.

The biggest voluntary health insurance plan in the world came into existence on July 1, 1960, when the United States government initiated its plan to offer protection to 1.8 million federal employees and their 2.2 million dependents. Two nation-wide systems were agreed upon, one under the direction of the Aetna Life Insurance Company with other commercial companies participating, the other run by Blue Cross–Blue Shield. Financing is jointly by the government and the employee. Employees have a choice between the commercial and the Blue Cross–Blue Shield plans. On July 1, 1961, a government-wide health coverage plan was offered under the Retired Federal Employees Health Benefits Act, administration by the Aetna Life Insurance Company but choice of qualified plans including Blue Cross–Blue Shield by the annuitant.

Expanding Coverage Under Health Plans

Comprehensive coverage under health plans is rhetorical, according to Anne R. and Herman M. Somers,[34] of Haverford College, Pennsylvania. They point out that less than one-fourth of our private medical care bills are met by health insurance and that only a little more than half of the total private hospital bill in the United States is met through insurance. They report some advances, however, such as:

[34] *Pub. Health Rep.*, January, 1961; condensed in *Hospital Topics*, April, 1961.

Group Health Cooperative of Seattle covers in its regular prepayment plan most prescribed drugs except insulin, other hormones, and vitamins (unless there is a clinical diagnosis of a vitamin deficiency) for each separate condition for up to a year. In 1959, GHC reported an average of $3\frac{1}{2}$ prescriptions per year per covered member and a total annual cost per member of $4.99. Compare this with the $36 spent by the average Health Insurance Plan of Greater New York member for noninsured drugs in 1957! The key to this low cost, according to GHC, is a formulary which provides a limited number of products, and so avoids duplications and prescribing by brand name.

Pressure is on the plans for coverage of mental illness—and, said Mike Gorman, executive director of the National Committee Against Mental Illness in 1959, not by "an extra rider for mental illness which asks the family to pay an extra charge for this coverage. This is actuarial nonsense. If the insurance companies of America cannot cover the most prevalent illness in the nation in their basic policies, they really forfeit the right to the patronage of the people." Gorman referred to the favorable experience of Blue Cross of Northeast Ohio (Cleveland), which has had mental illness provisions for hospitalization for twenty years and "the cost of such care has been running somewhat less than one per cent of total hospital claims of all types."[35]

Thomas P. Weils[36] concluded, after summarizing the experience of both Blue Cross–Blue Shield plans and commercial carriers when extending such coverage, that it is actuarially possible for prepayment plans to extend short-term hospitalization benefits for mental illness.

"Cut the Pain of Dental Bills," urged other authors,[37] and the way pointed out to do it was the nonprofit, prepaid, dental insurance plan.

The Washington State Dental Association organized the Dental Service Corporation in 1954 initially to serve the children of the members of several unions but later extended to other consumer organizations. It appears to have been the first state-wide dental plan.

In 1962 the Continental Casualty Company put into general operation a group insurance plan for dental care. The American Dental Association was one of the first groups to cover its employees.

Home care is being included in several plans and appears to have some possibilities in reducing the overutilization of hospitals by subscribers.

The major group that is creating gigantic problems for voluntary health insurance is the aged. The higher rate of illness and its frequently long-term nature in those over 65 make coverage on a break-even basis too costly for retired persons to pay the premiums, as a rule. Nevertheless, five million persons over 65 carry Blue Cross insurance. In an attempt to head off compulsory insurance under Social Security, all of the plans are working on special ways of covering insurance for the aged, and a few have already inaugurated plans, some of them including both medical and hospital service and nursing home care.

[35] From testimony before the New York State Joint Legislative Committee on Health Insurance Plans, reported in *Hospitals*, March 16, 1959, pp. 127–28.
[36] Health Insurance and Mental Illness. *Hospitals*, March 1, 1959.
[37] *Pageant*, May, 1961.

Dr. Karl S. Klicka,[38] former director, Hospital Planning Council for Metropolitan Chicago, proposed the application of annuity insurance principles to retirement health care. He quoted figures from studies published by the University of Michigan and by the Health Insurance Foundation showing that the average expenditure for all health services for persons 65 years and over is approximately $180 per year. Since a person at 65 years of age has an average life expectancy of 15 years, the average fund to be built up is $2,700. A person who bought such an annuity at age 40 would pay a premium of $63.80 per year until age 65, when premiums would cease. If bought at an earlier age the premiums would be less. Dr. Klicka cited the Blue Cross Plan of Cleveland as having announced that benefits will be continued for life at no charge for persons who have had 40 years of Blue Cross coverage.

Under a plan devised by a builder, Ross Cortese, of Los Angeles, the elderly can finance their medical care by buying a cooperative apartment in the price of which this service is included. Rossmoor Leisure World is a $150 million development south of Los Angeles. It has 6,750 apartments priced from $10,350 to $12,100, with monthly payments from $95 to $105 thereafter. The minimum age stipulated for purchasers is 52. Blue Cross of Southern California will administer the medical fund provided through about $10 of each purchaser's monthly payment. Outside medical services, except hospitalization, will be paid. The project will have 10 resident doctors, including a psychiatrist, 26 registered nurses on call around the clock, a free dispensary, a laboratory and x-ray room, and 24-hour ambulance service.[39]

In January, 1962, the American Medical Association and the National Association of Blue Shield Plans announced a uniform, nation-wide program of surgical and medical care benefits for persons age 65 and over whose income is $2,500 or less if single and $4,000 or less if husband and wife combine their incomes. It was recommended that all state medical societies cooperate fully with their local Blue Shield affiliates in implementing the program which will be available at an estimated $3 per person per month. It provides for surgery performed in a hospital or a physician's office and for medical care in a hospital or licensed nursing home. It also provides payments for anesthesia, radiation treatments, x-ray examinations, and laboratory tests and pathology services.

HOSPITAL WAGE AND SALARY ADMINISTRATION

O. K. STEPHENS[40]

Most of the subject matter concerning wage and salary administration in hospitals is of comparatively recent date. This is surprising when we consider that

---

[38] *Hospitals*, January 16, 1961, pp. 39, 40, 117, 118.

[39] As reported in *Time*, abstracted in *The Reader's Digest*, August, 1962.

[40] Condensed from his 1961 thesis submitted to qualify for the master's degree in hospital administration at Northwestern University. Mr. Stephens is hospital business administrator, Medical Health Center, State of Illinois, Chicago.

from 60 to 70 per cent of the total hospital budget is spent for payment of wages, salaries, or benefits to people who perform services in, and for, the hospital and its patients. Similarly, it is surprising that much of the literature regarding personnel management in the hospital is of comparatively recent origin.

Two recent developments are attracting attention and causing concern about the development of written personnel policies and sound policies of wage and salary administration. One of these developments is the rise in costs of hospitalization paid by the patient, an insurance carrier, or other agents. A second cause for concern is the interest of union organizers in a program of unionism for hospital employees. A lack of good personnel policies and sound wage and salary administration will play directly into the hands of these organizers.

To quote the words of Dr. Malcolm T. MacEachern:[41] "Few other institutions have so complex an organization as the hospital requires with the application of its various talents. Nowhere else are personnel and human relations so integrated and so strained, and nowhere else are such exactness of action and service required."

We find many conflicts which exert pressure in the determination of proper hospital wages and salaries from the patient, the relatives, the insurance carriers, and other third-party agents who join in the desire for the best possible care at the lowest possible cost.

Another factor producing a conflict in the hospital is the necessary wide divergence of training and experience among hospital workers. The janitor and the dishwasher come to the hospital with a minimum of training and experience and must be trained to produce services acceptable from the standpoint of hospital sanitation requirements. Above these qualifications are those expected of a hospital aide, a nurse, a laboratory technician, an x-ray technician, an EEG technician, progressing through the more or less specialized fields of dietary management, nursing administration, interns and resident physicians, to the chiefs of service of such complex medical specialties as radiology, pathology, and anesthesiology. Each employee, from the dishwasher to the top-ranking medical specialist, is expected to perform as though life hung in the balance, as it actually does.

Expressions of dissatisfaction that come to trustees from patients with whom they are acquainted, complaining about the high costs of hospital care, affect them when they are considering the merits of a new costly cobalt therapy machine, involving employment of special technicians to operate it.

There is a special grouping of hospital status symbols. This might be illustrated with the hospital key. The janitor must go to the floor housekeeper who has the key to the lock of the door behind which housekeeping and janitorial supplies, brooms, mops, and other necessities are kept. Another employee on the organizational ladder has to go to someone else who has the key to the narcotic cabinet. There is another key for other supplies of the pharmacy, and for every

[41] *Hospital Organization and Management,* 3rd ed. Chicago, Physicians' Record Co., 1957, p. 961.

key there are as many potential conflicts as there are employees supervised by the keepers of the keys. Other status symbols are the doctor's gown, the intern's gown, this cap, and that cap; and there are the shoulder patches of the various therapies where the gown does not produce the satisfactory distinction between your specialty and mine.

In the attitudes of staff members and volunteers and auxiliaries toward themselves and toward each other, conflicts of interests can easily appear. This is particularly true if the volunteer is energetic enough to serve more than one hospital and makes critical comparisons. Servicemen who call on several hospitals also make these comparisons. Physicians may produce discord if they find that another hospital provides a service needed by one of their patients but not available in their own hospital.

By contract or some agreement, the hospital pays for an employee's time, his presence at a given place, and his skills. For rare skills premium pay may be demanded by the possessor. A standard by which to measure these skills and motions is most desirable. Two-thirds or more of the hospital budget is spent for employee services, yet the purchasing department, responsible for from 15 to 17 per cent of the budget, is usually much more rigidly controlled.

Morale considerations temper the tendencies to pay as little as possible for satisfactory employee performance. Hospital employees must have a standard of living in keeping with the hospital's status in the community, as a good place in which to work, offering careers that fulfill employee drives to help fellow human beings during their times of trouble. This factor is related to the discovery, applying the findings of industrial studies, that there is close kinship between employee morale and efficient work and service. Other factors affecting wage and salary policy are pressure from unions and the fact that employee turnover if excessive is a waste of recruitment, induction, training time, effort, and expense.

The first basic consideration in developing wage and salary administration is conformance with federal, state, and local laws, statutes, or ordinances. The hospital program must observe laws relating to the minimum wage, statutes relating to the length of the workweek, limitations on the length of the workday, child labor restrictions, public health and sanitation requirements, building codes, and possibly fair employment practice acts.

In achieving the objective of equal pay for equal work, there should be no differentiation between the pay of a male and of a female who are accomplishing the same work in the same time and in the same place. The completed programs should imply no differences due to race, color, creed, and similar considerations. A governing board must deliberate carefully whether it intends to pay the lowest possible wage to fill its vacancies or whether to pay as much as is required to get people to do a quality job.

Job descriptions constitute a simple, clear-cut written statement of the duties and responsibilities for each position and help in constructing training programs and in comparing jobs with those performed in business, industry, other hospitals, and government jurisdictions. One of the most satisfactory means of establishing fair wages is through comparisons with those paid by all employers in a given community. Consideration must also be given the tendencies of mobile workers to be attracted to distant communities for higher wages and other considerations. Wage survey accomplishes the desired comparisons.

Consideration should be given in wage surveys to the manner in which the cooperation of other employers is enlisted. Offering a compilation of results, developing the community need for current wage data, expressing the dangers of competitive pressure from payment of wages at too high levels, as well as those of costly turnover in paying too low a wage, and strictly maintaining the confidential nature of the data will help to provide assurance and confidence and the desire to participate in wage surveys. Personal interviews with the employers and key members of their staffs are a great aid to harmony.

Probably the most significant factor in the compilation and presentation of results following a wage survey is the deliberate separation of wages from fringe benefits. The surveyor needs to know the unusual, the average, and the minimum effect on wage administration of the fringe benefits provided by each employer supplying the data which has been collected.

Current newspaper advertisements of job opportunities often carry the salaries to be paid. These are particularly helpful in the analysis of wages and salaries paid to clerical, maintenance, kitchen, and laundry employees.

The publications of the government through the Bureau of Labor statistics, Bureau of Census, United States Employment Service, the Veterans Administration, and other agencies should be obtained.

Specific salary scales established for the different groups of employees require a rate range consisting of minimum and maximum rate to be paid for each job. Such pay ranges provide latitude for seniority and proficiency and assist in the reduction of turnover. In establishing rate ranges, the administrator must determine whether or not administration of increases within the rate range is to be automatic. The increase plan could be based solely on length of service, failing to distinguish between the inferior and superior employee, with the resultant possibility of destroying incentive for superior performance. Under a system of progression through the rate range according to individual merit, the supervisor becomes responsible for planning the development of each person under his supervision.

Although incentive plans do not apply to some major areas of hospital services, there are some possibilities, as illustrated by the group incentive plans applied by some hospitals to laundry production. These plans have been used to reduce the number of employees required while maintaining the necessary production and quality of laundry processing. They may consist of nothing more than a fair wage to employees, to which is added the incentive of reaching the end of the workday when all of the necessary production has been obtained.

Payment of overtime will probably depend upon the practices of hospitals in a given area, but final determination should consider industrial and business experience in each locality. Consideration must be given to part-time people in respect to both the wage scale and fringe benefits. Study of the labor market in the hospital area and study of special jobs, such as tray girls needed at meal-time, will help toward appropriate decisions.

One of the objectives in administration of the personnel program should be uniform application to all employees, regardless of professional or nonprofessional status. Pioneering in this direction has already been accomplished by federal hospitals and by some state hospitals.

Fringe Benefits

There was a time in the history of hospitals when the importance of fringe benefits overshadowed the administration of salary payments. Today salary payments have outdistanced fringe benefits. Within the hospital a number of inequities are often found in the application of fringe benefits. This is directly related to the shortage of personnel during World War II when, in addition to salary payments, hospitals offered fringe benefits to attract professional workers.

Included in the fringe benefits offered to hospital employees in Illinois are holidays, sick leave, vacation, meals at cost or at no cost, uniforms, laundering of uniforms, payment of overtime, premium pay for evening and night shift duty, hospital care at low cost or no cost, bargain rates for drugs from the pharmacy, hospitalization insurance, accident and sickness insurance, life insurance, pensions, severance pay, and coffee breaks.

Too often hospitals fail to publicize the cost of these benefits. It is important to tell employees what the financial burden is. A hospital that gives a two-week vacation with pay to employees having less than ten years of service and three weeks to those having more than ten years spends a large amount each year to maintain services during vacations. We owe it to the public and to the patients served to publicize fully the cost of fringe benefits to each employee.

Annual Review

Recently more hospitals have begun to review both wages and fringe benefits annually. Certainly in the days that lie ahead more and more attention will be given to periodic review of these as a part of total hospital costs. The alternative dangers are pointed out succinctly by Robert M. Sigmond, quoted in an Illinois Hospital Association memorandum, March 29, 1961, who says: "These rising costs, if unchecked, will inevitably result in new undesirable forms of governmental control and limitations unless hospitals can assure the public that they are taking every possible step to avoid waste and inefficiency in every form."

Conclusions

The hospital economy, community economy, and national economy bear many relationships. National, regional, and community recessions are linked. Inflation of wages, of equipment costs, of the costs of building and servicing hospitals, will not begin and end solely within the hospital's walls. The cost of care for the patient is affected by some influences beyond our control, but those costs we can control need independent analysis, thought and determined effort.

Collective action of all hospital employees must be encouraged to produce the optimum qualitative and the optimum quantitative patient care for each hour of work and pay. Beyond this we must encourage unity of action among hospitals. Group discussions should consider every facet of cost, including particularly wages and salaries. Associations of hospitals should formulate group action to share opinions, knowledge, skills, facilities, equipment, and personnel. Illustrative of trends are those hospitals which share rare skills of registered medical record librarians, dietitians, pharmacists, or anesthesiologists, or the costs of electronic data processing.

Not all hospitals can establish methods engineering on a full-time basis, but this service can be acquired by consultation or contract. Every hospital can encourage methods improvement and work simplification. In an administrative atmosphere that encourages ingenuity, employees can become great assets in reducing costs.

There is need to improve the communications of the hospital to its employees, to patients, to third-party payers, to the community, to other hospitals, to hospital associations, and to government and the courts.

CHAPTER 15

Political Backgrounds; Public Health

> The state came into existence, that man may live. It continues, that man may live well.
>
> ARISTOTLE

POLITICAL SCIENCE is changing in approach and in emphasis. Two quite different directions are apparent in educational circles. One is to reduce the scientific element and enhance the practical, making it practically a study of government. The other is to combine the scientific and utilitarian aspects and adapt mathematical, sociological, psychological, and anthropological techniques to the political scene. With a different viewpoint if not goal from that of the sociologist, the political scientist of the new order conducts surveys of communities to aid them in solving problems such as housing, urban renewal, crime prevention, and disease control. Data gathering is used in analyzing and forecasting political trends.

Traditionally study of political science has been focused upon the doctrines propounded by political philosophers—Plato, Aristotle, Dante, Machiavelli, Bacon, Hobbes, Locke, Bentham, Mill, de Tocqueville, Bryce, Laski. Parkinson[1] insists that along with such study should be that of the men who have been actors on the political scene. His contention is that "no actual politician is greatly influenced by a book of political theory although many have been influenced by a book of religion." Further, he points out that politics are far older than political theory.

---

[1] C. Northcote Parkinson: *The Evolution of Political Thought.* New York, The Viking Press, 1960 (By arrangement with Houghton Mifflin Company), pp. 7–10.

HOSPITAL CARE BY GOVERNMENT

The earliest record of a government system of hospitals is connected with King Asoka of India. This Buddhist ruler of the third century B.C. was a socially minded individual, motivated by religious zeal. He commanded the establishment of hospitals and dispensaries throughout his vast empire, which extended from Afghanistan to Madras. A rock inscription records the founding and operation of 18 such medical centers, as they would be called today. King Asoka belongs to the whole social welfare realm. H. G. Wells[2] records:

> He organized a great digging of wells . . . the planting of trees . . . appointed officers for the supervision of charitable works . . . founded public gardens . . . gardens for the growing of medicinal herbs . . . created a ministry for the care of aborigines and subject races . . . made provision for the education of women . . . was the first monarch to make an attempt to educate his people into a common view of the ends and way of life . . . made vast benefactions to the Buddhist teaching orders and tried to stimulate them to a better study of their own literature.

The attendants in the hospitals established by King Asoka were, according to MacEachern in *Hospital Organization and Management*,[3] ordered "to give gentle care to the sick, to furnish them with fresh fruits and vegetables, to prepare medicines, to give massages, and to keep their own persons clean." It is recorded that the king's daughter headed the first known nursing organization.

No other ruler's name is prominently connected with hospital care until the middle of the fourth century of the Christian era. In the year 335 Constantine the Great issued a famous decree ordering the closing of the Aesculapieia and other pagan temples in which faith healing played the major part, and thus stimulated the building of Christian hospitals. It is not recorded that the great Roman emperor directly concerned himself with the establishment of hospitals, although the founding and building of Christian hospitals is reported to have proceeded rapidly, with Helena, the mother of Constantine, playing an active part.

Another fourth-century monarch who established hospitals was King Buddhadisa of India. He created many so-called wejasa, in which he is said to have nursed sick people himself.

The Roman emperor Justinian I concerned himself with care of the sick on a large scale when in the year 532 a terrible epidemic of plague occurred in Constantinople and threatened to spread throughout the empire. He had posts specially set up for the examination and "purification" of all travelers coming from the stricken areas. This preventive measure was an astonishingly enlightened one for the period. In 550 he built the great hospital of Saint John at Jerusalem, service in which was given by the new military orders established during the Crusades.

[2] *The Outline of History.* New York, The Macmillan Company, 1921, pp. 369–70.
[3] Chicago, Physicians' Record Co., 3rd ed., 1957, p. 2.

Glamor enters hospital history with the accomplishments of the caliphs. El Walid Ibn Abdel Malik, the sixth caliph of the Ommiad dynasty, founded at Damascus in the year 707 the first Arabic hospital. According to Sand,[4] resident doctors were attached to this establishment, and it included special wards for mental illness, blindness, and leprosy. Eighty-five years later, the caliph of *Arabian Nights* fame, Haroun al-Raschid, founded in Baghdad a great hospital with a medical school attached. Sir Mark Sykes, in *The Caliph's Last Heritage*,[5] lists among the achievements of the Moslem potentate the fact that through the vast dominions, "pestilence and disease were met by imperial hospitals and government physicians."

Although by the time of Charlemagne, who was crowned by Pope Leo III in 800 as head of the Holy Roman Empire, there were many large hospitals in Europe, he personally seems to have played no great part in building or developing them. In his day, as for a long time before and afterward, they were certainly not places in which scientific procedures were followed. He corresponded with Haroun al-Raschid but does not seem to have absorbed any of the caliph's interest in scientific medicine. Yet Charlemagne was socially minded. He showed concern for the welfare of his people. It is probable that indirectly, as was the case with many other rulers, he encouraged those who were engaged in care of the sick insofar as his understanding of their needs went.

A century later a caliph was again responsible for the establishment at Baghdad of a great hospital. Caliph al Muktadir asked the celebrated Persian physician Rhazes to select a healthful site and to give advice on planning and construction. Rhazes later became its chief physician. This hospital is a striking example of the fact that the passage of years too often brings retrogression rather than progress. About it the statement was made that the "comfort was such that some patients simulated illness in order to have the opportunity of enjoying it." This hospital was managed by a superintendent and a steward. It had a staff of 25 doctors. It had a library. Home care of convalescent patients appears to have been provided. Avicenna (980–1037), called the "prince of physicians," was later physician-in-chief in this celebrated hospital.

There was a king of Ceylon, Parakrama the Great, who reigned from 1159 to 1186, and who opened a hospital containing many hundreds of rooms. Each patient, according to Sand,[6] "had his own male and female attendant who shared the day and night watches, and the king personally saw to it that the diet, which constituted one of the cardinal features of the treatment, was abundant, varied, and of the highest quality." Further, "he used to visit the hospital once a week and distributed new clothes to the patients who were ready for discharge."

The sultan of Syria built a magnificent hospital at Damascus in 1160. It is said that until 1427 the furnaces of this hospital were kept burning night and day. About 1200 the sultan of Morocco built a great infirmary at Marrakesh. This

---

[4] René Sand: *The Advance to Social Medicine*. London, Staples Press, 1952, p. 71.
[5] London, Macmillan and Company, 1915, pp. 222–23.
[6] *Op. cit.,* p. 68.

hospital was lavishly decorated and furnished, and it was surrounded by beautiful gardens. The historian Abd el Wahid el Marrakehi[7] reported that every Friday after prayers "the Sultan used to go on horseback to visit the patients and inquire after each one, asking how they were and whether they were well looked after. He kept up this custom until the day of his death."

The emperor of China, Kublai Kahn, whose glorious reign was described by Marco Polo, ordered in 1271 the setting up of nursing establishments as part of a wide program of relief and social welfare.

In Cairo, Egypt, Sultan el Mansour Gilavun opened a great hospital in 1283. In it there was extensive specialization of services with special wards for dysentery, fever, eyes, injuries, and the like. The air was cooled by fountains ever playing. Nursing and dietary services were well organized. There were lounges for physicians, a library, a dispensary, and an herb garden. Musicians and storytellers were employed to entertain the patients.

Since the story of hospitals has its downs as well as ups, and spasmodic is the word that best describes hospital progress, a monarch must be mentioned who wrecked a whole hospital system. Henry VIII of England ordered the Catholic hospitals closed in 1530. The properties were confiscated along with other church properties. On his deathbed, however, he authorized the founding of the five royal hospitals of London as a replacement for those whose property he had seized. According to Sir Arthur Salusbury MacNalty,[8] in *The Renaissance and its Influence on English Medicine, Surgery and Public Health,* there were in England until the eighteenth century 23 counties which had no hospitals.

Writing about the Aztecs under Montezuma, Bancroft[9] says:

> For severe cases, the expenses of treating which could not be borne except by the wealthy classes, hospitals were established by the government in all the larger cities, endowed with ample revenues, where patients from the surrounding country were cared for by experienced doctors, surgeons, and nurses well versed in all the healing arts. Medical practitioners were numerous, who attended patients for a small remuneration.

Hernando Cortez, who conquered Mexico, established in Mexico City in 1527 the Hospital of the Immaculate Conception, now the Hospital of Jesus of Nazareth. This is the oldest hospital still in existence in the Americas. In the rules set by the founder there was a stipulation that each patient was to be visited by a physician and by the head nurse every day.

U.S. Public Health Service Hospitals

In Virginia as far back as 1708 the Council ordered that a house be hired to accommodate the sick men belonging to her Majesty's ship the *Garland* and that the rent be paid out of her Majesty's revenues, but not until 1780 were steps

[7] *Op. cit.,* p. 72.
[8] London, Christopher and Johnson, 1946. Cited in Sand, *op. cit.,* p. 366.
[9] *Works of Hubert Howe Bancroft,* San Francisco, A. L. Bancroft Company, 1882, 39 vols., Vol. 11, p. 596.

taken to establish a permanent marine hospital. In 1800 the hospital was transferred to the federal government and became the second federal institution of its kind in the United States. It was operated by the government until the Civil War. Its establishment was preceded by the signing by President John Adams in 1798 of an act "for the relief of sick and disabled seamen"—the first move of the federal government to care for the health of any group of its citizens—and the establishment in 1799 of the first marine hospital, the Marine Hospital of Boston.

Responsible for this action by the government was the Boston Marine Society, organized by captains of the ships that thronged the harbor. The captains were concerned about the needs of the seamen for medical care. In 1790 they drew up a petition to the Second Congress for a marine hospital, but it took seven years' work to get it passed. The act provided for the payment of 20 cents a month by every seaman, taken from his pay by the master of his ship, toward the support of marine hospitals. The Boston hospital was established in an old army barracks on Castle Island.

The marine hospitals are now known as Public Health Service hospitals and are operated by that agency under the Health, Education and Welfare Department. Besides the former marine hospitals which are general in nature and which total 18, the Public Health Service operates two neuropsychiatric hospitals, two tuberculosis hospitals, the National Leprosarium, Freedmen's Hospital, Indian hospitals, and some 20 full-time clinics. Complete medical and dental care and hospitalization is provided to the following major groups: American merchant seamen, coast guard officers and enlisted personnel and dependents, and federal employees eligible for compensation under the Federal Employees Compensation Act. Smaller groups included are persons with Hansen's disease and federal prisoners and voluntary patients who are narcotic drug addicts. The Veterans Administration may also hospitalize patients in P.H.S. hospitals on a reimbursable basis.

Veterans Administration Hospitals

The Veterans Administration, originally the Veterans Bureau, was created in 1921 as an independent agency to take over and conduct the duties of the Bureau of War Risk Insurance, the rehabilitation division of the federal board for vocational education, and some of the services then rendered to ex-soldiers by the Public Health Service.

As of 1963 the Veterans Administration was operating 165 hospitals, besides utilizing beds in other hospitals.

Veterans of all wars are admitted to VA hospitals, with priority given to those who are suffering from injuries or diseases incurred in or made worse by wartime service. Others who have nonservice-connected disabilities must state under oath that they are unable to pay for private treatment, and they must submit financial statements.

Military Hospitals

Hospitals were improvised for care of wounded and ill soldiers during the Revolution, the War of 1812, the Mexican War, and the Civil War. A Hospital Corps was authorized for the first time under a law enacted in 1887. Except for the Army and Navy General Hospital at Hot Springs, Arkansas, the Army had only small post hospitals at that time. Before the development of the national defense program in 1940, the permanent hospital facilities of the Medical Department of the Army consisted of 5 general hospitals and 110 station hospitals, with a total capacity of about 10,000 beds. There are now some 60 general and 450 station hospitals. The Navy has large hospitals at Great Lakes, Illinois, and at Bethesda, Maryland, the former established in 1911, the latter in 1942; also at Chelsea, Massachusetts, Long Island, New York, Annapolis, Maryland, at Philadelphia, and other places. The earliest naval hospital was established at Norfolk in 1830. The Hospital Corps was established in 1898 and the U.S. Naval Medical Bureau in 1907.

The Air Force also operates hospitals at its major posts, and all of the military hospitals are readily expandable on threat of war.

The War Department operates five local civilian hospitals maintained by the Panama Canal government on the Isthmus of Panama. They include the Gorgas General Hospital at Balboa; two general hospitals, one at Colon, the other at Margarita; a 350-bed mental institution at Corozal; and a 140-bed leprosarium at Palo Seco.

Total U.S. Government–Operated Hospitals

Hospitals operated by agencies of the federal government[10] totaled 444 out of the 7,028 hospitals in the United States. They had 177,677 beds out of 1,689,414. They admitted 1,591,796 patients out of the total 26,531,365.

INTERNATIONAL PUBLIC HEALTH

The Department of State of the United States has in its Agency for International Development (AID) an Office of Public Health. There is a Health and Sanitation Division of the Institute of Inter-American Affairs which is responsible to the Secretary of State.

There is a Pan American Health Organization whose operating arm is the Pan American Sanitary Bureau.

A voluntary National Council for Community Services to International Visitors cooperates with the Department of State and other government and private agencies, especially with respect to help and orientation services for students from other countries.

[10] As reported in the 1963 A.H.A. "Guide Issue."

DEPARTMENT OF HEALTH, EDUCATION AND WELFARE

Editor Edward W. Bok of the *Ladies' Home Journal,* editorializing in the February, 1911, issue, said that the government in Washington had information to give out for curing sick hogs but none for tuberculosis in people, and asked, "When will we have a national department of health and end this ridiculous situation?"

Not until 1953, Mr. Bok. It took a long and determined struggle to get health established as an executive department of the government with its head a member of the Cabinet. The Department of Health, Education and Welfare was established on April 11, 1953, replacing the Federal Security Agency. It brought the number of executive departments to ten, the others being the Department of State, the Department of the Treasury, the Department of Defense, the Department of Justice, the Post Office Department, the Department of the Interior, the Department of Agriculture, the Department of Commerce, and the Department of Labor.

Besides the Public Health Service, the organizations within the Department are Food and Drug Administration, Office of Education, Vocational Rehabilitation Administration, St. Elizabeths Hospital (for mentally ill), the Social Security Administration, and the Welfare Administration established in 1963. The department has administrative responsibility for the following federally supported organizations: American Printing House for the Blind, Gallaudet College and Howard University, and the Columbia Institution for the Deaf.

The then Secretary of Health, Education and Welfare, Arthur S. Flemming,[11] in 1959 referred to mental illness as one of the major health problems, saying:

> The resources we are devoting to mental illness today fall dreadfully short of meeting the problem. We have not yet mounted an effective attack on mental illness in this country. The fact is, we are barely holding the line. One does not need to dig very deep into this problem to uncover some shocking deficiencies. I am satisfied that, on the whole, we are beginning to make real progress in the area of research. But in the area of hospital care and treatment, we are far behind.

Legislation authorizing $329 million to treat and study mental health and retardation problems was enacted in November, 1963.

In October, 1963, former President John F. Kennedy signed the Drug Amendments Act to the federal Food, Drug and Cosmetic Act. The amendments establish new safeguards for drug research, manufacture, and distribution. They tighten control on preclinical tests.

[11] *Pub. Health Rep.,* July, 1959.

U.S. PUBLIC HEALTH SERVICE

The Public Health Service is a branch of the Department of Health, Education, and Welfare which was established in 1953, replacing the Federal Security Agency created in 1939.

The beginning of the Public Health Service is traced to the program of medical care for seamen of the American Merchant Marine established in 1798. The marine hospitals, now Public Health Service hospitals, and other hospitals operated by the Public Health Service were referred to earlier in this chapter.

The Public Health Service administers the National Hospital Survey and Construction program under the Hill-Burton Act of 1946. The activities of its Division of Hospital Facilities include financial assistance and technical advice and leadership to state and local governments and to nonprofit organizations, so that community needs for hospitals and health centers may be measured and met.

Among the other functions of the Public Health Service are:

Enforcement of national quarantine laws

Furnishing aid beyond the resources of state and local health departments to control epidemics in time of disaster

Promoting coordination of all facilities and resources pertaining to the provision of hospital and related care, and administering a grant program for the conduct of research in the fields of hospital and related care

Providing information on broad questions of national policy pertaining to nursing education and nursing service, and promoting the coordination of nursing facilities and resources

Developing comprehensive programs for the diminution or reduction of water pollution, including action to secure abatement of pollution having adverse interstate effect

Promoting the development and application of means for protecting and improving the health of workers through direct services to industry, official state agencies, investigations of occupational health problems, and other services

Developing and operating programs for the control of tuberculosis, heart disease, and diabetes; restorative services; hygiene of aging; and other chronic diseases

Licensing manufacture of biologic products (vaccines, serums, etc.) and their shipment in interstate traffic or importation from foreign countries or U. S. possessions

Conducting, in cooperation with state and local health agencies, scientific research, investigations, and demonstrations related to the cause, prevention, and cure of the diseases of man

Making loans of radium

Administering grants-in-aid to states for public health services for control of diseases

Administering grants-in-aid to qualified institutions and individual scientists for research in physical and mental diseases

Providing technical assistance and consultative services to the states and to federal agencies

Collecting and disseminating statistical and other information on health problems

Training professional persons in the public health and medical sciences through fellowships and grants

Collaborating with governments of other countries and with international organizations in world health activities, and with private national organizations and institutions concerned with health

In 1961 the National Advisory Health Council issued a report in which recommendations on the role of the Public Health Service were made. This was followed by formulation of the following seven objectives:[12]

1. In collaboration with the professional groups and agencies involved, assist in defining acceptable standards of medical care services and promote their widespread use; provide technical assistance to health insurers, state insurance commissioners, state departments of health, federal agencies, and others concerned with standards of medical care services.

2. Expand its activities and increase its emphasis on cooperative planning and development of comprehensive health care services among hospitals, group practice clinics, outpatient departments, nursing homes, home care programs, rehabilitation centers, homemaker services, and other health professional groups or individuals providing patient services.

3. Establish and conduct a continuing program of studies, technical assistance, and grants in support of research, training, and demonstration in the organization, administration, delivery, measurement, and improvement of quality and methods of financing of medical care.

4. Exercise vigorous leadership in recruiting and training all types of health personnel and encourage and support specialized training in the skills necessary to meet the changing demands of modern medical care.

5. Continue to promote research necessary to provide the knowledge essential to meet the medical care needs of the nation.

6. Expand its efforts to appraise the effectiveness of promising new developments, to disseminate related information, and to make available resource materials relating to programs in medical care administration.

7. Continue to promote the effective organization and delivery of high-quality medical services to its beneficiaries in its own facilities.

Public health authorities point out that the most fearsome environmental health hazards are of man's own creation and that they are being created so fast that controlling them is almost a vain hope. Radiation is the one of which the public has been made most conscious. Except in minor respects such as safeguards for patients and personnel using equipment and disposal of atomic wastes, not a great deal can be promised in the way of control as long as bombs are being tested. This is, however, only one of many dangers. New chemical products are being produced at a much faster rate than those in charge of testing projects can keep up with. Air and water are being polluted by toxic substances, and nobody knows what the long-term effect will be on human life.

The Public Health Service is attacking the problems through its water pollution, air pollution, radiological, and occupational health programs. A project

[12] Surgeon General Luther L. Terry: The Public Health Service Role in Medical Care Administration. *Pub. Health Rep.,* February, 1962, pp. 93–96.

that has won especially wide public attention has been the study[13] of automobile exhaust gases initiated in 1959 at the Robert A. Taft Sanitary Engineering Center in Cincinnati.

In 1961 the Public Health Service established three new divisions in its Bureau of State Services: the Division of Community Health Practice, the Accident Prevention Division, and the Division of Chronic Diseases. The Nursing Home Services Section established in 1960 operates under the last division. In 1962 a Migrant Health Section was formed. Migrants are estimated to number nearly a million persons and their interstate mode of life complicates the problem of serving them through state and community health departments.

Children's Bureau of the Welfare Administration

The Children's Bureau celebrated its fiftieth anniversary in 1962. Since its establishment by act of Congress in 1912 the mortality rate for infants under one year of age has dropped from 100 deaths or more per 1,000 to 25. Julia Lathrop was the first chief of the bureau. It was under her leadership that studies were made that led to such legislation as the Maternity and Infancy Act passed in 1921.

Services to crippled children were included in the Social Security Act in 1935 and were delegated to the Children's Bureau, which in consequence undertook the first federal-state program in medical care. At first the program was mainly orthopedic in nature, but it was broadened to include handicapping conditions such as rheumatic fever, epilepsy, and congenital heart disease.

The Children's Bureau was responsible for administration of the emergency maternity and infant care program during World War II.

The Children's Bureau was the first federal agency to use funds for training programs. Training for nurses was begun in 1922 under the Maternity and Infancy Act.

The bureau has always advocated integration into public health services of maternal and child health, early developing a team approach with medical-social interests.[14]

National Institutes of Health

The National Institutes of Health is the research arm of the Public Health Service.

On July 6, 1953, the Clinical Center, the largest hospital for clinical research in the nation, was dedicated in Bethesda, Maryland. This hospital gives the Public Health Service scientists in the National Institutes means to "carry their

---

[13] See David E. Price, M.D.: Is Man Becoming Obsolete? *Pub. Health Rep.,* August, 1959, pp. 693–95.

[14] See Katherine Bain, M.D., deputy chief of the Children's Bureau: A Half Century of Pioneering for Child Health. *Pub. Health Rep.,* April, 1962, pp. 307–10.

laboratory findings directly to patients and study their observations of the patients in nearby, fully equipped laboratories. The center was planned to house 500 patients and 1,100 laboratories."[15]

The National Institutes of Health gives stipends to persons preparing for careers in medical research, supports traineeships, gives grants to teaching institutions for the support of training courses, and conducts extensive research in its own laboratories and in cooperation with other organizations.

The Communicable Disease Center in Atlanta, Georgia, is one of the projects under the National Institutes of Health; also the National Institute of Mental Health. The latter provides advisory service and matches state funds to help communities build facilities and provide services for the mentally ill and offers mental health project grants.

Altogether there are nine institutes, this number having been reached in 1963 when the National Institute of General Medical Sciences, which was previously classified as a division, was established.

Civil Defense Emergency Hospitals

Stored in strategic locations in 50 states, the District of Columbia, Puerto Rico, and the Virgin Islands are 1,930 emergency hospitals each with 200-bed capacity. They can be set up in a little over an hour by personnel who have taken the course Medical Aspects of Health Mobilization at designated instruction centers.

The equipment for the hospitals is packed in 351 boxes which fit in a standard moving van.

Included in the unit are an admitting-triage area, shock ward, operating rooms, pharmacy, laboratory, central supply section with sterilization facilities powered by gasoline or bottled gas, generator, and x-ray machine with polaroid development process.[16]

The hospital can be set up in any existing structure or in conjunction with a regular hospital.

The hospitals are a project of the Division of Health Mobilization of the Public Health Service.

State and Local Health Departments

A typical experience in trying to get a public health program started is that of Illinois. In 1819 the first State General Assembly passed a medical practice act which included a provision for the reporting of births, deaths, and cases of communicable disease. This law was repealed at the next session, and similar

[15] From an article on the Department of Health, Education and Welfare by its first secretary, Oveta Culp Hobby, in *The American Peoples Encyclopedia-Yearbook*. Chicago, The Spencer Press, Inc., 1954, pp. 452–53.
[16] *Pub. Health Rep.*, June, 1960, p. 564.

legislation enacted in 1825 met the same fate. These early attempts at public health legislation were initiated by physicians. The opponents were quacks, herb doctors, and charlatans who wanted no regulation.

The medical profession continued to struggle for legislation. A request for legislation that would create a State Board of Health to regulate the practice of medicine and collect reports of births and deaths was presented in 1856 and again in 1861 by the Aesculapian Society of the Wabash Valley. Success came in 1877 with passage of the State Board of Health Act and of the Medical Practice Act. The State Board of Health was finally organized on July 12, 1877. The Illinois State Medical Society was directly responsible for the enactment of both of these laws.

The success was limited by the meager appropriation of $5,000 plus some $12,000 in license fees for the first two years for operating expenses. The first president of the Board of Health, Dr. John H. Rauch, served for 15 history-making years. In the very next year after its founding, the board had the problem of fighting a major epidemic of yellow fever which started at New Orleans and proceeded up the Mississippi River to Cairo, Illinois. Dr. Rauch instituted rigid quarantine against downriver travelers. He met with the newly created National Board of Health in Washington to assist in organizing to fight yellow fever. He organized in July at Memphis, and was appointed secretary of, the Mississippi Valley Sanitary Council, made up of large transportation interests.

In fighting smallpox these agencies were of no assistance. Despite success in vaccinating almost the entire population of the state, epidemics continued because of the heavy immigration. On June 29 and 30, 1881, Dr. Rauch held a conference in Chicago with all health authorities in the nation to discuss control measures. Establishment by the National Board of Health of an Immigration Inspection Service was the outcome of the conference. Inspectors were stationed at all important railroad terminals to see that all susceptible immigrants were vaccinated. Public support was lacking, so the system did not last long but at least probably led to the highly effective coast quarantine service which was later established. Dr. Rauch continued to campaign for vaccination, with the result that in 1882 he could say: "I doubt if the people in any other state of equal age are as well protected against smallpox as those of Illinois at the present time."

The establishment of local health departments was another project that Dr. Rauch strongly championed. With voluntary help he instituted a system of state-wide sanitary inspection. His dynamic leadership at the start gave the State Board of Health in Illinois a firm foundation on which to build an effective program as scientific developments rapidly broadened the public health role in the last decade of the nineteenth century and the early years of the twentieth. There was much left to do with respect to smallpox, diphtheria, typhoid fever, infantile diarrhea, and the infant death rate of 72.5 and the maternal death rate of 6.7 per thousand births.

The responsibility for the care and quarantine of contagious diseases and of the investigation and control of epidemics falls on state and local public health departments. Other functions are general supervision of water supply, disposition of sewage, food and drug inspection, laboratory facilities for prompt and free diagnosis of infectious and contagious diseases and supplying free biological products for diagnosing and treating these conditions. A few states go beyond these functions in providing health service. They assume control of venereal disease and supply diagnostic and treatment facilities for cancer to indigent or medically indigent patients. In metropolitan communities activities are greatly extended.

The sovereign power in the governmental system of the United States is the state. The federal government can only indirectly promote state and local public health service. It can appropriate money for allotment to states and make general rules as to its use, but states may take it or leave it. It is in the state that the administrative authority rests for using federal funds. Once it reaches the state treasury, the federal grant is state money, although it must be accounted for in accordance with the agreement under which it was accepted.

The state government grants authority and powers to the counties, municipalities, and townships. None of these is autonomous. The key governmental agency is the state. The administration of public health as well as other local services is determined in principle by the state. It can confer considerable autonomy upon local governmental units, but has the legal right to intervene and carry on essential activities when for any reason local authorities fail to perform their public health functions in epidemic emergencies.

Great disparity in local health services is a result of granting too much autonomy to local authorities. Yet the state health department cannot readily give direct service on the local level. In Illinois, county health departments throughout the state were authorized by law in 1943 as a result of a survey in 1941 followed with recommendations by representatives of the American Public Health Association. Regulations were included in the law for establishing and financing of the health services. It is possible under this law for as many as four counties to join in establishing a health department, which is an advantage in more sparsely settled sections. A public educational campaign continues for the establishment of departments in those counties which have not yet voted to have them. The rural and small town public health problems are acute.

By 1962 some 180 city-county health department mergers had been effected. Increased efficiency and probably reduction in costs are the reasons for and the results of mergers. There is a shortage of trained public health personnel, another good reason for consolidation when feasible.

The "urban fringe" is presenting somewhat new public health problems as subdivisions multiply without due planning and supervision from the standpoint of health. Sanitary regulations have to be quickly instituted and inspection services for food supply and other needs arranged.

City health administration, according to Surgeon General Luther L. Terry, "antedates other governmental organization in this field." Baltimore has the longest "documentary record of a permanent health organization," having begun the collection and systematic reporting of mortality and morbidity data as early as 1816. Philadelphia built the first public general hospital. In 1866, New York City "abandoned older forms of organization and created the first metropolitan health administration, setting a mark for municipal organization: indeed, a mark for public health administration at all levels. . . . Before the turn of the century New York made a world innovation by the organization of the first public bacteriological laboratory, serving private physicians and hospitals with diagnostic tests and biological products free of charge."[17]

In Chicago in September, 1959, at its third biennial meeting, the State and Territorial Chronic Disease Program Directors organized as an association and affiliated with the Association of State and Territorial Health Officers.

Among the current issues outlined were the needs for full-time medical and public health leadership, for standards for screening and diagnostic follow-up of diabetics, for licensing and continuing supervision of nursing homes as a function of state departments of health, for homemaker services, for development of programs for the disabled, for use of the epidemiological approach to chronic disease control, and for encouragement of the use by health departments of workers in the social sciences.

The concept of federal grants to local health agencies for chronic disease control activities was approved. Support of the community cancer demonstration project grant program by the Public Health Service was recommended.

The first state to adopt a policy of licensing nonmedical, full-time local officers of health on the basis of specified qualifications and training was New Jersey. This has been the practice in that state for nearly eighty years. An internationally famous sanitarian, Charles-Edward Amory Winslow, started his career as a local health officer in New Jersey, after receiving his baccalaureate degree from the Massachusetts Institute of Technology. Since 1925 the State Health Department in cooperation with Rutgers University has conducted special extension courses for health officers and sanitarians, and in 1956 the department instituted an in-service training program for full-time health officers, both physicians and lay personnel.

Legislation for Health

Law has strengthened life in every enlightened society ever since Hammurabi made his classification in the twenty-second century B.C. and Justinian the Great compiled his code of the Roman laws in the sixth century A.D. Its power has waxed and waned, as has that of science, in accord with the spirit of the times. Without its authoritative control, exploitation and fraud flourish. It is as much needed to safeguard health as it is to protect property.

[17] The City in National Health. *Pub. Health Rep.,* May, 1962, p. 378.

Anybody could play doctor in medieval Europe—and in colonial America in a much later period. It took legal action to protect the public. King Roger II of Sicily issued an edict in 1140 forbidding anyone to practice medicine without proper examination. His grandson, Frederick II of Germany, in 1224, not only made licensure through examination necessary but ruled that failure to comply would be punished by forfeiture of property and a year's imprisonment. His edict, which was followed in Spain and Italy also, included a wide range of subjects, including regular inspection of food, drugs, and apothecaries' mixtures.[18]

In 1683 Colbert, minister to Louis XIV, issued sanitary regulations for all of France.

It took legislation to give status to the surgeon. About the middle of the sixteenth century special laws governing surgery were passed, noteworthy among them being the edict of Charles V in 1548, renewed by Rudolph II in 1577, which provided that candidates in surgery had to pass examinations before they were permitted to practice.

Sanitary legislation in England did not come until the early nineteenth century, along with measures such as reduction of hours of labor to protect the workers. Then laws followed fast as the social reformers aroused the government officials to action.

Education of Physicians

Standard setting through state licensure boards and financial support of medical schools and hospitals are among the activities which give the government a role in the training of physicians. Forty medical schools are owned and operated by states and one by a city. Nearly half of the medical students in the United States are in government-owned and -operated schools. Federal support to all of the schools is mainly in the form of grants for research.

The evidence that there was a decline in the ratio of physicians to the population led the Public Health Service to appoint a consultant group on medical education in 1958. The report of the group, "Physicians for a Growing America," was published in late 1959 with recommendations for remedying the situation. It has been estimated that by 1975 there will be between 9,500 and 11,000 physicians less than will be needed to maintain the 1962 ratio. This shortage is anticipated even when new schools and expansion of present ones now planned are considered. One of the solutions that is being studied is the use of more auxiliary personnel to conserve the doctor's time.[19]

What former President John F. Kennedy termed "one of the most significant health measures passed by Congress in recent years" became law on September

---

[18] See Garrison's *Introduction to the History of Medicine,* 4th ed. Philadelphia, W. B. Saunders Co., 1929, pp. 238–39.
[19] See Paul Q. Peterson, M.D.: Government's Role in Meeting Physician Manpower Needs. *Pub. Health Rep.,* September, 1962, pp. 773–78.

24, 1963, when he signed the Health Professions Educational Assistance Act. The bill provides grants for medical and other health professional schools and scholarship loans for medical, dental, and osteopathic students.

The American Medical Association, the Association of American Medical Colleges, and other medical organizations are active in efforts to recruit and train more medical students.

Financial Aid

Benjamin Franklin began it. On January 23, 1751, he petitioned the Pennsylvania Legislative Assembly, then convened in Philadelphia, to assist citizens of that city in trying to establish a hospital by making an appropriation to the fund. As a result of the assistance thus obtained from the Commonwealth, the Pennsylvania Hospital was organized in that year and opened to the public in 1752, and has been open ever since, the oldest voluntary hospital in the United States. Franklin subscribed to the fund himself and went around getting subscriptions from others.

The aid from the Commonwealth was not easily obtained. There was a condition. As told in Franklin's *Autobiography:*

> The country members did not, at first, relish the project; they objected that it could only be serviceable to the city, and therefore the citizens alone should be at the expense of it, and they doubted whether the citizens themselves generally approved it. My allegation, on the contrary, that it met with such approbation as to leave no doubt of our being able to raise two thousand pounds by voluntary donations, they considered as a most extravagant supposition, and utterly impossible. On this I formed my plan. . . .

He drew up the plan so that if and when the citizens contributed 2,000 pounds, the legislature would grant an order on the provincial treasurer for the payment of 2,000 pounds in two yearly payments to the proposed hospital. In other words a scheme we think of as modern—a matching plan. Franklin wrote further:[20]

> This condition carried the bill through, for the members, who had opposed the grant, and now conceived they might have the credit of being charitable without the expense, agreed to its passage; and then, in soliciting subscriptions among the people, we urged the conditional promise of the law as an additional motive to give, since every man's donation would be doubled; thus the clause worked both ways. . . . The institution has by constant experience been found useful, and flourishes to this day, and I do not remember any of my political maneuvers the success of which at the time gave me more pleasure; or wherein, after thinking of it, I more easily excused myself for having made some use of cunning.

The first federal grant program is represented by the Northwest Ordinance of 1787 which provided that one section in every township be reserved for the maintenance of public schools within the township. The first federal grants-in-aid for public health purposes were authorized by the Chamberlain-Kahn Act

[20] Quoted in a news release, undated, from the Hospital Association of Pennsylvania.

of 1918, providing for appropriations to the states by the Inter-departmental Social Hygiene Committee for venereal disease control activities. This was followed by the Sheppard-Towner Act of 1921, which provided grants-in-aid for the protection of the health of mothers and children. Then with the passage of Titles V and VI of the Social Security Act in 1935, the federal grant method of assisting health projects either directly or through the states was well established.[21]

The appropriation in 1964 under the Hill-Burton Act alone was $226,200,000. Certain hospital construction and renovation projects were eligible for grants under the new public works appropriation bill. The 1963 ceiling under this bill was $900,000,000 total, the grants to go to areas of persistent and substantial unemployment. The program provides for grants of at least 50 per cent of the cost of the project. As much as 75 per cent may be given in areas of high unemployment. Administration is through the Hill-Burton agencies.

The Hill-Burton Act. For its impact on better distribution of hospital care and on improvement of facilities in general, the Hill-Burton Act stands at the peak of legislation for medical care in the United States.[22]

    The Hospital Survey and Construction Act of 1946 was sponsored by Senators Hill and Burton as an amendment to the Public Health Service Act. It had two primary purposes: to survey and inventory health facilities with respect to existing facilities and to make available funds for the construction of approved projects. The bill was primarily aimed at giving better distribution and increasing available hospitals in rural areas where such facilities were lacking. Grants under Part C of the act were made available for general, tuberculosis, mental, and chronic disease hospitals and public health centers. The federal allotment to states was on a basis of population and income, with federal participation fixed at one-third of the local project cost.

    In 1949 appropriations were authorized for research to improve hospital facilities and resources. The basis of federal participation in local projects was altered so that states could fix a uniform federal share for each project or could adopt a sliding scale of from one-third to two-thirds of local project costs.

    The Wolverton Amendment in 1954 extended coverage of the act to include diagnostic and treatment centers, hospitals for chronically ill and impaired, nursing homes, and rehabilitation centers, under Part G of the act. There was also allowance for transfers of funds among categories of hospitals.

    The program is administered at the federal level by the Surgeon General, who consults with the Federal Hospital Council. The director of the Division of Hospital and Medical Facilities and regional offices carry out the mechanics of administration.

    At the state level the program is administered by public health departments in all but eight of the states. There must be a state advisory council to consult with the state agency in carrying out the program.

---

[21] *See* The Role of Grants-in-Aid in Financing Public Health Programs. *Pub. Health Bull. No. 303,* 1949.
[22] The following description is abstracted from a paper read at an Alpha Delta Mu fraternity meeting by J. Frank Meisamer, now administrator of Tennessee Tuberculosis Hospital, Chattanooga, when he was a student in hospital administration at Northwestern University in 1960.

State construction programs have developed from the inventory of existing acceptable facilities. The Hill-Burton Act and the Public Health Service Regulations have established what the needs of the states are in providing adequate hospital facilities.

The state plan calls for division into areas which are the "trading areas," so to speak, of each hospital and are based on population distribution, geographic boundaries, and trade and transport patterns. These areas are designated as base, intermediate, and rural. A base area must contain a general hospital of 200 or more beds, with interns and residents in two or more specialties. An intermediate area will have one general hospital with 100 or more beds, and a rural area is any area not specified as base or intermediate. Regulations have specified general hospital bed needs in each area as 4.5 beds per 1,000 population in a base area, 4 beds per 1,000 in an intermediate area, and 2.5 beds per 1,000 in a rural area. Public Health Service Regulations state the distribution should be "as will meet the needs" but not less than 2.5 beds per 1,000 population in any area. Other regulations prescribe distribution factors for other types of facilities.

In arriving at the beds needed in an area, the state excludes certain existing beds which are not acceptable. The criteria used by a state to judge unacceptable hospitals are not uniform; however, lack of fire resistance or safety, obsolescence, poor design and construction, limitations on expansion, are some of the more common reasons used.

Local projects are given a priority rating by the state program as each annual construction program is planned. This indicates the order in which grants will be made available. Regulations have established general principles to be used in determining priorities. For example, in determining the priority of nursing home applications, projects are given priority based on (1) relative need for additional nursing home beds in the area; (2) extent to which beds will be made available to those groups less adequately served; and (3) nursing homes operated by hospitals.

The state plan must give assurance to applicants of fair hearings for dissatisfied applicants and must be publicized to newspapers thirty days before the plan is submitted to the Surgeon General for approval. Application is made on standard forms supplied to the state by the Public Health Service.

Part I is the form used for the original request for funds. A narrative description of the project, proof of nonprofit status, and a resolution authorizing a signature for the applicant are required. Preliminary drawings and outline specifications by the architect with an estimated cost and a separate cost statement by the architect accompany the request.

Part II deals with statements regarding building site and financial resources for construction.

Part III deals specifically with the building site, including legal description, site and soil investigation data, title status and a legal opinion on title to the land. The architect must prepare a "Survey of Building and Construction Wage Rates," which shows wage rates for three projects in the area, plus contractors' association rates and labor organization rates. This must be approved by the Department of Labor. Actual labor rates for each job title must conform to the wages so approved. The working drawings and the specifications must be signed. by the architect and the applicant. The bid date opening must be set.

Part IV gives summaries of estimated costs and actual costs and must be accompanied by supporting schedules, including tabulation of bids, itemized lists of equipment, etc. This is the firm figure upon which construction starts and upon which actual costs are presented.

Payment is made by the government in three stages, and approval of the costs must be obtained from both the state and the Surgeon General's office.

In 1963 the emphasis was on shifting Hill-Burton funds from general hospital facilities in rural areas to rehabilitation of existing facilities in urban communities, increase in funds for nursing homes, and grants to stimulate state-wide and regional planning of medical facility construction.

The Hill-Burton program, due to expire June 30, 1964, was extended for five years.

Other Financial Aid. The Community Health Services and Facilities Act, which was passed in 1961, is expected to stimulate the reorganization and expansion of community health services. All health agencies, both public and voluntary, are asked to re-examine their activities, create new approaches, and provide a sound basis for meeting the critical needs in health service organization. The act increased from $30 million to $50 million the annual appropriation authorization for federal matching grants to the states to assist them in establishing and maintaining adequate public health services. It also authorizes the earmarking of part of the appropriations for specific activities, including services provided in nursing homes, home health care programs, outpatient diagnostic services, and health referral and information centers. A new five-year program of up to $10 million annually is authorized for special project grants to public and nonprofit organizations for studies, experiments, and demonstrations of new or improved methods of providing out-of-hospital community health services, particularly for the chronically ill and aged. The annual appropriation for Hill-Burton grants for the construction of public and nonprofit nursing homes is doubled, and the eligibility requirements for rehabilitation center construction under the Hill-Burton program are liberalized. The annual appropriation ceiling for research, experiments, and demonstrations in utilization of medical facilities is increased from $1.2 million to $10 million. Appropriations for grants for the construction of experimental or demonstration hospitals and other medical facilities are authorized.

In citing these benefits under the new act, Dr. Milton Terris concludes: "Our generation must grapple with the mammoth task of reorienting and reorganizing community health services."[23]

A grant of $1,300,000 from the National Institutes of Health enabled Northwestern University to establish in 1963 the nation's first Bio-Medical Engineering Research Center. A second such center is being established at Johns Hopkins University. Two of the benefits expected from the programs are wider use of artificial organs and automatic patient-monitoring equipment in hospitals to cut rising health costs.

[23] The Future of Community Health Services. *Pub. Health Rep.,* October, 1962, pp. 849–54.

PUBLIC HEALTH

"Public health and preventive medicine in the United States," according to one authority,[24] "are emerging into roles entirely different from those defined by their apostles." These "early apostles," he indicates, were "crusaders for sanitary reform and care of the sick," whereas the present trend is toward "community medicine," a term which he proposes be used to define "a combined public and private effort for comprehensive health care in every American community." He points out that the emerging system of medical service in the United States is neither "state medicine," nor "private medicine," nor "socialized medicine," but what is in other countries called "social medicine," a term which "for cultural and political reasons well known to all of us" cannot be used here.

Certainly the scope of public health has expanded enormously since Southwood Smith founded the Health of Towns Association in England in 1839, Lemuel Shattuck published his *Sanitary Survey of the State of Massachusetts* in 1850, and the first General Board of Health was established in London following the passage of the first Public Health Act in 1848. A glance at the program of the ninetieth annual meeting of the American Public Health Association, October, 1962, quickly establishes this fact. There were more than 200 separate topics classified[25] into the following general headings: Health Economics, Medical Care, Community Relations, Family Service, Maternal and Child Health, Public Health Nursing, Chronic Diseases, Cancer, Communicable Diseases, Environmental Health, Occupational Health, Mental Health, Addiction, Dental Health, Food and Health, Records and Statistics, and School Health. The topics range from "Medicos Mending More Men on the Mend" to "Coccidioides Vaccine Protects Monkeys."

For true appreciation of the state of the public health program today it is imperative to study the past, the bit by bit contributions made by individuals. No more than in any other branch of medicine do they comprise a brick-on-top-of-brick type of development. Every once in a while the bricks came apart and a new start had to be made. In 532 B.C. Eupalinus of Megara tunneled the water supply of Samos from the Leucothean Spring; in 494 B.C. there were sanitary police in Rome; between 312 B.C. and A.D. 500 a number of Roman aqueducts were built, the longest, the Marcian Aqueduct, built between 144 and 140 B.C., having extended for 61.75 miles; in A.D. 97 a water inspector was appointed in Rome—but in the 1960's there are countless communities in which there is no good water supply and no inspection. WHO estimates that a fourth of the world's hospital beds are occupied by people who are ill because of poor water.[26]

---

[24] William H. Stewart, M.D., assistant to assistant secretary for Health, Education and Welfare: Community Medicine, An American Concept of Comprehensive Care. *Pub. Health Rep.*, February, 1963, pp. 93–100.
[25] *Pub. Health Rep.*, February, 1963.
[26] *Canad. Hosp.*, January, 1961, p. 72.

Among the ancient Hebrews the high priests acted as public health officers. For long centuries afterward most countries had no comparable officials, until in 1224 Frederick II of Germany issued an edict which included food and drug inspections and regulations in municipal and rural hygiene—proper depth of graves, disposal of refuse, etc.

Military sanitation principles were laid down by Sir John Pringle in a book published at London in 1752; by Jean Colombier's *Code of Military Medicine* published in France in 1772; and by James Lind, founder of naval hygiene in England, with his three treatises on scurvy, naval hygiene, and tropical medicine published between 1754 and 1768. But all this was almost forgotten at Scutari in 1854 until Florence Nightingale arrived on the scene, and there is little evidence of familiarity with the principles in America's War between the States, although Benjamin Rush had written a valuable pamphlet on the hygiene of troops back in 1777.

Denmark and Sweden set up national health councils about the middle of the eighteenth century, and in 1822 a central health authority was created in France.

Veterinary inspection and inspection of pharmacies were among the reforms instituted by Johann Peter Frank, of Austria (1745–1821), who produced a great four-volume work on public hygiene, *Complete System of Medical Polity,* between 1777 and 1788. These books are considered the foundation of modern public health. Von Haller was public health officer at Bern, 1753 to 1777.

Sir Edwin Chadwick (1800–1890) is credited by Garrison[27] with having initiated the sanitary era in public hygiene through his reports on poor law reform, health of the laboring classes, and cemeteries, which showed how public ailments could be diagnosed through the census and mortality statistics. Lemuel Shattuck used this method in starting public health activities in the United States.

Insignificant though it sounds, there cannot be omitted even from this most superficial dip into public health history John Snow's checking of the 1854 cholera epidemic in London by removing the handle of the Broad Street pump, demonstrating that impure water was a factor.

Brazil had a public health dictator in Oswaldo Goncalvez Cruz (1872–1917), who inaugurated drastic reforms, including a successful campaign against yellow fever, freeing Rio de Janeiro from the disease.

The first municipal bacteriological laboratory in the world was established by Hermann M. Biggs (1859–1923) in New York City. Dr. Biggs, following a teaching career in medicine, became public health commissioner of New York State. He was a believer in decentralization and established district health centers on a model which has been widely copied. He and his associates were especially active in the movement to utilize public education as a means for preventing and controlling tuberculosis.

[27] *An Introduction to the History of Medicine, op. cit.,* p. 660.

Education in Public Health

Twelve universities in the United States, six public and six private, have schools of public health. The school at Johns Hopkins University, Baltimore, was established in 1916 with an endowment by the Rockefeller Foundation and was directed by Dr. William H. Welch from 1916 to 1926. This event occurred 66 years after Lemuel Shattuck had declared that a sanitary professorship should be established in all colleges and medical schools and filled by competent teachers. He said that the science of preserving health and preventing diseases should be taught as one of the most important sciences.

Chairs of hygiene were established in 1794 in the schools of health of Paris and Strasbourg after the French revolutionaries had closed the medical schools. The subject was retained when the medical schools were reopened, but only as an adjunct to medicine. Several universities in South American countries established independent chairs of hygiene between 1813 and 1857, and one was instituted at Munich in 1865 for Max von Pettenkofer. A full-time professorship in the subject was established for the first time in Great Britain at Edinburgh in 1898.[28] Recently Johns Hopkins University established the first degree in international health.

Communicable Disease Control

In the pre–public health era communities were threatened with an epidemic started by any itinerant who appeared. A typical incident occurred in 1832 when a wanderer pitched his tent on the outskirts of the little village of Belleville, Illinois. The state was only 14 years old then and had only some 160,000 inhabitants. The occupant of the tent suddenly became acutely ill and sought help. The local doctor, notwithstanding the fact that he recognized the disease as cholera, kindly found a place for him in the local courthouse and attended him. The stranger died—and so did many citizens of this and surrounding communities. No respecter of rank, the disastrous epidemic included among its victims the able territorial and third governor of the state, Minian Edwards.

The town marshal of Grenada, Mississippi, sent a telegram on August 4, 1878 to the mayor of Wilmington, North Carolina, which read: "Help us to pay nurses and bury the dead. Our town is a graveyard. We need help. The Mayor is dying, and I am the only officer left." This occurred during one of the periodic marches of yellow fever up and down the Mississippi River Valley.

Contrast these incidents with one that occurred in the spring of 1962 in Chicago. An Italian ship, one of the first to come down through the Saint Lawrence River after the opening of the locks at the end of the winter freeze-up, sent ashore at Milwaukee a seaman who was found to have typhoid fever and

[28] René Sand: *The Advance to Social Medicine, op. cit.*, p. 286.

was put in isolation. The ship proceeded on to Chicago to unload both cargo and crew. But the city health department had been notified of the case by the Milwaukee health authorities. The health commissioner, Dr. Samuel Andelman, acting immediately, notified the Port Authority, which in turn ordered the captain to stay outside the harbor. The captain, taking the message literally, stopped at once, anchoring nine miles out, instead of the three or four anticipated.

The wind was high, Lake Michigan was rough, small craft warnings were out, and it was a Saturday which should have been a holiday for most of the staff, but Dr. Andelman's epidemiologists rose to the call of duty. They embarked in a small boat, and spent several hours making tests of the seamen, the food supply, water, and sanitary facilities. The tests disclosed nothing wrong. The coast guard sent out a boat to bring back the health department personnel, and the ship was given permission to land at Navy Pier so that the crew could enjoy at least part of their week-end leave. An amusing incident, perhaps, since all was found to be well, but significant because it shows how the city would have been saved from danger had there been others on that ship to spread disease.

An eighty-year-old quarantine story is that of the Italian ship *Matteo Bruzzo,* which set sail in 1884 for Montevideo. Cholera broke out. Passengers were refused permission to land at Montevideo. Then the ship sailed to Rio de Janeiro. It was chased out again. It returned to Italy and was quarantined at an island near Elba, Pianosa. The passengers were finally permitted to land four months after they first set sail and but 78 miles from the place where they had embarked.

Dr. Colter Rule[29] told this story as inducement to study the International Health Regulations and to be conscientious about taking the shots recommended for travel to certain places. He mentions the ten international health conferences held between 1850 and 1900 with no success in reaching an agreement. Around 1900 when discoveries about the spread of infectious disease were disclosed, including the role of carriers, some local action was incited, but not until 1946 was effective international action taken. Then the constitution of the World Health Organization provided authority ". . . to adopt regulations concerning sanitary and quarantine requirements to prevent the international spread of disease." This was followed in 1951 by the unanimous adoption of the International Sanitary Regulations, which involve accurate and speedy reporting of diseases within each country; prevention of disease in each country by improving sanitation, eradication of disease-carrying insects, and nation-wide programs of immunization; and minimum effective interference with travel across international boundaries.

The more than two million air passengers arriving at international airports in the United States each year are inspected for quarantine, and around 7 per cent are given surveillance notices. The notice is to be presented to the health

[29] *Travel,* September, 1961.

officer at his discretion in case the person becomes ill within a certain period. Detention and isolation are necessary when the traveler shows symptoms of a quarantinable disease.

Garrison[30] quotes Sir A. Newsholme as observing that "philanthropy was the motor power in initiating sanitary reform, but the driving power came from the great expense of sanitary Poor-Law administration and actual fear of the ever-recurring epidemics of communicable diseases."

An interesting account of the development of a public health program comes from the fiftieth state.

King Kamehameha III of Hawaii established a board of health in 1850. Fourteen years earlier, recognizing the importations of diseases that were decimating the native population, King Kinau had ordered the harbor pilot "to ascertain whether there has been any case of smallpox or other pestilent disease" on board an approaching vessel and, if so, to "direct the Master to hoist a yellow flag at the main and immediately give information to the constituted authority." Captain James Cook, whose exploration of the islands began in 1788, wrote in his journal, "The order not to permit the crews of the boats to go on shore was issued that I might do everything in my power to prevent the importation of a fatal disease into this island, which I knew some of my men labored under and which, unfortunately, had been already communicated to other islands in these seas." The ancient Hawaiian population was reduced from 500,000 to less than 60,000 before protective measures were developed to control the invasion of disease by immigrants. Now the infant mortality rate, 24 per 1,000, is below the average for the fifty states, the incidence of acute diseases is slightly higher than on the mainland, and the reported causes of death for the resident civilian population are about the same as for the mainland population. In 1929 in Hawaii 418.5 of every 100,000 residents died of a communicable disease. In 1960, the rate was down to 27. Tuberculosis and Hansen's disease are prominent afflictions; the former, however, dropped 90.8 per cent in the ten years from 1950 to 1960; the latter is being controlled by the sulfone drugs introduced in 1946.[31]

American Public Health Association

A highlight in public health in America came in 1872 with the founding of the American Public Health Association. It was organized, according to *Reports and Papers of A.P.H.A.,* Volume I, 1872, by "an informal conference of gentlemen . . . with the design to secure concerted effort, and establish some adequate plans in the cultivation of hygienic knowledge, and procuring more effective application of sanitary principles and laws," and for promoting the practical application of public hygiene.

---

[30] *An Introduction to the History of Medicine, op. cit.,* p. 777.

[31] Adapted from an article, "Ola Kino—Hawaiian Health," material for which was gathered by Jeanne Paty, director of health education, State of Hawaii; published in *Pub. Health Rep.,* December, 1961, pp. 1063–80.

Dr. Stephen Smith was the leader of the group and he became its first president. He had been largely responsible for the creation of the Metropolitan Board of Health in New York City in 1866, had served as commissioner of the board for nine years, had drafted the bill for a National Board of Health in 1879 (serving upon the board during the four years of its existence), and had formulated the law establishing the New York State Board of Health.

Membership in the association is drawn from the entire western hemisphere. Both medical and nonmedical public health workers are included. As a voluntary professional organization, embracing the entire field of preventive medicine, it exerts a particularly powerful influence in stimulating cooperation between public and voluntary health agencies of every nature.

Activities are conducted through numerous committees. One recently appointed, for example, is the Committee on Fringe Area Sanitation. Its publications include the monthly *American Journal of Public Health*. The association has a number of affiliated societies or branches organized on a state or district basis.[32]

THE WORLD HEALTH ORGANIZATION

The World Health Organization represents the most ambitious intergovernmental activity ever attempted in public health. Its accomplishments, in view of the maze of political procedure required in such an undertaking, have been little short of miraculous. Surgeon General Luther L. Terry,[33] of the United States Public Health Service, paid tribute to its achievements, saying in part:

> The United States has enjoyed 14 years of freedom from outbreaks of quarantinable disease known to have been introduced from abroad. We, like other countries, have our own foreign quarantine program. The Public Health Service has administered it for nearly 80 years. But I do no injustice to the vigilance of our quarantine officers when I say that we owe this protection primarily to the World Health Organization.
>
> Health and medical leaders in the United States and elsewhere have known for decades that true protection against the world spread of disease depends upon improved health conditions at the source of disease. This is what the World Health Organization and its member countries have been working toward these past 15 years. I cannot give you an eyewitness account. But every member of my staff, every colleague in outside institutions who has brought me accounts of world health conditions testifies to the striking improvements that have taken place. . . .
>
> Several hundred American professionals are serving with more than a thousand of their foreign colleagues on WHO expert committees. Also the United States Delegation to the World Health Assembly has included members of our health professions and leaders in public affairs. They have come from private

---

[32] *Voluntary Health Agencies, An Interpretive Study*, by Selskar M. Gunn and Philip S. Platt, under the auspices of the National Health Council. New York, The Ronald Press Company, 1945, pp. 229–32.
[33] *Pub. Health Rep.*, April, 1963.

practice, as well as from organizations devoted to medical research and teaching, public health, and hospital administration. International voluntary associations have participated in special sessions of the Assembly. . . . The Public Health Service will do everything in its power to support the objectives and programs of the World Health Organization. Let us remember that they are our objectives, our programs. For when our government signed the United Nations charter, when it adopted the constitution of WHO, it made every citizen a participant in the world's great struggle for human health and welfare.

It was in the spring of 1946 at the International Health Conference in New York that representatives of 62 nations assembled and decided upon the formation of WHO. The suggestion came from the representatives of China and Brazil. Permanent organization as a specialized agency of the United Nations became effective on September 1, 1948.

Previous efforts to establish a single intergovernmental health agency had resulted in the formation of such organizations as the Office International d'Hygiene Publique, the Health Organization of the League of Nations, and the Health Division of UNRRA. WHO inherited their functions.

The Preamble of the Constitution of WHO defines health as a "state of complete physical, mental, and social well-being and not merely the absence of disease or infirmity." Other principles emphasize the importance of health in the social development of the world and the interdependence of states in the development of higher levels of national health, the responsibility of governments for the health of their peoples, the importance of an informed public opinion in matters of health, and the extension to all peoples of the benefits of medical, psychological, and related knowledge. Particular emphasis is placed on the importance of the health development of the child.

Membership is open to all nations. By 1963 there were more than 100 member countries. Geneva, Switzerland, is the headquarters at the Palais des Nations, formerly the home of the League of Nations. The first director-general was Dr. Brook Chisholm, Canadian psychiatrist who was surgeon general of the Canadian Army during World War II. Dr. M. G. Candau, of Brazil, was elected director-general in 1953.

Delegates representing member nations meet annually for the World Health Assembly, at which program and policies are determined. The first assembly met in Geneva in 1948. It gave top priority to six major health programs: control of malaria, venereal disease, tuberculosis, and improvement of environmental sanitation, maternal and child health, and nutrition. Other major areas of activities outlined included improvement of public health administration, nursing, health education, mental health, research in parasitic and virus diseases, and provision of fellowships.

Through WHO scientific information, literature, and teaching equipment are exchanged, and research projects are coordinated. Periodicals on the technical aspects of health and reports of its meetings are issued. World-wide information service on the prevalence of epidemics is provided. Radio warnings are regularly broadcast from Geneva to airports, seaports, and national health authorities on every continent. Governments are assisted, upon request, in improving their health services. International demonstration teams work in selected areas of need. Emergency services are provided in epidemics and disasters.

The *International Digest of Health Legislation,* which is published quarterly by WHO, is the only periodical devoted solely to the publication of health legislation of international significance.

WHO publications may be obtained from the Columbia University Press, International Documents Service, 2960 Broadway, New York 27.

In recent years WHO has devoted much attention to the chronic diseases, particularly to cancer and cardiovascular diseases. Here its principal task, as described by Director-General Candau, is, for the present at least, "to promote the standardization of nomenclature and techniques and to stimulate the study of differences in the incidences of cancer and cardiovascular diseases in different countries and ethnic groups, in the hope that such studies may provide a key to the better understanding of their etiology."[34]

An especially important activity of WHO, from the viewpoint of administrators of health service organizations, is its role in relation to the "International Classification of Diseases." It is responsible for arranging the successive revisions of this publication and for ensuring that it remains continuously up to date and, in Dr. Candau's words, "ready to serve the needs of its many users in almost every branch of health activity." He adds that "without an international established classification of diseases the interchange of health information between countries would be greatly impeded and international cooperation in epidemiologic research would be much less effective."[35]

This function of WHO is currently limelighted in the American Hospital Association–American Association of Medical Record Librarians joint recommendation that the "International Classification" be adopted in all hospitals in the United States. The recommendation was contained in a joint statement issued by the two organizations on February 26, 1963. The 1963 statement supersedes a joint statement issued in June, 1959, that recommended deferring action until a comparative study of the ICDA and the Standard Nomenclature of Diseases and Operations could be completed. The study demonstrated

> . . . the economy of use of ICDA as well as its high degree of consistency in coding and retrieval. Specifically, the use of ICDA permitted significant savings in personnel time, but did not impair the usefulness of the index. . . . Since use of the ICDA is acceptable to the Joint Commission on Accreditation of Hospitals, administrators and medical record librarians are urged to benefit by the efficiency and economy its use provides.[36]

[34] Epidemiology and World Medicine. *Pub. Health Rep.,* September, 1961, pp. 793–96.
[35] *Ibid.*
[36] Editorial Notes. *Hospitals,* May 1, 1963, p. 35.

ICDA is not a nomenclature, however, the editorial adds, but a coding system only, and "to record diagnoses and operative procedures, physicians should use either the Standard Nomenclature of Diseases and Operations or the *Current Medical Terminology* of the American Medical Association."

A central office on the International Classification of Diseases adapted for hospitals was opened in May, 1963, in the headquarters building of the American Hospital Association. The office is sponsored by the AHA and the American Association of Medical Record Librarians by agreement with the National Center for Health Statistics of the PHS.

Another WHO activity of great importance to hospitals is development of uniform standards for the strength and purity of drugs and medical substances (vaccines, etc.). WHO's recommendations are incorporated in its "International Pharmacopoeia." The agency participates in international control of drug addiction and studies new synthetic drugs likely to become habit-forming.

The annual budget for WHO is around $25 million. Each member country pays a share calculated according to a fixed scale which takes into account both its size and its wealth. Besides funds received from membership fees, WHO solicits and receives voluntary contributions from governments and private sources.

HOSPITAL–PUBLIC HEALTH RELATIONSHIPS

From the head of the nation to the top-ranking officer of a village, the people who direct government activities must support public and voluntary efforts to preserve the health of their constituents and must be concerned about their care when they are ill. This is, in fact, one of the basic functions of government.

Mutual interdependence is most desirable in this area. The relationships between voluntary and government health agencies should be so close as to be virtually integrated in order to avoid duplication of effort and assure maximum health protection.

The health department has a policing function in connection with hospitals and nursing homes just as it has with other institutions and enterprises which have any effect upon the health of the people who patronize them. The administrator who is well informed about trends in public health welcomes these inspections and recommendations and actively supports all constructive measures to improve sanitation, to minimize the dangers of infection, and in general to assure healthful surroundings and practices for patients and personnel.

In 1948 the American Hospital Association and the American Public Health Association prepared a joint statement of recommendations for the "Coordination of Hospitals and Health Departments."[37] One of the opening statements was: "Preventive and curative medicine have reached the stage where they are no longer separable, and it is necessary at the present time to bring them

[37] *Am. J. Pub. Health,* May, 1948, pp. 700–701.

together physically and functionally. The close physical and organizational association of health departments and hospitals will provide a valuable step toward
this essential goal."

For some obscure reason, probably related to the different administrative
methods of the public and the private agency and of the preventive and the
curative approach, the movement to establish integrated physical facilities, which
was promoted especially by grants from the W. K. Kellogg Foundation, quickly
lost momentum. The economies were evident. As the joint statement reads:[38]

> It is strongly recommended that, wherever circumstances justify and permit,
> there should be joint housing of hospitals and health departments, and, if pos-
> sible, the offices of physicians and dentists. Although coordination of the activi-
> ties of hospitals and health departments can be accomplished even if they are not
> closely integrated physically, it is most feasible when there is joint housing of the
> hospital and health department. The common use of laboratory and clinic facili-
> ties, which is difficult to achieve when the two institutions are physically sepa-
> rated, occurs readily when they are housed together. The planning of integrated
> programs is facilitated by joint housing and their administration is made
> smoother and more efficient.

All true as true can be, but the theory did not work in practice except in a few
instances. Possibly the idea may be revived when actual coordination is more
complete, but at present the subject seldom comes up, prolific as the literature
about it was in the 1940's.

Particularly in rural areas, as the joint statement goes on to point out, the
hospital, the health department, and the community benefit greatly by joint
housing. In a few counties physical coordination is achieved through rental by
the health department of space in a hospital.

In Louisville and in Indianapolis there is integration in a medical center including the medical school, teaching hospital, and public health department.
These remain exceptions, rather than the rule, however.

Whether or not there is physical integration, actual integration is imperative
for the good of the community, and this was recognized long before the 1948
statement. The American Hospital Association had a Committee on Public
Health Relations the chairman of which was invited back in 1927 to become a
member of a subcommittee of the American Public Health Association to study
the relations of hospitals and health departments.

A survey conducted in 1949 and 1950 by the American Public Health Association showed close correlation between hospitals and health departments in
specific programs and considerable coordination of services; in a few cases there
was even a single administrator, as in Denver, where the health department
administered the hospital. Coordination was discovered to be not always the
best way in some places, as in one joint laboratory in which the public health
and the hospital personnel had to be separated because the more urgent nature

[38] *Ibid.*, p. 701.

of the hospital work led to a certain amount of neglect of the public health tests. In this survey it was found that there were some disadvantages in housing the health department in a hospital because the latter frequently needs more space and either encroaches on or prevents the former from expanding; the hospital may have financial problems which cause decrease in maintenance services to the health department; some danger of loss of identity by the health department; and confusion between the two types of service by patients.[39]

One of the reasons why, with the best intentions on both sides, coordination between health departments and hospitals is less than the ideal, is given by John Bigelow,[40] executive director of the Washington State Hospital Association. This is that the boards and agencies are all composed of, or are under the direction of, political appointees who have limited tenure. Bigelow states that at the end of ten years of organized effort to cement relationships, there have been five different directors of the Department of Labor and Industries, three directors of the Department of Public Assistance, and two directors of the State Health Department. He comments: "Perhaps it is significant that our area of greatest problems and fewest successes is in the department with the greatest turnover."

Relationships with state government fall into three groups, according to Bigelow. These are the legislature, state agencies concerned with hospital operations, and state agencies concerned with purchasing hospital services. The first is the most important of all, he says, adding:

> Hospitals have awakened to the fact that what occurs in the state capitol every two years can affect their daily existence more than what the well publicized group in Washington D.C. does continuously. All our dealings with state agencies are connected to the Legislature. Some problems we have can be solved only by the Legislature. Likewise we can prevent later problems with administrative agencies, if we are lucky, by taking steps in the Legislature. But the Legislature meets every two years and we have to work with agencies and boards continuously.

Mr. Bigelow's article gives a realistic picture of obstacles to coordination and of how to surmount them.

Hospitals as contributors to public health should "do everything possible to rehabilitate and restore to society as speedily as possible those placed under their care and play an important and definite part in the development and carrying on of services which have for their objective the promotion of health and the control of disease." This is not a new statement. It was made on October 22, 1929, at the eighth annual session of the New England Hospital Association, Boston, by Dr. C. F. Wilinsky,[41] now trustee, then superintendent, of Beth

---

[39] Milton Terris, M.D.: Joint Housing of Hospitals, Health Departments, and Laboratories. *Am. J. Pub. Health,* March, 1951, pp. 319–25.

[40] *Hosp. Forum,* June, 1962. *Hospital Forum* is published by the Hospital Council of Southern California. The title of Mr. Bigelow's article is "Hospital and State Government, a Study of the Varying Relationships," pp. 28–32.

[41] The Relation of Hospitals to Public Health. *Bull. Am. Hosp. A.,* January, 1930, pp. 81–87.

Israel Hospital, Boston. Dr. Wilinsky went on to cite some of the contributions of hospitals to the public health: training of physicians, training of nurses, social service, prenatal clinics, well baby clinics, diagnostic clinics, mental hygiene clinics, care of the chronically ill, cancer clinics, heart clinics, isolation of communicable diseases, and affiliations between hospital and health department laboratories.

Regulation of Hospitals

Wide variations exist in government regulation of hospitals in different states. Accredited hospitals would welcome strict and uniform licensing laws. The Michigan Hospital Association is asking for one state licensing law that is effective, instead of a patchwork pieced together by different governmental agencies. The public thinks that the hospitals are licensed in that state, but only the maternity sections are really licensed.

In Wyoming, on the other hand, when the State Board of Health was vested with legal authority in 1947 to inspect and license all hospitals and medical facilities built in the state under the Hill-Burton program, it created an advisory hospital council to consult with the newly formed division of hospital and medical facilities within the public health department. The limitation to Hill-Burton hospitals left out two-thirds of the hospitals in the state, and these were the ones, being older, that most needed regulation. As a result of suggestions from the Wyoming Hospital Association the law was amended to include all hospital facilities and to increase the number of hospital administrators serving on the advisory hospital council from one to three. Also recommended was a fire marshal's office separate from the licensure program, and this has been done. The hospitals now feel that they are helping to regulate themselves.[42]

The New York State Board of Social Welfare regulates medical care facilities of all kinds but licenses only a small group of dispensaries. The director of the state's Bureau of Adult Institutions, Gertrude Binger, makes the following distinction between legal and voluntary regulation:[43]

> Voluntary agencies are free to ignore substandard operations and concentrate on the development of institutions which set an example of superior service. There is a significant difference in that the voluntary agency is accountable to its membership or to the profession it represents, but the regulatory agency is accountable to all people of the locality which enacted the law it administers. . . . In governmental regulation "mandatory" means that facilities which do not meet minimum requirements may not, legally, continue in operation. Requirements

[42] Hale Laybourn, director, Division of Hospital and Medical Facilities, and Paul Mico, director, Division of Health Education, Wyoming Department of Public Health: How Wyoming Hospitals Regulate Themselves. *Hospitals,* August 16, 1958, pp. 45–48.

[43] Gertrude Binger: How Regulation Differs from Accreditation. *Mod. Hosp.,* May, 1960, pp. 113–14, 168.

of voluntary agencies have no such legal status. The only penalty for noncompliance with them is exclusion from accreditation or from membership in the standard-setting organization.

This explanation of the distinction makes obvious the fact that legal regulations are unlikely to present any hardship to the institution that is living up to high standards. They cannot go above a level that is necessary to assure a community of sufficient service, quantitatively speaking, although they can close up the lowest operators and force borderline ones to improve. Also, they can be raised from time to time, just as voluntary standards can, in line with progress.

In the state of Washington, the hospital association asked for licensing. Hospital administrators dominate the advisory board and actually write the rules and regulations and establish the policy of administering them.

The director of New York Hospital, New York City, Dr. Henry N. Pratt,[44] states that a recent incomplete count of licenses, permits, certificates, reports, and inspections required by governmental agencies of certain voluntary hospitals in New York City showed 65 required by the city, 29 by the state, and 11 by the federal government—a total of 105—besides reports, inspections, and accreditations by voluntary agencies totaling 38, and he concludes: "It appears that hospital business is everybody's business." And this, he indicates, is right. However, Dr. Pratt warns against the entrance upon the scene of state insurance commissioners who, concerned about rate increases by health insurance plans, use economic pressures as a reason for instituting new regulations. This trend, he declares, is ominous.

The state of Minnesota has a licensing law for hospital administrators.

[44] What Public Regulation Means to Hospitals. *Hospitals,* June 16, 1962, pp. 42–44.

CHAPTER 16

Religion in Medical and Hospital Service

> It is time that the established Churches take the responsibility
> of health and healing seriously. It is not enough to build
> great hospitals and turn them over to the medical profession
> to run as it sees fit. And I would be the first to argue that
> the doctor is a religious person; he may not always be a
> Christian by doctrinal standards, but he is religious. He knows
> and trusts the Force that makes for health, which most
> call nature, but which some call God.
>
> RUSSELL L. DICKS[1]

HOSPITALS ARE one of the early phenomena of human society.
They had originally little political, economic, scientific, or educational significance. They were simply places of refuge for the sick. Their social importance was considerable because besides fulfilling this custodial function
they provided, as they still do, opportunities for the expression of religious
and humanitarian impulses. Religion has always found practical application in
caring for the sick. It is safe to say that religiously motivated people still lead
action to provide health facilities and to serve in them. The origin and a large
part of the upkeep of voluntary hospitals in particular are traceable to church
affiliations.

What little is known about medical and, later, hospital care in ancient times
shows that it was a responsibility, largely, of the priesthood. The incantations

[1] From the preface to *The Church and Healing* by Carl J. Scherzer. Philadelphia, The Westminster Press, 1950, pp. 9–10.

of the medicine men and the witch doctors were, and where they remain still are, of a religious nature, propitiation of the gods. The forerunners of hospitals were temples of worship to which the sick came, as in Egypt and Greece, for ministrations by priests. A natural sequence as knowledge increased and medical science began was the combination of priest and physician in the same individual.

The great monotheistic religions, Judaism, Buddhism, Mohammedanism, Christianity, have given strong motivation for selflessness in caring for the sick.

When at the age of 29 a "great discontent" with the purposelessness of his life fell upon Gautama, later known as Buddha, the first things he saw that shocked him into a new way of life were a frightfully decrepit old man, a man suffering from a horrible disease, and the unburied body of one who appeared to have perished from starvation and exposure. Among the achievements that grew out of his and his disciples' dedication to service was the building of hospitals for the crippled and the poor—a great innovation for the sixth century before Christ. Upatiso, his son, is said to have built shelters for the diseased and for pregnant women. Buddhism teaches that every life is holy. The accomplishments of the Buddhist King Asoka were described in a previous chapter as the contributions of a ruler, but his primary motivation was clearly religious.

CHRISTIANITY AND HOSPITALS

Heading the list of Christian churchmen who founded hospitals is Saint Basil the Great, Bishop of Caesarea, who in A.D. 369 built the famous Basilias at Caesarea, which consisted of a group of charitable institutions including a hospital and a lazar house. Physicians and nurses were housed on the grounds. The deaconess Macrina, his sister, is believed to have functioned as its superintendent—perhaps the world's first woman hospital administrator.

Six years later Saint Ephraim established a 300-bed charity hospital at Edessa for the care of victims of the plague. He was a Christian deacon who came from seclusion in the desert with this special object. He bought 300 beds with money he raised, set them up in a public portico, served as doctor and nurse to the patients, and, the crisis over, retired again to his hermitage and to oblivion except for this one noble accomplishment.

About A.D. 390 Fabiola, a wealthy deaconess, opened the first charity hospital in Rome. She used a portion of her own large home for the purpose and nursed the sick with the help of other deaconesses. She was influenced in doing this by Marcella, a Roman matron who was a philanthropist. She in turn influenced her friend Paula, the best known of all the deaconesses, wealthy widow of a senator, who established a number of hospitals in Rome and later, inspired by Saint Jerome, founded a hospital, monastery, and convent at Bethlehem, impoverishing and wearing herself out in her work.

The wife of Emperor Theodosius the Great, Placilla, also a deaconess, not only nursed the sick in hospitals but made beds and scrubbed floors.

The Orders of Deacons and of Deaconesses, the rules and precepts for which are included in the Apostolic Constitutions of the early Christian Church, are one of the first known organized groups for care of the sick. They were enjoined not only to minister to patients but also to make known their needs to the congregation in order that others might help.

Although the deaconesses had other duties besides nursing, the nursing profession considers its history to have begun with them. The female diaconate of the early Christian Church disappeared as orders of nuns were organized.

A zealous reformer who had two hospitals erected at Constantinople about the year 400 was Saint Chrysostom, bishop and patriarch. Olymphia, a deaconess, served as a nurse in these hospitals and donated her great fortune to the church which sustained them.

For the modern board member and administrator it is interesting to note that these women not only gave of their own wealth and toil but literally made beggars of themselves, as auxiliary members and trustees continue to do to this day, soliciting funds and services for their institutions. In the early hospitals there was, of course, little real scientific care, but there were kindness, relief of suffering, nourishment, and shelter. Medical care was rendered by priests, mainly, who were physicians.

Nestorius, a priest who was made patriarch of Constantinople in 428, was about the first prominent physician whose name has come down in history in connection with both hospitals and medical schools. His fame rests mainly on the medical teachings which he and his followers and successors started, out of which grew Arabian medicine. He took up the study of medicine after the Christian sect of which he was head, known as the Nestorians, was driven into the desert. They took over control of the medical school at Edessa in Mesopotamia, with which two large hospitals were connected. In 489 the orthodox bishop Cyrus drove them out and they established in Persia the famous school at Gondispor. Moslem medicine was founded upon their teaching of medicine and hospital care. They preserved and translated the texts of Hippocrates, Aristotle, and Galen.

Of the Hospital of Augusta-Emerita, founded by the Goth bishop Masona in 580, it was recorded that its doctors scoured the town for sick people to take in. René Sand[2] records that six centuries later the brothers of the Order of the Holy Ghost, who served the Ospedale di Santo Spirito in Sassia, built in Rome about 1200 by Pope Innocent III, "made a weekly round of the city in search of sick and people in distress and took them to the hospital in one of the earliest known ambulances." Similar zeal was reported concerning the staffs of other early hospitals, a pioneer kind of medical social service that outstrips what has developed later as a distinct profession from medicine and the priesthood.

The religious orders figure prominently in the early history of Christian hos-

[2] *Advance to Social Medicine,* London, Staples Press, 1952, pp. 74, 75.

pitals, notably those founded by Saint Benedict of Nursia in 501, the Benedictines, first of the western monastic orders; by Saint Francis of Assisi in 1209, the Order of Mendicant Friars, to be known as the Franciscans; and by Saint Ignatius of Loyola in 1539, the Jesuits.

The Benedictines and some of the other orders included women as members. They nursed the sick in their homes as well as in hospitals. Many of the hospital and nursing orders originated during the Crusades. They form a long and fascinating chapter in the story of hospitals of yesterday and today, well repaying in appreciation of their importance the student who is beguiled by this bare mention of them to learn more about their enormous contributions.

A rather new type of hospital under religious auspices began with the founding in 542 of the Hotel Dieu at Lyons followed by establishment of a Hotel Dieu in each great city of France and of hospitals of the Holy Spirit in other cities of the Holy Roman Empire. Popes, archbishops, priests, and monks were the directors and supporters of these institutions. Up to the thirteenth century when control of these hospitals began to pass to civil authorities, hospital care was almost completely the responsibility of ecclesiastics in Christian countries. Bishop Landry founded Hotel Dieu at Paris around the middle of the seventh century, the oldest hospital that still exists.

In 1198 Pope Innocent III urged hospitals of the Holy Ghost in every important town. Study of the reasons for this and of the subsequent widespread establishment of municipal hospitals should be accompanied by study of the whole medieval movement toward town life, the beginnings of industrialization and of organized commerce, and the resultant growth of cities which created problems of unemployment, poverty, and disease.

Arabic Hospitals

Although the religious impulse was behind the movement for medical care and hospitals in Mohammedan countries, the caliphs were rulers and therefore their activities in this direction were mentioned in the preceding chapter as attributable to government.

Every major Moslem town had by the tenth century its own hospital. Well-qualified doctors provided the medical care. The caliph's officials made regular inspections. There were even mobile hospitals hauled by dromedaries in the caravans for the purpose of treating the sick during epidemics and the wounded and ailing soldiers on the march.

English Hospitals

Hospitals existed in England before the Norman conquest in 1066. Athelstane founded Saint Peter's Hospital at York about 937. Saint Alban's Hospital near London dated back to 794. Saint Thomas' Hospital, London, dates back to the thirteenth century, Saint Bartholomew's was founded in 1123 by Rahere, a jester at the court of Henry I, who afterward joined the priesthood. Saint Mary of Bethlehem, founded in 1247 near London by the Order of the Star of Bethlehem, began to admit mental patients in 1403. It was rebuilt as an exclusively mental institution in 1676. From its name comes the term "bedlam."

All these English hospitals were ecclesiastical institutions. In the sixteenth century Henry VIII closed all of them and seized their properties along with those of other Catholic institutions. Later they were reopened as civic hospitals.

AMERICAN RELIGIOUS HOSPITALS

Some evidence exists that one or more hospitals were established very early in the Spanish colony of Florida. A Spanish religious order called the "Confradias" was established in Florida in 1567, and according to the W.P.A. 1960 publication, *Stories of Florida,* a "Santa Barbara" hospital was founded by this order in Saint Augustine. No date is given and no record of it exists in Saint Augustine, it is said.

Generally, when homeless people became ill they were cared for in the homes of private citizens who were sometimes but not always reimbursed by the parish or the town. The heaviest demands were made upon clergymen and physicians. A French minister at Saint James, Santee, South Carolina, expressed his dissatisfaction with this custom as follows:

> I am obliged without charity to assist the sick poor people and to keep physic to cure her. Some time these be at my charge two months before she recovered her health.

As a result of this complaint and others an act was passed authorizing the Vestry of Saint Philip's Parish, South Carolina, in which Charleston was located, to raise a maximum of 2,000 pounds for the year 1734 and 1,000 pounds annually thereafter and to construct therewith "a good, substantial, and convenient hospital, workhouse and house of correction." The hospital, Saint Philips, is believed to have been opened in 1738 and it seems to have served mostly chronic patients. By 1789 the care of the poor in this locality had passed from the hands of the church into those of the civil authorities, and what happened to the parish hospital is not known.

In Pennsylvania the Philadelphia Almshouse was founded by Quakers in 1713, and sick inmates were cared for in a sort of infirmary; the institution was later used for care of the insane. Eventually it became the Philadelphia General Hospital.

A sailor, Jean Louis, left $2,500 to found "Saint John's Hospital" in New Orleans, then in the French colony of Louisiana. A memorandum dated May 20, 1737, addressed to the Minister in France, stated that the hospital had five patients and was both a hospital and an asylum for indigents. A hurricane in 1779 wrecked the building, and in 1786 the new Charity Hospital was established and endowed by Don Andres Almonaster y Rojas, becoming the City Hospital in 1811. A new site was acquired in 1832 and a building erected which is still in use. The Daughters of Charity of Saint Vincent de Paul took charge of the institution in 1834.

West of the Mississippi River the first hospital was what is now called the De Paul Hospital at St. Louis. This is the oldest hospital founded by a Catholic order in the United States. The Daughters of Charity of Saint Vincent de Paul opened it in 1828 in a two-room log cabin.

Another early Catholic hospital which still exists is Saint Joseph Infirmary, opened in Louisville in 1836, for emergency hospital service by the Sisters of Charity of Nazareth.

Nursing in the Catholic institutions was far superior to that in other early hospitals because of the devotion and better training of the members of the nursing sisterhoods. Occasionally Catholic sisters were called upon for emergency help in city hospitals.

The monastic and nursing orders continue to play a large part in care of the sick, some of them in an unusual way. In a 1960 book, *Benedictine and Moor,* Peter Beach and William Dunphy told the story of the Priory of Christ the King, which came to be known as Toumililine, after a nearby spring. Established by twenty Benedictine monks who left their abbey in southwestern France in 1952, it is the only community of Christian monks in Moslem North Africa. Among their welfare activities is the conduct of a dispensary in which some 2,500 patients a month are treated.

What is now the Congregation of the Alexian Brothers originated in the work of a group of charitable laymen during the Black Death at the beginning of the fifteenth century. Although the details of the early years are obscure, Brother Tobias is given the title of founder. The Holy See raised the society to the dignity of a religious order in 1469. The Brothers were given the Rule of Saint Augustine and permitted to make solemn vows. In 1481, the Cellites, as the Brothers were then called, adopted Saint Alexius as their chief patron and since then have been known as Alexian Brothers. The order was changed to a congregation when it was reorganized after the French Revolution, and foundations were established in Germany, England, Belgium, Switzerland, Ireland, and the United States. In 1866 Brother Bonaventure came to the United States and established Alexian Brothers Hospital in Chicago. A general and psychiatric hospital was started at St. Louis in 1869, a retreat for nervous and mental patients at Oshkosh, Wisconsin, in 1880, and a general hospital at Elizabeth, New Jersey, in 1893. A rest resort and residence for men was opened at Signal Mountain, Tennessee, in 1938.

EARLY CHURCH HOSPITALS IN CANADA

Dr. Angus C. McGugan,[3] former administrator, University of Alberta Hospital, Edmonton, Canada, tells how in the year 1634 one of the first Jesuit missionaries in New France, Father Le Jeune, made an appeal for a hospital to be

[3] Gleanings from History. *Canad. Hosp.,* December, 1960.

established there. The Duchess d'Aiguillon, a niece of Cardinal Richelieu and a follower of St. Vincent de Paul, founder of the order called The Sisters of Charity, heard the plea and sponsored the hospital. Three sisters of the order known as Hospitallers of the Mercy of Jesus were chosen to go, along with three each from two other orders. They arrived in New France in August, 1639, and established their hospital in a warehouse in Quebec. After a few years a hospital was built, the sisters assisting in the heavy manual labor. Indians, soldiers, and other patients were cared for. Many hardships, epidemics, and Indian massacres plagued the group. The same difficulties were encountered in Montreal, where the Hotel Dieu was founded in 1644 and dedicated to St. Joseph by Mlle. Jeanne Mance, who governed it until her death in 1673. There was no physician at this hospital in its early years, Mlle. Mance, the priests, and the nuns ministering to the patients.

Dr. McGugan comments:

> Without a knowledge of history there can be no intelligent appreciation of the contributions of the past; there can be no intelligent assessment of the present; and no intelligent planning for the future. Without a knowledge of the failures and successes of the past; without a knowledge of the contributions of each race and each civilization to the common weal of all society, we cannot achieve our universal hope for universal brotherhood.

VALUE OF RELIGIOUS MOTIVATION

The interest of the Church and of church people—Catholic, Protestant, Buddhist, Mohammedan, Jewish, or other—is proved historically by countless evidences of leadership in hospital care beyond those sketchily traced here as examples. On the whole the record is a glowing one, for the religious incentive was clearly dominant in the establishment and development of most early hospitals and many later ones. It must be admitted that at times it was almost too dominant in that too much concern for the patient's soul in the next world led to too little treatment of his body in this one. Medical science had a hard time forging ahead in this other-worldly atmosphere.

These comments on the place of religion in hospital service are made with full cognizance of the inclination of sociologists in general to discount religious motivation as an important element in their field. Emotion and sentiment pose difficulties for most scientists. They keep them from advancing social theory to a scientific level approximating that of the natural sciences. They like to leave these disturbing factors to the psychologist, overlooking the fact that sociology and psychology are intermeshed.

Talcott Parsons recognized this when in 1946 he established at Harvard University a Department of Social Relations, subordinating the specific disciplines of sociology, anthropology, and clinical and social psychology. Earlier Max Weber recognized it in his appreciation of religious values in social action, as did also both Vilfredo Pareto and Emile Durkheim, the latter particularly in his study, *Elementary Forms of the Religious Life,* published in 1912. In their forerunners of the eighteenth and nineteenth centuries there was a strong tendency to feel, with Herbert Spencer, that religion was the "product of ignorance and error" and to deify science.

Hospital people, along with members of other welfare groups, might well retort that out of that "ignorance and error" have issued many a movement and institution without which civilization would be in the state of chaos out of which the early sociologists unsuccessfully tried to rescue it by reason and intelligence alone.

Compassion is a highly complex emotion. It is something quite different from Theodor Lipps' doctrine of "empathy." Empathy is a more encompassing but also a colder, more objective concept. True compassion takes a person out of himself. Empathy may not. If a doctor or nurse or anybody in constant, everyday attendance upon and contact with numbers of sick people felt deep compassion for every patient, he would inevitably court an emotional breakdown. Empathy, identification in a calmer sense with the patient's problem, is both a compromise and a more scientific approach. Indulgence in genuine compassion for an extended length of time is possible under two conditions: for an individual or a comparatively small group of sufferers toward whom the relationship though close is voluntary; for a larger group toward whom the relationship is occasional or is fairly remote, and under these conditions it may be either voluntary or professional.

People who are not religious may, of course, be compassionate. They may be compassionate to the extent of taking significant social action to lessen the misery of the objects of their compassion. On the whole, however, history shows a religious foundation for this emotion as exhibited in the good works of most benefactors of mankind. The wellsprings of human behavior seem to be bottomed in mystic qualities as common to modern as to primitive man, though more hidden.

Religion in the hospital has surmounted creeds. Almost no hospital or related institution limits admissions to the denomination to which they may owe their origin and part of their support. They are open to the ministry of every faith. They attract as workers, both paid and voluntary, religiously inclined persons; but they have grown to be true religious melting pots, as if birth, suffering, and death know no creeds, but are the very essence of religion itself. Persons who have lost their religious faith, or who have never had any, frequently under the strain of suffering and fear of death welcome the ministrations of religious personnel. Therapeutic as well as spiritual values often result.

In most hospitals religion is nowadays not a conspicuous influence. It is there just the same. In Catholic hospitals it remains visible and inescapable, bringing some real advantages compared with its subduing behind a nondenominational front in other hospitals of religious origin.

Churchmen often dominate hospital boards. Their service is a practical expression of their religious convictions. The Catholic institutions, of course, are ruled by orders of priests and nuns. A few Protestant hospitals likewise are denominationally controlled. The Mennonites, the Brethren, the Seventh Day Adventists, the Methodists, the Lutherans, and the Baptists still closely control their institutions. Presbyterians and Episcopalians exercise limited authority, although board members and top administrative personnel are seldom expected to be of the same denomination. Usually, however, they must be Protestant. Jewish hospitals are not church controlled, but religious influences are strong, especially in the orthodox institutions. At the top of the hospital hierarchy, the board, religion and even denominationalism still hold a prominent place.

It therefore behooves the hospital administrator, for very practical reasons, to maintain good relations with religious organizations. Interchurch movements are especially interesting and rewarding for those who join them, because they signify the spirit of tolerance which the hospital practices in its admission of patients of all faiths. The appointment of a chaplain to visit patients not only accomplishes the internal recognition of the impact of religion on the hospital, but shows the outside world that it remains strong in the atmosphere of medical care, notwithstanding the too general acceptance of the notion of the ungodliness of the times.

The religious impact, though relatively unorganized, is growing, or rather returning. Authorities are constantly reiterating the conviction that a spiritual reawakening is occurring. Keeping abreast of the developments in this direction is a clear obligation of those who head organizations which depend in considerable measure for support upon the expression in good works of religiously motivated persons.

CATHOLIC HOSPITAL ASSOCIATION

The story of the beginning of the Catholic Hospital Association is well told in the obituary of the Rev. Charles B. Moulinier, S. J., written by Dr. Malcolm T. MacEachern.[4] Father Moulinier died on August 1, 1941, in his eighty-second year, at West Baden College, West Baden, Indiana. The following is abstracted from Dr. McEachern's article.

There has passed from this life one who left the impress of his remarkable personality on a leading activity of the American College of Surgeons—Hospital Standardization. Father Charles B. Moulinier crusaded for Hospital Stndardization in its critical early days, and in retrospect those of us who worked with him can appreciate more fully even than at the time, how the progress of the movement was speeded by his championship of it as a holy cause, and by his skill in communicating his enthusiasm to hospital people of every classification and rank.

This Jesuit priest, founder in 1915 of the Catholic Hospital Association, and its president for twelve years, was universally acclaimed for his great influence in

[4] *Bull. Am. Coll. Surgeons,* October, 1941.

improving Catholic hospitals. He is also to be remembered for his stimulating influence on *all* hospitals, through his voluntary alliance with the College in spreading the Hospital Standardization gospel.

Father Moulinier was a fighter, not of the grim, defiant type, but of that rare number of history makers who battle joyously and welcome obstacles as exciting incentives to greater effort. It was fortunate for Hospital Standardization that in 1915 this priest, then Regent of the School of Medicine of Marquette University and lecturer on Medical Jurisprudence, saw the need for cooperation among Catholic hospitals and organized the Catholic Hospital Association. That project could not have been conceived by other than a daring individual. In the words of the next president of the Association, Rev. Alphonse M. Schwitalla, the Association was organized "in the face of lethargy and mistrust, in the face of indifference and suspicion, in the face of opposition and disapproval. . . . His was then the voice of a new prophet preaching a new message. New prophets with new messages must convince an indifferent world that a new message is at the same time an urgent and an imperative one."

The new message that Father Moulinier brought to Catholic hospitals is well expressed by the themes of the first two conventions of the Association. The first theme was "Education in the Care of the Sick." The second was "Conservation of Human Life Through Teamwork—Cooperation in the Matter of Knowledge —by Everyone in the Hospital." How coincidental it was that these ideals were being implanted in a large section of the hospital world at the same time that the College was planning its program of hospital betterment. By 1917 this program had advanced to the calling of the momentous "Conference on Hospital Standardization" in Chicago, to which Father Moulinier contributed expressions of warm sympathy with the movement and stirred the group to loud applause by his vigorous acclamation of the undertaking as a "great privilege, a great honor, a great mission" for the "enlightenment for health of the people of America."

The Catholic Hospital Association and the American College of Surgeons were each destined to success by the dynamic leadership of their respective founders, but they have both made amazing progress because the paths of those founders met and converged. Franklin H. Martin and Father Moulinier were kindred souls, adventurers in reform, able communicators of their own glowing enthusiasms. Even before Hospital Standardization was accorded the official endorsement of the Church through His Eminence, James Cardinal Gibbons, Father Moulinier was preaching it to the Catholic hospitals, notwithstanding the fact that the doctors working in them did not, as he said, "want to be disturbed," and had "nothing but words of scorn for the American College of Surgeons at that time." Forcefully bringing the program to the attention of all who were working in Catholic hospitals, he chose for the third meeting of the Catholic Hospital Association, in 1918, the theme, "Hospital Standardization—The Soul of the Hospital," and for the fourth, in 1919, "Progress in the Standardization of Hospitals." This emphatic support by an association representing a large proportion of the hospitals of the United States and Canada, has been an appreciable factor in the success of Hospital Standardization.

Well do I personally remember the vehemence with which Father Moulinier, on trips to hospitals with Director John G. Bowman and myself, used to hammer on the essential principles of Hospital Standardization in his talks before hospital groups. Unforgettable as an example is the alliterative admonition which so repeatedly I heard him give: "Find the facts—filter the facts—fix the facts—and face the facts fearlessly."

Dr. Martin in his book, *Fifty Years of Medicine and Surgery,* expressed an admiration for Father Moulinier that strikes a responsive chord in the hearts of all of us who have known and loved them both, revealing as it does the appreciative spirit of the writer as well as the high qualities of his subject. He wrote:

"When that beloved and renowned American, His Eminence, James Cardinal Gibbons, embraced the movement of Hospital Standardization, Father Moulinier was already enthusiastic; he led the campaign, that was so ably endorsed, with the genius of a statesman and the persistence of a crusader.

"This cultured man, whom I love as a friend and with whom I have intimately associated at home and in travel, I learned to respect as a true priest. He loves his Church which he serves devotedly; he loves his people; he has endeared himself to thousands of hospital administrators who look to him for aid and sympathy, and to thousands of sick men and women who are cared for in the hospitals to which his jurisdiction and service extended.

"Father Moulinier is more than a priest, more than a mere organizer, more than an administrator, more than a teacher, more than a dean of a medical school, more than the founder and longtime president of the Catholic Hospital Association, more than the organizer and administrator of the first school for hospital administrators. He is a great statesman; he is a sympathetic counsellor; he is an orator of transcendent power and exquisite charm; he is a man of far-reaching wisdom and of poetic instincts. His humanitarianism is unbounded, and his practical methods have ever brought forth enduring results.

"Father Moulinier's work has been that of a genius and stands for tangible and enduring progress. His lieutenants and successors will envy us; but the 'Soul of the father' should be kept in the forefront of progress, or his great and inspirational work will lapse and become mechanical and commonplace."

The "Soul of the Father" has been kept in the forefront by the Catholic Hospital Association. When in the year following his retirement, Father Moulinier completed on July 23, 1930, fifty years of religious life as a member of the Society of Jesus, an article on his Golden Jubilee was published in the journal of the Association, *Hospital Progress,* written by Father Schwitalla, which ended with these words: "The president, the executive board, and all the members of the Catholic Hospital Association extend to the Reverend Founder in this his jubilee year . . . the assurance that the aims of their lives and of their activities for the Catholic hospital will ever be inspired by the principles upon which his Association has been founded."

Among those who supported the Very Rev. Charles B. Moulinier, S.J., in founding the Catholic Hospital Association of the United States and Canada in 1915 was Rt. Rev. Monsignor F. Griffin. He served as vice-president of the association for twenty years. He was president in 1947 and 1948 at the time the association was reorganized and the present headquarters in St. Louis purchased. Monsignor Griffin was a Protonotary Apostolic and pastor of St. Philomene's Church, Cleveland, Ohio.

On September 25, 1939, as senior trustee of the American Hospital Association, Monsignor Griffin made the presentation address on the occasion of the Award of Merit to Dr. MacEachern at the Toronto Convention. A year and a half later

Dr. MacEachern made the address when an anonymous donor gave to the association a portrait of Monsignor Griffin. Dr. McEachern said in part at the unveiling:

Long, arduous service for hospitals makes Monsignor Griffin deserving of this tribute while he has left to him, we hope, many more years to devote to Church and hospital duties. For more than twenty years a trustee of the American Hospital Association, and for 28 years identified with hospital work, he has a record with which few can compare in richness of contribution. He started his hospital career on a very practical level—raising the funds for the institution which was to become St. Elizabeth's Hospital, Youngstown, Ohio. He has continued it on a practical level, as all know who are familiar with his championship of plans for hospital care as a member of the Commission on Hospital Service of the American Hospital Association since its inception in 1935. Yet practical as he is, it is in the realm of humanitarian ideals and spiritual values that his influence has penetrated deepest in hospital work.

It is inspiring to go back nearly 22 years and read a short talk he gave as the representative of the Catholic Hospital Association at the 1919 meeting of the American Hospital Association. The subject was the human side of the hospital. He said that the genius and the efforts of others may be expended on marble and canvas, sticks and stones, but that those who work in the hospital work for and with man. And he said that all that head and heart, and all that science, and all that art can do, we should try to do for every patient who comes to our hospitals.

I have heard Dr. Bert Caldwell refer to Monsignor Griffin as the "sheet anchor" of the Board of Trustees for the whole period of his membership on it. He testifies to his unfailing kindliness, to his cheerful granting of every possible request. He declares that there never has been a forward, sound movement conceived by the Association since 1920 that has not had his active material and moral support. He led in advocating the purchase of the headquarters, the establishment of the magazine, *Hospitals,* the development of hospital service plans under the sponsorship of the Association, and has been active in the work of the joint advisory committee of the Catholic, Protestant and American Hospital associations. Is it any wonder that he has been asked again and again to serve on the Board, until he has attained a longer total period of service than any other elected member has ever reached?

Monsignor Griffin's first choice of a career was law, which accounts for his special interest in legislation affecting hospitals. He appeared before congressional committees several times. He died in 1961, in his eighty-sixth year.

In 1928, Reverend Alphonse M. Schwitalla became president of the Catholic Hospital Association and served until his resignation in 1947. Reorganization of the association followed, with provision for the election of a president annually and for a permanent executive director. The governing board is composed of sisters, brothers and priests. There are state, regional, and provincial conferences which embrace all of Canada and all but seven or eight states of the Union. An office is maintained in Ottawa, Canada, on behalf of the Canadian Catholic hospitals. Rev. John J. Flanagan, S.J., is executive director.

The Catholic Hospital Association is associated with the Catholic Hospital Conference of Bishops' Representatives, which is composed of diocesan directors of Catholic hospitals, the Hospital Chaplains' Conference, and the Catholic

Physicians' Guilds and is affiliated with the Bureau of Health and Hospitals of the National Catholic Welfare Conference.

The association conducts workshops, institutes, and refresher courses for religious and lay people working in Catholic hospitals—a program of continuing education. The St. Louis University's graduate course in hospital administration operates in close cooperation with the association.

Publications are *Hospital Progress,* a monthly periodical; *Linacre Quarterly,* official journal of the Federation of Catholic Physicians' Guilds; and manuals, proceedings, booklets, and departmental newsletters.

The Catholic Hospital Association of Canada has its headquarters in Ottawa.

A new member of the association in 1963 is the Catholic Hospital Association of Quebec which was founded August 8, 1962, to replace the Comité des Hôpitaux du Québec, the Montréal Conference, and the Québec Conference.

NATIONAL JEWISH WELFARE BOARD; JEWISH HOSPITALS

The outstanding contribution to health, hospitalization and welfare of Jewish groups is plainly evident in their great institutions. From these hospitals have come such renowned leaders as Dr. Sigmund S. Goldwater, Dr. E. M. Bluestone, Dr. Charles Wilinsky, and many others. The Jewish hospitals appear to work together very well indeed without need for a separate national organization other than the Welfare Board. They participate actively in the activities of the American Hospital Association and local hospital groups.

When the Jews' Hospital was first opened in New York in 1855 the intention was to restrict it to Jewish patients, and it was with this understanding that donations came from many Christians, including $250 from a Catholic priest.[5] In 1861, however, the board passed a resolution "That the board of directors tender to the state authorities a ward in this hospital for the accommodation of such soldiers who may be wounded in the service of the United States." A year later when draft riots occurred in New York City, the hospital admitted and cared for all injured, and again in the same year colored children who suffered injuries when their orphanage was destroyed by fire were admitted for treatment. Emergency cases of all faiths were therefore accepted even in the early years, and the Civil War made obvious to the directors the wisdom of making the facilities available for anyone. The 1855 rule "that the visiting committee be instructed not to receive any patients other than Jews" was discarded. The name of the hospital was changed to Mount Sinai and the constitution amended to read: "To give medical and surgical aid, nursing and dispensary service, and medical social service, to the sick and disabled poor of the city of New York and to others of any race, creed or nationality."[6]

[5] Story of a Hospital That Grew Up with Modern Medicine. *Hospitals,* January and February, 1944.

[6] From a term paper by Marguerite M. Ducker, administrator, Sewickley Valley Hospital, Sewickley, Pennsylvania, when she was an administrative resident from Northwestern University at Mount Sinai Hospital.

That there was strong religious motivation in the founding of Mount Sinai Hospital is shown by the way in which the ground-breaking ceremonies were conducted in 1853. Invitations went to the

President, Trustees, and Hazanim (Cantors) of the several Hebrew congregations in the city and vicinity; also the president, directors and other officers of the various Hebrew charitable societies, and to others who were interested. Guests were asked to meet the officers and directors at the synagogue in Crosby Street on November 24 at 2 o'clock. The minutes record that the board and their guests "having formed in procession, proceeded by cars of the Eighth Avenue Railroad at Canal Street to the ground in 28th Street."[7]

Thus it was from a synagogue that the procession began, and the services in laying the cornerstone were performed by rabbis.

Jewish Hospital, Cincinnati, had been established earlier, in 1850. Michael Reese Hospital, Chicago, dates from 1868. The Home for Aged and Infirm Hebrews of New York was founded in 1870, Montefiore Hospital in 1884, and the great procession of Jewish hospitals in the United States was well under way.

AMERICAN PROTESTANT HOSPITAL ASSOCIATION

The Catholic hospitals resisted organization at first because the different orders that operated them feared loss of individuality. Protestant hospitals likewise were too denominationally minded in the early twentieth century to yield readily to the idea of working together through an association. The Interchurch World Movement after World War I impressed a few hospital leaders with the idea that hospitals should move toward unified effort also. They held meetings at the annual conventions of the American Hospital Association in 1919 and 1920. Spearheading the effort to organize was Frank C. English, then superintendent of St. Luke's Hospital, Cleveland, Ohio. An organizational meeting was held in 1921 in West Baden, Indiana, where the American Hospital Association was holding its convention. Some seventy hospital personnel enrolled at this first meeting to form the nucleus for the association.

It was originally intended that this association become a part of the American Hospital Association, but this was impossible because of a clause in its constitution which recognizes only geographical representation. Incorporation of the American Protestant Hospital Association was effected under the laws of the state of Ohio on January 3, 1924.

For 25 years the Protestant association met just prior to and in conjunction with the American Hospital Association convention. This policy was changed in 1951, and it now holds its meetings separately but in conjunction with the various denominational meetings. Figuring prominently in its growth besides Rev. English have been Dr. Albert G. Hahn, the association's executive secretary from 1937 to 1956 and president in 1957; Rev. Herman L. Fritschel, president in 1928; Bryce L. Twitty, president in 1939; Dr. Malcolm T. MacEachern,

[7] Jane Benedict: The Story of Mount Sinai Hospital. *J. Mount Sinai Hosp.*, April, 1942.

president in 1951; and Leo M. Lyons, president in 1952 and executive director since 1956.

The affiliation between the various denominational boards and the American Protestant Hospital Association is based purely on voluntary cooperation. The various denominational hospital conventions meet just prior to and in conjunction with the association. The boards include in their scope such closely affiliated institutions as homes for the aged, children's homes, hostels, as well as hospitals.

The constitution provided for a chaplains' section, the members all to be personal members of the association. The section, now known as the Chaplains' Association, is an autonomous unit, with its own executive secretary, electing its own officers and committees, and conducting its own program. Its secretary is responsible in administrative matters to the executive director of the Protestant Association.

Under the reorganization effected in 1961, the American Protestant Hospital Association operates through four councils—education, church-hospital relations, governmental relations, and association development—each made up of ten members representing the ten regions of the association.

Organizations which met just prior to and concurrently with the association as part of its annual convention in 1963 in Cincinnati were:

American Baptist Convention, Institutional Ministries
Brethren Homes Conference
National Association of Methodist Hospitals and Homes
Division of Health and Welfare Services of the United Church of Christ
The Salvation Army, Conference of Hospitals and Homes
Assembly of Episcopal Hospitals and Chaplains
Lutheran Hospital Association of America
Baptist Hospital Association
Southern Baptist Association of Hospital Chaplains
American Baptist Institutional Ministries
National Presbyterian Health and Welfare Association
Christian Churches—Disciples of Christ
Association of Mennonite Hospitals and Homes
Chaplains' Association of the American Protestant Hospital Association

The practice of holding the denominational meetings with the association began in 1950.

The association limits membership on its board of directors and house of delegates to persons who are active in hospital administration. There are ten delegates at large and 40 members of the house of delegates, 4 from each of 10 regions. Each of the regions is represented by a member on the association's four councils.

Following is a brief resumé of some of the facts about a few of the organizations of church hospitals which are included in the membership of the American Protestant Hospital Association.

The first hospital in America founded under Protestant church auspices was a small one in Pittsburgh started in 1849 by a Lutheran minister, Rev. William A. Passavant. Rev. Passavant on a visit to London to attend a religious conference became interested in hospital service and went to the Continent after the meeting to see hospitals in several cities, including Dusseldorf in Germany, near Kaiserwerth on the Rhine, where Rev. Theodore Fliedner had re-established the order of deaconesses through his training school for nursing and other tasks. At Rev. Passavant's urging, Rev. Fliedner came to the United States with four deaconesses to establish the Order of Protestant Deaconesses. Several hospitals, among them a hospital in Milwaukee and Passavant in Chicago and in Jacksonville, Illinois, owe their origin to Rev. William Passavant and his deaconesses.

During the Civil War the deaconesses were among the first nurses in the country to be called to serve in camps and hospitals. Rev. Passavant served as a chaplain and helped to organize hospital facilities for the wounded.

Because they took in victims of cholera and other contagious diseases, the Passavant hospitals were fought by their neighbors, even to the extent of legislative action, stoning, and arson. It was feared that the hospitals would spread contagion. The Pittsburgh hospital had to be moved for a while to a schoolhouse in the country.

Literally starting his hospitals on a shoestring, Rev. Passavant spent a large part of his life raising funds for them and for the 34 charitable educational institutions he established along with several homes for orphans and handicapped persons. He collected more than one million dollars for his institutions before he died in 1894.

Some 120 hospitals are operated by the Lutheran denomination and its branches in the United States. One of the unusual projects is a group method for helping small hospitals in relatively isolated communities, known as the Great Plains Lutheran Hospitals, which includes hospitals in Kansas and Nebraska. A similar branch plan in Wyoming is operated by the Lutheran Hospitals and Homes Society, Fargo, North Dakota.

The oldest Baptist hospital in the world is Missouri Baptist Hospital, St. Louis, Missouri, which was founded in 1884. This 525-bed hospital, including its special unit for the chronically ill opened in 1959, began with one patient in a doctor's home.

Some fifty hospitals are under Baptist auspices, all but five or six of them in the South.

Although the impetus for the establishing of Presbyterian Hospital, Chicago, now Presbyterian–St. Luke's, came from Rush Medical College in 1879 and the building had begun, a group of Presbyterian laymen were asked to form a corporation to manage it and the site and building were turned over to the hospital corporation. The largest and oldest Presbyterian hospital is the 1,500-bed Presbyterian Hospital in the City of New York, established in 1868. The church has been quite active in establishing mission hospitals in the Southwest.

Altogether it maintains or assists some 50 hospitals and 80 dispensaries in the United States and 17 in other countries. There are also 18 hospitals which are self-supporting.[8]

Each diocese of the Episcopal Church has its own bishop and has responsibility for its own institutions. Funds are solicited and are included in the budgets of the churches in the diocese. Many of the nearly 100 hospitals in this denomination are specialized, some of them for children, others for the chronically ill, like St. Barnabas, New York, established in 1866.

The Seventh Day Adventist denomination credits Dr. John Harvey Kellogg (1852–1943), of the famous Battle Creek Sanitarium, with much of the responsibility for rational development of Adventist medical work. He became in 1876 physician-in-chief of the denomination's first hospital, which had been founded in 1866, only three years after the Adventists were organized (although the movement had begun in 1818). The original name of the Battle Creek Sanitarium was the Western Health Reform Institute. Dr. Kellogg headed the sanitarium for 67 years, and his brother, W. K. Kellogg, was business manager for 25 years beginning in 1879.[9]

Some 200 hospitals, clinics, and dispensaries are now owned and operated in more than 70 countries. The individual hospitals are autonomous. Two of the hospitals, White Memorial in Los Angeles and Loma Linda Sanitarium and Hospital, are connected with the Seventh Day Adventists' educational institution, Loma Linda University, whose medical school was formerly named the College of Medical Evangelists.

The Salvation Army owns and operates in the United States and Canada some 30 hospitals and several infirmaries. The earliest hospitals are those in Boston and in Cleveland, which were established in 1892.

The hospital movement of the Methodist Episcopal Church began in 1881 in New York City with a gift of $410,000 from a Methodist layman, George I. Seney, who had been inspired by an editorial in the *Christian Advocate* in which the failure of the church to establish hospitals other than in missionary fields was deplored. The hospital was opened in 1887. Christ Hospital, Cincinnati, and Wesley Memorial Hospital, Chicago, were established the following year. The Methodist Hospital of Philadelphia dedicated its first building in 1892. Bethany Hospital and Deaconess Home, Brooklyn, New York, was established in 1893 by the East German Conference and became the first hospital under the German Methodist Episcopal Church. Bethesda Hospital, Cincinnati, was organized in 1898 under the central German conference.

Most of the hospitals now under the supervision of the Methodist Church were started separately and attached to the church later. For example, Warren A. Candler Hospital, Savannah, Georgia, was established in 1808 as a private

[8] John S. Glass: Presbyterian Hospitals in the U.S.A. *Hosp. Forum*, July, 1961, pp. 25–26.
[9] See *W. K. Kellogg, A Biography*, by Horace B. Powell, Prentice-Hall, Inc., Englewood Cliffs, N.J., 1956, pp. 21, 46, 48, 52–68; and "The Seventh Day Adventist Hospitals" by Irwin J. Remboldt, *Hosp. Forum*, March, 1962, pp. 17–26.

institution and later operated by the city before it was acquired by the North Georgia conference of the Methodist Church in the South in 1830 and organized as a Methodist hospital. White Cross Hospital, formerly the Protestant Hospital of the South, now Riverside Methodist Hospital, was founded in 1892 and adopted after its founding by the Ohio Conference of the Methodist Church.

The largest Methodist hospital, the Methodist Hospital of Indianapolis, was founded in 1908. Barnes Hospital, St. Louis, opened in 1914 with a million-dollar plant and a million-dollar endowment, its financial support having originated in 1892 with the bequest of one million dollars by Robert A. Barnes to Southern Methodists to establish a hospital.

Related to the Board of Hospitals and Homes of the Methodist Church are 77 hospitals, 113 homes and facilities for older persons, and 46 agencies for children.[10]

CHAPLAINCY SERVICE IN INSTITUTIONS

Formal chaplaincy service in Protestant hospitals has grown rapidly in the past few years. Surveys conducted by the Chaplains' Association, or in its behalf, showed 18 full-time chaplains serving in member hospitals of the American Protestant Hospital Association in 1931. In 1945 there were 38. In 1962 there were 412. The Chaplains' Association has an accreditation program under which 285 of the 412 members have been approved. The American Hospital Association has issued a *Model Guide for a Hospital Chaplaincy Program.*

Accreditation is limited to chaplains who have theological degrees, are ordained by the church to which they belong, have ministered at least three years in a pastorate, and have had a minimum of six months of full-time clinical training in a hospital under an accredited supervisor.

The chaplain is usually an employee of the hospital.

The father of clinical pastoral training is generally conceded to have been Rev. Anton T. Boisen who, as hospital chaplain at Worcester (Massachusetts) State Hospital, accepted in 1925 three theological students to receive training under his guidance. Physicians and psychiatrists participated in the instruction. With Dr. Richard Cabot, he and one of his former students, A. Philip Guiles, initiated in 1930 the incorporation of the Council for Clinical Training, of which Dr. Cabot became the first president.

In 1929 a young clergyman, Russell L. Dicks, had a lengthy personal experience with hospitalization which led him to see the need for pastoral care along with medical. He associated himself two years later with the Council for the Clinical Training of Theological Students and later went to Worcester State Hospital to study the needs of mental patients. Dr. Cabot became interested in him and invited him to Massachusetts General Hospital as chaplain, paying his

[10] *Hospitals and Homes of The Methodist Church.* Evanston, Illinois, Board of Hospitals and Homes of the Methodist Church, 1962.

salary himself for four and a half years and later endowing the position. Dr. Cabot, impressed with his methods, asked his collaboration on a book which was completed in 1936 under the title, *The Art of Ministering to the Sick*. This book was widely acclaimed and won many recruits to chaplain service. At this time few hospitals had chaplains, except Church-controlled institutions such as Roman Catholic, Lutheran, and Episcopalian. Most of the incumbents were retired ministers, and the ministry was mostly for the dying.

For three years from 1938 to 1941 Rev. Russell Dicks was chaplain of the Presbyterian Hospital, Chicago, whose superintendent, Asa Bacon, was a leader in the American Protestant Hospital Association. Bacon was responsible for his giving an address, "The Work of the Chaplain in a General Hospital," at the 1939 meeting of the association in Toronto, which was enthusiastically received. Rev. Dicks was then asked to help in the formulation of standards; these were adopted in 1940. He was also given teaching appointments in four theological seminaries in Chicago. In 1941 he accepted a call to teach at what was then known as the Southern Methodist University School of Theology and to become associate minister in a Dallas, Texas, church. With others, when the war came, he was asked by the Commission on Religion and Health of the Federal Council to conduct seminars for chaplains in the armed forces, for Y.M.C.A. and U.S.O. workers, and for other clergy.

In 1944 Rev. Dicks returned to Chicago, and for four years was chaplain of Wesley Memorial Hospital, conducted classes in clinical training at the hospital, and taught in several theological seminaries, also writing a couple of books and a manual. In 1946 he was elected first chairman of the Chaplains' Section of the American Protestant Hospital Association, which he and others had helped to organize. In 1948 he went to Durham, North Carolina, to accept an appointment as professor of pastoral work at the Divinity School of Duke University and, later, as chaplain of Duke University Hospital. Several other universities have followed his lead in establishing clinical training in conjunction with hospitals.

A number of others have done pioneer work in establishing the essential educational and training programs for the chaplaincy.[11] Along with many of the new programs, as well as separately, short courses have developed for the general clergy in connection with their ministry to the sick in hospitals and homes.

The doctors have been responsible for the progress in this field also, as Dr. Cabot's part in the beginning establishes. Rev. Carl J. Scherzer illustrates this by telling of a physician's referral of a patient to the young minister of a rural church in North Carolina, saying, "I have done what a doctor can do for you. You should call the preacher. He can help you." Later the same doctor said to the same minister, "We are entering upon a whole new understanding of the nature of disease. I believe this will draw the minister closer to the work of the

[11] See the chapter, "Chaplaincy Programs in Hospitals" in *The Church and Healing* by Carl J. Scherzer, *op. cit.*, pp. 229–48.

doctor. You train yourself for this." The minister followed his advice. He was Wayne E. Oates, who by 1946 was offering at Kentucky Baptist Hospital, Louisville, a ten-week course in clinical pastoral training and by 1948 was assistant professor of psychology of religion and pastoral care at Southern Baptist Seminary.[12]

Many physicians, however, opposed Richard K. Young when he established the School of Pastoral Care at North Carolina Baptist Hospital, Winston-Salem, in 1946, but "there hostility has given place to an understanding of the worth of the program." He states that he finds it interesting that the move toward cooperation comes more enthusiastically now from leaders in the medical field than from those in the religious field. He states, "By inviting clergymen to join physicians in their total approach to the total person, medical science is affording the church its greatest opportunity since Christ commanded His disciples to 'preach the gospel and heal the sick.' "[13]

Plans for a national program of cooperation between physicians and clergymen were made at a meeting of the advisory committee to the American Medical Association's Department of Religion in November, 1961, in Chicago. The program is at the county medical society level, stressing counseling, the role of faith in treatment, special problems of terminal illness, and information on the moral codes of ethics of the various faiths. The director of the department said at the meeting:

> Medicine recognizes that it represents all faiths within its profession and therefore has the common ground to invite the clergy of all faiths to participate in such a program. Medicine can and wants to take leadership in bringing the two professions together to discuss this vital, challenging opportunity for better health for America.

Among the subjects discussed were:

Encouraging more physicians to participate in overseas medical missions
Augmenting medical school and nursing school training to include medically significant information on the various religious faiths, including dietary laws, extreme unction, and canons on blood transfusions
Augmenting theological training to provide clergymen with an understanding of the degrees of illness
Developing methods in which pastoral clinical training centers can inform the medical profession of the specific qualifications of various clergymen in dealing with various illnesses
Establishing qualification and standardization codes for hospital chaplains
Cooperation with the A.M.A.'s Council on Mental Health

The meeting was attended by clergymen of the major faiths and by physicians representing the various areas of medical practice.[14]

---

[12] *Ibid.*, pp. 242–43.
[13] From *A.M.A. News*, August 20, 1962.
[14] *Ibid.*

Hospitals and Church-State Relations

After having read Bishop William T. Watkins' address, "Church and State Relations," delivered at a meeting of the National Association of Methodist Hospitals and Homes, of which he was president, in Columbus, Ohio, on February 17, 1960, nobody could presume to discuss the subject when the text of his message is available for reproduction. The text was provided in a news release at the meeting and was widely distributed by mail. Bishop Watkins is from Louisville, Kentucky.

Church and State Relations

BISHOP WILLIAM T. WATKINS

Shall the Methodist Church continue to accept federal aid for the construction or expansion of its hospitals? Does such aid violate the American doctrine of the separation of church and state?

Let it be noted at once that this is a controversial matter. Men of equal intelligence and devotion to the Methodist Church differ about the matter. This statement, therefore, aims to avoid a dogmatic tone that might be offensive to those who differ from it, but intends within these bounds to argue for the continued acceptance of such funds.

The question is not new but has been an issue, explicit or implicit, for at least sixteen centuries. From the Edict of Constantine in A.D. 311 to the Hill-Burton Act, some kind of official position has been necessary. Within this sweep of history, three viewpoints or doctrines have been developed, and it may be pointed out that these positions seem to be exhaustive; that is, there does not seem to be a possible fourth viewpoint, though various modifications and combinations of these three are possible.

The oldest viewpoint is the Roman doctrine of the superiority of the church over the state. This viewpoint came to its summit of expression under Innocent III in the early thirteenth century. Innocent made and unmade kings. The Vatican ruled the then known world, and Innocent III has been named by some historians as the most powerful ruler in all history.

The opposite view is Erastianism, which doctrine was developed during the Protestant Reformation and took its name from its chief promulgator, Erastus. In the beginning Luther subscribed to this doctrine which held that the princes in power had the right and the duty to reform the church. Luther's position at times was desperate and whatever you may think of the doctrine, without the aid of the secular powers, Luther would have failed and the Reformation would have been abortive. England is the best contemporary example of Erastianism. While it is a very mild Erastianism, in England the Crown, and not the Archbishop of Canterbury, is the head of the church. Not a line of the prayerbook can be changed without the approval of Parliament. Only the well-known common sense of the Englishman has made the theory workable. While technically the state is superior to the church, at the level of practice each stays out of the way of the other.

The third theory of the relation of church and state is the American doctrine of the separation of these powers, neither infringing on the rights of the other. The author of this doctrine was Roger Williams, who had felt the heavy hand of the state in the sphere of religion and had been banished from the colony of Massachusetts for his religious views. He established the colony of Rhode Island, proclaimed the doctrine of separation of church and state, and guaranteed religious liberty in this colony. It has been said that Williams should be honored as a discoverer of first principles along with Copernicus, Newton, and Kepler.

Something more than a century later this doctrine was written into the American Constitution and is now known around the world as the American doctrine of the separation of church and state. However, the statement in the Constitution is very brief and very limited. It simply states: "Congress shall make no law respecting an establishment of religion, or prohibiting the free exercise thereof . . ." It should be noted that this restriction is laid solely on Congress. It does not apply to the states. Any state that so wished might have an established state church, and several states continued the state church for a period. The last state to abolish the state church was Connecticut, which continued the established state church for more than forty years after the adoption of the Constitution. No state now has an established state church, but that is solely by act of the state itself, and there is nothing in the legal situation to prevent any state from changing its own constitution and establishing a state church if it so wishes. This fact is often overlooked in the discussion of this subject.

There has been a strong tendency in popular thinking to overlook the religious matters which the Constitution does not prohibit. Thomas Jefferson, in one of his state papers, used the phrase "a wall of separation between church and state." Legal minds have pointed out that this phrase from Jefferson has influenced popular thinking more than the language of the Constitution itself. Of all possible religious acts, and they are many, only one religious act is denied to Congress by the Constitution. Congress may not engage in any act which looks toward establishing a state church. That and that alone is prohibited.

The constitution does not erect "a wall of separation between church and state." The federal government may and does inscribe "In God We Trust" on the silver dollar, offers prayers in the House and in the Senate, provides chaplains for all branches of the armed services, and by act of Congress has made Thanksgiving a legal holiday. These illustrations alone are enough to destroy the figment of an absolute separation between church and state.

When these things are considered, it may be affirmed that the American people simply do not wish an absolute separation of church and state, and it may be doubted that even the advocates of such separation wish it to be made absolute. Suppose for illustration that the Supreme Court should declare the Hill-Burton Act unconstitutional. This would mean that the Supreme Court has struck off in a certain direction, and as later cases are brought before it, the court will have to follow that road to its end. This would mean taking "In God We Trust" off the dollar, the elimination of prayer in the House and the Senate, the abolishing of the chaplaincy in the armed services, the rewording of the Declaration of Independence to avoid any reference to deity, outlawing the use of the Bible in administering oaths of office, canceling Thanksgiving as a national holiday, a return of the postmen to delivering mail on Christmas day, and doubtless a number of other undesirable things.

Since the states have always followed the federal lead in matters of this kind, it is to be assumed that in time reference to the Bible or the name of God would be forbidden in the public schools, all tax exemptions of church property, which are after all a form of contribution, would be canceled, all laws protecting the Sabbath would be repealed, and all exemptions from taxation of church-owned institutions such as hospitals, homes, and schools would be set aside. All of these matters, state and federal, hang together, and the elimination of one means ultimately the elimination of all. It is doubtful that more than a mere splinter group in the population wishes all these things abolished.

As long as the federal government does not favor one group above another, but treats all alike who qualify, it is difficult to see even a remote sense in which the Hill-Burton Act violates the principle of the separation of church and state. Does anyone seriously think that a federal appropriation of funds to help build a Methodist hospital is looking toward the establishment of The Methodist Church as the state church of the United States?

Actually, the election of a Methodist minister as chaplain of the Senate is much closer to a violation of this principle than is the mere appropriation of funds, for in the latter case The Methodist Church is only one of several denominations receiving such aid, whereas in the former case only one denomination can be so favored at a given time. However, since this post of honor is filled from time to time by ministers of different denominations even this has no tinge of favoritism in it. In fact, none of the examples cited above as religious acts of the federal government creates any danger whatever that Congress is about to set up a state religion, and so long as this is true no one of them violates the Constitution.

It appears, therefore, that the Hill-Burton Act does not violate the American principle of the separation of church and state. Moreover, none of the fifty state constitutions prohibits the acceptance of such funds, nor have the legislatures of these fifty states enacted any statutory law that prohibits such. Any thought that the acceptance of such funds would prove to be illegal and unconstitutional if the matter were tested in the courts may be dismissed as an unnecessary concern.

But even if legal and constitutional, is there some moral consideration which would forbid the acceptance of such funds? Moral principles are not vague rules of action. They are clear principles of conduct whether the case be individual or social. Generally speaking, a moral principle is self-evident and self-validating. For example, the moral principle that men ought always to speak the truth requires no explanation. The matter is self-evident and validates itself. Moral principles are like that, and anyone who would make a moral issue of accepting federal funds for hospitals or other institutions must state just what moral principle is violated. Even a casual examination of the matter will reveal that no moral principle is applicable in this connection. It is easy to refer vaguely to moral principles, but to cite specifically what moral law is violated is another matter. Neither the law of Moses nor the ethics of Jesus can be appealed to as condemning the social benefits that accrue to the nation under the Hill-Burton Act.

On the other hand, moral considerations may require that we use federal funds. A moment ago we used the term "moral principles." Actually there is but one moral principle: whatever helps men is good and therefore moral; whatever harms men is evil and therefore immoral. This one supreme moral principle may require that we use federal funds for the common good. A case in point would be the Methodist Evangelical Hospital in Louisville. This structure should be ready for occupancy in the late summer. It is a 320-bed six-story building with the most modern appointments throughout. For more than ten years the Louisville Conference has struggled toward this objective. The need for it is great. Louisville has an inadequate number of hospital beds. There is a waiting list in all hospitals. There are instances of death before hospitalization could be secured. Without federal aid this hospital could not have been built. Ten years of effort proved that beyond question.

Those who have scruples about the use of federal funds must face this question: which is the greater evil, to refuse federal aid and thereby have no hospital to relieve a desperate situation or to accept federal aid, thereby relieving suffering men and women, but sacrificing your scruples? This, of course, must be answered by the individual for himself, but for your speaker there can be but one answer. Moral demand requires that we relieve suffering humanity.

If then the use of federal funds is both legal and moral, there remains the question: Is the use of federal aid wise? There is some sort of popular belief that when the government gives aid to a hospital it lays down a number of conditions that must be met and that it retains some kind of control over the institution it aids. Actually, the government requires but two basic things: First, the plant must be built to conform to Class A hospital construction. The government will not aid a second-class structure. Second, if the structure ceases to be used as a hospital, the government will seek to recover the amount it has invested. This is thoroughly reasonable. The National Division of our Board of Missions requires this of churches aided by its funds. So far as ownership, management, and policy making are concerned, the government is completely hands off. Any hospital receiving federal aid remains a completely autonomous institution.

Of course, there are good citizens and good church members who are simply opposed to the welfare state as such. Under our democratic standards this is any man's privilege. Such a person would naturally be opposed to the Hill-Burton plan of aid. If such a person will carefully analyze his thinking, however, it is believed that he will find that what he opposes is the Hill-Burton Act itself rather than opposing a particular hospital receiving this aid. In other words, his fight should be in Washington rather than opposing the building of a local hospital with federal aid. In still other words, it is not inconsistent for a man to be opposed to the Hill-Burton Act and yet, since it is law, be in favor of his local hospital receiving such aid. His community pays its part of the taxes. Why then should it not receive its part of the benefits so long as this law is in effect?

In conclusion, no valid reason can be seen for refusing this form of aid to suffering humanity. The welfare state is here to stay. Neither major party dares to oppose it. It has now passed through two different administrations without serious modification. It apparently has the approval of the American people, regardless of party lines.

Special Religious Considerations

The hospital administrator needs to be aware of differences in religious beliefs and customs that affect care of patients. Guides are obtainable to help.[15]

The attitude of the various religious groups toward autopsy is important to know. The subject was clearly presented in an article, "The Dead Teacheth the Living," by Dr. Samuel A. Levinson.[16] Quoting several authorities he concludes that in neither the Roman Catholic nor the Jewish religions are there any fundamental objections and that in general the Protestant sects are likewise not opposed when good reasons are presented for the procedure. Personal prejudice rather than doctrine accounts for most of the objections.

---

[15] Such as *Routine Spiritual Care Procedures for Laymen, Doctors, Nurses,* by Gerald H. Fitz-Gibbon, S.J., published by the Catholic Hospital Association of the United States and Canada, St. Louis, in 1950.

[16] *Hospitals,* August 16, 1961.

Part five

THE EDUCATIONAL, RESEARCH, AND COMMUNICATIONS ENVIRONMENT

CHAPTER 17

Emphasis on Research and Education

> At some point following exhaustive laboratory and animal studies, every new drug must be clinically evaluated in human beings. Hospitals, because of their very nature, provide the logical place for such clinical trials. . . . The use of investigational drugs in hospitals places heavy responsibility not only on the investigator but on the hospital administrator, nurses, pharmacists and others concerned with patient safety.
> GROVER BOWLES, JR.[1]

MANY AND varied are the obligations and opportunities for conducting research in hospitals, research that is coordinated with that being carried on in the wide range of fields that constitute the external environment of the hospital. In medical schools, in scientific laboratories, in industry, in numerous social, economic, educational and governmental agencies, research activities flourish that have significant impact upon hospitals. To a degree undreamed of in past epochs, the latter half of the twentieth century is keyed in every aspect of its life to research.

Pharmaceutical research has been selected for particular emphasis in this chapter, not because it is any more important than several other kinds of research, but because it seems so specific, so direct in its possibilities, and dangers, of application to patient care. Also, it is such an outstanding example of the necessity for and potentialities of coordination of effort by basic scientists, medical scientists, medical schools, government, industry, doctors, and hospitals

[1] Patient Safety Comes First in Drug Trials. *Mod. Hosp.,* November, 1962, pp. 132, 134.

that it gives exceptional opportunity for study of the current "emphasis on research" in all fields and a supplement to the many references in this book to research, especially the discussion of medical research in Chapter 8.

The remainder of the first part of this chapter is contributed by Arthur J. Glazebrook, M.D. It is adapted from parts of his thesis submitted to Northwestern University in 1961, other parts of which were used in Chapter 4 in the section on pharmacy.

As an introduction to Dr. Glazebrook's discussion, the following quotation seems apt:[2]

> Every discovery is building upon foundations laid by others. . . . Innumerable discoverers who might have achieved fame remain unknown. Perhaps the time was not ripe for their discovery. Acceptance came only when the climate of opinion was favorable. There have been other discoverers who did not grasp the significance of their own work, and it was left to others to explain and to apply at some later date. . . . When we praise famous men, let us also think of the unknown pioneers who "have no memorial, who are perished as though they had never been." In any case, discoveries are merely the peaks in the chart of progress, made possible by the spade work of many obscure and forgotten researchers. . . .
>
> The essential basis or starting point to the solution of every problem is a theory or premise, an assumption, a hypothesis—call it what you will. A hypothesis is to science what inspiration is to art. . . . The investigator begins his work after having formulated his hypothesis, which of course is only a scaffolding or framework, to be altered or even discarded as the work of construction proceeds.
>
> All the experiments are designed to confirm or to refute the hypothesis. There should be no hesitation to alter the plan, if the hypothesis is no longer serviceable. As Huxley said, "the tragedy of all enquiry is that a beautiful hypothesis may be slain by an ugly fact." Nevertheless, the observer notes what he sees, not what he expects to see, or what he would like to see. The unusual and the unexpected may be of great importance.
>
> The result of an investigation may be the discovery of an error in the accepted knowledge. This may be quite as valuable as a new discovery. Lister once wrote: "Next to the promulgation of truth, the best thing a man can do is the recantation of error."

THERAPEUTICS RESEARCH IN DRUGS

ARTHUR J. GLAZEBROOK, M.D.

Organization of Pharmaceutical Research and Production

Basic research is exploration for new knowledge which may or may not be directly useful. The effects of drugs elude direct observation and can be disclosed only through experience. We are bound to ask how ancient man came to select substances which even today are employed therapeutically on a vast scale. Was it "instinct," either of man or of the animals he watched, that led

---

[2] D. Guthrie, M.D., F.R.C.S.: The Way of the Investigator; published originally in the March, 1956, issue of the *Irish J. Med. Sc.*, reprinted in the August 4, 1956, issue of the *J. A. M. A.*, and reprinted again in the January, 1957, issue of American Hospital Association's *Trustee*.

to their discovery? Or was some reasoning process used, based perhaps on a false premise?

Alexander Tschirch relegates any attempt at explanation along these lines to the realm of fable. However, one possible clue was given by Oliver Wendell Holmes when he wrote: "Opium, which the Creator Himself seems to prescribe, for we often see the scarlet poppy growing in the cornfields as if it were foreseen that wherever there is hunger to be fed, there must also be pain to be soothed."

Maclagan[3] spelled out the implications of Holmes' feeling in 1874 when he described the "hunch" that led him to the use of salicin:

> In connection with the action of quinine on the various forms of intermittent fever and remittent fever, one fact had strongly impressed me—that the maladies on whose course they exercise the most beneficial action are most prevalent in those countries in which the Cinchonaceae grow most readily—nature seeming to produce the remedy under climate conditions similar to those which give rise to the disease. Impressed with this fact, and believing in the miasmatic origin of rheumatism, it seems to me that a remedy for that disease is most hopefully to be looked for among those plants and trees whose favorite habitat presented conditions analogous to those under which the rheumatic miasma seemed most to prevail. A low-lying, damp locality, with a cold, rather than warm climate, are the conditions under which rheumatism is more likely to prevail.

Thus Maclagan was led to use a principle, salicin, derived from willow bark—but the value of a decoction of willow bark as a remedy for painful joints had been recognized by the Hottentots for hundred of years, the secret having been passed down from generation to generation of tribal doctors.

It seems likely, then, that ancient man discovered valuable drugs by a screening process. He took anything handy, and was just as prone to prescribe camel dung, decoction of snakes, or powdered rhinoceros horn, as he was to give quinine, salicin, or opium. As the centuries passed, the value of the latter substances emerged because of experience, while the former became discredited.

Today the development of new products is the lifeblood of the industry, yet the costs and risks are immense. The huge market for influenza vaccine in 1957 eventually disappeared because of some uncontrollable and little-understood change in the life cycle of the virus. Expenses may be assigned to a program which eventually produces a different asset from that for which they were appropriated. A drug house may be faced with the invention of a new substance, with its indications unexplored and its potentialities quite unknown. Iproniazid, introduced for the treatment of tuberculosis, came to be employed in psychiatric illness, and was finally withdrawn because of toxic effects which did not become apparent until it had been used for five years. Market research, which attempts to predict the sales volume of new drugs, may produce erroneous figures, and a drug estimated to gross $30 million a year in sales may, in fact, gross only $1.5 million.

[3] J. Maclagan: *Rheumatism*. London, Pickering and Company, 1881.

The "screening" process has now become a formidable undertaking. Thirty-four million organisms per teaspoon of 100,000 samples of soil from all over the world were "screened" before Pfizer's discovered Terramycin. The subtle complexities are illustrated by the antifungal agent, griseofulvin. This substance occurs in penicillin cultures, but remained unknown for two decades because no one thought to test penicillin broth for antifungal activity.

In the nineteenth century every attempt was made to improve the few active drugs. They were "powdered, sifted, granulated, desiccated, percolated, macerated, distilled, sublimed, comminuted, dissolved, precipitated, filtered, strained, expressed, clarified, crystallized, ignited, fused, calcined, tomefied, and deflagrated into pills, powders, wafers, capsules, ampules, extracts, tinctures, infusions, decoctions, syrups, cordials, essences, magmas, suppositories, tablets, troches, ointments, plasters, abstracts, liniments, collodions, cataplasmas." Dr. Upjohn virtually founded the Upjohn Company on his "friable pill," as some of the competitive pills of the day became so hard with age that they could be hammered into a board without cracking their coating.

This manipulation of drugs by simple physical processes foreshadowed the "molecule manipulation" of modern research. Paul Ehrlich, an assistant of Robert Koch, was the pathfinder and coined the word "chemotherapy." Observing that certain dyes stain bacteria more readily than the tissues they infect, he argued that compounds could be found which would kill organisms and spare the host's tissues. After 606 experiments he developed the compound Salvarsan for the treatment of syphilis. For the first time a man-made compound had cured disease, and Ehrlich had transformed the art of drug making into a science. He got his financial backing from the chemical firm of Leopold Cassella and Company of Frankfurt, and in return the firm received the patent rights to Salvarsan. This transaction established something of a pattern for the industry.

"Molecule manipulation" is now an established tool of pharmaceutical research, but it has become infinitely more complex. It has taken years of patient effort and the collaboration of scientists in two countries (Britain and the United States) to "manipulate" the penicillin molecule and make it active against staphylococci resistant to the ordinary penicillins.

While "screening" and "molecule manipulation" account for much of the approach to basic research, a chance observation may be crucial. Such was that of Alexander Fleming when a mold from the air accidentally dropped into one of his culture plates of staphylococci. He noticed that the organisms around the mold died off, and in 1929 he named the active substance from the mold "penicillin." The pressures of World War II and the resources of the American chemical and pharmaceutical industry were required before Fleming's discovery could be applied to the healing of the sick.

Another way to get started on basic research is provided by physicians and biologists, who ferret out the fundamental nature of the disease and point the way to its chemical cure. Dr. Addison connected the fatal disease, now termed "Addison's disease," with destruction of the suprarenal capsules a little more than a century ago. Four decades later it was shown that the capsules were in fact glands, and after another decade, zoologists studying fish showed that the glands contained two parts, of which only the cortex is essential to life. Between 1929 and 1931 three teams of workers, one associated with Parke Davis and Company, succeeded in preparing adrenal cortex extracts which could maintain life in adrenalectomized animals, and the scientific treatment of Addison's disease became possible.

Glazebrook and Cummings[4] in 1943 showed that a disturbance of blood copper existed in Wilson's disease, and this led to the employment of chelating agents to correct it.

A much more important and dramatic event was the discovery of insulin. That pancreatectomy produces diabetes was known because of the work done by Mering and Menkowski at the turn of the century, and in 1921 Dr. Frederick Banting and a medical student, Charles Best, in Toronto, set out to find an extract from the pancreas that would cure diabetes. They succeeded on November 19 of that year. However, serious problems of stability, purity, and cost had to be solved. Eli Lilly and Company set 100 workers to attack the difficulties, and by the spring of 1923 insulin was obtainable in quantities. One of those whose life was saved by the new preparation was Dr. G. R. Minot, of Boston. He more than paid his debt by discovering that liver extracts cured people with pernicious anemia.

Besides basic research, two other activities have to be included in the departmental organization:

1. Applied research. Existing knowledge is applied to the creation of a new drug.

2. Product improvement. Existing knowledge is applied to improving a drug or process or evaluating new uses for it.

Since by definition, basic research may not produce anything of value for a drug house, some adopt policies which encourage it, e.g., staff scientists may be permitted to spend 10 to 20 per cent of their workweek on projects of their own choosing. In order to support the activities mentioned and at the same time to safeguard against a disastrous loss in one particular field, there is an increasing tendency toward diversification of products and of interests.

A good library is a necessity, for much is based upon past investigations. The patent division is of vital importance, for the filing of a valid patent on a drug or a process, sound enough to prevent imitation, must be done as soon as possible. Few realize that in the United States, the patent system has played a tremendous part in encouraging initiative. It guarantees the holder of a patent on a good drug a reasonable return for his investment; countries without

[4] A. J. Glazebrook and W. Cummings: Wilson's Disease. *Edinburgh Med. J.*, February, 1945.

enlightened patent laws fail to progress. One of the unfortunate results of the recent Kefauver inquiry is the proposal to cut the tenure of patent rights from 17 years to 3 years in the case of drugs.

The clinical research division sees to it that adequate evaluations are carried out by physicians. These must be done in such a way that patients are not deprived of adequate therapy or exposed to risks. Because of this it is usually conducted in three phases:

Phase 1. The drug is entrusted to a small circle of carefully selected investigators in medical schools and teaching hospitals.

Phase 2. The drug, with known activities and hazards brought out by Phase 1, is entrusted to a larger group of physicians, including a sizable number in private practice.

Phase 3. The drug, now on sale as a result of passing Phases 1 and 2, is evaluated by physicians for as long as interest can be maintained. This may result in learning new uses for the drug or in the discovery of unexpected difficulties with it. Also, Phase 3 serves to provide the detail man with continuous support for his promotional efforts.

At the end of Phase 2 all of the data is assembled for submission to the Food and Drug Administration in Washington. If the administration is satisfied as to the safety of the product, the submission is made effective, and the drug may be put on the market. Safety is a relative term. In benign illnesses it is of prime importance; in fatal diseases, a risk of some toxicity is allowable. The establishment of the efficacy of the drug has not been required in the past, but new regulations seem likely to be imposed which will demand proof of this. Submission to the F.D.A. may be made by the Clinical Research Group or, in some firms, by a new products division.

Despite the tests and complexities, and the competition from many small drug houses which can cut costs because they do no research, the major drug firms spend an ever-increasing proportion of their resources on the search for new drugs.

> The pharmaceutical industry is as highly competitive as any that can be named. This industry is very much aware that the physician-patient relationship is such that the physician does not consider the matter of price if there is any choice open to him in selecting prescriptions. All of the evidence is that this severe competition forces the industry to do almost as much research to achieve cheaper production and marketing as it does to develop the new or better product. As soon as one producer of these products is able to market them more cheaply, he will certainly do so, with the object of forcing his higher priced competitors out of the market. This will cause other producers to accelerate efforts to improve their own production and marketing techniques. Further price cuts, with eventual stabilization at a lower level, will be the result. Penicillin, streptomycin, and cortisone have all had price histories that seem to demonstrate the validity of this conclusion.[5]

[5] Editorial. *J. A. M. A.,* June 23, 1956, p. 772.

Besides research, production has to be thought about, and at a fairly early stage in the research the products development division decides on the dosage form, whether tablet or capsule, liquid or ointment, oral or injectable. Questions of color and of taste are sometimes involved, especially in pediatric prescriptions. Then ways to make the pure drug in bulk must be studied in a pilot plant. Here sources of crude material are developed; the cost of operation must be kept at a minimum, with maximum use of by-products; and safety factors must be considered.

The Relief of Pain

A drug which afforded complete relief from pain without other action would be a boon to humanity. Pain has always been the predominating symptom in diseases of man; and the science of analgesia is of great antiquity. References to it are found in all the early schools of medicine, the Chinese in 500 B.C. and afterward in the Persian, Indian, and Greek. Preparations were made from mandrake, hellebore, poppy, hemlock, henbane, mulberry, lettuce, and hops, and while the concoctions were made heroically, they were often useful.

During the dark period of the Middle Ages medicine fell into the hands of the Church, and no advances in analgesia were made—indeed, uncertainties as to the preparation of opium mixtures often led to fatalities. This, coupled with religious objections, caused them to fall into disuse. In the seventeenth century we find Nicholas Bailly, a French barber surgeon, being accused of witchcraft because he prescribed opium, and a law was passed in France banning its use.

In course of time opium came to be recognized as the only potent analgesic, and it retained this place until comparatively recently. Sydenham said that without opium the healing art would cease to exist, and while this is not true today, there can be few doctors who would care to be without it or its derivatives for their practices.

The first real step forward was the isolation by Serturner of morphine in 1806 and the recognition that it was the main analgesic alkaloid in opium. This enabled standardized preparations to be made which could take the place of unreliable tinctures. More confidence could be placed in the prescription of the drug, and its clinical applications were increased.

In 1876 Maclagan investigated extracts of the willow, and he hit upon salicin. The fact that salicylates had analgesic properties was soon seen, and in 1889 aspirin was produced commercially and rapidly became a household analgesic and antipyretic. Further research into aniline derivatives produced many pain-relieving compounds, the two most important groups being those derived from aniline and the closely related phenetidin such as acetanilide and phenacetin, and those derived from pyrazole such as antipyrine and amidopyrine. Aspirin administration has recently been helped by the discovery of a stable soluble calcium salt.

All of these products have an undoubted pain-dulling action, but the extent of it is not to be compared with that obtained by the opiates. In view of their relatively weak analgesic action T. Fourneau in an article in 1938 suggested that they be separated from true analgesics and called antalgics.

Attempts were also made to improve opium and morphine preparations. These took two main lines—the purification of opium to obtain a product with all of its alkaloids intact and the treatment of morphine to make, by part synthesis, closely related compounds.

H. Sahli in 1909 prepared the first compound containing the total opium alkaloids free of gums, resins, and other inert and irritating ingredients. Its main advantage over morphine is that it is less likely to cause smooth muscle spasm. It was the first successful intravenous preparation of opium alkaloids, although Sir Christopher Wren, assisted by Boyle (1656) had injected opium experimentally into the veins of dogs.

Part synthesis from morphine and related alkaloids and separation of the naturally occurring alkaloids in opium led to the production of compounds such as Dionin, heroin, Dilaudid, Dicodid, apomorphine, metopon, and the naturally occurring codeine. These products all vary greatly in analgesic action, toxicity, and power to cause the development of addiction or tolerance. Apomorphine, for instance, is used clinically in 5-mg doses for its emetic effect, its mild analgesic action being valueless, while metopon in doses of 6 to 9 mg has a powerful analgesic action with fewer side effects than morphine.

However, it was Serturner's isolation of morphine which had really set the stage for the fascinating but laborious work of chemical detection which followed. The next step was to establish the chemical structure of morphine. If this could be done it might then be possible to track down that portion of the morphine molecule responsible for its analgesic action and produce a substance with enhanced therapeutic power and diminished side effects.

The structure of morphine proved to be exceedingly complex, but it is generally accepted today that it is an arrangement of five rings in a spatial relationship of three dimensions, and eventually it came to be realized that the rupture of one of these, the piperidine ring, led to an almost complete loss of analgesic power.

In 1938 one of those curious and completely accidental discoveries which occur so frequently in medicine was made and suddenly illuminated the whole field of analgesic research. O. Eisleb and O. Schaumann, while performing toxicity trials on a new spasmolytic drug dolantin (ethyl 4-phenyl-1-methylpiperidine-4-carboxylate) discovered that it caused tail erection in the test animals, a phenomenon described by Straub (1911) as occurring in animals given morphine. This acute observation led directly to the testing and establishment of dolantin (pethidine, Demerol) as an analgesic and the realization that pethidine, in its structure of a 4-phenyl piperidine derivative, constituted a fragment of the morphine molecule.

This discovery of the first true synthetic analgesic led to attempts to modify its simple structure in all possible ways, and some promising analgesics were produced.

It might have been thought that the chapter which had opened with the isolation of morphine was now concluded, from the analgesic activity of certain of the 4-phenyl piperidine derivatives such as pethidine, and the known loss of analgesic potency brought about by the opening of the piperidine ring in morphine, and that the piperidine ring was an essential feature of an analgesic.

Further work, however, in subjecting the morphine molecule to intensive dissection provided the framework of many new compounds, some of which were found to possess analgesic properties. In the diphenylpropylamine class the most potent was found to be the ketone first referred to as Hoechst 10820.[6]

This powerful analgesic, in contrast to pethidine and morphine, does not possess a piperidine ring. It is now produced commercially and known variously as amidon, physeptone, miadone, Dolophine, methadone, etc. A closely related compound is phenadoxone.[7]

Although at first sight the molecule of the diphenylpropylamine derivatives (represented by amidon and phenadoxone) is markedly different from that of the 4-phenyl piperidines (represented by pethidine) and the natural prototype morphine, when an atomic model is made the structural similarity of amidon and pethidine to morphine becomes apparent. Thus F. Bergel and A. L. Morrison[8] have concluded that the shape or fit of the molecule as a whole is more important in determining its analgesic activity than any one duplication of precise fractions of the morphine molecule.

The most undesirable action of the opium derivatives is their tendency to cause addiction. This fact has been kept in mind during the search for better analgesics in the hope that one will be found free from this trait. Addiction may be defined as the insatiable desire for repeated doses of a substance; after a patient has taken a true drug of addiction for some time his cellular metabolism becomes disturbed because of the constant presence of the drug and eventually his tissues come to function well only if the drug is present. The patient is now dependent upon it, his tissues crave it, and the problem is a much greater one than that of simple deprivation of a favorite tipple, for withdrawal symptoms can be very severe and prostrating. Cases have been recorded in which babies have been born drug addicts, their tissues demanding the presence of the drug just as clamorously as those of their drug-addicted mothers.

Certain drugs are better euphorigenics than they are analgesics. *Cannabis indica,* for instance, undoubtedly has a low analgesic activity, but is capable of

[6] B.I.O.S. Final Report 116, 9 24, p. 52, 1945.
[7] W. M. Wilson and R. B. Hunter, *Brit. M. J.,* **11:** 553, 1948.
[8] *Quart. Rev. Chem. Soc.,* **11:** 349, 1948.

producing marked euphoria, and this is also true of the synthetic cannabis preparation synhexyl.[9] Extracts from natural cannabis have been classified with the morphine alkaloids under the Dangerous Drugs Act.

There is a tendency, at first, for all new potent analgesics to be considered nonhabit-forming. Heroin, for instance, produced by acetylation of the morphine molecule, was acclaimed as being free from any such tendency, but soon after its introduction this drug became a favorite of the drug addicts of the world. Codeine, on the other hand, a naturally occurring methyl ether of morphine, is relatively safe, but has lost much of the analgesic power of its parent substance.

Meperidine is euphorigenic and for this reason alone will produce habit formation in susceptible subjects. However, the cellular metabolism is not disturbed to the degree found in morphine addicts. Discussing meperidine addiction, P. Polonio[10] states, "physical dependence on the drug is not great and all authors are agreed on the mildness of the withdrawal syndrome." B-Pethidine,[11] a closely related compound, produces much less euphoria than pethidine, but also has less analgesic activity. Another 4-phenyl piperidine derivative, Nu 896, has very powerful analgesic powers, much more so than pethidine, but it also has marked euphorigenic properties, patients becoming very lively and talkative after its injection.[12]

Amidon undoubtedly produces euphoria, although to a lesser extent than Nu 896. This subjective reaction has been described by former morphine addicts as entirely comparable with that experienced with morphine. Most commonly these addicts describe the effects of amidon as very like those produced by heroin, especially when amidon is given intravenously. There is production of tolerance to all of the morphinelike effects; and withdrawal symptoms, differing from those of morphine in time relationship and intensity, but definite and characteristic, can be produced (Commission on Narcotic Drugs).[13] Phenadoxone has similar euphorigenic properties.

It can be said that despite the intensive research of the past few years no perfect analgesic has been produced entirely free from the dangers of addiction, and where temporary control of pain is needed great caution must be exercised in prescribing these drugs. The universality of pain, and the dangers inherent in the more active compounds, have led to aspirin becoming the most important of all drugs, in terms of quantity. In 1956 a total of 16,603,000 pounds of aspirin were produced, and 12 billion 5-grain tablets were prepared from this.

[9] C. S. Parker and F. Wrigley: *Lancet,* **11:** 223, 1947; and same authors, *J. Mental Sci.,* **96:** 276, 1950.

[10] *Lancet,* **1:** 592, 1947.

[11] A. J. Glazebrook and A. W. Branwood: *Lancet,* **11:** 528, 1945.

[12] A. J. Glazebrook: *Edinburgh M. J.,* **56:** 206, 1949.

[13] British Commission on Narcotic Drugs. Extract from report to the Economic and Social Council, 1948.

Impact of Research in Analgesics on the Hospital

Analgesic drugs have not directly affected the productivity of the hospital, but their continued improvement has caused a profound change in the therapeutic milieu. The agonies of a burned child, the screams of women in the throes of a painful labor, the angor animi of a coronary thrombosis, or the long-drawn-out tortures of death from incurable malignant disease can be greatly alleviated by their use. Pity, suffering, and anxiety have been replaced with optimism, comfort, and hope. These emotional factors are of incalculable value in the treatment of any illness.

In the future we may expect that a nearly perfect analgesic will be found— long-acting, nondepressant to blood pressure or respiration, and nonaddictive. With reference to euphoria, it is not necessarily a bad thing, for it may confer a priceless boon to both a pain-racked, depressed patient and the harassed and anxious attendants, replacing listlessness and apathy with brightness and an urge for conversation. The dangers of addiction may be ignored in the incurable case dying of malignant disease; indeed it is difficult to understand the attitude of those who would deprive such people of the merciful relief to be obtained from potent analgesics on the grounds of habit formation.

As regards the administration of a hospital, the introduction of powerful yet nonaddictive pain killers will ease problems of narcotic and dangerous drug control.

Cancer Research

One of the cruelest ironies in the annals of medical science is the fact that Marie Curie, discoverer of what was to become one of the two known methods by which cancer can be cured, was herself struck down by this disease.

With her husband, Pierre Curie, she isolated the first few particles of radium from pitchblende, to lay the groundwork for the use of radiation in the treatment of malignancies and to establish the role of radioactivity in physiological research.

Her tragic, yet triumphant, story is an illustration that here is a killer that strikes all people, young and old, learned and unlearned, rich and poor. It has claimed the lives of some of our most distinguished citizens: Secretary of State John Foster Dulles in international affairs, Oscar Hammerstein II of the Broadway theater, and baseball's immortal Babe Ruth in sports. The list is long. One of every six deaths in the United States is attributable to cancer.

At present surgery appears to offer the best cure. The development of new techniques, an increased understanding of the body's chemical balance, of replacing blood loss, of preventing shock, and of controlling infection, have added to its effectiveness. Unfortunately, surgery may be extremely mutilating, as in the hindquarter amputation and in treatment of sarcoma of the hip. It may be impossible, because of the close relationship of important structures, as in tumors of the brain. It may fail, although the tumor may be completely excised, because of the escape of cancerous cells from the operation site to distant parts of the body, where they grow and reproduce the tumor. Finally, the tumor may be eradicated by surgery, but a second tumor of a different type, unrelated to the first, may grow somewhere else in the patient.

When the diagnosis can be established early, as in cancer of the cervix uteri, the chances of complete extirpation are good. In fact, it is now stated that a regular screening of all women over 30 by the cervical smear technique, which has been vastly facilitated with fluorescent methods, would reduce the mortality from cervical cancer to nil. On the other hand, where diagnosis is likely to be established at a late stage, as in cancer of the stomach, all of the hazards mentioned are possible, and the five-year cure rate is not much better than 5 per cent.

Radiation treatment is being improved by new instruments, better methods of administration, and a resultant lower incidence of side effects. Fundamentally it suffers from the same drawbacks as does surgery, for it cannot guarantee complete destruction of the tumor; it may harm healthy tissues; and it does not deal with the problem of the tumor-prone individual.

The basic problems of cancer research are the elucidation of the precise nature and cause of the disease and discovery of effective measures of control. How do cancerous cells escape the normal metabolic controls of growth, and how do cancer cells differ from normal cells? To this end, scientists in the physical, chemical, and biological disciplines are intensively probing the details of cell metabolism, growth, reproduction, and nature's intricate controls of these processes. Complete understanding of these fundamental mechanisms of life should lead to effective methods for control, cure, and prevention of cancer.

Hundreds of collaborating scientists are participating in the massive cancer chemotherapy screening program administered by the National Institutes of Health. The Charles Pfizer organization is centered in the John L. Smith Memorial for Cancer Research in Maywood, New Jersey. Many thousands of fermentation broths and synthetic chemicals are being tested for antitumor activity for the first time, using rapid screening methods such as tissue culture techniques and test animals against which the repressive action of compounds may be measured. The Maywood researchers are not seeking modifications of known molecules but brand new compounds which are chemically unique and which may act in beneficial ways utterly different from drugs presently used in chemotherapy of cancer. Compounds being screened are derived from soil microorganisms, plant materials, or are synthesized by organic chemists.

Possibilities of "tailor-making" anticancer drugs by deliberate molecular design have been expanded by elucidation of the structure and functions of deoxyribonucleic acid (DNA), the principal molecular entity of the cell nucleus. The structure proposed by Watson and Crick, of Cambridge University,

England, allows us to picture DNA as a giant molecule built of two chains winding around a common axis in the same direction, a double "spiral stairway" cross-linked by purine and pyrimidine bridges. The precise order of attachment of these bases probably controls the precise reproductive processes of the cell. Alterations of structure by external or internal agents would produce an abnormal DNA molecule—a mutation—which would reproduce daughter molecules repeating the same abnormality. Such molecular alterations of DNA are thought to be the cause of many forms of cancer.

Drugs which modify cell growth have had significant success in cancer chemotherapy. Purine antagonists, particularly useful in treatment of leukemia, interfere with cross-linkage of bases in nucleic acids and inhibit cell growth. Folic acid antagonists, developed after discovery of folic acid itself and elucidation of its structure, deprive cells of an essential vitamin and thereby inhibit growth. These have been of considerable value in treatment of childhood leukemia. Nitrogen mustards and derivatives have also been useful in treatment of leukemia and a few other forms of malignancies. There are many molecular modifications of such compounds in clinical use, but in general each group of compounds acts similarly and has the same limitations. A great need to be fulfilled by research is that of finding compounds, perhaps entirely new ones, which will be unerringly selective of cancer cells without doing harm to normal cells.

Steroids have also been useful in treatment of cancer. Massive doses of synthetic corticosteroids sometimes will induce leukemia remissions. Estrogens curb the growth of prostatic cancer, and androgens have been used in treating mammary cancer. The opposed effects of male and female hormones in breast and prostate cancer underline the fact that cancer is not a single disease entity but one that varies with the tissues affected and with the patient's own intricate biochemistry. Cancer also varies in rate of growth, invasiveness, and many other ways. Human cancer cells do not "take" when transplanted into healthy volunteers, and a new and exciting area of investigation is immunology, now being explored with unprecedented vigor in the United States and other countries by oncologists, virologists, serologists, and related workers. Underlying it is the concept of "infective molecules," such as the nucleic acid of viruses, that may enter and alter the genetic constitution of living cells.

That host resistance factors are involved in the growth of cancer has been recognized by perceptive physicians for years. The often unpredictable course of the disease—varying from dormancy to widespread dissemination—and the phenomenon of spontaneous remissions which can occur even in the wildest growths, obviously suggest the presence of natural defense mechanisms within the host.

Other apparent immunological manifestations are the occurrence of local inflammatory reactions, as in Paget's cancer of the breast, and the frequent occurrence of lymph node hyperplasia, suggestive of a nonspecific defense mechanism.

Thus, when tumors are removed from the original host, they may show amazing proliferative powers, perhaps because they have been released from these defenses. At the Sloan-Kettering Institute, a slowly growing sarcoma of minute size (0.5 gm) was removed from a patient six years ago. Today this tumor, propagated in rats and hamsters, multiplies itself a hundredfold every two weeks.

That some tumors are caused by viruses has been recognized since Ludwig Gross demonstrated a mouse leukemia virus, and autoimmunization has become a dependable procedure in laboratory animals. The most common technique is to implant a tumor into the tail of a rat or a mouse, permit it to grow for a week, and then cut off the tail. This renders the animal immune to further exposure by the same type of tumor.

All this work indicates the possibility of finding a vaccine, or other preventive method, directed against the causal agent, rather than against the tumor cells themselves.

Both surgery and external radiation treatments are crude and perhaps unscientific; their replacement by more refined, accurate, and certain methods, such as specific chemotherapy or immunotherapy, can only be a matter of time.

Impact of Cancer Research on the Hospital

The growth of radiation therapy has involved many a hospital in a complicated and costly program. Usually a radiologist is employed on a full-time basis, for there are few in private practice. He has to be assisted by competent technicians, at least one of whom is likely to be a qualified physicist. The apparatus is bulky and expensive, and personnel must be protected by shielding devices; frequently new construction is necessary to house the cobalt bomb because of the thickness of concrete which is necessary. Hospital administrations feel obliged to get the best equipment possible. They must compete with neighboring hospitals and do not like to have to transfer patients elsewhere because of lack of facilities. However, in some cases the decision to install cobalt equipment, is taken although it may not be in the best interest of the hospital's economic position.

The introduction of successful chemotherapeutic or immunological agents, which seems entirely possible, perhaps within the next decade, would abolish the necessity for separate departments of radiotherapy. The trend seen during recent years of splitting the x-ray department into the two divisions of diagnosis and of treatment would be reversed, with economic gain to the hospital.

A goodly proportion of surgery today is concerned with the extirpation of cancers. The operations performed are not infrequently heroic and entail difficult postoperative care and nursing in intensive-treatment units. A reduction in the number of surgical procedures may occur as cancer comes under chemical or biological control, but the economic benefits to the hospital may not be as significant as in radiotherapy. The operating theaters and staff will still have to be maintained for other types of surgery—indeed, the growth of surgery for congenital and degenerative disease may offset the reduction of load resulting from a falling off in cancer surgery.

Politically, some interesting changes may be visualized. At one time consultant physicians or internists held influential positions, for recourse to a surgeon was a last resort, with a better than 60 per cent chance of dying from the operation. Over the years their power has been weakened by the growing strength of the surgeons, who are now dominant. Supply to the internist of potent anti-cancer agents, which may well demand his special skills for their employment, may restore him again to his former pre-eminent position on hospital staffs.

Psychiatric Care—Research Provokes a Peaceful Revolution

A good many treatments were available for the mentally ill some twenty years ago when the writer (Dr. Glazebrook) first became interested in psychiatry. The views of Freud, Jung, Adler, Kraepelin, and Pavlov held the stage, and psychotherapy of one sort or another, ranging from psychoanalysis to hypnosis, was practiced as it is today. Recourse could be had to electroshock or insulin-shock when psychotherapy failed, while the powerful barbituates were available for the recalcitrant. There was always a strait jacket or padded cell ready for use when nothing else controlled the behavior of the sick patient. These treatments did nothing to solve the fundamental difficulty—the admission of patients to mental hospitals at a rate in excess of discharges.

In 1952, Smith, Kline and French acquired patent rights to a phenothiazine which had been produced by the French chemical house of Rhone-Poulenc. The drug was given the trade name of Thorazine in the United States. Like many drugs, it was produced for one purpose and used for another. Originally tailored to be an antiallergic preparation, it came to be used as a preoperative medication in surgery because of its remarkable sedative powers. However, a side effect of producing a fall in blood pressure was considered dangerous enough to outweigh the other advantages. The research workers at Smith, Kline and French were impressed, not with its antiallergic or preoperative value, but with its capacity to block what might be called neurotic activity in laboratory animals. By 1954, clinical trials had proved its power of calming disturbed mental patients, and it was introduced to the medical profession as a tranquilizer.

While this work was under way, chemists in the pharmaceutical houses of Hoffman-LaRoche, of Squibb, and of Bayer were pursuing a costly development program for the production of antituberculosis agents based on isoniazid. One of these, iproniazid, was found to cause a curious side effect. Depressed patients became active and elated, and since rest was a cardinal principle of the treatment of active phthisis, this side effect was not welcome. However, the drug was given to people with other kinds of chronic physical illness who were depressed, with good results as far as their emotional state was concerned. In 1956, a New York psychiatrist, Dr. N. Kline, used the drug in the mentally ill, purely for its antidepressant properties. The success he obtained led to its wide employment in depressed patients; but unfortunately an outbreak of jaundice associated with iproniazid occurred in 1957, and dosage restrictions were placed on it which severely limited its value. The cardinal action of iproniazid seemed to lie in its power of inhibiting an enzyme concerned with catecholamines and serotonin metabolism, called monoamine oxidase, and that part of the brain most intimately concerned with emotional control has a rich supply of all of these substances. It seemed that a cure of depressive illness, perhaps worse than any other because of the depth of sadness and melancholy it produces, was just around the corner. If iproniazid was too toxic, substances with a similar power of inhibiting monoamine oxidase, but without its dangers, could soon be found. Indeed, after an intensive research, several were marketed by 1960, including niamid, Marplan, nardil, and Monase.

Unfortunately these drugs, although safe as compared with iproniazid, and useful in therapy to a degree, did not fulfill entirely the bright promise of their predecessor. On the other hand, their discovery and application have illumined many paths of further inquiry into the role of catecholamines, serotonin, and related substances in the production of mental diseases.

A drug whose major function in psychiatry has been to uncover biochemical mechanisms, rather than to cure patients, is reserpine. This substance was isolated, by the Ciba Company, from the Indian plant *Rauwolfia serpentina*. Long used in India as a folk medicine, its roots were chewed by Mahatma Ghandi to quiet his nervousness and may well have helped him adhere to his policy of passivity and nonviolence. Reserpine has many side effects, one of them the production of a severe depressive illness in susceptible individuals. Chemically, its administration causes the catecholamines and serotonin to be washed out of the midbrain. Since one of the catecholamines, norepinephrine, is a neurohormone concerned with the transmission of messages from one nerve to another, its loss from the area controlling emotions is of import. There is much evidence that norepinephrine, especially when in excess supply, is concerned with hostility and aggression. Conversely, its lack may lead to a shackling of the will to fight back, so Gandhi's nonaggressive tactics may have been drug-related. As for the value of reserpine in treatment, it will control aggressive, hostile, and paranoid behavior, but generally it is not as useful as Thorazine.

The success of Thorazine led to the production of many competitive phenothiazines. One of these is Sparine, made by Wyeth. The Swiss firm of Geigy developed a product very similar in configuration to Sparine, with the idea of getting into the tranquilizer market. On clinical testing, the drug, which is called Tofranil, was found not to be a tranquilizer but to have antidepressant properties. It is believed to act through norepinephrine, but instead of increasing the amount of this catecholamine, as do the monoamine oxidase inhibitor anti-depressants, it appears to sensitize the nerve ends so that they will respond to subnormal levels of norepinephrine.

What of the future? While the phenothiazines have made the mental patient more manageable and have caused the biggest impact, they are not curative. The new antidepressants, on the other hand, are used to correct a possible bio-chemical imbalance and seem to restore some patients to normal. In addition, they are tools of investigation and therefore a challenge to create something better. We may expect, therefore, that great improvement will take place in the chemotherapy of the affective disorders, and doctors will turn less and less to electric and insulin shock in this area.

A large proportion of the patients in mental hospitals suffer from brain disease due to atherosclerosis. Since cholesterol is associated with atheromatous lesions, control of its metabolism might prevent or even reverse established atherosclerosis, with great benefit to sufferers from degenerative diseases of the brain, heart, or kidneys. Already products which prevent the absorption of cholesterol, aid its transport in the blood stream, or prevent the manufacture of cholesterol by the liver are available. Recently it has been shown that niamid, a monoamine oxidase inhibitor, protects the siliconelike property of the lining of the blood vessels. By its use, sticking of white blood cells or platelets to the vessel's walls, which can be caused by the injection of epinephrine, the smoking of a cigarette, or the taking of a cholesterol-rich meal, can be prevented. This phenomenon may turn out to be crucial. In any case control of atheroma seems likely to be accomplished within the next decade, and this would have an even more profound impact upon mental hospitals than the tranquilizers in terms of admission of people with hitherto progressive and incurable chronic brain syndrome caused by arterial diseases.

Mental Illness: Impact of Recent Research on the Hospital

The impact on the mental hospitals of the use of these drugs, particularly Thorazine, has been profound. In 1955 psychiatric hospitals cared for 54 per cent of the total number of patients hospitalized. But between April, 1955, and April, 1956, following widespread use of tranquilizers, there was a 23 per cent increase in discharges from mental hospitals in New York, and increased discharge rates were also reported from Indiana, Illinois, Ohio, Tennessee, and South Dakota. By 1959, only 40 per cent of all sick patients were hospitalized for mental diseases, as compared with 54 per cent in 1955.

The state hospitals were badly overcrowded in 1955. Since the population is growing, it has been calculated that during the half decade between 1954 and 1959, some $880 million has been saved in new mental hospital construction which would have been necessary were it not for the introduction of the tranquilizers.[14]

[14] Department of Health, Education and Welfare: *Report on Mental Hospitals,* 1959.

In other countries, a similar picture is seen. In Britain, the local mental hospital in one area has been abolished as an experimental procedure, with a view to finding the practicability of treating disturbed patients in general hospitals now that tranquilizers are available. In the United States, more and more general hospitals are opening psychiatric wards for short-term therapy of mental patients.

The most tangible result of the use of tranquilizing agents has been the marked improvement of the environment within the hospital. Physical restraint and seclusion have been reduced. Greater hospital freedom has been granted to patients, and the concept of the "open ward" has been freely applied. In some hospitals 90 per cent of the population is kept in wards which are unlocked during the day, the patients being free to come and go as they will. There is less use of the various shock therapies. Since the patients are more easily managed, the attendants and nurses can spend more time on psychotherapeutic treatments ordered by the doctors, because they are less distracted by behavior problems.

It is impossible to cure by drugs mental diseases due to defects in brain structure, and perhaps the more malignant types of schizophrenia will elude chemotherapy too; but the prevention of atherosclerotic brain disease and the cure of affective disorders seem quite probable. This will cause the present massive and overcrowded state mental institutions to shrink, and the general hospitals will become more important as centers for psychiatric treatment as new advances are made.

A more humane approach to the mentally ill is developing as the possibilities for cure increase. Significant changes in the laws relating to certification and detention will surely follow.

Reduced Death Toll from Infections

In 1850 average life expectancy in the United States was only 38.2 years. The figure had risen to 48.2 years by 1900, primarily because of improvements in sanitation and hygiene which helped to control infectious disease. Wide use of immunizing vaccines, great strides in the science of nutrition, and other advances contributed to a rise in average life span to 59.1 years by 1931. Yet Americans born as late as the early 1920's can recall vividly the frequency with which pneumonia, typhoid, blood poisoning, mastoiditis, peritonitis, tuberculosis, and other infectious diseases caused prolonged illnesses and death. Within a generation, the diminishing incidence of such infections and the infrequency of death from them have greatly reduced fear of infectious diseases in general.

Paul Ehrlich was the first man to use the word "chemotherapy" when he developed Salvarsan for the treatment of syphilis. However, the first major breakthrough in chemotherapy of infectious disease was the discovery in Germany in 1932 of sulfanilamide, the original sulfa drug. Sulfa drugs not only gave physicians new weapons to control dangerous streptococcal and other infections but gave enormous impetus to further research in chemotherapy. The antibiotic era began in 1941 with the British discovery of the clinical effectiveness of penicillin. A crash development program in this country and Great Britain, involving collaborative efforts of governmental, academic, and industrial research laboratories, soon made penicillin available for widespread clinical therapy. By 1950, the list of controllable infections had been greatly extended by the advent of broad spectrum antibiotics, including oxytetracycline and others.

Immunizing vaccines and antisera have cut the toll due to diphtheria, smallpox, tetanus, whooping cough, and poliomyelitis to negligible proportions, and these vaccines have also undergone improvement and refinement. The live poliomyelitis vaccine marketed in 1961 by the Pfizer Company is beginning to replace the three injections plus booster shot of the old vaccine, with two drops of the new being taken by mouth on a piece of sugar. This progress is quite remarkable, for only ten years ago poliomyelitis was a major cause of disability or death.

Although medical science has won impressive victories over infectious diseases, the war is by no means over. Viruses continue to be a major cause of infections for which no effective treatment is now known. Drug-resistant bacteria continue to emerge and new ways are needed to cope with them. Infections caused by hardy gram-negative bacteria, still relatively unresponsive to chemotherapy, are increasingly important clinical problems. Effective agents are needed against systemic fungal diseases which, although not widespread, are serious for the afflicted patient.

Many so-called tropical diseases are completely uncontrollable. Helminthic infestations are world-wide, common even in the United States; it has been estimated that half a billion people are infested by ascarids and hookworms. Fifty million people in tropical regions suffer from schistosomiasis, and existing treatments are far from adequate. Innumerable compounds of theoretical effectiveness are found to be clinically useless. For poorly understood reasons, these substances when administered to the host do not reach the required site of biochemical action in adequate concentration or are metabolized to inactive molecules. Horizons of basic chemotherapeutic research must be widened to embrace not only cellular metabolism but also the absorption, distribution, deposition, metabolism, and excretion of potential drugs and the relationships between these and the chemical and physical properties of molecules. The challenge is one of complete understanding of cellular metabolism.

The "natural wisdom" of microorganisms which synthesize antibiotics has given the organic chemist dramatically novel points of departure for his work. A number of chemically modified antibiotics of the penicillin and tetracycline types already are well known to possess superior therapeutic properties. As further knowledge develops it may become possible to predict, within a given molecular framework, the effects of structural changes upon biological activity.

Design of agents selectively toxic to viral particles is peculiarly difficult, since these "living molecules" commandeer the metabolic processes of the host cell in order to reproduce themselves. Nonetheless, differences between viral and human nucleic acids, as revealed by fundamental biochemical studies, should provide a key to antimetabolite attack. Drugs which stimulate natural defense mechanisms of the body may one day displace or augment compounds acting directly on the pathogen itself. Such agents might stimulate antibody-producing centers, increase the vigor or numbers of phagocytes, or stimulate production of nonspecific immunity agents such as properdin.

Dramatic developments of the past quarter-century have resulted from chance observations, painstaking testing, and massive empirical screening programs. The organic chemist has been highly successful in discovering selectively lethal molecules. He has accumulated and correlated a large store of knowledge relating molecular structure and biological activity. He has become skilled in the now classical technique of systematic analogue synthesis.

Also during this era, chemotherapy took a giant step toward becoming a rational discipline. This requires integration of many scientific specialties. Bacteriologists, biochemists, and enzymologists are attempting to clarify the mechanisms by which organisms assimilate and transport nutrients and transform them into essentials required for life, growth, and reproduction. Delineation of differences in biochemical pathways utilized by a pathogenic microbe, on the one hand, and the host (man), on the other, can provide a key to selective destruction of the pathogen without damage to the host. This might be accomplished by alteration of cell permeability, derangement of protein or nucleic acid synthesis, or disruption of energy-producing mechanisms.

Several great American drug houses play a major part in these efforts. Among the leaders is Charles Pfizer and Company, Inc.; this firm gained its present eminent place in the ethical pharmaceutical industry because of its knowledge of fermentation processes which was applied to the manufacture of antibiotics.

Impact on the Hospital of Control of Infections

The control of infections made possible by chemotherapy and immunotherapy has had a remarkable impact on the hospital. The effect of today's drugs on the course of infectious disease can be seen in the rapid drop in the death rate from pneumonia following the introduction and widespread use of sulfonamides and antibiotics. In the 20 years from 1935 to 1955 the death rate per 100,000 declined from 60 to almost zero.

The cost of illness for a pneumonia patient has dropped drastically. Instead of five weeks of hospitalization and a period of convalescence with doctor, hospital, and nursing bills, plus loss of earnings, totaling perhaps $1,000, most cases of lobar pneumonia today are cleared up in less than two weeks with the use of antibiotics—and often at home instead of in the hospital.

Successful treatment of tuberculosis with streptomycin, isoniazid, and PAS has also had a profound impact, for without question the greatest single factor in the improvement of treatment has been the development of antimicrobial agents active against the tubercle bacillus. Outpatient treatment now often takes the place of long-term hospitalization. In 1946 there were 412 nonfederal tuberculosis hospitals. Even this bed space was insufficient to accommodate all of the sick, and the City of Chicago Municipal Tuberculosis Sanitarium had a long waiting list, to cite one example. In 1956 there were only 315 nonfederal tuberculosis hospitals, representing a drop of 8,771 beds. (By 1963 the total had dropped to 203 hospitals.)

The smallpox hospital disappeared years ago. Of more recent demise are the hospitals which were set up in the 1930's for women suffering from puerperal fever. The special isolation hospitals for infectious diseases are largely empty.

Probably the most important immediate problem, as regards hospitals, is control of antibiotic-resistant staphylococci, which still plagues the best efforts of hospital administrators and their infection committees. The synthesis of a form of penicillin, by the joint efforts of American and British scientists, which is effective in staphylococcal infections resistant to the ordinary penicillin has been accomplished, and the drug is now available.

Further advances will also have some impact, but it is doubtful whether any future change will be as dramatic as were those occurring during the past 25 years in hospitalization procedures for the control and treatment of infectious disease.

Research and the Rise of Surgery

Without anesthesia and antisepsis, many of the intricate surgical procedures of today would be impossible.

Before Lord Lister introduced his phenol spray for sterilizing operation areas, the death rate from "hospital gangrene" was about 60 per cent, and to accept advice to undergo surgery was a fateful decision. Childbirth was a hazard. The reduction in maternal mortality recorded by Semmelweis after he introduced Lister's methods to Vienna was dramatic.

Phenol is an unpleasant antiseptic, harmful to the tissues and irritating to the surgeons and their helpers, so Swiss and German drug houses got to work and soon produced effective and noncaustic materials to replace it. In the meantime, the introduction of antiseptics had shown the importance of keeping bacteria away from surgical wounds, and aseptic methods were adopted. The blood-stained frock coat was replaced by the sterile gown, cap, and mask, and trained nurses presided at surgery to see that asepsis was maintained by the team.

The anesthetic properties of nitrous oxide and of ether had been shown by Priestley and his associates in the eighteenth century, but for decades no application was made of the discovery except as an amusement for visitors to fairs and circuses and as an escape from reality at the so-called ether parties. In 1842, Dr. Crawford Long of Georgia removed a tumor from a patient under ether, and in 1846 the Boston dentist William T. Morton demonstrated the use of ether as an anesthetic for tooth extraction and later for operations for tumors of the neck and of the shoulder at Massachusetts General Hospital. In 1851 when young Dr. E. R. Squibb took leave from the Navy to do a six-month refresher course at Jefferson Medical College, Philadelphia, he found that surgeons were using the new "sulfuric ether" quite extensively.

The early ether was dangerous. Made of crude sulfuric ether mixed with aromatics, it had gotten the name of "letheon," and its potency was so unreliable that it was difficult to control the depth of anesthesia. Squibb felt that the fault lay partly in the crude method of manufacture, and partly in the type of container used, which allowed deterioration.

In 1853 Squibb turned his attention to the problem. For months he analyzed all the commercially manufactured ether. The differences in color, limpidity, specific gravity, and purity amazed him. Next he experimented with stills. He designed twenty before he made one which would operate on a moderate head of steam. Then he found impurities in his first batch. He discovered ways to wash these out, and finally, in November, 1854, he distilled pure ether of uniform strength. He did not patent his invention but described it in detail for the whole pharmaceutical industry.[15] More than a century later the giant still in the Squibb plant in New Jersey is basically the same design Dr. Squibb developed at the Naval Laboratory at Brooklyn in 1854. This plant provides ether for much of the world, and ether remains perhaps the safest anesthetic there is, especially when facilities are limited and experienced anesthetists are not at hand.

Ether was not the only anesthetic improved by Squibb. He developed chloroform of uniform quality, but while chloroform is more comfortable to the patient, its toxic effects on the liver caused it to be abandoned. He also invented improvements in the technique of anesthesia and designed an ether inhaler to replace the "rag-and-bottle" method. This inhaler prevented more than a predetermined quantity of ether being used on any one patient. He also stabilized a solution of cocaine for local anesthesia and later made anodynes and hypnotics on a large scale.

With antisepsis, asepsis, and anesthesia, surgery soon became commonplace and the surgical theaters and their ancillary departments an outstanding feature of any general hospital. The concept of "central supply" became established and anesthesiology blossomed into a separate discipline of medicine. The surgeons grew in stature from the "barbers" of the sixteenth century to leaders of the medical community, for since they could do more for the patient in a more dramatic way than could physicians, their power and influence grew. Leading medical centers, such as the Mayo Clinic, were founded by surgeons. Under these pressures, anesthesiology became more scientific, more complex, and more

[15] E. R. Squibb: Manufacture of Ether. *Am. J. Pharmacy,* September, 1856.

efficient. Resuscitation and monitoring devices were added to the machinery, and more refined inhalant gases, such as cyclopropane and Fluothane, displaced ether and nitrous oxide. Cocaine was modified by the pharmaceutical chemist into less toxic derivatives, and the use of surface, local, nerve-block, and spinal anesthesia developed for minor procedures and for those too ill to undergo general anesthesia.

The hypnotic barbiturates were tailored into short-acting ones, suitable for intravenous use where surgery was not likely to be prolonged, and agents such as meperidine and hydroxyzine added a further refinement—the reduction of anxiety before anesthesia.

There remained the problem of obtaining good muscular relaxation in a difficult patient without pushing the anesthesia too deeply. It was known that curare, the Indian arrow poison, was powerful enough to paralyze animals because of the muscular relaxation it caused, and several companies sent expeditions into the jungles to seek the active principle.

While they were gone, an amateur botanist, Richard Gill, attracted by the Squibb record of pioneer work in anesthetic products, walked into the firm with a supply of the material. With an initial investment of only $6,000 the firm developed a series of important muscle-relaxant products which sold for years, although afterward other companies succeeded in marketing similar substances.

These refinements have made fantastic feats possible, such as operations on the open heart, replacement of major blood vessels with plastic tubes, and construction of new joints with metal grafts. Eye banks have been set up for corneal grafts, but the ability to transplant whole organs successfully seems to be limited. Before organ transplantation can be generally practiced it will be necessary to develop the science of immunology and to create conditions which will make it possible for the host to accept the implant without protest.

Improvements in anesthesiology are still attainable. Very rarely, a patient dies from an anesthetic; further refinements may prevent this. Improved methods of combating preoperative anxiety and postoperative nausea, pain, and discomfort are likely.

Will a pill displace the anesthetic machine, the anesthetist, and his department? It is doubtful. Inhalation anesthesia offers such advantages in terms of absorption and excretion of the anesthetic and control by the anethetist that it is doubtful whether it will be superseded in our time. Also, the anesthesiologist has become invaluable in the more serious operations, for he can monitor all of the vital signs and warn the surgeon of trouble, besides being an important member of the resuscitation team.

Impact on the Hospital of Surgical Progress

Antisepsis, asepsis, and anesthesia, by stripping surgery of its horrors, have made it a leading specialty. Hospital construction has to take into account the special demands of operating theaters, of sterilization, of central supply, and of the ready availability of diagnostic aids to the surgeon such as radiology and rapid pathological techniques. In contrast to infectious disease control, which has reduced the demand for hospital beds, the vast increase in the variety of surgical techniques has added to the number of patients seeking surgery. The help requested may involve some relatively unimportant cosmetic correction or an elaborate and lifesaving procedure. This trend has had great economic impact on the hospital—but what of the future?

It would seem that as far as cancer is concerned, there is great hope that the development of chemotherapeutic and of immunological agents will better the results produced by surgery. Should this prediction prove true the number of operations performed in general hospitals will lessen to a significant degree.

Advances in the drug treatment of hitherto intractable illnesses, such as Buerger's disease, peptic ulcer, regional ileitis, and ulcerative colitis, would further reduce the need for surgery, and there is little doubt that such advances will be made.

Mastoidectomy is rarely performed these days since the discovery of penicillin, and the mastery of adenoviruses should make tonsillectomy equally uncommon.

Progress in surgery will be made in correcting congenital defects and in tissue repair after injury by physical trauma or burning, but in many other areas the importance of surgery seems likely to decline.

The Influence of Modern Drugs upon Hospital Productivity

Hospital productivity may be assessed by the number of patients served, the amount of pain and disability which is avoided or reduced, and by the extension of life made possible by treatment. When these measures are applied to a typical metropolitan general hospital, the Beth Israel Hospital of Boston, the comparison between 1932 and 1952 is quite impressive.[16]

These twenty years represent a distinct era in medicine and hospital care, i.e., before and after the current era of sulfa drugs, antibiotics, and other great advances in therapy and in broader understanding of the nature of disease.

During the period there was a decrease in the average length of stay per admission from 12.8 to 9.8 days. The hospital's occupancy ratio rose from 70 per cent in 1932 to 93 per cent in 1952. The mortality rate declined by a third between 1932 and 1952—from 52 to 34 per 1,000 admissions. This saving in life occurred despite the higher average age of patients admitted during the latter year. Similar changes were evident elsewhere, and the average length of stay in all nonfederal short-term general and special hospitals declined from 9.1 days in 1946 to 7.7 days in 1956.[17]

As has been shown earlier, a considerable expansion of the drug industry, from its present sales value of around $2 billion yearly, will occur during the

---

[16] Health Information Foundation: *Progress in Health Services.* New York, September, 1957.
[17] *J. Am. Hosp. A.* Guide Issue, Part II, August 1, 1959.

next 15 years, partly because of population growth and economic factors, and partly because of the introduction of new drugs. These drugs are likely to be introduced especially in the areas of cancer and mental diseases, although advances will probably be made on all fronts. Thus, a prediction of a total sales value of $5.2 billion has been forecast for 1975.

This expansion of drug sales will be paralleled by an increase in the productivity of the general hospitals, and the trend seen during 1946 to 1956 will undoubtedly continue. Special hospitals, such as the tuberculosis hospitals, will decline in importance.

As for mental hospitals, some change has taken place since 1955. Discharges now exceed admissions, and the total inpatient population in the United States has declined by better than 5 per cent during the period. More drastic and fundamental changes are likely during the next decade. With improved chemotherapy, more patients will be treated in psychiatric wards of general hospitals or at home as outpatients of general hospitals. One of the biggest burdens of the mental hospital, the care of persons afflicted with chronic brain syndrome due to atherosclerosis, seems likely to be removed. It can be predicted that by 1970 no new mental hospitals of more than 1,000 beds will be tolerated, and the vast "concentration camps" or "snakepits" seen today, containing upward of 10,000 or more souls, will disappear. Concomitant with this, the increasing influence of drugs in treatment will facilitate the growth of the public's conception that mental disease is no longer to be regarded with fear and aversion as the diagnosis of tuberculosis once was. This will lead to drastic changes in the laws.

Thus, judged by one of the criteria stated, the productivity of the state mental hospitals will fall, since it is expected that they will lose their curable cases to the general hospitals and will serve fewer persons. Their population will consist largely of patients with chronic brain syndrome with organic damage or with congenital lesions and the more malignant schizophrenics and other severe psychotics. Since their total patient load will be so much lessened, they will become efficient workshops of enlightened research, and progress may be looked for even against those intractable and hitherto incurable diseases.

Summary

Development of American pharmaceutical research, made possible by the investment of a large part of the profits of the leading drug houses in research programs, has caused a tremendous growth of the pharmaceutical industry during the last quarter of a century.

Discoveries of new potent drugs and reductions in the cost of drugs have greatly increased the productivity of the general hospital, while some of the special hospitals have tended to fall out of use.

During the next 15 years, a continued growth of the drug industry will be reflected in a continued increase in productivity of the general hospital. With the use of new, powerful medications, the number of surgical and radiation treatments undertaken will decline. The diminished importance of the special hospital will be especially shown by shrinkage of the large mental institutions. The tendency for mental disease to be treated in general hospitals will become more marked, while changes in the laws regarding certification will occur.

Federal interference with the drug industry by changing the present enlightened patent laws, or by interfering with the pricing structure, may have the effect of slowing down an increase in general hospital productivity.

RESEARCH BACKGROUNDS

With the current almost frenzied popularity of research, training in research methods becomes a vital part of every graduate program, whether it is education, the natural and social sciences, engineering, law, medicine, hospital or business administration.

Gordon and Howell devote an entire chapter to "Research in the Business Schools" in *Higher Education for Business,* the report of a three-year study of collegiate business education which was undertaken at the request of The Ford Foundation. Since many of the statements apply equally to hospitals and to business organizations, a few extracts follow from the section "The Kinds of Research That Are Needed":

> Our understanding of business behavior is clearly of the most rudimentary kind, and in most business fields there is a paucity of significant generalizations that can be taught in the classroom or used by businessmen and other administrators. . . . Much if not most research in the business schools attempts merely to describe current practice or, going a short step further, to develop normative rules which summarize what is considered to be the best of prevailing practice. The business literature is not, in general, characterized by challenging hypotheses, well developed conceptual frameworks, the use of sophisticated research techniques, penetrating analysis, the use of evidence drawn from the relevant underlying disciplines—or very significant conclusions. . . . In some professional fields, the professional school is, in effect, the research arm of the profession. Through its research activities the professional school creates the new knowledge on which future professional practice will be based. Thus, the university blazes the way for the practitioner, providing him with ever more powerful tools with which to deal with once intractable problems. Medicine, of course, is the classical case of this. . . .
>
> It is fair to say that, at least so far, more significant knowledge of ultimate value to business has come out of the nonbusiness departments of the university than out of the business schools. This is true, we think, even if we exclude the physical sciences and engineering. Major contributions to our understanding of business behavior and to the ability of business to deal with some types of problems have come from psychology, mathematics and statistics, economics, and sociology. . . .[18]

[18] *Higher Education for Business* by Robert Aaron Gordon and James Edwin Howell, New York, Columbia University Press, 1959, pp. 379–81.

The authors then differentiate between fundamental and applied research. Stating, "Research on organizational problems is still in its infancy," they continue:

> Here clearly the behavioral sciences have much to contribute. We still have little tested knowledge on such problems as how alternative organizational arrangements affect various kinds of decision-making, the conditions of organizational viability, and the factors that influence the interactions between the individual and his organizational environment. There is need for more of a "behavioral" approach to the study of organization, particularly to the study of large groups. . . .[19]

Even in medicine, however, which these authors hold up as a model, the importance of research in the medical school is not as great as it should be and has been slow of development, as Professor Sten Axel Friberg, M.D., of Stockholm, Sweden, pointed out in an address, "The University and Society," at the 1959 Convocation of the International College of Surgeons:

> There was a time when our institutions of higher learning were concentrated on instruction rather than research; when the researcher was a lone wolf, by necessity an ascetic, whose work and discoveries were recognized as valuable only as they served the purpose of waging war. . . . From being a means by which a man could study the world around him, science has become a tool to transform it. Research is no longer the poor relative, supported by charity as a balm to our cultural conscience; it has achieved status; is more purposeful and can be carried on in a more favorable climate. . . . This generation is only at the beginning of a great era of research in medicine. . . .[20]

In hearty agreement with Professor Friberg's conviction that a great future is ahead for medical research are hospitals in the United States, whose research departments are expanding at an unprecedented rate.

The scientists who man the laboratories of the great Mount Sinai Medical Research Foundation in Chicago spur themselves on with the conviction, "Man's conquest of disease has barely begun; millions will die this year who could have been saved if *next* year's medical discoveries were available *now*." Cancer, body chemistry, and hematologic research are the major activities. The foundation is affiliated with Mount Sinai Hospital and with the Chicago Medical School. This school also strengthened its affiliation with the Michael Reese Medical Center, according to an announcement in November, 1963.

"Improving Hospital-Physician Relations through Education" is the subject of a four-year research project started in 1960 by North Carolina Memorial Hospital of the University of North Carolina, Chapel Hill, financed by a $114,494 grant from the National Institutes of Health. The principal investigator is Dr. Robert R. Cadmus, professor of hospital administration at the university's school of medicine, and director of the hospital. A curriculum is being

[19] *Ibid.*, pp. 382–84.
[20] Rector, University of Stockholm, Surgeon in Charge of Orthopedics, University Clinic, Stockholm. *J. Internat. Coll. Surgeons*, May, 1960, pp. 605–10.

developed the objective of which is to give the medical student better understanding of the administrative implications of medicine, particularly in the hospital setting.

The research program at Chicago Wesley Memorial Hospital in 1963 was carried on by 7 full-time physicians on the research staff and 1 consultant to the department of research; 7 other physicians devoted full time as research fellows. Other full-time staff included 4 scientists with Ph.D. degrees and 1 with a master's degree in chemistry. Additional workers included 23 technicians and 5 laboratory aides. Twenty-seven physicians on the medical staff were actively engaged in the activities of the department, which were conducted in 38 well-equipped research laboratories and 11 offices.

Among the research projects under way were artificial heart valves; artificial lung for heart surgery; blood disease; brain; steroid hormone; leukemia; obstetrics and gynecology; infectious disease; orthopedic conditions; electrolyte metabolism; tissue culture; urological disorders; cancer diagnosis; heart station; intermediary metabolism; metabolic unit; and temporal bone bank.

Saint Barnabas Hospital, New York, conducts

> . . . a wide range of investigations, both of a clinical and an experimental nature, although our primary interest continues to be the role of the basal ganglia and related structures in sensory and motor function, as well as in higher integrative areas of behavior. It is our continuing goal to combine and coordinate our research program so that clinical data are always supplemented and coordinated with anatomic data, animal investigations, and material derived from physiologic studies.[21]

Dr. Leona Baumgartner,[22] then commissioner of health of New York City, now head of the Office of Human Resources and Human Development, AID, and Assistant Secretary of State, declared:

> Our vast national investment in medical research has indeed created the possibility of medical miracles. But the scientific observations, the creativity which has led to these miracles, has not been matched by similar objective observations, by a similar ingenuity in creating administrative innovations, a similar courage in examining and changing old ways to make certain that the scientific miracles will reach everyone whose health they can maintain and restore.

This need for research in directions other than medical is beginning to get response in hospitals. Among the projects of the operations research division of the Johns Hopkins Hospital has been an investigation of effective use of nursing resources, in which several academic disciplines are represented in the research group.[23]

A few of the projects which have been carried out under the Public Health

[21] From the 96th Annual Report, 1961–1962.

[22] In an article, "Hospitals and the Tragedy of Unused Medical Knowledge," taken from a paper delivered at the 150th anniversary convocation of the Massachusetts General Hospital, Boston, February 1, 1961. *Hospitals,* August 16, 1961, pp. 67–70.

[23] A report by R. J. Connor, Dr. Eng., was published in *Hospitals,* May 1, 1961.

Service grants program have been development of organizational patterns for the provision of patient care; hospital utilization; personnel needs and training; architectural, engineering, and equipment design; quality of care appraisal; methods improvement and work simplification; coordination of facilities and services in small hospitals; ambulatory patient care; and legal aspects of hospital administration.

Dr. Jack C. Haldeman,[24] then assistant surgeon general and chief, Division of Hospital and Medical Facilities of the Public Health Service, pointed out guidelines for federally supported health facilities research.

Declaring that administrative research and improvement are a "survival" item for hospitals, the administrator of the Roswell Park Memorial Institute, Buffalo, New York, A. A. Lepinot,[25] urges that the hospital provide a "creative environment" for research. He says: "We must not only try to improve what we now have but to adapt quickly to constant and frequent technological change. Even this is not enough; hospitals themselves must produce technological improvements and innovations by conducting research programs as part of their operations."

EDUCATIONAL BACKGROUNDS

The administrator who is fired with zeal to make his hospital a progressive institution will be educationally minded. He will study the school systems in his community and the nation, from the elementary through the professional levels, in order to absorb the philosophy of education in its practical applications and to familiarize himself with the current thinking of educational authorities. He will want to study the effects that education has upon the development of individuals and their influence on other lives and on society.

Besides curricula and teaching methods, the administration of educational institutions of all kinds will be studied by the hospital executive who visualizes himself as administering one of them. As an educator himself, directing other educators on his staff, he will want to know how this kind of administration differs from his responsibilities for patient care and how it correlates with them.

Between university administration, in particular, and hospital administration there are some similarities. Both involve administering professionals as the most difficult part of their function. Faculty members, like doctors, are independent but not to the same degree, since they are employees and most doctors are not.

If the administrator in his role as an educator becomes acquainted with Socrates, Plato, and Aristotle; Quintilian, Alcuin, and Anselm; Abelard, Aquinas, and Erasmus; Rousseau, Spencer, and Dewey, he will have enriched his life with a new interest and will go on to study systems and innovators. He

---

[24] New Horizons for Hospital Research. *Hospitals,* December 16, 1961.
[25] *Hospitals,* May 16, 1960, pp. 42–45.

will become acquainted with the meaning in an educational sense of scholasticism, formalism, realism, the scientific method, the commentary method, the disciplinary theory, absolutism, the democratic ideal, naturalism, the monitorial system, Herbartianism, individualism, and so on.

Professor Alfred North Whitehead said:[26]

> Culture is activity of thought, and receptiveness to beauty and humane feeling. Scraps of information have nothing to do with it. A merely well-informed man is the most useless bore on God's earth. What we should aim at producing is men who possess both culture and expert knowledge in some special direction. Their expert knowledge will give them the ground to start from, and their culture will lead them as deep as philosophy and as high as art. . . . We are only just realizing that the art and science of education require a genius and a study of their own; and that this genius and this science are more than a bare knowledge of some branch of science or of literature. . . . Education is the acquisition of the art of the utilization of knowledge. This is an art very difficult to impart.

He asserts that "training should be broader than the ultimate specialization."[27]

In a report of the proceedings of the Inter-Professions Conference on Education for Professional Responsibility held a few years ago, appears this statement by Dr. John Romano:[28]

> Many (medical) students are interested in but frequently do not have an opportunity to learn more about the costs of medical education, of hospital care, of community, State and Federal subsidy; in fact, they are eager to know more about the projection of medicine into the total social and economic scene. The physician, if he is to be a comprehensive human biologist, should have had the opportunity of acquiring a certain body of knowledge and of learning methods appropriate to the use and application of this knowledge.

This is the dominant theme of all criticism of modern education—broaden the background, enlarge the perspective, build specialized study upon a more firm foundation of liberal education. The administrator needs to take it to heart for himself and for his educational planning for others. What it amounts to is a raising of the aim from education for making a living to education for life.

The retiring dean of Columbia College, Columbia University, Harry J. Carman, speaking at the Fifth National Conference on Higher Education, said this about over-specialization:[29]

> Unfortunately, during the past hundred years liberal education in this country has suffered from the inroads of overspecialization, vocationalism, and professionalism. Our colleges have become collections of departments with little organic connection between them. Courses reflect the specialized interests of the scholar who intends to devote his entire life to a small aspect of a single subject.

---

[26] *The Aims of Education*, New York, The Macmillan Company, 1st printing 1949, 4th, 1953, pp. 13, 16.

[27] *Ibid.*, p. 65.

[28] *Education for Professional Responsibility*, Pittsburgh, Carnegie Press, 1948, pp. 165–66.

[29] A Dean Takes Inventory. *Current Issues in Higher Education*, Department of Higher Education, National Education Association of the United States, Washington, D.C., 1951, pp. 28–29.

Seeking to understand society, the student is confronted with a plethora of specialized courses, ofttimes not related other than on a departmental basis. Men and society disappear from the student's vision as men and specialties crowd them out. The situation as a whole is, as my colleague Dr. Ordway Tead puts it . . . intellectual fragmentation, befuddlement, philosophical anarchy, and spiritual blindness. We are without a common intellectual background on which to stand.

To this academic separatism and specialization has been added a glorified vocationalism. Courses leading to vocations or professions have multiplied almost as rapidly as highly specialized instruction in the common disciplines. As a result our colleges and universities have graduated men and women technically trained as accountants, librarians, physicians, lawyers, or social workers, with little or no interest in the cultural implications of their professions, much less in those things which would enable them to formulate for themselves a satisfying philosophy.

The concern is international in scope. At the same time that the specialties demand more education because they become ever more complex, the world around them grows more complex also, and the only solution is a generally lengthened and more efficient educational system aided by television, programmed instruction, teaching machines, and whatever other devices technical progress and human wisdom may contribute.

THE EDUCATIONAL COMMUNITY

It is one of what might be called the consolations of the much-criticized hospital community that it by no means stands alone as the target for attack. Education, which has some similar problems, is certainly coming in for its share. In fraternizing with educators the hospital administrator should keep an ear open for ideas that can be translated into improvements in his own educational operations.

Because of the keen competition for admission to the colleges, barriers have been set up in the selective process. The easiest one of these to administer is the scholastic average in the secondary school. Hence it has become in some institutions the sole, or at least the chief, determinant of who gets in and who stays out.

Anyone who has studied previous scholastic records of current students in graduate work and of those who have completed their formal academic courses and gone out into the field knows all about the fallacy of the "average" grade record as a clue to performance. If the "average" grade represents a consistent achievement in all subjects, that is one thing; the student can be judged by it as brilliant, average, or poor. It is quite another thing if the record varies among subjects. Here are clues to interest. Many a student with high potential in a career which he chose early in life will neglect subjects that seem to him unrelated. It takes adulthood usually to realize the values of wide knowledge and interests.

Sometimes late motivation, a restless, unhappy confusion about choice of a career, leads a student to pick at subjects without any real interest in studying them. Suddenly through some contact or event such a student gets enthusiastic about some field for which he would like to prepare himself. What a difference ensues in his grades and in his impression upon his instructors. But this happens perhaps in the senior year, high school or college as the case may be, and it is much too late to do anything to bring up that grade average. This is a not uncommon occurrence in a field such as hospital administration, which gives emotional as well as intellectual incentives to the student who likes people and who is unintrigued by the mysteries of chemistry and physics before he has a good reason for wanting to penetrate them.

Then there are the students with high vitality who excel in extracurricular activity but for whom the classroom means boredom. They change too when they grow up and acquire an interest—but too late to bring up that grade average enough to appeal to college admissions officers.

The tense struggle for grades to the detriment of real learning was deplored by Oscar Handlin, professor of history at Harvard University:[30]

> Those great big beautiful A's so avidly sought, those little, miserly C's so often found, were meant for another time and another student body. . . . The cruelty of the contest is clearest in courses which establish grades on the basis of a statistical distribution curve. No matter how hard they work, or how able they are, one half of the class will fall below average.

The instructor is caught in the network because if he grades too many too high, the university concludes that his course is too easy; if he grades too many too low, the students rebel and the university wonders whether he is a good teacher.

The trend to tighten rather than to loosen the competitive examination system is unmistakable and disheartening. "The distorted emphasis nullifies much of what the colleges aim to do," states Professor Handlin, but he sees no solution. Each stage of education selects its entrants by the scores they have made in the previous one. Scholarships, fellowships, and other awards go to those who have the high marks, under this system that places as the educational goal knowing the right answers to the questions in the examinations. Instead, in the words of Professor Handlin, their education should have been an experience which, "by the exposure of one mind to the thinking of others, creates not answers but a lifetime of questions," encourages probing "alone beyond the limits of what is handed to them," and shows them "how to be creative original thinkers."

This is an unfortunate trend. Another that is, in general, good but which is being carried too far in some instances, is the high favor in which general education is held, with a somewhat scornful attitude toward specialized education. There are unquestioned examples of overstressing of career goals, but the pendulum can swing too far the other way.

[30] Are the Colleges Killing Education? *The Atlantic Monthly*, May, 1962.

THE HOSPITAL AS AN EDUCATIONAL INSTITUTION

Just as the hospital is affected by, and in turn affects, research in general, so it is a force in the field of education that is influenced by current general trends. Second only to its primary object of the best possible care of the patient, and inseparably tied in with that object, is its responsibility to educate and to train. This responsibility is not limited to personnel who come specifically for that purpose but extends to patients and public as well.

Joseph E. Garland expresses this educational relationship for physicians, and the need for analysis and possible change, as follows:[31]

> The concept of hospitals as educational institutions is as old as hospitals themselves. The medical student today immerses himself during the first two years of medical school in the basic sciences of medicine, anatomy, physiology, biochemistry, pharmacology and microbiology. These have been regarded as essentially classroom and laboratory subjects, and the student has little or no contact with patients and disease—the *human* equation in medicine—until he has mastered this fundamental knowledge. Then, during his second two years of medical school, he enters the hospital and begins to learn how experienced clinicians apply this information at the bedside. After his graduation he serves as a house officer in the hospital and is given increasing responsibility for the actual care of patients. Many medical educators believe that this system . . . tends to cleave the educational process for the student between the basic, or preclinical, and his clinical training . . . and tends to isolate the basic scientist in the school from the clinical in the hospital. . . . One solution may lie in compromising these divergent tendencies at the level of the university hospital.

The danger lies in accepting any student, doctor, nurse, technician, or other into the hospital and letting them become buried with little guidance in the everyday, institutional routine. The aim is impaired if a hospital, any hospital, falls short of attaining its highest potential in functioning as an educational institution. Its obligation in this endeavor extends beyond its internal operations involving doctors, nurses, dietitians, technicians, and all of its other staff members. Patients, visitors, and the community in general are also its pupils. Only if hospitals meet this obligation with increasing effectiveness can medical and allied sciences continue their rapid advancement and the social, political, and economic advantages of maximum health conservation be enjoyed by the nation and its people.

Those hospitals which are affiliated with medical schools in the education of their students in medical and allied professions obviously rank as schools in the accustomed sense as indicated by their accepted designation as "teaching hospitals." Those which are approved for the training of medical interns and for residents in the various medical specialties are also entitled to this distinction, whether or not they are directly affiliated with a medical school. These teaching

[31] From *An Experiment in Medicine: The First Twenty Years of the Pratt Clinic and the New England Center Hospital of Boston.* Cambridge, The Riverside Press, 1960.

hospitals usually also have formal educational programs for nurses, technicians, therapists, dietitians, and perhaps medical social workers, medical record librarians, and administrators. Outside of the recognized "teaching" hospitals are many which must also be included in this category because they conduct schools of nursing and other formal professional educational programs.

The formal programs are, however, only the beginning of a hospital's educational responsibility. Continuation education is the field in which it has its most compelling, exacting, and promising role. The atmosphere of the hospital, within and without, is one of rapid, exciting change. Human problems in adjusting to the changes are monumental. What was learned in medical school yesterday may have to be unlearned tomorrow. The obsolescent knowledge that the doctor must discard may involve radical changes in technical procedures in which many personnel participate. It may also mean the scrapping of costly equipment and the purchase of new, involving the retraining of operators.

Technological advances likewise dictate changes that may temporarily throw several interrelated departments into chaos unless educational preparation for change has been practiced. And chaos in a hospital may have tragic consequences upon patient welfare. Progress in concepts of administration similarly involves keeping all personnel attuned to a dynamic spirit in which every organizational pattern and every established routine are understood to be constantly under scrutiny for improvement.

The hospital as a school benefits by consciously allying itself with other educational institutions and activities. Better than it now does, it should fit itself into the educational scene and earn recognition of its place in that scene from educators. Developments and trends in education in the broad sense need to be studied by hospital people. Tradition and individualism must be subordinated. Methods of teaching should be changed to conform with the newest ideas. Goals must be set higher as vision grows.

Having acquired a background in general educational principles and trends, the administrator as an educator himself and as the head of an educational institution will want to acquaint himself with the application of those principles in all fields related to health, studying his hospital for policies and practices which he can improve through educational methods. Perhaps a good place to begin is "standing orders," upon which hospitals have placed much reliance for many years. These have decided value in spelling out the detail of techniques. But they can also be deadly impediments to progress if personnel are not educated to subject them constantly to rigorous analysis and to offer recommendations for changes. "Standing orders," in the way of thinking in the 1960's, can be permitted to "stand" only for the period in which they stand up to the best current knowledge.

In a hospital, lives depend upon alertness for improvements instilled in a staff through a deliberately directed, never-ending, continuation education program clear down to the detail of the simplest everyday procedures.

Medical Education

A slow evolution occurred in the concept of the hospital as a medical educational institution. Only in exceptional hospitals in the past was there any attempt made to utilize the clinical facilities of the hospital for the teaching of medical students and interns. Most hospitals were merely places of refuge for the sick, unthought of as teaching assets by the medical schools. There were individual physicians, of course, who were superb teachers, and some of their teaching took place in hospitals. But medical education in the eighteenth century was didactic. The exceptions were mainly in England, where at Guy's Hospital in 1723, the Edinburgh Hospital in 1736, the Meath Hospital at Dublin in 1756, and the London Hospital in 1785, hospital medical education really began. Sir Astley Paston Cooper, of Norfolk, England (1768–1841), is known as one of the first surgical teachers to substitute practical demonstration upon an actual case for the didactic teaching of theory which prevailed in surgical training in his day. It was a long time before this innovation was generally adopted.

Now the concept is:[32] "The hospital is, by any reckoning, the keystone of our health structure, the instrument by which medical science is brought to the people, and the fountain of scientific knowledge from which young people go forth to practice the healing arts."

Dr. T. C. Laipply, director of medical education at Chicago Wesley Memorial Hospital, expresses the effect of an educational atmosphere upon the whole hospital as follows:[33]

> Those intimately associated with a teaching hospital soon find its progressive attitudes a way of life. Satisfaction, rewards and benefits are forthcoming to all —physicians, students and patients. The teaching-minded physician remains alert, up to date and retains a youthful outlook on change and progress. He may experience satisfaction beyond measure in appreciating the degree of success attained by those who received his guidance. The student, intern and resident obtain enthusiastic encouragement, learn what others have done and should attain the degree of humility essential to professional progress. They should soon appreciate the dictum of Hippocrates: "To know is one thing, merely to believe one knows, is another. To know is science, but merely to believe one knows is ignorance."
>
> Noteworthy benefits also accrue to the patient who is sufficiently fortunate to be admitted to a teaching hospital. He is assured of a high degree of excellence in medical care because of the alertness of physicians which prevails in an environment filled with questions originating in the minds of the young and eager to learn.

Foreign Medical Graduates

Hospitals in the United States and Canada, short of interns, residents, and house physicians from their own schools, must rely quite heavily upon foreign

[32] *America's Health: A Report to the Nation,* by the National Health Assembly. New York, Harper & Brothers, 1949, Chap. 2, p. 40.
[33] From *Wesley Life,* Chicago Wesley Memorial Hospital, spring, 1961.

medical graduates for medical service. The American Medical Association and the Association of American Medical Colleges formerly issued an approved list, on which around 1950 there were some 50 schools. Evaluation was impossible, however, so the list was withdrawn. In 1957 the Educational Council for Foreign Medical Graduates was established, at which time there were some 20,000 physicians from other countries in the United States for permanent residence and some 6,000 interns and residents, about a quarter of the total.

By 1960 there were around 9,500 physicians from other countries in training in hospital programs approved by the American Medical Association, and many more in unapproved programs. Of the 9,500, around 2,600 were interns and 6,900 were residents.

The council set up an examination plan with a deadline of April 4, 1961, for removing uncertified or unlicensed graduates of foreign medical schools from patient care situations in United States hospitals and for certification of new ones. Physicians who do not pass the examinations apply to hospitals with unapproved programs, but if they accept them such hospitals jeopardize their listing by the American Hospital Association, which is a prerequisite for accreditation by the Joint Commission on Accreditation of Hospitals.

Eight states will not license a foreign graduate, and some 30 states require foreigners to become citizens before licensing them.

For hospitals, the certification plan has been a great relief, for previously they had no reliable way of knowing whether their patients were sufficiently protected by their selections. Negotiations with foreign medical schools directly gave no assurance of the quality of physicians who were coming. Shortages make it desirable, in fact almost imperative, to recruit foreign physicians. With more than 7,000 internships and residencies vacant in hospitals each year, there is a critical situation which is leading some medical school heads and some hospital administrators to question the entire intern-resident system from the standpoints of both education and patient care.

Deficiencies, admitted by the trainees themselves and evident to their supervisors, must be remedied by special training courses instituted by hospitals for their interns and residents from other countries. These trainees are frequently not familiar with the laboratory equipment or the terms used in the laboratory and have little background in infection control or in medicolegal aspects of medical practice. Some of their difficulties, however, are the result of insufficient familiarity with the language. Hospitals are having to arrange language classes to help them.

C H A P T E R 18

Educating the Administrator

> For the betterment of our hospitals we should have, in the
> first place, trained superintendents. Can they be secured?
> Where are they? You can count on the fingers of two hands
> what we may call expert superintendents in this country. . . .
> Where did they get their training? They snatched it from
> the heart. They were born to it. They created their
> opportunities. If we expect to have a sufficient number of
> men of power, of great executive ability to take charge of
> our hospitals, we must provide some school or method of
> training. What is to be done, and what is the first step?
> The first step is to establish some school for the training
> of hospital executives.
> EDWARD MARTIN, M.D., in 1917[1]

THE DARK AGES of hospital administration were not so long ago, as
Dr. Martin's statement, and expressions of other speakers at the 1917 Conference
on Hospital Standardization, disclose.

It was some time before the school visualized by Dr. Martin came into existence, and the first one was short-lived because the field was not quite ready for it.

The first major investigation of the subject was made by a committee of the
American Hospital Association, headed by Dr. Warren L. Babcock, which reported in 1913 on the desirability of university training of hospital administrators.
Then came the war with its urgent problems, which, while they retarded action
on this idea, at the same time disclosed the acute need for especially trained persons to administer hospitals.

[1] From an address, "The Hospital and its Community," presented at the Conference on Hospital
Standardization, Joint Session of Committees on Standards. Dr. Martin was professor of surgery,
University of Pennsylvania School of Medicine, Philadelphia. *Bull. Am. Coll. Surgeons,* Vol. 3, No. 1
(undated).

The next important milestone was reached in April, 1922, when a report was presented by a Committee on the Training of Hospital Executives, financed by the Rockefeller Foundation, of which Dr. David L. Edsall was chairman and Dr. Willard C. Rappleye, then superintendent of the New Haven General Hospital, was executive secretary. The committee felt that its report "presented a reasonable basis for training hospital executives and for attracting into the field a group of individuals with proper qualifications for the work." The committee recommended that "a course or courses of training of this general character be inaugurated under university auspices."

The major points in this 1922 report were summarized as follows in a report made by a later committee in 1925:[2]

1. The conception of the hospital as a coordinating social and educational agency in striking contrast to the conception of the hospital as a hotel for the sick and a mere convenience for the medical profession.

2. The need, consequently, of constructive, even creative, social and educational leadership of the highest quality in the hospital itself in order to realize the new conception of the hospital. There is need for the training of creative thinkers and leaders as directors of coordinated programs of community health service in addition to training the administrators of the smaller hospitals.

3. The necessity for clearly defining the duties of hospital superintendent, holding him responsible at the same time for the achievement of all the purposes of the hospital, and giving him the opportunity and the authority in accordance with his responsibility and the community function of the hospital.

4. The provision for giving this training definitely under university auspices on a graduate basis.

5. The training should extend over a period of not less than twelve, nor more than 18 months "since it requires about four months to adequately cover a period of practical instruction in hospital operation, and a period of two months should be allowed for visiting other institutions and for final conferences, a total period of 15 months seems to be the optimum length of the basic course, allowing a full nine months (corresponding to a university year) for the theoretical-demonstration work. Possibly additional work in summer session should be given."

6. The proposed distribution of time of the curriculum is interesting as a first serious formulation of the curriculum, indicating the range of subject matter, its distribution and emphasis. The major topics with the relative percentage of time to be given are:

1.	Public Health	20%
2.	Social Sciences	15%
3.	Organization	15%
4.	Hospital Functions and History	10%
5.	Business Science	10%
6.	Institutional Management	10%
7.	Personnel Administration	5%
8.	Community Hospital Needs	5%
9.	Physical Plant	5%
10.	Jurisprudence	5%

[2] Report of the Committee on Training of Hospital Executives. *Bulletin No. 65*, American Hospital Association, July, 1926, pp. 5, 6.

The curriculum in detail presented in the 1922 report and reprinted as Appendix A of the 1925 report is most interesting from the standpoint of many topics that are still important, a few that are outdated, and several that should be added. It is reproduced at the end of this chapter.

In 1919 Dr. Arthur C. Bachmeyer, later to be the director of the first school that is still in existence, started in 1934 at the University of Chicago, announced a one-year course in hospital administration to be offered by the University of Cincinnati, and in 1922 Yale University included in its catalogue a series of four postgraduate courses in its school of medicine, one of which was in dispensary practice and administration, the other three in hospital administration. A few other sporadic short courses were announced, but it appears that for lack of demand, none of these offerings materialized, or if they did it was only briefly.

In 1924 a Committee on Training Hospital Executives of the American Hospital Association reported that it felt the immediate need was for the encouragement of research and particularly for a "small group of investigators analyzing some of the fundamentals of community hospital needs and some of the problems ramifying from the contact"; and it recommended that "effort be made to establish several fellowships in hospital administration under the National Research Council or other auspices, to finance qualified individuals to work on the problems of hospital administration under such conditions of freedom from routine work as will permit of productivity and training."

Around this time several short courses were established in different universities, among them one at New York University directed by Edgar Hayhow, Ph.D., who at the time of his death in 1958 was director of East Orange (New Jersey) Hospital. Dr. Hayhow in 1924 stressed the fact that there was no thought of "making hospital superintendents in thirty 2-hour lectures" but that the purpose was simply "to give the students a definite knowledge of how large institutions are organized and administered" and to give housekeepers, dietitians, nurses, and clerks "a clear conception of the other fellow's job."

Relative to short courses, a report of the 1925 committee, of which Dr. Malcolm T. MacEachern was chairman, stated in part:[3]

> The original demand of hospital people is almost always for short practical courses. This comes about largely, I think, after interviewing hospital people, not only from too narrow a conception of the social, health and educational opportunity which the hospital offers, but also from a limited knowledge of the rich fields of public health, and of the sciences of chemistry, bacteriology, psychology, and preventive medicine, and of the new sciences of business organization and administration in their relations to hospital service. It may be said that almost universally as this vista is presented, these people are perfectly willing to consider longer training. The need is for an educational program.

In a footnote to this statement in the report appears this comment: "It was to meet this immediate demand for short practical courses of those in the field that

[3] *Ibid.,* p. 14.

Mr. Bacon (Asa S. Bacon, president of A.H.A. 1923) appointed the committee of this Association in 1923, though recognizing the longer courses as the ideal to be sought."[4]

The 1925 report, which was approved by the association upon the recommendation of the resolutions committee, recommended the establishment of a standing committee to be known as the Central Committee on Training Hospital Executives, the duties of which would be

. . . (1) to make a thoroughgoing job-analysis of the hospital superintendency; (2) to undertake a recruiting campaign which would bring in an intelligent and interesting way the opportunity of service through the new profession of hospital administration; (3) to furnish the machinery in the large cities for a clearing house service for observation work particularly over extended periods for hospital administrators seeking special information or desiring aid on special problems; (4) to see that local members of the Association (and their institutions) cooperate with universities (a) in the general program of training for hospital administration, (b) give leaves of absence, if necessary, to members of staff desiring training, (c) furnish facilities for practical training under proper educational supervision of the university and without interfering with the hospital purpose but helping it rather for the longer courses, and (d) stimulate attendance, provide facilities for observation and furnish as far as possible special lecturers for the short courses; (4) to point out to foundations or wealthy donors the public service that could be rendered by the (a) endowment of university professorships in hospital administration and (b) university research fellowships in hospital administration; (6) to secure the cooperation of universities in the other sections of the hospital field; (7) to make intelligent experimentation in all aspects of the educational problems involved in training for hospital administration as Marquette University has done for the Central West. What is needed now is not multiplication of agencies of training, but a few institutions to undertake the solution of the educational problems in actually rendering the service in training executives.[5]

The Marquette University program referred to in these recommendations was described quite fully in the 1925 report. The university also published in August, 1925, a bulletin, "The College of Hospital Administration," in which the following statement occurs:

Marquette University established in 1924 a College of Hospital Administration for the training of hospital executives, hospital technicians, dietitians, and other hospital specialists. This step in 1924 was part of a comprehensive plan on the part of Marquette University to develop a great medical and hospital center in Milwaukee.

The movement for hospital standardization and improvement, so important and fruitful and to which the Catholic Hospital Association of the United States and Canada has given so much energy and effort, requires for its complete realization, the presence in each hospital of trained and expert executives, familiar with the best and most efficient method in hospital organization. Hitherto, the training of such executives has been carried on in too haphazard

[4] *Ibid.*, p. 14.
[5] *Ibid.*, pp. 46–47.

and uncertain a manner, through actual experience in hospitals. In this way, the development of executives has been slow, their experience only partial, and they have missed much of the rounded training which would come from definite courses carried on by skilled instructors. Hence there is need of a college of hospital administration where those destined to hospital work or who are already engaged in it, may come for regular training and may at the conclusion of their course receive a definite degree which will mark them out as competent for the important work which they are to undertake.

The president of the university, Rev. Albert C. Fox, announced the following appointments to the new college:

Rev. C. B. Moulinier, S.J., Acting Dean (founder and president of the Catholic Hospital Association since 1915)

Edward A. Fitzpatrick, Educational Director (Professor of Education and Dean of the Graduate School, Marquette University)

Joseph Carl Bock, Professor of Physiological Chemistry, Marquette University School of Medicine

Rev. John P. Donaghey, Professor of Physics, Marquette University

Max Gilbert, Assistant Professor of Physiological Chemistry, Marquette University School of Medicine

Clarence Winfred Geyer, Professor of Roentgenology

Malcolm T. MacEachern, Professorial Lecturer in Hospital Administration (Associate Director and Director of Hospital Activities, American College of Surgeons)

Edward L. Miloslavich, Professor of Pathology and Bacteriology and Director of the Department, Marquette University School of Medicine

E. Freeman Pyle, Professor of Business Administration (Dean, College of Business Administration, Marquette University)

Carl Zollman, Professor of Law, Marquette University

In the same bulletin the conferring of honorary degrees of doctor of science in hospital administration upon three leaders in the field at the commencement exercises on June 10, 1925, is reported:

To signalize the establishment of the College of Hospital Administration, Marquette University gave the honorary degree of Doctor of Science to three distinguished persons in the field of hospital administration: Dr. S. S. Goldwater of Mount Sinai Hospital, New York City, whose services are known nationally and even internationally; Dr. Malcolm T. MacEachern, Director of Hospital Activities of the American College of Surgeons, whose influence reaches all hospitals; and Mother Mary Concordia, whose service is typical of the great services of the Catholic Sisterhood. This is the first time the degree has been given for distinguished service in the field of hospital administration.

Marquette University's College of Hospital Administration offered undergraduate, graduate, and short courses in 1925–1926, 1926–1927, and 1927–1928 and then, auspicious though its beginning, is heard of no more. Inquiry around the university brings forth a consensus that although a great deal of interest was manifested at first, there was not sufficient enrollment to keep the operation in existence. Medical personnel who were there in those days feel "it was just too soon" for the venture.

The 1926 Committee on the Training of Hospital Executives, of which Professor Edward A. Fitzpatrick of Marquette University was chairman, conditioned its deliberations on the recommendation of the 1925 committee that the American Hospital Association "could best function in this educational field as a co-operating and supplementing agency with educational institutions actually training administrative personnel, rather than to directly initiate and undertake professional training itself." The 1926 report concerned itself in the main with a job analysis of the superintendent. The analysis is preceded by the following statement:[6]

> A study of the requirements of a modern hospital will show that the relationships between the various departments are so interwoven, and that authoritative decisions must be available promptly upon so many occasions, that it necessitates an organization plan whereby absolute authority must be centralized in one controlling individual. Such an executive is the hospital superintendent (by this or any other name).

The committee suggested that the next step for consideration should, for its effect on recruiting as well as a service to the medical student, be the inclusion in every medical curriculum of a course on hospital organization and administration from the physician's and the surgeon's viewpoint.

In 1928, continuing as chairman of the Committee on the Training of Hospital Executives, Professor Fitzpatrick[7] complained bitterly about the delay in implementing the recommendations of the several committees, saying in part:

> What the hospital field will become is dependent to a considerable degree on what kind of hospital superintendents we have. The central figure in the hospital field is not the doctor, nor the nurse, nor the business manager, but the hospital superintendent. On his outlook upon life, on his conception of the social responsibility of the hospital, on his vision of the possibility of hospital service, will depend ultimately the character of the American hospital. It is, therefore, of the utmost importance that the general level of the hospital superintendent should be raised and that the quality of the leadership furnished by him in his own hospital, and in national hospital associations, shall be characterized by intelligence, by vision, and by common sense. . . . It would seem, therefore, that an effort aiming directly at the training of the hospital superintendent would be fundamental to an improvement of the hospital field. . . . The Committee on the Training of Hospital Executives this year has reported a fairly thorough-going job analysis of the superintendency with the multiplicity of relationships of the superintendent analyzed into their various elements. . . .

Around this time medical schools, as a part of the curriculum for medical students, seem to have begun to teach some elements of hospital administration. In a brief biography of Dr. Louis H. Burlingham, president-elect of the American Hospital Association in 1927–1928, published in the same *Bulletin* from which the preceding quotation is taken, he is referred to as lecturer in hospital admin-

---

[6] Report of the Committee on the Training of Hospital Executives—1927—the 1925 Report. *Bull. Am. Hosp. A.*, October, 1927, pp. 95–112.

[7] *Bull. Am. Hosp. A.*, January, 1928, pp. 66–67.

istration in the medical school of Washington University, in addition to being superintendent of Barnes Hospital, St. Louis.

An international note was sounded in 1929 when at the First International Hospital Congress, held in Atlantic City, Dr. J. Wirth, medical director, Municipal Hospital, Sachsenhausen, Frankfort on the Main, Germany, a member of the International Hospital Committee, declared:[8]

> There should be a systematic training of those aspiring to become superintendents of hospitals. Medical training is an advantage, but the superintendent must also be conversant with principles of administration, fundamentals of technology, social problems and statistics.

Doubtless the depression was the reason why no report of a Committee on the Training of Hospital Executives appears in the 1930 convention program of the American Hospital Association. Attention seems to have been diverted to short-term training programs in the next few years. The need for action was nevertheless recognized as urgent. For example, Paul H. Fesler,[9] then superintendent of Wesley Memorial Hospital, Chicago, said in his presidential address to the American Hospital Association in 1932:

> It is deplorable to notice that some of the best hospitals in this country are administered by men with no experience or training in hospital administration. . . . It is ridiculous to think that men without any training whatsoever are permitted to head institutions responsible for the saving of lives and representing millions of dollars. This would not be possible in any business organization.

Need Combination of General and Special Education

In this age of specialization—compulsory specialization because of the vast accumulation of knowledge which necessitates a high degree of differentiation for excellence in any area—it is of supreme importance that in educating the specialist he be made fully aware of precisely how his field impinges on the fields around it. Generalization has a value equal to that of specialization. This seems particularly essential for the medical service administrator to understand. Like the doctor's, his ultimate concern is for a person, the patient. His concern is for everything about that person because the deeper we get into the scientific principles of treating disease and injury, the more it becomes evident that recovery depends upon much more than technical skill.

The patient's education, his emotions, his social and economic situation, his religious convictions, his position in the community, his reaction to the hospital surroundings, his motivation to get well, all enter into his response to surgery, medication, and whatever other therapy may be employed. He is as complex an entity and as hard to understand in toto as the universe of which he is a part.

---

[8] Proceedings of the First International Hospital Congress, Atlantic City. New York, New York Academy of Medicine, and Paris, p. 120.
[9] *A Venture Forward, A History of the American College of Hospital Administrators,* Chicago, The College, 1955, p. 8.

The manufacturer of steel beams has no such puzzling problem at the end of his production line. He can streamline his operations without concern for the feelings of his product. Even if the comparison is stretched to include those who buy his beams, he has to deal with impulses infinitely more simple than those that move the seeker of relief from physical and mental distress. The administrator in the health field cannot be a good administrator unless he directs all of his thoughts and acts to improving patient care, in complete awareness that the efficiency and economy for which industry strives must not infrequently give way to higher goals in the hospital.

Role of the American College of Hospital Administrators

In 1933 an organization was founded which had as one of its primary purposes the development of plans and projects for the training of hospital administrators. In the history of the college[10] the following statement about its origin appears:

> Since the late 1920's there had been considerable talk at hospital conventions about the obvious need for an organization of hospital administrators. Dr. Malcolm T. MacEachern, Associate Director and Director of Hospital Activities, American College of Surgeons, had frequently urged not only the desirability of such an organization, but had insisted that its existence was essential to the effective management of American hospitals. Many hospital administrators had begun to point to the American College of Surgeons and the American College of Physicians as examples of successful societies which might be emulated in the administrative field. These administrators believed that only through their own organization could they originate standards of administrative competency, promote formal academic training, attract able persons to the field, lessen opportunity for the incompetent, and give administrators professional prestige. . . .

The founder of National Hospital Day, Matthew O. Foley, editor of *Hospital Management,* brought up the subject of organized effort one day in a talk with Dewey Lutes, superintendent of Ravenswood Hospital, Chicago. Lutes then sounded out Dr. MacEachern on the idea, who, according to the history, "gave the project his immediate and influential support."

The organization was quickly accomplished. A study committee of the college presented in 1935, under the chairmanship of Dr. Fred G. Carter, a report, "The Hospital Administrator." In October, 1936, there started to function a Committee on the Training of Hospital Administrators, of which Dr. MacEachern was chairman. The committee agreed with Dr. MacEachern that the college should assume the responsibility for placing the training of hospital administrators on the same plane as the training of physicians. In 1937 the committee made a report, *University Training for Hospital Administration Career,* the foreword of which was written by Rev. Alphonse M. Schwitalla, then president of the Catholic Hospital Association, who stated in part:

[10] *Ibid.,* pp. 7–8.

From a functionary viewpoint there can be little doubt but that hospital administration must be regarded as a distinctive and highly complex area of endeavor. The hospital administrator must be cognizant not only of the intricacies of finance, the complexities of patient care, public relations of the institutions, the relation of his hospital to other professional groups, certain aspects of sociology and psychology, of community organization and inter-relationships, but also of a literally vast number of technical procedures in four or five professions. These specialized procedures he must understand at least in their significance. He must be possessed not only of a wealth of knowledge, but what is even more important, of tact, diplomacy and sympathy to a degree that may make it possible for him to apply his knowledge prudently and effectively for human betterment. Nothing that may happen in the institution can or should be foreign to his interests, from housekeeping to the significance of postmortem examinations. Hospital administration therefore seems to "cut through" all the larger human and institutional interests.

Arguing that the apprenticeship type of training was outmoded, and that other professions demand the acquisition of at least a master's degree for qualification for a profession, Father Schwitalla declared that "in trying to formulate general requirements for hospital administration we commit ourselves to the program that hospital administration requires at least the basic preparation which is ordinarily implied in the master's degree."

One of the basic principles outlined in the report reads:

In what subjects the master's degree should have been taken to constitute adequate preparation for the hospital administrator is, of course, a matter for discussion. It would seem, however, that the more specific the program leading to the degree can be made, and the more the whole curriculum can be pointed directly towards hospital administration, assuming as basis the need for an adequate general education, the more effectively will an educational program favor the uplifting of the profession of hospital administration.

In its "Statement of Principles and Recommendations" the recommendation relative to graduate education is theoretical instruction and education in skills in the following administrative fields:

1. General administration including executive and administrative meetings, departmental conferences, admission office, etc.
2. Management with reference to services and personnel
3. Plant management including physical plant as well as maintenance features
4. Medical and nursing staff administration
5. Intensified experience in at least two of the hospital's professional departments

The report also included provision for a four-year undergraduate program in recognition of "conditions existing at present," and it promulgated general principles of training for graduates in medicine and nursing who might be admitted. In connection with the former it declared that "obviously the M.D. degree by itself is no guarantee of success in hospital administration" and enumerated as "indispensable" courses for the physician in accounting, financial administration, and one or two courses in statistics and in management.

Joint Commission on Education

Then the schools began to get started—Chicago in 1934, Northwestern in 1943, Columbia in 1945—but these were not enough to meet the demand. The college planned action to interest more universities in this field of education. The first step was formation, under a $94,700 grant from the W. K. Kellogg Foundation, of a Joint Commission on Education with the American Hospital Association for a three-year study. Charles E. Prall, Ph.D., member of the staff of the American Council of Education and formerly dean of education, University of Pittsburgh, directed the study, with Dr. Robert H. Bishop, Jr., as chairman of the commission. The first meeting was held in Chicago in March, 1945, with Dr. Prall presenting a proposal for a curriculum plan:

> 1. The core should provide an adequate orientation in the hospital as an organism in itself and also as the central feature in a more inclusive community effort; it should supply understandings of the origin and nature of administrative problems with which the hospital administrator must deal; it should develop the place or importance of operating skills and techniques, and carry some of these in the intern period to elementary levels of proficiency.
> 2. Courses in allied fields and subjects may be visualized in two groups which do not have a sharp line of demarcation:
> (a) those providing specialized preparation which can be offered outside the core without greatly limiting their usefulness, e.g., accounting, bacteriology, orientation in medicine, nutrition, statistics, etc.; and
> (b) those taken with students going into allied occupations and carried in part for their "rounding out" or perspective creating value, e.g., community organization, public health organization, public health problems, industrial hygiene, personnel administration, the labor movement, health and old-age insurance, mental hygiene, race hygiene or race relations, etc.
> 3. Pre-professional courses will be determined by the needs of individual students and student groups who must carry courses as outlined in 2 (a) and 2 (b).
> 4. The internship should be conceived as part of the core; it is to be distinguished from extern and other types of experience connected with the work of the first year.

The director of the study visited the following universities to arouse interest: University of Minnesota, Washington University, Catholic University of America, Duke University, University of Oklahoma, University of Colorado, Medical College of Virginia, Stanford University, State University of Iowa, University of Southern California, and Vanderbilt University. The Commission's *Newsletter* of November 1, 1945, reported that Columbia University had opened with 5 full-time and 10 or 12 part-time students and had established six required and three elective courses in the fall quarter; that Northwestern at the start of its third year had 15 full-time students and 77 who were enrolled for one or more of its six special courses and seven electives; and that the University of Chicago had 9 full-time students and 1 auditor and was offering three courses in the business school and one each in the law school, school of biological sciences, and the social work school, besides the seminars, field trips, and lectures in hospital administration.

In 1946 graduate programs were started at the University of Minnesota and Washington University and in 1947 at the University of Toronto, Johns Hopkins, and Yale. Workshops on curriculum planning conducted under the auspices of the joint commission brought together the directors and faculties of all of the programs.

Hospitals were also visited by the director of the study who reported his observations in *Problems of Hospital Administration* (Chicago, Physicians' Record Company, 1948).

An especially historic meeting of course directors, because of the group action taken on administrative internships, was held in Chicago on February 10, 1947, attended by Dr. Frank R. Bradley, Washington University; Ray Brown, representing Dr. Bachmeyer, University of Chicago; Dr. MacEachern, Northwestern; James A. Hamilton, Minnesota; Drs. Claude W. Munger and John Gorrell, Columbia; Dr. A. L. Snoke, Yale; Dean Conley, executive director of the college; and the commission staff.

Further cooperative action on curricula developed from later workshops. At the end of 1947 the commission published *The Administrative Internship in the Hospital—A Manual and Guide,* much of the material for which grew from a conference, "The Hospital Administrative Internship," sponsored by the joint commission and the Columbia University School of Public Health in January of the same year. The *Manual* has since been revised and reissued periodically.

The work of the Joint Commission on Education culminated in a final report published in 1948 under the title, *The College Curriculum in Hospital Administration.* The report, together with the workshops sponsored by the commission during the three years of the study, proved to be a great stimulus to coordinated planning. Outstanding among the workshops were two of five days each which were held in Chicago in June and in August, 1947. Assignments were made to different small groups, later meeting together, to develop definitions, formulate objectives, and consider methods of teaching the following subjects: medical service; professional audits and accounting; dietetics and food service; financial accounting and management; and theory of organization. The approach was from the standpoint of training hospital administrators. Outlines were prepared by specialists in each of these fields who participated in the discussion with the course directors and faculty members. A course directors' session was concerned with services to faculty and control of subject matter, and with seminar direction and individual projects and assignments.

The 1948 Report

Hospital Administration; a Life's Profession, is the title of the 86-page report published by the college in 1948, the work of a committee consisting of Howard E. Bishop, Robert H. Bishop, Jr., M.D., Arden E. Hardgrove, and Edgar C.

Hayhow, Ph.D. The report is a fairly comprehensive portrayal of the hospital situation of the day, how it got there, and where it is heading, with emphasis on the role of the administrator and his educational preparation. It gives a general description of each of the programs in hospital administration, seven in number, which were being conducted at the time. Chapter 13 of the report is devoted to a discussion of the administrative internship, indicating its indispensability.

Continuing Leadership of the College

Direct assistance to the graduate programs in hospital administration has been given in every possible way. Especially helpful have been the institutes for administrative residency preceptors held in different regions of the United States and Canada each year. These were started in 1949 in response to an expressed need by the course directors, the first having been held December 18 to 20 of that year at the University of Minnesota. The first one was not so much for preceptors as for course directors and faculty, with emphasis on preceptor training. It gave the first opportunity for the school group to get ideas from the preceptors as a group, 21 of the latter having been included in the 50 participants. The Minnesota conference was followed by a "Pilot Study Program for Preceptor Training" held at Chicago in April, 1950.

At the end of each year's preceptor conferences, copies of the deliberations of the problem study sessions held in conjunction with each of the conferences are distributed to all of the graduate programs.

As a part of its annual congress on administration the college arranges a luncheon for preceptors and their present and former residents and dinner meetings for each of the alumni groups preceded by a reception for the alumni of all of the schools.

Naturally an increasing proportion of the nominees, members, and fellows of the college is made up of course graduates.

Association of University Programs in Hospital Administration

The work of the Joint Commission on Education had brought the course directors together and instilled a desire to continue to meet. During the American Hospital Association convention in Atlantic City in the fall of 1948, representatives of six of the university programs met with the following stated purpose:

> To organize a group for the exchange of ideas and experience; to consider establishment of reasonably uniform policies and practices where feasible; to consider some relationship to the appropriate committee of the A.C.H.A. if and when funds are available to the College; methods which would be of greatest value, in an advisory way; other business pertinent to such a group.

The University of Chicago was represented at this meeting by Ray Brown; Columbia by Dr. John Gorrell; Northwestern by Laura Jackson; Toronto by Dr. Leonard Bradley; Washington by Dr. Frank Bradley; Yale by Dr. Clement Clay. James Stephan, of the University of Minnesota, had been invited but was unable to attend. It was decided that the group to be organized at a meeting set for the weekend beginning Friday evening, December 17, would consist of graduate teaching groups of these seven programs. It was agreed that for specific purposes, other persons could be invited to attend certain sessions. Dr. Arthur C. Bachmeyer was unanimously selected to head the group. A workshop was scheduled for December 18 and 19 at the Roosevelt Hospital, New York.

At the New York meeting in December, 1948, Dr. Bachmeyer who had accepted the chairmanship, presided; the name, Association of University Programs in Hospital Administration, was selected; the purposes and qualifications for membership were discussed; formal organization was agreed upon; and a committee was appointed to draw up bylaws.

School affairs discussed at the New York workshop included selection of students, work experience, testing devices, prerequisites, grades, residencies, and a report from a subcommittee of the American Association of Medical Social Workers on the teaching of students in hospital administration what they should know about social work.

The first meeting as an organized group was held in May, 1949, at the headquarters of the American College of Surgeons, Chicago. Subsequent meetings were held in December, 1949, at Minneapolis; May, 1950, at the Kellogg Foundation headquarters in Battle Creek; December, 1950, at the University of Chicago; May, 1951, at Guild Inn near Toronto; September, 1951, at Barnes Hospital, St. Louis; April, 1952, at Brooke Army Medical Center, San Antonio, Texas; September, 1952, in connection with the American Hospital Association convention in Philadelphia; May, 1953, at the State University of Iowa, Iowa City; February, 1954, at the Lake Shore Club, Chicago; June, 1955, at the Grand Hotel, Mackinac Island; September, 1955, in connection with the A.H.A. convention in Atlantic City; December, 1955, at the Biltmore Hotel, Atlanta; June, 1956, at Yale University, New Haven; September, 1956, at the Palmer House, Chicago; December, 1956, at the Gramercy Park Hotel, New York; May, 1957, at the Chase Hotel, St. Louis; September, 1957, in connection with the A.H.A. convention in Atlantic City; May, 1958, at the University of Minnesota; August, 1958, in connection with the A.H.A. convention in Chicago; May, 1959, at the University of Pittsburgh; August, 1959, in connection with the A.H.A. convention in New York; May, 1960, as guests of the Medical College of Virginia in Williamsburg, Virginia; May, 1961, at Brooke Army Medical Center, San Antonio; May, 1962, at the State University of Iowa, Iowa City; May, 1963, in Dearborn, Michigan, with the University of Michigan as host. The University of Montreal is host for the 1964 session.

Chairmen, serving for one year, have followed the order of the establishment of the programs. In 1964 seventeen universities were members: University of Chicago, founded in 1934; Columbia University, 1945; University of Minnesota, 1946; Washington University, 1946; University of Toronto, 1947; University of California, 1947; Yale University, 1947; St. Louis University, 1948; University of Pittsburgh, 1948; State University of Iowa, 1950; Baylor University–Army, 1950; Medical College of Virginia, 1950; University of Michigan, 1955; Cornell University, 1955; Université of Montreal, 1956; George Washington University, 1959; University of Mexico, 1959.

Although no accreditation of schools has been attempted by the association, admission to membership is generally considered as tantamount to approval.

Conferences and Workshops

With the aid of grants from the W. K. Kellogg Foundation, conferences and workshops are held once or twice a year. An outstanding conference was one held at Mackinac Island in June, 1955. Objectives were discussed, and the following five major goals for the development of students were outlined:

1. Understanding of the hospital (a) as an important community health institution; (b) as an important interprofessional institution; (c) as an important research and educational center; and (d) the hospital administrator's responsibility
2. Ability to recognize and define a hospital problem, gather the facts, draw conclusions, and implement them to the fullest possible extent
3. Ability to draw upon various fields of knowledge to be used as guiding principles in making conclusions and decisions
4. Ability to exercise leadership role in working with associations and the public
5. Ability to develop attitudes appropriate to effective hospital administration

Discussion of ways of implementing these objectives was held at the succeeding conference in Atlanta in December, 1955, in preparation for which the various schools selected an objective and drew up and circulated descriptions of teaching efforts aimed to develop it.

For 1(a) Michigan uses lectures, case problems, seminars, field trips, and collateral reading and courses, under the following heads: I, Learning to Define the Community (as related to provision of health services) in terms of consumer demand, social organization, topographic or geographic considerations, supplier restrictions, health service duplication, and examination and analysis of various patterns; II, Determining the Nature of Communities, according to classifiable types and patterns by social, economic, and environmental characteristics and the effect of these forces on health organization; III, Knowing Available Patterns of Community Health-Directed Resources—Private, Voluntary, and Public, from the standpoints of structure, health goals, functions, financing, and methods of operation; IV, Identifying Specific Health Goals Applicable to the

Community, including preventive and diagnostic, therapeutic, rehabilitative, and education and research services; V, Integrating the Hospital with Other Community Health Resources, from the standpoints of effects on recipients of services and on community health resources.

Pittsburgh, also with relation to 1(a), conducts introductory discussions by students and faculty to develop understanding of the nature and magnitude of physical environmental factors affecting man and conditioning his response; such understanding, it was stated:

> . . . is indispensable in making decisions in regard to such problems as housing and physical facilities for patients and employees; plant location; design and maintenance; heating, lighting, ventilation and color; contamination, sterilization, sanitation, waste and refuse disposal; vermin control; water, air, safety hazards; fire protection; and a host of other aspects of basic public health and engineering. Biological factors are considered, their identity, relative importance, variations in both man and the biological environment, as well as their impact on the health of the public, on needs and demands for medical care and on planning and management of programs and institutions. Environmental physiology, nutrition and similar courses provide the student with necessary background in the basic principles of healthful living, well-being, productivity, general health, recovery and rehabilitation.

Other courses mentioned were social psychiatry, introduction to human ecology, statistics, public health seminars, and principles of public health practice.

California, for 1(b), interprofessional aspects, presents these as a basic part of the discussions of organization and human relations, which include sessions on medical staff organization; hospital standards and accreditation; dietary, nursing, social service, medical records, admitting, pharmacy, x-ray, laboratory, anesthesia, physical therapy and rehabilitation, and nursing education departments; intern-resident education; specialist services in the hospital; and various relationships. Methods of instruction include seminars, lectures, and special interdisciplinary field studies. The conclusion reached was that in this area "we can use more of what anthropology, sociology and social psychology have already developed, but the need for further development remains great."

Chicago, concerned with 1(c), the hospital as an important research and educational center, stated that in programs of education for hospital administration "the development of proper attitudes toward the research and educational responsibilities of the hospital must be one of the major objectives" and added that this can be achieved "only if the student has a clear understanding of those concepts which make and require the hospital to serve as such a center." The concepts given were:

1. The hospital is a community agency and as such has a responsibility to maximize its service to the community.

2. The hospital is the largest employer of the health professions and must have a constant supply of such personnel.

3. The hospital is the only source of much of the clinical material necessary in the training of the health professions.

4. Organized educational programs within the hospital serve to stimulate the best thinking and practices of all those who participate in, or come into contact with, such teaching programs.

5. Teaching programs help the hospital meet its responsibility to provide the best possible environment for encouraging the continuous education and upgrading of its medical staff.

6. The best doctors tend to be attracted to hospitals with active teaching programs.

7. The patient receives a dividend in better care as a by-product of the educational program in which he is involved. Likewise the best teaching is dependent upon the best possible patient care.

8. The hospital gains prestige and added community support from its educational activities.

As for the hospital as a research center, the concepts, summarized, were (1) responsibility, as a community agency, to contribute to the betterment of medical care through research; (2) primary function of prevention of disease furthered by research; (3) having the patients, personnel, and facilities necessary for research; (4) having unique characteristics for attracting research support; (5) being a repository of clinical data useful in research because of maintenance of detailed medical records for long periods; (6) better professional practices and higher level of care stimulated by active research; (7) best clinical research derived from best possible patient care; (8) best doctors and other professional personnel attracted by an active research program; (9) prestige and community support gained by active research program.

Objective 1(d), the hospital administrator's responsibility, as developed by Columbia included seven topics: planning, organizing, staffing, directing, coordinating, reporting, and budgeting. How these are taught was summarized as follows:

> Essentially, the basic principles are presented and set forth in lectures in the first semester. This is followed by the year of residency period, in which the student learns from observing his preceptor in action, and is also given the opportunity to apply theory gained in classrooms in actual situations under the guidance of the preceptor. The residency year is followed by seminar work, case study and problem solving. Here the students have an opportunity to become acquainted with the differences between the various hospitals in which they served their residencies. It is in this period too that a concerted effort is made by the faculty to fill in possible gaps in their education and residency experience, correct ideas, or help them to overcome weaknesses in certain areas.

Minnesota reported on goal 2, problem solving, with an excellent chart showing the subject broken down into the following elements: steps in problem solving; tools of problem solving; interpretation of administrative situations; barriers to problem solving and facilitating skills; awareness to problems in situation—definition, listing of areas of consideration; problem-solving practice; current management problem in a local hospital; conference technique of problem solving; presentation of solutions and implementation; written problem-solving practice. Under "aims of instruction" the content of each ele-

ment, the attitudes to be cultivated, and the skills to be developed were outlined. Methods of teaching used are lectures, discussions, illustrations, seminars,
student presentations, written reports, conferences, role playing, and written
examinations and quizzes.

Baylor–Army, discussing the same objective, presented similar ideas, listing
the following steps: problem identification, statement of problem, fact collection, evaluation of facts, conclusions, recommended course of action, and implementation.

Northwestern, concerned with objective 3, "ability to draw upon various fields
of knowledge for guiding principles in making conclusions and decisions," said
in part:

> The utilization of so-called "outside" sources—that is, outside of the hospital
> administration curriculum—to influence the behavior and attitudes of the pro-
> spective administrator has two values. First, it introduces him to fields of
> knowledge in which he will find many related concepts and ideals; second, it
> helps him to appreciate that the whole of life and living encompasses countless
> worthy activities and objectives besides that of healing the sick, highly important
> though this effort is. As far as behavior is concerned, therefore, what we are
> seeking to develop is a sense of balance. . . . A sufficiently well rounded education
> will . . . develop in him an appreciation of the value of work in many other
> fields, and of the way all workers fit together to form a more or less smoothly
> functioning social and economic structure. This appreciation will help him to
> get along much better with members of boards of trustees, personnel and the
> public, than would otherwise be the case. It will make his decisions, when action
> is needed, more acceptable and practical. . . . Naturally the courses in hospital
> administration are not devoid of elements designed to help develop in the stu-
> dents the attitudes and understanding described. As has been remarked many
> times, there can be no sharp separation between the curriculum within the field
> and that without.

Toronto developed the theme of objective 4, importance of exercising the
leadership role. Michael M. Davis was quoted as saying:

> Universities should educate administrators to serve as leaders. The task of such
> leaders is to guide their hospitals toward the full realization of service to the
> public. . . . The basic policies and the most important technics of each type of
> agency are determined by its primary objectives . . . in the case of the hospital,
> up-to-date medical service. . . . The hospital must assemble and utilize an excep-
> tional variety of technics in order to attain its primary purpose of medical
> service. . . . This unusual array of technics requires an exceptional degree of co-
> ordination, guidance and leadership in administration. . . . Graduates of univer-
> sity schools of hospital administration must be educated in the arts of utilizing
> and organizing a variety of business and community skills, skills which they
> may not themselves possess but which they must understand in purpose and
> relation. . . .

Content aspects of the objective were listed as human relations, communications, hospital associations, hospital economics, and the hospital as a community
health center. Devices used to develop leadership qualities in the student include
encouragement to give talks in the classroom, to attend and study the programs

of hospital meetings, to cultivate broad community interests, to discover and interpret source materials, to acquire skill in written communication, to familiarize himself with health and social welfare organizations and agencies, and to learn to think independently and to make decisions, at the same time recognizing and utilizing the abilities of others.

Duke, which was not a member but was invited to contribute to the discussion in view of its pioneer status in establishing an apprenticeship type program in 1930 which was still in existence at the time of the meeting (and has since, 1962, instituted a full graduate program), working on objective 5—ability to develop attitudes appropriate to effective hospital administration—listed 13 methods. In summary, they were:

1. Capitalize upon the "institutional attitude" of the teaching institution
2. Select faculty and staff personnel who have a teaching attitude and are interested in passing on their knowledge and skills
3. Provide sufficient time to associate with these people so that attitudes can be transferred and assimilated
4. Utilize psychological tests to determine attitudes and preferences
5. Assign special projects which have bearing on shaping attitudes
6. Arrange close relationships with top administrative staff at hospitals
7. Provide routine duties that have some responsibility for independent thought and action
8. Provide opportunities for attending board meetings, staff and planning conferences and let student or resident participate
9. Provide opportunities for observing different administrators at work
10. Arrange lectures by people who are outstanding in their fields so that attitudes as well as technics and principles can be learned
11. Provide opportunities for the student to express himself
12. Cultivate interaction of students with other students at different stages of development
13. Provide reading assignments and journal sessions for reading well-known administrators' works

Washington and St. Louis universities reported jointly on the same objective concerned with development of attitudes. Differentiating between "understanding" and "attitude" it was pointed out that whereas "a person may understand why social segregation has been abolished in the tax-supported institutions in the country, his attitude concerning segregation may be entirely different." Therefore the following definition of attitudes was presented: "Appropriate attitude may be defined as a feeling of responsibility manifested by service to the board of trustees, the community, the medical staff, the patient and the hospital employees."

Four "learning experiences" were listed by the St. Louis schools for developing appropriate attitudes:

1. Assimilation from the environment
2. Emotional effect of certain kinds of experiences which may be deliberately planned, preferably in the residency year

3. Traumatic experiences—possible in residency year
4. Direct intellectual processes by means of formal lectures, case problems, demonstrations, mock board meetings, field trips, training films, hospital meetings, staff meetings, clinical pathological conferences

The preceding papers were written in 1955, and the world has moved on since then and so have the courses, but they are presented to show the way the workshops stimulate analysis and thinking and to portray through the expressions of the program directors and faculty members themselves what they feel to be the objectives of graduate education in hospital administration.

Thanks to grants from the W. K. Kellogg Foundation, it has been possible to add to the benefits of interchange of experiences by the group the advantage of ideas and guidance from authorities in the educational field. Prominent among the speakers and discussion leaders at the different meetings have been John Dale Russell, director of the Center for Study and Development of Higher Education, New York University; Daniel R. Davies, Professor of Education, Columbia University; Robert T. Livingston, Professor of Industrial Management Engineering, Columbia University; Ralph Tyler, director of the Center for Advanced Study in the Behavioral Sciences, Stanford University; Leo W. Simmons, Professor of Sociology, Yale University, Wallace S. Sayre, Professor of Public Administration, Columbia University, and John Ivey, director of the Southern Regional Educational Conference Board. The positions listed are those which they held at the time of their participation in the workshops.

Among the comments by the discussion leaders on the papers submitted by the courses at the Atlanta meeting on objectives were:

Dr. Wallace Sayre:

The more familiar he gets with them the less the hosiptal administration student and administrator is inclined to feel that we should borrow from business administration techniques—use them with care and caution. Borrow business techniques in part but not whole. . . . How the needs of the community are being met is the measure of success of the administrator.

Dr. Ralph Tyler:

Systematic planning of a curriculum and the development of a program of instruction and of procedures for evaluation require clearly defined objectives. These are the guiding purposes which provide a basis for selecting instructional materials, developing teaching plans and assignments, and indicating the kinds of appraisal to be made in order to find out how far the objectives are actually being reached. The objectives of any educational program are behaviors, that is, ways of thinking, feeling or acting to be developed by the students.

Dr. Leo W. Simmons:

Certain guides are needed on the practical limitations of curriculum planning. These are the considerations of (a) time and resources available for studying the hospital; (b) scope and depth in the theory and material to be presented; (c) teaching techniques and procedures to be employed; (d) checks on progress attained in the teaching objectives—namely, ability to understand hospitals.

The Olsen Report

In 1952, through a committee, the Association of University Programs in Hospital Administration appointed a Commission on University Education in Hospital Administration to study education for administration in hospitals as envisioned for the future, to survey existing university programs in the field, and to make recommendations for the improvement of present programs as a group. The commission, of which James A. Hamilton, director of the University of Minnesota program, was chairman, was independent of the association. Its members included two hospital trustees, two hospital administrators, one representative of the field of public health administration, one representative of organized education on a national scale, and three professional educators in the field who were also hospital administrators and consultants. Herluf V. Olsen, long-time dean and professor of the Amos Tuck School of Business Administration at Dartmouth College, was selected as the director.

The report of the commission, *University Education for Administration in Hospitals,* was published by the American Council on Education in 1954 with this preamble:

> As the report of an independent commission and study staff, this document does not presume to represent the views of and is not to be construed to be endorsed by the American Council on Education, the W. K. Kellogg Foundation, the Association of University Programs in Hospital Administration, or any of the universities now conducting a university graduate program in hospital administraton. The study and publication of the report were made possible by a grant of funds by the W. K. Kellogg Foundation.

The tenor of the report as reviewed prior to its publication was disagreed with by many of the directors of the programs; hence the guarded preamble. The bone of contention was such statements as, "The establishment of graduate programs in hospital administration may be said to mark the coming of age of an *industry"*—a word that the Dr. MacEacherns and the Dr. Snokes did not like to see applied to hospitals. The recommendations that "the program be located in the school of business administration" provoked considerable dissent, as did the emphasis throughout on the business aspects.

On the whole, the report was an important and constructive event in the history of the association. Professor Leo W. Simmons summed up the reaction beautifully in a statement he made at the Atlanta conference:[11]

> The Olsen report served a fine purpose—it challenged and frustrated you; and it forced upon you a major decision—whether to accept for yourselves the model of the business administrator or try to do something else. In spite of many similarities, you sensed fundamental differences between business and hospital administration and you began to wonder whether what works in business will fit also into the health field.

[11] From the original manuscript, Training for Hospital Administration.

Research Project

A further major project of the Association of University Programs in Hospital Administration was a three-year study, between 1956 and 1959, under a Public Health Service grant, of the needs for research in the hospital field. It was instigated by Dr. John R. McGibony, then chairman of the association's research committee and director of the program in hospital and medical administration, University of Pittsburgh.

The study was conducted under the direction of a national advisory committee consisting of Dr. McGibony as chairman and the following members: Dr. E. Dwight Barnett, then director, Palo Alto Stanford Hospital Center; Ray E. Brown, then superintendent, University of Chicago Clinics; George Bugbee, president, Health Information Foundation; George S. Buis, then director, Course in Hospital Administration, Yale University; John E. Ivey, Jr., then executive vice-president, New York University; Dr. Jack Masur, assistant surgeon general, Public Health Service; Maurice J. Norby, deputy director, American Hospital Association; and Ralph W. Tyler, director, Center for Advanced Study in the Behavioral Sciences, Stanford University.

The reports of the results of the study were under three main headings: A Study of Problems in the Hospital Field; Hospital Problems in Changing Times; and The Role of Research in Graduate Education.

THE SCHOOLS

Experimentation in the application of the principles in the various committee reports was already going on at the University of Chicago, whose graduate program was in the planning stage at the same time that the American College of Hospital Administrators was being organized in 1933. The first students were accepted in the fall of 1934. With the distinction of being the earliest program which is still in existence, the University of Chicago celebrated its twenty-fifth anniversary in 1958 with a National Symposium held December 12-13.

The instigation for the pioneer program came from a leading authority in the hospital field, Michael M. Davis, who as a member of the Committee on the Costs of Medical Care which rendered its report in October, 1932, resolved to take action on this statement in the recommendations:[12]

Hospitals and clinics are not only medical institutions, they are also social and business enterprises, sometimes very large ones. It is important, therefore, that they be directed by administrators who are trained for their responsibilities and can understand and integrate the various professional, economic, and social factors involved. . . . Definite opportunities should be provided, either in universities or in institutes of hospital administration connected wth universities, for

[12] Quoted in *Graduate Education for Hospital Administration,* Ray E. Brown, ed., Chicago, Graduate Program in Hospital Administration, University of Chicago, 1959, p. 1.

the theoretical and practical training of such administrators. The administration of hospitals and medical centers should be developed as a career that will attract high-grade students.

Dr. Davis was director for medical services of the Julius Rosenwald Fund and had professorial rank in the Department of Sociology of the University of Chicago at the time. He found the atmosphere of the university favorable to innovations. The dean of the School of Business, William H. Spencer, agreed that the objectives of hospital administration were fundamentally medical, but he also perceived that the basic principles and practice of administration extended to nonprofit areas as well as to business. The dean of the School of the Biological Sciences, which included the medical school, agreed that hospital administration was a field worthy of an educational project on the university level.

It was for purely practical reasons, as was the case later at Northwestern, that the course was placed under the School of Business. The dean of the Medical School supported the idea but his faculty were not interested. Dr. Davis felt that it would have been "theoretically correct" but "practically stupid" to place the course under the Medical School, and the dean agreed.

Taking note of the fact that several of the programs established later have been set up in schools of public health, Dr. Davis said that this choice was not possible in 1933–1934 because at that time such schools were not developed. He acknowledged, in an address at the twenty-fifth anniversary celebration, the "theoretical appropriateness" of placing hospital administration in schools of public health, but concluded:[13]

> Unhappily, the schools of public health have rarely measured up to their opportunities. They have also shown little flexibility in adapting educational programs to the needs of particular fields. An example is the requirement that certain courses in public health must be taken by every student in hospital administration who seeks a degree, apparently irrespective of the relevance of these courses to the hospital field.

Utilization of existing courses as far as possible was the aim in the establishment of the University of Chicago program, and only two new courses were introduced: one in the history and development of medical agencies and institutions, taught by Dr. Davis in the Department of Sociology, and one of supervised field work conducted by the hospital administration staff. The other work was in the School of Business, the School of Social Service Administration, and the Departments of Sociology and Economics. Opportunities for observation and study of administrative practice were provided in the teaching hospital and outpatient department, but "the School of Medicine offered nothing sufficiently unspecialized for our classes."[14]

Dr. Davis stated that the policy of utilizing existing courses "led instructors

13 *Ibid.*, p. 12.
14 *Ibid.*, p. 13.

in accounting, statistics, business policy, community organization and other courses given in various departments of the University gradually to enrich their material by additions from the field of medical administration."

Dr. Arthur C. Bachmeyer assumed direction of the program in 1937 when Dr. Davis left, giving it medical leadership in his position as associate dean of the School of the Biological Sciences. Upon Bachmeyer's death in 1953 Ray E. Brown, administrator of the University Clinics, became director, the first graduate of a program to head his own school. Upon Mr. Brown's appointment in 1961 as vice-president for administration of the university, George P. Bugbee, president of the Health Information Foundation and former executive director of the American Hospital Association, assumed the directorship.

World War II may be given as one impetus for starting the program in 1943 at Northwestern University, as well as the others that started soon afterward. The American College of Hospital Administrators had prepared and mailed a questionnaire to 10,000 members of the Army Medical Administrative Corps asking about their training, experience, and future interest in civilian hospital administration. Of the 2,500 replies that were received, 1,450 indicated desire to prepare for a career in this field. Partly as a result of this, and partly because of their own knowledge of the needs, Dr. J. Roscoe Miller, then dean of Northwestern University Medical School, and Edgar Blake, then superintendent of Wesley Memorial Hospital affiliated with the university, asked Dr. MacEachern to start a program at Northwestern.

This, too, was set up in the School of Business for much the same reason as Chicago's—administratively it fitted best into that school. The Medical School had no courses to which students in hospital administration could be admitted, and the university has no school of public health. All of the prerequisite courses and electives in business—accounting, finance, business economics, business organization, statistics, office management, personnel administration, and so on— were obtainable in the School of Business and in the closely integrated evening divisions' offerings in biology, sociology, psychology, and public administration. The program left a narrow margin of opportunity at first, which was gradually discontinued, for an undergraduate degree, limiting admission to mature students who already had two or more years' experience as administrators or assistant administrators.

The Medical School cooperated by furnishing an instructor for the basic medical orientation course, fundamentals of medical science, Dr. Theodore Van Dellen; also by contributing the services of many special lecturers through the years on subjects in which the medical viewpoint was needed, especially in rehabilitation, laboratory and x-ray service, maternal and infant care, and medical staff relationships.

For teaching in public health, a professor was recruited from another university.

Several changes in administration of the School of Business, and the death of Dr. MacEachern in 1956, together with desire to discontinue specialized courses, led to termination of the program in 1961. Between 1943 and that date there were 729 graduates. They form a strong alumni association, which is developing a unique program for continued service to the field.

A five-year grant from the Rosenwald Foundation followed by a one-year one from the Commonwealth Fund and later support from the W. K. Kellogg Foundation helped to finance the University of Chicago program. Northwestern University's program was started with the aid of grants from the Johnson & Johnson Research Foundation and the American Hospital Supply Corporation, with supplemental aid from several industrial sources. The later programs have likewise received substantial support from foundations, especially the W. K. Kellogg Foundation.

Characteristics of the Schools

Mere listing of the course titles of the seventeen universities that are members of A.U.P.H.A. for the purpose of comparative analysis would be misleading. A program that lists many specialized subjects in its curriculum may nevertheless incorporate within them as much emphasis upon general principles as does another program that lists mainly three or four broad general areas. The latter in turn may incorporate considerable specialized teaching in its seemingly broad framework. The style of the school catalogue may well be a limiting factor in descriptions of course content, rendering comparisons unreliable. Changes from year to year, and even from semester to semester, in a still new field of education also make unwise any attempt to differentiate among the programs from the standpoint of curricula.

For the student and for the field the differences are minor. The important facts are that the programs exist, that 17 leading universities have recognized the need for special preparation for hospital administration through graduate education, that promising students are being attracted to the courses, that except for an infinitesimal percentage graduates stay in hospitals and related organizations, and that the university-trained administrator has quickly established a favored position. The last fact can be proved by requests to the schools and employment agencies from governing boards.

The necessity of conforming to the policies of the diverse schools in which they are established imposes rather wide apparent variations in the administration and curricula of the programs. Four of the 17 programs are set up in schools of medicine, 7 in schools of public health, 3 in graduate schools, 3 in business schools, or in combined schools of business and public administration.

Nonmember Schools

New schools are not eligible for consideration for membership in A.U.P.H.A. before they have graduated their first class, so that generally two years elapse before they apply.

Duke University has started a master's degree program in its Medical and Graduate School, an outgrowth of a long-established apprenticeship type program conducted at Duke University Hospital, Durham, North Carolina, in conjunction with the university. Started in 1930, this is actually the earliest training program for hospital administrators in America that survived.

The University of Florida at Gainesville and the University of Alabama Medical Center at Birmingham have announced plans to start graduate programs in the fall of 1964.

The University of California at Los Angeles has established a graduate program under the direction of Dr. Paul Lembcke who formerly was with the Johns Hopkins University course which was discontinued.

Undergraduate courses have been conducted by the University of Georgia, Oklahoma Baptist University, University of Mississippi, and others. The U.S. Naval School of Hospital Administration has been operating for several years. Recently a cooperative education program has been arranged with George Washington University whereby students satisfactorily meeting the academic requirements of both will be granted credits toward an associate in arts or a bachelor in arts degree in the field of business administration.

Xavier University, Cincinnati, has a certificate and a degree program.

A program in hospital administration not leading to a degree was established in 1948 by Rev. Hector L. Bertrand, S.J., mainly for Catholic sisters, under the auspices of the Committee of the Hospitals of Quebec.

In Britain, Australia, and a few South American countries, programs are being conducted and additional ones are planned.

The Canadian Hospital Association conducts an extension course in hospital organization and management extending over two years, with a four-week summer session in residence at a university, leading to a certificate. The program is conducted in cooperation with the Department of Hospital Administration of the School of Hygiene of the University of Toronto. It was started in 1955.

With the aid of a grant from the W. K. Kellogg Foundation, the University of Saskatchewan started an extension course in hospital organization and management in 1960. It is a long-term, formal educational program aimed at the specific needs of executive personnel in hospitals with less than 50 beds.

Columbia University conducts courses by correspondence in a special program. In 1962, in cooperation with the U.S. Public Health Service and the International Cooperation Administration, a ten-week intensive course was held for eight foreign physicians. In 1962–1963 the extension department sent lecturers to Chicago to conduct a program for administrators of nursing homes similar to the longer one which it has established in New York.

Northwestern University conducted a 32-session course in principles of administration for personnel of medical service institutions in 1961–1962.

Most of the universities which have graduate programs in hospital administration hold special courses, in addition, for different types of hospital personnel as a community service.

Much has been written about the administrative residency from the viewpoints of the university and of the preceptor, but little from the reaction of the resident himself. Here is the viewpoint of Don L. Arnwine when he was a resident from Northwestern University in 1959 at the University of Colorado Hospitals, of which he is now the administrator.

Administrative Residency

DON L. ARNWINE

The administrative residency can be tremendously important if it is entered into and utilized properly. It can increase the student's personal growth in hospital administration and sow the seed that will bring a good harvest to the hospital field in general.

The administrative residency can be described as many things. It can be a "learning situation," a "testing ground," an "experience provider," and many other things. More than anything else, though, it is "opportunity," in every sense of the word. The value and the results of the residency will depend on the degree to which the resident takes advantage of the opportunity.

A resident has at his disposal an established and operating hospital. It lies before him like a giant erector set and he can mentally disassemble, renovate, or build what he wishes with it. The hospital is also like a watch with a glass case, and the resident has the opportunity to observe its functioning parts, detect the necessary coordination, and learn how to wind it to make it tick.

Because the hospital administrator is his preceptor and he is a free lance member of the administrative staff, the resident's position could be described as enviable. He has an objective vantage point from which to view the hospital operation. In his association with the administrator and administrative staff the hospital as a whole can be clearly visualized. The resident has the opportunity to become familiar with departmental problems but they do not reduce him to subjectivity because of his vantage point. He has a front-row seat at policy decisions and can then carry his chair to the units that the policies affect. Conversely, he can witness the evolution of a problem and follow it step by step up the ladder through its resolution by a policy or administrative decision.

If the preceptor is properly interested in his education, the resident has a key to every door, and what escapes his scrutiny is due to his own passiveness or lethargy.

Though the resident is in an enviable position, it is also often a precarious one. Because of his position, he may become a holder of confidential information or knowledge that demands much discretion. To be able to maintain possession of his key and stay in a position to take advantage of his opportunity will largely depend upon his discretion.

He may find himself in an unfavorable relationship with certain employees.

This can be regarded as natural because in a short period of time he gains advantages that many long-time employees do not have. It is a test of his ability to work with people to overcome this situation without jeopardizing his position.

If the resident's study or observations result in a change that affects employees, he may gain the reputation of being the administrator's "spy." The protection of his position in this situation will depend upon his ability to implement and sell ideas diplomatically.

The Resident's Attitude. The opportunity that an administrative residency offers and the position that the resident holds is of little value if he does not have the right attitude. An attitude is intangible and hard to define. The distinction between an attitude of "learning" and an attitude of "teaching" should be made. That is to say, the resident should consider his primary purpose to further his knowledge and capabilities in administration. This may seem rather elementary but it is not. Most residents have had several years of hospital experience, as well as nine months of graduate study. They may already feel a considerable mastery of their subject. It is not unusual for a resident to have an improper attitude.

The dangers of an improper attitude are twofold. One is that if the resident is not seeking to learn, he will not even see the opportunity, much less take advantage of it. Second, he will alienate the administrative staff and other personnel who can be of great value in furthering his knowledge and administrative growth.

An example of an improper attitude is depicted in the following true incident: A resident had been in a hospital two weeks when a department-head meeting was called. The administrator thought this would be a good opportunity to introduce the resident and invited him to the meeting. He introduced him and asked if he would like to say a few words. The resident responded by saying: "I have only been here two weeks but I can see that we have a lot of work to do."

In so stating he showed the attitude of a reformer rather than a learner, and he destroyed any possibility of cooperation from the department heads.

Another extremely important attitude is the way he feels about the role of a hospital administrator. If he is fully dedicated to the task, his learning experience and his potential are greatly enhanced. If to him hospital administration is just another job, the residency will lose much of its significance.

Curriculum Recommended by the Committee on Training of Hospital Executives, 1922[15]

    I. *Public Health* (20%)
        Major disease groups, their causes, methods of treatment and prevention
        Communicable disease control, community, institutional

[15] In the 1925 committee's report. *Bulletin No. 65,* American Hospital Association, July, 1926, Appendix A.

Social factors in disease, ignorance, poverty, vice
Vital statistics, hospital statistics
Statistics of morbidity for community, patients' records
Health insurance, sickness insurance, contract medicine
Mental hygiene, delinquency, relation of crime to mental diseases
Community sanitation and hygiene, application of principles to hospital
Industrial hygiene
Relation of hours of work, sleep, diet, fatigue and normal physiology to health and disease
Activities of public health departments, state, national
Organizations in field of public health, their aims, ideals and operation, group medicine, visiting and public health nursing, etc.

II. *Social Sciences* (15%)
General definitions, principles, history
Standards of living, poverty, education, recreation, unemployment
Urbanization, causes, results of concentration of population
Principles and agencies of relief, voluntary, governmental, local
Health as a sociological problem, responsibility of government for health protection
Rural problems, factors relating to health
Principles of community organization, political science, economics
Tendencies in sociology
Publicity
State medicine, problems incident to it

III. *Organization* (15%)
Fundamentals of organization, responsibilities, governing boards, machinery for administration
Internal hospital organization, departments, advisory groups, delegation of activities and responsibilities
External contacts, agencies of the community, professional groups, political machinery
Correlation of laboratory, x-ray, radium, social service, nursing, dietetics, ambulance service, visiting nurses, operating rooms, outpatient department, follow-up and after-care services, etc.

IV. *Hospital Functions and History* (10%)
History of medical and nursing practice, traditions and education
Present tendencies in medicine and nursing, various suggestions to meet problems
History of laboratories, social service, dietetics, special therapies, their relationship to each other and to other activities
History of hospitals and their tendencies, foreign and American
Position of hospital in community activities, present conception, tendencies
Functions of hospitals and modifications of such functions
Methods of care of sick, hospital and other methods

V. *Business Science* (10%)
Definitions, theories of production and distribution
Distribution of industrial risks, insurance of various kinds
Cost accounting and interpretation, elements of bookkeeping
Budget making, various types of accounts, collections

Purchasing and selling, financing of capital and maintenance charges of hospitals

Various forms of revenue, endowments, sustaining funds, community chests, state or municipal support, contributions, bonds, trust funds

Records of performance of departments, office records and reports

VI. *Institutional Management* (10%)

Principles, definitions, purposes, lines of responsibility and contact, management of departments such as kitchen, laundry, engineering, office, units of the hospital, store-room, housekeeping, etc.

Economics and methods of curtailing expenses of operation

VII. *Personnel Administration* (5%)

Labor problems and labor management

Psychology of work

Efficiency, rewards, methods of increasing responses of workers

Functions of labor in production

Handling professional groups and departments

VIII. *Community Hospital Needs* (5%)

Classification of hospitals

Needs of the community for medical and nursing services

Needs for hospitals and dispensaries, for various types of hospital beds, determining factors of industrial and social life, area to be served, population to be served, living conditions, etc.

Distribution of hospitals and their size, relative to present and probable future demands

Other facilities in community for medical and nursing care

Support in sight for an adequate program

IX. *Physical Plant* (5%)

Location, construction, ventilation, heating, lighting, refrigeration

Maintenance, alterations, repairs, equipment, depreciation, fuel consumption, etc.

X. *Jurisprudence* (5%)

Elements of contracts, testimony

Responsibilities of and legal requirements for the practice of medicine and nursing

Legal responsibility of hospital in matters of autopsies, accidents, compensation, operations, laboratory findings, professional care

Principles of privileged communications

Professional testimony

CHAPTER 19

Communications and Communicators

> I believe that social study should begin with careful
> observation of what may be described as communication:
> that is, the capacity of an individual to communicate his
> feelings and ideas to another, the capacity of groups to
> communicate effectively and intimately with each other.
> This problem is, beyond all reasonable doubt, the outstanding
> defect that civilization is facing today.
>
> ELTON MAYO[1]

COMMUNICATING SEEMS such a simple thing to create such a furor about as is going on today. By a tone, a look, a word, an act, everyone is communicating all the time, and people have been doing so ever since they appeared on the earth.

Yet this simple process is not simple at all but the most complex of the arts and sciences. The community of the professional communicators is one of the hardest with which to establish rapport. It becomes more self-conscious every day because of the current subjection of its techniques to intensive analysis. The lateness of the realization of its importance is one of the reasons for the present dominance of communications in discussions of the future of society, whether it be in terms of the neighborhood, plant management, health improvement, or world affairs.

Technology has much to do with it also. The means and the media of communication are tremendously advanced over what they were even ten years ago.

[1] *The Social Problems of an Industrial Civilization.* Andover, Massachusetts. The Andover Press, 1945, p. 22.

Hollywood star Edward G. Robinson suffers a heart attack while on location in Africa. In a Nairobi hospital the electrocardiogram impulses recorded in the ECG are transmitted to the actor's cardiologist in Los Angeles—the first intercontinental sending of an electrocardiogram, according to the Foundation for Diagnostic Research Education. A device called a sonlink was used to send and receive the heart recording. The apparatus converted the electrocardiogram into sounds which were sent to London by radio, to New York by oversea cable, and then to the cardiologist by telephone. That was in 1962.

In early 1963 Syracuse University announced embarkation upon an "extensive program to meet the challenges posed by revolutionary developments in the field of mass communications . . . with establishment of the world's largest and most advanced center." The reason given was the placing of the communications satellite Telstar in orbit. The university's plans, according to a dispatch dated January 13 from the Chicago Tribune Press Service:

> . . . call for construction of a complex of three buildings linked by a central terrace to form an architectural unit. Work had already begun on a new school of journalism building, a second will contain radio and television facilities including an educational television station and a sight and sound library. The third building will house a major information library and an institute for advanced study of communications and provide facilities for international and national seminars. . . . stress will be placed on developing new ideas and techniques. The center is a part of a 76 million dollar construction and endowment program. . . . Samuel Newhouse, owner of a chain of newspapers and radio and television stations, and Mrs. Newhouse have contributed 15 million dollars toward the communications center.

With spectacular developments such as these, and of course Telstar itself, communications gains concrete foundations. Not since the invention of printing has the outlook been so revolutionary.

Industry is so communications conscious that it hinges almost all its hopes of progress, both within and without the organization, on better communications. *Managing by Communication*[2] is the title of a book by Willard V. Merrihue, manager of community and business relations, General Electric Company. In his introduction he assigns it a new role in business, brought about by rapid changes; increased size, complexity, specialization and decentralization; technological progress; increasing social consciousness; influence of unions; and antibusiness propaganda. He convincingly depicts its importance in every kind of operation in a business organization, saying:

> Gradually we have learned that leadership in work groups cannot be long effective unless it is by persuasion rather than by command. We have learned the hard way that, in the long run, we cannot get effective work accomplished in groups, corporations, armies, churches, or governments, unless we can get it accomplished by individuals.

To which should be added hospitals and other health organizations.

[2] New York, McGraw-Hill Book Co., 1960.

In their teaching, the communications experts prove the fallibility of oral communication by describing a not too complex situation to a member of the class, who retells it to his neighbor, and so on down the line, and then the last one is asked to give his version. There is almost never any resemblance between the final story and the original one. Features have been added and subtracted in the communications process.

The Industrial Research Foundation labels "filling the communications gap" as "industry's biggest frontier," asserting that it finds evidence that a growing communications crisis exists in industry and that there is almost universal concern with the problem. In a series of studies the foundation made in 1961–1962, reported in the *Chicago Tribune,* the lack of adequate communications lines was listed by 86 per cent of close to 20,000 participants as the chief reason for labor-management disputes. The foundation rates "people power" as 97 per cent of the strength of any business and urges explanations to employees of how the individual worker's interest is affected by what the company is trying to do.

COMMUNICATIONS AND PSYCHIATRY

An interesting acknowledgment of the fundamental importance of good communications in promoting a cause was a Conference on Special Problems in Communicating Psychiatric Subject Matter to the Public held at Swampscott, Massachusetts, in 1955. It was organized and conducted by the American Psychiatric Association in cooperation with the National Association of Science Writers and the Nieman Foundation for Journalism. The conference was made possible by grants from the Ittleson Family Foundation, the Albert and Mary Lasker Foundation, the Division Fund, and the Harris Foundation. The conference report, published in 1956 by the association, states the purposes as follows:

> The Conference was envisaged as a first step in a long-range effort to further the public's understanding of psychiatry. Such a meeting, it was believed, could give direction to this effort and carry it forward intensively by focusing on the problems of communication and by exploring the relationship of psychiatry and the press. The stated purposes were:
> To further understanding among psychiatrists and laymen who work together in communicating psychiatric subject matter to the public.
> To clarify certain basic problems in communicating psychiatric subject matter to the public and to shed some light on how best to resolve them.
> To provide the participants with significant information.
> To furnish material for a published report which will be of use to all concerned with communicating psychiatric and other medical subject matter to the public.

In Chapter 3 of the report, "Working Together, People and Mechanisms," reference is made to the specific historical background of the differences between psychiatrists and writers:

In the 1880's the press became interested in institutional psychiatry, which was about the only psychiatry that existed at that time. A flood of exposés about insane asylums, as the mental hospitals were then called, followed. The classic example is Nelly Bly's series of articles, *Horrors of the Mad House,* written after she had spent ten days at the New York City Lunatic Asylum, now the Manhattan State Hospital.

This uninformed, sensational approach to mental hospital problems became a prototype for articles about mental hospitals. Such exposés made good copy for a headline-hungry public, but they were singularly lacking in any constructive suggestions for improving the lot of the mentally ill.

As late as the 1930's, a reporter on a New York City newspaper got himself into a New York state mental hospital and wrote a series of articles about the hospital that were almost as lurid as those written by Nelly Bly fifty years before. Incidentally, it is said, he had a hard time getting out again because the psychiatrists there were convinced he needed treatment.

The report goes on to say that this "black and white approach" embellished "with all kinds of sensationalism," naturally resulted in "considerable antagonism between institutional psychiatrists and the press." The doctors developed an antipress attitude that has not vanished to this day, although after World War II the situation improved when actual surveys began to be conducted with cooperation between the hospitals and the press.

Among the suggestions made at the conference was that psychiatrists should spend a week now and then on a newspaper writing science stories, and writers should spend some time working in mental hospitals!

Another suggestion was that encouragement be given a new form of magazine writing—the editorial review and the documentary in which a complete, detailed analysis is given and the research behind the story is described.

PUBLIC RELATIONS BACKGROUND

Public relations has grown into a big business vying with advertising in size and importance. It began as a defense against the "muck-rakers" who were mentioned in a previous chapter as turning the glare of publicity and public opinion on the "curse of bigness" in business. Conspicuous among them were David Graham Phillips, Lincoln Steffens, Ida Tarbell, and Upton Sinclair. Their success led to recognition by industry of the power of publicity. Sinclair's *Jungle* led to new laws affecting public health and food standards. Industry rose to the defense with whitewashing, an attempt to gloss over the abuses and highlight the constructive aspects. The pioneer among the whitewashers was Ivy Lee, retained in 1914 by the Rockefeller interests and later by the Pennsylvania Railroad.

Ivy Lee did more than whitewash, however. He stimulated action to make his stories true. He had a conviction that business should be operated in the public interest. In the days when business was out to grab everything it could, that was a revolutionary idea. By enunciating the principles of good public relations,

Lee proved to be a leader of reform in business operations. Many of the tenets which he expressed remain valid today.

A few public relations people were trained just in time to respond to the needs of the government for propagandists in the First World War period. This introduced what might be considered the second stage of the development of public relations. All kinds of media were used to sell the war aims and ideals of the government to the people. "Words that won the war" became the slogan, such as "Make the world safe for democracy"—"the war to end wars." Business used publicity to show cooperation with the war effort and in so doing created a new image for itself.

The third stage of public relations was the ten years between 1919 and 1929. During this period industrial publicity was introduced on a large scale. The practitioners had the advantage of the successful tests of principles and practices during the war. Soon universities and hospitals joined industries in harnessing publicity to promote their cause. Among the examples were Light's Golden Jubilee honoring Thomas Edison and the electric light Mazda bulb on postage stamps; and the opening of Greenfield Village by Henry Ford, with guests carried to the ceremonies in buggies, victorias and barouches, horse-driven, to dramatize the passing of the horse-and-buggy age. Vice-presidents were installed during this period whose function was to build good will. The American Telephone and Telegraph Company appointed Arthur W. Page vice-president in charge of public relations in 1927.

Public relations literature began to appear. Ivy Lee published a collection of his addresses in 1925 under the title, *Publicity: Some of the Things It Is and Is Not*. Robert Holman Wilder and K. L. Buell published in 1923, *Publicity: A Manual for the Use of Business, Civic or Social Service Organizations*. There was even a textbook, published in 1926, *Principles of Publicity*, by Glenn C. Quiett and Ralph D. Casey. And a handbook, *Public Relations*, by John Cuthbert Long appeared in 1924. Edward L. Bernays authored *Propaganda* in 1928.

The first request to have "counsel on public relations" listed in the New York telephone directory was made in 1923. Twenty years later there were more than 120 listings.

Edward L. Bernays introduced the fourth stage of public relations in 1929 and became known as United States Publicist Number 1. He served on the U. S. Committee on Public Information during the first World War, was with the committee at the Paris Peace Conference, was a member of President Hoover's Emergency Committee for Employment in 1930–1931; and was co-chairman of the Victory Book Campaign and chairman of the U. S. Treasury's National Publicity Committee for the Third War Loan during the second World War. He has served as public relations counsel to a number of corporations, trade associations, newspapers, theaters, governments, foundations, individuals, educational institutions, and medical organizations. Besides *Prop-*

aganda, his books include *Crystallizing Public Opinion; Speak Up for De-mocracy; Take Your Place at the Peace Table; Public Relations, a Growing Profession;* and *Public Relations.* The last-named was published in 1952 and is a definitive analysis and survey of the field.

What Bernays started in the public relations field was a totally new approach —an academic and research trend for one thing, and high ethical standards for another, marked by the idea that the private and the public interests must co-incide, with public relations activities furthering this goal. The new approach created a dignified, recognized profession that quickly gained stature, with other social forces appreciating its importance.

The profession began to organize in 1939 with the formation of the American Council on Public Relations started by Rex Harlow, then associate professor of public relations at Stanford University, California. A local group of health, welfare, and civic agencies in New York preceded this in 1921 with formation of the National Publicity Council, which is still in existence and publishes *Channels.* In 1948 came the first annual meeting of the Public Relations Society of America, Inc., now the most representative national organization in the field.

Boston University pioneered in education, starting its School of Public Rela-tions in 1947, offering both baccalaureate and master's degrees. In the foreword to the catalogue of the 1949–1950 sessions these statements were included:

> Public Relations represents an all-embracing conception of human relationships. It recognizes that society will progress substantially in proportion to the success with which its members develop understanding and appreciation of one another. Thus, Public Relations impinges upon all media of social communication and contributes to their development. . . . The Division of Public Relations gives new academic recognition to the emerging profession for which it is named. The Senior College program emphasizes continued study in the social sciences with a broad introduction to the objectives and procedures of Public Relations. It de-velops ingenuity and initiative in the organization of Public Relations programs. It seeks to develop skills in the communications media, such as writing and speaking. The Graduate division emphasizes research and teaches its students to think creatively on problems of Public Relations policy within an organization. All divisions are aiming toward preparation of men and women for ultimate policy-making positions rather than for merely their first employment.

The groping stages of public relations are not over and hopefully never will be, for an activity that is based on such a changing foundation as communica-tions must be constantly analyzing and redirecting itself. Even the dictionary definition in *Webster's* first carried in 1945 and revised in 1951, indicates by its use of the word "adapt" that the process is fluid:

> Public relations. 1. The activities of a corporation, union, government, or other organization in building and maintaining sound and productive relations with special publics such as customers, employees or stockholders, and with the public at large, so as to adapt itself to its environment and interpret itself to society. 2. The state of such activities or the art of organizing them.

What might be considered the fifth stage of public relations began in the 1950's with the concept of "corporate citizenship"—a much larger, more active visualization of its function than in the past. Publicity has become an aid but no longer the main vehicle for building good will and understanding. The concept is really not new, but its more general acceptance is. More than 70 years ago the National Cash Register Company, Dayton, Ohio, started garden plots, not just to beautify its grounds, but to give mischievous youngsters something to do, an early effort to curb juvenile delinquency. Seeds, fertilizer, and space were donated and a gardening instructor employed; prizes were offered. But projects like this were few before the present era.

The use of the word "helping" in the headings of six of the chapters in Louis B. Lundborg's book, *Public Relations in the Local Community,*[3] gives a key to the new trend. The headings are "Helping Local Causes and Organizations," "Helping Schools and Colleges," "Helping in City Beautification and Improvement," "Helping in Community Promotion," "Helping Agriculture and Other Business in the Community and Locality," and "Helping Local Government."

The enlistment of the aid of company personnel in all of these "helping" objectives, as a preliminary to which there must be a program for informing them of company affairs and of its interest in the community, is represented as essential and valuable. This necessity brings the public relations director and staff into a close cooperative relationship with the personnel department.

Opinion surveys are another development of the times that is making public relations more scientific. They form a basis for planning the direction of work with employees and the public. The Institute for Research in Mass Motivations, Inc., of Croton-on-Hudson, New York, is among the agencies that have done notable research aimed at creating a better climate for good public relations within and without an organization.

An enlarged and revised edition of the *Public Relations Handbook* edited by Philip Lesley was published by Prentice-Hall in 1962. This is an 869-page volume. It includes summaries of research findings on why publicity succeeds or fails to produce the effects desired by the publicist. In recognition of the broader concept of public relations in the 1960's, chapters have been added on community relations and on industrial and employee relations. The new edition contains a quite comprehensive bibliography of literature on communications psychology and semantics, public relations, and propaganda.

HOSPITAL PUBLIC RELATIONS

Along with the rest of the world in the 1920's, hospitals became more definitely aware of the need for informing the public about their services. In 1927 Matthew O. Foley, then managing editor of *Hospital Management,* made the following remarks at a meeting of the American College of Surgeons:

[3] Published under the sponsorship of the Public Relations Society of America by Harper & Brothers, New York, 1950.

When a state hospital association last summer assigned to Dr. MacEachern the subject of the most important problems before the field, he listed as No. 1 the matter of *development of community interest and support* by means of an educational program. In discussing this point, others suggested legislation and finance as of widespread interest, but Dr. MacEachern replied that in a hospital-wise community, harmful legislation would be defeated, and also in such a community the people would understand the necessity of greater financial support.

Here and there a few other persons were preaching the need for public education through the press. Ahead of his time was, for example, Dr. H. Sheridan Baketel,[4] of Jersey City, who urged that the A.M.A. "establish a publicity bureau, the chief of which should map out the plan of campaign, oversee the preparation of articles, and communicate with the editors of the large papers concerning their acceptance of special articles." Dr. Baketel's concern was to combat the "idiotic and inane medical tales which often appear in newspapers," but he also made specific reference to hospitals when he stated: "There is a wide-spread prejudice among the masses against hospitals and operations. Surgeons are looked on as butchers, seeking whom they may knife. Carefully prepared articles could combat these foolish notions and could bring out the benefit derived from hospitals and operative procedures."

The American Hospital Association took historic action in 1932 when it published as *Bulletin No. 92* a "Report of the Committee on Public Relations." The committee consisted of Lola M. Armstrong (later Mrs. Thomas Ponton) of the *Western Hospital Review;* Matthew O. Foley of *Hospital Management;* Robert Jolly, administrator of Memorial Hospital, Houston, Texas; John A. McNamara, managing editor of *Modern Hospital;* Mrs. Alice Taylor of All Saints Hospital, Fort Worth, Texas; and Dr. MacEachern, the chairman. The introduction to the report stated in part:

> We are entering into a new era of hospitalization. Economic conditions have changed the entire picture so that in the future we must be prepared to meet every demand of the public, and, furthermore, be able to tell the public exactly what our institutions stand for, what we are striving to do, and how we fit into the general scheme of society.
> Every economic crisis that the world has known has brought forth ideas, and means and methods of organization that have been of the utmost benefit to mankind. By the proper education of the public as to the hospital and its work, we may hope to relieve suffering and to lengthen the life of the people within our communities. This is our opportunity to contribute to the welfare of the entire nation.

That the 1932 committee's concept of hospital public relations was far from being confined to the aim of publicity for hospitals but extended to the use of communications media as a way of promoting health is proved by the following statements:

> By cooperating with health officers, visiting nurses, and welfare workers in their work generally, hospitals can aid in furnishing the public with the latest,

[4] *J. A. M. A.,* December 23, 1905. From a reprint by the American Medical Association dated 1906.

most scientific, and progressive knowledge of preventive medicine. The hospital should encourage frequent health examinations, offer an immunizing service for school children if desired, provide accommodations and facilities for clinics, cooperate with the health department to care for infectious diseases, and work side by side with health and welfare organizations in every possible manner for the betterment of humanity. . . . The hospital can in no way be disassociated from the health problems of its community. . . . It is dealing with people; it is concerned first, last, and always with the welfare of human beings. Since its very existence is so commingled with the lifeblood of the community, it is, therefore, both fitting and proper that serious consideration be given to the question of how the hospital can best relate itself to the public--how can it most successfully fit into the community plan of things?

After outlining the various ways in which the hospital should assume leadership in community health activities, and referring to a 1931 report of the A.H.A.'s committee on public health relations, the report recommended such public relations activities as "the health education forum," "the health inventorium," and public education about hospitals through the patient, the medical staff, hospital personnel, superintendent and governing body, visitors, women's auxiliaries, business and service clubs, churches, schools and extracurricular groups, the radio, newspapers, contests and school papers, magazines, bulletins, annual reports, house organs, booklets for patients, bulletins published by outside organizations such as business firms and churches, letters to relatives or friends of patients, follow-up letters, tours, exhibits, slides and motion pictures, National Hospital Day observances, and public meetings of many kinds.

The 43-page report spelled out in some detail how these activities could be planned and carried out and included a 4-page bibliography of articles and reports on public relations and related subjects.

The committee issued a second report in 1933. In 1934 it was enlarged to 18 members, with Dr. MacEachern remaining as chairman and the name changed to Committee on Public Education. The 1934 report expressed disappointment at the slow response to the suggestions on organizing public relations activities in hospitals, emphasized the specific benefits to be expected, and made new recommendations. As addenda, a "calendar of events" for a program of public education and suggested topics for talks, lantern slides, films, and articles were presented.

In 1935 came the publication of the first edition of Dr. MacEachern's book, *Hospital Organization and Management,* with a chapter on "Public Education." In 1939 appeared the 369-page book, *Hospital Public Relations,* by Alden B. Mills, then managing editor of *Modern Hospital.* Hospital public relations had established itself in the literature.

Positive Public Relations

Strong incentives for a positive approach to hospital public relations were outlined in an editorial, "A Role for Hospitals in Preventive Health Measures," in the December, 1962, issue of *Hospital Forum:*

Instead of the constant negative campaign for funds to build more beds to serve the sick and injured, why not a positive campaign that asks the community to "help us keep our beds empty!" Why not place the responsibility for future hospital expansion squarely on those who will make it necessary? How many hospital beds are required to care for the victims of carelessness? How many of your patients, for instance, might not have been patients if their automobile had been equipped with seat belts? And how much is it costing to build and staff those beds? This is a simple public relations approach to preventive health care. If every hospital—or even half the hospitals—would use it, it could be very effective. . . .

There are many safety measures which could be taken in boxing to protect the boxer—and boxing itself. But there has never been a voice of leadership from the health field to inform the public what those safety measures might be, so that the public may draw its own intelligent conclusions.

The editorial continued with mention of the dangers in present-day designs of ladies' shoes and the controversial subject of cigarette smoking and its relationship to cancer.

This brings to mind an incident that occurred in the press room at a surgeons' convention which may serve to illustrate the positive public relations attitude the administrator should have.

A flustered, disheveled crank-type woman with a bandaged hand forced her way through the reporters to the publicity director's desk. Holding up her hand, she shouted for all to hear: "The surgeons should do something about this. I've had four operations on this hand, all because I ripped it on the jagged top of a can when I was opening it; they should make cans easier to open; the surgeons should make them do it."

It had been a heavy day. The incident was a sort of last straw. The publicity director pacified the woman and eased her out of the room with promises to tell the surgeons what she had said. Later he did mention it, in the tone of relating an amusing kind of convention problem, to one of the country's leading surgeons. The surgeon, however, was not amused, not in the least. He said the woman was absolutely right. He maintained that every time a surgeon had such an injury to treat he should investigate the cause and use his influence to correct it.

Nor is this a new attitude on the part of doctors and other hospital people. In *Hospital City—the Story of the Men and Women of Bellevue*,[5] John Starr tells of Dr. Lewis Albert Sayre's diagnosis in the 1850's of lead poisoning in a girl who came to him in a spinal brace with her arms completely paralyzed. The author tells how Dr. Sayre reacted:

It suddenly dawned on him that the limpness of the hands, which could be extended but not flexed, was symptomatic of lead poisoning. But it still remained for him to prove this. Questioning revealed that the girl had not drunk water from lead pipes. Dr. Sayre suggested champagne from a bottle that had been washed with lead shot. But the patient assured him that never in her life had she tasted champagne at all. Nor had her house been recently painted. But finally the

[5] Published in New York by Crown Publishers, Inc., 1957, pp. 88–89.

girl brought Sayre a bottle of liquid face powder labeled "Bloom of Youth." Analysis showed that it contained compounds of lead. Dr. Sayre not only cured the girl of her paralysis by giving her an antidote, *but he headed a vigorous campaign to prevent cosmetic manufacturers from using the poison in balms and lotions.*

Going back two hundred years, we find a hospital administrator who was also a city magistrate, Philippe-Nicolas Pia, establishing rescue stations along the banks of the Seine and inventing apparatus for forcing air into the lungs to resuscitate victims of drowning.

Carried to its logical conclusion this means that doctors and hospital administrators should be active in accident prevention and should have cooperative relationships with the manufacturers of cans and of every other device, piece of equipment, and food or drug product the use of which has potential dangers to the buyer. Such relationships do exist and have operated to prevent an untold number of injuries, illnesses, and deaths. They need to be extended. Promotion of safety and of health precautions is only one of the many ways in which the hospital can and should reach out and serve while at the same time it furthers its own main purpose of saving lives and restoring health. Minimizing the need for some of its services should be, paradoxically, a leading objective.

The line between preventive and curative medicine shifts constantly. Influential persons in the community shift with it. Practicing positive public relations brings recognition and support of the entire hospital operation.

Annual Reports

A sort of climax in the use of the annual report in public relations was achieved in 1957 by Charles Pfizer & Company, Inc., when it distributed its 1956 report as a Sunday newspaper supplement in the *New York Times,* the *Chicago Tribune,* and the *Los Angeles Times.* The 16-page advertising insert was received with such interest that in 1958 a second climax was reached in the publication of the 1957 report as a special supplement of the *New York Times* with inclusion of a seven-page illustrated commentary on the operations of the company by John Gunther, entitled "Inside Pfizer." This was believed to be the first article written by a top-ranking author to appear as part of a corporate report. The newspaper edition was identical in format and content with the one mailed to the pharmaceutical company's 25,000 shareholders.

It is open to argument whether it is a waste of money for hospitals to produce elaborate annual reports. In an article in *Modern Hospital,*[6] Dr. Robert S. Myers of the American College of Surgeons, contends, under the title, "Are Hospitals Going to the Hucksters?" that "a lavish display" antagonizes contributors, who wonder how and why the hospital can spend so much in this way. He refers to a 1961 report on the "finest paper stock" and "full of multi-

[6] September, 1962.

colored illustrations" with some 50 pages of descriptions of activities but no "record of the actual care of patients by departments."

Long criticized for their dull, unattractive reports, some hospitals have, of course, gone to the other extreme in imitating the reports put out by large business corporations. They have employed the same experts who get out the business brochures and these experts, knowing little about hospitals, have used the same techniques. However humble he may feel about his knowledge of typography and layout, the hospital administrator has to step into this picture and make the decisions on what are the important features to be played up, what have been the *really* vital accomplishments. To say, however, "There is no valid reason to distribute this report to the public," as Dr. Myers does, is to ignore the public education possibilities of this medium. Granted that the hospital should have a record of its work, with scientific statistics "incomprehensible to the lay public," this is something else entirely, a specially drawn up record for the archives. The annual report for public distribution should be an interpretive presentation of medical results like that which the science writer prepares for the press—in fact, if rightly handled and distributed to newspapers there should be newsworthy material in it. Also, the hospital owes the public a financial accounting, although as Dr. Myers indicates this should not be as dominant a feature as it is in many annual reports. Yet the annual report provides one of the best ways in which the cost-of-service story can be given to the community.

Attractiveness and novelty can be accomplished without making a report "fancy" and expensive. Bethany Hospital, Chicago, published its 1958 annual report as a "Family Album"—12 pages and cover, size about 5 inches by 6 inches—headings, "Our Family Through the Years," "From Whence We've Come," "Some Changes," "Our Administrative Family Heads," "Our Family's Medical Staff," "Comparative Yearly Statistical Report—What We've Been Up to These Past 8 Years," "What We Did Last Year," "How We Managed to Do It!" (this was the financial report), and "Look At Us Today."

Press Relations

Hospitals might well adapt some of the ideas used in industry for working with the press. The New York Central Railroad Company issues to its division and local officials a booklet, "How to Meet the Press." In it there is explanation of how a newspaper functions, of the speed that is necessary for a reporter to make the edition for which his story is intended, of the way the wire services work—the whole background needed to create understanding of the people in newspaper work and their problems. The railroad personnel are urged to take the initiative in making facts known to the press, whether it be the arrival of a celebrity or the collision of two passenger trains. The object is to stop wild rumors. The booklet was compiled with the aid of suggestions from newspaper editors, reporters, and public relations men.

A public relations firm prepared a manual on press relations for the Textile Committee on Public Relations based on surveys of what newspapermen did and did not like about their relations with industry, and how industries with good press relations achieved their results.

Hospitals have departed somewhat from their stand-off treatment of reporters as they too have learned that cooperation pays. Back in March, 1948 it was reported in the *Public Relations Newsletter* of the American Hospital Association that at a session of the American Press Institute attended by A.H.A. representatives they were as much as told by the city editors that hospital-press relations "stunk." The complaint was that accurate sources of news are not made readily accessible to newspapers, that nobody was assigned to give information. The hospital press codes in Cleveland and Chicago were discussed, but discounted as likely to become "iron curtains" and result in less information than before.

Since that time the Chicago Hospital Council has published a pamphlet that is more than a code. It is called "A Guide to Ethical Hospital Press-TV-Radio Relationships." It was prepared by a joint committee of hospital and newspaper representatives, and on June 5, 1956, the Council of the Chicago Medical Society voted to concur with the principles. Topics covered for the news media are deadlines, diversity of interest, equal access, ready access, exclusives, public interest, responsibility, patient welfare, authorized sources, privacy and authorization; for the hospital, medical judgment, prognoses, records, delays, legal restraints, deaths, features and human interest stories, maternity cases, medical news, police cases, and well-known persons.

Hospitals and related organizations unquestionably have an advantage over commercial interests in getting information into the newspapers. There is always a distrust of free advertising with the others. Editors know that every reader wants to learn how he and his family can live longer and happier lives. It has been proved by polls that health news ranks near the top. Therefore editors feel justified in expecting and even demanding news from health agencies. They appreciate knowing where they can get, and from whom, answers on what's new in medicine. Nevertheless the waste basket is still handy if the news release does not contain real news or if it is poorly written.

Articles can be contributed that overcome ancient fears, senseless traditions, and fallacious beliefs. Doctors constantly struggle against ignorance and prejudice because supposedly sensible persons still are victims of quacks and charlatans. When it comes to health, any kind of lotion or potion which advertisers promote as a panacea for all ills is bought and used. Think of the amazing success in selling "Hadacol" through one of the most outrageous advertising campaigns that ever disgraced the patent medicine field!

Distortions are not at all uncommon in the writings of journalists. Sometimes they are deliberate in order to gain attention, but usually they are the result of hasty and superficial investigation. Answers to the charges seldom get the conspicuous display that the original article did. Some protection against a succeeding offense is to bombard with corrections and explanations every writer who makes misstatements. At least he will not repeat the same errors, and he may be more careful the next time. Everett W. Jones, when he was vice-president of the Modern Hospital Publishing Company, made a practice of doing this; as a hospital consultant now it is probable he still does.

Frequently headlines are deliberately misleading just to attract attention. Magazine publishing is a highly competitive field. Doctors and hospitals have to learn to live with this fact. With a large picture of a surgeon in cap and mask, the cover of *Look* for June 19, 1962, carried in large type the statement, "A Doctor Denounces Fee Splitting, Knife-Happy Surgeons, Mercenary Doctors." So he did, in the article inside, but in sober, unsensational tone, with far more emphasis on the positive than on the negative side. In sounding his justifiable note of caution, Dr. Virgil G. Damon left a clear picture of what good surgery is like and of the way to evaluate doctors when seeking medical care. He properly blamed the patient for some of the evils—simple folk who think only of a good bedside manner, hypochondriacs who demand attention for non-existent disease, persons who seem to need an operation to give them a sense of importance. The article is an appeal to the reader to use intelligence in seeking medical care; the shock is mainly in the glaring headlines.

The press is learning, with exceptions, scientific caution. Going fast are the days when headlines blazoned "CURE DISCOVERED" for anything from tuberculosis to cancer. More and more better papers are steering away from sensationalism. They are trying to report the truth, which usually is that with such and such a new treatment a disease can sometimes be arrested in certain stages or in certain types of cases.

The medical profession, hospitals, and the press were all adversely affected by the old exaggeration of medical news which gave rise to so many tragedies through raising false hopes among readers. The press learned its responsibilities through floods of calls which followed exaggerated news stories. Editors would call to check with medical societies only to discover that reporters had omitted essential modifying clauses.

The gross errors which made scientists scoff at reporters are disappearing. Only once in a while do blunders occur like one the *J.A.M.A.* picked up from a story in a Springfield, Massachusetts, paper: "This city's first case of infantile paralysis this year was reported today when a 6-year-old girl was operated on at a hospital for *tracheotomy, a form of the disease.*" Mostly nowadays reporters and editors check with hospitals and doctors or their own medical dictionaries on such terms. New reporters have to be watched, though, and worked with tactfully.

The change in the interpretation of medical news in the lay press has come about through the development of specially trained science writers.

Working with the Press

One who works with newspapers needs to have a feeling of the greatness of the newspaper as an institution, and he needs also to have a feeling for the possibilities of the specific newspaper, editor, and reporter in his community. The paper should be studied and compared with other newspapers. Sometimes a young reporter can be helped by showing him how another paper handled a story similar to the one he is preparing, perhaps at the administrator's suggestion. Comparison with other papers makes it possible to reveal to the editor or reporter knowledge of what might be called the individual differences of the particular paper, so far as policy and aims are concerned. Understanding and appreciation go a long way if they are genuine and not just expressed for a purpose.

Genuine appreciation will involve watching a reporter's whole effort, not just those stories that concern your hospital, and commending him upon them.

Anybody who prepares material aimed at publication in newspapers should have the newspaper point of view, which is that every day the sun dawns on a new world and that anything under the sun can happen that day. Life is sparkling, changeable, always moving on. More than that, life is charming, fascinating, amusing, pathetic, tragic—offering many a tug at the heartstrings. The newspaperman thinks that his is the most absorbing vocation in the world—to keep people awake to these qualities that eyes and souls blinded by routine might otherwise not see and feel. His passion is one that those who work with newspapers should share, or their material will be dull. The hospital should be interpreted with feeling, from leap-year babies to the trying out of a new type of anesthesia. There is the simple human interest story about the crippled child long in the hospital who cries for her nurse after she is returned to her home— reversing the usual order of homesickness—and there is the scientific story of the lowering of the death rate from pneumonia through the use of penicillin. Sometimes the human interest and the scientific angle can be coupled, as when the crippled child is a cripple no longer thanks to a new procedure.

Business concerns are conscious, and hospitals should be, of the reaction to publicity on the part of the institution's own personnel. Pride and loyalty can be cultivated throughout the staff from the doctors to the moppers when the news about achievements is reported in the press.

Some points to keep in mind about working with newspapers are:[7]

1. Take their initial friendliness for granted and meet it in the same spirit.
2. Get the newspaper point of view toward your hospital.
3. Cultivate personal interest in the paper and those connected with it.
4. Prepare your copy according to high journalistic standards.
5. Realize that you are engaged in competition with others working with and for newspapers, and do not expect more than a fair share of space.

[7] Adapted from Laura G. Jackson: Working with Newspapers. *Mod. Hosp.,* December, 1940.

6. Build press relations in ordinary times so that under extraordinary conditions, a feeling of mutual confidence will exist between you and the newspaper, thus ensuring fair treatment in the press.

7. Feel enthusiastic about your hospital—so enthusiastic that you want to tell about its work to the best of your ability.

8. Avoid dullness by letting genuine feeling for the hospital dictate the tone of the copy you write and communicate itself to the editors and reporters with whom you work.

9. Feel as if you were working *for* the newspaper as well as with it, which brings an obligation not to let news possibilities escape you.

10. Consider the reaction of the people within the hospital to what they see about it in the press, and deliberately try to deepen their enthusiasm in this roundabout fashion.

It is a good situation for a hospital when the editor of the newspaper, who may perhaps be a member of the hospital board, starts to question whether the hospital is as good as it might be and wants to do something about it. We do not begin to give sufficient credit to the press for the strides of progress which are being made in health work. Their cooperation is taken for granted, which is, of course, in a way a tribute to them, too, but proper recognition is a needed incentive for continued support.

An issue of a hospital magazine some time back carried an article about the successful promotion of a building fund for a hospital in Erie, Pennsylvania. Throughout the article there was mention of the regular distribution of press releases to the two newspapers of the city. In this instance, the newspapers were given due credit for the success of the campaign by the administrator of the hospital who was quoted as saying:

> We might stress that one of the most important parts of the campaign promotion was the series of publicity articles released periodically to local newspapers, who cooperated 100 per cent during the campaign. A total of 54 photographs were taken to go along with these releases. The *Dispatch-Herald,* the only local Sunday newspaper, gave us feature space every week, which was very gratifying.

The newspapers in this instance were aware that a United States Public Health Service survey had disclosed a dangerous shortage of hospital beds in Erie, and they were interested in assuring adequate health protection for the community.

It will be noted that even some of the front-page stories in the local newspaper are about things that did not just happen—they were made to happen—"managed news." Editors like to crusade for worthy causes. Such crusades constitute newspaper public relations.

Notwithstanding the favorable attitude toward health news, it must be expected that a great deal of the material furnished to the papers will not be used. The hospital is competing with every kind of enterprise, group and personal activity; competing with national news, politics, catastrophes, crime. There is slim chance for regular publicity however important when there happens to break at the same time a national or local election, a hurricane, a big scandal. The volume of material that comes to a large newspaper every day is so great that it cannot all even be looked at, let alone read.

The tendency of doctors to duck when a reporter appears must be forestalled by getting them acquainted with representatives of the press. Young doctors should be briefed on what information it is ethical to give the press and should be urged to give reporters prompt attention and told why this is desirable.

Actually a whole new era in medical-press relations was ushered in with the way Dr. Paul White of Boston gave the facts of President Eisenhower's condition to reporters when he suffered a coronary attack in Denver. He gave a lecture to the group and used a blackboard to illustrate what he was saying. A reporter who was present hailed the frankness of the presentation as more than giving the world assurance that the President was likely to recover—in a spectacular way, because of the person concerned, it spread hope to people everywhere that with present-day medical treatment a heart attack need not be fatal and educated them about the different kinds of heart conditions. When former Presidents became ill, Cleveland, Wilson, Harding, the utmost secrecy was observed which gave rise to false rumors and unrest.[8]

Sometimes on an important occasion a hospital can get a newspaper to publish an entire supplement about its activities. The *Sunday Telegram,* Worcester, Massachusetts, published a 20-page illustrated section on May 7, 1961, on the occasion of the dedication of the City Hospital's new five-million-dollar consolidated services building (these services were formerly sprawled through 11 scattered buildings). Many activities of the hospital were described along with historical features. The advertisements which appeared in the section were mainly those of suppliers of materials, equipment, and services for the hospital, so they, too, served to give information.

Radio and Television

The approach for getting information to radio and television people is much the same as that to the newspaper. The contacts are with individuals. In the licenses issued by the government to the stations there is the stipulation that the service be maintained "in the public interest, convenience and necessity." Prestige and popularity follow a station's "integration with community activities," so the production manager of WEEI, Boston, and educational director for the Columbia Broadcasting System in New England, L. G. del Castillo, said at a hospital conference of the American College of Surgeons some years ago. Mr. del Castillo emphasized that any organization which has a place in the community's philanthropic activity, and a need for publicizing specific activities, has a legitimate claim for publicity and "need not go with hat in hand as an

---

[8] Adapted from an article by Frances Burns, science reporter for the *Boston Daily Globe: J. Am. A. Med. Rec. Librarians,* April, 1959.

humble petitioner." He favored the forum type of program, if it fits the subject, as more interesting than the straight talk and the interview, saying that "comparatively innocuous subjects such as the average philanthropic institution might select can be highly entertaining in the hands of an experienced moderator and a carefully selected panel of speakers representing the different aspects of the question to be discussed."[9]

Dramatizations must be very well done or had better be omitted. Announcements should be most carefully worded and timed, clear and accurate. A brisk pace is needed.

Radio and television programs which are more than announcements should be promoted in advance. This pleases the station and makes it receptive to another. Local groups should be informed, notices sent to the press, and people asked to send in reactions.

The National Association of Broadcasters has pointed out that radio represents the oldest means of communication because the human voice, with its intimacy, directness, and personality, has swayed millions down through history. Radio made its mass projection possible. Radio and television reach people in their homes where they are relaxed and receptive. Along with the advantage of the warm, friendly voice is the disadvantage of the evanescence of the spoken word. When the telephone or doorbell rings you can put your reading aside and go back to it. When this happens with radio, the continuity is lost—words that have gone out over the air cannot be called back. The radio speaker must get full attention and hold it, must make points several times yet in a way that does not sound like too much repetition. The appeal has to be universal because there is always a mixed audience, and the factor of entertainment plays a larger part than in the press.

DEVELOPMENT OF JOURNALISM

Thomas Carlyle, in the second volume of his *French Revolution,* written in 1837, made this comment: "Great is Journalism. Is not every able Editor a Ruler of the World, being a persuader of it?"

Dictionary definitions of journalism go little farther than to say that it is a record of events of the day. This, of course, overlooks the element of persuasion to which Carlyle refers, and which enters into all but purely factual matter— and frequently even into that, for facts, too, can be so selected and presented that they are exceedingly impressive and persuasive. Henry Justin Smith, of the *Chicago Daily News,* wrote a delightful little book several years ago on this subject, called *It's the Way It's Written!*

Not the least of the factors that have speeded hospital progress has been the so-called rise of the press. Along with scientific advances and technical improvements, the hospital has enjoyed increasingly the advantage of being able to tell

---

[9] From the original manuscript.

and circulate its story far and wide, to the people of all creeds, classes, and colors whom it professes to serve. The modern hospital was idealized in printer's ink before it could come into being. Ideas, and their expression in such a way as to win the support of the reader or audience, must always precede the establishment of a project and the steps in its development ever afterward if it is to grow.

Speaking of ideas and the importance of getting them expressed quickly is a reminder of the story of the man who was trying to think up a way to get his hospital mentioned in the paper on National Hospital Day. He woke up at midnight, with a brilliant idea flashing through his mind. He got up, got down on his knees to thank God for it, but when he got back into bed and tried to resume the train of thought, lo the idea had vanished.

Journalism began before printing. Letters giving the news were sold and circulated long before the invention of the printing press. When Julius Caesar became consul at Rome, in 60 B.C., he decreed the issuance of a document called the "Daily Acts" in which births and deaths, illnesses of prominent people, and the like, were recorded along with political and financial news. Items concerning hospitals frequently appeared in the early newsletters. A French source book exists which is a collection of documents—newsletters, itineraries of pilgrims, chronicles of the Crusades, the registers of the popes, archives of monasteries, and personal journals and memoirs—many of which mention hospitals, particularly the Hotel Dieu at Paris. Thus, for the historical background from which we draw to enrich our writings about hospitals today, we are indebted to the primitive journalism of the Dark and Middle Ages and to the stone carvings and papyri of the ancients.

Among the English handwritten documents about hospitals that have been preserved is the appealing "Manuscript of John Howe," written in 1582. It is addressed to three men who were officers and benefactors of Christ's Hospital. John Howe was a grocer who gained some proficiency in writing while serving as secretary within the Grey Friars to Richard Grafton, first treasurer-general of the order. John Howe's position with the hospital was to collect rents from its properties and to see that the legacies left it were duly paid. From the tone of his manuscript it is apparent that he used his powers of persuasion, also, to stimulate donations and legacies. After telling the story of the hospital, and giving an accounting, he concludes his manuscript thus:

> At the fyrst erection, God moved the harts of a number of good men to gyve greate things. And I hope that the same good mynde be in a nomber still and that they will shewe the fruits of the Gospell which God graunte wee maie all doe . . . and I praie you be myndefull of your promyse made in the beginning touching reformacion of the abuses of the tyme presente.

An example of a printed newsletter, from a period about two hundred years later than John Howe's manuscript, is John Aikin's *Thoughts on Hospitals,* published at Warrington, England, in 1771. John Aikin was a surgeon, and he wrote his little piece with the object of "serving the cause of humanity." He praises the spirit of compassion which has led to the founding of hospitals, but, he says:

> One thing appears wanting to compleat the wishes of humanity; and this is, that a proper direction of the means should accompany the well-meant intentions of doing good. Without a due regard to this object, the most benevolent designs may be frustrated, and instead of a blessing, prove an additional misfortune to the afflicted. Having turned my thoughts somewhat particularly to this subject, several reflections occurred to me which appeared of importance enough to be communicated to the public. . . .

Obviously the idea of the importance of communicating with the public, of public relations, is not new. John Aikin goes on in this document to communicate to the public some facts about the evils of poor ventilation and crowded wards and of the indiscriminate admission and mixture of patients suffering from all kinds of diseases. No doubt good came of it. Perhaps the next conspicuous journalist on hospitals, John Howard, read it. Anyway, in 1773, two years after it was published, John Howard began the series of inspection tours to the prisons, hospitals, and other institutions throughout the British Isles and the European continent that were to continue for 17 years until his death in 1790.

The graphic reporting of his observations has made Howard the outstanding hospital journalist of all time from the viewpoint of the purpose of reform that inspired him to portray the horrible conditions that existed. He would visit a hospital, stir up the authorities and the public by reporting on its deficiencies, and then go back time after time to see what improvements had been made and to criticize until changes occurred that won his praise. If his reports had been private documents for the eyes of the few insiders, the reforms would never have resulted so promptly. The fact that Tenon, at about the same time, was doing similar work in France, also helped, because Tenon's disclosures corroborated those of Howard in instances where they concerned the same institution.

This was journalism in which the facts spoke for themselves. Shocking facts. In the telling, however, they certainly lost nothing by being presented in Howard's vivid narrative style:

> Cavan County Hospital (Ireland)—All the rooms very dirty; little or no bedding; an upper room full of fowls; a dunghill in the small front court.

> The infirmary at Maryborough—an old house, four rooms, walls black and filthy, the floor of the room below was of dirt. . . . In the tower room, the ceiling covered with cobwebs, and in several places open to the sky. Here I saw one naked, pale object, who was under the necessity of tearing his shirt for bandages for his fractured thigh. No sheets in the house; the blankets dirty. No vault, no water. The diet a threepenny loaf and 2 pints of milk. The surgery was a closet about 10' by 6. Furnishings, 10 vials, some of them without corks; a little salve stuck on a board; some tow; and pieces of torn paper scattered on the floor.

Of Lifford Hospital in the County of Donegal he says he has been well informed that the surgeon, Mr. Spence, spent 500 pounds in procuring votes to ensure his election—the "same scandalous abuse by which the lives and health of the poor are in a manner put up to auction that prevails, as is well known, in many London hospitals." He balances this with an account of another hospital in which the surgeon is paid 100 pounds, but "generously gives 50 pounds towards the maintenance of the poor in the hospital, and pays for all the medicine."

Howard's report of his visit to the celebrated hospital at Malta has an amusing note:

> My letter from Sir William Hamilton to the Grand Master flung open every place to me. At the first visit he promised to supply me from his own table with butter, and about a pound was sent to me, with promises, compliments, etc. In a week after, I waited on the Grand Master, who asked me what I thought of his hospitals. I told him freely my opinion, and pointed out many glaring abuses and improprieties which, if His Highness would but at times look into his hospitals, would be redressed. Alas! Here was an end of all my presents; so my tea was ever after with dry bread. I did not, however, cease visiting those places even to the last day, as there was a placidness in the countenances of the patients through the many alterations that were then made.

We are not lacking in this type of journalism, aimed at reform, today—for example, a few years back, the newspaper accounts of the contaminated water situation at Manteno State Hospital in Illinois. Newspapers not infrequently assign reporters to investigate certain hospitals, hoping to find some sensational examples of neglect, or worse. Sometimes there is good reason for suspicion and needed reforms result. Occasionally the efforts are even inspired from within the hospital, by persons who are eager to see conditions remedied and feel that the only effective method is to arouse the public.

John Howard could append to his disapproving report of some features of the London Hospital, in Whitechapel Road, this note: "By a letter lately received, I am informed that the committee are exerting themselves, and making several improvements in this hospital."

That happens nowadays, too.

On the other hand, sensationalism for its own sake, when a writer eager to make a sale of an article to a journal dramatizes and exaggerates a situation, is currently a menace. Since defense is weaker in gaining attention than attack, it is hard to counteract the effect of the misinformation upon the reader.

Another extremely important English contribution to hospital journalism was Florence Nightingale's *Notes on Hospitals,* consisting of two papers read before the National Association for the Promotion of Social Science in 1858 and 1859 at Liverpool, and first published in 1859, going through several editions.

Among the earliest important pieces of literature that had to do with hospitals in the United States was the little book written by Benjamin Franklin and printed in May, 1754, called "Some Account of the Pennsylvania Hospital, from its First Rise to the Beginning of the Fifth Month, May 1754." The first hospital in the country, therefore, inspired the first hospital journalism. This book was written for circulation through the colonies and in Great Britain in order to procure subscriptions to the hospital, which had been started in 1751 and was on the point of moving to a new site. Franklin also publicized the project in his newspaper, and before long the new building was a reality. He published a second edition of the book, bringing it up to date in May, 1761.

It was more than a century after that before the publication of hospital periodicals began. In 1877 there started in New York a publication called *The Hospital Gazette,* but it lasted only six months, when it united with the *Archives of Clinical Surgery,* so probably it was of a medical rather than hospital nature. In England, Burdett's *Hospitals and Charities—a Year Book of Philanthropy and Hospital Annual,* began publication in 1895. Sir Henry Charles Burdett was a great figure in hospital affairs; he came to Chicago in 1893 to represent his country at a hospital conference during the city's first World's Fair.

In 1897, in Detroit, publication of the *International Hospital Record* started. It lasted until 1915, when it merged with *The Modern Hospital,* which had been started in 1913 at St. Louis by the publisher of the *Interstate Medical Journal,* Dr. Otho Ball.[10] After Dr. Ball's death in 1953 *The Modern Hospital* was taken over by the F. W. Dodge Corporation, now McGraw-Hill Book Company, but continues under the editorship of Robert M. Cunningham, Jr., with Raymond P. Sloan as chairman of the editorial board.

Hospital Management is another early periodical in the field. It was founded in 1916 by G. D. Crain, Jr., and associates. Matthew O. Foley, the founder of National Hospital Day, was its managing editor for several years. In 1952 its publication was taken over by Paul E. Clissold, Kenneth C. Crain continuing as vice-president and eastern editor, and Frank Hicks as executive editor. The present executive editor is Dr. Charles U. Letourneau.

Hospitals, the official journal of the American Hospital Association, actually began, in a sense, with the *International Hospital Record* (started in August, 1897, under the name *National Hospital and Sanitarium Record,* with the change of name in 1908) because that publication served as the official organ of the Association of Hospital Superintendents, formed in 1899, and of its successor in 1907, the American Hospital Association. After merger of the *Record* with *The Modern Hospital,* the association published a *Quarterly Bulletin* carrying news items, reports of meetings, and articles based on talks given at the meetings. In 1935 the Committee on the Official Publication, consisting of Dr. Walter E. List, chairman, Dr. G. Harvey Agnew, and Asa Bacon, recommended the publication of an official monthly journal. The first issue appeared January 1, 1936, under the editorship of Dr. Bert W. Caldwell, former executive

[10] For details of the origin and development of *The Modern Hospital* and the influence that a journal and its staff can have in stimulating constructive action, there is at the end of this chapter an article by Bessie Covert of the editorial staff which was written while she was a student in the program in hospital administration at Northwestern University and published in the school's journal, *Hospital Administration Review,* in July, 1950.

secretary of the association. The journal became a semimonthly publication in 1956. James E. Hague is editor.

The Trained Nurse and Hospital Review started publication in 1888, essentially as a journal devoted to nursing. As Helen Pruitt, then (1949) librarian of the American Hospital Association, stated in "A Review of the Bibliographic Sources in the Field of Hospital Administration" (mimeographed by the association), it had "some emphasis on administrative nursing problems" and is still being published "with even more emphasis on nursing."

Hospital Progress, the official journal of the Catholic Hospital Association, dates back to May, 1920.

Other hospital journals with national and international circulation are *Hospital Topics, Canadian Hospital, Hospital Administration* (Australia), *Hospital Administration* (American College of Hospital Administrators), *Hospital and Health Management* (England), *Hospital* (London), *Hospitals' Association Journal* (Australia), *Mental Hospitals* (Washington, D.C.), and *New Zealand Hospital,* to mention only a few of those published in English. *El Hospital,* published by the Panamerican Publishing Company, New York, is the inter-American review of hospitals. Its September, 1962, issue was devoted to a directory of suppliers and supplies, showing offices in the different countries.

Journals of the medical and allied professions also publish many articles on hospitals and related institutions.

A few regional periodicals such as *Southern Hospitals, Texas Hospitals,* and southern California's *Hospital Forum* are well worth including in the administrator's required reading, as they carry articles of general interest.

In the semiannual *Hospital Literature Index,* published by the American Hospital Association under the direction of Helen Yast, librarian, will be found a great number of journals listed outside the hospital field which publish from time to time articles on hospital affairs. This index, a great service to hospital personnel, has been published by the association since 1945. Every five years a cumulative index is published. Since each semiannual index is now around 100 pages ($8\frac{1}{2} \times 11''$, 3 columns), it furnishes an excellent idea of the volume to which hospital journalism has grown. Its classification into more than 400 main subjects also shows the vast scope it has attained.

Writing for the Journals

Editors are busy people. Material that requires little editing, that is vividly told, stands the best chance of getting into print. Speaking of newspapers, a prominent public relations man urges publicists to be even better reporters than the ones employed on the paper and to use a blue pencil even better than the editor.

In writing for any medium, there is a great appeal in contrasts. In order to visualize the growth in clinical laboratory service, it helps to know and to state that in 1895 there were only six microscopes in Chicago, compared with thousands today. Articles can be spiced with historical incidents to show progress. For example, young John Coolidge with today's chemotherapy would probably have recovered from the septicemia which resulted from a blister on his foot. A writer and speaker should be steeped in historical facts—a rich treasure mine from which to dig for adding interest.

The distinction between the way a paper should be prepared for oral presentation and for written was clearly made by John M. Storm, editor of *Hospitals* from 1943 until his death in 1951, in a lecture he gave each year to students in hospital administration at Northwestern University. He said that most non-professional writers do not realize that there is a difference, making the serious error of thinking of the reader as a listener. But, said Mr. Storm:

> The listener rather likes to be warmed up. He is seated and prepared to stay right where he is. In contrast, the reader does *not* like to be warmed up. He is perpetually in a hurry. If the article does not tempt him, he will not even start it. If he starts, and the text is uninteresting, he will not go on. In either case, in order to escape, he has only to flip a page—and this is somewhat easier than turning the dial on his radio.

Books about Hospitals

Hospital literature of book length is relatively meager but is growing, as the reviews in the journals prove. Aside from a few histories of individual hospitals, the past has not much to offer. Dr. Ferdinand C. Stewart wrote a 432-page book in 1843, published by A. Burke, Buffalo, titled *Eminent French Surgeons, with a Historical Account of Hospitals of Paris*. Earlier, 1819, Harry W. Carter had a 255-page book published by T. and G. Underwood, London, called *A Short Account of Some of the Principal Hospitals of France, Italy, Switzerland and the Netherlands, with Remarks on Climate and Disease of Those Countries;* and in 1820 Sir James Clark, M.D., using the same publishers, authored another long-titled book, *Medical Notes on Climate, Disease, Hospitals and Medical Schools in France, Italy, and Switzerland, Comprising an Inquiry into Effects of a Residence in the South of Europe, in Cases of Pulmonary Consumption, and Illustrating Present State of Medicine in Those Countries*.

In 1863 Luoisa May Alcott wrote her *Hospital Sketches,* 102 pages, published by J. Redpath, Boston. In 1868 Edwin R. Maxson wrote *Hospitals, British, French and American,* 122 pages, published for him by a Philadelphia printer. In 1876 Dr. Walker Gill Wylie delivered the Boylston Prize Essay of Harvard University, on *Hospitals: Their History, Organization and Constitution,* which was published by D. Appleton and Company in 1877, 240 pages.

In the 1890's such notable works were produced as Sir Henry Charles Burdett's four-volume *Hospitals and Asylums of the World—Their Origin, History and Administration,* published by the Scientific Press, London, in 1893, and by the same publishers and author, *Cottage Hospitals; General, Fever, and Convalescent: Their Progress, Management and Work in Great Britain and Ireland and U.S.A.*, 379 pages. Sir Henry was surgeon and general superintendent, Queen's Hospital, Birmingham, England.

In 1893 another surgeon, Dr. John S. Billings, published as editor the papers and discussions of the International Congress of Charities, Correction and Philanthropy, Section III, under the title, *Hospitals, Dispensaries and Nursing* (see Chap. 23 for further discussion).

In 1909 Rotha Mary Clay wrote *Mediaeval Hospitals of England*, 357 pages, published by Methuen and Company, London. In 1911 W. B. Saunders Company, Philadelphia, published Charlotte Albina Aikens' *Hospital Management*. John Allan Hornsby and Richard E. Schmidt produced *The Modern Hospital; its Inspiration, its Architecture, its Equipment, its Operation*, 644 pages, in 1913.

In 1918 appeared *Dispensaries, Their Management and Development*, a 438-page book by Michael M. Davis, Jr., Ph.D., then director of the Boston Dispensary, and Dr. Andrew R. Warner, then superintendent of Lakeside Hospital, Cleveland. The book was published by The Macmillan Company, New York. In 1927 Michael Davis wrote *Clinics, Hospitals and Health Centers* in collaboration with staff members of the Committee on Dispensary Development of the United Hospital Fund of New York, 546 pages. In 1924 *Hospital Organization and Operation*, 270 pages, was published by The Macmillan Company, New York; the author was Frank E. Chapman, then administrator of Mount Sinai Hospital, Cleveland, later director of University Hospitals of Western Reserve University, Cleveland.

In the 1930's the new books on hospitals began to add up to a long list, even including fiction—*Hospital*, a novel, by Norah C. James was published by Duckworth, London, in 1932.

Selections from this period and later appear in the bibliography.

How a Hospital Journal Contributes to the Progress of Hospitals[11]

BESSIE COVERT

The first issues of *The Modern Hospital*, the pioneer monthly magazine devoted exclusively to hospital administrative problems, appeared in September, 1913, from St. Louis, Missouri.

The publisher and founder, Dr. Otho F. Ball, was familiar with the publishing business through his periodical, the *Interstate Medical Journal*. Associated with him were a number of young doctors who had recently returned from medical studies in Europe and who were later to become leaders in their respective spe-

[11] *Hospital Administration Review*, Northwestern University, July, 1950, pp. 17–20.

cialties. They read several languages and were supplied with all of the important medical journals and books. From the current medical literature from all countries, these special editors wrote "Collective Abstracts," a unique feature of the *Interstate Medical Journal*. Many of the now familiar developments in medical science were reported and interpreted in these abstracts.

These young medical men, including the publisher, Dr. Ball, who had been sidetracked from his original ambition to practice ophthalmology through his greater interest in the larger problems of medical journalism, discussed the need for a closer tie between doctors and hospitals and commented on the haphazard growth of hospitals and the political hold on public hospitals which was reducing rather than increasing their usefulness. The result of these discussions was the suggestion that there be some interest taken in hospital problems as part of the editorial program of the *Interstate Medical Journal*.

At about this time John D. Barnard of St. Louis became interested in the St. Louis Free Skin and Cancer Hospital, which was overcrowded and had many patients clamoring for admission. He gave the money to build a modern institution. This later became known as the Barnard Free Skin and Cancer Hospital. In the planning stage, Mr. Barnard and Dr. Martin F. Engman, later chief of staff of Barnard Hospital, came to Dr. Ball for help in finding information here and abroad on planning and equipping this special type of hospital. An extended study of special and general hospitals was begun which brought to light the fact that there was little organized material on hospital construction, organization, equipment, and administration available from any source.

The mayor of St. Louis, in a speech before a civic group during this period, made the statement that "the St. Louis City Hospital has the lowest per capita cost and the lowest food cost of any similar institution in the country." Dr. Ball was certainly impressed by this statement, but not in the way the mayor intended. He was impressed rather with the seriousness of the situation when a city like St. Louis was more interested in lowering the cost of hospital care than in improving its quality.

"Efficiency" drives were beginning in business and industry in this era. A few hospitals became interested in improving their efficiency, although most of them went on in their usual, rather disorganized way. There were 6,665 institutions which called themselves hospitals in the United States at the time with a reported capacity of more than 600,000 beds. The investment in lands, buildings, and equipment was estimated at a billion and a half dollars. Certainly, such a field needed some means of exchanging ideas and some source of information for its own interests.

Dr. Ball had traveled throughout the country and knew the need for organization among hospitals, particularly organization of information, as well as the need for all types of hospitals to get away from their isolation and individualism. Instead of discussing hospital problems in the already existing *Interstate Medical*

Journal, he saw the need for a special publication devoted to them. The only existing publication in the field was the *International Hospital Record,* a small newspaper-type magazine published by Del T. Sutton, a Detroit printer who was also its editor. It was a monthly publication of limited editorial content and limited circulation. After *The Modern Hospital* was established, this publication was taken over by The Modern Hospital Publishing Company and discontinued.

Monthly Publication Planned

With his program for a hospital magazine outlined, Dr. Ball visited with his friend, Dr. John T. Hornsby, then superintendent of Michael Reese Hospital, Chicago. Together they worked out the details for a monthly publication of which Dr. Hornsby would be editor. As a preliminary step it was decided that Dr. Hornsby, collaborating with Richard E. Schmidt of Schmidt, Garden and Erikson, the hospital architectural firm, should write a book on hospitals. This was done, and the book, also called *The Modern Hospital,* was published by W. B. Saunders and Company in March, 1913.

Drs. Ball and Hornsby felt that the hospital field would benefit if the American Medical Association were to authorize a section on hospitals with the idea of educating physicians in regard to the changing status of these institutions. To that end the interest of Dr. George H. Simmons, then head of the association, was enlisted, and such a section was formed and held its first meeting in 1912. The report of that meeting, which appeared in the first issue of *The Modern Hospital,* shows that the ideals toward which they were working then were much the same as they are today.

When Volume 1, Number 1, of *The Modern Hospital* appeared in September, 1913, it totaled 144 pages, approximately the same page size as the present magazine. Copies were sent to 8,000 hospitals in the United States, in Canada, and abroad. The magazine was received with enthusiasm, but it is interesting that the director of a prominent hospital, in his letter to the publisher regarding the first issue, wrote: "Dear Doctors: Your first number is excellent, but after a few issues you will exhaust all possible topics in hospital architecture, organization, equipment and administration and what then?" Of course, as time has gone on the problem has been, rather, how to use all of the material available.

The cover design of the new magazine was developed by Walter Dorwin Teague, who has since become internationally famous in industrial design. It represented the Golden Circle of Charity within which a typical hospital was pictured. The picture on the first cover was an architect's sketch of the new Peter Bent Brigham Hospital in Boston, whose story was told in the magazine.

The original board of editors included Dr. Henry Hurd and Dr. Winford H. Smith, of Baltimore; Dr. Frederic A. Washburn, of Boston; Dr. James G. Mumford, of Clifton Springs, New York; Dr. W. L. Babcock, of Detroit; and Dr. S. S. Goldwater, of New York, in addition to Dr. Hornsby.

Hospital Standardization Suggested

In its second issue *The Modern Hospital* made a suggestion which, at the time, was considered startling and revolutionary—the need for inspection and standardization of hospitals. Dr. Hornsby, as editor, wrote an editorial and an article on the subject, the first of a series continued over the years. The next month the newly organized American College of Surgeons held its first convention. The college, which later absorbed the Clinical Congress of Surgeons of North America, then had no planned program except the annual clinical congress.

Early in 1915 Dr. John G. Bowman, chancellor of the University of Iowa, learned that members of the faculty of the medical school were guilty of fee splitting and, when informed of all the facts, asked for the resignations of a considerable number of the faculty. He let out a blast against fee splitting as immoral which made front-page news throughout the country. Dr. Franklin Martin, the founder and director general of the American College of Surgeons, was quick to see the importance of the issue raised by Chancellor Bowman and promptly negotiated with him to head the educational program of the college.

One of Dr. Bowman's first tasks was to orient himself to the hospital field, and this was mainly done through reading the back issues of *The Modern Hospital*. The articles on hospital standardization commanded his attention and resulted in visits with Drs. Ball and Hornsby. The outcome of these visits was the broadening of the educational program of the college to encompass hospital standardization. Dr. Bowman felt that the moral issues involved, such as fee splitting, competence of surgeons, adequacy of hospital care, were issues that should be taken up with the trustees of the hospitals of the country and with the general public because only with such backing could a real program of betterment get under way.

In December, 1917, *The Modern Hospital* announced

... the most important meeting for the hospitals of this country that has ever been held occurred in Chicago on Friday and Saturday, October 19 and 20, unfortunately too late for a full account to be published in our November issue. The hospitals of the United States are to be standardized. It looks very much now as though we were on the threshold of some very radical progress.

The indicated meeting was that of the American College of Surgeons announcing its standardization program. Dr. Bowman was director of the educational program of the college from 1915 through 1921 when he left to become chancellor of the University of Pittsburgh.

Dr. Malcolm T. MacEachern, general superintendent of the Vancouver General Hospital from 1913 to 1922, was one of Dr. Bowman's and Dr. Martin's volunteer workers who helped spread the gospel of hospital standardization. He spoke extensively on the subject, both in Canada and in the United States. Much of his material was published in early issues of *The Modern Hospital*. He was director general of the Victorian Order of Nurses for Canada for a year and then became associate director and director of hospital activities of the college, succeeding Dr. Bowman.

Catholic Hospitals Organized

One of the complications of the early period of the American College of Surgeons' standardization program was the seeming inability of the Catholic Sisters to take an active part in the various conferences held over the country. It became obvious that an organization of Catholic hospitals was an essential step in the standardization program. Drs. Ball and Hornsby arranged with Father Moulinier of Marquette University for an organization meeting of Catholic Sisters in Milwaukee in June, 1915. The transactions of this very successful meeting were published in a special book by The Modern Hospital Publishing Company for the association, and copies were sent to all Catholic hospitals and Catholic dignitaries throughout the country. The association was off to a good start, and Father Moulinier, the first president and the founder, made a very real contribution to the betterment of hospital service. He collaborated actively with Dr. Bowman and the American College of Surgeons in carrying this new concept of hospital responsibility forward.

Because of specialized problems affecting Catholic hospitals, particularly religious problems, which had to be discussed and for which there was no logical place in *The Modern Hospital,* Father Moulinier came to the conclusion that this growing association should have its own official publication, and he approached The Modern Hospital Publishing Company with the idea of such a bulletin or magazine for the Catholic field. It was not logical for the publishers of *The Modern Hospital,* who were serving the entire field with their own magazine, to publish a second bulletin or magazine which would cover only a segment of it, hence the suggestion was made by Dr. Ball to Father Moulinier that he approach the Bruce organization in Milwaukee, publishers of several Catholic papers and of the *American School Board Journal.* The Bruces were affiliated with the Catholic Church and the sons were Marquette University graduates. A satisfactory publishing arrangement was entered into with this company. This was the origin of *Hospital Progress* (now published at the Catholic Hospital Association headquarters in St. Louis).

War Gave Impetus

During the first World War *The Modern Hospital* had done a fair job of reporting on the base hospitals in Europe and on new developments in surgery and equipment. When the United States entered the war, hospital and surgical equipment and supplies, doctors, nurses, and technicians were needed at once and in volume. The Council of National Defense and officials of the Army and Navy turned to *The Modern Hospital* for information. Drs. Ball and Hornsby conferred with officials and manufacturers, obtained buildings for official use, and turned out a mass of information for the government. From the digging that was necessary to obtain the information required came the realization of the need for a hospital reference source, and the first issue of the *Hospital Yearbook* appeared in 1919. This has grown and developed as a source of general information on equipment for hospitals and is now known as the *Hospital Purchasing File*.

When the war ended, *The Modern Hospital* set up a free placement bureau and for two years aided superintendents, nurses, technicians, and hospital war workers of all sorts in getting jobs.

The Modern Hospital was moved to Chicago in 1918, and in 1920 the company purchased an old mansion at 22 East Ontario Street where it was located for ten years. The first permanent home of the American Hospital Association was in the drawing room of that mansion, which became known as a National Hospital Center.

The Hospital Library and Service Bureau, established at the instance of Dr. Ball and backed by the interest of the late Edwin Embree, then vice-president of the Rockefeller Foundation, occupied the library of the mansion. This bureau was set up as a reference library for all hospital people with free "package" libraries of clippings on all phases of hospital administrative problems. *The Modern Hospital* helped to finance the bureau which eventually evolved into the present library of the American Hospital Association.

From its first number *The Modern Hospital* has emphasized hospital planning, and each issue has contained descriptions of one or more hospitals or hospital departments, or articles on hospital planning. Prior to the publication of this magazine only a few architects and hospital administrators had any specialized knowledge of hospital planning. Usually those interested in a new hospital took trips throughout the country to look at existing institutions. The result was that each member of the group became impressed with the importance of some particular feature of some hospital visited, and each insisted upon his idea being incorporated in the plans. The results were not always happy.

In 1922–1923 *The Modern Hospital* conducted its first competition for small hospital designs. Cash awards were made to the architects who designed the winning plans, and for years requests were received from readers for copies of these elevations and floor plans.

The idea of improved planning is consistently promoted by the magazine and in 1944 another competition was conducted for the best plans for a small modern hospital and community health center. The prize-winning plans were published in the March, 1945, issue, and later the company published a book, *The Small Modern Hospital and Community Health Center*. It contains plans and descriptive information on all of the prize-winning entries, those that received honorable mention, and 34 additional institutions, as well as general information on hospital planning. The magazine has continued its progressive program in this field, collaborating with the Public Health Service in some of its activities along this line.

Some responsibility for the stimulation of academic training in hospital administration can be credited to *The Modern Hospital,* since in 1920 it helped interest the Rockefeller Foundation in setting up a committee to study what should constitute the training of hospital administrators. As part of a long-range program in the editorial pages of the magazine there were presented several "reading courses" in hospital administration. The last of these, consisting of 24 lessons published consecutively, began in the issue of January, 1927, and was for some time the basis for study and the nearest that many successful hospital administrators ever came to academic or graduate study in hospital administration.

The Modern Hospital has had a continuing interest in the improvement of hospital facilities, hospital service, and hospital administration and has been a strong progressive influence in the field since its inception.

CHAPTER 20

Administration and Administrators

> This is the great age of administration . . . Administration is
> the attainment of a purpose: it is scientific when the purpose
> has been rationally defined and deliberately accepted, when
> the means of attainment have been rationally made appropriate
> to the object, with neither more nor less or other resources
> than those required to be successful.
> HERMAN FINER[1]

IN *Managing by Communication*[2] Willard V. Merrihue states:

The past decade should be chronicled by historians as the age in which businessmen discovered communication as their principal tool, first, to build understanding and cooperation by the employees they were trying to lead within their
enterprise, secondly, to project their leadership among the employees and the
publics they served, and thirdly, to discredit their detractors (many of whom are
sterile nonproducing talking chiefs stalking the public forest). The American
business leader's appreciation of the importance of communication has been
further heightened by a series of changing conditions within industry and
within the sociopolitical environment in which business operates.

Judging by the outpouring of literature on the art and science of administration, the value of communication is fully realized by teachers and practitioners
in administration. As a means to the end of assuring that his hospital is run according to the latest principles of good administration, the administrator of the
1960's is striving to absorb the complicated and often confused thinking of the
hundreds of writers who are producing articles and books on the subject. He is

---

[1] *Administration and the Nursing Services.* New York, The Macmillan Co., 1952, pp. vii, 18.
[2] McGraw-Hill Book Co., New York, 1960, p. 5.

having a hard time in selecting and trying to apply what seems best to fit the proper conduct of his institution.

As the viewpoint of a student who has had long experience in the management of business as well as of health agencies, there is presented in this chapter, with some adaptations, the thesis submitted to Northwestern University in 1961 by Robert J. Marsh for his master's degree in hospital administration. Mr. Marsh is now administrator of Warren A. Candler Hospital and Candler Telfair Hospital, Savannah, Georgia.

The Impact on Hospital Administration of the Growth and Development of Administrative Theory

ROBERT J. MARSH

Management method, administrative science, executive action, the art of administration—regardless of terminology this matter of seeking better ways to attain objectives through others has been, since the advent of the Industrial Revolution, a subject of intense interest. Psychologists, sociologists, anthropologists, engineers, experts from the schools of business administration and practitioners engaged in administrative functions in industry, finance, transportation, education, communication, distribution or service, all have studied, experimented, analyzed, and reported their findings and conclusions. The literature on the subject is vast. The indications are that the evolution of research into the science and art of administration is being accelerated and that the groundwork done thus far will make it possible to evolve tested basic principles which may improve results of administrative endeavor wherever sincerely applied.

Thinking managers, aware that the ever-increasing size and complexity of modern organizations can become self-limiting, are acutely conscious that the growth and successful functioning of enterprise and/or government depend upon the development, advancement, understanding of, and skill in application of the art and science of administration.

Unlike most inquiries into the arts or sciences, administrative theory has no one closed school of qualified experts. Biology, physics, astronomy, and music each have their specialists devoting largely undiluted effort toward progress in their respective areas. The relatively young and dynamic science of administration has attracted, since its inception, the thought, imagination, and energies of thinkers and probers whose basic orientations were not directly, and sometimes not logically, related to the problems of organizing, planning, decision making, communicating, controlling, or evaluating. This has been a mixed blessing. At times the products derived from these many and varied frames of reference have been contradictory. They have certainly contributed to an unstable and ambiguous terminology that often confuses rather than clarifies otherwise sound propositions. In many instances enthusiastic acceptance of new insights into facets of administration has bred the formation of cults or led earnest but impulsive seekers of truths of administrative technique into tangents of thought and behavior that have proved costly and occasionally disastrous.

On the other hand, this multifaceted approach has created ever new and intriguing horizons. It has unlocked, and will continue to unlock, the doors to the mysteries encountered in attempts to harness the productive and creative energies of an entire civilization. To satisfy the goals of maximum, efficient production and service and the ethical, moral, and physical needs of all who participate in modern society we must utilize fully the talents and resources of every art and every science that can make useful contributions.

Among hospital administrators and in the hospital literature no subject receives more widespread attention than the problem of understanding and improving the administration of hospitals. The emergence of hospital administration as a profession and the heightened awareness of the urgent need for improved administration are relatively recent developments. The past 25 years have witnessed full-scale revolution in the field. Involved in the revolution are the size, the number, and the complexity of hospitals; changes in financing of patient care and capital needs; alteration of the hospital's social role; technical changes in medical science; significant changes in labor markets; and the birth of formalized educational programs to fulfill the needs demanded by advancing technology.

Perhaps of equal impact, particularly on administration, has been the actualization of a principle first enunciated by Dr. Malcolm T. MacEachern at a meeting of the American College of Surgeons in October, 1922. For several years the college had perceived the vital need to raise the standards and improve the quality of patient care rendered by the hospitals. The primary emphasis had been to establish workable standards and to evangelize their propriety. This by 1923 was on its way to accomplishment. In addressing the college Dr. MacEachern, with prophetic foresight, focused the thinking upon a then-revolutionary concept. His words were, "The hospital authorities do not have a divided responsibility for the care of patients. They are responsible for both the hospital care and the medical treatment."[3]

This concept, although not yet fully operative, has been the foundation for the most profound changes in hospital organization and in the growth of the role of administration from an embryonic state to that of a maturing profession. Unfortunately this philosophy has had a more widespread acceptance in theory than in practice. Many members of the medical profession have been disinclined to relinquish what they have considered their prerogatives. Many have feared that administrators were not competent or would take meddlesome actions which could weaken the effectiveness of patient care. Administrators themselves, especially those with little hospital orientation, were reluctant to accept responsibility

[3] Report of Hospital Conference Held at Chicago, October 22–23, 1923. *Bull. Am. Coll. Surgeons,* **8:** 61, 1924.

commensurate with such a philosophy as that stated by Dr. MacEachern. They were inclined to an attitude of "Let the doctors and nurses take care of the patients; we (the administrators) will be concerned with the building, equipment, supplies, and finances." This attitude has frequently been reinforced by trustees and nurses.

On the theory that to know a river best it is well to explore its tributaries, let us take a look at some of the developments of modern management or administration.

Development of Modern Management

The Industrial Revolution, which took place during the eighteenth and nineteenth centuries, exerted profound pressures upon society and gave the impetus toward mass organization of society which continues at a rapid pace. The great developments in the physical sciences spurred the opportunity for varied manufacturing enterprise. The growth of such enterprise was accompanied by widespread and enthusiastically garnered material wealth. The owners of the means of production profited with such relative ease, due to the new demands for manufactured goods and their ability to secure cheap labor and power, that they were not conscious of a need to examine their administrative processes critically. The development of the factory system brought with it many new problems connected with the organization and management of labor and the technique of production. Early solutions were crude.

With the enormous increase in demand for manufactured products, in the need for capital, and in the number of workers, plus the ever keener competition, the early methods soon proved to be inadequate to meet the new problems. The time was ripe for the introduction of scientific management—management the aims of which are to "correlate and systematize all the best of modern developments in . . . administration, and to push development farther in accordance with the principles discovered."[4]

In 1832 Charles Babbage, a mathematician-scientist who had become greatly interested in the phenomena surrounding the manufacturing processes, wrote his famous *Economy of Machinery and Manufactures*. Babbage foresaw the importance of the human organization, the need to analyze operations and to devise organizational tools, if efficient use of men and machines was to result. Babbage by and large was much ahead of his time. Although he undoubtedly influenced many toward efficient production (his book sold 10,000 copies) the times were not right during the great era of exploitation for his emphasis on organization and control to gain the attention it deserved.[5]

Perhaps the accepted prophet of scientific management, Frederick Winslow Taylor, was able to exert his great influence partly because, for him, the times

---

[4] C. Bertrand Thompson: Scientific Management, *Quart. J. Economics*, **28**, 506–7, 1914.

[5] L. Urwick: The Making of Scientific Management. *Management Publications Trust*, London, 1941, Chap. 2.

were right. Taylor (1856–1915), an American engineer, matured with the Industrial Revolution. In a sense the great concepts which are the basis of large-scale industrial organization came into being during his lifetime. The tremendous advances in technology since 1915 may well be seen as logical extensions, refinements, and continued growth and spread of concepts born in those years.

During this period means of power were transferred mainly from muscle and water power to coal, oil, and electricity. During his lifetime the transition was effected from small-shop and craft-based production to large factories. The division of labor and separation of planning concepts, which have made possible the swift development and expansion into large-scale operation, changed all manner of human activity. The changes have made possible large governmental operation, large communications organizations, giant distributive enterprises, and, just as surely, as the needs developed, large hospitals, large universities, and so on.

No one person had a greater impact upon the social and economic genes of the twentieth century than Frederick Winslow Taylor. He was a leader in the truest sense of the term. He conceived broad principles which would materially alter the form and pattern of the future. He instructed and motivated others to the recognition of the worth of these principles. Today's writers might say he was an "activator" and an "actualizer." He performed his work with higher goals than personal acquisitive achievement.

Like most men who affect society broadly, Taylor was widely misunderstood and widely misinterpreted. Labor characteristically feared any innovation which, even on a short-term basis, threatened dislocation of workers, and so labor ignored much of the best of Taylor's ideas and fought viciously to discredit, as being detrimental to the workingman, the management tools he espoused. Time has partially vindicated Taylor on this score, for at least in the material benefits derived from better organization and planning the working people have received substantial rewards.

Beyond just a series of factory techniques, Taylor based his life on a conviction that management had an obligation to apply the scientific method to the study of its human problems and of its nonhuman problems of organization. One of his early lessons was that to expect a high level of planning at the foreman's level was a delusion. Hence his separation of planning from performance and the evolution of the idea of "functional foremanship."

Taylor was interpreted as being a coldly scientific person. In fact he was a man of great human sympathy. He saw the logic of his methods as improving production and proportionately improving the status of the worker.

Nearly all contemporary writers on administrative methods, when referring to scientific management, picture it as a concept of cold, dehumanized, calculated manipulation of worker-pawns by a management employing a sort of hocus-pocus trickery upon them. Many allude to Taylor as a sort of managerial ogre who, while an acknowledged production genuis, was somehow personally responsible for all poor human relations and psychological frustration which have grown out of industrial relaions.

Insofar as scientific management is concerned, it can be viewed from Taylor's own point of reference. He testified before a committee of Congress:[6]

> Scientific management is not any efficiency device . . . nor is it any bunch or group of efficiency devices. It is not a new system of figuring costs; it is not a new scheme of paying men; it is not holding a stop watch on a man and writing things down about him; it is not time study; it is not motion study nor an analysis of the movements of men; it is not the printing and ruling and unloading of a ton or two of blanks on a set of men and saying, "Here's your system; go to it." It is not divided foremanship or functional foremanship; it is not any of the devices which the average man calls to mind when scientific management is spoken of.
>
> Now, in its essence, scientific management involves a complete mental revolution on the part of the working man engaged in any particular establishment or industry . . . (and it involves an equally complete mental revolution on the part of those on the management's side, the foreman, the superintendent, the owner of the business, the board of directors) . . . and without this complete mental revolution on both sides, scientific management does not exist.
>
> The great revolution that takes place in the mental attitude of the two parties under scientific management is that both sides take their eyes off the division of the surplus as the all-important matter, and together turn their attention toward increasing the size of the surplus. There is one more change in viewpoint which is absolutely essential to the existence of scientific management. Both sides must recognize as essential the substitution of exact scientific investigation and knowledge for the old individual judgment or opinion, either of the workman or the boss, in all matters relating to the work done in the establishment.

Taylor's work came at the right time, the optimum stage in technological development, to be universally accepted in those respects which would contribute to increased production efficiency. However, he failed to comprehend the practical barriers to the acceptance of his required revolution in the minds of men. Unfortunately, the behavioral sciences were unprepared to supply the knowledge which might have brought about a revolution of a magnitude that staggers the imagination and which might have prevented uncounted waste, strife, and suffering in the intervening years.

It is true that within a few years a great increase began in the efforts to supply this knowledge. Industrial psychologists began to study and develop useful knowledge of why workers and management behave as they do. The first real fruits of these efforts are beginning to be felt. Taylor was somewhat aware of the lacks inherent in his system when he said, "There is another type of scientific investigation which should receive special attention; namely, the accurate study of the motives which influence men."[7] He was also thinking in terms far in advance of most of his contemporaries in this respect. Just as Babbage's thought preceded the readiness to understand by his contemporaries, so it might be that Taylor's attempt to influence men toward genuine mutual concern for human

[6] *Ibid.*
[7] *Ibid.*

values was lost because the pressure of the need for understanding was not at that time great enough.[8]

Mary Parker Follett (1865–1933) was a political scientist and philosopher who was drawn into contact with industry through her able and vigorous pioneer work in developing social centers and evening educational programs in Boston. She saw business from the point of view of the worker. She was keenly aware of the emotional and psychological influences that underlay the frictions existent in the commercial world. She comprehended the realities of business structure and organization and was exceedingly competent in setting forth the fundamental principles involved. Her mind and personality were probably the motivating spark which gave rise to what has come to be known as the human relations school in administration. In 1924 she presented a series of papers explaining the psychological factors upon which any undertaking must rest.

Mary Follett had a sound knowledge of group dynamics and could interpret to business executives the implications of her insight. She saw that authority, leadership, control, acceptance of orders, all derive from the "facts of the situation" and that it was no longer desirable for authority to be concentrated on any other basis. This then would imply recognition that authority and control would fall wherever function and responsibility in the organization, the "facts," dictated they should be. One of the great gains from this shift in viewpoint would be the "depersonalization" of orders. In other words, orders (decisions) would become a part of a natural activity of people acting in response to the functional needs of organization. They would thus be accepted and the personal offense she held to be inherent in subordination would cease.[9]

This was new. It was not paternalism nor anything else than practical, usable knowledge steering administrative people and those who study administration into areas of investigation which have led into new understanding of behavior and new levels of achievement.

Many others made great contributions to the advancement of a science of management during this period. However, men such as Henry L. Gantt, Frank B. Gilbreth, and Edward T. Elbourne, great and important though their work was, did not define new directions for growth. They advanced techniques, they contributed perspective, they evangelized and expanded understanding, but they did not and could not do what had already been done by Taylor and Follett, who had led the way into a new era of social organization.

What Is Scientific Management?

Few terms, really, have been so severely misconstrued as "scientific management." In the science of medicine, the "basilar membrane" means one thing only, and that meaning is attributed to it by all who practice medicine. But in the

[8] Frederick W. Taylor: *Principles and Methods of Scientific Management*. New York, Harper & Bros., 1914.
[9] L. Urwick: *op. cit.*

science of management, it has not yet been determined precisely what "management" means. A vague terminology is evidence of loose, unformed, or confused thinking, which makes it difficult to consider applications to such a field as hospital operation. For the sake of definition the idea might be accepted that scientific management is that form of management in which the objects and methods of any activity have been determined, not by the opinion of any one individual, but by the (scientific) analysis of all the available facts and the determination of "standards" on the basis of those facts. Included by implication are the methodical investigation, measurement, definition, classification, standardization, and evaluation of a proposition, a process, a program, a function, or a job. It must be agreed that scientific management takes place only when the foregoing are accompanied by a process of analysis and review of all components, whereby some elements are expanded, others curtailed or eliminated, and when the final result is a harmonious flow of a clearly understood and controlled set of operations.

According to this definition, scientific management is obviously applicable to nearly every conceivable form of organized human endeavor. As it applies to industry, so should it apply to all forms of management, including hospitals'. However, none of the mechanisms of scientific management should be mistaken for the thing itself; otherwise there is degeneration into assumptions unworthy of the word science. With Taylor it may be concluded that "it is possible to use the mechanism of scientific management for bad, but not scientific management itself. It ceases to be scientific management the moment it is used for bad."[10]

By the mid-1920's widespread concern over, and revolt against, the concept of a "machine" industry was under way. The pendulum began its swing toward a "human" concept. Instead of seeing industry as a vast maze of machines, buildings, systems, and materials, a few began to see it as a complex form of human association. This was not only a second industrial revolution but a social movement. It was a deep-rooted seeking for more effective methods of organization and a searching for ways to inject ethical bases for meeting and satisfying human needs in work relationships. In much of the writing of this period are statements to the effect that "management is primarily an art," "the need is for leadership in management," "management is the art of moving, guiding, inspiring, and bringing and welding together masses of men and women." Thus attention tended to be directed to structure of organization, to the use and location of committees, and, much later, of course, to the "scientific" investigations into human behavior and the more recent "motivational research."

The work of Roethlisberger and others in the famous Hawthorne experiments set the stage for the development of a new school of administrative method. This has been widely labeled as the human relations school of management. Its ramifications seem endless. Each investigator has seemed impelled to coin and attempt

[10] Oliver Sheldon: Development of Scientific Management. *Harvard Business Rev.*, **3**: 129–33, 1925.

to establish a new school in order to give identity to his unique contributions to the expanding body of knowledge of the behavioral sciences in industry. Consultative management, group leadership and group conference technique, nondirective counseling, bottom-up management, benevolent autocracy, management by objective—all have been expertly advanced as management methods.

All have this in common: a realization that employees are people, human beings who are by the nature of things impelled to seek satisfying social relationships through the establishment of working relationships which will yield a secure social position within a stable group. As these developments are reviewed and their significance and influence pondered, it is difficult to escape the feeling that administrators are confronted with two opposing, irreconcilable philosophies. The demands of scientific or formalized management appear to preclude optimum utilization by administrators of the techniques and skills advocated by the social scientists.

In attempts to reconcile the two approaches to effective administration, numerous methods have been advanced. Many business consulting firms have developed into rather large and prosperous organizations by employing a single method which they attempt to apply as a cure-all for the ills of a given enterprise. The creators of organization charts are an example. These so-called professional consultants are often able to bring a measure of order into chaotic situations. They prepare elaborate and detailed charts showing exactly the position and relationships of every person and function in the organization to every other person and function. The fault is that they oversimplify administrative problems and leave the organization a legacy of charts whose defects soon become apparent. Others sell their services as specific medication for a single organizational disease.

The still more narrowly limited consultants are at least honest by not implying that they are able to deliver total solutions. They are typified by those who confine their activity to "scheduling" or "engineering business forms" or "job analysis." They have their uses and often contribute toward the better functioning of a sick part of an organization. However, the administrator who relies too greatly on these crutches is in danger of developing administrative hypochondria with resultant enrichment of the "doctors" and no basic improvement of the patient's health.

Analysis of the Administrator

Most of the writing in the field of administration has concerned itself with analysis of the executive profile or the make-up of the administrator; or it has tended toward a delineation of what he does, how he behaves, how he solves problems. Along with this there have been attempts to clarify his role by investigating "leadership," "delegation," "authority," "control," "integrity," "planning," and other abstractions. Much of the writing has contributed a great deal to the administrator's growing knowledge of the social responsibilities he faces within and outside his own organization. All such thinking is helping administrators in their efforts to perfect a workable concept of their role as professional managers.

In 1936 Wallace B. Donham[11] summed up his thinking about administration as follows:

> Administration is itself a social science with its own specialized logics, techniques, and theories. It centers around a concept of action through human organization. Administration tries to and indeed must integrate the psychological, biological, physical and social sciences. In actuality it is comparable to the practice of medicine. Skill and wisdom in handling men and things in action is not easily acquired, yet the successful administrator is required almost hourly to demonstrate such skill.

Since World War II the major emphasis in administration has been upon the needs for greater human understanding and the development of skills in handling people. A typical expression of this realization is given by T. H. Nelson.[12] He states that "the basic qualifications for administration are separate from, they are different from, and they are over and above experience and abilities in specialized areas. Today's administrator thinks in terms of policies and the development of persons."

This same thought is found in Robert Saltonstall's book, *Human Relations in Administration*.[13] Nelson viewed administration's greatest need as the need for control of people and operations in a manner which would obviate the defects of authoritarian control. It was imperative during the war and postwar expansions that management devise better and more workable methods of control, for the rate of expansion threatened a disastrous loss of control. In addition to spelling out the means of securing control through various information-gathering procedures, considerable emphasis was placed upon the necessity for administrators to realize that "control is not authoritarian decision making, or the declining to state policies so that others must come to the administrator to 'find out' what should be done."[14]

Another theory of administration appealingly and logically presented is referred to as consultative management. The consultative administrator, as the term suggests, brings together his key people regularly. In conference with them he fully discusses goals, progress, and problems. He suggests plans, encouraging his department heads to do the same with their subordinates. Through open and free discussion and analysis of policies and administrative decisions, clear understanding and honest support are obtained both "up" and "down" the line. If department heads clear with one another through periodic conference, horizontal communication is established.[15]

[11] Wallace B. Donham: The Theory and Practice of Administration. *Harvard Business Rev.*, **14**, 408, 1936.

[12] Changing Concepts of Administration. *Am. J. Nursing*, February, 1949, p. 70.

[13] New York, McGraw-Hill Book Co., 1959.

[14] *Changing Concepts of Administration, op. cit.*

[15] National Industrial Conference Board Inc.: Consultative Management. *Management Rec.*, **17**: 438–39, 1955.

The successful practitioner of consultative administration will be a good planner. Successful conferences are not off-the-cuff talk sessions. The key questions to be considered must be well thought out and clearly presented. The administrator must know what it is he wants to accomplish. The leader must have the ability to ask pertinent questions that will lead to an orderly progression toward a solution. The administrator will get little or no benefit from a conference if he uses it as a means of "selling" his own solutions or ideas, or if he merely calls busy people together to "tell" them what he wants done. Conferences can be either great time-wasters or the best possible way of solving problems; the results depend almost wholly on the leader. If he has the sincere desire to get the thinking of those present, and if he is honestly unafraid to face free discussion, and if he is not pride-bound about his own prowess, he can utilize the consultative role confidently and successfully. Conferences enable him to capitalize on the previously unused knowledge, experience, and judgment of his staff; he can develop persons as well as direct them; he should obtain better results with less effort and with greater harmony and loyalty.

Herbert A. Simon[16] expresses the philosophy that management (or administration) is a matter of making decisions and that decision making is learnable like putting a golf ball. Therefore if decision making is properly (and scientifically) taught to persons with the same natural aptitude and sufficient diligence, the result will be the production of able administrators. Many books and articles have been written describing the art (or science) of decision making. Most recognize that decision making is one of the administrator's functions and make serious attempts to help him increase his proficiency in it. It is somewhat surprising, however, to find that there are those who advocate a theory that administration, as such, is purely a decision-making process.

Interestingly, A. Zaleznik,[17] associate professor of business administration at Harvard University, takes the position that science in this connection will have the following basic ingredients:

> First, systematic study, that is, the development of a body of data showing how people in organizations actually do behave. Second, the creation of appropriate research methods that are communicable, simple and can be duplicated by others who desire to do so. Third, the scientific approach depends upon the use of empirical investigation to aid us in making action decisions in the field of human behavior.

This, of course, is precisely what the leaders in behavioral science have been attempting. However, as Chris Argyris[18] says, "It is impossible to understand others unless we understand ourselves and we cannot understand ourselves unless we understand others."

[16] The New Science of Management Decision. *Personnel,* American Management Association, January–February, 1961.
[17] Zaleznik, A.: Science vs. Common Sense in Human Relations. *Harvard Business Rev.,* November–December, 1960.
[18] *Personality and Organization.* New York, Harper & Bros., 1957.

According to Zaleznik the "common sense" approach to the problems of human relations in organizations is based on human values; they are ethical and moral issues; and the resolution of such questions depends primarily on the insights that have come down to us through the ages. Certainly much in the way of insight is to be gained by the use of the case method of teaching. The recent book by Peter Stryker[19] is perhaps an indicator of the direction which the case method may take. Stryker makes his cases come alive by employing the simple device of narrative-styled memoranda between principals involved and reports from a junior management consultant to his superior and the superior's replies, which present analyses and counter thoughts.

In the struggle to clarify thinking about administrative methods and roles, there is evidence that certain words gradually take on new prominence. Leadership is becoming one of these new words. The qualities of leadership are being scrutinized, and there are now many writers who advance the concept that "leadership" is the essence of administration. The term "reality-centered" leadership is advanced by W. J. Humber[20] as being central to effective administration. By "reality-centered" it is meant that leadership prerogatives must be willingly assumed by management and clearly understood by the entire organization. All ambiguity as to where these prerogatives reside must be eliminated. The elimination of status factors waters down decisive leadership and fails to satisfy the employee need for confident and purposeful leadership. Humber further implies that anything less will result in overdevelopment of the strength of the informal organization as a substitute leadership.

This line of thought has many aspects of similarity to that advanced by Walter Bennis.[21] He rather neatly combines most of the current thinking into an expression which is rapidly finding wide acceptance. The philosophy it refers to may not be so willingly embraced as the term. His term is "benevolent-autocracy"; it has overtones of human relations, leadership, formalized management, control, delegation; in fact it could be defined in such a way as to include nearly all current theories. For example, how neatly the following observation fits into the several currents of contemporary thought: "A leader cannot avoid the exercise of authority any more than he can avoid responsibility for what happens to his organization." Again, "It just isn't possible in business to delegate much autonomy below the top echelons of management."[22] This is a principle of the benevolent-autocratic school, but it could have been an expression used by F. W. Taylor in explaining his concept of management's responsibility for skilled planning of work.

This approach by modern theorists is further reinforced by Douglas McGregor.[23] He states that "authority is the central indispensable means of man-

---

[19] *The Men from the Boys.* New York, Harper & Bros., 1960.
[20] Major Factors Affecting Organizational Health. *Personnel Psychol.,* **13,** No. 3, Autumn, 1960.
[21] Revisionist Theory of Leadership. *Harvard Business Rev.,* January–February, 1961, p. 26.
[22] *Ibid.*
[23] The Human Side of Enterprise. *Consulting Psychol.,* 8: 55–63, 1944.

agerial control." He differs from some of the early writers only in that he advocates that authority, or leadership, be based upon more than "role" or "status"; that it should come about as a result of a joint effort in which superior and subordinate attempt to develop ground rules for work and productivity. Interwoven here are the ideas of "management by objective" and control through "target setting." Roethlisberger's principle of "collaboration" is also identifiable as a part of this latest enunciation of administrative theory.

Dr. E. H. Litchfield, former dean of the Graduate School of Business and Public Administration, Cornell University, now chancellor of the University of Pittsburgh, and others have stressed the universality of administrative action whether it is public or private, hospital or educational, industrial or retail. This observation of universality of root principles should not be taken to imply, as some have, that technical or specialized knowledge is not essential to success in most areas of administrative action. Stressing the commonality of administrative problems is dangerous when mistakenly interpreted as meaning that the executive can absorb administrative theory and proceed to function with no further orientation.

The increasing realization that proficiency in managing people depends largely on insights into social structures and psychological aspects of organization adds substance to the need for knowledge specific to the field of administrative performance. It is unlikely that administrative science alone can bridge the gap for a step from public school administration to a bank presidency or from a railroad to a department store. It can be of tremendous aid to functioning managers in all fields, but it is highly dangerous to make assumptions which ignore those aspects of organizations which are unique to them.

It should be clear that "the administrator who believes his accomplishments will turn chiefly upon his adherence to any given technique is . . . courting disappointment."[24]

Basic Principles of Administration

The underlying and basic principles of the science of administration which appear as settled, at this time, as the result of investigation, research, and equipment, divide themselves into a set of major and minor propositions advanced by Chancellor Litchfield which provide a clear guide to the elements which comprise formal administrative method.[25]

I. Major Principle
   The administrative process is a cycle of action which devolves upon these specific activities:

[24] Erwin H. Schell: The Changing Philosophy of Management. *Advanced Management*, Vol. 23, December, 1958, p. 18.
[25] E. H. Litchfield: Notes on a General Theory of Administration. *Administrative Sc. Quart.*, January, 1956.

      a. Decision making
      b. Programming
      c. Communicating
      d. Controlling
      e. Reappraising

A. Minor Proposition

Decision making may be rational, deliberative, discretionary, purposive, or it may be irrational, traditional, obligatory, random, or some combination. If it is rational, deliberative, discretionary, and purposive, it is arrived at through the application of

      a. Definition of issues
      b. Analysis of existing situation
      c. Calculation and evaluation of the alternatives
      d. Deliberation
      e. Choice

In actual performance all elements are seldom apparent; they are nevertheless present, if only in a fleeting way.

B. Minor Proposition

Decisions, once made, become the guides to action, but only after they have been interpreted in the form of specific programs.

C. Minor Proposition

The effectiveness of a programmed decision will vary with the extent to which it is communicated to those of whom action is required. (For the moment, at least, to serve the purposes of the statement, it is assumed that reception of knowledge by the person or persons receiving it will act as the necessary stimuli for the action required.)

D. Minor Proposition

Action required by a programmed and communicated decision is more nearly assured if standards of performance are established and enforced.

E. Minor Proposition

Decisions are based on facts, assumptions, and values which are subject to change. To retain their validity, decisions therefore must be re-evaluated and revised as rapidly as change occurs. Reappraisal is vital because of the possible imperfection of the original decision, which is revealed by time and circumstance.

II. Major Principle

The administrative process functions in the areas of (a) policy; (b) resources; (c) execution. Policy is the definition of the objectives which guide the actions of the whole organization or a significant portion of it. Resources of administration are people, money, authority, and physical things. Execution is a function of integration and synthesis and is aimed at achieving a dynamic and total organism.

A. Minor Proposition

The action cycle described in I applies to action in each functional area. Policies are not only made but also programmed, communicated, controlled, and reappraised.

B. Minor Proposition

Each function seeks a value which when realized is its contribution to the administrative process. For instance, policy seeks purposive direction of the organization. The resource function seeks economy in the sense of productivity and of frugality. Execution seeks, and is evaluated by, the degree to which it achieves a state of dynamic coordination.

C. Minor Proposition

Each function has distinctive characteristics which govern the application of the action cycle to it. Policies involve questions of value and fact. Values are plural and facts are contingent; consequently the action cycle in the policy cycle is modified. People are actuated by varying stimuli and combinations of reward and punishment. Money is moved by factors of scarcity. Authority has properties which determine the way it may be allocated and exercised. The executive function achieves synthesis and dynamism by observing the laws of equilibrium and decay as they are variously perceived.

D. Minor Proposition

The functional areas of administration are integrally related to one another. No one, or the influence of one, can be isolated from the other; they are actually reciprocating parts.

III. Major Principle

The administrative process is carried on in the context of a larger action system, the dimensions of which are (dimension is referring to a category of variables):

a. The administrative process
b. The individual performing the administrative process
c. The total enterprise within which the individual performs the process
d. The ecology within which the individual and the enterprise function

Parson's "theory of action" postulates three systems of action: personality, social, and culture.

The variables inherent in the concept of the "total enterprise" and the ecological setting of the enterprise are those which tend toward and make necessary the study of special fields of administrative endeavor. The commonness of administrative function cannot be interpreted in such a way as to eradicate the essential variables or to subvert the need for a study of, or proficient interpretation of, the variables present and peculiar to the area of operation in which any practitioner of administration chooses to practice.

A. Minor Proposition

While constant in basic structure, the administrative process will vary in important aspects, depending upon the personality of the person who performs it. Different administrators will have radically different effects upon the whole organization, for they will perform each function in varied ways based upon the myriad facets of the factors of which their administrative personality is composed. A Wilson might gather his own facts, an Eisenhower would assemble his information by means of an elaborate staff organization. In either case the process of analyzing the situation is carried out.

B. Minor Proposition

While constant in basic structure, the administrative process will vary in important respects, depending upon the character of the total enterprise within which it is performed. The study of difference occasioned by enterprise variations is necessary, but only following a prior understanding of the constants in this process.

C. Minor Proposition

While constant in basic structure, the administrative process will vary in important respects depending upon the environment in which the individual and the total enterprise function—culture, professional setting, regional effects, community differences, religious force, etc.

D. Minor Proposition

The types of relationships existing among the three dimensions other than the administrative have an effect upon the administrative process. Relationships between the whole enterprise and the dimension of the environment may be competition, bargaining, cooptation, and coalition. In this major proposition are seen:

1. The way in which variations in any one of the three dimensions directly affect the administrative process.

2. The way in which variations in the total combination of the three affect the administrative process.

3. The varying relationships between any two (other than the administrative process dimension) will have corresponding variable effects upon the process per se.

IV. Major Principle

Administration is the performing of the administrative process by an individual or a group in the context of an enterprise functioning in its environment. The administrative process is a series of interdependent steps which can be isolated and described in the abstract. Administration is the performance of the process in the specific contexts of enterprise and environment.

A. Minor Proposition

Administration as a totality has definable attributes. They are (a) it seeks to perpetuate itself; (b) it seeks to preserve its internal well-being; (c) it seeks to preserve itself against others; (d) it seeks growth.

B. Minor Proposition

The attributes of the totality of administration have significant effects upon administrative behavior (properties of organic compulsion).

V. Major Principle

Administration and the administrative process occur in substantially the same generalized form in industrial, commercial, civil, educational, military, and hospital organizations (cyclical and other processes occur universally).

Elements Peculiar to Hospital Administration

Inasmuch as most of the effort and literature on administration has been concerned with general business administration, hospitals have been forced to look to that area for most of their indications of trends in administrative method. The hospital field has not been devoid of leadership or initiative in developing administrative theory and proficiency, although it did not receive the impetus of the Industrial Revolution as did business organizations.

Fundamentally there appear to be three elements which tend to be useful in arriving at a method of classifying institutions or organizations. These are (1) the social role of the institution; (2) its economic aspects; (3) its internal structure.

The first inquiry should be, how does a given institution fit into its cultural environment and what social evaluation is it given? Next, what is the pattern of the social organization of which it is a part?

To understand the modern hospital its historical background must be known. In our society hospitals began as an expression of Christian charity. Many early ones were given the designation "poorhouse and hospital." It was as such that they became rooted in the social fabric. Those who supported them with gifts proclaimed their own virtue and demonstrated their participation in the upper-class traditions. Patients were viewed as recipients of charity.

The advance of the medical sciences, particularly anesthesia, radiology, asepsis, and surgery, brought changes. Hospitals became places in which the prospect of cure was stressed. De luxe services were devised in order to accommodate the well-to-do. The disgrace and the hopelessness that were formerly attached to hospitalization were removed. The "poorhouse" connotation disappeared. Finally improved economic conditions and prepayment plans made it possible for the middle classes to utilize hospitals, which have come to be regarded as necessary community services for the entire community irrespective of the individual's financial circumstances. Despite the changed perspective, the old traditions which involve altruism remain. It is the administrator's task to reconcile the new and the old ideals.

Hospitals attract to their support and to their boards of trustees persons of high social prestige who feel a civic responsibility, who have yearnings of service to their fellow citizens.

With enlarging social concepts of the hospital as a health center active in preventive medicine, in education, and in research, as well as in treatment of the ill and injured, its complexities have multiplied with consequent evolution of the administrative function. The administrator is confronted with an unusual organizational structure. He is responsible to a board that not only has economic power over him, but functions also as a promoter of ethical and humanitarian values. Its judgment, even on minor matters, is of importance in the daily routine of the hospital. Its members typically are more concerned with particular cases and more prone to "interfere" in administrative detail than are their counterparts in industry, although improved administration is slowly alleviating this situation. The medical staff in the hospital is at the pinnacle of the scale of status and prestige and in a position to exert great power in its internal structure. The administrator must meet the need for efficiency and for smooth and dynamic coordination; he must accommodate and compromise among these and other power groups.

Other voluntary and governmental agencies in the community have in general far less difficulty in administrative control than the hospital. Closest to it is the large private university. Both have a major public service aspect. Both attract notable persons to their boards without financial compensation. Both have peculiar administrative problems in dealing with professional personnel. The university's scope of service, however, is limited to a distinct type of people, most of whom, usually, come from outside the community in which the university is situated. This difference radically affects the administrative process.

Rated as the fourth largest industry, hospitals create a false image of a colossus. Actually, since their function is service, they make little impact on the economy as compared with producing industries, although they suffer from economic pressures generated by the industries, their occupancy dwindling disastrously in times of depression. Unlike most businesses, they lack flexibility and cannot contract services in such periods. Facilities must be held in readiness for disaster, epidemic, or other acute human need. Furthermore, despite its gross dimensions, the hospital industry is weak in terms of organized economic strength. In fact it is inappropriate to speak of the "hospital industry," for there is little economic cohesion within it. Associations on the national, state, and local levels bind hospitals together after a fashion, but in a quite different and less economic-oriented way than industry's trade associations.

The colossus image fades when it is considered that some 4,000 of the 7,000 hospitals have less than 100 beds and that the average of all short-term general hospitals is only 235 beds.

Few organizations achieve the intimate customer relations in which hospitals are involved. Their consumers stay on the premises 24 hours a day for an average of 7.8 days per hospital admission, and the nature of the care is about as personal as can be imagined.

The economics of hospital care get their most unique aspect from the fact that practically 100 per cent of its users are unwilling customers who are deeply involved in crisis situations which make extreme emotional demands on them and their families.

The administrator's fund-raising problems differ from those of industry. Money for new buildings, capital equipment, and many social services continues to be provided largely by private donations, by public subscription, and through volunteer services. Since World War II federal funds have been made available in increasingly substantial amounts for new building, and it appears that this source of capital funds will play a growing part in aiding hospitals to adjust to the changing social demands.

Pricing policies are undergoing swift evolution toward realistic rate-setting based upon full cost, which is a trend away from the traditional below cost or according to ability to pay philosophies.

Another unique economic aspect is equipment and supplies. Each small hospital must have almost the entire range of possible items. Traditionally these widely diversified lines have been filled by small local or regional supply houses, and although there is some evidence of larger units emerging, this traditional pattern still applies in general.

It has become increasingly difficult for hospitals to get and retain a stable work force because of traditionally lower wage scales; personnel in medical and paramedical fields are too specialized to transfer for promotion purposes and therefore lack incentive to stay; and volunteers are frequently unreliable and difficult to fit into certain services.

The rate of technological change complicates the economic situation.

Generally in the past doctors dominated hospital routine, and their orders activated all or nearly all services. Governing boards were self-perpetuating bodies. The administrator was clearly third man; he was a superintendent of buildings and grounds and saw to it that doctors' orders were carried out. World War II brought a great change. Competition for employees became fierce. Changes arose in the role, responsibility, and authority of administration, although too often this is still not adequately defined. Hospital boards are learning slowly the same lessons learned earlier in industry—that the board had best delegate operations to paid, trained executives. The doctor still finds it hard to relinquish his prerogatives within the hospital.

For administrators, managing proud people can be rewarding but difficult. Working with many proud occupational groups can be likewise. The hospital administrator today cannot use authoritarian methods to coordinate his organization. Few, if any, institutions contain an equal number of alert, well-informed tightly organized, and sternly principled professional groups.

In order to understand and to compare the administrative task in any institution its structure, its functions, its internal and external personal relationships, and its pattern of operation must be studied and evaluated.

After consideration of the social status, economic position, and internal structure of the modern hospital, the next step is to study the development of hospital administration as a distinct art and science. An early indication of the need for the board and administrator to broaden into the professional area their authority for work done in the hospital occurs in the 1916 "Report of the Director of the American College of Surgeons." Here is raised the question as to whether "superintendents and trustees . . . responsible for the administration of the hospital take pains to assure themselves that the work of laboratories . . . is competent."[26] In its pioneering effort to raise the standards of hospital care this crusading group of doctors found themselves deeply involved in all phases of hospital operation, particularly in administration. This same report carried a statement that "this leads us to the whole problem of hospital administration. We cannot avoid it."[27] Roles and relationships had to be questioned; rights and privileges had to be examined.

By 1917–1918 the first hospital survey of the college was made and a report issued on the standard of efficiency of hospital operation. The opening statement made a point reiterated countless times since: "As a people we are accustomed to hospital service; we look upon that service no longer as a luxury which we may buy, but rather as an inherent right."[28]

At this point the college was concerned almost entirely with the establishment of criteria which would permit evaluation of the quality of patient care. The emphasis was on need for organized and standardized medical records and the development of orderly presentation of the facts of patient care, with some real concern about postmortem examinations and with the level of training given interns and nurses. The first survey report closes with this statement, "Dietetics, anesthesia, accurate and intelligent financial accounting, hospital administration, the pharmacy and supervision of prescriptions, and the library and encouragement of research are among other important subjects which merit consideration."[29]

During the 1920's the college continued to supply leadership and to apply pressure for the adoption of and development of better methods of administration. Dr. Malcolm T. MacEachern's forceful advocacy of hospital inspection as part of the standardization program produced new insight into the need and aroused nation-wide support for education in hospital administration.[30]

[26] *Bull. Am. Coll. Surgeons,* Vol. 2, Parts 1-2, 1916.
[27] *Ibid.*
[28] *Bull. Am. Coll. Surgeons,* Vol. 3, Parts 1-2-3, 1917–1918.
[29] American College of Surgeons: *Standards of Efficiency—First Hospital Survey of the College,* Chicago, The College, 1918.
[30] Relations of the Board of Trustees to the Superintendent. *Bull. Am. Coll. Surgeons,* Vol. 12, No. 2, April, 1928.

Illustrative of the growing and widespread concern over the deficiencies in hospital administration was this statement in 1928 by Charles F. Neergaard:

> The trouble is that relatively few superintendents have sufficient prestige and experience to be able to take a position of leadership with their trustees. They are too often looked upon as super-housekeepers or clerks. Many a trustee thinks that the hospital job is composed of two parts: one, a hotel business, which he feels he knows as much about as his superintendent, and the other, professional matters, which he thinks the doctors and nurses know more about.

Also, in 1928, Major Edward A. Fitzpatrick[31] came directly to the crux of the hospital dilemma with these statements:

> It would seem . . . that an effort aiming directly at the training of the hospital superintendent would be fundamental to an improvement of the hospital. This interference (by members of boards of trustees), cited as a principal cause of high turnover, can only mean that the fundamental principles of organization applied to the hospital are not generally understood or enforced. One simple principle— that a board of trustees has no power except in a meeting. Individual members of a board have no powers as such. Board could most intelligently use its time and its power if it confined itself to a formulation and development of policies for the institution, rather than to administrative routine.

The first Institute for Hospital Administrators is described as follows:[32]

> This institute conducted by the American Hospital Association at the University of Chicago was a gratifying success. A course of lectures, seminars and administrative clinics extending over a period of three weeks and instructed by faculty members of the School of Business Administration of the University and by eminent guest lecturers (hospital authorities) was the bellwether of formal graduate training for hospital administration. Approximately 180 hospital executives attended as students and came from hospitals throughout the nation.

In 1935 an eloquent plea for hospitals to realize the need for expertness in the special demands for hospital administration was made by J. Dewey Lutes,[33] director-general of the young American College of Hospital Administrators. He foresaw that an instrument such as the college would be the ultimate means of raising the status of administrators for all hospitals.

By 1936 the college had a committee on training hospital administrators, of which Dr. MacEachern was chairman. Out of the work of this and subsequent committees came short courses and ultimately complete graduate programs in hospital administration in leading universities. Formal education for hospital administration has had, and doubtless will continue to have, a profound influence on the quality of hospital administration.

There is growing evidence that governing boards are becoming well aware of the existence of formally educated hospital administrators and are using this

[31] Why Train Hospital Executives? *Bull. Am. Hosp. A.,* Vol. 2, No. 1, January, 1928.
[32] *Bull. Am. Hosp. A.,* October, 1933.
[33] The Importance of Efficient Hospital Administration. *Bull. Am. Hosp. A.,* Vol. 9, April, 1935.

as a criterion with increasing frequency when seeking to employ an administrator. Some authorities believe that by 1970 it will become virtually impossible for noncourse graduates to enter the field except in small rural hospitals.[34] Leading placement agencies report that currently more than half the requests from governing boards include graduate degrees in hospital administration as a requisite for candidates. About half the applications being received by the American College of Hospital Administrators are from program graduates.[35] Degree administrators are contributing an impressive proportion of the articles published in hospital magazines.

Although the academic approach of the formal graduate programs has not been uniform, they have thus far trained what amounts to a new generation of hospital administrators.

It seems important that after reviewing the birth of the science of administration, its maturing as an art as well as a science, and its adaptation to hospitals, a pause be taken to take a sharp look at the species.

Dr. Edwin L. Crosby[36] says, "The administrator is the catalyst between the governing board, the medical staff, and the public. He must have the skill of a tactician and the equilibrium of a philosopher."

Dr. MacEachern in the bible of the hospital world, *Hospital Organization and Management*,[37] describes the administrator as "a person endowed by nature with special qualifications; these must be supplemented by careful education and wide experience, and the person lacking these qualifications and education cannot successfully administer so complicated an institution as the modern hospital."

Here are a few additional but helpful attempts.

Quoting Louis E. Newman:[38] "If I had to name the one most important quality of a top administrator today, I would pick his personal integrity."

Ordway Tead:[39] "The administrator's struggle is against confusion, against ineffectiveness, against waste, against inefficiency." This is not a definition but it certainly conveys an impression of some of the qualities an administrator should possess.

A few years ago the job of the administrator and some of its peculiar aspects were set forth with unusual insight. The writer, J. Elliott Janney,[40] listed these as some of the principal things an administrator had better be emotionally prepared for:

[34] Richard L. Johnson: Influence of Graduate Programs of Hospital Administration on the Hospital Field, paper presented before the National Symposium on Graduate Education for Hospital Administrators, University of Chicago, December, 1958.

[35] *Ibid.*

[36] The Hospital Administrator. *Mod. Hosp.*, August, 1948, p. 56.

[37] MacEachern, Malcolm T.: *Hospital Organization and Management*, 3rd ed. Chicago, Physicians Record Co., 1957.

[38] Some Philosophies of Management. *Advanced Management*, Vol. 24, February, 1959.

[39] *Administration: Its Purpose and Performance*. New York, Harper & Bros., 1959.

[40] Company Presidents Look at Themselves. *Harvard Business Rev.*, Vol. 30, May–June, 1952.

1. He must live alone and like it. Camaraderie with the rest of the organization just cannot exist; when it seems to be present it is a false image, a phony.

2. Decisions are terminal and final. The administrator must constantly be aware that the nature of his position precludes any escape from this aspect of his decision-making activity.

3. He is the model for the rest of management. Inescapably he sets the tone, the quality of behavior, the standards that will be emulated by his subordinates.

4. He has a stereotype imposed on him, whether he likes it or not. He inherits a position about which every other person in the organization has definite feelings, and these feelings dictate each person's criteria for judging the administrator's every act.

5. He cannot afford the luxury of being competitive with anyone else in the organization. As the top man he can only destroy the morale of any person with whom he enters into competition. He must direct his competitive drives outward toward other organizations.

6. He must serve as his own "inspector." Everyone else has someone whose responsibility they are; not the administrator, he is on his own and must "glow with his own light."

It is not enough to analyze the currents in the slow process of establishing administration as a distinct function. All that has contributed to its progress should reveal some degree of measurable advance in the actual operation of specific hospitals. This is a nearly impossible task, for there exist no concrete measures that can be applied to a hospital that will yield an acceptable efficiency score. Accreditation by the Joint Commission on Accreditation of Hospitals is the most frequently applied test; it, however, cannot satisfy as certification of excellence of administrative performance, important though this element is conceded to be in attaining the required high standards of care.

Counseling Service Provides Information

The American Hospital Association's counseling service for member hospitals appeared to be a good source of information. The program, financed by grants from the Ford Foundation, has since 1957 been conducting, on request, management audits of hospitals. This involves prior study of a detailed presurvey questionnaire submitted by the administrator.

The presurvey data are intended to show the type of institution, the nature of its governing authority, its social and financial stability, its internal organization, the background of its managerial hierarchy, and details to support these elements affecting the administrative process. This material is analyzed by staff personnel who have been selected from the hospital field because of their organizational skills. They steep themselves in the data drawn from the questionnaires in preparation for the on-premises audit.

The audit consists of inspection tours of the hospital, depending primarily upon the examination of documents, reports, and records and personal interviews with members of the governing board, the administrative team, members of the medical staff, and department heads. The audit is guided by somewhat elaborate statements of principles that have been evolved by the staff. These principles have been established, through experience, as the nearest thing to measuring rods of administrative proficiency. Their effectiveness is highly dependent upon the skill and experience of the persons conducting the audit. The concept involved is one that says, for example, "We believe that good administration is evidenced, in part, by the degree to which the environment of the hospital and the personnel give evidence of effective support of patient care." This principle is then applied to the hospital under study and specific inquiry is made and results recorded that will demonstrate to what extent this principle is being fulfilled.

This process is applied to various elements of the hospital such as the governing authority, the medical staff, the external relationships of the hospital, and its internal operations. In each area of inquiry conclusions are drawn and recommendations are made. The final result of the audit, which is, of course, confidential in all respects, is delivered only to the administrator. Council staff members discuss the findings with the administrator and counsel with him in order to aid the administrator in gaining a maximum benefit from the audit and in improving his administrative performance.

Up to June, 1961, some 85 hospitals were audited; the first 54 were available for the purposes of study. Hospitals from nearly every state have participated, and they represent nearly every size and form of organization, except federal and state-owned institutions.

In this study the primary interest was in finding out what, if any, correlation might exist between the degree of formal training in administration of administrators of hospitals audited and the results being obtained by that administration. Several beclouding issues appeared immediately. The greatest was the question of gauging fairly the results being obtained. After much frustration it was decided to assess the recommendations made by the counselors to the administrator. This could not be done on a numerical basis, for the recommendations varied greatly in seriousness. Obviously a recommendation that might result in a major overhaul of a department could not be weighed equally with one suggesting improved wording of a report. Therefore resort was taken to the subjective process of scaling the recommendations to indicate the number of recommendations made for a given hospital involving major, moderate, and minor categories.

Attempt was made to identify from the descriptive material in the audit reports the administrative techniques employed by the administrator. This was an edifying but largely unproductive task. The tenure of several administrators was too short to indicate fairly that the methods in evidence were their own. In a few cases, frankly, there was no discernible evidence that there existed any method in the performance of the administrator.

The only defense against the charge of subjectivity is to liken the problem to that of an actuary. Actuaries assemble massive bodies of statistical data, complicated tables, and all available facts in as close to mathematical precision as possible. This done, they invariably find many imponderables, any of which could exert decisive effect upon the result. What do actuaries do? In the final analysis they become very subjective, and despite all their higher mathematics, they are privately fond of saying "the best actuary is the best guesser."

Perhaps, then, the dilemma can be understood. Certain things become clear; some approach demonstrability, but much remains about which it cannot be said, "add up the figures and see for yourself."

An additional factor should be mentioned. Of course, the sample of 54 hospital case studies, despite their wide range geographically and by size and type of sponsorship, cannot be assumed as statistically adequate or meaningful. Yet the tentative conclusions have a measure of validity and usefulness if accepted for what they are—tentative indications showing how administrative theory is being utilized currently by administrators in hospitals, and with what results.

Ultimately the administrative achievement of each hospital was reduced to a four-part score: superior administrative achievement, commendable, acceptable, and questionable. Each of these terms is subject to challenge. The next task, classifying the administrative methods which could be identified from the material available, was difficult. First, there is such a welter of so-called administrative techniques, many of them little more than twigs on the tree of administrative theory, that to maintain a semblance of clarity only the six primary methods which appear most common were used. The terms chosen are formal, informal, consultative, committee, traditional, and authoritarian. The word "formal" implies the use of management tools which result in positive, tangible, preservable, and presumably readable forms, reports, statements, manuals, minutes, and other memoranda that enable management to carry on in an orderly manner the functions described earlier in the section on general theory of administration.

Informal administrative action could have both "good" and "bad" connotations, as could nearly all methods when carried to extremes. As used here the term signifies the substitution of personal contact and word-of-mouth communication for the more formal reports. It has been assigned as an identifiable administrative method only in those instances where it was clearly so substituted.

Consultative administration has much in common with informal administration, the major difference being that the consultative manager relies largely upon his own personality and persuasive powers and close, frequent personal contact with his subordinates to accomplish his objectives. Many a successful administrator makes considerable use of the method to promote collaboration between himself and subordinates and between his subordinates and the staff. It is in the area of consultative technique rather than the "informal" category that we would place those who apparently are "human relations" oriented.

The committee method, heralded a few years ago as "the answer for all who would be successful administrators," was used because some administrators make conscious and excellent use of the method. Committees have been called a curse of hospital organization, for they seem to proliferate in the hospital atmosphere. Because of their omnipresence the method might have been assigned to every case under consideration, but it is assigned only in those situations where evidence pointed to conscious employment by the administrator of committees for explicit accomplishment and not for the purpose of rounding out an organization chart.

The reason for the use of the designation "tradition" as an administrative method is that much hospital committee activity has no other basis than tradition. No author has been found who advocated, as worthy, a reliance upon tradition as an acceptable administrative way of life. On the contrary, most books on the subject identify tradition as the pitfall of the unwary and the undoing of the incompetent. Hospital tradition, insofar as it expresses the ideals of humanitarian and charitable service, is laudable, but as a basis for planning, programming, decision, or policy making it has no values. That it is widely relied upon in exactly this way is a somewhat shocking indictment of modern hospital administrators.

Authoritarian management, or autocratic if preferred, is used to identify those cases where administration was seen to be placing emphasis upon the authority of position to enforce acceptance or support for its programs. For instance, wherever it was seen that a lack of clear-cut policy was tolerated by the administrator so that subordinates were forced to turn to the administrator as the dispenser of "the word," the use of authoritarian methods has been assigned. Such administrators apparently relish the role of commander in crisis situations.

In a few instances it was impossible to identify operations or performances that would permit application of any of these types of administrative technique. In others, in fact in most cases, two or more methods were clearly identifiable.

For the most part the distributions as to results compared with formal education (graduates of hospital administration programs), membership in the American College of Hospital Administrators, age of the administrator, his years of hospital administrative experience, his tenure in his present position, the age of the institution, its size or type of ownership, have failed to produce any significant correlations. The only item of interest along these lines was indication that those who were surveyed during their first year in their present position were experiencing difficulties. It appeared probable that these persons were utilizing the counseling service as an aid in their attempt to bring order out of a chaotic situation.

Classified according to this estimate of administrative results being obtained the following was arrived at:

Superior administrative results	12 hospitals
Commendable administrative results	20 hospitals
Acceptable administrative results	12 hospitals
Questionable administrative results	10 hospitals

It might be expected that a solid relationship would exist to the quality of patient care as indicated by approval by the Joint Commission on Accreditation of Hospitals. There is some indication of a relationship. It would be interesting to be able to carry out such a distribution on a more substantial sample.

	Accredited	*Not Accredited*
Superior administrative results	11	1
Commendable administrative results	18	2
Acceptable administrative results	11	1
Questionable administrative results	6	4
	46	8

Since the absorbing interest here centers around administrative method, what, if anything, does the tabulation of administrative results show to indicate the frequency with which each method identified was compared with the various categories of results? The tabulation disclosed that of the 32 administrators showing superior and commendable results, 19 were making substantial use of the formal tools of management. It is significant that in no instance were those in the superior result category showing evidence of being tradition-bound.

Of the 54 administrators with identifiable methods, 32 were informal to a notable degree, and 20 were making considerable use of consultative techniques. Whether this is an indication that hospital administrators are generally inclined toward informality and a human relations approach to administration can only be speculated upon.

There is some indication that those achieving better results are perhaps more flexible and adaptive than are those whose results are less satisfying. In the superior and commendable and acceptable categories a total of 86 identifiable methods were found—a ratio of two to one. In the questionable category the ratio was one and one-half to one.

In an effort to determine the reasons for the surface contradiction indicated by finding 2 of the 10 in the questionable class using the formal method identified with 10 of the 12 in the superior class, a re-examination of the audits of the two questionable results was made. In one case—a 150- to 200-bed, unaccredited hospital—the administrator stated that he was applying three different techniques, each to an exaggerated degree, to different areas of his responsibility. His primary orientation was in the business office. He had spent 16 years working in that area at another hospital. All business departments were highly formalized, and he had excellent financial control; however, his use of the tools of management ended there. The board of trustees' meetings were poorly attended; no agenda were prepared or distributed; there had not, in ten years of his administration, been developed a set of written policies for guidance of administration. Departments functioned on the basis of tradition, each department head doing things in accord with custom. Personnel policies were not written and there was little centralization or standardization outside the business office.

The other case presenting a picture of questionable results and use of the accepted formal management method is equally interesting. This is a 40-bed community hospital, not accredited by the joint commission. The administrator had no administrative experience or training prior to appointment two years before the date of the audit. The community has never had a hospital before, and the governing authority is inexperienced. The medical staff is composed of two warring cliques of doctors. No faction understands the role of the other nor has any clear ideas of its own role. The authority of the governing board is challenged and that of administration unrecognized. Nursing refuses to report to anyone but the chief of the medical staff. In this state of anarchy the administrator has attempted to impose rigid formality far beyond the reasonable needs of a 40-bed hospital and has resorted to purely autocratic methods of dealing with his subordinates. Faced with rebellion and chaos his use of the formal tools of management only emphasizes the observations made earlier about the need for balance in the application of administrative method.[41]

Perhaps the only observation not already made and worth stating is that of the hill farmer confronted by a federal agricultural agent desirous of teaching him improved agricultural methods. The lanky, sweaty man tucked his big, clumsy hands into the bib of his overalls, shifted his chew, spat and snorted, "Hell, I ain't farmin' half as well as I know how right now!"

This seems eminently true of the majority of hospital administrators. Evidence is abundant that ample technical knowledge and reasonable technical competence exist. There is, of course, much room for improvement. Yet one cannot escape the impression, when studying the reports of the counseling program, that the greatest barrier to better administrative performance is frustration—not only personal frustration, but frustration toward the general idea of management improvement for hospitals.

Strangely, the sources of this frustration appear to generate within the two groups which most closely share over-all responsibility with administration: the medical staff and the governing authority. The medical staff in theory accepts its role as guardian of the quality of patient care and has no hesitancy about taking action whenever its prerogatives are challenged. Rarely, however, does a medical staff act to enforce the rules and regulations against one of its members unless there are circumstances forcing the action. Moreover, the administrator who attempts to correct an abuse within the staff or to secure improvement in its functioning is in real danger. It is agreed by all that he is the sole representative of the governing authority, but this does not mean that he does in actuality have authority commensurate with his responsibility. Only

---

[41] American Hospital Association: Audit reports and files of survey data of the Counseling Program of the Council on Administrative Practice.

rarely have governing boards clearly met this issue by firmly asserting that the administrator has the authority equal to his responsibility.

This lack of comprehension of roles by the governing boards and the medical staffs, then, poses the great dilemma of today's hospital administrators and can be summed up in three words, responsibility exceeding authority.[42]

It will be essential to the future of the field of hospital administration to develop organizational skills and to apply existing knowledge of the processes of administration to yield a sound solution which will contribute to improvement of patient care as well as to enhancement of the opportunity for administrators to serve more efficiently and effectively.

---

[42] Richard L. Johnson: The Dilemma of the Hospital Administrator. unpublished paper presented before the Alabama Hospital Association, January, 1961.

Part six

THE HEALTH
SERVICE COMMUNITY

The Other Hospitals

If we'd had enough money in the early days of the National
Health Service to do what we wanted to do, we should have
made some appalling mistakes. With unlimited funds we
should probably have covered the East Anglian Region
with hospitals for tubercular and mental patients. By now
the T.B. hospitals would be out of date and mental hospitals
not far from it. We should have built general hospitals
on the old lines—large wards with rows of beds. The pattern
of the future will be to lay far more stress on outpatients
and greater diagnostic facilities. We don't want to put
people into hospital. We want to make inpatient treatment
unnecessary.

SIR STEPHEN LYCETT-GREEN, BT., J.P.[1]

LOOKING AROUND at the other hospitals is a good exercise that
usually leads to restraint. Changes are coming so fast that the mistakes in past
and present planning teach caution in venturing into a building or expansion
program. The wise administrator guides his board and staff in vicarious experiences through observation and study of what the other hospitals are doing
and what their results are. In a give-and-take spirit he welcomes discussion of
his own planning problems with personnel of other hospitals. Exchange of
ideas with the hospital community in general is a necessary ingredient of good
planning and operation. The other hospitals are one of the most important of
the individual hospital's "publics."

Hospitals are in an exciting period of development, one in which every procedure and policy is open to question. Among the methods used in analysis of

[1] *Hospital and Health Management,* December, 1961, reprinted in *Canad. Hosp.,* February, 1962,
p. 107. Sir Stephen Lycett-Green is chairman of the East Anglian Regional Hospital Board, England.

present-day practices is study of their evolution. How, why, and when did this way of doing things come about? In such a study of the past, some things are disclosed that could be resurrected to advantage, forgotten though they have been because of disrupting circumstances and changes in personnel. The germ of most of the good ideas of the present can be found in the thinking of past leaders. Technological advances make practical some of the ideas that were only dreams in the past; so dreams such as the vision of hospitals in Sir Thomas More's *Utopia* written in the sixteenth century provide food for thought in the twentieth: "The hospitalles in Utopia were so well appointed and attended, that though no man be sent thether against his will, yet, notwithstandinge, there is no sicke person in all the citie that had not rather lye there than at home in his own hawse."

Progress in hospital care as well as in other fields depends upon individuals who are creative thinkers, planners, and doers, and who have the ability to influence associates and groups to action. Society has grown too complex for the individual to accomplish very much alone, yet organization effort can quickly languish without the guiding enthusiasm of an inspired leader. The hospital and related fields have produced many such leaders. The few who are mentioned in connection with activities outlined in this and the three following chapters are examples of many more whose contributions have been invaluable.

A debt is especially owed to those who constructively criticize. Without them, organizations sink back into complacency and deteriorate. The John Howards of the early days and the joint commissioners of the present keep attention focused on the main goal, improved care of the patient. Their role takes courage, patience, persistence, and vision.

EARLY REFORM MOVEMENTS

Significantly Pope Clement V and the Council of Vienna issued in 1311 an edict condemning the "administrators of xenodochia, lazarettos, hospices and hospitals who unfeelingly refuse to carry out the founders' wishes and shamefully consume the revenues of these establishments."[2] Instead of caring for the indigent sick, as they were supposed to do, some of the administrators took in paying guests and diverted the profits to themselves. Sometimes the administrators were members of the donors' families. Abuses were frequent under the ecclesiastical system as well as under manorial control.

In 1579 King Henry II of France had the Ordinance of Blois passed, declaring that "the major part of the revenues of the said Poor-houses and Lazar-houses has been usurped and applied to the profit of those who have the management of them." He ruled that "no person may henceforth be appointed Commissioner for the management of the revenues of the said Lazar-houses and Hospitals

[2] From René Sand, *The Advance to Social Medicine*, London, Staples Press, 1952, p. 365.

other than common Burghers, Merchants or Labourers, and not members of the Clergy, Gentlemen, Constables, public officers, their servants or other agents."[3]

But all of the edicts and laws were evaded. In 1612 Louis XIII formed the Chamber of General Reform of Hospitals. It functioned for sixty years with little success. Reforms instituted by a commission appointed by Louis XIV in 1693 introduced a managing committee for each workhouse and hospital; but its function was mainly to control property and funds, and there was little concern about medical care or equipment.

An individual reformer occasionally created a bright note. In Paris there was, for instance, Claude-Humbert Piarron de Chamousset (1717–1773), a philanthropic citizen, who not only set up hospitals but conceived a scheme of linking all hospitals to a national organization financed by a common fund. He was appointed general superintendent of military hospitals in France. He even outlined in 1757 a plan for a benefit society, with premiums payable monthly, which would provide medical care in case of illness, either at home or in a nursing home. Nought came of these schemes, but they were the germs of later developments.

In Germany and Austria also there were reformers. Holy Roman Emperor Joseph II, king of Germany, whose reign extended from 1765 to 1792, established in Vienna a coordinated network of hospitals. He made the Allgemeines Krankenhaus (1784) with its 2,000 beds the center of the network.

Johann Peter Frank (1745–1828), a great clinical physician and public health pioneer, carried out such extensive reforms in this central hospital, where he taught and was superintendent, that he made violent enemies who publicly denounced him because of the financial losses. His answer was to the point: "The saving of human lives is the only saving that matters, and any system founded on inadequate protection of the productive classes defeats its own object."

Jacobus René Tenon, a physician, was the chief exposer of hospital horrors in France. His story began with a fire in 1772. Part of the largest hospital in the world, the Hotel Dieu at Paris, was destroyed. The fire drew the attention of Louis XVI to the hospital. He asked the Academy of Sciences to appoint a committee to submit a plan for rebuilding. Because he went a bit further and asked also for a thorough investigation of conditions and for recommendations for improvement, this weak and doomed king is himself part of the reform movement. Tenon was appointed chairman of the investigating committee. He and his committee made a complete survey, disclosing findings from time to time.

The final report, submitted in 1786 and published in 1788, was a revelation of horrors—average mortality, 25 per cent; recovery from surgery rare; only 486 beds for single patients; 1,220 beds occupied at times by four to six patients

[3] *Ibid.*

each; many patients lying on vile heaps of straw on the floor; no ventilation; almost no segregation of infectious cases; filthy, verminous surroundings; stifling odors.

The committee reported that convalescents occupied the same rooms as the sick, the dying, and the dead; that the room allotted to the insane was near that of "the unfortunate creatures who had suffered from most cruel operations and who can obtain no repose in the neighborhood of these madmen, whose frantic cries are heard by day and night." The committee reported the ventilation in the hospital to be so bad that the attendants and inspectors would not enter without holding to their faces a sponge dipped in vinegar.

The report proposed the practical scrapping of the whole hospital. Replacement with four separate buildings of 1,200 beds each was recommended. The plans included ample provision for sunlight and fresh air. The government accepted the proposal in 1787. But in vain for the time being at least was all the effort—there was a revolution in France, and Louis XVI was beheaded.

Afterward the state assumed control of the hospitals. Reforms followed in 1803 so far as nursing, management, and sanitation were concerned. But not until fifty years later was a hospital built in Paris which followed Tenon's plans. One concrete result of the report was establishment in 1802 at Paris of the largest children's hospital in Europe, the present Hôpital des Enfants Malades.

Sir John Pringle (1707–1782), of Scotland, contributed to hospital progress mainly through his work with military hospitals. He is known as the founder of military medicine and the originator of the idea which led to the organization of the Red Cross. England's first military hospital, the Greenwich Hospital, was founded in 1705. Pringle was a surgeon on the continent during the wars around the middle of the eighteenth century and was surgeon general of the English Army from 1742 to 1758, during which time he supervised the building of military hospitals made of hutments. He led a movement for hospital reform, being particularly concerned with better ventilation. Principles of military sanitation were presented in his *Observations on the Diseases of the Army* published at London in 1752. He was a pioneer in preaching and practicing antisepsis; in fact the word "antiseptic" was first used by him in a series of papers which he read before the Royal Society between 1750 and 1752. He called this series "Experiments upon Septic and Antiseptic Substances." The papers were republished in 1752 jointly with the work previously mentioned.

John Howard (1726–1790) has been mentioned before in these studies. His influence cannot be overestimated, and his story is interesting. He was a Quaker who when he was appointed in 1773 to the post of high sheriff of Bedford County, England, put his heart into his duties, one of which was to supervise the county jail. It happened that 17 years earlier Howard had sailed for Lisbon to relieve the sufferers from the 1755 earthquake. On the way the vessel was captured by a French privateer, and the crew and passengers were imprisoned at Brest. The treatment of the prisoners and the condition of the jail set him aflame with indignation at man's inhumanity to man. The starvation diet, the filthy, dark, unventilated dungeons, the exploitation and mistreatment of the prisoners, stayed in his mind like a nightmare. So he took particular note of the irregularities that he discovered in the Bedford jail.

He immediately set out to compare conditions there with those in other prisons. The result, in his own words: "I beheld scenes of calamity, which I grew daily more and more anxious to alleviate." From jails his concern extended to almshouses, orphanages, homes for the aged, quarantine stations, and hospitals in England, Scotland, Wales, and Ireland, and also in Europe and Asia. From his forty-seventh to his sixty-fourth year, that is from 1773 to 1790, he made seven long tours of inspection of the corrective, custodial, and medical institutions of Europe, covering practically every country on the continent and visiting some of them several times. His travels covered more than 50,000 miles. He spent 30,000 pounds of his own fortune.

How does a visitor of Howard's type get into hospitals? Nobody likes snoopers. In most places he was without authority; even in his own country he was without portfolio for this work except in his county. What he did was to pose as a regular do-gooder visitor who came to succor the inmates and patients. He gave alms. He brought gifts. And in so doing he looked around!

What he saw was eventually published in two books. The first, which appeared in 1777, is entitled *The State of the Prisons in England and Wales, with Preliminary Observations, and an Account of Some Foreign Prisons and Hospitals*. The second came out in 1789 and is called *An Account of the Principal Lazarettos in Europe, with Various Papers Relative to the Plague: Together with Further Observations on Some Foreign Prisons and Hospitals: and Additional Remarks on the Present State of Those in Great Britain and Ireland*.

Prior to the publication of each of the books Howard reported his observations to Parliament. He told them of patients lying "untended upon a sanded or straw-littered floor, unbathed, covered with rags, in dark, unventilated, unheated rooms which reek with filth and vermin." From the House of Commons he received in 1774 a vote of thanks. The press took up his cause. The public was aroused. A reform movement was under way.

Along with Howard's criticisms he wisely presented plans to remedy the conditions. In many communities his suggestions were followed. Frequently he revisited institutions, praised publicly what reforms had been made, and suggested further improvements. Not a carping critic he, but a constructive one. He praised as well as blamed. In not a few places his visits were welcome. He won for himself the title of the "Father of Prison Reform." In his native land and in Europe he was warmly acclaimed.

Means of prevention and treatment of the plague were his last self-assigned study. While so engaged he himself fell prey to the disease. On January 12, 1790, he succumbed in the village of Cherson in Russian Tartary. In accordance with his wishes he was buried in the neighboring village of Douphigny.

In tribute to his memory a statue was erected at St. Paul's Cathedral, London. Among the thoughts recorded on the pedestal are these words:

> Our National Prisons and Hospitals, Improved upon the Suggestions of his Wisdom, bear testimony to the Solidity of his Judgment and to the Estimation in which he was held. *He trod an open but unfrequented path of immortality.*

Czar Paul of Russia, son of Catherine the Great, was, according to Garrison,[4] "horrified with the condition of the Moscow Hospital and ordered its reconstruction" when he came to the throne in 1797. The new one opened in 1802 with facilities for accommodating 1,200 patients.

A celebrated medical and hospital reformer in early nineteenth-century Russia was Nicolai Ivanovich Pirogov (1810–1881), the founder of modern Russian surgery. He fought a terrific battle to improve the hospital in St. Petersburg where he was chief of the 1,000-bed surgical department. He had to struggle against unsanitary conditions, administrative abuses and routines, but emerged victorious. Less successful were his efforts to reform the country's military hospitals and medical services as a whole, although he gained wide fame as an authority on the conduct of military medicine.

The Fliedners, Rev. Theodor and his wife, Frederike Munster, entered the reform scene in 1836 when they established a hospital and a training school for deaconesses at Kaiserswerth on the Rhine. Their encouragement to do this came from having visited similar institutions conducted by the Mennonites in Holland. Another incentive was distress over the poor nursing service they found in hospitals that they visited in England and other countries.

Mrs. Fliedner became the administrator. The teaching was designed to train the girls for teaching nursing to others as well as to learn how to nurse. As the work grew Rev. Fliedner gave up his pastorate and established branch schools and hospitals. He traveled widely, establishing deaconess homes and hospitals in Jerusalem, Constantinople, Smyrna, Alexandria, Hungary, Holland, France, England, Scandinavia, and the United States. His visit to the United States in June, 1849, at the request of Rev. W. A. Passavant was mentioned in Chapter 16.

The Fliedners are especially important in this brief narrative of hospital reform because both Elizabeth Fry (1840) and Florence Nightingale (1850) visited Kaiserswerth, the latter to go back in 1851 and spend four months in training there. Miss Nightingale then went to Paris and worked in the hospitals with the Sisters of Charity and French surgeons. On her return to England she was appointed superintendent of nurses at King's College Hospital, but before she took that position the British government sent her officially to the Crimea to take charge of the care of the wounded and sick. Among the nurses she took with her were some who had been trained in the program instituted by Elizabeth Fry. What she found in the Crimea and the stir she made about it are

---

[4] Fielding H. Garrison: *An Introduction to the History of Medicine.* Philadelphia, W. B. Saunders Company, 4th ed., 1929, p. 400.

well known—dirt, disorder, chaos, misery. The medical officers opposed her changes. She persevered. The results were a reduction in the death rate from 42 to 2 per cent and the absolute proof that improvements in environment and in nursing care save lives and minimize disability.

It was 1856 when Miss Nightingale returned to England. From then until her death in 1910 she labored unceasingly for better hospital care and became the first real hospital administrator in the modern sense. She founded at St. Thomas' Hospital in 1860 a nursing school which set a pattern for many others. Her work is too well known to dwell upon here except to quote *Hospital Care in the United States,*[5] which says of her career that it "completely changed the concept of nursing service and education," and:

> Miss Nightingale was responsible for fundamental reforms in hospital organization and administration, in construction, sanitation, and dietary service. . . . Miss Nightingale's prolific writings revealed to the world her sound theories of health organization. Her books were the first to acquaint the people concerning the problems of hospitals and nursing. *Notes on the British Army* marked a turning point in the history of military medicine. *Notes on Hospitals* published in 1858 is considered a most valuable contribution and revolutionized hospital construction, emphasizing sanitation rather than beauty. . . . *Notes on Nursing* appeared in 1859 and remains a classic to this day for the principles she laid down are still followed. The practical application of her ideas proved the value of a definite plan of education for nurses.

AMERICAN REFORMERS

The Nightingale school figured in the first hospital reform project in the United States. Its leader was the great-granddaughter of Alexander Hamilton, Louisa Schuyler. After serving as president of the Women's Central Association for Relief during the Civil War, she became interested in Bellevue Hospital and related institutions. She studied the horrible conditions and decided that the reform needed most was improvement in the nursing service which could only be accomplished through establishing a training school for nurses. She organized a committee of society women to inspect the conditions and to promote the project. One of the Bellevue doctors, young W. Gill Wylie, who had proved to be sympathetic, was asked to serve on the committee. The members were required by Miss Schuyler to keep notes on their observations at the hospital, and these notes disclose such conditions as no night nurses, rats running over the floors and beds, and filthy bedding. Some of the evils were remedied by the committee, but the original goal was always kept in sight.

At the opportune time Miss Schuyler presented the idea to the commissioner, telling him about the Nightingale school. He had difficulty in winning over the medical board—the doctors were afraid educated nurses would not follow orders and would encroach upon the medical domain! Then Dr. Wylie, at his own

[5] Commission on Hospital Care: New York, The Commonwealth Fund, 1947, pp. 459–60.

expense, went to England to study the schools at St. Thomas' Hospital and at the University of Edinburgh. A letter filled with practical suggestions from Miss Nightingale, whom he had been unable to see in England because of her illness, came just before the next meeting of the Board of Charities. The influential ladies had succeeded in raising $20,000 by public subscription with the aid of 35 leading physicians. The medical board of the hospital and the Board of Charities of the city succumbed. The nursing school became a reality in 1873 with Sister Helen of All Saints Sisterhood, London, in charge, and six carefully selected students. Thus, thanks to a group of determined women, the first permanent nursing school in America was established.[6]

A tireless worker for the public welfare was Dr. Stephen Smith, surgeon and commissioner of health in New York from 1868 to 1875. Dr. Smith helped to organize Roosevelt Hospital, New York; Johns Hopkins Hospital, Baltimore; and several other large hospitals. He pioneered in improving conditions in the state mental hospitals. He induced a corps of Sisters of Charity to run the smallpox hospital on Blackwell's Island when he discovered that the nurses there were chronic drunkards recruited from the detention quarters. He began the campaign that resulted in the formation of the American Public Health Association in 1871.

Dr. James Alexander Miller revolutionized the care of tuberculous patients at Bellevue Hospital when he joined its staff in 1910. Previously little medical attention and no trained nursing service were given these patients, and no records were kept on them. Dr. Miller started a tuberculosis clinic in the out-patient department. With financial help from some of his patients he established a day camp on an old ferryboat. He worked hard to gain help for the tuberculosis service from city officials, and finally in 1926 he won the interest of Mayor James Walker. Thereafter the tuberculosis service became renowned for its high standards of service and exceptional rate of arrested cases.

A plea for help in reforming his country's hospitals was made by a doctor from Chile at the Conference of Hospitals, Dispensaries and Nursing during the International Congress of Charities at the Chicago World's Fair in 1894. After telling about the founding in 1556, the destruction by earthquake in 1647, and the reconstruction in 1702 of San Juan de Dios Hospital in Valparaiso, Dr. Louis Asta-Buruaga remarked with respect to Chilean hospitals that the "only conclusion that can be formulated is that they urgently need a total reform." He added: "It would be most gratifying to me if some day I could see the hospitals in Chile based upon the same laws as the International Conference of Hospitals at Chicago may deem it proper to propose for the construction and management of charitable institutions."

The advanced ideas and missionary zeal of Dr. John S. Billings and Dr. Henry Mills Hurd stirred the hospital world to many reforms. Dr. Billings created Johns Hopkins Hospital and Dr. Hurd ran it. In his series of articles,

[6] From *Hospital City* by John Starr. New York, Crown Publishers, Inc., 1957, pp. 103–23.

"They Made Hospital History," Dr. Otho F. Ball[7] said of Billings' work on Johns Hopkins Hospital: "His plan called for the highest type of teaching hospital, with physiological and pathological laboratories, outpatient dispensary, and a system of records, historical, clinical, and financial. Medical students received their firsthand training at the bedside, not subjecting the patient to amphitheater exhibitions, 'lectured over as if he were a curious sort of beetle.' The hospital was opened in 1889 and Billings' *Description of the Johns Hopkins Hospital* became a classic in the field of hospital construction." Dr. Billings also planned the Peter Bent Brigham Hospital of Boston and the Barnes Hospital (Soldiers' Home of the District of Columbia).

Dr. Hurd began his career in hospital administration in 1878 as superintendent of the Eastern Michigan Asylum, Pontiac, leaving that post in 1889 to become the first superintendent of Johns Hopkins Hospital. He retired from that position in 1911 at the age of 68, but continued as secretary of the board of trustees. His influence was greatly enhanced through his contributions to the literature and to association work. He became an active member of the American Hospital Association in 1904 and was its president in 1911–1912. From 1913 to 1920 he was on the editorial board of *Modern Hospital*. He was at different times editor of the *American Journal of Insanity;* editor of the *Institutional Care of the Insane in the United States and Canada;* and co-editor of *Hospitals, Dispensaries and Nursing*. He served as president of the American Medico-Psychological Association and as professor of psychiatry at the Johns Hopkins University School of Medicine. He died in 1927 at the age of 84.[8]

The reformers, the innovators, the leaders in hospital affairs, have been numerous since the days of Billings and Hurd. Among those who have passed from the scene but whose influence lives on are:

Dr. Richard C. Cabot, of Boston, who, among other contributions to improvements in hospital service, promoted, publicized, and enthusiastically encouraged the new profession of medical social service.

Drs. Franklin H. Martin, John Gabbert Bowman, and Malcolm T. Mac-Eachern, of the American College of Surgeons, who founded and developed the college's program of hospital standardization, still a most effective means of continuing hospital reform and improvement under the auspices of the Joint Commission on Accreditation of Hospitals directed by Dr. Kenneth B. Babcock.

Dr. Bert Caldwell, Asa Bacon, and many others who directed the early development of the American Hospital Association in its efforts to promote coordination among hospitals.

Arthur J. Swanson, president of the Canadian Hospital Association from 1945 to 1949, George Findlay Stephens, and many others who helped to guide the destinies of the association to its present effectiveness.

[7] *Mod. Hosp.*, February, 1951.
[8] Obituary. *Bull. Am. Hosp. A.,* October, 1927, p. 202. See also, Otho F. Ball, M.D.: They Made Hospital History—Henry Hurd of Hopkins. *Mod. Hosp.*, September, 1952.

So many have shouldered the responsibilities of those who have finished their work, and have taken on new ones as the times changed, that naming them would require too long a list, and anyway they and their activities can be traced in the literature. One, however, who celebrated his eighty-fourth birthday in 1963, stands out as an innovator, thinker, idealist, and hospital philosopher. Founder in 1934 of the first graduate program in hospital administration that is still in existence, Michael M. Davis gave the opening lecture, "America Challenges Medicine," on May 23, 1963, in the lecture series established in his honor at the University of Chicago. As a social scientist and medical economist (Ph.D. in sociology, Columbia University, 1906), Dr. Davis has served as consultant to the United States Congress and to other governmental and nongovernmental groups in matters ranging from health legislation to the organization and financing of medical services and has helped greatly to focus attention on the hospital in its broad social significance. Always forward-looking, never avoiding expressing his views on controversial issues, in his book published by Harper in 1954, *Medical Care for Tomorrow,* he has summarized his thinking.

CONTROL OF INFECTIONS

One of the leading problems in all hospitals is control of infections. The most valuable aid in establishing safeguards is study of the experiences and procedures in other hospitals.

The American Hospital Association published in 1962 a monograph, *Control of Infections in Hospitals.* The report was summarized by J. C. Colbeck,[9] chief of the pathology service at Shaughnessy Hospital, Vancouver, British Columbia. The summary mentions that in 1958 the Joint Commission on Accreditation of Hospitals recommended "that every hospital have an 'infection committee' charged with the responsibility of investigation, control, and prevention of infection within hospitals."

Extensive publicity in both public and professional journals has aroused everyone to the dangers of hospital-acquired infections. *McCall's Magazine* carried a seven-page article about them in July, 1961, under a banner headline, "The Hidden Epidemic: A Warning!" Sensational though this article was, it did not exaggerate the facts.

Among the most effective devices being employed to teach hospital personnel how to guard against spreading infection is the motion picture. A film, "Hospital Sepsis: A Communicable Disease," was prepared in 1959 under the auspices of the American Medical Association, the American College of Surgeons, and the American Hospital Association. It was directed by Dr. Carl W. Walter, of Peter Bent Brigham Hospital, Boston, and distributed by Johnson and Johnson, New Brunswick, New Jersey. A discussion manual supplementing the film was com-

[9] *Hospitals,* January 16, 1963, pp. 58, 59, 139.

piled and annotated by Dr. Walter and Dorothy W. Errera, R.N., and edited by Dr. John Henderson, medical director of Johnson and Johnson; it is also distributed by that firm. This 44-page illustrated manual presents the problems and the way to attack them, mainly in question-and-answer form.

A later film under the same auspices with the addition of the American Nurses Association and the National League for Nursing is entitled "I Dress the Wound." It was also produced under the direction of Dr. Walter and is available from Johnson and Johnson.

In 1961 a third film, "Disinfection of Skin," was released under the auspices of the same organizations. This film was produced by the American Cyanamid Company, and co-sponsored by Winthrop Laboratories and the Aeroplast Corporation. Narration was written by Dr. Walter. The film deals with disinfection of the skin of both patients and personnel.

Everything in the hospital is suspect when infections occur. Investigations have disclosed contaminated water in unsterilized bedside carafes, contaminated ice prepared and handled without adequate safeguards, contaminated filters in air conditioning systems, defective autoclaves, insufficient emphasis on cleanliness throughout the hospital, and many other flaws in aseptic technique.

The current infection problems, which are as acute in Europe as in the United States, appear to focus around overconfidence in antibiotics. When they were introduced, the infection rate fell sharply. It has gone up again. Bacteria have become resistant to the many preparations on the market. Emphasis is being placed upon aseptic technics, with less reliance upon antiseptic measures, although these continue. Prepackaging and disposables are aids in reducing infections, but this virtue is destroyed when the hands that handle them have not been freshly washed.

The price of relaxation of vigilance, not just in the operating room but in the corridors, the kitchen, the laundry, and the corners of the patient's room, is hospital-caused death. The lifesaving necessity is firm administrative control.

Everybody in the hospital is involved in the battle. A reprint from *Canadian Hospital*'s March, 1958, issue includes articles from a symposium, "Controlling Staphylococcus." The first, by Dr. Arnold L. Swanson, is on "Hospital Organization"; the second, by Dr. George Dempster, is on "Bacteriological Fact Finding"; the third, by M. K. Ruane, R.N., is on "Nursing Techniques"; the fourth, by Dr. D. J. Buchan, is "On the Medical Wards"; and the fifth, by Dr. Eric M. Nanson, is "On the Surgical Wards."

A rather new theory about infections is that the drug-resistant germs are probably not new but have emerged as important sources of trouble only after others, such as the pneumococci, which formerly accounted for most bacterial infections, were brought under control with antibiotics. Experiments have shown that infection with one kind of bacteria usually prevents infection with another. The presence of certain germs in the environment was masked by bacteria that were more infective then but that are sensitive to the new drugs.

Kenneth Van Bree,[10] then an administrative resident at Saint Luke's Hospital, Racine, Wisconsin, now administrator of Marinette (Wisconsin) General Hospital, said:

> The control of hospital infections may be exceedingly difficult. The establishment of an infection committee, supported by adequate funds and a well-staffed laboratory service, to study and report on hospital infections, is essential. The return to the time-tested methods of aseptic techniques, and the rigid maintenance of them, should be the starting point of the program. Improving housekeeping, laundry, and kitchen procedures can be a valuable aid in eliminating sources of infections. Operating room and nursery procedures should be given special consideration. The search for and the removal of dangerous carriers from the medical and hospital staff should be carried out. The indiscriminate use of antibiotics should be carefully controlled.
>
> There should be no let-up of this program even though the bacteriological studies have been completed and corrective measures have been installed. Even the discovery of a new "miracle" antibiotic should not permit the program to be discontinued. The new antibiotic may also leave more resistant organisms to plague the hospital. There is no doubt that resistant organisms are "here to stay."

EMERGENCY SERVICE

What are "the other hospitals" doing about providing service for the victims of accidents and of sudden critical illness? Not nearly enough if the barrage of criticism is justified, as it seems to be, by the facts. Many millions of people every year face these emergencies. The problem is one of gigantic proportions. It has been estimated that the emergency room patient load has quadrupled since 1940. Hartford (Connecticut) Hospital reported multiplication by six from 3,000 in 1944 to 18,000 in 1954, with the estimate for 1960 of 26,000. "No other single service, if poorly run, will do more to alienate public support and good will," declared Dr. Ernest C. Shortliffe,[11] then associate executive director of Hartford Hospital.

Often termed "the weakest link in hospital care," the emergency service is confronted by unique problems such as the fact that almost any kind of patient may appear at any moment and there has to be instant readiness to give him any kind of treatment indicated.

"Give it the status it deserves," pleads Dr. Robert H. Kennedy,[12] surgical director and president of the medical board at Beekman-Downtown Hospital, New York City. His fellow orthopedic surgeons in the American College of Surgeons are uniting to insist upon better quarters, better personnel, better equipment in the emergency department. The president of the college in 1961, Dr. I. S. Ravdin, complained in an interview that "in many instances there isn't even an

[10] Master's thesis, The Control of Hospital Infections, submitted to Northwestern University in 1958.
[11] Emergency Rooms . . . Weakest Link in Hospital Care? *Hospitals*, February 1, 1960, pp. 32–34; 107.
[12] Editorial. *Trustee*, March, 1957.

intern on duty." He advocated in this interview with a science writer for the Scripps-Howard Newspaper Alliance that regional emergency hospitals with good facilities be provided. Pittsburgh's St. John's Hospital built one in 1963.

As director of the trauma field program of the college, Dr. Kennedy, referring to studies of emergency room care financed by a grant from the John A. Hartford Foundation, stated:[13]

> We are in the midst of an evolution of the old "accident room" into an emergency department which may be destined to become the medical center of the community. We must be certain that our emergency medical facilities are organized to accept this responsibility which the public is placing upon them.

A member of the college's Committee on Trauma and chief of Regional Section XII, Dr. Frank P. Patterson, of Vancouver, was chairman of a committee which reviewed and finished a study entitled "A Study of Emergency Departments in Hospitals in the Metropolitan Area of the Lower Mainland of British Columbia, 1960–1961."[14]

A review[15] terms the monograph "outstanding" and states that the statistics collected "appear to show that visits to emergency departments can be expected to double every 10 or 15 years; that the principle of a separate hospital for accidents only does not seem to be justified; and that an accident service should be attached to a large parent general hospital."

A manual, *The Emergency Department in the Hospital: A Guide to Organization and Management,* was approved by the Board of Regents of the college and by the Board of Trustees of the American Hospital Association and made available for distribution in November, 1962, through A.H.A. A country-wide survey by special committees preceded preparation of the *Guide.* A trauma research group at Cornell University also participated.

Twenty-four-hour medical coverage is an ideal that is fast becoming a myth in many smaller hospitals. Lois R. Chevalier[16] convincingly presented the facts. She told of parents rushing a small boy who had suffered a severe head injury to the nearest hospital. It was Christmas Eve. A nurse in the emergency room cleaned the wound and put a patch over it. Asked where the doctor was, she said there was none and offered to call the family doctor. He was away on holiday. From the hospital's on-call list she telephoned a doctor. It took him three hours to get there. The boy recovered, but the parents suffered extreme disillusionment about the security which a local hospital can offer.

Responsible for the shortage of physicians for off-hour duty are several factors. One is that there are only about 7,000 medical graduates each year to fill around

---

[13] *Bull. Am. Coll. Surgeons,* March-April 1961.

[14] The monograph was prepared and published by the Metropolitan Planning Council of Vancouver. It has 87 pages, 20 tables, 10 figures, 13 maps, appendices, and an "invaluable 63-item bibliography," according to a review in *Bull. Am. Coll. Surgeons,* April, 1963, p. 80.

[15] *Ibid.*

[16] *Reader's Digest,* September, 1961, pp. 135–38.

12,800 internships approved in 1964 by the American Medical Association. Only 75 per cent of the approved internships and residencies are filled; some 9,000 more residents could be used. The supply of foreign-trained doctors has been drastically reduced by the new justifiable regulations by the American Medical Association against appointment by hospitals of unlicensed or uncertified graduates for direct service to patients. On-call systems are in effect in close to half of the hospitals in the United States, a recent survey by the American College of Surgeons disclosed. A number of solutions have been proposed and are being tried, but the situation in general is a disturbing one for hospital boards, medical staffs, administrators, and the public. Accidents and acute illnesses have a way of striking down their victims mostly in the depths of the night.

Ways can be found to overcome the staffing problem, but the complete co-operation of the medical staff is necessary. Dr. Vernon C. Abbott[17] answered the question of "How to Staff a Hospital Emergency Department" by telling how the 381-bed Pontiac (Michigan) General Hospital operates. The administration put the problem up to the medical staff, which formed a group of some 25 doctors to work in 8-hour shifts, furnishing 24-hour coverage. The group organized as the Professional Medical Service Group, agreeing to examine and treat all patients presenting themselves to the department at fees in accordance with the service rendered, with a minimum of four dollars. The members of the group are paid monthly at an hourly rate for the number of hours worked. Most of the doctors in the group are young men and have more time than those who have a well-established practice. The minimum fee paid by the patient is ten dollars, a six-dollar service charge being added to the minimum fee for medical attention. The 24-hour intern coverage of the department continues, but under the new arrangement he is always under the supervision of the staff doctor.

The ever-increasing demands on the emergency service are doubtless a result of the passing of the family doctor. A great many persons nowadays have no personal physician. When they need medical care, they do not know how to select a doctor, one of the reasons being uncertainty over who is a specialist or who is not, and another whether their condition needs the service of a specialist or a generalist. They feel that the hospital gives the easiest answer to their problem. The hospital atmosphere in itself gives them some assurance of safety, far more than the strange doctor's office over the corner drugstore. That doctor may be eminently qualified, and the emergency department doctor may be a new graduate. They do not know the difference. They trust the hospital. This is evidence that the hospital has succeeded in creating an image that it had better live up to or all its public relations efforts along other lines are in vain. The opportunities here are ready-made, but making the most of them brings many problems, not the least of which is avoiding the charge of competing with private medical practice.

[17] *Bull. Am. Coll. Surgeons,* July-August, 1962.

DISASTER PLANNING

Closely related to emergency service problems are those of preparation for disaster. It is an obligation to the community for the whole hospital to be geared to instant action in case of hurricanes, floods, fires, wrecks, and every other imaginable catastrophe. The civil defense program has the great value of spurring planning to meet any emergency, under any circumstances.

Besides the inside preparations including frequent tests and drills, alert hospital administrators look around outside for potential resources. When two New York commuter trains collided near Suffern, New York, in 1958, Good Samaritan Hospital although almost full at the time found ways of accommodating the injured; but had there been more, the administrator, Sister Miriam Thomas, would have known what to do. She had her eye on the Augustine seminary across the road and knew exactly how much space was available in the corridors of their building and even how long it would take to move a patient there from the emergency room.[18]

Civilian hospitals in Nassau County, Long Island, have organized medical teams whose personnel, along with volunteer members of the civil defense medical service, have been trained in the operation of emergency hospital units which in a case of major catastrophe would be set up in three large shopping centers which have medical supplies and equipment stored below ground. These three sites are among fifty located in New York State, where the federal government is stockpiling supplies near the nation's critical target areas. Altogether, 1,000 such emergency hospitals are being developed. Shopping centers are especially suitable, administrators in the area believe, because of their accessibility, parking space, and supplies of food and other necessities.

The hospital cannot overlook its own vulnerability in a disaster. Evacuation plans are part of disaster planning. The disastrous fire in southern California's San Fernando Valley in August, 1962, forced evacuation of 1,100-bed Olive View Hospital in the foothills of the San Gabriel mountains. The personnel were prepared when a shift in the direction of the blaze threatened the hospital. Fire and evacuation drills had been held monthly for a long period. The 100 separate buildings scattered over 250 acres were emptied of patients, who were transported in buses, station wagons, and ambulances to three other county hospitals which had put their disaster plans in action in order to receive them. Evacuation was completed none too soon; a fire storm developed and several buildings were destroyed, although it was possible to return the patients to the hospital 48 hours later.

As is always true in such instances, some procedures, it was decided, could have been improved. Experience is a good teacher. Assistant Administrator Robert Frauens, in charge during the emergency, helped other hospitals by giving

[18] Preparedness Pays When Disaster Strikes. *Hosp. Topics*, November, 1958, pp. 31–34.

the author of an article in *Hospital Forum*[19] his ideas about what worked well and what could be improved. Hospital personnel are generous in giving others the benefit of their experiences, as articles in the hospital journals prove.

The Canadian Council on Hospital Accreditation has included a disaster plan as an integral part of the standards on accreditation. In an editorial in *Canadian Hospital,* April, 1962, it was stated that while disaster institutes have been held across Canada for almost a decade, only about half of Canadian hospitals have developed disaster plans. "There are plenty of examples from across Canada and the U.S.A.," the editorial goes on, "to show that when a hospital is faced with a sudden influx of patients and there is no prepared disaster plan, situations arise which can only be described as chaotic." And the added threats of "the hydrogen bomb, the intercontinental ballistic missile, and radiation fallout" make it imperative for every hospital to be able to "accept a large number of casualties on short notice," to sort them speedily and to give "adequate and prompt treatment." It is pointed out that *every* hospital is involved because it would be the institutions in the nontarget areas that would have to "bear the brunt of the disaster situation" by receiving the casualties and other evacuees from the areas directly hit.

Similar disappointment at the failure of hospitals in the United States to respond to the planning need was expressed in the *Bulletin of the Joint Commission on Accreditation of Hospitals,* December, 1961:

> Over five years ago the commissioners . . . made the request that in every hospital there should be a written plan for the care, reception and evacuation of mass casualties, and that this plan should be coordinated with the inpatient and outpatient services of the hospital. The plan should be rehearsed by key personnel at least twice yearly. . . . For the most part, hospitals have cooperated. . . . Our reports still show, however, that close to 30 per cent of the hospitals surveyed have not carried out our recommendation on this specific item. This should be done immediately.

The *Bulletin* then calls attention to the President's emphasis on the need for expediting all facets of civil defense, making it essential

> . . . that every hospital disaster plan be reviewed constantly in light of developments, local and national. If it is to prove effective, it must be disseminated and known not only to the staff and personnel but to the community, its police,, fire and welfare departments, public utilities, communications and transportation facilities. In turn it should be an integral part of the State Operational Survival Plan.

A written disaster plan under which periodic drills are conducted is now a requirement for accreditation by the joint commission.

The American Hospital Association and the Department of Defense issued a joint statement in late November, 1962, to the effect that "in the event of nuclear attack, the primary responsibility of the hospital will be to provide shelter space

[19] Irene Isherwood: Fire! *Hosp. Forum,* October, 1962, pp. 18, 42, 44.

for its patients, personnel, and as large a segment of the public as possible." The secondary function was stated to be to "protect its capabilty to function as a health facility during the postattack period." The joint policy statement was prepared after a series of meetings between the A.H.A.'s Committee on Preparedness Planning and the Department of Defense and stated that it was the view of both that

> ... in these times every hospital has the responsibility to take practical and sensible measures to minimize loss of life resulting from radioactive fallout in the event of nuclear attack. In addition, it is imperative to preserve the skilled manpower of our country's hospitals in order that we might survive as a nation and recover from the attack.

The A.H.A. sent the statement to 7,000 hospitals, and the Department of Defense sent it to all local civil defense authorities. It set forth the guiding principles applying to hospitals.[20] Through civil defense agencies the government is making stockpile supplies available to hospitals, and in 1963 legislation was being considered for financing fall-out shelters in hospitals. In the fall of 1962 the Presbyterian Inter-Community Hospital, Covina, California, received a $10,000 grant from the Department of Defense for making architectural studies for a contemplated $3,500,000 dual-purpose shelter. The shelter would provide space for 256 automobiles in an underground garage which could be converted into a 500-bed emergency hospital and a fall-out shelter for 15,000 persons. This was the first proposal of its kind submitted to the department and the first to receive a grant.[21]

OUTPATIENT DEPARTMENT AND CLINICS

Once confined to service to the indigent, and still so conceived of by some hospitals, the outpatient department with its special clinics is becoming more and more a service for all types of ambulant patients. As was discussed in the section on emergency service, the passing of the family doctor and the publicity about hospital resources are leading many persons to avoid physicians' offices in favor of the hospital clinic or emergency service. Financial circumstances have little to do with the trend. Locating physicians' offices in or adjoining the hospital is one solution to the problem.

With modern medical practice tending to keep people up and about, with even critical illness and surgery usually confining them to bed for only a few days, the outpatient department acquires increasing importance. Expansion of outpatient services was given as one of the answers to the problem of overutilization of inpatient facilities by Carl C. Lamley, administrator of Stormont-Vail Hospital, Topeka, Kansas, at a 1961 conference of hospital trustees, administrators, and

[20] See *Hospitals*, December 16, 1962, pp. 99–101.
[21] *Hosp. Forum*, September, 1962, p. 41.

chiefs called by the Illinois Hospital Association. Mr. Lamley said that there was "a void today between the doctor's office and the hospital" and recommended that "more outpatient services and programs be developed to fill that gap," with hospitals and physicians working together to provide for specific needs of the patient short of hospitalization.

Dr. Harvey Agnew[22] predicted:

> One change will probably be to keep to a minimum the use of beds for patients undergoing diagnostic study, e.g., laboratory or radiological. . . . such patients, if not bedridden, would come to the hospital as outpatients on appointment and would probably go directly to the department concerned. In the case of larger hospitals with a considerable amount of referred work, one foresees the patients from a distance staying at an adjacent hostel, possibly operated by the hospital, and reporting at appointed hours for examination. . . . It is easy to envisage the development of entire units designed solely for diagnostic purposes. These units would be maintained primarily for short-stay patients who do not require total bed care; they would therefore be planned to provide for an uppatient lounge room, dining room and a patio or open sun deck if possible. Such a unit would be heavily staffed by technical personnel but would require no intensive nursing care. There would be a strong concentration of x-ray and laboratory services of the diagnostic type, electrocardiography, basal metabolism and electroencephalography, where feasible, plus a good supply of examining rooms.

Special clinics link the hospital with the community in an exceptionally effective way. The services should be well publicized and referrals promoted. Their type is almost limitless, and their value incalculable. They range from prenatal, postnatal, well-baby, nutrition, cardiac, cancer, arthritis, orthopedic, neurological, diabetic, rehabilitation, and mental health clinics, to the comprehensive follow-up clinic which is being widely advocated as essential to complete medical service.

The follow-up clinic has research and educational values for the physicians. When early ambulation following major surgery first began to be practiced, some doctors agreed that there were mental and physical advantages to the patient but questioned the effect upon wound healing. In a follow-up clinic at Mount Sinai Hospital, New York, studies were made of two groups of postoperative patients. One group had been kept in bed in accordance with tradition, the other had been allowed early ambulation. It was discovered that the patients who stayed in bed were more susceptible to wound weaknesses and hernias.

The Veterans Administration is conducting a new program, authorized by Congress in 1960, of prehospital and posthospital care. V.A. hospitals can now perform certain medical services for nonservice-connected patients without placing them in hospital beds. The program is limited to veterans who are scheduled for admission to, or are patients in, V.A. hospitals. It is designed to shorten the period of stay as inpatients and has already proved to be a factor in increasing the turnover rate.

[22] The Tempo of Change. *Canad. Hosp.,* October, 1958.

Hospitals for the Mentally Ill

Concern over the inadequacy of many existing state facilities as well as the lack of long-needed community-based programs and services for the mentally ill prompted the formation in 1959 of the Ad Hoc Committee on Planning for Mental Health Facilities by the Surgeon General of the Public Health Service. The report of the committee was published in 1961. It showed 620 nonfederal and 42 federal psychiatric hospitals and 264 nonfederal institutions for mental deficiency. Of the nonfederal psychiatric hospitals 259 were proprietary, with a total of 16,621 beds. Total beds in nonfederal psychiatric hospitals were 503,301, in federal hospitals 64,932. Total beds in nonfederal institutions for mental deficiency were 93,287. Only 3.3 per cent of the beds were in proprietary psychiatric hospitals and 1.9 per cent in voluntary nonprofit psychiatric hospitals, indicating that the nongovernmental hospitals were small in size. This was also true of institutions for mental deficiency.

In the conclusions of the report it was observed:

> In spite of recent dramatic advances in the treatment of mental illness, little progress has been made in providing the various types of facilities which would offer the most appropriate environment for carrying out the latest treatment methods. The inadequacy of present facilities is considered one of the primary impediments to more rapid progress in the treatment of mental illness—one of the nation's major public health problems.

For many years the American Psychiatric Association in cooperation with other agencies such as the American College of Surgeons and the Joint Commission on Accreditation of Hospitals has labored to raise the standards of care in mental hospitals. Standards were published in 1945 and revised in 1951. They were applicable to outpatient psychiatric clinics as well as to hospitals. The association established a Central Inspection Board for inspecting and rating hospitals which ended its work in 1960, although the surveying and consulting functions were continued under the association's Mental Hospital Service. The reports of this service show deficiencies and make recommendations. Assistance to the Joint Commission on Accreditation of Hospitals is given "to aid development of a realistic appraisal of mental hospitals." The commission has surveyed mental hospitals on request since 1958.

Building design as well as treatment procedures reflect a new era in the care of the mentally ill. In the September 1, 1962, issue of *Hospitals* was an illustrated article on the new 150-bed Moccasin Bend Psychiatric Hospital, Chattanooga, Tennessee, a state facility. The very design of the structure, with its large plate-glass windows and essentially one-story plan, makes it an exhibit of the "open-door" policy which is the dominant pattern of patient care. Rules are few; the atmosphere is friendly. Patients can bring their own personal belongings, even such things as television sets, radios, lamps, and sewing machines. When the article was written, a day-care program was in the planning stage, the aim of which would be to free more beds for immediate occupancy and to aid in returning the patients to the community more rapidly. Patients of all ages and with all types of mental illness are accepted.

Tranquilizing drugs "have helped in smoothing the path to the open door," according to a psychiatrist[23] from the Bristol Mental Hospital, England. He warned, however, that the doors should be opened gradually, starting with the best-behaved patients. Individualization and keeping the patients active are the aims of the new therapy.

In England the recent Mental Health Act is operating to bring psychiatric hospital standards up to those of general hospitals. The open-door pattern can be and is more widely practiced because the hospitals are much smaller. They are appalled at the giant-size units in the United States which prohibit individualized care. The changes in their concept of hospitalization for the mentally ill are so drastic that they visualize the main focus in the future will be on the psychiatric units in general hospitals, with much less need for long-term inpatient facilities.

Through affiliations with general hospitals, the mental hospitals are endeavoring to dispense with medical-surgical activities in their own facilities. In cases in which hospital care as an inpatient for a physical condition is not needed, relationships are being established with outpatient medical services and individual physicians who can see patients in their own offices. These changes are made possible by the decreasing fear of the mentally ill by the public, including the staffs of other health facilities, and are occurring in almost every country.

There is a growing belief, based on experience, that readmissions to psychiatric hospitals can be reduced by a system of gradual discharge—in other words, establishment of halfway houses. These have been in existence in England since 1879. Some are run by hospitals, others by various other community agencies.

"Mental hospitals should be chiefly places of remedy not custody." That flat ten-word statement at the beginning of an article[24] commenting on the 1960 report of the British Ministry of Health epitomizes the philosophy behind the changed administrative and professional needs of institutions for the care of the mentally ill. Quoting further from the report the article states, ". . . and there is a widening scope for treatment of the mentally ill outside hospitals." Visualized now as having important roles are not only the halfway houses, but training and social centers and visiting services, both for preventive reasons and for care after increasingly short stays in hospitals. In Britain, as elsewhere, the mental hospital and the psychiatric service in the general hospital are evolving into short-term facilities. Separation in a different type of institution seems to be indicated for the custodial type of care needed by patients who have passed the stage of being benefited by treatment, but even for these new discoveries may change the picture.

That the dramatic changes brought about by advances in treatment produce

---

[23] *Mental Hospitals*, April, 1960, condensed in *Hospital Topics*, January, 1961.
[24] *Roy. Soc. Health J.*, September-October, 1961.

other social problems was brought out by the Minister of Health in an address to the Royal Society for the Promotion of Health on July 11, 1961 when he said: "The prospect that active treatment may be substituted for custodial care has excited the public at large as well as those in the medical field; but this prospect brings with it the duty of sustaining in the community many who previously would have been severed from it."

The largest psychiatric hospital in the world is New York's Pilgrim State Hospital with 16,000 patients.

Among the recommendations in the final report of the Joint Commission on Mental Illness and Health, "Action for Mental Health," released in 1961, were the following two with respect to mental hospitals: (1) No state mental hospitals of more than 1,000 beds should be built in the future. (2) Not one patient should be added to any existing mental hospital of more than 1,000 beds.

The Veterans Administration has decided to build no more neuropsychiatric hospitals, planning to utilize general hospitals in the future in accordance with the trend toward psychiatric units.

Day Hospitals

The day hospital is somewhat of an innovation on the psychiatric scene. Dr. Sigmund L. Friedman[25] said the first such hospital in the English-speaking world was started in Montreal in the mid-forties as part of a psychiatric teaching hospital, the Allen Memorial Institute. Since then, he declared, "they have grown slowly in North America, much more rapidly in England." The idea is new only in its present concentrated pattern, individual patients having been accepted as day, or night, patients by psychiatric hospitals for many years. Actually, the day hospital concept is spreading to geriatric and physically handicapped patients who return to their homes at night and therefore do not require rooms or beds in the institution. The Menninger Clinic, Topeka, Kansas, has such a plan. Its patients are divided between full-time, half-time, and quarter-time classifications. Dr. Friedman warns that the day hospital idea is in an early, experimental stage.

An example of a day hospital operated by a general hospital is the "treatment center" at Montreal General Hospital, opened in October, 1950. Most patients report at 8:30 in the morning and return home at 4:30 in the afternoon, except Saturdays and Sundays. Beds are available for insulin therapy and electroshock. Luncheon is provided. Only acute psychotic conditions necessitating constant supervision are refused admission.

Medical Audit

Research on a medical audit plan for psychiatric hospitals is being conducted at the Veterans Administration Hospital, Perry Point, Maryland, sponsored by the School of Hygiene and Public Health of Johns Hopkins University and sup-

[25] *Hosp. Topics,* March, 1962.

ported by grants from the Veterans Administration and the National Institute of Mental Health, Public Health Service. The project, started in 1961, is designed to develop a method for appraising the effectiveness of public psychiatric hospitals.[26]

Home Care

Montreal's Verdun Protestant Hospital launched a foster home care program in 1957 for the rehabilitation of patients who were mentally ill or hospitalized over a period of time and could not readily adjust to their former environment. By 1963 the hospital's social service department had placed more than 170 patients in 100 homes. Doctors have been encouraged by the successful integration of many patients back into society, although some patients have had to return to the hospital and about 60 are still under home care. It has been discovered that elderly patients adjust more readily. In Quebec, legislation provides for an allowance to a home care foster mother which is sufficient to meet the expenses.[27] Home care programs are common in European countries.

Open Staff

At Western State Hospital, Olympia, Washington, the State Department of Institutions is experimenting with a plan to permit physicians who meet certain qualifications to continue to serve their patients after they are admitted to the state mental hospital. A few private mental hospitals have open-staff policies.

The Therapeutic Community

Following are extracts from a thesis submitted to Northwestern University as partial qualification for his master's degree in 1957 by Neil S. Cooper, now hospital administrator at Eastern State Hospital, Knoxville, Tennessee:

> In the spring of 1955, Dr. B. F. Peterson, superintendent of Eastern State Hospital, Knoxville, realized that as a result of the new tranquilizing drugs, mainly chlorophomazine and reserpine, many of the long-term schizophrenics at his hospital were improving to the extent that they would possibly be able to return to their home communities. The first experience with these long-term patients on discharge was that a great number of them were unable to adjust to the home-life situation. Dr. Peterson felt that this inability to adjust to the home community was the result of the fact that the patient had become completely institutionalized. After considerable planning, he conceived the idea of setting up a therapeutic community project which would place the patient in an environment freeing him from the confining atmosphere of the hospital and yet providing some of the hospital security. The underlying philosophy was to find a method of bridging the gap between the hospital and the home.

[26] The social restoration phase of the study was reported in the May, 1961, issue of *Pub. Health Rep.,* pp. 437–46.
[27] *Canad. Hosp.,* March, 1963.

In August, 1955, Eastern State Hospital embarked on a new and somewhat daring approach in the treatment of these patients, especially those who were considered to be chronic cases, by setting up a therapeutic community. A Y.M.C.A. camp in the Smoky Mountains, some 30 miles from the hospital, was rented for 23 days. The camp area had living and dining room facilities for 100 people, as well as suitable recreational facilities, such as a swimming pool, lake, shelter house, and sports area. The surrounding area was excellent for hiking. Five cabins were located at opposite ends of the camp site, each one able to accommodate eight patients and one attendant. The director of adjunctive therapies was in charge. His staff included attendants, nurses, an occupational therapist, recreational workers, a life guard, a truck driver, and cooks.

Dr. Peterson felt that in order to make the community a success, as much hospital restriction and atmosphere as was possible should be eliminated. The first step was elimination of employee uniforms. Patients and employees alike wore sport shirts and slacks. The women, both patients and employees, wore various colored slacks and blouses. Attempts were made to vary the styles and colors of all clothing to prevent any duplication.

It was felt that the dining room was one of the best places to break down some of the tension that existed during the first few days of operation. All meals were served family style, with patients and employees eating together, at different tables and places for each meal. Special attention was given to the menus, with the very best of food being purchased and prepared. The food included prime sirloin steaks and shrimp. This one change in the usual employee-patient relationship tended to break down many of the barriers.

After the first few days there was a noticeable relaxing of tension as the patients accepted the lack of window guards, locks, and their greatly increased freedom, as well as the changed relationship with hospital personnel.

The patient was given as much freedom of choice in daily activity as possible. In the morning he could choose between classes in archery, folk and square dancing, nature study, swimming instruction, or community improvement projects. No organized classes were conducted in the afternoon; but the patient might participate in any of the many sports available—swimming, hiking, fishing, boating, horseshoes, or just resting in the shade of a tree. Nighttime activities were quite diversified, with such programs as stunt and skit night, cooking out, counsel ring fires, community singing, game night. Each night ended with a period of social and square dancing. Since all activities were coeducational, supervision was required, but the atmosphere of surveillance was minimized by having supervising attendants join the groups and participate in the activities on the basis of their own interests.

One drawback of renting an established camp is the fact that most of them are in use during the summer months and are not available for rent until the camping season is over. This means that a therapeutic program cannot be begun before fall and cooler weather. This was true of the Y.M.C.A. camp in the Smokies.

As to the results accomplished with this first venture at a therapeutic community, of 70 patients selected for the first experiment, 35 were discharged in the period immediately following the closing of the project for the year 1955. Of the 35 discharged, 1 man and 2 women were returned to the hospital the following year; the remaining 32 continued to live normal lives at home. Indications are that a community operated on a year-around basis would enable a great number of chronic patients to return home to stay. A one month's stay would indicate whether the patient is able to go home or should be returned to the hospital for more treatment.[28]

PSYCHIATRIC DEPARTMENTS IN GENERAL HOSPITALS

In 1940 only 40 general hospitals in the United States were treating psychiatric patients. By 1963 some 580 had established psychiatric units and many others were accepting mentally ill persons for short-term treatment.

One of the recommendations in the final report of the Joint Commission on Mental Illness and Health, "Action for Mental Health," issued in 1961, was: "No community general hospital should be complete unless it provides a psychiatric unit for short-term hospitalization of mental patients." This report was the result of a five-year study authorized by the Mental Health Study Act of 1955.

Dr. M. Ralph Kaufman,[29] director of the new Institute of Psychiatry at Mount Sinai Hospital, New York City, said: "We are about at the point in this country where a general hospital of no matter what size that lacks an appropriate psychiatric unit of its own may be considered an anachronism."

"More general hospitals should have psychiatric units" was the conclusion reached at the American Medical Association's First Mental Health Congress, held in October, 1962.

"Increased use of the general hospital for treating the mentally ill is essential to successfully combat the isolation of the mentally-ill patient."[30] Dr. C. H. Hardin Branch told of the 28-bed unit operated in a general hospital by the University of Utah, Salt Lake City, which in a six-month period admitted 160 patients and discharged 71 per cent of this group to their homes as either recovered or sufficiently improved to cope satisfactorily with life outside the hospital. Of the 160 patients, 133, or 79 per cent, were discharged within 28 days, 68 per cent within 21 days.

The psychiatric unit established in 1950 at the Salvation Army's Booth Memorial Hospital, Covington, Kentucky, is succeeding in rehabilitating more than 92 per cent of acutely ill patients.[31] Only acute cases with a good potential for rehabilitation are accepted.

A "comprehensive community psychiatric program" has been set up at City Hospital, Elmhurst, New York City, a 1,000-bed general hospital. The psychiatric department has 120 beds. However, the distinctive feature of the department is a "trouble-shooting clinic" which offers first-aid for emotional problems. It is regarded as a public health and preventive medicine service, open 24 hours

[28] B. F. Peterson and Sidney H. Acuff: An Experiment in Living. *Mental Hospitals,* November, 1955, pp. 8, 9.

[29] *Hospitals,* April 1, 1963, p. 17.

[30] Opening statement of a condensation by *Hosp. Topics,* November, 1962, of a talk by the president of the American Psychiatric Association, Dr. C. H. Hardin Branch, at the fourteenth Mental Hospital Institute held in September, 1962, in Miami Beach.

[31] *Hosp. Topics,* June, 1959.

a day. Other unusual features of the "comprehensive program" are a psychiatric clinic for general practitioners, a psychiatric seminar for chaplains, a teachers' consultation service, and a seminar for lawyers.[32]

Evanston (Illinois) Hospital reported[33] that the average stay in 1958 for the 541 patients admitted to its psychiatric unit was 16.2 days.

The advantages to the patient are, all agree, removal of the social stigma of commitment to a mental hospital; treatment in the community of which he is a resident; usually some health insurance coverage whereas there is none in a mental hospital; medical diagnosis, along with mental; and intensive treatment, which greatly speeds recovery.

CARE OF THE CHRONICALLY ILL

How far are hospitals going in establishing their own facilities for patients who need extended care? A few examples will show the trend.

Harrisburg (Pennsylvania) Polyclinic Hospital purchased in 1957 a small hotel building located five miles from the hospital and adapted and renovated it to a 40-bed long-term care unit. The beds have practically been filled ever since. After a reasonable test period the operation proved to be financially successful, so the hospital will construct a special building for long-term care on the hospital grounds.

The Fairview Hospital, Minneapolis, opened a 150-bed, $1.5-million convalescent and long-term care unit in August, 1963. The four-story building can be expanded to ten stories. Costs are estimated to be about half those of care in the acute hospital facilities.

At Bellevue, Washington, the hospital is planning a 65-bed long-term nursing and convalescent facility, and additional land is being reserved for a future new general hospital, nursing home, convalescent home, and scientific care facilities. A future home for the aged is planned on a nearby site by another group.

The University of Florida Teaching Hospital and Clinics at Gainesville has a 26-room "ambulant" wing. Probably this should be classified as a stage in progressive care rather than as service for the chronically ill, but the unit houses orthopedic and arthritic patients who need long-term care, so the line is hard to draw. This facility has a most unique feature that may well give a clue to reducing the cost of care and at the same time enhance the benefits to the patient. In Japan and other Asiatic countries members of the family come into the hospital and care for the patient. This has always seemed to Americans to be a poor, unscientific practice—maybe not, in the convalescent stages anyway. At Gainesville in the ambulant unit each patient's room has an extra bed for relatives or friends. This person gives all of the nonmedical service. The hospital sees a great

---

[32] A General Hospital As a Focus for Community Psychiatry. *J.A.M.A.*, December 31, 1960.
[33] November, 1959 issue of its publication, *The Pilot*.

advantage in the fact that the relative or friend learns how to care for the patient when the time comes for him to be discharged to his home. Especially for the very young and the very old patient, the feeling is that he improves faster with this kind of treatment.[34]

Smaller hospitals are finding just as much need as larger ones for special facilities to care for long-term patients. Gibson (Illinois) Community Hospital, a 48-bed institution in a rural community, opened a 40-bed annex in 1961 for long-term nursing care and rehabilitation and for care and treatment of the aged.

Three voluntary hospitals in Rochester, New York, are cooperating in the construction of extended care units. The units differ from nursing homes, since more services normally provided by hospitals will be required. Patients will be admitted only for a certain length of time and only if it is anticipated that their condition will be improved by the services of the extended care unit. The three units will have a total of 144 beds and will be nonprofit and separately administered.

The Christian Hospital, St. Louis, has facilities in its new six-story addition opened in 1963 for 50 beds for the chronically ill.

Rancho Los Amigos Hospital, a Los Angeles County institution for the chronically ill, is integrated with the main county hospital.

Government insurance plans in British Columbia did not in the beginning cover the extended care necessary for many patients. As a result the acute hospitals are overcrowded by long-stay cases. In response to pressures the British Columbia hospital insurance service began in September, 1960, a rehabilitation, chronic treatment, and convalescent coverage program. Certain hospitals were selected as centers in which coverage would be provided. The veterans' hospitals also admit patients entitled to the government insurance. Surveys are being made to determine the need for rehabilitation, convalescent, and chronic services.[35]

Special Hospitals for the Chronically Ill

Montefiore Hospital, New York City, pioneered in the care of prolonged illness. It was founded in 1884 on the hundredth anniversary of the birth of Sir Moses Montefiore. Custodial care was all that the hospital could give for many years. Today it has all of the facilities of a general hospital for the scientific care of patients. It has comprehensive rehabilitation facilities and conducts a home-care program. It is affiliated with sheltered workshops for vocational rehabilitation. For teaching purposes it is affiliated with Columbia University.

In Brandon, Manitoba, Canada, is Assiniboine Hospital, an extended treatment center for long-term patients in western Manitoba. This 200-bed former military hospital served for more than ten years as a treatment center for Indians and Es-

---

[34] M. D. Bellomy: Ambulant Patient Program Pays Off! *Hosp. Topics*, April, 1962, pp. 33–34.
[35] L. F. Detwiler, assistant deputy minister of hospital insurance for British Columbia: Activation Program for the Chronically Ill. *Canad. Hosp.*, December, 1960, pp. 36–37, 80–81.

kimos with tuberculosis and other respiratory and orthopedic diseases, and was converted to its present purpose in 1937 when the demand for tuberculosis beds declined. It is operated by the voluntary, nonprofit corporation known as the Sanatorium Board of Manitoba. Most of the patients are elderly and have multiple complaints. The board operates three other extended-care hospitals.[36]

The Hillcrest Convalescent Hospital, Toronto, was opened as a 36-bed shelter for homeless convalescent patients in 1887 through donations of $10,000 by a young Englishwoman and of land by a local citizen. In the next year it came under the Charity Act, becoming eligible for a grant of 15 cents per day per patient (reduced to 7 cents a day in 1897). Capacity was increased to 54 beds by addition of a new wing in 1892. In its first 50 years of service more than 11,000 patients passed through the hospital. It was replaced by a new building in 1963, with capacity for 120 patients.

The Highland View Cuyahoga County Hospital, Cleveland, Ohio, is a general hospital that accepts only patients with long-term illnesses. It is owned by the county but operated by a lay board. Admission is limited to patients 12 years of age and older who require at least 30 days' hospitalization. Patients pay or do not pay, according to their financial circumstances. Mental illness, tuberculosis, and narcotic conditions are not treated nor are patients accepted who require only domiciliary care. Most of the patients are suffering from arthritis, cerebral palsy, cancer, cardiovascular disorders, and paralytic conditions such as poliomyelitis, strokes, and injuries. The patient capacity is 748, and admissions and discharges are at the rate of more than 700 per year. The hospital is affiliated with the School of Medicine of Western Reserve University.

A similar type of hospital in that it is a general hospital in its scope of service but limits its admissions to long-term patients is Masonic Memorial Hospital, Minneapolis, a part of the University of Minnesota Medical Center. Intensive treatment is given in the main hospital when indicated before a patient is transferred. An interesting statement in the description of the services of Masonic Memorial Hospital is that "many patients have been referred to the hospital for 'terminal' care, with subsequent cancer improvement and rehabilitation as a result of facilities and therapy available."[37]

Hospital-Run Homes for the Aged

One of the most comprehensive programs undertaken by a general hospital for care of the aged is that of the Flower Hospital, Toledo, Ohio. After thorough survey of the needs, the hospital formed a separate corporation and built a residential unit of 170 apartments with the help of an F.H.A.-insured 40-year

[36] Patricia A. Holting: Extended Treatment at Assiniboine Hospital. *Canad. Hosp.*, March, 1962, pp. 47–49.

[37] B. J. Kennedy, M.D.: Less Than a General Hospital, but More Than a Nursing Home. *Hospitals*, December 16, 1962, p. 42.

loan. Life lease fees range from $7,000 to $29,500 with a monthly maintenance fee of $150, which includes standard hospitalization and doctor and surgeon fees. For prolonged illness beyond ten days $50 a month extra is charged for infirmary care. The apartments vary in size and life lease fee, from one-room hotel type to two bedrooms. Eventually a medical center is planned on the grounds; in the meantime an infirmary and Flower Hospital provide the in-patient facilities according to need. The site is ten miles from downtown Toledo and public transportation is two blocks away. The master plan calls for accommodations for 2,500 residents and building of a chronic and convalescent hospital. Services in this unit are planned to be made available to other persons in the community beside the residents of the home. Outpatient service will also be provided. In the final phase of the program an acute general hospital, a professional office building, and a residence for nurses will be built; also such facilities as a central meeting house, band shell theater, pitch-and-putt golf course, and a motel for resident visitors, medical center visitors, and other outsiders. The first unit, the 171-apartment house, was completed in 1960 and is fully occupied.[38]

The "Hopedale Complex" is the response of a rural village in Illinois to a combination of needs. About to lose their only doctor, the citizens built and equipped a 20-bed hospital for him; the hospital was no more than built in 1955 when other needs were discovered, so adjoining it was opened a 40-bed nursing home in 1958. The nursing home, which includes rehabilitation services, relieved the hospital of long-term care and reduced charges to patients by 65 per cent, but it made immediately obvious a further need. So the Hopedale Retirement Apartments were opened in 1961 providing quarters for 44 aged persons who were staying in the nursing home because they had no place else to go. This village of 500 people has completed the complex by building a residence for six nurses on the grounds of the retirement home.

The Princeton (New Jersey) hospital answered the challenge of care of the aged by building the Merwick Unit. Replying to the question of why practically every authority states that the facility for the care of the chronically ill and aged should be attached administratively, and if possible physically, to the general hospital, Administrator John W. Kauffman[39] states: "Because the development of these units as elements of the general hospital is the only forceful way to raise the standards of these institutions."

The New Mount Sinai Hospital, Toronto, is integrated with the Jewish Home for the Aged and with Baycrest Hospital, a facility for the chronically ill. The medical staff of the general hospital is responsible for the medical program at the other two institutions. Baycrest Hospital and the Home for the Aged are

[38] From a thesis submitted to Northwestern University in 1959 by James F. Shepherd, then an administrative resident at Flower Hospital, now administrator of Putnam County Hospital, Greencastle, Indiana.
[39] From a talk, Eight Facets of Care for Aged Challenge Hospital Administration, reported by *Hosp. Topics,* October, 1960, pp. 21–22.

housed in the same building although they are two distinct operations and have their own separate boards.[40]

The New York City Department of Hospitals introduced in 1958 the "Homestead" concept. This is recognition of the fact that whereas general hospitals were overcrowded because of having to accommodate so many chronically ill patients, institutions for the chronically ill have in turn become overcrowded with custodial-type patients, mostly very old, who have no place else to go. In 1957 the first "Homestead" unit of 360 beds was opened for truly long-term and practically permanent patients who have been given in other hospitals the maximum rehabilitation but who still must have care. By the fall of 1962 the Department of Hospitals had a total of 2,148 beds, in different places, designated as "Homestead" beds. Paraplegic, blind, and aphasic patients are among those cared for in these institutions. Close integration with the main hospitals is maintained to permit transfer of patients back and forth.

Rehabilitation Service

"Rehabilitation Belongs in General Hospitals" is the title of an article by Dr. Howard A. Rusk,[41] professor and chairman, department of physical medicine and rehabilitation, New York University Medical Center.

This is one of the signs of the future that may be seen in studies of the other hospitals. Only a few of the larger ones have taken major action as yet, but the obligation is clear. The comprehensive rehabilitation center completely separated from any hospital is a most expensive and perhaps uneconomic stopgap that has arisen because hospitals are failing to complete their jobs in patient care.

The separate facility is desirable after the acute stage is passed, but it should be so closely connected with the hospital as to practically be a part of it. Because of the special appeal of the crippled, separate financing can be arranged for distinctive aspects of care, but duplication of many facilities can be avoided by unifying the operation.

Says Dr. Rusk:[42]

> To ignore the development of rehabilitation services within general hospitals is to guarantee the continued deterioration of many less severely disabled persons until they reach the severely disabled stage of dependency. . . . As an area of specialized activity within a number of professional disciplines, only the general hospital can bring these services to the patient at the earliest possible time and with costly and damaging sequelae to the disability alleviated or minimized. . . . The neglect of disability is far more costly than an early, aggressive program of rehabilitation. . . . Although hospitals complain the chronically ill are responsible for overcrowded conditions, few provide the rehabilitation that would permit many patients to leave.

[40] Sidney Liswood and Sam Ruth: A Program of Integrated Medical Care. *Canad. Hosp.*, September, 1957, pp. 39–40.
[41] *Am. J. Nursing*, September, 1962.
[42] From a condensation in *Hosp. Topics*, February, 1963, p. 26.

Although the immediate and early rehabilitation procedures should be provided in every hospital, not all institutions can be expected to follow through to the extremes of vocational and social rehabilitation. Planned regional programs are therefore indicated. Such a plan is being developed around the comprehensive regional rehabilitation center planned at St. Vincent's Hospital, Billings, Montana. This city is the center of what is known as the Midland Empire, encompassing south central Montana, northern Wyoming, and the western Dakotas. Rehabilitation centers which are not completely comprehensive are being established in Great Falls, Butte, and Missoula in Montana and Thermopolis in Wyoming. Patients whose needs cannot be met in these more limited centers will be referred to Billings from all of the hospitals in the area. The largest of the outlying centers, at Great Falls, is for outpatients only. The one at Thermopolis has no neurosurgeons, orthopedic surgeons, or other specialists.[43]

The University of Florida's Rehabilitation Center is directly integrated with its teaching hospital and clinics and with the College of Health Related Services. Besides having the latest treatment and teaching equipment indoors, the center has a large outside courtyard which provides space for outdoor rehabilitation activities. Psychodiagnostic and psychotherapeutic services and speech and hearing services are offered in the rehabilitation area to hospital patients and also upon direct referral from community physicians.[44]

The National Jewish Hospital in Denver, a tuberculosis Hospital, has a Department of Rehabilitation Services housed in the National Rehabilitation Center building on the hospital grounds. Many other tuberculosis hospitals provide excellent rehabilitation services for their patients to help them resume normal living in their communities upon their discharge.

Iowa Methodist Hospital, Des Moines, has its own three-million-dollar Younker Memorial Rehabilitation Center. This is a 120-bed unit dedicated in 1958 connected to and completely integrated with the 400-bed main hospital. The center also provides facilities for 150 outpatients. Before this center opened, the only rehabilitation facility in Iowa was at the University Hospital in Iowa City. Admission to the Methodist center is through the general section of the main hospital when a referral for rehabilitation is made through a patient's physician. All medical and surgical problems are taken care of before admission to the center. The Iowa State Division of Vocational Rehabilitation supplies a full-time vocational counselor and supervises the vocation planning and ultimate vocational rehabilitation of patients.[45]

The 1,200-bed University of Alberta Hospital at Edmonton has a rehabilitation department in which on a randomly selected day are a total of 318 patients (35 per cent of all patients in the hospital). Of these, 193, or 60.7 per cent, suffered from either disorders of the locomotor system such as fractures and ar-

[43] Sister Ann Raymond, S.C.L.,R.N.: Plan for a Regional Rehabilitation Center. *Hospitals,* September 1, 1960, pp. 37–39, 97–98.
[44] They Give Ability Back to the Disabled. *Mod. Hosp.,* October, 1961, pp. 94–96.
[45] Robert Black: Center Provides Integrated Rehabilitation. *Mod. Hosp.,* December, 1959, p. 6.

thritis, or disorders of the nervous system such as poliomyelitis, cerebrovascular accident, and others. The six most common disorders are arthritis, poliomyelitis, cerebrovascular accident, back conditions, fractures, and spinal cord injuries. About 3 per cent have amputations or brain injuries. The director of rehabilitation, Dr. M. T. F. Carpendale,[46] comments:

> Even after appropriate treatment, the patient with a cerebrovascular accident will still remain paralyzed down one side of his body, the patient with spinal cord damage will still be paralyzed from the waist down, and the amputee still will be minus a limb. Clearly, none of these patients unassisted will be able to leave hospital and resume his normal daily activities at home and work. To do this, he must undergo a rehabilitation program oriented to his special needs and this is most effectively provided by a special department *within the hospital*. From 25 to 35 per cent of all patients admitted to a general hospital will require the services of such a rehabilitation department.

Michael Reese Hospital and Medical Center, Chicago, conducts an extensive rehabilitation program which includes research. An especially interesting project was a geriatric rehabilitation study conducted between 1957 and 1959, under a National Institutes of Health grant, jointly with the Cook County Department of Public Aid and Rest Haven Rehabilitation Hospital. The Illinois Public Aid Commission subsidized the total cost of patient care at both hospitals. The aim was to restore nursing home residents to noninstitutionalized living. The subjects, aged 65 years or over and on old-age assistance, were taken from nursing homes. Of 112 selected for admission to Michael Reese Hospital, 91 regained functional capacity sufficient to live more or less actively in a community setting. The mean age of the group was 76 years. After an average follow-up of 16 months, stability of the favorable response was observed. Included was improvement in adaptive and social behavior. The director of the hospital's department of physical medicine, Dr. Edward E. Gordon, stated in the conclusions that "the outcome points up two gaps in the nation's care of the aged: (1) omission of rehabilitation management at the onset of the disability; (2) abandonment of sound modern medical procedures in nursing home practices."[47]

The Eugene duPont Memorial Hospital is a 60-bed rehabilitation facility, the idea, the space, and the financial means for which were conceived and supplied by Mr. DuPont. It is an adjunct to a general hospital, Memorial at Wilmington, Delaware, and is situated on ten landscaped acres just outside of the city. It was opened in September, 1955. Patients are admitted from any hospital or from home upon application from their personal physicians. Meals are prepared and sent from the main hospital by means of a thermal-pack system. The convalescent-rehabilitation unit has its own administrator but is under the general direction of the managing director of the Memorial Hospital.[48]

[46] Rehabilitation Bridges Gap Between Hospital and Home. *Mod. Hosp.*, October, 1961, pp. 97–100.

[47] From the Final Report of Project RG 6137 (C1 and C2), "Evaluation and Rehabilitation of Indigent Subjects."

[48] Charles E. Vadakin and Mrs. Grace L. Little, R.N.: Costs to Patients Are Lower in This Convalescent/Rehabilitation Unit. *Hospitals*, February 1, 1960, pp. 35–37.

The Government Program for Rehabilitation

Mary E. Switzer, director of the federal Office of Vocational Rehabilitation since 1950, says that it was "learned long ago that in most cases rehabilitation begins in a hospital" and that "one of the finest happenings of recent years was the amendment to the Hospital Survey and Construction Act in 1954, which linked rehabilitation facilities with hospitals as beneficiaries of this legislation." She states further:

> It is gratifying to all of us in the public program that so many hospitals are adding rehabilitation facilities to their operations. The links they are forging in the state-federal partnership in vocational rehabilitation are impressive, for they tie a large potential of disabled persons in local communities to the public program. Thus they contribute materially to our hopes for exceeding by a wide margin the 92,500 disabled persons who were rehabilitated into employment through state rehabilitation agencies in the year that ended June 30, 1961.
>
> The growing interest in rehabilitation on the part of our hospitals is progress in the right direction. Fine as it is, however, there is feeling in some quarters that the true philosophy of rehabilitation is not invoked enough in these operations, because too many times these efforts end with physical restoration—which to us in the public program is only half the battle. . . .
>
> In the philosophy that underlies the public program of vocational rehabilitation, a congenitally malformed person, or one accidentally injured, or one struck down by a disabling disease should have not only the benefits of modern medicine, but a full chance to live productively afterward.
>
> Almost always there are morale-shattering considerations in long-term illness, so that there must be brought to bear the abilities of the psychologist or psychiatrist, the social worker, the physical and occupational therapist, the trained counselor to prepare a severely disabled person to face successfully a competitive world of work. . . .
>
> We shall continue to hope that hospital rehabilitation programs shall be integrated more than ever into community and state efforts to help the disabled, and that there shall be closer relationships among hospitals and state rehabilitation agencies so that they may merge themselves into a common beneficial effort. . . . We hope that hospital administrators will remain alert to their opportunities to achieve the true end of rehabilitation, and shall broaden their perspective so that their rehabilitation efforts with physical restoration will be followed with post-hospital service to complete the task. . . .

Probably the emphasis on vocational rehabilitation has another seldom considered aspect. This is the release for employment of the person who was previously tied down to serve the disabled patient before he was taught to carry on for himself the activities of daily living, even though he could not be rehabilitated to the extent of re-employment.

SPECIAL HOSPITALS

Even for mentally ill and tuberculous patients there is a reversal of the trend toward special hospitals. There are obvious advantages, particularly of a scien-

[49] *Mod. Hosp.*, October, 1961, pp. 91–92.

tific and educational nature, in concentration of patients who are suffering from the same kind of pathological conditions. These advantages are somewhat offset by the disadvantages of separation from the full resources of the general hospital in view of the fact that afflictions seldom come singly. Also, advances and discoveries may quickly change the demand for specialized types of care. This has certainly occurred in the past—where are the "fever" hospitals now? Yet for the sake of the advantages that remain, and for providing concentrated opportunity for study and training, some special hospitals are likely always to exist, and the present and future administrators should be aware of them. Brief discussions of a few typical ones follow.

Cancer Hospitals

The Princess Margaret Hospital, Toronto, opened in September, 1958. It is part of the Ontario Cancer Institute, which functions under a board of trustees representing the Ontario Cancer Treatment and Research Foundation, the University of Toronto, and five major teaching hospitals. The hospital has 87 beds for inpatients, including a ten-bed children's ward. The top three floors of the seven-story building are concentrated on research. Radioactive gold, phosphorus, chromium, iron, and iodine are stored on the top floor. Also on this floor are laboratories for research with animals, particularly mice, and for research in nuclear physics. On the sixth floor are the biological research laboratories. On the fifth floor clinical investigations are made with cancer patients. Patients who come for radiation therapy are all referred by other hospitals or practicing physicians throughout Ontario. No general cancer surgery is done, only surgery connected with the giving of radium therapy. A unique facility is an adjoining 53-bed hostel financed by the Canadian Cancer Society for out-of-town patients who do not need inpatient care but must have regular treatment and supervision.[50]

In Buffalo the state of New York owns and operates the 516-bed Roswell Park Memorial Institute, a cancer and research hospital with a large outpatient department.

Adjacent to the Winnipeg General, the Children's, and the Rehabilitation Hospitals in the Manitoba Medical Center is a hospital completed in 1963 by the Manitoba Cancer Treatment and Research Foundation. The foundation and the Canadian Cancer Society are housed in the building.

Memorial–Sloan Kettering Cancer Center, which includes the James Ewing and Memorial Hospitals, is the world's largest cancer treatment and research center.

Communicable Disease Hospitals

The most rapidly disappearing of the specialized hospitals is the communicable disease institution. Almost every large community still has one for the

[50] *Canad. Hosp.*, January, 1959, pp. 45–48.

exceptional smallpox or diphtheria case, but the census is gratifyingly low.

A famous hospital that remains is the Carville, Louisiana, Institute for the treatment and rehabilitation of patients with Hansen's disease, operated by the U.S. Public Health Service since 1921. Previously the hospital was operated by the state of Louisiana as a home rather than a hospital for its residents with leprosy. In the early days of administration by the state the hospital was staffed in large part by the Daughters of Charity of St. Vincent de Paul, and this Order still gives service to the institution. No member of the medical or nursing staff has ever contracted the disease and thanks to new drugs and treatment many patients have been rehabilitated and returned to civilian life.

For well over a decade authorities have agreed that there is no longer need for special hospitals for patients with communicable diseases and that these patients should be cared for at home or in general hospitals. Precautions against contagion can be taken by following established rules.

Eye, Ear, Nose, and Throat Hospitals

London established its Royal Westminster Ophthalmic Hospital in 1816. In Dublin the National Eye Hospital was founded in 1814. The Royal Ear Hospital opened in London in 1816, the Metropolitan Ear and Throat Hospital in 1838, and the Throat Hospital in 1863.

In the United States in 1928 there were 77 EENT hospitals with 2,879 beds; by 1944 the number had dropped to 42 hospitals with 2,695 beds. In 1962 there were 38 with 2,035. The decline is best appreciated when the rise in population in the 34 years is considered.

Heart Hospital

There is only one hospital in the United States devoted entirely to research and treatment of cardiovascular disease—the $30-million, twin-towered, 24-story Heart Institute, construction of which was started in 1963 in New York City. The hospital is sponsored by the New York Medical College as a branch of its facilities in the city. Congenital, rheumatic, degenerative, and hypertensive heart diseases will be studied and physicians will be educated and trained in research and clinical cardiology.

Maternity Hospitals

Maternity hospitals have a history dating back to ancient times. In the Christian era, John the Almsgiver endowed four maternity hospitals in Alexandria in 610. There is known to have been one in Metz as early as 1334. Mostly, however, maternity patients were received in wards attached to the general hospitals and poorhouses, until the eighteenth century when independent institutions appeared in many of the larger European cities. They were known as lying-in hospitals in London.

Private maternity hospitals were set up in Philadelphia in 1762. Boston's Lying-in Hospital was founded in 1832. By 1931 there were in the United States 145 maternity hospitals with 8,078 beds; in 1944 they had declined to 107 hospitals with 5,762 beds; in 1962 they had dropped much farther to 44 hospitals with 2,238 beds, while births had risen from 2,135,327 in 1946 to 3,908,121 in 1962.

Accident Hospitals

A new kind of special hospital to meet a new problem is the hospital for the care of persons injured in accidents. An example is the Hospital of Trauma, Rome, Italy. An orthopedic surgeon is in charge of the 340-bed new hospital, the choice of this specialist being based on the fact that about 80 per cent of patients with injuries have an orthopedic problem. Many of the major cities in Italy have similar hospitals. After visiting them Dr. Edward L. Compere,[51] head of the orthopedic department at Northwestern University Medical School, Chicago, wrote: "In no country in the world can an injured person receive better care than in these hospitals in Italy. This is because of the planning and organization and the careful staffing of these hospitals with men who know just exactly what they are expected to do and how to do it."

Tuberculosis Hospitals

Although special hospitals for tuberculous patients are still with us and will be for quite a long time, they are decreasing in size and in numbers. Resistance of the bacillus to the new drugs, however, is creating considerable alarm.

In 1962 a 310-bed hospital in the Bronx, New York City, St. Joseph's Hospital for Chest Diseases, was closed to make way for an expanded medical center for St. Francis Hospital.

The decline in need for accommodations as a result of lower incidence and improved treatment is creating excess beds which can and are being used for patients suffering from other long-term illnesses.

In Michigan in a ten-year period, 11 tuberculosis hospitals closed, and 7 of the 15 county sanatoriums remaining converted their institutions to admit chronic disease patients. The combination has some disadvantages, but these can be minimized with certain adaptations.

Podiatry Hospital

The only hospital in the world to treat foot ailments exclusively was opened in May, 1960, in San Francisco—the California Podiatry Hospital. It is equipped

[51] *J. Internat. Coll. Surgeons,* August, 1960, pp. 34–35.

to accommodate 2,000 inpatient surgical cases a year for major and minor foot surgery. It is operated on a nonprofit basis. An additional 20,000 outpatients a year can be handled through the clinical facilities of the California Podiatry College which adjoins the hospital.

Proctology Hospital

Another unusual special hospital field is proctology. The Ferguson-Droste-Ferguson Hospital, Grand Rapids, Michigan, a 92-bed institution, accepts only this type of patient. It was established in 1929.

Age Group Divisions

How far is it feasible to divide patients according to their ages? This is a consideration in establishing special hospitals for children and for the aged as well as in organizing special departments in the general hospital.

The number of children's hospitals in the United States declined from 65 with 5,669 beds in 1928 to 44 with 4,459 beds in 1944, but has risen since that time to 59 hospitals with 7,078 beds in 1962.

The first modern hospital for children was opened in Paris, France, in 1802. The first one in the United States was the Philadelphia Children's Hospital opened in 1855.

Canadian Hospital reported in its March, 1963, issue that children's wards were overcrowded in 20 British Columbia hospitals and that 40 other hospitals had reached or exceeded a saturation point in the use of their beds for children. The Metropolitan Planning Council of British Columbia was therefore calling for construction of a 100- to 150-bed child care unit specializing in diagnostic and therapeutic facilities to be built at the University of British Columbia.

Within the children's hospital group are some that specialize in treating certain conditions, such as La Rabida Jackson Park Sanitarium, Chicago, which specializes in the treatment of children with rheumatic fever.

Kauikeolani Children's Hospital, Honolulu, is the only children's hospital in the whole Pacific area. Jets and helicopters bring in children from remote islands.

In general hospitals, the separation by age has brought up the problem of teen-agers, who are unhappy in the children's quarters and do not belong with adults. Occupancy problems arise with divisions into pediatrics, adolescents, mediatrics, and geriatrics. The teen-ager units seem to be popular and good for the patients. If this is a service the community wants, it should be provided if at all feasible. Apparently no hospital that has made the arrangement has discontinued it.

Separation of aged patients is more commonly arranged through affiliation with another institution than through establishing a special geriatrics unit (examples are given in another section). An additional instance of such cooperation is provided by Rochester (New York) General Hospital's Northside Division, which made an agreement in 1960 with the new 354-bed St. Ann's Home, under construction adjacent to the hospital at the time, to provide care for its acutely ill residents and to make available to its medical staff the hospital's clinical laboratories, x-ray department, diagnostic and therapeutic facilities, and administrative consultation. The St. Ann's Home had been operating in a different location since 1906. Of the home's 354 beds, 216 are designated for nursing care patients, 138 for the aged. Patients from the hospital may be referred to the home for admission in accordance with its procedures.

Classification by Sponsorship

Besides the usual classifications of hospitals into Veterans Administration, Public Health Service, military, state and local government, voluntary, and proprietary, there are a few other classifications according to sponsorship such as industrial, prison, and osteopathic. Industrial hospitals are decreasing in number. Prison hospitals operated by the U.S. Department of Justice total 20 with 1,854 beds.[52] Some 400 hospitals with a total bed capacity of around 12,000 located in 22 states are designated as osteopathic hospitals. Most of them are nonprofit charitable corporations, licensed under state hospital laws on the same basis as medical hospitals. The largest single nonprofit osteopathic hospital is in Detroit, Michigan, and has 420 beds.

PROGRESSIVE PATIENT CARE

Enthusiasm for the idea of setting up, formally, in every hospital five complete stages of patient care is waning; nevertheless, the concept of progressive patient care remains exciting and worthy of thorough consideration for adaptation to the conditions in the individual hospital.

How the idea started is explained in a 1958 news release by the American Medical Association:

> A hospital care plan that could set off "a chain reaction of improved hospital care" is now under way in the town of Manchester, Connecticut, according to an article in the *Journal of the American Medical Association*. Since April 1957 the Manchester Memorial Hospital has been achieving "remarkable results" for patients and physicians in an entirely new approach to hospital care called "progressive patient care." . . .
> It is a comprehensive system designed to adapt hospital facilities to the patient, rather than the other way around. The Manchester plan may "foreshadow new thinking, new planning, and new policies in many of the 7,000 hospitals in the country," the editorial said. . . . The plan is a three-phase program of gradually placing the patient in transition from special surveillance to self-help. Or it may

---

[52] The Medical Center for Federal Prisoners at Springfield, Missouri, was described in an interesting article in *Hospitals,* November 16, 1962, pp. 53–58, 138.

work in reverse—from a diagnostic work-up in the self-help unit, to surgery and
the intense care unit, and then back to self-service by way of an intermediate care
unit. . . .

Last July, encouraged by preliminary results, the U.S. Public Health Service
decided to finance a detailed and continuing study of the Manchester experiment
by a team of experts. There were to be no recommendations, just scrutiny of the
system in operation.

Meanwhile, the idea was fast becoming known in scattered parts of the nation.
By February 1958 there were reported to be 30 hospitals in the country handling
patients in stages similar to the Manchester plan and last week the Public Health
Service found nearly 150 hospitals doing it.

The article cited the beneficial changes as (1) because only the doctor would
decide when his patients were ready for transfer from one unit to another, he
would be brought into more intimate contact with the hospital than he is under
most existing conditions; (2) installation of expensive equipment in only one
section of the hospital, the intensive care unit, would bring about substantial
reduction in over-all construction and operating costs; design and structure of
the buildings also would be changed greatly; (3) the accumulated savings might
very well bring costs within the means of communities which are now struggling with the problem of financing new hospitals or enlarging existing ones;
(4) concentration of the most thoroughly trained nurses and ancillary medical
personnel in the intensive care units would allow more effective use of their
skills; this is particularly important at a time of severe shortages in these fields;
(5) individual patient costs could be less because of varying room rates.

By March, 1960, *Hospital Topics* was reporting that the patient care plan
at Manchester had moved "out of experimental stage" as the hospital added
a $2.5-million wing.

The questions asked in an article in *Medical Economics,* December 21, 1959,
were: "Do doctors who have given it a try find they have trouble keeping track
of their patients? Or that they lose control of the patient to nurses and the
administration? Or that the best nurses are drained off by the intensive-care
unit, leaving the average patient to the care of second-raters? Can progressive
care be forced on staff physicians who don't want it?" The fact that Santa
Barbara Cottage Hospital closed its experimental intensive-care unit after 21
months because some doctors did not like it and there was a shortage of qualified
nurses, and then reopened it because other doctors who liked it won over their
colleagues, is reported in this article; also the closing of the intensive-care unit
at Chicago Wesley Memorial Hospital because its occupancy rate of 67 per cent
was too low to warrant the necessary concentration of equipment and nurses.

The Public Health Service conceives of progressive patient care as having
five elements: (1) an intensive care unit for the critically ill; (2) an intermediate
care unit for patients whose condition has stabilized and who require remedial
care; (3) a self-care unit for patients who are physically able to care for themselves and who require restorative care or diagnosis; (4) a continuation care

unit for long-term patients requiring prolonged care; (5) an organized home care program that is hospital-based. Not many hospitals are providing all these elements. In its June, 1959, issue *Hospitals* reported that St. John's Lutheran Hospital, St. Paul, Minnesota, was the "only hospital known to have established all five of these units" and that it "became a pioneer in progressive care in 1952." Quite a few have the first four elements. For example, the new and renovated Peterborough Civic Hospital, in Ontario, provides intensive, intermediate, convalescent, and two types of long-term care—rehabilitative and chronic—all planned with the idea of offering the necessary steps toward progressive patient care.

As the administrator of Manchester Memorial Hospital, Robert Thoms, explained, only a small proportion of patients—smaller than the advance estimate —go through all three of the intensive, intermediate, and self-care stages. Many come into intermediate and stay there. Terminal patients are usually put into this area.

In a symposium on progressive patient care conducted by the American Hospital Association,[53] one of the questions among several that were asked was "Is it better for patients to be moved about to accommodate the staffing pattern of a hospital or should the hospital staff and services be geared to accommodate the needs of the patient, regardless of his location?" Moderator George Bugbee asked panel member Charles G. Roswell to make the final statement, which was a plea that

> . . . the potential savings to hospitals and patients not be over-emphasized until more facts are available to justify such statements. A low per diem cost in a self-help unit, for example, is no indication that the over-all cost of providing care to patients is going to decline. This has yet to be proven, particularly if we think in terms of cost to the patient or cost to third parties.

Panel member Oliver G. Pratt added:

> I feel that in a hospital with clinical services and house staff teaching programs, the answer is "no" for the active clinical services except, of course, we should have postanesthesia recovery rooms and an intensive care unit for all patients. . . . I certainly feel that the housing facilities for patients on an active rehabilitation program might be self-help. . . . When you get into a less highly geared hospital without scientific teaching, the more community type hospital—the pattern may well be different. However, I continue to feel that we are still in the pioneering stage. The pattern for one hospital may not be the pattern for another hospital and I continue to feel that in certain circumstances, with an average stay of eight days, several transfers are not wise. But it is wise for us to study patterns of patient care, and I think anyone who is experimenting or pioneering is entitled to commendation.

The controversy quietly continues. About the first phase, however, there is fairly general agreement. Intensive patient care units are believed to have many

[53] *Hospitals,* January 16, 1959.

advantages. *The Modern Hospital* devoted a special section,[54] to them in its January, 1963, issue, introducing the subject by stating:

> Many authorities believe that intensive patient care units are likely to become the fastest spreading hospital service of the next few years. The reasons, they think, are unpretentious and logical; it simply makes good sense to assemble into one unit specialized equipment and nursing personnel to help patients who require continuous skilled care. Five years ago, there were perhaps 25 hospitals in the country with intensive care units, according to Public Health Service estimates. Now, a P.H.S. official states, more than 20 per cent of all short-term community hospitals larger than 100 beds have them.

A prediction by Dr. Kenneth B. Babcock, director of the Joint Commission on Accreditation of Hospitals, is then quoted: "It's only a matter of time before the commission makes the existence of a good intensive care unit an accreditation standard—for larger hospitals, at least."

Included in the special section in *Modern Hospital* is a report of a survey made by the magazine which includes data from 106 hospitals of all sizes; the questionnaires were sent to 450 hospitals known to have intensive care units. Returns, the report states, "showed that many hospitals with the units have trouble deciding (1) who goes in, (2) who stays in, and (3) who takes care of patients while they are there." The occupancy rate of the units is "capricious," hard to control, impossible to predict. Frequently patients cannot be transferred as soon as desirable because of lack of bed facilities on other nursing units. Ninety per cent of the reporting hospitals charged higher rates for intensive care beds than their regular rates.

Jewish Hospital of St. Louis reported[55] that it combined intensive care and recovery units. Grace–New Haven Hospital (Connecticut) split its intensive care zone into two self-sufficient units.[56] Cedars of Lebanon Hospital, Los Angeles, remodeled a solarium, an ECG room, and a 3-bed ward into an intensive care unit.[56] A nurse consultant and an architect tell why "intensive care units should not be open wards but small enclosed areas that give patients the privacy they need and should have."[57] St. Luke's Hospital, Denver, reported that the doctors are enthusiastic about intensive care; one of them is quoted as saying:

> When you place a crew of intelligent nurses to work with seriously ill patients hours each day, you will observe a growing power of observation on their part that is most useful for all concerned. When one lives with danger, he unconsciously trains himself to early recognition of the more subtle changes in vital signs that may forestall a medical catastrophe.[58]

Warning that "intensive care units are not an unmixed blessing," Frances Ginsberg, consultant on operating room nursing and hospital aseptic technics, comments:[59]

[54] Pp. 67–110.
[55] *Mod. Hosp.*, January, 1963, p. 79.
[56] *Ibid.*, p. 87.
[57] *Ibid.*, p. 92.
[58] *Ibid.*, p. 99.
[59] *Ibid.*, p. 112.

Intensive care is not a new idea. Further, in spite of the fact that there has been a wide acceptance of the idea and many intensive (special, acute) care units are now in operation, there has been some rejection of the plan and a number of such units have been discontinued. . . . Safeguarding and improving patient care is, of course, the primary motivation for the development of this idea. However, there are other factors to be considered, including costs, maximum utilization of facilities, equipment and personnel. All of these can be studied from four points of view by both those who favor the idea and those who have come to disagree with it—from the point of view of the patient, the physician, nursing and administration.

The patient, Miss Ginsberg states, is given "a maximum of efficiency, conscientious and continuous care at a minimum of cost by obviating special nurses and the cost of special equipment," but some patients (or their relatives) "frown on the ward concept and want maximum privacy and liberal visiting privileges."

Most physicians support the idea, she has found, "although some prefer that their patients be given special care in private rooms."

Nurses vary in their reactions, some being well adapted to caring for critically ill patients, others arguing that "a better quality of care is possible within an environment with which the patient has become familiar."

Administrators are confronted with "severe financial implications . . . it poses problems in terms of keeping beds filled and staffed," and most prepaid insurance plans and other third-party payments "do not provide for such service."[60]

The Kellogg Foundation supported studies of the operation of intensive care units in two quite different hospitals.[61] The first was the "Hospital in the Round," a prototype unit developed by the Rochester Methodist Hospital—Mayo Clinic, Rochester, Minnesota. The second study was undertaken by the University of Michigan Bureau of Hospital Administration. It was an evaluation, published in late 1961 by the university, of the same unit, with before and after analysis, that is described in the Kellogg brochure. In the conclusion of this brochure it is stated:

Certainly the principal question confronting any hospital in a study of the feasibility of an intensive care unit is, "Will it materially improve patent care?" Judging by the experience of Community Hospital, there is evidence that the reply is in the affirmative. The reaction of Community's medical staff, board of trustees, hospital and nursing administration, as well as patients, is highly favorable. . . .

Admittedly, the special care unit at Community Hospital is expensive, with costs per patient day materially above those prevailing on all other services. The

[60] *Modern Hospital's* special section includes a condensation of *Elements of Progressive Patient Care,* Chapter 3, Part 1, "Intensive Care," Public Health Service Publication No. 930-C-1, September, 1962. Another good reference is *The Planning and Operation of an Intensive Care Unit* available from the W. K. Kellogg Foundation, Battle Creek, Michigan, published in September, 1961 to recount the experience of Community Hospital of Battle Creek, in planning and establishing an intensive care unit for acutely ill patients.

[61] The American Hospital Association published the results of this study in the monograph, *Comparisons of Intensive Nursing Service in a Circular and a Rectangular Unit.*

high ratio of hours of care per patient is, of course, a major aspect of this cost, together with the fact that such patients utilize a great deal more medications, treatments, and supplies than does the average patient. However, for those patients who might otherwise have had a private duty nurse, the cost of SCU would be materially less than the total paid for private duty nursing plus the usual hospital charges. It must also be noted that the total charges for SCU patients exceeded the total costs by some 9 per cent. Even so, and granting that an intensive care program results in a higher per patient day cost than do other patient care units, the hospital must still weigh this fact against the potentiality of improved community service.

The self-care phase of progressive care has many ardent proponents and substantial patient support. According to a Gallup poll in 1962, nearly six out of ten persons favor self-care hospital units. The question asked was: "It has been suggested that communities build a less expensive hospital for those not dangerously or critically ill. These hospital buildings would not have so much equipment or so many nurses. The daily rates would be about half those now in force. Do you think there is a need for this kind of hospital in this area?"

The national response was 58 per cent in favor, 11 per cent no opinion, 31 per cent not needed.

HOME CARE

As costs of hospital care—and of hospital insurance—mount, medical and nursing care of the sick in their homes is being increasingly brought to the fore as a solution of part of the problem. Formerly conceived of as applying only to the indigent, the concept has grown to embrace all classes of patients.

Frank E. Wing,[62] then director of the New England Medical Center, Boston, predicted back in 1935 that home care "is likely to assume considerable importance in the medical economics of the future." He told of the establishment in 1796 of the Boston Free Dispensary which served the sick poor in their homes, and which in 1935 was still supplying "more than two-thirds of the total service of the entire city, the other third being divided between the Massachusetts Memorial Hospitals, the Medical Mission Dispensary, and the Jamaica Plains Dispensary." In 1856, in conformance with a new policy of requiring patients who could leave their homes to go to a central place, a clinic service was established which did not supersede the original plan of caring for those who could not leave their homes. In 1894 there were 11 district physicians who made 27,125 visits to patients. The service gradually diminished to about 6,000 visits in 1922, but it rose again to some 25,000 in 1935 by which time it was being intensively used for the training of students from Tufts College Medical School in domiciliary medicine. Mr. Wing emphasized the saving to the city in the numerous cases which it was unnecessary to hospitalize or whose hospital stays were shortened.

[62] *Bull. Am. Hosp. A.,* April, 1935.

Dr. E. M. Bluestone[63] tells of an orthopedist, Dr. Victor Jacques Jacobsohn, who organized in 1933 the Home Visiting Rehabilitation Society in New York. This was a response to the continuing needs of his ward patients following their discharge. Weak support and the depression made it short-lived, but it gave Dr. Bluestone the inspiration which caused him to inaugurate in 1947 in Montefiore Hospital the extramural program known as "Home Care," which has been widely copied.

Mount Sinai Hospital, Chicago, began its home care program in 1953 after the need had been proved by an extensive study. It was aimed at the indigent and medically indigent. The doctors who participate in the program are on the regular medical staff and are paid by the hospital for their visits. In an emergency, ancillary services and nursing care, as well as medical care, are furnished. The social worker is a key member of the team and since 1957 there has also been a rehabilitation team. Bedside nursing is provided by the Visiting Nurse Association on referral of the patient's physician. The home care plan, Director Nathan W. Helman[64] states, "has definitely contributed to fewer readmissions and shorter hospital stays. More patients have done better in a shorter time, and more patients have returned to their homes."

The home care plan of Pekin (Illinois) Public Hospital includes housekeeping, light laundry, and food service after evaluation of the needs by the visiting nurse. The unit is completely hospital-based and hospital financed. Regular hospital rates prevail for most services, with nursing calls varying according to distance from the hospital from $3.00 to $5.00. The "meals-on-wheels" charge is $1.25 per day. Any chronically ill patient is eligible for home care who can be safely cared for in the home. The home care program is conceived of as the fourth and final step in a progressive patient care plan.[65]

That a small hospital can successfully operate a home care program has been shown by the experience of Sheldon Memorial Hospital, Albion, Michigan, a 75-bed institution. In cooperation with the Calhoun County Health Department and with the assistance of the W. K. Kellogg Foundation plus a $5,000 a year subsidy from the state, the hospital embarked on a home care program in late 1960. The hospital utilization at the time was comparatively heavy, averaging 93 per cent occupancy, the ambulatory service was active, and there was a shortage of long-term care facilities in the area. Special automotive equipment with double side doors was provided. An informal case-finding committee was developed which, when candidates were found, consulted the physician and encouraged him to use home care. As the work became known, the committee became less important. The health department took over the nursing care, setting the rate at $4 per visit, $6 per day for active care.

The first year cost was $27,300 with no charge for administration or space.

[63] Reader Opinion. *Mod. Hosp.*, March, 1954.
[64] From a talk at the 38th annual meeting of the Illinois Hospital Association. *Hosp. Topics*, January, 1961, pp. 41–42.
[65] *Ibid.*, p. 42.

Collections were poor despite the low charges, nearly half remaining uncollected. Blue Cross went along, but many did not have it and other carriers refused. More than half of the patients were aged 65 or over, and there was a frequency of multiple diagnoses. It was felt that the program was proving sufficiently successful to demonstrate that "a program can be made available in a small community by a smaller hospital."[66]

The American Hospital Association published in 1961 a monograph, *Home Care,* which is a report of the results of a comprehensive study of home care programs. The report is from the Medical Care Research Center of the Jewish Hospital of St. Louis and the Social Science Institute of Washington University, and the study was supported by a grant from the National Institutes of Health. In a summary of the study by Drs. David Littauer, I. Jerome Flance, and Albert F. Wessen[67] the following statements are made:

> Home care *per se* is not a device to save money on hospital care. Although this goal may be realized ultimately by reducing the need for hospital beds, at present it must be considered as another health benefit that increases the total community health bill. . . . At least three major types of home care programs are now recognizable: those sponsored by and based upon hospitals; those conducted by visiting nurse associations; and those operated by public health or welfare agencies. . . . The cost of operating these programs ranges from approximately $3 to $7 per patient per day. The sources of financing have been principally from tax funds or private and public grants-in-aid, with only a smattering of payments coming from patients or from voluntary prepayment health insurance. . . . To date, organized home care has shown its greatest usefulness in meeting the health, social and economic needs of that segment of the population represented by the elderly chronically ill.

The home care program of the Jewish Hospital of St. Louis, according to the report, was started in 1955. Patients in foster homes and in proprietary nursing homes have been included in the service. Private philanthropy has made up the difference in operating expenses between fees paid by patients, which represent only 10 per cent of the cost.

Fifteen home care programs were compared in the conduct of the study. Among the hindrances to growth found are the exclusion of care in the home from the framework of hospital and medical insurance plans except in a very few places; the indifferent and questioning attitude of the practicing physician; the lack of enthusiasm by hospital administrators and their governing boards; shortages of qualified personnel; deficiencies in community organizations; and lack of knowledge of this health resource on the part of the patient and his family. The conclusion (as stated in the summary) was:

> Although home care may be organized under a variety of auspices, the general hospital must in any event play a key role. Patient population comes from all age groups and economic classes and needs treatment for a broad spectrum of ill-

[66] John R. Griffith: *Hospitals,* June 16, 1962, pp. 58–60.
[67] *Hospitals,* January 16, 1961, pp. 41–43.

nesses. The hospital is accustomed to meeting requirements for standards, controls, records and statistical data. It already possesses the basic personnel and diagnostic and therapeutic services, as well as the administrative "know-how," essential to the successful organization and operation of a coordinated home care program. It can give assurance of hospitalization for the patients when they need it.

It is, therefore, concluded that a program sponsored and administered by a general hospital which sees itself as a true community health center offers the type of home care which is best for patients, for hospitals, for the health professions, for participating service organizations and for the community.

In a symposium, "Health Services at Home," held at the National Health Forum, Miami Beach, Florida, in March, 1960, Dr. Claire F. Ryder, chief, Health of the Aged Section, Chronic Disease Branch, Public Health Service, said that home care is being furthered by official and voluntary agencies at the national, state, and local levels. Working at the national level are the American Medical Association, American Hospital Association, Blue Cross, Blue Shield, and the Public Health Service. The last, Dr. Ryder said, in addition to collecting and disseminating information on home care, has stimulated and supported pilot projects as another source of information for guidance materials. The Service, he said further, has aided, through federal formula grants to states, categorical and over-all chronic disease programs. He mentioned that rural home care services are being supported by the Kentucky State Department of Health.

Alcoholism

That the "general hospital, recognized as the health care center in the community, is the only logical place to treat alcoholism effectively" is the conclusion of the thesis submitted to Northwestern University by Karl D. Glunz who received his master's degree in hospital administration in 1959. Mr. Glunz is assistant administrator at St. Joseph's Hospital, Milwaukee. He further concludes that

> ... the general hospital should represent the concentration of medical minds, means and methods to all citizens of the community—a place close to their living environment which they can depend upon for assistance in meeting health problems; by eliminating the alcoholic from this available service, the general hospital is neglecting the responsibility to the community for complete health care.

The following discussion of alcoholism is adapted from Mr. Glunz's paper.

The alcoholic is an individual who can keep an interest in life only by using large quantities of alcohol, or who cannot stand up to the requirements of life without the aid of alcohol. Harold W. Demone, Jr., the nation's first commissioner on alcoholism, describes the typical alcoholic as a "39-year-old, well educated, third generation American, once divorced, who likes to nip to 'get in the mood' before going to a party." About half of this country's five million alcoholics are third generation Americans; half of them are under 40 years of age; 20 per cent are women, and of these women 96 per cent have been married —in 45 per cent of the cases to an alcoholic husband. So, strange as it may seem, only a small portion of alcoholics fall into the category of drunkards or skid row bums.

When does the alcoholic actually become an alcoholic? When he can no longer drink on a social basis—instead cannot stop his consumption of alcohol after that ever so dangerous first drink, after which he depends upon alcohol for daily living. Approximately 2 per cent of any community's drinking population is potentially capable of reaching this status.

The community attitude toward the alcoholic might be classified as both active and passive—active insofar as its readiness to classify him as a drunkard who should be locked up, passive insofar as neglect to look upon him as a human being, afflicted with a serious disease which needs professional care, is concerned.

The biggest problem to any community is the common drunk. He is not a compulsive drinker who has lost control; he gets drunk because he wants to get drunk, deliberately. This group in the main is uncooperative, unruly, unreliable, and unpredictable. The drunk, often mistaken for the alcoholic, is unwanted wherever he goes, especially in hospitals, where he is a troublesome, demanding patient, undeserving of hospital care.

The alcoholic, on the other hand, is neither a drinker nor a drunk. He cannot drink socially, and he does not drink in order to get drunk. The alcoholism subcommittee of the World Health Organization describes the alcoholic as one afflicted with a "chronic disease, disorder, or behavior, characterized by the repeated drinking of alcoholic beverages to an extent that exceeds customary dietary use or the ordinary compliance with the social drinking customs of the community, and that interferes with the drinker's health, interpersonal relationships, and economic functioning."

Most communities of substantial size have various types of facilities which are available to the alcoholic. There are institutions, both private and tax-supported, which are directed specifically toward the treatment of alcoholism. Mental disease hospitals admit the alcoholic as a matter of routine, and many emergency hospitals offer limited care (often to the common drunk mistaken for an alcoholic). Often the alcoholic spends his first and last phase of institutionalization in the lock-up or the jail or even a workhouse of some sort. In all of these facilities the care and treatment are short-termed with inadequate follow-up, and therefore ineffective. Something more than merely affording the alcoholic a "drying-up period" must be offered, or he will only go out into the community and start on another binge. Present general hospital facilities are indeed lacking. For example, in New York State, only 25 per cent of the public general hospitals and 20 per cent of the voluntary general hospitals will admit patients with a primary diagnosis of alcoholism, with 24 per cent of this admitting total having no provisions whatsoever to treat the alcoholic. Seventy-five per cent of the public general hospitals and 45 per cent of the voluntary hospitals actually state within their regulations that they will not accept alcoholics.

Community facilities for the treatment of alcoholism are written into Corwin's and Cunningham's Report of 1944,[68] and after considering facilities offered today, most likely this statement still holds true:

> The . . . General Hospital, as well as other local institutions, have all adopted the same policy due to overcrowded conditions, that "alcoholism is a self-induced condition, therefore, why take up space that might be given to an acutely ill person who might be cured." . . . If, however, the hospital is used repeatedly merely as a place to sober up instead of being put in jail or being cared for by friends or relatives, with no intention of quitting the practice, it seems futile and a gross misuse of medical or hospital facilities. . . . To our house staff, they (alcoholics) are a disgusting and disagreeable annoyance.

Although there are approximately 70,000,000 users of alcoholic beverages in the United States, the population developing the illness of alcoholism is relatively small—about 5,015,000. No matter how small this number may seem in relation to the total, it is large enough to list alcoholism as the fourth major public health problem. Alcoholism alone does not account for this high rating, even though it is the basis of all related problems. Alcoholism in many cases will "mask" other serious disorders to the extent that they are never diagnosed, therefore leaving a seriously ill person loose in the community to spread his undiscovered sickness to the remaining population, whether it be tuberculosis, pneumonia, or some other disease.

Tuberculosis is ten times as prevalent among alcoholics as among the general population. Alcoholics spread more tuberculosis infection than any other segment of the population. Since alcoholism is concentrated fifty times as great in skid-row areas as compared with other proportionally sized areas, it is plainly seen that from the public health standpoint these skid-row areas are a "hot-bed" of tuberculosis. Mental disease requiring hospitalization is also a frightening public health problem to which alcoholism is attributed as the third most frequent cause.

Considering the alcoholic as an individual in contrast to a public health problem, certain undiagnosed medical disorders are very detrimental and often fatal to the alcoholic because of the lack of communication between him and the average health agency. Studies have proved the high incidence of medical conditions, particularly liver disease, in alcoholics. Yet, today, in the majority of hospitals, these medical needs are overshadowed by alcoholism, and when and if the alcoholic is admitted, it is usually for the medical need only. The alcoholism factor is disregarded completely, even though it is probably the principal etiological factor behind the medical problem.

[68] E. H. L. Corwin and E. V. Cunningham: *Institutional Facilities for the Treatment of Alcoholism.* New York, Journal of Studies on Alcoholism, Inc., 1944.

The solution calls for use of case studies, preventive measures, research, education, treatment, within a concentrated unit of organization in the community—the general hospital.

Restoration to normalcy—is this possible? A certain proportion of the alcoholic population exhibits a rather poor prognosis because certain personal assets are lacking. However, general hospitals do not hesitate to offer treatment for other disease conditions in which the prognosis may be extremely dubious—for example, cancer or schizophrenia. If members of the healing professions acknowledge that alcoholism is a mixed medical and social problem, that it is an interrelated physical and emotional disability, that the medical treatment of the body alone is not sufficient to bring about recovery, and that the community has a responsibility to provide the kinds of resources that in time will reduce the prevalence of alcoholism, progress may then be expected.

To exemplify this, a southern hospital completed an extensive survey in 1957 to classify the progress made in the 85 alcoholics they treated in a certain period of time. The results were gratifying. Unemployment within this group was reduced from 60 to 11 per cent; complete sobriety was attained by 35 per cent; 18 per cent were greatly improved; and only 10 per cent were absolutely nonreceptive. Restoration to normalcy, then, is possible.

The chief method of attack is clearly set forth by the American Medical Association and the American Hospital Association. At the November, 1956, annual meeting of the A.M.A. in Seattle, Washington, a report of the board of trustees dealing with hospitalization of alcoholic patients stated:

> Alcoholic symptomatology and complications which occur in many personality disorders, come within the scope of medical practice. . . . With improved means of treatment available and the changed viewpoint and attitude which places the alcoholic in the category of a sick individual, most of the problems formerly encountered in the treatment of the alcoholic in the general hospital have been greatly reduced. In any event, the individual patient should be evaluated rather than have general objection toward him on the grounds of a diagnosis of alcoholism. It is recognized that no general policy can be made for all hospitals. Administrators are urged to give careful consideration to the possibility of accepting such patients in the light of the newer available measures and the need for providing facilities for treating these patients. In order to render a service to the community, provision should be made for such patients who cooperate and who wish such care.

The administrators noted the doctors' message. In October, 1957, the board of trustees of the American Hospital Association recommended that the

> . . . primary point of attack [on alcoholism] should be through the general hospital. Because of the completeness of its facilities and of its accessibility, it is the logical place to which an alcoholic or his family should turn. . . . The American Hospital Association urges general hospitals to develop a program for the care of alcoholics. . . . This progressive step would keep pace with increased recognition of (1) the general hospital as the community health center, and (2) alcoholism as a medical problem requiring broad-scale attack if it is to be solved.

Does a general hospital need specialized facilities in treating the alcoholic patient? This is certainly a controversial question, in fact, one of the most controversial points. The consensus of hospital authorities is that some type of segregation is necessary, whether it be coordinated with the psychiatric section, a few rooms set aside within the medical division, or even a ward completely separated from all other hospital activity. On the other hand, there are those who insist that the alcoholic be placed as any other patient upon admission, in the most convenient bed no matter where it may be in the hospital. Segregation of the alcoholic ward necessarily means specialized facilities, ranging from a specially trained nursing staff to specially equipped rooms with various sound-proofing, protecting, and restraining devices. The advantages of treatment in the general wards are often three-sided: in favor of the alcoholic, the hospital, and the other patients involved. No stigma is placed on the alcohol addict as there is when he is placed in an "alcoholic bed" shut off from other hospital life. He appreciates being treated like others; psychologically this is often the very best medicine. By being placed among nonintoxicated, nonalcoholic patients, the alcoholic may receive self-assurance and kindness from these other ill people. Much tension and work is removed from the nurses and orderlies because of the presence of these other patients in the room. This not only helps the hospital but also affords a certain satisfaction to the patient giving the helping hand. Finally, since the alcoholic is frequently inhibited when drinking, the morale of the entire ward may be improved through his aggressive and jovial spirit on recovery.

Although the weight of opinion is that special facilities are not needed, the correct attitude on the part of the hospital, physician, nursing staff, fellow patients, and the public is a necessity. A certain degree of segregation in the initial stages of his recovery permits the intensity of care which is needed by the alcoholic.

The community as a whole must be made aware that the alcoholic is a sick person and must be treated on a parity with any other person who is admitted to the hospital. An educational program by the hospital is needed to emphasize this. Included in the program should be education of the hospital staff from the janitor all the way to the administrator and the board. It must be remembered that alcoholism is often primarily a psychological problem which has resulted in a physical disorder; therefore the method of attack must take into consideration both the mental and the physical aspects.

Clinical research should be conducted on such questions as: Are there personality characteristics peculiar to the alcoholic? Are there some factors in metabolism, in body chemistry, in hormonal functioning, which distinguish the uncontrolled drinker from the other millions of ordinary users of alcoholic beverages? What determines the onset of alcoholism in one group and not in another? Research is needed to dig into the unknown as well as to evaluate the existing theories on the causes of alcoholism. Much should be known about the effectiveness of different types of treatment and the techniques which must be developed in order to handle a large number of cases with minimum expenditure of professional skills and monetary budget.

A hospital needs, in fact must have, at least one active physician who is thoroughly interested and specifically trained in the problems of alcoholism if an alcoholic ward is to have any chance of success. Some members of the medical profession look upon the alcoholic as one who is outside the proper concern of medicine. Many others hesitate to devote to a disorder of this sort time which past experience has led them to believe will be unproductive. Certainly the idea commonly shared by some doctors that the only thing that can be done with an alcoholic is to lecture him is not sufficient. A cooperative attitude is mandatory and should be encouraged among internists, psychiatrists, neurologists, chemists, and pathologists. Working as a team along with the other members of the medical staff, such a group could accomplish real progress.

The role of the psychiatrist is stressed, for many authorities diagnose alcoholism as "cancer of the ego" in which early recognition and proper psychiatric treatment are of the utmost importance. The ego characteristics which the alcoholic lacks are independence, freedom to think and act at a mature level, power to manage routine situations and assume responsibilities, and prestige—self-assurance and feeling of adequacy. The psychiatrist can help the patient overcome these weaknesses.

The house staff physician in any general hospital cannot be overlooked. His potentially close affiliation with the alcoholic should positively be beneficial to the patient. Also, since he will eventually come in contact with this type of patient in practice, his education and training in treating this illness should come while he is a resident officer.

The nurse is also in a particularly advantageous position to make a constructive contribution to the patient's recovery. The nurse, not being an authoritarian figure to the alcoholic as the physician, clergyman, or social worker appear to be, can get his response by exhibiting personal concern for his improvement. She can suggest, after consultation with the social worker, community agencies that might be helpful to him, and her suggestions might have a stronger appeal than those made by others.

Screening and admission of patients involve deep understanding of the general problem and rapport with other community agencies as sources of information. Whenever possible, admission should be refused to unwilling, uncooperative, and unmanageable patients, or patients with violent delirium tremens. The opinion of a family physician or attending staff doctor is usually considered enough authority to admit a patient, but his opinion should be supported by the patient's desire to stop drinking and to get back to the normal living cycle.

Acute alcoholic intoxication can be, and often is, a medical emergency and in some cases a surgical emergency. As with any other acute case, the merits of each individual situation must be considered.

The hospital is surely not the place to sleep off a drunk and utilize valuable space in so doing. An inebriated patient should be given proper outpatient care and returned home (if possible) and advised to come back when sober. If he returns and is classified as an alcoholic he can be admitted.

Care, however, must be taken in sending an inebriate home, for if he is an alcoholic, delirium tremens normally occurs eight to ten hours after his last drink, and by proper treatment and sedation this can be prevented. There are times, however, when a person coming off a drunk or off a spree, having remorse, shame, and humiliation, along with his hangover, the "jitters," tension, befuddled mind, dehydration, or electrolyte imbalance, really needs help. Usually at this time he is as gentle as a lamb, no longer drunk but sick, and is most appreciative of everything that is done for him. But the Saturday night jail population and the payday playboy are to be avoided.

A five-day hospital stay should be a minimum with no maximum time set forth except in accordance with the severity of the case. Unless there is extreme emergency, readmissions within the period of a year should not be permitted. He should not leave the hospital with the attitude, "I feel fine now, but if I slip again, all I have to do is to come back here." Word gets around skid row! The policy of only one admission for the diagnosis of alcoholism is popular because it is believed that the psychological effect of mixing repeaters with new patients is detrimental to the prognosis of a good rehabilitation.

The hospital chaplain should be a familiar figure around the alcoholic ward, encouraging the patients to attend religious services and to ask God's assistance in their struggle.

The alcoholic, no matter what the type or intensity of his treatment, can never really be cured. The disease remains for life. No matter how long the time interval, one drink inevitably sends him off. He should be followed up with constant rehabilitative measures for the duration of the disease—for life. On release from the hospital he should be given appointments to return as an outpatient at least monthly. Follow-up is ideally accomplished through scheduled clinics for alcoholics. Remembering that alcoholism is a medical disorder, periodic physical examinations and check-ups to evaluate physical stamina should be offered within the clinic facilities. Medical therapy is not necessarily given unless the patient has had a recent bout with alcohol and is nauseated, restless, or nervous. Keeping the alcoholic healthy is in itself considered a preventive measure insofar as he realizes the comfort and pleasure of good clean living and loses the wish to return to that ever-present "morning after" feeling.

Alcoholics Anonymous

Probably the most active and most effective community agency in dealing with the alcoholic (before, during, and after hospitalization) is that organization known as Alcoholics Anonymous. The basic attitude of most A.A. members is quite unique. All of them having gone through the hardships of alcoholism and the upward struggle for the recovery of their self-respect, health, and happiness, they believe that in the initial phase of treatment, the alcoholic does not accept the type of counseling offered by psychiatrists and social workers.

The alcoholic, if properly oriented toward recovery, believes himself to be sick, not queer, and he accordingly wants a doctor to treat his sickness and not a person to analyze his problems. The typical member of A.A. sees "red" at the mere mention that some underlying problem which arose when the alcoholic was a youth is basically the cause for addiction, and in order to conquer this, the problem must be discovered and overcome. A fellow alcoholic is actually the only one who can really place himself in the position of the patient and is many times the only one who can offer sound advice and communicate sound mental hygienic principles without being "preachy," antagonistic, or seeming to pass judgment.

To ensure success in the operation of the alcoholic service in the general hospital, many hospitals have looked toward Alcoholics Anonymous as the backbone of their admission and follow-up procedure. Working relationships with A.A. will vary from community to community and even from hospital to hospital; however, the principle involved remains the same. Most hospital administrators feel that the only way to be positive you are receiving a patient who wants to stop drinking and who is willing to cooperate without causing administrative and patient care problems is to confine admissions to the A.A-sponsored patient. This would reduce the hospital's screening responsibility, since the A.A. sponsor would make sure the alcoholic is absolutely ready for hospitalization, notify the hospital, give all the necessary admission information, notify the family physician as well as the physician in charge of the service, and orientate the family as to hospital procedures in treating cases of this nature; finally the A.A. sponsor would bring the patient to the hospital and actually admit him and get him settled in his bed.

A.A. sponsorship should not stop with this. In fact, even in hospitals where A.A. sponsorship is not required, members of A.A. make daily visits to previously assigned patients, which affords the alcoholic an opportunity to talk with someone capable of understanding him. Visits are made on a very friendly and personal basis in order to acquaint the alcoholic with this "new friend." Visits are not directed toward counseling or problem finding. These relationships with A.A. while yet in the hospital bed should condition the alcoholic to the fact that someone is truly interested in him as an individual and that someone can be counted upon for help even after hospitalization.

Mrs. Marty Mann, the executive director of the National Committee for Education on Alcoholism, summed up the A.A. relationship with the general hospital in her address given before the South Carolina Legislature in 1946. Mrs. Mann, an alcoholic, said in essence that hospitalization is extremely necessary, but alone it helps only a little and quite temporarily; psychiatry helps a little more when applied to the hospitalized alcoholic; but the real clincher is the aid offered by A.A., for here is *living proof* that the alcoholic can be and is worth being helped.

Alcoholics Anonymous is in itself a type of outpatient therapy on a group basis. Hospital outpatient clinics which are regularly attended by members of A.A. offer the alcoholic much on his way to recovery, and insofar as these clinics are not held daily, A.A. feels that the time between clinic visits should also be closely watched. Therefore, each alcoholic, depending upon the severity of his addiction, is in contact with his sponsor anywhere from three to four times a day to once or twice a week. Whenever, no matter the time or place, the alcoholic gets the urge to drink, he calls his A.A. sponsor, who also being an alcoholic understands the situation and immediately takes action to prevent that first drink. Contacts continue as long as they live.

The general hospital neglects its responsibility to the community for complete health care if it eleminates the alcoholic from its services.

CHAPTER 22

The Other Services

We are in the most demanding era of our history. We must
build for the future in hospital services and medical care
as daringly and as energetically as we have built other aspects
of our national economy such as industry, transportation,
agriculture and housing. Our thinking and aims must
be at the level of the dramatic, not the commonplace. We
are no longer living in a frontier world, nor even in an
individualistic world, but one demanding cooperation and
interdependency. It is, therefore, necessary that each of the
major agencies in any community seek understanding
of the functions and responsibilities of other organizations,
institutions, professions, and the current trends in the
health program required for constructive planning.

WILLARD C. RAPPLEYE. M.D.[1]

THE OTHER agencies are all geared to render services to cooperate with
hospitals in health conservation and restoration, but it takes exploration to
learn about them. A few of the social agencies were mentioned in Chapter 13,
and public health services in Chapter 15. The medical social service worker is
the liaison person to recommend referrals of patients to other services, but only
one-sixth of the nonfederal short-term general and other special hospitals in the
United States reported having social service departments in 1962.[2] Obviously the
administrator of most hospitals must assume the responsibility in cooperation
with the medical staff and with the assistance of such coordinating agencies as
may exist in his community.

[1] From an address before the Greater Detroit Area Hospital Council, Inc., November 18, 1958.
Quoted in *Trustee*, published by the American Hospital Association, July, 1959.
[2] *Hospitals*, Guide Issue, August, 1963.

Effective working relationships with the other health and welfare services are a public relations asset. Disseminating knowledge of the hospital through outside groups is often more successful in building good will than direct communication through the press or other media.

In this chapter a few of the most prominent organizations with which affiliation should be made are discussed.

NURSING HOMES

There is considerable difference of opinion on how far the general hospital should embrace care of the chronically ill. On the negative side, venturing a prediction on "The Next Ten Years in Medicine," Dr. Caldwell B. Esselstyn, consultant and lecturer in group medical care, Department of Preventive Medicine and Community Health, Seton Hall College of Medicine and Dentistry, Jersey City, has this to say about nursing homes:[3]

> Over the past few years the mushrooming of proprietary nursing home syndicates all over the country has been a cause of increasing alarm. The spectacular financial returns that these syndicates are providing speculators, many of whom are doctors, is disturbing. Some 90 per cent of nursing homes providing approximately 71 per cent of the available beds belong to this category today. This percentage will diminish in the years ahead.

> If expansion of the Hill-Burton Act is not possible, some other legislation will be passed to make possible the construction of needed facilities other than hospitals. The time has come when physicians will be turning their attention to the care of patients outside the hospital and avoid the overcentralization of services in institutions. Although the hospital is an important link in the medical-care chain, it must always be considered not as the last word but as the last resort. The extent to which this movement will succeed will be governed by the degree to which some sort of compromise can be made with those dedicated to the creation of greater and greater hospital empires.

On the other side, the Joint Committee of the American Hospital Association and the United States Public Health Service in its report issued in March, 1963, "Areawide Planning of Facilities for Long-Term Treatment and Care," declared:

> The general hospital and its organized medical staff should accept responsibility for providing facilities for long-term treatment and care, either through the construction or allocation of facilities or through relationships with one or more established facilities.

The committee stated that planning should include the entire complex of facilities and services for the long-term patient and that "responsibility for planning for both short-term and long-term facilities should be vested in the same planning agency."[4]

[3] *New England J. Med.*, January 18, 1962.
[4] P.H.S. Publication No. 930-B-1. Washington, D.C., Superintendent of Documents, U.S. Government Printing Office, 1963.

That effective relationships with proprietary and other nursing homes can be and are being established is proved by many examples, a few of which are:

In Traverse City, Michigan, through a unique arrangement, a county-operated nursing home was located adjacent to and on a site donated by a voluntary general hospital. The hospital furnishes heat, laboratory, x-ray, food, laundry, and some other services to the 90-bed nursing home, which is designed for both county and full-pay patients. The buildings are connected by a covered, glassed-in corridor. More than one-fourth of the admissions to the nursing home are transfers from the general hospital. The general hospital also has a home care program which is available to patients from both institutions. Nearly 90 per cent of the patients admitted to the long-term facility are more than 65 years of age, and about the same percentage are in the welfare classification. A problem that is arising, however, is the increasing length of stay of patients in the nursing home facility, so that its beds are tied up with custodial care patients for whom no other place is available. Obviously a third-stage facility is needed.

Hackley Hospital, Muskegon, Michigan, selected a nursing home in its area with which to contract for referral of patients, with the understanding that the hospital would be an adviser and special consultant in the operation of this proprietary home without interfering with its independence. An eight-point agreement on the relationship was included in the contract. The project, which was started in 1961, is financed by a federal grant as a prototype of a way in which nursing home operation can be upgraded by an affiliation with a general hospital that helps to raise its standards of care.[5]

Near Tacoma, Washington, a 400-bed medical facility is planned which will include a 100-bed retirement home, a 100-bed ambulatory nursing home, and a 100-bed home for the mentally deficient. There will be a resident physician, clinic and therapy facilities. Relationships will be established with the local general hospitals.

The state of Washington is well in advance of most of the other states in developing nursing home facilities; in fact its ratio of nursing home beds per 1,000 population is more than three times the national average. The stimulus to nursing home construction in that state came about through favorable legislation passed in 1949 which provided for hospital and nursing home care and free choice of physician, drugs, and other supplies and made the Department of Social Security (now the Department of Public Assistance) responsible for administration. There is a nursing home bed for about every 190 persons in the state, as compared with the ratio of 2 beds per 1,000 which most authorities give as desirable. The program has proved to be expensive for the state. The reaction of one hospital spokesman, as quoted by John H. Westerman,[6] was:

Of every $1 spent by the state for health care of those over 65, 60 cents is paid to nursing homes, 24 cents to hospitals, 11 cents to physicians and 5 cents to drug-

[5] See Bob D. Dann: Hospital-Nursing Home Cooperative Project. *Hospital Topics,* June, 1962, pp. 41–43.
[6] *Hospitals,* January 16, 1962, p. 76.

gists and dentists and for minor services. . . . It would be interesting to see what a month's hospital stay at a cost of $1,000 or less would do for one of these patients compared with a year's nursing home stay at a cost to the taxpayers of about $2,500.

A limited number of the nursing homes in the state of Washington have established relationships with hospitals.

John Hackley[7] points out that discussions of hospital–nursing home affiliations almost always give the inference that the nursing home would be upgraded and benefited by the connection, and overlook the advantages to the hospital of continuing contact with the patient. He states:

> Affiliation which provides an uninterrupted program of care for patients makes the staffs of the participating institutions co-workers and—with proper administrative climates—co-partners in the teamwork required for effective care. By a free interchange of visits, personnel of the affiliated institutions can become acquainted with a patient and his current program of care before he is transferred to the other facility. No small side effect is the reassurance the patient receives with such a practice and the resultant minimization of his problems in adjusting to a new setting. Beyond direct care to individual patients, the device of affiliation can work to strengthen feelings of mutuality of interest and effort. Affiliated institutions in a community can become the aggregate spokesman on behalf of all the long-term, disabled, and aged patients, serving as their interpreter to the community and its health resources. As a spokesman, too, the institutions can be a dynamic factor in stimulating community development of the necessary programs and resources which presently are inadequate or do not exist.

An exceptionally comprehensive program for long-term patients is conducted by Beth Abraham Home in New York, which was opened in 1920 as a voluntary nursing home for the care of long-term ill and disabled adults. According to its 1961 report, the home observes orthodox Jewish regulations and customs, although it is nonsectarian in admissions. It is a member agency of the Federation of Jewish Philanthropies of New York City.

Of the 510 beds, according to the report, 211 are in the Hirschman Pavilion, which was opened in 1958. Thirty-one beds are operated as a private pavilion for patients able to afford a more expensive type of accommodation. All of the other floors serve patients who are either self-maintaining or on public assistance. Seven beds are reserved for isolation cases. Admission is limited to patients who are 18 years of age and older. Persons suffering from tuberculosis, mental illnesses, communicable or contagious diseases are not eligible. Short-term rehabilitation and convalescent patients are not admitted except to the private pavilion.

Services include a completely coordinated program in medicine, nursing, social service, physical therapy, occupational therapy, arts and crafts, recreation, music therapy, speech therapy, dentistry, laboratory, diagnostic x-ray, podiatry, and volunteer services. A sheltered workshop is being developed.

Special diagnostic procedures, surgery, and consultation services are provided

[7] *Hospital Topics*, March, 1962., p. 42.

by nearby Montefiore Hospital, with which the home has a medical affiliation. The home has a home care program in cooperation with Montefiore Hospital and a private residence (foster home care) arrangement with the hospital and the Jewish Community Services of Long Island. Bronx House provides consultation on the recreation program, and the Jewish Guild for the Blind on blind patient care. Applicants who were victims of Nazi persecution are processed through an arrangement with Self Help.

The foregoing information from the introduction to the annual report gives a basis for comparison with many of the commercially operated nursing homes that are springing up today. It is inconceivable that with this quality of facilities, services, and direction of transfers to affiliated services, there could possibly be any profit from the proper operation of a long-term care institution. With the growing emphasis on rehabilitation of the chronically ill and disabled, the capital investment in plant, equipment, and trained personnel is becoming prohibitive for the seeker after profit. Cost per patient day was $13.17 in 1961 in the Beth Abraham Home; only 24 per cent of the patients were self-maintaining, and only a small number of these met the actual cost of maintenance. "The large deficit of the Home was made up primarily by generous grants from the Federation of Jewish Philanthropies, of which the Home is a member agency."

A breakdown of patients in the home is interesting. The percentage of elderly patients is increasing, 77 per cent in 1961 being 60 years of age and over. As of December 31, 1961, 35 per cent of the patients were male, 65 per cent female. Nearly one-fourth of the patients have been in the home for five years or more. Patients are admitted mainly from hospitals and from their own homes. The patient group is sicker, and in need of more care, than in previous years. The most prevalent primary diagnoses are paralysis agitans (parkinsonism), encephalomalacia due to thrombosis, arteriosclerosis generalized, multiple sclerosis, arthritis, arteriosclerotic heart disease, diabetes mellitus, and neoplasms (in that order). These diagnoses account for 68 per cent of the total primary diagnoses. The facilities available in the institution for senile and terminal cancer patients are limited and therefore many of these applicants must be rejected.

Nursing Home Survey

Findings of the second national inventory of nursing homes and related types of facilities were reported by the Public Health Service in November, 1962. They showed that there has been almost a doubling of the capacity of such facilities since 1954, although a shortage remains.

The survey showed a total of 23,000 nonhospital facilities that provided nursing or supportive services to chronically ill and aged persons with a capacity for 592,800 residents.

Of the 23,000 facilities, 9,700 are skilled nursing care homes which average

25 in capacity. About 87 per cent are proprietary and account for slightly more than 70 per cent of the available beds.

Personal care homes totaled 11,100, and residential care facilities totaled 2,200.

The total capacity of the 9,700 skilled nursing homes was reported as 338,700, compared with 180,000 beds in 1954.[8]

Accreditation and Listing

The American Nursing Home Association announced in 1962 a "crash program" for accrediting nursing homes under which each state association was directed to establish an accreditation board.

The association negotiated with the Joint Commission on Accreditation of Hospitals about an accreditation program. If the commission had undertaken such a program, the association's program would have served as a screening plan. However, as announced in April, 1963, by the president of the American Hospital Association, the joint commission's program was halted by the refusal of the American Medical Association to concur in its establishment. In the same month the American Medical Association and the American Nursing Home Association jointly announced a plan to establish a national accreditation program for nursing homes.[9]

The American Hospital Association had registered more than 600 nursing homes at the beginning of 1963. The listing program for inpatient institutions other than hospitals was begun in 1958.[10] The listing requirements include:

1. The facility shall be licensed by the state and must comply with local governmental regulations.

2. Each patient must be under the care of a duly licensed physician who must see the patient as his need indicates.

3. A duly licensed doctor of medicine must supervise the clinical activity of the institution and advise on medical administrative problems.

4. A medical record must be maintained for each patient.

5. The nursing service must be under the supervision of a registered nurse, or a licensed practical nurse with a registered nurse regularly serving in a consultive capacity.

6. Food must meet the nutritional and dietary requirements of patients.

7. Care must be provided for patients on a 24-hour per day basis and arrangements must be made to provide diagnostic services on a regular and convenient basis.

The South Carolina Hospital Association voted in 1963 to revise its bylaws to allow the acceptance of nursing homes to membership. The homes will become members of a special section. Nursing homes are also eligible for membership in the Alabama Hospital Association, and other state associations are expected to broaden their membership accordingly.

[8] Reported in *Hospitals,* January 16, 1963, p. 133.
[9] *Mod. Hosp.,* May, 1963, p. 21; *Hospitals,* May 1, 1963, pp. 107–8.
[10] The survey procedures were described in *Hospitals,* January 16, 1962, pp. 53–56.

Standards

Concern about the quality of care that is given in nursing homes is widespread. A three-year study aimed at answering the question of what happens when the hospital patient goes to a nursing home was announced in April, 1963, by Brandeis University and Boston College. The project is financed by a $362,000 Public Health Service grant. The study will commence with patients just before they leave hospitals and will follow them through some 60 nursing homes in Greater Boston. It is anticipated that the study will cover some 1,000 patients.

Because of deficiencies in proprietary nursing-home care, the city administration of New York City recommended in 1961 that a self-regulating effort be instituted. This was done. Among the accomplishments were the organization of a central dietary service for member homes; establishment of self-policing inspection teams that regularly visit and evaluate each home; and initiation of a nine-month compulsory training program for administrators at the School of Public Health of Columbia University. The self-regulating program was discontinued on January 15, 1963. In 1962 the Department of Hospitals of the city created a Nursing Homes and Home Care Service which will concentrate on revision of the nursing home code to substantially raise the standard of care.

The Public Health Service has issued a *Nursing Home Standards Guide;* also *General Standards of Construction and Equipment—Long-Term Care Facilities.* A study by the California Bureau of Hospitals under a Public Health Service grant aimed at improving patient care in nursing homes resulted in the publication of a textbook, *Nursing Home Administration,*[11] written by two educators and a hospital administrator, which is a minutely detailed "how-to-do-it" manual.

The Illinois Hospital Association has prepared and adopted a "Guide for Hospital—Nursing Home Affiliation" with the object of stimulating at the local community level (1) better continuity of care for patients with chronic and disabling conditions; (2) more effective utilization of available institutional facilities; (3) more effective pooling of resources to provide specialized services and personnel so that they can be available to nursing home as well as hospital patients; and (4) better care at the lowest possible over-all cost to the community.[12]

Evidence of the high degree of interest in nursing homes by the hospital field is shown in the periodical literature. *Hospitals* devoted some fifty pages of its January 16, 1962, issue to "The Nursing Home—A Health Care Resource" and published a special section on the design of long-term care facilities in its March 1, 1963, issue. *Modern Hospital* published a 27-page section on "What Is Needed in Planning for Long-Term Care" in its March, 1960, issue; included among the articles were descriptions of facilities in European countries.

---

[11] By John D. Gerletti, C. C. Crawford, and Donovan J. Perkins. Downey, California, Attending Staff Association. 1961.

[12] Leonard P. Goudy: *Hospitals,* June 16, 1962, pp. 49–50, 140.

Administering the Nursing Home

Awareness of the differences in administering acute hospitals and those rendering long-term care is being shown by inclusion of special sessions on the subject in graduate programs for training hospital administrators. The educational trend against over-specialization in graduate study practically prohibits the setting up of special programs in each health care administration field. No one can predict in exactly which field the student will land, notwithstanding advance plans he may have made. There will be much transferring back and forth by administrators among the different types of institutions. Therefore the graduate programs must be broadened to cover administration of all health facilities, and special instruction given in institutes, postgraduate courses, and field studies. It has been concluded that poor administration is responsible for many of the deficiencies in care that are found in nursing homes. Education of the existing and future administrators is therefore an acute need. Columbia University's special courses offered in New York City and in Chicago in 1961–1963 have set a good pattern for the longer type of program. The American Nursing Home Association and the state associations are also conducting workshops and institutes.

Legislation

Licensing programs for nursing homes started around 1945. The American Nursing Home Association has encouraged state licensing agencies to strengthen their regulations. Many states, however, still limit their rules to physical factors. These are important in view of the many tragic fires in nursing homes, but other considerations having to do with quality of care should be included.

At the federal level legislation is helping greatly to improve the quality of care, partly through focusing attention on the long-term care facility. The Community Health Services and Facilities Act of 1961 provided substantial financial aid. The Kerr-Mills program for medical services to the aged inaugurated in 1960 mentioned "skilled nursing home services" as one of the types of medical assistance to be provided. Proprietary nursing homes are eligible for federal aid on construction loans made through the Small Business Administration. Federally guaranteed mortgages may be obtained by proprietary nursing homes which are unable to obtain commercial help.

HOMES FOR THE AGING

Hospitals that do not have homes for the aging directly under their control or closely affiliated have an obligation to acquaint themselves thoroughly with the facilities in their communities so they can refer patients to them in accordance with individual circumstances. Since few homes have facilities and personnel for all types of illness, hospitals should also establish relationships so that patients can readily be referred to them from the homes.

Care of the aged is a problem that looms large in the civic consciousness these days, stimulated by federal government and social agency concern and publicity. A general view of the accommodations is depressing from the standpoints of both quality and quantity. Performance falls so far short of promises in many instances that action is sorely needed to protect a group that is unable to protect itself.

The big problem is the high cost of providing good care. Unpredictable to both the home and the individual is the extent of medical service that the person who comes in well is going to need in the future. In order to provide for all contingencies the home should be, besides a hotel, an institution for the chronically ill, a rehabilitation center, a recreational facility, and a hospital for the mentally as well as the physically ill. The scope of service implied in this concept is leading some authorities to feel that there would be advantages in admitting patients of all ages to certain of the facilities and that segregation of the aged may not be the best answer to the problem.

The new thinking stems from the fact that so much can be done nowadays in rehabilitating the chronically ill of any age. Not until the outlook is hopeless is it necessary to keep the patient in bed and give full hospital care.

Day Resident Plans

A few homes for the aged have established day resident plans. Under these plans older residents of the community are given the advantages of the facilities of the institution from early morning until departure to their homes at night. They receive three meals and are under supervision. Medical and nursing care are available when needed.

The day resident plan is a preventive plan in two ways: it prevents deterioration of the resident by giving him stimulation and social life; it prevents over-construction of homes for the aged by keeping aged persons in their own homes or those of their children or other friends and relatives.

The Orthodox Jewish Home for the Aged, Chicago, established in 1899, instituted its day care program in 1948. In 1956 it invited a Golden Age group to affiliate with the home and to hold its meetings and socials there. In the same year it introduced a sheltered workshop.

The executive director of this home, Jacob G. Gold, endorses a hotel-like operation, called a club-residence, for persons who like to retain their independence. He sympathizes with the resistance to entering a home because of its "closed-end" nature. After the probation period, the resident must stay there until he dies. The club-residence idea offers registration for a day, a week, a month, or any longer period the person wishes. It can be terminated at his desire. When such a facility is an auxiliary to a home, patients can be transferred back and forth. The club-residence offers a social atmosphere not obtainable in a regular hotel patronized by aged persons.[13]

National Association of Non-Profit Homes for the Aged

Hopeful signs for improvement of care are the formation of organizations for the exchange of experiences and the setting of standards. In November, 1961, an organizational conference was held for a National Association of Non-Profit Homes for the Aged. Among organizations represented in the group that attended were the National Council on the Aging, the National Conference of Catholic Charities, American Association of Homes for the Aged, the Federal Council on Aging, the National Association of Jewish Homes for the Aged, and the Division on Aging of the Federation of Protestant Welfare Agencies.

A few of the problems facing nonprofit homes were discussed, among them the general lack of understanding of the purpose, role, and function, as distinguished from nursing homes. Another problem was the lack of any "central spokesmanship" through which influence could be brought to bear upon local, state, or national legislation. A third problem was need for a channel through which nonprofit homes could "come together around important operating and other problems facing them every day, such as guides for standards of care; sources for training personnel; unresolved problems in relation to senile patients; the role of social work; rehabilitation services; relationship to the community and to government and voluntary agencies at every level."

Membership in the new association is open to two representatives, one board member and one staff, from each institution, and to representatives of national, regional, state, or local associations of nonprofit and/or governmental homes. The latter are organized in a standing committee or council, and each organization is entitled to one vote. There is also an associate membership for doctors, social workers, lay persons, and others serving homes for the aged. The association is administered through the National Council on the Aging.

As one speaker at the November, 1961, conference said, homes for the aged are undergoing a transition because of the rapidly increasing number of persons over 65 in the community. Whereas traditionally "most homes have admitted only the relatively well older person who was capable of a maximum degree of self-care and independence and have provided care and services for the remaining lifetime of this type resident" simply being places where the older person retires and lives out his life "as comfortably as possible in a sheltered and protective environment," today most applicants are "already in need of some one or more of the supportive and/or protective services that institutionalization in this enlightened era might properly imply. The overwhelming extension of the average

---

[13] Condensed from material prepared for a field visit by students in hospital administration from Northwestern University.

life span has resulted in many more handicapped, many more with varying degrees of disability, and many more chronically ill among the elderly than formerly."[14]

There are nearly 3,000 nonprofit voluntary and governmental homes for the aging in the United States.

Varying Patterns of Care

The Charitable Research Foundation, Inc., of Wilmington, Delaware, after a two-year study conducted by Booz, Allen and Hamilton, management consultants, published in 1959, with a second printing in November, 1962, *Effective Standards for Institutional Care of the Infirm Aged*. The 271-page report is in three parts: (1) Nature of the Problem; (2) Standards of Adequate Care; (3) Implementing an Adequate Program of Care. In a section on integration of services for care of the aged the statement is made:

> The most economical way to provide adequate institutional services with competent personnel is to organize a facility that combines the services of (1) the acute hospital, (2) the chronic hospital, (3) the nursing home, (4) the old age home and (5) home care. The savings that make this the most economical approach of all arise from the opportunities afforded to integrate common services when these operations are combined.

It is further stated that "an institution offering integrated services provides substantial advantages to patients . . . greater efficiency of operations . . . and economies in design and capital cost of facilities." Disadvantages are listed also; among them, that "the fully integrated institution is feasible only in a few of the large cities," that there may in some cases be extra costs, and that an institutionalized environment of this scope might be extremely distasteful to some people.

Complete hospital facilities in a separate building are provided residents of the Mary Manning Walsh Home, New York City, operated by the Catholic Order of the Carmelite Sisters. Every kind of special care is given, including physical medicine and rehabilitation, psychiatry, psychology, neurology, ophthalmology, and dentistry. No resident need be referred elsewhere, although he may if he prefers use the services of his personal physician. This home requires no down payment nor turning over of capital funds and, for those who can afford to pay, the charge is $150 a month. In an article entitled "Who Has More Fun Than Old People?" Raymond P. Sloan described the home.[15]

The Home for Aged and Infirm Hebrews of New York is accredited as a hospital by the joint commission. It has some 40 physicians on its medical staff. Eight people compose the resident staff. The home has two main centers, two apartment residences, and also serves an extramural care group. For ward and out-

---

[14] From a copy of a talk by Hobart C. Jackson, administrator of Stephen Smith Home for the Aged, Philadelphia, prepared for the National Council on the Aging Organizational Conference for a National Association of Non-Profit Homes, November 28, 1961.

[15] *Mod. Hosp.*, January, 1957, pp. 69–150.

patient care, relations are maintained with four general hospitals. Transfers to these hospitals are for ophthalmological services, general surgery, urological services, orthopedic services, specialized diagnostic and therapeutic services, and electric shock therapy. The physicians on the staff of the home do some of the surgery through their general hospital appointments. Convalescent care and rehabilitation are usually provided in the home or its infirmaries. Visits of residents in the home to outpatient clinics in the four hospitals average less than one-sixth of those to clinics at the home itself and to the offices of the home's consultants.[16]

Beth Israel Hospital and Home Society, Denver, Colorado, has found that today the average person who seeks admission to the home for the aged

> . . . presents evidence of multiple disease entities, which are virtually "sticks of dynamite" that could explode into acute disease flare-ups at the least provocation. Because of Beth Israel's unique structural and functional relationship which provides a home for the aged and an acute general hospital on the same grounds, we have had the opportunity of adopting a preventive medical program. . . . The annual medical evaluation of our entire resident population as of June 30, 1960, disclosed an increasing incidence of chronic diseases. Of the 72 residents, whose average age was 81.2 years, 58 were ambulatory and resided in the home for the aged building and the balance of 14 were patients in the chronic disease section of the hospital. The latter group, due to crippling conditions, such as complete paralysis, degenerative disease processes, etc., are bedfast residents of the chronic disease section and have been transferred to this unit because of their need for more intensive care. Of the 58 in the ambulant section, there were none that were devoid of any disease process. . . . The mean average was four per resident.[17]

Willamette View Manor, eight miles south of Portland, Oregon, is a nonprofit cooperative apartment house project for the retired which includes a hospital with infirmary wings. Infirmary quarters and care entail additional charges; full hospital care a higher rate. Medical insurance covers such charges as major surgery. Many medical services are included in the monthly fee for food, laundry, and maid service.

Two of the homes for the aged under the auspices of the United Church of Christ are the Phoebe Home at Allentown, Pennsylvania, and the Devitt Home at Allenwood, Pennsylvania, which have the same administrator. The first was established in 1903, the second in 1955. The Phoebe Home began as a training school for deaconesses as well as a home for the elderly. It is now the largest home for the aged in the denomination, with capacity for 175 residents, about 100 of whom are usually in the infirmary receiving full nursing service. Nearly 100 persons are usually awaiting admission to the two homes, and this is a common occurrence in all homes for the aged.

Circular design has entered the homes-for-the-aged field. Ohio Presbyterian Homes announced in 1963 plans for a two-million-dollar "Rockynol" home for

---

[16] From an article by Manuel Rodstein, M.D., and Frederic D. Zeman, M.D., condensed in *Hosp. Topics*, May, 1961, from *Am. J. Pub. Health*, December, 1960.

[17] Harry Yaffe, administrator, Beth Israel Hospital and Home Society: A Working Program of Health Care for the Aged. *Hospitals*, September 1, 1961, pp. 58–62.

the aged near Akron, Ohio, to accommodate 158 persons. Two main buildings, both circular, one with four stories, the other with six, will be connected by a one-story entrance, lounge, lobby, and office area.

A trend to convert hotels into nonprofit homes for the aged was reported at the 1963 convention of the American Protestant Hospital Association by an executive of the Pacific Homes Corporation, Los Angeles. This is not as new a trend as it sounds. Without a doubt elderly persons who could afford to pay the rates have always lived in hotels when keeping up homes became too strenuous for them. The new idea is to confine admissions to the retired, which may not be a good idea as there are psychological advantages to mixed-age groups. However, the possibilities of installing special assistive devices, rails, etc., special diets, and perhaps exercising some friendly supervision, will probably be an attraction, besides the promised lower rates.

Focus on the Aging

The White House Conference on the Aging at which the great need for a coordinated program was emphasized was followed up by the American Hospital Association, the American Medical Association, and the American Nursing Home Association. A.H.A. established a new Council on Long-Term Care and approved a "Background Statement on the Role of Hospitals in Long-Term Care" in September, 1962.[18] The American Medical Association announced early in 1963 an eight-point program for helping persons 65 and over who need help, involving:

1. Re-evaluation of attitudes toward the elderly
2. Implementation and revision of the Kerr-Mills Act
3. Changes in income tax laws
4. Continued expansion of health insurance and prepayment plans
5. Realistic retirement policies
6. Increase in nursing home facilities
7. Expansion of community programs for the aged
8. Emphasis on mental health in the aged

Progressive Care for the Aging

The progressive care concept is spreading to homes for the aged. Geriatric programs are becoming more active all the time. Studies and experiments have proved that the rehabilitation possibilities are much greater than most people realize. The discovery makes desirable the sorting of residents according to their requirements. The acutely ill or terminal, the independent but frail, and those who need little or no nursing care should be in separate areas, as should also be those who require rehabilitation or functional restitution.

[18] *Hospitals,* November 16, 1962.

Dr. J. A. MacDonell[19] of Winnipeg (Manitoba) Municipal Hospital states:

The keynote of prevention and treatment is the avoidance of bedfastness. While early ambulation is an accepted practice for the surgical patient, it is an essential for the geriatric patient. The "special approach" necessary in geriatrics is a combination of patience and optimism. Patience is necessary because the recuperative powers of the elderly are slow, and their day-to-day progress may be imperceptible. The optimistic attitude is essential because the patient must feel your conviction that he can and will improve.

MENTAL HEALTH CLINICS

One of the most promising developments in the mental health field is the movement to establish mental health clinics. Many are already in operation. In 1962 the state of Illinois began construction of six community-centered clinics, each to have about 300 beds and special sections for the treatment of alcoholics, geriatric patients, and emotionally disturbed children.

A clinic opened in 1962 at Kelowna was reported by *Canadian Hospitals* to be the first step in the development of regional mental health services in the province of British Columbia, the pattern to include both day hospital and intensive-treatment centers. The Mental Health Services Branch of the Department of Health of British Columbia plans for the clinics to provide professional diagnostic and consultative services to the physicians and agencies of the regions, with teams consisting of psychiatrists, psychologists, social workers, public health nurses, and clerical personnel.

There are around 1,400 outpatient psychiatric clinics in the United States. The first national report on community-oriented services of psychiatric clinics was published in *Public Health Reports* in March, 1961. In this report community mental health service activities were classified by primary purpose into (1) information and education services for the general public; (2) in-service training for professional groups; (3) consultations and conferences with personnel of other agencies concerning emotional problems of individuals served by the agency as well as general mental health problems; and (4) participation in community mental health planning and coordination. The community agencies with which the clinics work are schools, courts, social and welfare agencies, health agencies, medical groups and individual physicians, visitors, and the general public. Services to the patients in the clinics tend to be brief. Some of them are follow-up care clinics attached to state mental hospitals.

REHABILITATION CENTERS AND FACILITIES

Perhaps in no other direction today should the hospital be so closely interrelated with other social institutions and with socially minded citizens as in the rehabilitation movement. The emphasis upon this aspect of patient care being

[19] A Crying Need for Understanding Rehabilitation. *Canad. Hosp.*, January, 1962.

rather new and attracting many zealots, the duplication of effort is tremendous, confusing, and hampering. The logical agency to take the lead in coordination is the hospital, but it has not usually done so. The reasons for this are clear. They are the same ones which keep hospitals from leading any health effort that goes beyond the actual acute hospitalization stage. Hospitals lack the unity which could make them a driving force. If they had the cohesion of such industrial empires as the telephone system—but they probably never will have, so why speculate upon the power they could wield if they did?

The opportunity to help substantially in the rehabilitation effort is therefore to a considerable degree the privilege of the individual hospital, to take advantage of or not as its policies and the interests of its staff may permit. If it stands aside, however, limiting its activity to the procedures which are carried on within its confines, it is shirking its complete obligation to its patients and to society and is foregoing its chance to escape from its historic isolationism.

Government hospitals, particularly those under federal jurisdiction, are working together with respect to rehabilitation, as well as certain other aspects of patient care, rather more closely than is possible for voluntary institutions. In many ways the latter may learn from their work. It was from military hospitals, in fact, that the impetus initially came for concentrated and extended effort to promote rehabilitation.

A few large hospitals can undertake rehabilitation of the severely incapacitated patient clear through to his maximum potential of recovery. Other hospitals and nursing homes must rely upon transfer to special institutions which concentrate upon furnishing rehabilitation service. *All* hospitals and nursing homes should maintain close relationships with such institutions in order to keep abreast of advances. Constantly new procedures are being discovered that make possible rehabilitation of patients with disabilities heretofore deemed impossible to overcome. Evidence of this is supplied by the theme of the eleventh annual workshop of the Association of Rehabilitation Centers, Inc., held November 28 to December 1, 1962, in Boston: "Changing Patterns in Rehabilitation."

The scope of rehabilitation center services is shown by the four major areas covered in this workshop—administration, psychosocial, medical, and vocational services—and by the topics discussed, a few of which were:

Barriers to utilization of center resources
Hospital rehabilitation centers' provision of vocational services
Involving the private physician in a rehabilitation center program
Can centers justify their fee schedules?
Problems with rehabilitation services in an organized home care program
Do hemiplegics benefit from rehabilitation services?
Experiences with spinal cord injuries
Problems in rehabilitation of amputees
Family involvement works two ways
Rehabilitation: a process of weaning without the withdrawal of love
The team approach: cliché or reality

The rehabilitation center in rehabilitating the emotionally disturbed
Obstacles and gaps in the placement of the severely disabled
Effects of government research and demonstration grants on center development

Standards for rehabilitation centers are being developed by the Association of Rehabilitation Centers. Such centers would have been included in the program for accreditation of nursing homes if it had been developed by the Joint Commission on Accreditation of Hospitals. The commission's approved list at the end of 1962 included facilities that had beds for inpatients such as the Rehabilitation Institute of Metropolitan Detroit, the Rehabilitation Institute of Chicago, and the Georgia Warm Springs Foundation.

The A.R.C. has published a *Directory of Rehabilitation Centers* which contains a complete description of each of the 140 member centers, including information on personnel, plant, facilities, and types of patients served.

The modern concept of rehabilitation has grown out of a long and stumbling effort to do things to promote convalescence. The impetus to an active battle against disability has come from scientific advances in treatment. Previously about all that could be done for the patient was to provide pleasant and relaxing surroundings, with some employment of hydrotherapy and limited exercise.

Back in 1640 Hotel Dieu and the Charité Hospital, Paris, were making special provisions for the care of convalescent patients, the former opening in 1645 through the generosity of Monsieur and Madame de Fieubet a convalescent hospital branch, and the latter starting in 1650 a convalescent hospital opened by Madame de Faure. In 1755 John Howard inspected Hotel Dieu at Lyons and reported that there were two large upper rooms, airy and pleasant, named "Chambres de Convalescence" to which were removed patients who were recovering.

In England the first of a series of convalescent homes, conducted for the poor of London, was established in 1844 by the Metropolitan Convalescent Institution of London. In 1875 the Liverpool Convalescent Institution was opened.

Emperor Napoleon III in 1855 decreed the foundation of special hospitals in which convalescent patients of the working classes would be cared for, especially those who had been injured while at work. One of these was founded in the same year at Vincennes, opened in 1857 with 460 beds, enlarged in 1861 to 522 beds. Another was completed at Vesinet, France, in 1859 with 350 beds. In 1867 a 100-bed public convalescent hospital for men, the Asile Sainte-Eugenie, initiated by the Empress Eugenie who gave 200,000 francs, was opened at Lyons. The Vesinet Hospital was renovated and reopened in 1924 after having served as a military hospital during the war; likewise the Vincennes Hospital.

In 1877 St. Luke's Convalescent Home and the Convalescent Home of the Massachusetts General Hospital, Waverley, were opened at Boston. The latter was closed in 1914.

At the beginning of the twentieth century there were 278 recognized convalescent homes in England, of which 13 were connected with the hospitals in

London, and an estimated 20 per cent of patients from English hospitals were sent to these homes. In the United States, however, the value of supervised care during convalescence was practically unrecognized, only 10 per cent of patients of Massachusetts General Hospital being sent to Waverley and other hospitals having little or no resources for transfer of patients needing further care.

After thorough study of the importance of physical and occupational therapy in overcoming disability, the Burke Foundation Hospital for convalescents was opened at White Plains, New York, through the bequest of his entire fortune of several millions by a merchant of New York City who died at the age of 97. The hospital was opened in April, 1915, with 300 beds. It had a receiving station in New York City for the convenience of patients being transferred from affiliated hospitals. The hospital, which is fully accredited, still exists with accommodations for 150 patients.

In the early literature on convalescence there is an emphasis on "fatigue" almost as a disease in itself that with the passing of time has given way to recognition that this is a sign of some other disorder that can be treated. The idea of "rest cures" has been supplanted by activity programs. It is therefore difficult now to draw the line between the convalescent and the rehabilitation center, for the first, in order to be effective in the modern sense, must employ rehabilitation procedures. This applies to the aged as well as to the younger patient. The aim of rehabilitation is to restore the utmost possible ability to live an active life, even though that be limited in some cases to routine self-care. The merely custodial institution for the mentally as well as the physically ill is on the decline, and hope is growing that the term "chronically" ill will pass out of existence before long as did the name "incurable" in connection with certain long-term care institutions.

The medical aspects of rehabilitation were briefly discussed in Chapter 7. The organizational problems of the center that is not connected to a hospital directly are being studied by the Association of Rehabilitation Centers, which was organized in 1954 under the name "Conference of Rehabilitation Centers and Facilities." Sponsoring organizations were the National Society for Crippled Children and Adults and the government's Office of Vocational Rehabilitation. One of the first major projects was publication of *Planning of Rehabilitation Centers*, obtainable from the Government Printing Office. Next, after study of some 75 to 80 major facilities came the publication *Rehabilitation Centers Today*. A later project conducted in cooperation with the National Society was a series of three reports prepared by a research team headed by Basil J. F. Mott entitled (1) *Basic Accounting Procedures for Rehabilitation Centers and Facilities;* (2) *Cost Accounting, Budgeting and Statistical Procedures for Rehabilitation Centers and Facilities;* and (3) *Financing and Operating Rehabilitation Centers and Facilities.* The third one was published in 1960. All are obtainable without charge from the National Society for Crippled Children and Adults, Chicago.

The Association of Rehabilitation Centers operated with a voluntary staff until 1960 when a full-time director was appointed and headquarters established at

Evanston, Illinois. Charles E. Caniff is executive director. The 1963 president was Richard D. Burk, M.D., director of the Ohio Rehabilitation Center of Ohio State University, Columbus, and the president-elect was Sedgwick Mead, M.D., medical director of Kaiser Foundation Rehabilitation Center, Vallejo, California.

Substantial aid has been given the association by the Office of Vocational Rehabilitation. In 1949–1950 this agency conducted a study of comprehensive rehabilitation centers with the assistance, among others, of Dr. Howard A. Rusk, of the Institute of Physical Medicine and Rehabilitation, New York; Dr. Henry H. Kessler, of the Kessler Institute for Rehabilitation, West Orange, New Jersey; and Bell Greve, of the Cleveland Rehabilitation Center. In delineating the needs, the report states:[20]

> A convincing case for establishment of comprehensive centers in adequate number throughout the country is found in their major role in expediting the rehabilitation of the severely disabled. This task has been laid squarely at the door of rehabilitation agencies and if it is to be accomplished then special rehabilitation facilities must be made available. Considerations of human rights and economic and social well-being dictate such a course.

In London, England, there was opened in 1962 the first specially designed social and rehabilitation center for physically handicapped persons. *Canadian Hospital* reported in May, 1962, that this center has a full range of specially planned craft rooms and ancillary accommodation for the use of all kinds of handicapped persons attending rehabilitation courses and clubs. Among the facilities is a fully equipped household unit, including a model kitchen designed to show disabled housewives how to cope with their household tasks. One of the courses is for the newly blind with instruction ranging from mobility training to clay modeling, carpentry, basket work, Braille and Moon-type, Braille shorthand and typing, and switchboard operating. Each week about 250 people attend the center. A permanent exhibition of aids and gadgets for the handicapped and articles made by them is open to the public on the ground floor of the building.

A very special kind of modest but sorely needed rehabilitation project is the "Stroke Clinic" sponsored by the Newton County Heart Council at the little town of Covington, Georgia. It is held twice a month and is free. It meets in the courtroom of the city hall. The 54-bed county hospital is closely involved, having arranged for the training of two staff nurses in the technique of reactivating muscles rendered useless by a stroke. It also selects and gives training to nurses' aides to work with the stroke victims in their homes and at the clinic. Consulting physicians on the heart council directed the medical aspects of the clinic organization. The physicians have become so interested that they have stimulated and helped the setting up of similar clinics in other parts of the state. Homemade devices and equipment keep the costs low.[21]

[20] *Rehabilitation Centers,* Report of the Committee on Rehabilitation Centers, Washington, D.C., Office of Vocational Rehabilitation, 1950, p. 4.

[21] Mrs. W. V. Dickinson and Mrs. Mary Mallard: Georgia Stroke Clinic Helps Patients Help Themselves. *Hospitals,* December 16, 1961, pp. 51–52.

St. Barnabas Hospital, New York, has graduated from the care of the chronically ill stage to a true rehabilitation facility. A significant sign of the improving prospects for the chronic disease patient is the successive name changes of this hospital. It was originally the "Home for Incurables." Then it became the "St. Barnabas Hospital for Chronic Diseases." Now recoveries from so-called chronic diseases are so frequent that the "for Chronic Diseases" is not always used. In May, 1959, the hospital dedicated a new surgical center designed exclusively for chronic disease treatment and research. An especially high success record for treatment of sufferers from Parkinson's disease and other neurological disorders has been achieved by this hospital. St. Barnabas is the oldest voluntary hospital for the care of long-term illness. It was founded in 1866 as a custodial institution caring for 33 patients. It now has 500 beds including the facilities of the affiliated Braker Memorial Home for the Aged. Although a specialized hospital, it has all of the diagnostic and therapeutic facilities of the general hospitals. From an administrative standpoint its operation is very different, with patient stays for months or years and only infrequently for the few days common in the acute hospital. Rehabilitation covers a wide range of activities.

Rehabilitation centers are set up in many different ways. Dr. Rusk's Institute of Physical Medicine and Rehabilitation is part of the New York University Medical Center. The Rehabilitation Institute of Chicago is affiliated with Northwestern University Medical School. The Institute of Physical Medicine and Rehabilitation, Peoria, Illinois, has two branches, one in the Methodist Hospital, the other in the Forest Park Home of St. Francis Hospital. The Detroit Rehabilitation Institute is situated on the grounds of Harper Hospital and is connected with it by a tunnel. Prepared food, laundry, x-ray, pharmacy, pathological, and clinical services are purchased from the hospital, but the institute, like the others, remains an independent organization with its own board and staff.

Canadian Hospital (February, 1961) reported the beginning in 1957 of a rehabilitation center for handicapped Eskimos, situated on Baffin Island, established by the Northern Affairs Department. The center was started to train Eskimos, returning from southern hospitals, to become self-supporting again. Hunting and trapping are strenuous activities, and the Eskimo who has had an illness or injury requiring hospitalization cannot always return to his former way of life. Other employment can be obtained after rehabilitation on the air base or in the new town being built on Frobisher Bay. The Eskimos build their own one-room cottages with lumber supplied by the center.

Many rehabilitation facilities are specialized. Some limit themselves to cerebral palsy, others to cardiac conditions or strokes, hearing or speech disorders, neuroses, poliomyelitis, arthritis, orthopedic cases. A few are sheltered workshops, emphasizing vocational training. The comprehensive center is a combination of every kind of treatment for any disability.

Comprehensive rehabilitation is a long drawn-out process in many instances and is expensive and complicated because so many different kinds of personnel and equipment are involved. As Sister Ann Raymond said in her description of the regional center plan at Billings, Montana:[22]

> The cost of rehabilitation is so prohibitive that without the aid of supporting and contributing agencies, any total rehabilitation program would be doomed to failure. Rehabilitation is not a money-making project. There must be some subsidy or supporting fund, for very few disabled persons can pay for their own rehabilitation. Support must come from nationally affiliated agencies and volunteer groups. In all communities, each of these organizations is distinct, limited by its own directives and organizational structure, and each serves a definite need in the field of rehabilitation. However, no single group has either the capacity or the financial resources to develop a complete service; herein lies the difficulty. Total rehabilitation, regardless of who provides the services, must be *community oriented* rather than *agency centered*. All must work together.

Visiting Nurses

An invaluable service to the sick has been provided for more than 75 years by visiting nurse associations whose members, under direction of the physician, care for patients in their homes. These associations are community agencies set up to supply nursing and ancillary health services, and they are found in most cities of more than 50,000 population. The associations have been responsive to change. Physical therapy, for example, was added in 1926, occupational therapy in 1933, nutrition and mental health in 1938, homemaker service in 1955, and medical and social work consultation in 1956, to the activities of the Detroit Visiting Nurse Association. The Detroit association tried unsuccessfully to gain the cooperation of hospitals in referral plans for some ten years, and then in 1955 took the initiative in organizing a program under a grant from a local foundation. A four-year demonstration aroused physicians and hospital personnel to the need for and value of such a program. Says Emilie G. Sargent, executive director of the Detroit V.N.A.:[23]

> The hospital must supply the bridge to home care. Every hospital has a responsibility to plan for patients needing continued medical and nursing care after discharge. If the patient has a private physician, he, of course, is captain of the planning team. Hospitals set up certain routine procedures which physicians who bring their patients to that hospital must follow. It would seem that a system of planning for the patient who needs continuing care after hospital discharge could be part of such established hospital policy. . . . The nonindigent post-hospital patient can be well cared for in the home by the simpler and less expensive method of a centralized system to refer patients to a community agency, such as the visiting nurse association, which will coordinate with other agencies whose services are needed by the patient.

A tie-in of the type suggested by Miss Sargent is under way in Seattle where the Seattle-King County Visiting Nurse Service, in conjunction with Providence

[22] Plan for a Regional Rehabilitation Center. *Hospitals,* September 1, 1960, p. 37.
[23] Visiting Nurse Service. *Pub. Health Rep.,* December, 1960, pp. 1140–42.

Hospital, is conducting a study on the role of private hospitals in promoting continued nursing care for home-bound patients. The progressive patient-care unit being planned for the proposed new wing of Providence Hospital is the reason for that hospital's particular interest in the project.

As reported in *Hospital Forum,* August, 1962, a visiting nurse is located at the hospital on a part-time basis to assist in selecting dischargees who would qualify for service under the program. Standard rules of the Visiting Nurse Service remain in effect, such as the provision that home nursing care must be ordered by the patient's physician. If the pilot study proves successful, the V.N.A. plans to expand the program to other hospitals.

Hospital Associations

At about the turn of the century there sprang up in the United States an association of hospital superintendents, the first organization in the Western Hemisphere of men whose efforts were devoted to the improvement of hospital conditions. The declared object of the association was the promotion of economy and efficiency in hospital administration. A review of the earlier transactions of this association shows that the hospital superintendents of America were at that time concerned chiefly with the care of buildings and the economical purchase and distribution of supplies. Hospital management was conceived by them to be scarcely more than a form of household administration. How strikingly does this point of view contrast with that of the progressive executive of our day, who, without relinquishing his interest in the problems of internal institutional management, is concerned lest the hospital fail to measure up to the health needs of the community.

S . S . G O L D W A T E R , M . D . [1]

W H A T U N I T Y there is in the hospital world has been achieved mainly through local, national, and international associations. Yet even here, some division of effort has occurred by the formation of special interest groups, such as the American Protestant Hospital Association and the Catholic Hospital Association. While these contribute to cohesion and joint planning toward their specific goals, they inevitably cause some dilution of the strength of the whole front. Nevertheless, they are active and influential, and the hospital picture is far from complete without portraying their evolution and accomplishments, which have been sketched briefly in Chapter 16.

[1] *On Hospitals,* New York, The Macmillan Co., 1947, pp. 4-5.

To a high degree, it is through the associations that the leadership that ensures hospital progress has been and is being developed. Also, they provide the opportunities which champions of specific causes need to get their messages across to the whole field. An outstanding example is the way in which heads of the hospital standardization movement of the American College of Surgeons sought their support in starting the activity, and through cooperation with them helped in their growth and progress.

Dr. W. Douglas Piercey,[2] executive director of the Canadian Hospital Association, has stated succinctly the objectives of associations:

> The basic purpose of a hospital association is to enable hospitals to act collectively on problems of common concern and to carry out in cooperation activities which they cannot undertake so efficiently or economically as individual hospitals or agencies.
> There are many forces in our modern society which almost compel organization for mutual action. The complex culture in which we live has, to a large extent, submerged the voice of the individual person. Because we live in a democracy and believe in this way of life, it is necessary for us to speak as a group and very often to make representations as a group.
> Today, this business of representation is vital to hospitals. It is the only way in which hospitals can be given a voice at provincial and national levels. It is the only effective means by which hospitals can be heard on issues that affect them directly or indirectly. The public expects that those who have a story to tell will develop a means by which to tell it.

The first real sign of an attempt at large-scale coordination among hospitals occurred in 1893. An International Congress of Charities, Correction, and Philanthropy was held that year during the World's Columbian Exposition at Chicago. There for the first time in history, by one of the sections of this Congress, the Section on Hospitals, Dispensaries and Nursing, hospital problems were discussed on an all-encompassing, international scale.

Among the papers presented was one written by Florence Nightingale. Her subject was "Sick Nursing and Health Nursing." In it she declared that the "main object of the whole hospital organization" was "to carry out effectively the orders of the physicians and surgeons with regard to the treatment of patients." She also stated:

> There is no such thing as independence. As far as we are successful, our success lies in combination. . . . The Chicago Exposition is a great combination from all parts of the world to prove the dependence of man on man.

John S. Billings, M.D., Surgeon, U.S. Army, was chairman of the section. In his address on the subject, "The Relations of Hospitals to Public Health," he said:[3]

---

[2] *Canad. Hosp.,* October, 1960, p. 86.
[3] From *Hospitals, Dispensaries and Nursing—Papers and Discussions, International Congress of Charities, Correction and Philanthropy, Section III,* Chicago, June 12–17, 1893. John S. Billings and Henry M. Hurd, eds. Baltimore, The Johns Hopkins Press; London, The Scientific Press, Ltd., 1894.

The business of this section relates to cooperative means for the care of those suffering from disease or injury . . . primarily hospital aid was intended and provided solely for the benefit of the poor—of those who were unable to obtain at their own expense or by their own efforts, proper care in case of sickness; but its field of work has been steadily extending; it now has relations with the interests of almost every class of the community, and its results have greatly modified the methods of treatment of many forms of diseases among the well-to-do classes as well as among the poor.

It is largely by hospital organization and work that skilled physicians, surgeons and nurses are provided for the public; and in the absence of hospitals, their proper and complete training is practically impossible. Each succeeding year more people resort to hospitals and dispensaries for treatment and this is especially the case in the United States. Forty years ago the number of hospital beds in our cities was very small in proportion to the population when compared with the amount of such accommodation in the countries of western Europe, and the demand for such accommodation was also small. People did not go to hospitals if they could help it . . . hospitals were for sick paupers and we did not have many paupers in comparison with European countries. The war of 1861–65 and the great influx of immigrants have produced many changes in public opinion upon these points. . . .

The war taught us how to build and manage hospitals so as to greatly lessen the evils which had previously been connected with them and it also made the great mass of the people familiar with the appearance of and work in hospitals, as they had never been before. . . . The demand is now relatively greater in the United States than it is in Europe.

Dr. Billings quoted the lugubrious thought expressed 250 years earlier by Sir Thomas Browne that he "counted this world not an inn but a hospital, a place not to live in but to die in."

The honorary chairman of the section was Sir Henry Charles Burdett of Birmingham, England, surgeon and general superintendent, Queen's Hospital. He said in part:

At my first visit to Chicago in 1882 I found its largest hospital in such a condition that I felt I must do as I did on a similar occasion in Dublin—return to my country with sealed lips; because I believe that if a correct and literal account had been given of the condition of affairs which I found in it, it would have staggered this city and it certainly would have astonished others.

In an allusion to the surveys of hospitals which were being made under his supervision, Sir Henry said: "The work which we endeavor to do is done in the interest of all hospitals, not in the interest of any individual person at all." His reference here was to the fact that from Chicago his only response to a request for reports for his *Hospitals and Asylums of the World* came from St. Luke's Hospital.

Afterward, in discussing a paper, "Relation of Hospitals to Medical Education," by the secretary of the section, Dr. Henry M. Hurd, superintendent of Johns Hopkins Hospital, Baltimore, Sir Henry said:

Those who are interested in seeing the result of what Dr. Hurd has referred to should certainly go to the hospital at the World's Fair. It is situated between the Fine Arts Building and the Government Building of the United States, and you will find there objects of the greatest interest to everybody who is connected with hospitals. And speaking as a practical man and one who has visited most expositions during the past twenty years, I venture to say fearlessly that the exhibit in that building is the most valuable, as I believe it to be the most interesting, to scientific visitors to this city during the Fair. Dr. Billings has had a great deal to do with that exhibit and you will see there illustrated in the most interesting manner the action of photography and all the other appliances relating to bacteriology and the sciences which are now included in the study of medicine.

Graft, too, was among the aspects of hospital administration reported. In a talk, "The Trustee of the Hospital," Richard Wood of the University of Pennsylvania Hospital, speaking of the Philadelphia Hospital, said:

Its great copper roof, by an act that outdid the carrying away the gates of Gaza by Samson, has, by one of its political superintendents, been stolen and put into his pocket, a feat accomplished by substituting for the copper a tin roof, selling the former as old metal and pocketing several thousand dollars by the trick; this and like performances finally providing the superintendent with free lodging in jail.

Some of the remarks made at the meetings sound astonishingly like those that are being made in the 1960's. For example, speaking on "The Relations of the Medical Staff to the Governing Body," Dr. Edward Cowles, superintendent of McLean Hospital, Somerville, Massachusetts, said:

The management of a hospital is often likened to a business such as that of a manufactory or a mercantile house. It is more than that by having a different human element in it; the special work of the hospital is done by a family, and should be governed with due regard for its domestic unity. The competent head of the household should have training and capacity for conducting the business, and have sole charge of all administrative affairs, under the direction of the governing body.

Because the Johns Hopkins Hospital at Baltimore was so advanced in its planning, a little of its history as recounted by its superintendent, Dr. Hurd, at this congress, is interesting:

In 1873 Johns Hopkins, a retired merchant of Baltimore, placed in the hands of trustees a large sum of money for the erection of a hospital. In a subsequent letter he gave specific directions as to its location and general arrangement. Upon his death the trustees after consultation with many eminent medical men in this country and Europe selected Dr. John S. Billings, Surgeon of the United States Army, to act as their medical adviser in the perfection of plans and the erection of the buildings. The work was commenced in 1875 and the buildings finally completed in 1889. Wards were formally opened for the admission of patients in May, 1889. . . . 310 beds—when completed according to the original plan will be 400 beds.

Upon the opening of the hospital arrangements were made to use a large room in the private ward for an operating room. This arrangement was satisfactory at first when the number of serious operations was comparatively small and its use was infrequent, but a rapid and unprecedented increase in the amount of operative work soon suggested a change. It was accordingly decided in the Spring of 1891 to erect a building to be used exclusively for operative work. . . . Adjoining the operating room is an etherizing room 10 × 12. Communicating with this is a recovery room of the same size.

Who said recovery rooms were a new idea!

Special training for administration was mentioned several times at this 1893 meeting. Especially interesting are the following extracts from a talk, "Trained Nurses as Superintendents of Hospitals," by Miss E. P. Davis, superintendent of the University of Pennsylvania Hospital, who was an honorary vice-chairman of the Hospital Section:

A woman who has taken the training required to fit her to graduate from any of our well organized, well conducted training schools for nurses must, it can easily be seen, have many advantages and therefore be better prepared other things being equal to be the superintendent of a hospital than the man or woman who has little or no hospital experience. . . . I see but one disadvantage to a hospital having a trained nurse for a superintendent and in some instances that may not exist—the total lack of business training. . . . Seeing that trained nurses are taking their places as superintendents it behooves us who are in the work to look to it that they are properly fitted for it. . . . The time has come either to add the necessary business course to the present curriculum of the school, to have an extended term devoted to this course, or a postgraduate course, eligible only to those showing a special inclination or aptitude for the work. Let her not be handicapped by want of preparation, but be fully equipped to do justice to the school from which she graduates, to herself as a woman, and to the people who employ her. . . .

In the nursing subsection there was much talk of organizing a society of nurses. On this subject Edith A. Draper, superintendent of the Illinois Training School, Chicago, said:

Our success for the future depends upon our unity . . . we have as a profession just emerged from infancy and attained our majority, it being 21 years since first an Englishwoman introduced the system of training nurses in this country. A passing tribute to Sister Helen, the first superintendent of Bellevue, would not come amiss now. . . . The plan so ably sketched sometime ago in our nursing periodical through some misfortune has not matured. Whether the time was not propitious or a competent leader not forthcoming or because energy and enthusiasm were lacking or whatever the reason, to the majority of toilers for the sick in this broad land even the name of such an organization is utterly unknown.

We have gathered here from East and West, from far and near, activated by the desire to take part in the World's Exposition, this union of nations, in one vast representation. It would be fitting to commemorate the time by adding our mite to the history of the Exposition and becoming a unit organization, a body of women trained to be of unquestioned benefit to mankind and not lacking in love and sympathy for each other. . . . We represent a number of schools, our English friends are here to give us their experience and advice, the medical fraternity are ready to offer their support and the way seems clear; our combined efforts will truly be crowned with success . . . the standard for membership should be high . . .

Three years later, in 1896, the American Nurses Association was formally organized.

One speaker told of the formation of an organization of hospital administrators in New York City. He was Frederick F. Cook, general agent and organizer of the Hospital Saturday and Sunday Association of New York, who said:

> Recently there has come into existence in New York an association of hospital superintendents which meets frequently for conference upon administration methods and economies, and this practical means to reform is the direct corollary and effort of Hospital Saturday and Sunday methods and influence.

A sort of climax to the congress from a hospital administration standpoint was the following remark by Dr. Billings: "Before the Congress adjourns it is desirable that we should hold a superintendents' meeting with the view to form a superintendents' society."

It is not recorded in the transactions whether or not such a meeting was held or what came of the idea, but certainly the seed was sown. It led to meetings of hospital administrators from time to time thereafter and doubtless was the true origin of the organization meeting that came six years later.

AMERICAN HOSPITAL ASSOCIATION

An epochal date is September 12, 1899, when a group of eight hospital administrators, meeting in the Colonial Hotel at Cleveland, organized the Association of Hospital Superintendents, which thereafter met each year. At the eighth annual meeting on September 18, 1906, at Buffalo, attended by 83 persons, the name "American Hospital Association" was adopted. Sir Henry Burdett was the guest speaker.

The stated objects of the Association were

> . . . to promote the general welfare of the people by the pursuit of such studies and measures as may best increase efficiency and economy in the management, organization, equipment and construction of institutions engaged in the care and treatment of the sick and injured and to aid in procuring the cooperation of all organizations with aims and objects similar to those of this Association.[4]

Starting with the 201 active and 10 honorary members of the Association of Hospital Superintendents prior to 1906, the American Hospital Association by 1913 had 996 active, 15 honorary, and 20 associate members. Among the prominent administrators who served as president in the early days were Daniel D. Test, of the Pennsylvania Hospital, Philadelphia, 1904; Dr. Sigismund S. Goldwater, of Mount Sinai Hospital, New York, 1908; Dr. W. L. Babcock, of Grace

[4] *Bull. Am. Hosp. A.,* Vol. 1, No. 3, October, 1927; Vol. 4, No. 10, October, 1930.

Hospital, Detroit, 1911; Dr. Henry M. Hurd, of Johns Hopkins Hospital, Baltimore, 1912; Dr. F. A. Washburn, of Massachusetts General Hospital, Boston, 1913; Dr. Winford H. Smith, who in 1926 succeeded Dr. Hurd at Johns Hopkins Hospital, 1916; Dr. Andrew R. Warner, of Lakeside Hospital, Cleveland, 1919; Dr. Joseph B. Howland, of Peter Bent Brigham Hospital, Boston, 1920; Dr. Louis B. Baldwin, of University Hospital, Minneapolis, 1921; Dr. George D. O'Hanlon, of Jersey City General Hospital, 1922; Asa S. Bacon, of Presbyterian Hospital, Chicago, 1923; Dr. Malcolm T. MacEachern, of the American College of Surgeons, Chicago, 1924; Eugene S. Gilmore, of Wesley Hospital, Chicago, 1925; and Dr. Arthur C. Bachmeyer, of Cincinnati General Hospital, 1926.

The membership of the association fluctuated somewhat during the war years. In 1918 an institutional membership classification was added with an initial enrollment of 98 hospitals. In 1916 the constitution was changed to provide for recognition of sectional or state associations. The first geographic section accepted was the Ohio Hospital Association in 1920; that association was organized in 1915. (The Hospital Association of Pennsylvania was founded in 1900.) The first local hospital council, Cleveland, was formed in 1916. The second and third geographic sections accepted were the Wisconsin and the Michigan state hospital associations in 1921. Currently there is a hospital association in all 50 states, and 8 regional associations.

In 1917 Dr. MacEachern founded the British Columbia Hospital Association, then the only active association of its kind in Canada. In 1920 the first regional association in Canada was formed, the Western Canada Hospital Association embracing the provinces of Manitoba, Saskatchewan, and British Columbia. In that year the American Hospital Association held its annual meeting in Montreal.

Institutes

Institutes for hospital administrators were started by the American Hospital Association in 1933 under the leadership of Michael Davis, Asa Bacon, and Dr. MacEachern. The first one, consisting of lectures, seminars, and administrative clinics, was held at the University of Chicago from September 18 to October 6, 1933, and attracted more than 200 registrants. A little of the comment on the early institutes intimated that too wide a variation of backgrounds hindered fruitful discussion, and thereafter more care was taken to screen applicants and limit registration to persons with fairly high executive positions. The Chicago institutes were continued annually under A.H.A. sponsorship until 1938 when the American College of Hospital Administrators accepted an invitation to become joint sponsor. It had participated since its organization in 1933. Complete control of the Chicago institute was turned over to the college in 1948.

The association's institute program has ballooned to impressive size and seems to grow each year. The 1964 schedule listed 67 institutes. Some 35 subjects give an idea of the scope, and the groups ranged from administrators' secretaries to volunteer service. Nursing service led in number of institutes, with 12. All nursing institutes were conducted in cooperation with the department of hospital nursing of the National League for Nursing. Among the other institutes of a cooperative nature were dental service, with the American Dental Association; dietary service, with the American Dietetic Association; social service, with the National Association of Social Workers; medical records, with the American Association of Medical Record Librarians; pharmacy, with the American Pharmaceutical Association and the American Society of Hospital Pharmacists; physical therapy, with the American Physical Therapy Association; and occupational therapy, with the American Occupational Therapy Association.[5]

Councils and Committees

The activities of the American Hospital Association are carried on mainly through a coordinating council and eight other councils: Administrative Practice; Association Services; Blue Cross, Financing and Prepayment; Government Relations; Hospital Auxiliaries; Long-Term Care; Professional Practice; and Research and Education. Each of the councils has several committees. The association is also represented on a number of joint committees of other organizations.

Counseling Program and Research and Educational Trust

A counseling program for hospitals was started in 1958 and has been conducted under contract with the Hospital Research and Educational Trust. On-the-scene surveys and counseling are offered to hospitals requesting them.

The project, "Hospital Administrative Services," is financed by a grant from the W. K Kellogg Foundation and is conducted by the Trust as mentioned in Chapter 12. The total Kellogg grant to the Trust is $591,154.82 for the period from February 1, 1959, to June 30, 1965.

The Research and Educational Trust originated in 1944 as an educational trust sponsored by the association to create a fund for encouraging and engaging in professional education and scientific research to improve hospital services. Among the early projects were the studies of the Commission on Hospital Care and the Commission on Financing of Hospital Care. The name was changed in 1957 with no change in aims and purposes, but the trust then began to have its own staff. Up to 1958 grants of more than four million dollars had been received for a variety of research projects. The trust has its own board of governors, consisting of the president, treasurer and secretary of A.H.A., and four representatives from the fields of education, research, industry, and commerce.

[5] Check List for Educational Planning. *Hospitals,* November 1, 1962, pp. 68–72.

Direction and Offices

The American Hospital Association has benefited by having directors who stayed with the organization for many years. Dr. Bert W. Caldwell served from 1928 until his retirement in 1943. His successor, George Bugbee, served for 11 years, leaving to become president of the Health Information Foundation in 1954, since which time Dr. Edwin L. Crosby has been executive director. Dr. Crosby is also vice-president. William Henry Walsh was executive secretary from 1916 to 1928.

The association had its headquarters until January, 1959, in an old school building and adjacent small apartment buildings on Division Street, Chicago. With rapid increase in activities the surroundings became crowded and inefficient. In January, 1959, the association moved to its magnificent new 12-story building on the lake front, occupying ground made available to it by Northwestern University. Space is rented in this building by a few hospital-related organizations such as the American College of Hospital Administrators, the Illinois Hospital Association, and the Chicago Hospital Council.

The Washington Service Bureau of the association, opened in 1942, has its headquarters in Washington, D.C. In 1962 an office was opened in New York City. A West Coast regional office was established in San Francisco in the fall of 1963.

Library and Publications

The Asa S. Bacon Memorial Library has the most comprehensive collection of hospital literature in the world, including more than 15,000 books; complete sets of bound periodicals in the hospital, health, and nursing fields; an extensive file of magazine articles, classified by subject; and collections of hospital annual reports, patient booklets, and hospital bulletins.

Besides its semimonthly journal, *Hospitals,* mentioned in Chapter 19, a monthly journal, *Trustee,* is published for hospital governing boards. More than 50 manuals have been completed and distributed. Monographs are published from time to time.

CANADIAN HOSPITAL ASSOCIATION

The Canadian Medical Association created in 1928 a Department of Hospital Service, with Dr. Harvey Agnew as secretary. Canada at that time had 886 hospitals with some 75,000 beds. Establishment of the department was made possible by a generous grant from the Sun Life Assurance Company. The aim was to stimulate the interest of the doctor in the general and nonprofessional problems of the hospital. A section of the *Canadian Medical Association Journal* was allotted to the hospital department.[6]

In 1931 the department became associated, although remaining a separate organization, with the newly created Canadian Hospital Council, a federation of the provincial and regional hospital associations of Canada. Also associated in the membership of the council were the Federal Department of Health and the health departments of the various provinces. The Hospital Service Department of the medical association gave personal assistance and office space, and Dr. Agnew, its secretary, became also secretary of the Council. *Canadian Hospital*, which had been founded in 1924 by Charles A. Edwards as *Hospital Buying*, became the official journal of the council in 1935, Mr. Edwards remaining with the publication as business manager. He retired in 1964.

In 1939 the council and the Ontario Hospital Association were hosts to the American Hospital Association convention in Toronto. Preparations had also been made for holding the International Hospital Congress simultaneously, but they had to be canceled at the last minute because of the war.

The Canadian Medical Association discontinued its hospital department in 1945 and the council took over most of its activities. The name was changed in 1953 to Canadian Hospital Association.

Although provincial associations began in British Columbia and Saskatchewan in 1917, the Quebec Hospital Association held its first convention in 1959. Previously in that province, because of the varied cultural and religious backgrounds, there had been several organizations with overlapping memberships. Another unifying event occurred in the same province in 1962 when the newly formed Catholic Hospital Association of Quebec replaced the Comité des Hôpitaux du Québec, the Montreal Conference, and the Quebec Conference. The school of hospital administration conducted by the Comité since 1948 is now integrated with the Catholic Hospital Association of Quebec. Both the latter and the Quebec Hospital Association are members of the Canadian Hospital Association.

On the local level, the first regional hospital council in Canada was organized in 1955 by 12 hospitals in southwest Saskatchewan.

In Canada it is agreed that the hospital associations have greater opportunity than ever before to serve their members through coordinating efforts to preserve the autonomy of hospitals under the Hospital Insurance and Diagnostic Services Act enacted by the federal parliament in April, 1957, and followed by the establishment of hospital insurance plans in all of Canada's provinces. This "opened up a new and certainly not an entirely happy or satisfactory era for those engaged in the actual operations of hospitals," said Chief Judge Nelles V. Buchanan[7] in his presidential address at the 1962 Canadian Hospital Association convention. Judge Buchanan continued:

---

[6] Condensed from the presidential address of Dr. George F. Stephens delivered at the fifth biennial meeting, Toronto, September 22–23, 1939. *Canad. Hosp.*, October, 1939, pp. 11–14.

[7] The Future of Hospital Associations in Canada. *Canad. Hosp.*, July, 1962, pp. 32–34, 64–68.

Though financial difficulties were in part relieved, innumerable new problems were introduced. In the solution of these new problems, hospital associations have acquired a new importance—a role in which they can be of outstanding value or little worth. This is dependent upon the realization by hospital people that in this period while insurance plans are being adjusted, changed and pushed into what may well be permanent shape, hospital associations form the most effective arm available. . . . At this moment in hospital history, for any provincial hospital association, this activity outclasses in importance all others combined.

Across the country hospital people are concerned at the direction which government financing of hospitals is taking. If the introduction of hospital insurance plans in all the provinces is to be a boon and not a misfortune, then hospital associations must act. They must plan their actions with care and skill. They must deal with ministers, cabinets, governments and paying authorities, in wise and statesmanlike fashion.

The Canadian Hospital Association has issued a *Guide to Hospital-Government Relations.*

For information on the regular current activities of the association reference is made to an article by its secretary, Dr. W. Douglas Piercey.[8]

AMERICAN COLLEGE OF SURGEONS

The American College of Surgeons belongs in the hospital organization picture by virtue of its initiation of the great reform movement for hospitals, hospital standardization. Its other activities have been sketched in several sections of these studies.

A meeting which served as the springboard for action was held at Chicago, October 19–20, 1917. It was a joint session of the international, state, and provincial committees on standards which had been formed by the college, and some 60 leading hospital superintendents.

The outcome of the conference in general terms was reported in the 1917 *Bulletin* of the college as follows:

First, the idea of organized standardization advanced among those present from a mere intellectual conception into real enthusiasm.

Second, the interest in the project was shared by hospital administrators, whether they came from little hospitals or from great hospitals, as well as by physicians and surgeons.

Third, the proper care of the patient was, throughout all of the papers and discussions, held as the test of efficiency in the standardization program. The hospital is for the patient; it is for his convalescence and complete recovery from illness. The right sort of care of the patient, it was emphasized, could be provided in a small hospital as well as in a great hospital.

Fourth, time and time again the need of closer cooperation between hospital staffs and hospital trustees was urged, and the need also of strong administrative authority.

Fifth, firmness in all procedure and quick action were judged fundamental to successful policy.

[8] Appendix 2, *Modern Concepts of Hospital Administration,* edited by Joseph Karlton Owen and published by W. B. Saunders Company, Philadelphia, 1962, pp. 792–94.

The establishment of a standard was the first need. John G. Bowman, director of the college (later the chancellor of the University of Pittsburgh, deceased 1963), drew up the Minimum Standard for Hospitals in 1918. Hawthorne Daniel, a writer who was assigned by *World's Work* to describe hospital standardization, said of the standard in his article published in the June, 1920, issue:

> The statement is simplicity itself, and yet, with all of its simplicity it contains just the suggestions that go to make good hospitals of mediocre ones; just the suggestions that lead to the conservation of lives and the elimination of unnecessary operations; just the suggestions that bring about the conscientious care that every patient in every hospital has a right to expect.

A bulletin entitled "Standard of Efficiency for the First Hospital Survey" was published and distributed by the college to hospitals and the fellows in March, 1918. A quotation from the introduction follows:

> As a people we are accustomed to hospital service; we look upon that service no longer as a luxury which we may buy, but rather as an inherent right. The humblest patient is entitled to the best of medical service. In the last twenty years especially this idea has taken hold of us. We regard the right to health today much as we regard the right to life. It follows now that in so far as the right to health is a right of society, all hospitals in a broad sense are public service institutions. On the one hand, hospitals in which sound honest care is given patients may reasonably ask the confidence, good will, and support of their communities; on the other, all hospitals are accountable to the public for their degree of success. By general consent the time has come for an accounting on both sides of the equation. Such an accounting is inevitable. If the initiative is not taken by the medical profession, it will be taken by the lay public; and this entire accounting is what we mean by Hospital Standardization. It is an analysis of the obligation of the public to support hospitals; and it is a practical accounting to the public of the business and scientific efficiency of hospitals.

Field representatives visited 671 hospitals of 100 beds or more in the United States and Canada in 1918 and 1919, while a crusade was led by Director General Franklin H. Martin, Director Bowman, and Rev. Charles Moulinier, S.J., founder of the Catholic Hospital Association. Of these 671 hospitals, 89 were approved as meeting the Minimum Standard in 1918—but the report and the list, which were to have been released in October, 1919, were burned because too many important hospitals failed to meet the requirements, and altogether the results of the survey would have had terrific repercussions from the public. Now nobody knows which hospitals were among the 89 approved.

The surveys and the campaign went on with renewed vigor. By 1919 the College could list 198 hospitals as approved. In the same *World's Work* article mentioned previously, published in June, 1920, Mr. Daniel stated:

> From coast to coast the idea is changing the conditions in hospitals. Everywhere there is the ferment of development, the activity of improvement. In great centers of medical affairs the changes have been startling. In Baltimore, the greatest center of medicine in America, there is not a hospital of 100 beds or more that has not put into effective operation the Minimum Standard.

In New York and other cities the hospitals have made almost as great an advance. The world of the hospital is changing. An advance normally to be expected in twenty years has come in three. For this opinion I am indebted to President Henry E. Pritchett of the Carnegie Foundation.

The Carnegie Foundation had made a grant of $105,000 for the inauguration of the program. This was the only outside fund ever received by the college for hospital standardization. Time, energy, and funds were poured into the program in a spirit of service to hospitals, to the medical profession, to hospital personnel, and above all to hospital patients.

The American Hospital Association had endorsed the program in 1916 and appointed a committee to cooperate in its launching and conduct. The Catholic Hospital Association through its officers and His Eminence, James Cardinal Gibbons, endorsed the program on January 11, 1917, and offered to aid in the work. The American Protestant Hospital Association likewise gave its official endorsement as did also the Board of Hospitals and Homes of the Methodist Episcopal Church, and the Baptist hospitals.

By 1922 a total of 1,012 general hospitals of 50 or more beds had been approved, an accomplishment that was a result of an intensive educational campaign throughout the United States and Canada.

On June 1, 1922, a physician who had been superintendent of Vancouver General Hospital, British Columbia, was appointed associate director for Canadian activities of the college, and joined the crusaders for hospital standardization. In August of the following year this physician, Dr. Malcolm T. MacEachern, was appointed director of hospital activities. Through his leadership in this great hospital reform movement he came to be known internationally as "Mr. Hospital."

In the year 1923, out of 1,786 hospitals surveyed, 1,181 or 66.1 per cent were approved. Twenty years later the number surveyed had grown to 3,900 of which 2,963 or 76 per cent were approved. As of December 31, 1951, approved hospitals totaled 3,352, of which number 2,991 were fully approved and 361 provisionally approved, in the United States, Canada, and a few other countries. Hospitals under consideration for approval in 1951 numbered 4,111. Surveys were never made except upon request by the hospital, the activity having been entirely on a voluntary basis.

The 1951 approved list was the last one issued by the college. The transfer of the hospital activity to the Joint Commission on Accreditation of Hospitals, and the reasons for the change, were summarized as follows in the March, 1952, *Bulletin* of the college:

> This year the American College of Surgeons brings to an end an era of primary responsibility for establishing and maintaining the standards of the nation's general hospitals. Henceforth, the Joint Commission on Accreditation of Hospitals will conduct the hospital program initiated and developed by the College. This cooperative arrangement automatically broadens the scope of the hospital standardization work already under way and opens up new fields.

Tentatively, the date set for formally transferring the program to the Commission is June 30, 1952. . . . The problems of transition will be somewhat alleviated by the fact that the Commission has agreed to accept as its initial list the roster of hospitals furnished by the American College of Surgeons. Essentially, this roster will consist of those hospitals listed in this issue of the Bulletin with the exception of any changes which may be made between now and the time the Commission assumes this responsibility.

Dr. Gunnar Gundersen, of La Crosse, is chairman of the Joint Commission, and the member organizations . . . are: American College of Physicians, American College of Surgeons, American Hospital Association, American Medical Association, Canadian Medical Association. . . .

In 1950 the College, recognizing that not only surgeons but also other members of the hospital medical and administrative staffs should participate in an approval program for hospitals and share the burden of the expense entailed, upon its own initiative broached the subject of sharing this responsibility to the organizations listed above. In 1951 these member groups arrived at an agreement acceptable to their respective governing boards.

The Joint Commission on Accreditation of Hospitals took over the program as planned in 1952.

JOINT COMMISSION ON ACCREDITATION OF HOSPITALS

Although its leadership historically and currently is predominantly medical, the approval and accreditation activity is concerned with hospitals, and the Joint Commission on Accreditation of Hospitals may properly be classified as a hospital organization. Its primary consideration, however, is the quality of medical care that is being rendered in the hospital, with recognition that able administration, qualified personnel, a good and safe physical plant, and adequate up-to-date equipment are important factors that affect service to patients. No question appears on the questionnaire form about financial affairs, nor does the surveyor report on this subject. The patient and what happens to him are the foci of attention.

The official ceremony of conveyance of the hospital standardization program from the American College of Surgeons to the Joint Commission on Accreditation of Hospitals was held on December 6, 1952, in the college's John B. Murphy Auditorium, with the Honorable Lister Hill, United States Senator from Alabama, delivering the main address. Senator Hill emphasized that for 35 years the college had "labored for the program of accreditation. It is apparent how great is the power over hospitals that lies in the administration of the program. The American College of Surgeons has never usurped this power in its own interest; rather, it has used it again and again in the interest of the public."

This ceremony was the culmination of activity begun in October, 1950, when the college started discussions of a joint program with representatives of the American Hospital Association, the American Medical Association, and the

1. That physicians and surgeons privileged to practice in the hospital be organized as a definite medical staff. Such organization has nothing to do with the question as to whether the hospital is open or closed, nor need it affect the various existing types of medical staff organization. The word *staff* is here defined as the group of doctors who practice in the hospital inclusive of all groups, such as the active medical staff, the associate medical staff, and the courtesy medical staff.

2. That membership upon the medical staff be restricted to physicians and surgeons who are (a) graduates of medicine of approved medical schools, with the degree of Doctor of Medicine, in good standing, and legally licensed to practice in their respective states or provinces; (b) competent in their respective fields; and (c) worthy in character and in matters of professional ethics; that in this latter connection the practice of the division of fees, under any guise whatsoever, be prohibited.

3. That the medical staff initiate and, with the approval of the governing board of the hospital, adopt rules, regulations, and policies governing the professional work of the hospital; that these rules, regulations, and policies specifically provide (a) that medical staff meetings be held at least once each month; (b) that the medical staff review and analyze at regular intervals their clinical experience in the various departments of the hospital, such as medicine, surgery, obstetrics, and the other specialties; the medical records of patients, free and pay, to be the basis for such review and analysis.

4. That accurate and complete medical records be written for all patients and filed in an accessible manner in the hospital, a complete medical record being one which includes identification data; complaint; personal and family history; history of present illness; physical examination; special examinations, such as consultations, clinical laboratory, x-ray, and other examinations; provisional or working diagnosis; medical or surgical treatment; gross and microscopical pathological findings; progress notes; final diagnosis; condition on discharge; follow-up; and, in case of death, autopsy findings.

5. That diagnostic and therapeutic facilities under competent medical supervision be available for the study, diagnosis, and treatment of patients, these to include at least (a) a clinical laboratory providing chemical, bacteriological, serological, and pathological services; (b) an x-ray department providing radiographic and fluoroscopic services.

---

[9] From the *Manual of Hospital Standardization,* American College of Surgeons, 1948.

American College of Physicians, informing them that it was prepared to "solicit from its membership additional support to strengthen and improve its standardization program and to conduct it permanently if a better plan could not be developed."

Several conferences were held afterward by the 20-member interim committee appointed at the first meeting. About a year later the committee reported with recommendations for the commission's organizational structure and suggestion that the Canadian Medical Association be invited to participate. The invitation was extended and accepted.

The commission was incorporated on December 15, 1951. Under the initial corporate structure each of the colleges had 3 votes, the American Hospital Association had 7, the American Medical Association 6, and the Canadian Medical Association 1. When the Canadian group withdrew in 1958 to conduct its own program, the American Medical Association vote was raised to 7. The Board of Commissioners consists of 20 representatives of the constituent organizations in the same ratio as the votes.

The first chairman of the Board of Commissioners was Dr. Gunnar Gundersen, of the American Medical Association; the vice-chairman, Dr. LeRoy H. Sloan, of the American College of Physicians; the treasurer, Stuart K. Hummel, of the American Hospital Association. Dr. Edwin L. Crosby, formerly administrator of Johns Hopkins Hospital, had been appointed executive director of the commission and also served as secretary of the commission. Upon his appointment as director of the American Hospital Association in 1954, he was succeeded by Dr. Kenneth B. Babcock, formerly director of Grace Hospital, Detroit, and a Fellow of the American College of Surgeons.

The beginning of the joint commission's activity was eased by acceptance for accreditation in 1953 of all hospitals which were fully approved by the American College of Surgeons, with accreditation continued until an inspection of the hospital could be made under the commission program. Also accepted for use as a basis of approval of hospitals were the standards and the point rating system developed by the college, with the understanding that changes were to be made when indicated. The hospital files of the college with their wealth of information were turned over to the commission. Also adopted was the agreement between the college and the American Psychiatric Association for surveys of mental hospitals, with the commission continuing to survey psychiatric units of general hospitals on the basis of standards established by the psychiatric association. The latter was to evaluate surveys made under the commission auspices of public and private mental hospitals, and the commission was to be the accrediting agency.

The standards are being revised from time to time. A revised *Manual of Hospital Accreditation* and *Accreditation References* were substituted for the *Manual of Hospital Standardization,* and periodically adjustments of criteria are made to conform with advances in practices, policies, and thinking in the medical and hospital fields. It is imperative that every administrator and prospective administrator of medical services of any kind keep himself informed of the commission's pronouncements.

The surveyors of the joint commission are in the direct employ of the commission. Hospitals are scheduled for survey, and following the survey, the findings of the surveyors are submitted directly to the commission for evaluation and subsequent action. Each surveyor submits a written report on each hospital that he surveys. This report is reviewed and evaluated by staff at the commission. The staff synopsizes the report and submits it to the commissioners, who review the recommendations of the surveyor and of the staff, and then assign accreditation for three years, accreditation for one year, or nonaccreditation to the hospital. The hospital is then notified of this fact and is sent a complete list of recommendations and comments concerning the findings.

Essentially the spirit of the accreditation program is the same as that of hospital standardization, strengthened by the joint support of four organizations. The formal inclusion of the association representing hospitals is significant. Dr. Crosby, in the first issue of the Commission's *Bulletin* in November, 1952, expressed the feeling in this way:

> ... The Joint Commission on Accreditation of Hospitals has a great heritage— taking over the work of the American College of Surgeons that has been so capably handled by Dr. Malcolm T. MacEachern—which we accept with humility, conscientiousness, responsibility and a determination in our hearts to carry on at the same high level established by our predecessor.

Almost immediately the commission was faced with new problems that were arising as a result of changing conditions, and committees were formed to study them. A few of the first were problems of the multiplicity of staff meetings, of the department of general practice, of radiology and fluoroscopy services, of accreditation of mental hospitals, of standards for the dental staff, and of requirements for consultations. Among the changes have been discontinuance of point rating and of provisional accreditation. In place of the latter, accreditation is granted for one year instead of the usual three years and resurvey scheduled the following year.

Up to January 1, 1964, hospitals paid no fee for surveys for approval or accreditation. As of that date the charges became $60 per hospital, plus $1 per bed (exclusive of bassinets) up to 250 beds. This means that the smallest eligible hospital of 25 beds pays $60 plus $25, or a total of $85. A hospital of 250 beds or more pays $60 plus $250, or a total of $310. The four member organizations of the joint commission are continuing to pay the administrative costs of the program, but the charge for the actual survey is now being passed along to the hospital. By 1964 some 4,000 hospitals were accredited.

JOINT COMMISSION ON ACCREDITATION OF HOSPITALS
STANDARDS FOR HOSPITAL ACCREDITATION
(DECEMBER 1, 1960)

Basic Principles

The following basic principles must be followed in order for a hospital to be accredited by the Joint Commission on Accreditation of Hospitals.

I. *Administration*
  A. Governing Body
     The governing body must assume the legal and moral responsibility for the conduct of the hospital as an institution. It is responsible to the patient, the community, and the sponsoring organization.
  B. Physical Plant
     The buildings of the hospital must be constructed, arranged, and maintained to insure the safety of the patient; and must provide facilities for diagnosis and treatment and for special hospital services appropriate to the needs of the community.
  C. The following facilities and services must be maintained:
     1. Dietary
     2. Medical records
     3. Pharmacy or drug room
     4. Clinical pathology and pathological anatomy
     5. Radiology
     6. Emergency care for mass casualties
     7. Medical library
II. *Medical Staff*
     There must be an organized medical staff which is responsible to the patient and to the governing body of the hospital for the quality of all medical care provided patients in the hospital and for the ethical and professional practices of its members.
III. *Nursing*
     There must be a licensed, graduate, registered nurse on duty at all times and graduate nursing service must be available for all patients at all times.

CANADIAN COUNCIL ON HOSPITAL ACCREDITATION

The Canadian Medical Association resigned from the Joint Commission on Accreditation of Hospitals on January 1, 1959, in order to give its full support to the program of the Canadian Council on Hospital Accreditation which was assuming the responsibility of accrediting hospitals in Canada.

Planning for the Canadian program began in 1951 when the Canadian Hospital Council (now the Canadian Hospital Association) declared itself in favor of such an activity. The inaugural meeting of the Canadian Commission on Accreditation was held in 1952, and its work culminated in the incorporation in 1958 of the new council. Its members are the Canadian Medical Association, the Royal College of Physicians and Surgeons of Canada, L'Association des Médecine de Langue Francaise du Canada, and the Canadian Hospital Association. Each organization is entitled to 11 representatives on the board of directors.

The Canadian program has the same goal as that of the Joint Commission on Accreditation of Hospitals in the United States—improved hospital service. One advantage of the separation, which was also one of the main reasons for it, is the conduct of the activity on a bilingual plane. The same standards, survey procedures, and report forms are used, with translation into French for the French-speaking areas. Close liaison between the programs in the United States and in Canada has been established.

In the last year of its operation in Canada, the Joint Commission on Accreditation of Hospitals made 125 surveys. This was increased by the Canadian Council to 134 in 1959 and to 158 in 1960. Accredited hospitals totaled 328 at the end of 1960, compared with the joint commission's total of 323 at the end of 1958.

By 1962, 99 per cent of hospitals with more than 300 beds had achieved the standards, but only 70 per cent of those with 100 to 300 beds, and 16 per cent of those with 25 to 100 beds could be accredited. The Canadian Council announced in 1963 the inclusion of hospitals with less than 25 beds in their surveys.

The Canadian council, in connection with its surveys, renders reports on junior intern training to the Canadian Medical Association and on advanced graduate training to the Royal College of Physicians and Surgeons of Canada.

As a result of the council's solicitation, nine of the ten provinces (as of July, 1961) agreed to give financial support to the council by grants and to claim federal general public health grant funds for this purpose. This financial support is given without any control over the conduct of the program which is completely "voluntary in its origin, its support, its establishment of standards, its visitation of hospitals, and its granting of certificates," in the words of the executive director of the council in his progress report in May, 1961, to the Canadian Hospital Association.

At the inaugural meeting of the council on January 17, 1959, the Canadian minister of national health and welfare said in part: "Hospital accreditation has been a spontaneous effort on the part of the medical profession and hospitals to put their own houses in order—to set their own ideals of service and efficiency and to translate these into practice. They have been their own conscience and watchdog." He praised the Joint Commission on Accreditation of Hospitals for the work it has done in the United States and Canada and for the assistance it rendered in making possible the all-Canada accreditation program.[10]

AMERICAN COLLEGE OF HOSPITAL ADMINISTRATORS

The American College of Hospital Administrators is, for the hospital administrator, the equivalent of the American College of Physicians and the American College of Surgeons for members of the medical profession. It is a

[10] W. I. Taylor: Progress in Hospital Accreditation. *Canad. Hosp.*, July, 1961, p. 74. Dr. Taylor is executive director of the Canadian Council on Hospital Accreditation.

college in the sense of being a status-conferring body by virtue of its restrictive qualifications for membership and its dedication to the continuing education and advancement of its members. In order to attain the highest rank, fellowship, the candidate must progress through the first two stages of nomineeship and membership.

The three types of membership are described as follows in a pamphlet published by the college:

> *Nomineeship* status is granted those persons who have fulfilled all of the requirements for admission to the College.
> (Who is eligible for membership: Men and women engaged in hospital administration as a career in the United States, Canada, and other countries may request membership in the College. The candidate must be in a responsible position in an acceptable hospital either as the administrator, assistant administrator, administrative assistant, or in a post of comparable responsibility. In addition, membership in the College is open to members of the faculty of approved courses in hospital administration.)
> *Membership* is granted to those persons who have been Nominees in good standing in the College for at least two years and who have fulfilled technical requirements for advancement. These requirements include successfully passing both an oral and a written examination and in all other respects complying with the Constitutional provisions for this status.
> *Fellowship* is awarded to men and women who have been Members of the College in good standing for at least *five* years and who have been found technically eligible for advancement to Fellowship by the Credentials Committee of the College. To be eligible for this status, the candidate must have submitted an acceptable Fellowship project. This project may be a thesis, four case reports, a bibliography of four published articles, or any combination of case reports and bibliography totaling four. In addition, he must comply in all other respects with the Constitutional provisions of the College for Fellowship.

Eligibility of candidates for membership is determined by the Credentials Committee of the college. This committee is a specially appointed group of members with fellowship status. It normally meets twice a year. Review and approval of its decisions are made by the Board of Regents, which is the governing body of the college.

The requirements for memberships are specifically defined in the constitution. Primary consideration is given to three factors: education, experience, and position. These factors are described in the same pamphlet previously mentioned.

Admission takes place only once a year at the convocation in the fall, which is held in connection with the annual convention of the American Hospital Association.

Listed in the Articles of Incorporation are the following objectives:

> To elevate the standard of hospital administration.
> To establish a standard of competence for hospital administration.
> To develop and promote standards of education and training for hospital administrators.

To educate hospital trustees and the public to understand that the practice of
hospital administration calls for special training and experience.

To provide a method for conferring Fellowships in hospital administration on
those who have done or are doing noteworthy service in the field of hospital
administration.

Toward the furthering of these objectives the college operates in three major
areas: education, publications, and special services. The first is carried on through
institutes, fellows' seminars, preceptor conferences, regional members' conferences, the annual convocation ceremony, and an annual Congress on Administration. Publications consist of a quarterly journal, *Hospital Administration;* a
monthly newsletter, *ACHA News;* a monthly *Administrator's Digest* "of significant current literature on organization, management, and human relations";
and such books as *Hospitals Visualized,* a manual of questions on all major
phases of hospital operation; *The Administrative Residency in the Hospital,*
a guide to the establishment of a sound administrative residency program; and
A Venture Forward, the official history of the college; other books are in progress. The third major area, special services, is described as follows: "The staff
and facilities of the College are organized to expedite, correlate, and coordinate
special educational projects and research activities directly related to hospital
administration." Recently a Board of Administrative Development was added.

The strong position of the college and its impressive impact on the profession
of hospital administration have been achieved in a relatively short time, since
this "venture" in a new kind of association dates only from the year 1933. Its
rapid progress can be attributed to the fact that leaders thoroughly seasoned in
association work were behind its birth and nurture. In *A Venture Forward*[11]
it is stated in the chapter, "The Charting" that

> Since the late 1920's there had been considerable talk at hospital conventions
> about the obvious need for an organization of hospital administrators. . . . Dr.
> Malcolm T. MacEachern, associate director and director of hospital activities,
> American College of Surgeons, had frequently urged not only the desirability of
> such an organization, but had insisted that its existence was essential to the
> effective management of American hospitals.

In 1932 the president of the American Hospital Association, Paul H. Fesler,
superintendent of Wesley Memorial Hospital, in an address at an association
convention, strongly expressed the need for such an organization, saying in part:
"It is ridiculous to think that men without any training whatsoever are permitted to head institutions responsible for the saving of lives and representing
millions of dollars." Later the same year Matthew O. Foley, editor of *Hospital
Management* and founder of National Hospital Day, discussed the subject with
J. Dewey Lutes, then president of the Chicago and Illinois Hospital Associations
and superintendent of Ravenswood Hospital, Chicago. The latter sought and

[11] *A Venture Forward, a History of the American College of Hospital Administrators,* compiled
under the direction of the history committee by Ira A. Kipnis, Chicago, The College, 1955, p. 7.

instantly received the enthusiastic "and influential" support of Dr. MacEachern, support which was ardently continued for the remaining 24 years of his life. Lutes then met with three Chicago area administrators, Maurice Dubin of Mount Sinai Hospital, Ernest I. Erickson of Augustana Hospital, and Charles A. Wordell of Saint Luke's Hospital, to discuss ways and means of establishing the association, and a plan basically similar to the present one was adopted. Afterward 48 administrators were selected to form the nucleus of the organization, 6 of whom were from Canada. Twelve were physicians.

The next important meeting was held on February 2, 1933, at the offices of the American College of Surgeons with Dr. MacEachern, Lutes, Erickson, Wordell, and Fesler attending. Letters of support from administrators were read. Wordell was appointed chairman of the organizing committee and called a meeting at the Palmer House, Chicago, on February 13, which was attended by 18 administrators and 2 hospital magazine editors. Dr. MacEachern gave the keynote speech, following which a motion to form the organization was adopted unanimously. There was also a unanimous vote for the first officers: Charles A. Wordell, president; Robert E. Neff, first vice-president; Joseph G. Norby, second vice-president; J. Dewey Lutes, director general; Rev. Herman Fritschel, Maurice Dubin, and John Smith forming the executive committee. The constitution and bylaws presented by Dubin were adopted with slight changes.

A list of names for charter membership was submitted and discussed at a meeting on September 10, 1933, in Milwaukee, and a secret credentials committee of five was appointed to pass on the names proposed. Those approved were invited by the secretary to a meeting on September 12. Forty-three fellows and members of the new college out of 70 who had been approved for charter fellowship and 11 for honorary membership attended this first official meeting of members.

In *A Venture Forward* the statement is made:[12]

> The anonymous chairman of the Credentials Committee, and the man who was to remain chairman for many years, was Dr. MacEachern. This gave the College a unique advantage, for no other individual knew so many administrators personally nor was acquainted with the actual administrative conditions in so many hospitals. Consequently, from the first the College was able to select those administrators who were really outstanding and with whom other administrators of integrity would be eager to associate.

The first convocation was held on September 23, 1934, in the Benjamin Franklin Hotel, Philadelphia. John Smith, superintendent of Hahnemann Hospital, Philadelphia, was chairman of local arrangements. By the time the convocation was held there were 100 charter fellows and 16 charter honorary fellows. Some 100 new members were admitted at the convocation. Robert E. Neff, then president, conferred the fellowships, and Dr. Joseph C. Doane gave the convocation address.[13]

[12] *Ibid.*, p.15.
[13] *Bull. Am. Hosp. A.*, July, 1934, p. 72.

The college immediately began to participate with the American Hospital Association in the conduct of institutes and in 1948 took over complete control of the Chicago institute. On a two-week schedule, usually in September, the institute has been continued. A few regional institutes are also conducted.

In the original plans for the institutes, the college function was limited to sponsorship and counseling, programs and other arrangements being left to local associations and the university involved. Length of the institutes varied from a few days to one or two weeks. In 1940 the first inter-American institute was held at San Juan, Puerto Rico. Two were held in 1944, one at Mexico City, the other at Lima, Peru. Canadian institutes were held in 1947, 1948, and 1951. Between 1933 and 1943 some 28 institutes were held which were attended by more than 2,000 persons.

In 1943 the policy was changed by the appointment of a central committee on institutes with responsibility for initiating, organizing, and controlling the institutes, with financing by the college. It was decided that participation by a university was desirable and that cooperation by state and regional hospital associations should be invited.

Advanced institutes have been held following each University of Chicago and a few other institutes since 1950 for specially selected advanced students.

Two-day conferences for residency preceptors have been held each year since 1949.

As a part of the celebration of its twenty-fifth anniversary, the college held its first congress in Chicago in February, 1958; this event proved so successful that it is being continued annually.

Progress of the College

The tribulations and successes of the college, the brink-of-disaster events and the resumption of the upward swing, are vividly told in *A Venture Forward*— "must" reading for administrators and would-be administrators of hospitals —and need no repetition here, except to name some of those, besides the initial planning group, who figured in the story with especially noteworthy contributions. These men and women are prominent among the makers of mid-twentieth-century hospital history.

Gerhard Hartman was appointed assistant to Lutes in 1937, while studying for his Ph.D. degree at the University of Chicago, and soon became full-time executive director except for teaching at the university, serving until 1941. His connection with the A.C.H.A. was the beginning of a brilliant career in the field leading eventually to directorship of the Program in Hospital Administration at the University of Iowa while serving as administrator of the University Hospitals. His successor, Dean Conley, has led the college to a position of unquestioned prestige.

All of the presidents of the college have also been active in the affairs of the

American Hospital Association and in hospital progress in general. In the order of their terms of office they are: Charles A. Wordell, Robert E. Neff, Dr. Fred G. Carter, Dr. Basil C. McLean, Howard E. Bishop, Dr. Robin C. Buerki, James A. Hamilton, Dr. Arthur C. Bachmeyer, Dr. Lucius R. Wilson, Joseph G. Norby, Dr. Robert H. Bishop, Jr., Dr. Claude W. Munger, Dr. Frank R. Bradley, Edgar C. Hayhow, Jessie J. Turnbull, Dr. Wilmar M. Allen, Frank J. Walter, Ernest I. Erickson, Dr. Fraser D. Mooney, Dr. Merrill E. Steele, Dr. Albert C. Kerlikowske, A. J. Swanson, J. Dewey Lutes, Frank S. Groner, Anthony W. Eckert, Ray E. Brown, Melvin L. Sutley, Tol Terrell, Dr. Frank C. Sutton, and Robert W. Bachmeyer.

Other widely known administrators who have directed college activities and helped to shape its policies include John R. Mannix, Dr. Benjamin W. Black, George P. Bugbee, Sister Mary Patricia, Jewell W. Thrasher, Oliver G. Pratt, Amy Beers, Mildred Riese, Grace T. Crafts, Ray Amberg, Mother Loretto Bernard, Clyde L. Sibley, Ada Belle McCleery, Dr. John C. Mackenzie, Guy M. Hanner, and James Russell Clark, among many others.

INTERNATIONAL HOSPITAL FEDERATION

The International Hospital Federation is the successor to the International Hospital Association. This association was formed in Vienna in 1931 by representatives of 23 countries, with the objects of fostering the international exchange of information on hospital work and practice; the promotion of study tours and conferences in various countries; and conducting research in hospital matters. Formal organization followed the holding of the First International Hospital Congress at Atlantic City, New Jersey, June 13-15, 1929. Dr. E. H. L. Corwin, then with the New York Academy of Medicine, had proposed the meeting in 1926 to Dr. Arthur C. Bachmeyer, then president of the American Hospital Association, and Dr. Bachmeyer upon approval of the board appointed a Committee on International Hospital Relations, with Dr. S. S. Goldwater as chairman and Dr. Corwin as secretary.

The A.H.A. committee arranged a meeting in Paris on September 19, 1927, to organize a representative international committee. The result was the election of Dr. René Sand of Belgium as chairman and of Dr. E. H. L. Corwin as secretary general of the executive committee.

The delegates to the congress from the other countries began to arrive in the United States in May, 1929. While gradually assembling, they were shown the hospitals of New York City and Westchester County. The New York Academy of Medicine gave a banquet to all of the foreign delegates on June 5. On June 6 the party left by boat for Boston, thence to Niagara Falls, Montreal, Rochester, Washington, Philadelphia, and Atlantic City, arriving on June 12. In the proceedings of the congress it is stated that "everywhere they were met by the mayors and other dignitaries and also by the local hospital committees."

In Atlantic City in addition to the program of the International Hospital Congress there were joint meetings with the American Hospital Association, whose convention and exhibit were opened immediately following the close of the International Congress. There were also meetings of the various allied societies such as the American Protestant Hospital Association, American Dietetic Association, National League of Nursing Education, American Occupational Therapy Association, Children's Hospital Association of America, and the American Association of Hospital Social Workers. The foreign delegates participated in these meetings both as speakers and listeners. Thirty-five countries sent delegates to the congress.

Included as an appendix in the proceedings of the first congress is the draft of a proposed constitution for an international association submitted by Captain J. E. Stone of England, stipulating headquarters in New York.

Among the resolutions passed was one to organize a second International Hospital Congress to be held at Vienna in 1931. The executive committee was instructed to formulate plans for the organization of a permanent association. In a section of the proceedings headed "Considerations Concerning the Creation of an International Hospital Association," which was presented by the president, M. J. E. Brizon, and the secretary general, M. A. Gouachon of the Hospital Federation of France, is this statement:

> The American Hospital Association, which has rendered so many services to hospitals and showed so much courtesy and kindness to the foreign delegates, will be hailed by all as the agency naturally fitted to discharge the functions of the future International Association. . . . We feel that the headquarters should be in the United States; this choice will not only be a fit compliment to a nation we all esteem, but it will ensure the wholehearted cooperation of every country in the development and success of the International Hospital Association."[14]

This was not to be. At the Vienna Congress in 1931 headquarters were established in Germany, and that is where they were, with a German secretary-treasurer, Dr. Alter, when the second World War began. The congress which was to have been held at Toronto under the presidency of Dr. Malcolm T. MacEachern had to be canceled.

In order to hold the association together as much as possible, a war emergency committee was established at a meeting on November 24, 1939, with W. McAdam Eccles, of England, as chairman. Headquarters were transferred to Switzerland, and Dr. O. Binswanger, president of the Swiss Hospital Association, acted as secretary-treasurer.

As the result of the changed conditions brought about by the war it was resolved to dissolve the association and establish a new organization. This action was approved by the representatives of 12 countries present at a meeting held at Lucerne in 1947, when the name "The International Hospital Federation"

[14] *First International Hospital Congress.* New York, New York Academy of Medicine, 1929, p. 267.

was chosen. Headquarters were established at London, England, with Dr. René Sand, of Belgium, as president and chairman of the provisional executive committee and Captain J. E. Stone of King Edward's Hospital Fund for London as honorary secretary and treasurer.

By 1950 the hospital associations of Australia, Belgium, Denmark, Egypt, Eire, England, France, India, Italy, Jamaica, Northern Ireland, Norway, Scotland, Sweden, Switzerland, and the United States were full members of the federation. Other countries represented among the associate members were Holland, Portugal, and South Africa and among the individual members, Brazil, Canada, Wales, and Ethiopia.

Under the old association, five congresses were held, the last one at Rome. After the war the federation conducted the sixth congress at Amsterdam in 1949 and the seventh congress at Brussels in 1950 under the presidency of Dr. René Sand, then emeritus professor of social medicine at the University of Brussels. In 1953 the eighth congress was held in Church House, London. Subsequent congresses were held in 1957 in Lisbon, 1959 in Edinburgh, 1961 in Venice, and 1963 in Paris. In November, 1962, D. G. Harington Hawes, former deputy secretary of King Edward's Hospital Fund for London, was appointed director general upon the retirement of Captain J. E. Stone.

In those years in which congresses are not held, study tours are organized. The first tour in the United States was conducted in September, 1960. The 1962 tour was in Belgium.

The federation is expanding its activities and conducting a membership drive in the western hemisphere. The Washington Service Bureau of the American Hospital Association is the Pan-American office for the International Hospital Federation, whose American committee is headed by Dr. Robin C. Buerki, executive director of Ford Hospital, Detroit.

Dr. Edwin L. Crosby, vice-president and executive director of the American Hospital Association, was installed as president for a four-year term at the 1963 congress.

The 1965 meeting is scheduled to be held in Stockholm and the 1967 meeting in New York.

INTER-AMERICAN HOSPITAL ASSOCIATION

The Inter-American Hospital Association grew out of an Inter-American Conference of Hospitals held at Atlantic City during an American Hospital Association convention in 1941 and an institute conducted by the American College of Hospital Administrators in Puerto Rico in 1940. The first regional institute sponsored by the association jointly with the Panamerican Sanitary Bureau of the United States was conducted at Mexico City in January, 1944. The association was incorporated in 1945 with Dr. Gustavo Baz, then Secretary of Health and Assistance, of Mexico, as president.

The purpose as stated in the bylaws is

. . . to encourage and maintain a close union among the hospitals of the Americas; promoting and facilitating the interchange of ideas and experiences among those engaged in hospital activities; coordinating all humanitarian efforts for the betterment of hospitals; promoting the improvement of hospital organization and management; establishing programs for the education of hospital personnel, including institutes and conferences; establishing systems for the interchange of technical and professional personnel through fellowship awards; and organizing university courses in hospital administration.

The second institute was held in Lima, Peru, in December, 1944 and the third in Rio de Janeiro, Brazil, in June, 1950. The programs of these early meetings show extensive participation from the United States, including such internationally known hospital leaders as Dr. Arthur C. Bachmeyer, James A. Hamilton, Gerhard Hartman, Dr. Malcolm T. MacEachern, Dr. Robin C. Buerki, and Dr. Edwin L. Crosby.

Under the Latin American program of the American Hospital Association directed by Dr. Jose Gonzalez, an intensive cooperative program has been developed with the Inter-American Hospital Association and the Agency for International Development of the Department of State. Hospital associations have been organized in Latin American countries that previously had none, and others have been strengthened through the accelerated activities, which include the holding of institutes and seminars. An *Inter-American Bulletin of Hospitals (Boletin Interamericano de Hospitales)* in Spanish began publication in February, 1956, by the Latin American program of the A.H.A.

OTHER HOSPITAL OR RELATED ASSOCIATIONS

The very first hospital association in the United States that was national in scope was the Association of Medical Superintendents of American Institutions for the Insane, established in 1844, with an official organ, the *American Journal of Insanity,* first published in the same year. This association during the next thirty years occupied itself with study and formation of guiding principles which at least brought about many improvements in buildings and surroundings for care of the mentally ill. Among the existing hospital associations in the mental health field are the Neurological Hospital Association and the National Association of Private Psychiatric Hospitals. The American Psychiatric Association is, of course, very active in hospital affairs.

Nursing homes are represented in the American Nursing Home Association.

Rehabilitation centers are organized in the Association of Rehabilitation Centers, formerly named the Conference of Rehabilitation Centers and Facilities, Inc.

Osteopathic hospitals are organized in the American Osteopathic Hospital Association, and their administrators have formed an American College of Osteopathic Hospital Administrators.

The International Catholic Confederation of Hospitals has its headquarters at The Hague.

CHAPTER 24

Communities and Publics

Too many populations of different kinds are called communities indiscriminately. . . . What are the common denominators in the concept of communities? Is there always a geographic or ecological base; a common "bonding" element or interest; a clustering of institutions; an interlocking structure; centers of power and an identifiable leadership, etc.? . . . What are the implications of community stratifications and segmentations for the kinds and volume of ailments treated in the hospital? How are the possibilities of "preventive" or "rehabilitative" medicine conditioned by these community factors? Are there grounds for assuming that *what* the hospital may accomplish as an institution and *how* it may do this are substantially determined by the existing community components?

LEO W. SIMMONS[1]

OVERSIMPLIFICATION has been a fault in the general concept of the community, as Dr. Simmons points out. The same thing is true of the concept of the public. There they are out there, a mass of humanity with which to interact. Generally it is thought that the interaction can be accomplished through mass media with a mass approach as if they had one mind and one heart. It is not that easy. There are many communities within the community and many publics within the public. Relationships and communications have to be varied by understanding of the differences. The administrator of a hospital must establish some common ground with the several communities and the

[1] Professor of Sociology, Yale University. Quoted from a talk, Training for Hospital Administration, presented at a meeting of the Association of University Programs in Hospital Administration, Atlanta, December, 1955.

several publics before he can interact well with the community in general. Gradations of culture, of social status, of wealth, enter in, as well as vocational and professional identification and geographic characteristics.

The different communities are not as external, either, as some of them may have been made to appear in these studies. Many of them get inside the hospital as trustees, staff, volunteers, and most of them at some time or other as patients and visitors. A hospital is a public place, a community center. The more the fact of mutual interest is appreciated, the better are the prospects for hospital progress.

Nor are the communities separate and distinct. That should have been obvious in these studies. They have been mixed up, deliberately and unavoidably. There are social-minded doctors and health-minded sociologists. Both get frustrated over the economic problems that they try to do something about. Everybody supposedly has some church connection. Government people get involved in almost everything. They had to be brought into every "community" in these studies. Businessmen, churchmen, and editors are on the boards of educational and welfare institutions. Labor builds apartment houses and becomes a capitalist. Geographically speaking, also, the lines are confused. In cities, mansions are in the same block as tenement houses. In rural areas, luxurious country estates adjoin the shacks of tenant farmers. Yet for the purposes of study and of planning interaction, artificial dividing lines must be assumed.

The general trends in the several communities should be familiar to the administrator. In many respects the future of his own institution is correlated with and governed by them. In this chapter the two most intriguing developments, both demanding and depending upon the support of all of the publics, are discussed. These are *comprehensive medicine* and *regional or area-wide planning*. Neither is new as a concept. A long, slow build-up under different terms is behind them. Disappointment has come to those who promoted the ideas in the past. Both are due for long struggles to achieve any measure of success. It looks, however, as if the time has come, as if both the health field and the public are ready, to push these ideals which really interlock as a single alluring goal.

The Medical Community—Comprehensive Medicine

If there is one trend above all others in the medical community that promises to change hospital-medical relationships for the better, it is the concept of comprehensive medicine. The term is explained as follows:[2]

On occasion medicine consciously incorporates knowledge from areas outside of its own, particularly as this knowledge becomes useful to medicine and

[2] From William A. Steiger, M.D., Francis H. Hoffman, M.D., A. Victor Hansen, M.D., and H. Niebuhr, Ph.D.: A Definition of Comprehensive Medicine. *J. Health and Human Behavior*, summer, 1960, Vol. 1, No. 2. See also Jacob Tuckman, Ph.D., and Alice T. Dashiell: A Mental Health Program for the Later Years. *Pub. Health Rep.*, October, 1959, p. 853.

socially acceptable to it. The last period of integration would appear to coincide with the founding of Johns Hopkins and the initial inclusion of the physical and biological sciences into the medical curriculum. The present day "comprehensiveness" arises out of the incorporation into medical thinking, teaching and practice of the applicable knowledge of dynamic psychiatry, psychology and sociology. Comprehensive medicine, then, is the conviction, born out of experience, that the medical care of patients can be improved now by the utilization of psycho-dynamic knowledge and sociological knowledge, along with the generally available biological skills.

At the Temple University School of Medicine, Philadelphia, is a Comprehensive Medical Clinic supported in part by the Commonwealth Fund and the National Institute of Mental Health. The authors of the article from which the quotation was taken are on its staff. Besides defining what comprehensive medicine *is,* they define what it *is not:*

> Comprehensive medicine is not bringing together into one clinic area a number of biologically (organically) oriented specialists. Such group care may have certain advantages to the patients, to the administration, and to the students, but it is not really a qualitatively different approach to patient care. It is a re-grouping rather than a reorientation. It can be part of a truly comprehensive program but it is not basic to it. Moreover, since it consists largely of a change in clinic geography, it can hardly be expected to induce major changes in student attitudes.

It is pointed out that "although these are always welcome," improved care under the comprehensive medicine concept does not have to await new biological discoveries "but can be achieved by the process of incorporating existing knowledge and skills from psychiatric, behavioral and social sciences." Its most significant feature is declared to be that "it is patient-oriented as opposed to the disease orientation of most of present day medicine."

Lest comprehensive medicine be confused with "traditional psychosomatic medicine with its preoccupation with causality," the authors emphasize these significant differences:

> The primary concern of psychosomatic medicine in a patient with ulcerative colitis has been the causal role of the emotional conflicts (the psychiatric disease) upon the somatic alteration in the bowel (the pathophysiologic disease). Comprehensive medicine prefers to emphasize the view that all areas of the patient that are sick deserve consideration, since we are treating a person, an indivisible unit, regardless of the causal role of the area. This viewpoint allows the physician to assess his patient along several parameters and to decide on the basis of his findings in the particular patient the need for psychotherapy, diet and drugs, surgery or a combination of these. The physician, then, is not excluding indicated therapy because of lack of proof of causality, personal bias or near-total unfamiliarity with one of the techniques of understanding and treating his patient.
>
> We would like to state emphatically, however, that we do not necessarily prescribe a multidimensional workup of every patient, merely for the sake of being comprehensive. Thus the patient with prostatic obstruction and a distended bladder needs a catheter and not an extensive social history. If, however, his anxiety about surgery and its castrating connotations prevents him from getting the

necessary resection, psychiatric understanding and management are indicated. On the other hand, the patient with a complaint in every bodily system needs prompt evaluation of his social and emotional problems and this should not be delayed until every complaint has been tracked down by extensive biological tests. . . .

The educational implications of the comprehensive medicine approach are described as follows:

> What is generally needed to teach this comprehensive understanding of patients at present is a team (internist, pediatrician or gynecologist, psychiatrist, social worker and at times sociologist, psychologist and cultural anthropologist) wherein each team member has relatively equal prestige. Moreover, each team member should be responsible for patient management and should not be allowed the easy disengagement that is characteristic of many consultant-patient relationships. We feel that no apology is necessary for this use of multiple teachers. Certainly if a team of anatomist, biochemist, and physiologist is necessary to teach the cell, teaching about the whole person demands no less. . . .

So the pendulum swings between specialism and comprehensiveness, and the clock will not run properly unless they are equally balanced. The hospital by bringing the two together provides a balancing mechanism, and its administrator may be a key figure in the process by instituting administrative procedures that will encourage the necessary teamwork.

Entering conspicuously into the comprehensive medicine picture is the general practitioner. There is ebb and flow in the attitude toward him, and at present the tide seems to be running high, at the same time that the ratio of doctors entering the field is declining. In 1950 only 18 per cent of the graduating medical school seniors planned to enter general practice; only 2 per cent of residents were in general practice; and only 2 out of 80 medical schools were operating a separate department of general practice. In 1955 the American Medical Association took action and discouraged arbitrary restrictions by hospitals against general practitioners as a group regardless of their qualifications as individuals.

"The general practitioner is the keystone of the medical arch, the support of all the workers in the field," said a member of the Bowman Gray Faculty of Medicine of Wake Forest College, Raleigh, North Carolina, in an article[3] two decades ago. Elaborating upon this assertion, he said:

> We have begun to look upon disease as a comprehensive problem to be solved for the good of the sufferer, and we are learning to lean upon one another for the solution. Fortunately we cannot all be specialists, but it behooves us all, specialists included, to be good doctors. More and more the general practitioner by exclusion is becoming a genuine specialist; he is expected to know a little about everything.

Doubtless the current great emphasis upon geriatrics and gerontology has much to do with the development of the concept of comprehensive medicine as well as with the new focus of attention on general practice. The aged patient is more likely to have a combination of diseases than is the younger person,

---

[3] Hubert A. Royster, M.D.: Unity of Medicine. *J. Bowman Gray School of Med.*, November, 1943.

frequently chronic in nature rather than acute; besides he may be prey to more mental and emotional disturbances. The general practitioner is the logical physician to see him first, at any rate, and perhaps all the way through, and the comprehensive medicine approach is the one that will benefit him most.

A Section on the General Practice of Medicine was established by the American Medical Association in 1945. There are American and Canadian Academies of General Practice. The American academy issues a *Manual on General Practice Departments in Hospitals,* which is revised from time to time.

Of course, every physician, whether he be general practitioner or specialist, is ideally a devotee of comprehensive medicine. A warm light is shed, in a realm beyond the scope of the operating table and scalpel, by this episode in the experience of a founder of the American College of Surgeons, Dr. Robert T. Morris, of Stamford, Connecticut. It is best told in his own words:

> I have never forgotten one case of a great fibroid tumor in which the patient was nearly dead from hemorrhage in advance of the operation. On the following morning she was barely living. Speaking in a low whisper she said, as I bent over close to catch her words, "Doctor, I am dying." She really was dying, but I replied: "Oh, you must not think that, for it will spoil my statistics." This was not heartless levity. It was giving her something to grasp quickly, at a moment when a tear drop in sympathy might have been as fatal as a bullet in its effect. Some months after her recovery, she said one day, "Do you know what saved my life? On the morning when I was barely holding on and everything was nearly a blank, you said if I died it would spoil your statistics, and I determined to make one last effort to live for the sake of your statistics. I was too far gone to care anything about myself—in fact really wanted to die and end it all." This matter of thoughtfulness for others is characteristic of woman.

Dr. Morris said the surgeon should have "a kind of self-deluding helpfulness —a persistence even to the degree of obstinacy—stupid obstinacy to the point that he won't let the patient die." He added, "Firmness is will power, and obstinacy is won't power," and "the surgeon needs both."

The wholistic concept, which is another term for comprehensive medicine, was the subject of part of a thesis[4] by George H. Yeckel, submitted in partial fulfillment of the requirements for his master's degree in hospital administration from Northwestern University in 1958. Extracts from his paper follow.

The Wholistic Concept

GEORGE H. YECKEL

The development of new concepts of mental illness, neurosis, emotional problems, psychosomatic reactions, etc., has effected drastic changes in the operation of psychiatric institutions. These new concepts of personality are also having a profound influence on the general theories of illness and disease which are affecting the functioning of the general hospital. This concept is the wholistic

---

[4] George H. Yeckel: The Changing Role of the Hospital in the Community. (Mr. Yeckel is now associate administrator, St. Luke's Hospital, Kansas City, Missouri.)

concept—the idea that the patient is a whole organism existing in a society and that malfunction in any aspect of his life will have an effect on his whole life. Thus, when a person becomes ill, the *whole* person should be treated, not just the disease, or the organ, or the body, or the psyche, but the entire psycho-socio-biological organism. People today, including physicians, are as intractable and resistant to change as they were in the days of Semmelweis, so these newer ideas are taking hold only slowly, but the trend is there. This concept is one of the major indicators of the direction in which the hospital's role is changing.

Conflict

In many parts of the world today can be seen the evolution of a really human-istic approach to the problems of life, but in the United States, while the seeds of the philosophy are there, the economic system is not compatible with or con-ducive to its growth. One of the major tenets of capitalism is that the indi-vidual is entitled to anything he can buy, and nothing else, and this extends to his health and well-being the same as to any other possession. According to this system everyone has the opportunity, through rugged individualism and hard work, to make enough money to take care of his needs and wants, and if he does not, it is simply because he was not clever enough or did not work hard enough, so he should try again. There are, of course, many reasons why this does not work.

Circumstances over which the individual has no control may affect his earning ability seriously, or perhaps the individual has lost, or has never had, the abilities to struggle ahead in the labor market. These people have been allowed to de-generate into poor excuses for human beings because of the misdirected and erroneous thinking behind the idea of charity as a means of taking care of the unfortunates. Only in recent years has there been effort to restore the individual to some degree of effectiveness, productiveness, or usefulness in his own eyes, through programs of rehabilitation. In today's society it is necessary to "sell" the idea of rehabilitation on a financial-gain basis because many adherents to strong material capitalism do not advocate social programs without some economic gain involved. It almost seems that one must not waste the time and energy to rehabilitate a man just because he is a human being, but it is justifiable only if he can be productive and make someone some money. Fortunately it is possible to show conclusive evidence that rehabilitation does pay off, so this factor is assuming more importance as an influence.

Despite tremendous advances in the technical aspects of medicine, the practice of medicine is basically an art. It is often said that really good medicine is avail-able only to the wealthy and the very poor, but this is not true. The poor do get excellent technical care, but they are usually not recipients of the *art* of the practice of medicine. Charity patients are all too often treated as if indigence were an expression of gross immorality and sin. This is hardly a humanistic approach to life. The large middle class in this country gets more of the art of medicine than the technical, because the technical is quite expensive. The very wealthy get whatever they need and want. This is not a new point of conflict by any means.

What of Tomorrow?

Toynbee[5] says: "The twentieth century will be chiefly remembered not as an age of political conflicts or technical inventions, but as an age in which human society dared to think of the welfare of the whole human race as a practical objective."

The facilities and services of the future are clearly evident in the trends of today, found primarily, though certainly not exclusively, in the large medical centers. These are the centers of intellectual medicine, of probing curiosities, of sensitiveness to the human needs, and it is in this setting that the wholistic concept of human organization and function is being nurtured and put into practice; where life is being extended in years; where new techniques are being devised; and where principles of education become facets of a way of life.

Historically, and even to a great extent today, the role of the hospital has been related to the concept of definitive care of illness, injury, or disease. This concept related the treatment directly to the specific problem or symptom. The wholistic concept, on the other hand, puts the emphasis of approach on the total patient who in some fashion is not functioning adaptively, be that maladaptive behavior related to structural changes (as in injuries), biophysiological disturbances (as in bacterial and viral infection), psychosociologically (as in neurosis), or any other area or combination thereof. It further emphasizes the fact that an injury, illness, or other type of malfunction has an effect on all aspects of the person's life to one degree or another, and the treatment must be geared to the totality.

This concept is resulting in the figurative dissolution of the walls of the hospital, since the care provided must extend beyond its walls into the community life of the patient. This trend is seen most dramatically in the development of modern rehabilitation programs. Rehabilitation has been, and all too often still is, a service that is eventually tacked on long after definitive treatment is concluded, frequently months and sometimes years later. Experience has shown this delay to be inefficient and actually productive of the permanency of disability. The newer approach is to plan the rehabilitative program from the very beginning as a part of the general treatment of the patient. The results of this approach have been rewarding, both financially and personally, to the patient.

The Span of Life Lengthens

What happens when a civilization extends the chronicity of infirmity and increases the span of life beyond its adaptive facility, as we are doing now? The

[5] Arnold J. Toynbee: *A Study of History*. Oxford, England, Oxford University Press, Vol. 10, 1957.

aged require services of a kind not previously found outside the home itself. Since living conditions have changed, with the family unit shrinking to a two-generation unit rather than three or four as once was true, and since children no longer assume responsibility for the care of parents or grandparents, the burden of providing care falls on society. Because of the complications involved in this care, the hospital will be the logical source of the service, in terms of either the actual care or coordination of the services.

The Complications of Diagnoses

Good health care rests on the foundation of completely adequate diagnosis. Within the framework of the wholistic concept, adequate diagnosis necessitates availability of a great many specialists in divers fields, including, for example, medicine, psychiatry, psychology, social work, religion. At present these services are scattered and are often not even available because of lack of trained people or high cost. Tomorrow's hospital will be expected to provide them, just as today's hospital is providing diagnostic x-ray and laboratory facilities.

The Hospital's Newest Role

We move toward the day when hospital administrators must think in terms of total, comprehensive patient health services, and the acute general hospital will function as only one part of the total scheme. In order to promote the best of health care, all of the various services necessary should be available to the various disciplines working with the patient, and the most efficient and effective way of doing this is to provide a central administrative structure within which they may operate.

The health center (instead of hospital, or medical center, both of which will be misnomers) may be departmentalized in terms of such services as general diagnostic, rehabilitation coordinating, therapeutics, with subdivisions more like the present arbitrary divisions: surgery, medicine, psychiatry, physical therapy, etc.

Eventually patients will be categorized in terms of causation rather than on the basis of symptom syndromes, because therapeutics will be more directly related to etiological factors than is now true. Treatment today is too often palliative rather than therapeutic, partly because of ignorance, and partly because of resistance to anything new.

Mr. Yeckel's thesis, and the concept of wholistic or comprehensive medicine, lead naturally to consideration of the movement that shows promise of making possible the application of this philosophy of all-encompassing health care—area-wide or regional planning and operation of hospitals and related health services.

REGIONAL PLANNING

Foremost among the forces that are operating to make hospitals community conscious is the regional planning movement. Before planning can be attempted, the community in all of its aspects must be studied, with complete analysis of all of its health needs.

Another consideration is that hospital planning should be coordinated with general community planning. The exercise of imagination combined with practical good sense in controlling the pattern of growth of urban, suburban, and countryside areas has popularized the idea of checking haphazard development as practiced in the past. Hospitals must work with the over-all planners (when they exist) to fit into the whole-area concept. As the headline on a newspaper article in 1962 expressed it, "Interwork of Group Gains As a Theory." The article was a report on a meeting of 30 regional planners from eight eastern metropolitan areas to consider the problems of a "megalopolis"—the designation for a vast urbanized region running from Boston to Washington, where one-fifth of the nation's population lives, and similar areas.

Hiram Sibley, then director of the division of hospital community resources of the American Hospital Association, now director of the Hospital Planning Council for Metropolitan Chicago, traced the development of the area-wide planning idea in an article.[6] He described seven metropolitan-area programs, those in Columbus, Ohio; Chicago, Illinois; Detroit, Michigan; Rochester, New York; Allegheny County, Pennsylvania; Los Angeles, California; and New York City. He indicated the following common threads: (1) enthusiastic leadership of a trusted public figure; (2) skillful steering by the council's director; (3) the cooperative support of hospitals, related health agencies, health departments, community health and welfare agencies, and county medical societies; (4) some control over the financing, either from Hill-Burton grants, fund raising, or borrowing.

In July, 1961, the report of a two-year study by a joint committee of the American Hospital Association and the Public Health Service, *Areawide Planning for Hospital and Related Health Services,* was published.[7] It set forth goals, guide lines, and principles for organizing and carrying out the functions of a planning agency.

A "Guide to Development of Effective Regional Planning for Hospital Facilities and Services" was issued by the American Hospital Association in 1962.

Twelve grants totaling $1,026,359 for area-wide planning surveys and demonstrations were made to seven agencies by the Public Health Service in 1962 and 1963. The planning agencies which received the grants are in St. Paul, Toledo, Washington (D.C.), Topeka (state-wide), Columbus, Rochester (New York),

---

[6] *Am. J. Pub. Health,* November, 1962; condensed in *Hosp. Topics,* April, 1963.
[7] A digest of the report by George Bugbee was published in *Hospitals,* July 16, 1961.

and Detroit. The grant to the last is for developing and testing a method of measuring the physical and functional obsolescence of existing hospitals. Awards were also given to two state health departments, those of Oregon and Minnesota; to two state hospital associations, in Colorado and Hawaii; and to a hospital council in southern California for establishing planning groups.

The regional plan movement has been nationally organized in the American Association for Hospital Planning.

State-wide Planning

California is one of several states that are engaged in state-wide planning. California enacted a regional planning law in June, 1961. It permits the state advisory hospital council to authorize special regional planning programs for Los Angeles and San Francisco regions and to appoint regional planning committees. Recommendations to the state legislature for the enactment of future laws will be based upon studies of and experience in regional planning over the next few years.

The Wisconsin State Board of Health developed in 1958–1959 a 252-page state plan for hospitals and medical facilities, with a survey of the needs for construction of general, mental, tuberculosis, and chronic disease hospitals; public health and diagnostic and treatment centers; nursing homes; and rehabilitation facilities.

The Department of Health of the Commonwealth of Puerto Rico began a pilot-scale regionalization experiment in health and welfare services in 1956, calling the plan "Operation Regionalization." The method of regionalization starts with community health and welfare centers linked operationally with a central or district hospital, the latter in turn being integrated with a school of medicine and with schools for the disciplines associated with medicine, "to produce the effect that the area is served by one giant hospital with branches geographically distant but functionally as closely related as if they were wards or units of a large medical center."[8]

Metropolitan Area Planning

One of the early area-wide metropolitan plans was that formulated by the Rochester (New York) Hospital Council with the aid of a large grant from the Commonwealth Fund. A report of the first year's experience with its regional hospital plan was published by the council in 1946. The region originally included seven counties in the trading area of Rochester. In this region are a medical school, 6 urban voluntary hospitals, and 17 general hospitals outside of the city. It was predicted in the report that additional counties would be

[8] From the report of the experiment published in 1957. San Juan, Department of Health, Commonwealth of Puerto Rico.

included to coincide with the region established by the Joint Hospital Board of
.the New York State Postwar Public Works Planning Commission, set up
primarily for the allocation of capital funds under the Hill-Burton Act.[9] In
1961 the Council of Rochester Regional Hospitals was reorganized to include
functioning as the official general review and planning body for the area. Under
the reorganization the majority of the board members are representative of the
general public. The council now has 33 member hospitals from 11 counties.

Regional Planning in Canada

In Canada, regional planning is going forward in practically every province
since the government has made funds available for health surveys, and such
surveys are required before certain other funds are available.

Ontario's approach to planning was through the establishment in 1959 of a
government agency, the Ontario Hospital Services Commission. Its chairman,
Dr. R. W. Ian Urquhart, described the plan at the April, 1962, meeting of the
Ohio Hospital Association in Toledo, saying that the philosophy was to preserve
the traditional community hospital guided by its own board of trustees. The
aim is to provide a basic plan of hospital benefits available to all yet with minimum involvement in the internal affairs of the hospitals.

The Metropolitan Hospital Planning Council was established in 1959 by the
British Columbia Hospital Association. A 102-page report, *A Pilot Study of
Professional Utilization of the White Rock District Hospital and the Surrey
Memorial Hospital,* was published by the council in 1962. At the same time
other surveys on referral patterns, emergency services, and pediatric facilities
were being made, report of one of them, *A Study of Paediatric Bed Use in the
Province of British Columbia,* having been published in 1961.

Gradual Steps to Area-wide Operations

The numerous evidences of closer affiliations and even mergers among hospitals may be good initial steps toward regional planning. Economies are also
possible, forced by the rising costs.

In Los Angeles, Cedars of Lebanon and Mount Sinai hospitals have developed
a long-range program to coordinate their services and facilities. The merger
creates the largest private nonprofit hospital facility in the western states, with
combined bed capacity of 790. At least until 1965 the hospitals will continue at
their present sites, but future plans call for a unified medical center.

It was recommended in a report by the Federation of Jewish Philanthropies,
New York, that ten Jewish hospitals in that city consolidate into coordinated
hospital centers.

---

[9] From a report, *The Regional Hospital Plan—The First Year's Experience,* Rochester, New York,
The Council of Rochester Regional Hospitals, 1946.

A successful example of coordination is the creation in one Florida county of a board of public assistance which controls all health-related facilities, including a home for the aged, a home for children, outpatient services, a rehabilitation center, hospitals, and public welfare activities. The board was created in the fall of 1961 by an act of the state legislature. The county is Hillsborough, and the problems which instigated its creation were "deplorable" conditions in some hospitals, a "deteriorating" medical educational program, and a poorly managed welfare department. By April, 1963, the director of the board was reporting more efficient operation of the hospitals, more careful screening of persons seeking assistance, and centralized accounting, purchasing, laundry, and employment services.[10]

Four hospitals in Pittsburgh joined forces in 1962 to pool resources and cut costs. The four hospitals are Allegheny General, Divine Providence, St. John's General, and Suburban General. A joint referral plan was one of the first steps. Physicians at all four hospitals can refer patients from acute general hospitals to the convalescent unit started by St. John's Hospital at Valencia.

The "Outer Rings"

Metropolitan hospital planning is complicated by the development of outer rings of population which began in the 1920's with the use of automobiles. Whereas in 1900 only about 11 per cent of the total population of standard metropolitan areas lived in the rings, by 1950 the percentage had risen to 24 per cent. Some of the problems related to this development were described by Masaichi Tasaka, assistant administrator of Highland Park Hospital, Highland Park, Illinois, in his thesis for his master's degree in hospital administration submitted to Northwestern University in 1955.

Population Growth and its Effect upon Suburban Hospitals

MASAICHI TASAKA

The suburbs are the result of industrialization and the growth of cities and have grown as a corollary of people's desire to live away from the city to enjoy the advantages of country living while at the same time being close enough to enjoy the advantages of the city. As Wilbur C. Hallenbeck[11] described the suburbs:

> One of the phenomena of American cities of any size is a suburban zone which lies between city proper and country. It is not precisely definable by municipal or other boundary lines. In some instances it looks like a country village; in others, like a miniature of the city's modern mode, but its people are unmistakably of the city.

[10] *Hospitals*, April, 1963, p. 157.
[11] *American Urban Communities*. New York, Harper and Brothers, 1951, p. 202.

The man who came to the city in his youth from rural areas has a nostalgic yearning for the country life, and the man raised in the city has heard much of the good country living. Suburban development has also been dependent upon the development of communication and transportation facilities. Distance is no longer measured in terms of miles but rather by time. Mass building geared to the ordinary wage-earner's means made it possible for the average man to move to the suburbs. The building of large shopping centers, the providing of transportation facilities, food stores, and services, have added to the impetus of suburban movement.

Suburbs can be typed into three different categories according to the composition of the population and the kind of work they do for a living. First is the residential, or suburb of consumption, which has a high proportion of people in trade and professional services and domestic services. The people generally are better educated and have a higher standard of living. In this type of suburb, there is usually an excess of women with proportionately more single women than single men. Second is the industrial, or suburb of production, which is characterized by a large concentration of peoples of one racial extraction. It has a large proportion of women workers, low literacy rate, and a large portion of people in the working-age group. Third is the mixed suburb, a combination residential-industrial neighborhood.

These three broad classifications can be further broken down into planned and unplanned suburbs, specialized suburbs, suburbs with active community life and traditions, suburbs with different occupational levels, and young and old suburbs.

In 1950 the suburban areas with a population of approximately 36 million constituted 24 per cent of the total population of the United States, whereas in 1900 the suburban population was only 15.4 per cent of the total.

Although most of the suburbanites select their sites of residence with the hope of living in a country atmosphere, they do not realize that they are caught in a process of change. "So frustrating is this process to dreams of rural peace that most suburbanites hate to look ahead and envision the future; they can hardly help wishing that time would stand still."[12]

It is interesting to note that new adult residents in the suburbs do not readily take part in the civic life of their community. Their children, on the other hand, have shown more willingness to participate in youth organizations. The lack of interest by the adults may be due to differences in the cultural background between new and old settlers or in the standard of living, values, and behavior patterns. Some newcomers have also felt resentment by the established residents when they attempted to take an active part in the civic affairs of the community.

Participation in community activities by newcomers as well as old-timers is an important objective of a community hospital. As new settlers inevitably increase the demand for and the utilization of hospital facilities, the hospital should endeavor to create an avenue of community approach to these new members.

[12] Frederick Lewis Allen: Crisis in the Suburbs. *Harper's Magazine,* July, 1954, p. 50.

As the movement to the suburbs continues, the need for regional planning is indicated. City plans must be augmented by regional planning to bring about a coordinated and integrated metropolitan pattern. Master plans must be made and reviewed constantly to preserve good residential areas, recover blighted areas, maintain and preserve the wooded land, plan zoning regulations, and plan tomorrow's suburbs. Political ties must be reviewed and adjusted to bring about an equitable tax structure.

Health is gradually becoming recognized as a social problem, since illness deprives the community of the productive capacity of its citizens. Cost of sickness is high, and the cost of hospitalization is slowly becoming beyond the reach of the ordinary person. The present-day concept is the prevention and early detection of disease in order to prevent costly hospitalization and to return the patient to productive work as soon as possible. The increase in movement toward the suburbs affects hospital planning to such a degree that reappraisal of existing conditions and study of future trends must be made constantly by suburban hospitals if they are to serve community needs effectively. There is no accurate method of estimating future population growth inasmuch as mass home-building programs are taking place in areas where large tracts of land are obtainable. It seems, therefore, that the groundwork of suburban hospital planning must be flexible enough to meet an ever-increasing demand for hospital beds and facilities.

Geographic factors, such as distance from the medical centers in the central cities, will to a great extent affect the utilization of suburban hospitals. The suburbanites who are accustomed to commuting into the city may prefer to use the city hospitals. Those who have recently moved to outlying areas may prefer to continue going to their family doctors who maintain their offices in the city and who are affiliated with the larger city hospitals. It should be remembered that many of the suburbanites were formerly residents of the central city. They may not have been thoroughly assimilated into the community activities of the suburb. Then, too, the highly trained medical staffs of the medical centers have a strong attraction for prospective patients. Furthermore, the superhighways have brought the city much closer to the suburban town. This mobility of the population suggests the need for a flexible, coordinated attitude toward hospital planning.

It should be remembered that hospitals in the suburban communities usually must rely solely upon patient incomes to finance patient care, since they have not had the advantage of receiving large endowments as have the older hospitals. Financial support and utilization of suburban hospitals depend upon the ability of the hospitals to sell themselves to the communities through an educational program. A consideration in suburban fund-raising campaigns, especially in the residential suburbs where contributions from industry are negligible, is the public relations potential of the women. The wealth of the nations is slowly getting into the hands of women, and women are therefore increasingly controlling the economic life of the nation. This fact, plus the fact that the suburban life of the commuter is generally left in the hands of his wife, makes it advisable for fund raisers to gear their campaigns toward the housewives in the community as a large source of contribution and good will. The commuter whose economic life is primarily centered in the city is unlikely to be easily influenced to take active part in a suburban hospital fund campaign. A great deal of the public relations work should be directed to educate the commuter concerning the importance of the hospital to him and his family. The women's auxiliary is a good source of help in this direction.

It is the responsibility of suburban hospitals to determine the extent to which specialized services will be offered on the basis of need and efficient and effective utilization.

Although the future supply of physicians seems reasonably assured, as the percentage of increase in graduates from medical schools has kept ahead of the increase in population, the suburban hospitals, in order to attract these graduates, must seriously consider developing teaching environments for them, inasmuch as many of these graduates seem to seek surroundings that are similar to those of the medical schools. In the face of the increase in growth of population and utilization, the boards of all suburban hospitals must re-evaluate their basic policies. They must decide on the hospital's future in relation to the increasing population and the resultant demand for better and more comprehensive patient care. They will have to decide (1) to expand their hospitals to meet all the demands or (2) to rely on the larger city hospitals to care for the most difficult cases or (3) to expand their bed capacities only.

"Satellite" Hospitals

Regional planning has undoubtedly been partly responsible for the introduction of "satellite" hospitals. The term is new but not the idea, according to Philip B. Hallen, project director of the current study on satellite hospitals, reporting at the 1962 American Hospital Association convention in Chicago. Mr. Hallen said that the Youngstown (Ohio) Hospital which was established in 1881 opened its Northside Unit in 1929 and that Grace Hospital, Detroit, established its Northwest Division in 1942. The branch units at these hospitals were of almost the same bed capacity as the central units, although in most of the later branch units the second units are smaller. In the postwar years regional systems were organized by the United Mine Workers, the Bingham program in Maine, the Kaiser Foundation, and others.[13]

On June 1, 1962, Memorial Baptist Hospital, Southwest, was opened in Houston, Texas, with the announcement that it was the "first of several planned neighborhood branch hospitals" in the Memorial Baptist Hospital System. Three more 100-bed units are planned on four quadrant freeways leading to downtown Houston, at intersections of a "belt" highway connecting the units.

[13] Some Characteristics of Multiple-Unit Hospitals (research project of the Hospital Planning Association of Allegheny County, Pennsylvania). *Hosp. Topics*, November, 1962, p. 49.

Fairview Hospital, Minneapolis, besides adding a 150-bed convalescent and long-term care unit in 1963, plans to build a branch hospital in the suburbs southwest of the city and has acquired a 15-acre site adjacent to a medical building which is part of a total planned community development.

One of the benefits of the new satellite hospitals is to forestall the development of small, inadequately staffed and equipped, proprietary hospitals in the suburbs.

PROBLEMS IN AREA-WIDE PLANNING

A warning that a rough road is ahead for regional planning was sounded by Dr. Anthony J. J. Rourke, hospital consultant, a past president of the American Hospital Association, in an address at the 1962 New England Hospital Assembly. Dr. Rourke called an "oversimplification" the thesis that effective planning requires the support of the whole community and the full cooperation of hospitals and related health facilities, asserting:

> In reality there is conflict between voluntary and proprietary hospitals, damaging doubt between doctors and hospitals, jealous competition between service benefits and indemnity plans, laissez-faire attitudes between voluntary and governmental hospitals, eternal vigilance between industry and labor, suspicion between curative and preventive medicine, and vested self-interests among the voluntary hospitals. . . . Every planner with objectivity knows the heartache of trying to hammer out a better future for the community on the anvil of tradition, vested interest, personal prejudice, pride of ownership and conflicting interests.

Dr. Rourke did not end on this note, however. "Heartaches are no reason for not trying," he declared.

The inevitable conflicts were also brought out by Tasker K. Robinette,[14] administrator of Island Hospital, Anacortes, Washington. He strongly opposed the active participation of hospital administrators in planning councils. He thinks the councils should be independent, consumer-operated groups, with no hospital representation, for the reason that hospital boards "may not appreciate sacrificing status to the cause of area planning," or "because their institutions may be voted out of existence." He lauds the motives which are leading hospital people to originate, sponsor, push, and sell area-wide planning, but he is sure that only consumer groups can make it work.

Another warning against overconfidence in regional planning as a solution to hospital problems was given by T. J. Ross, president of the Hospital Council of Greater New York, in a talk at the 1961 meeting of the Greater New York Hospital Association. Mr. Ross said in part:[15]

> It seems to me that if there is one major fallacy in the field of hospital planning it is assumption that the development of a "plan" or setting up an organization or "task force" solves anything. The Hospital Council has contributed to the propagation of this heresy with its so-called Master Plan for Hospitals and Related Facilities. I am not referring to the content of the plan but to its name.

[14] Reader Opinion, *Mod. Hosp.*, July, 1962.
[15] *Hosp. Forum*, August, 1961, pp. 15–18, 34.

The word "Master" implies an omniscience and an authority that we have never claimed or believed in. The word "plan" implies a static blueprint rather than a continuous planning process. What is called for is not an authoritarian plan but a continuing application of such skill and judgment and wisdom as we possess to the solution of the problems that are always besetting us, but in constantly changing form.

In 1962 the Hospital Council of Greater New York was reorganized and expanded to include 14 counties with the five boroughs, and the name was changed to Hospital Review and Planning Council of Southern New York.

The danger of making overprecise calculations of hospital utilization by residents of a neighborhood was indicated in a study made by the Citizens Hospital Study Committee of Cleveland. One of the findings was that "few hospitals serve as many as half of the residents of their own immediate neighborhoods, most nearby residents going to other hospitals that may be located at some distance." Total area needs are therefore more important than neighborhood ones.

CONCLUSION

Of all the forces existing and impending that show promise of improving hospital-community interaction, regional planning is in the leading position. One administrator, Raymond Farwell of Swedish Hospital, Seattle, Washington, has a "profound conviction that the survival of the American hospital system as we know it today depends in large measure on our ability as a group to plan collectively for the public good where that good is involved with our activities and services."[16] That conviction is echoed from all parts of the land.

Among the newer developments that brighten the prospects for progress are: (1) the 1961 AHA-PHS report mentioned on page 778; (2) the 1963 supplement to this report on long-term treatment and care; (3) the AHA 1963 guide for hospital membership associations; (4) the AHA 1963 statement on the relationship of a planning agency with a community health and welfare council;[17] (5) the grants available under the expanded Hill-Burton program; (6) the study of community health needs by the National Commission on Community Health Services, sponsored by the American Public Health Association and the National Health Council.

Area-wide planning is achieving such strong support that the administrator of the present and the future must be educated to think and act for the good of the community at large, with knowledge of all of its aspects, as well as for the best interests of the patients in his institution.

[16] From *Hosp. Forum*, April, 1962, p. 23.
[17] *Hospitals*, November 16, 1963, pp. 78 and 141.

Bibliography
and
Suggestions for
Supplementary Reading
and Reference

ADMINISTRATION

AMERICAN MANAGEMENT ASSOCIATION: *The Dynamics of Management*. New York, The Association, 1958.

ARGYRIS, CHRIS: *Understanding Organizational Behavior*. Homewood, Ill., The Dorsey Press, 1960.

BAKKE, E. WIGHT; KERR, CLARK; and ANROD, CHARLES W.: *Unions, Management, and the Public,* 2nd ed. New York, Harcourt, Brace and Co., 1960.

BROWN, MILON: *Effective Work Management*. New York, The Macmillan Co., 1960.

DALE, ERNEST, and URWICK, LYNDALL F.: *Staff in Organization*. New York, McGraw-Hill Book Co., 1960.

DALTON, MELVILLE: *Men Who Manage*. New York, John Wiley and Sons, 1959.

DAVIES, DANIEL R., and LIVINGSTON, ROBERT T.: *You and Management*. New York, Harper and Brothers, 1958.

DELL, WILLIAM R.; HILTON, THOMAS L.; and REITMAN, WALTER R.: *The New Managers*. Englewood Cliffs, N. J., Prentice-Hall, 1962.

GABRIEL, H. W.: *Techniques of Creative Thinking for Management*. Englewood Cliffs, N. J., Prentice-Hall, 1961.

GREENBERGER, MARTIN, ed.: *Management and the Computer of the Future*. Cambridge, M.I.T. Press, 1962.

JENNINGS, EUGENE E.: *The Executive: Autocrat, Bureaucrat, Democrat*. New York, Harper and Row, 1962.

LEVINSON, HARRY, *et al.*: *Men, Management and Mental Health*. Cambridge, Harvard University Press, 1962.

LIKERT, RENSIS: *New Patterns of Management.* New York, McGraw-Hill Book Co., 1961.

MC FARLAND, DALTON E.: *Management: Principles and Practices.* New York, The Macmillan Co., 1958.

MANLEY, ROBERT, and MANLEY, SEON, eds.: *The Age of the Manager, a Treasury of Our Times.* New York, The Macmillan Co., 1963.

NILES, MARY CUSHING: *The Essence of Management.* New York, Harper and Brothers, 1958.

SIMON, HERBERT A.: *Administrative Behavior,* 2nd ed. New York, The Macmillan Co., 1958.

TERRY, GEORGE R.: *Principles of Management,* 4th ed. Homewood, Ill., Richard D. Irwin, Inc., 1962.

URIS, AUREN: *The Management Makers.* New York, The Macmillan Co., 1962.

BIOGRAPHY AND AUTOBIOGRAPHY

ABBOTT, EDITH: *Some American Pioneers in Social Welfare.* Chicago, University of Chicago Press, 1938.

BARUCH, BERNARD M.: *Baruch, My Own Story.* New York, Henry Holt and Co., 1957.

BECKER, CARL: *A Biographical Study of American Intellectual History.* Boston, M.I.T. Press, 1961.

BLOCHMAN, LAWRENCE G.: *Doctor Squibb.* New York, Simon and Schuster, 1958.

BRUCE, HERBERT A.: *Varied Operations* (autobiography). New York, Longmans, Green and Co., 1958.

BRUCHEY, STUART WEEMS: *Robert Oliver, Merchant of Baltimore, 1783–1819.* Baltimore, Johns Hopkins University, 1957.

CLAPESATTLE, H. B.: *The Doctors Mayo.* Minneapolis, University of Minnesota Press, 1941.

COPE, ZACHARY: *Florence Nighingale and the Doctors.* Philadelphia, J. B. Lippincott Co., 1951.

COPLEY, FRANK BARKLEY: *Frederick W. Taylor, Father of Scientific Management.* New York, Harper and Brothers, 1923.

CUSHING, HARVEY: *Life of Sir William Osler.* 2 vols. New York and London, Oxford University Press, 1925. (Also 1 vol., 1940.)

DOOLEY, THOMAS A.: *The Edge of Tomorrow.* New York, Farrar, Straus and Cudahy, 1958.

DORFMAN, JOSEPH: *Thorstein Veblen and His America.* New York, Viking Press, 1947.

ENGEL, L.: *Medicine Makers of Kalamazoo.* New York, McGraw-Hill Book Co., 1961.

ERICKSON, CHARLOTTE: *British Industrialists, Steel and Hosiery, 1850–1950.* Cambridge, England, Cambridge University Press, 1960.

FINNEY, JOHN M. T.: *A Surgeon's Life*. New York, G. P. Putnam's Sons, 1940.

FLEMING, D. H.: *William H. Welch and the Rise of Modern Medicine*. Boston, Little, Brown and Co., 1954.

FLEXNER, J. T.: *Doctors on Horseback, Pioneers of American Medicine*. New York, Viking Press, 1937.

FULTON, JOHN F.: *Harvey Cushing: A Biography*. Springfield, Ill., Charles C Thomas, 1946.

GRAVES, FRANK PIERREPONT: *Great Educators of Three Centuries*. New York, The Macmillan Co., 1929.

HAYMAKER, WEBB, ed.: *The Founders of Neurology*. Springfield, Ill., Charles C Thomas, 1953.

HEILBRONER, ROBERT L.: *The Worldly Philosophers: The Lives, Times and Ideas of the Great Economic Thinkers*. New York, Simon and Schuster, 1953.

HOLBROOK, STEWART H.: *Dreamers of the American Dream*. New York, Doubleday and Co., 1957.

JOHNSON, EDGAR: *One Mighty Torrent: The Drama of Biography*. New York, The Macmillan Co., 1955.

KELLOGG, W. K., FOUNDATION: *Selected Papers of Dr. Haven Emerson*. Battle Creek, Michigan, The Foundation, 1949.

KEYNES, JOHN MAYNARD: *Essays in Biography*. New York, Horizon Press, 1951.

LOVEJOY, ESTHER POHL: *Women Doctors of the World*. New York, The Macmillan Co., 1957.

MC MENEMEY, WILLIAM H.: *Life and Times of Sir Charles Hastings, Founder of the British Medical Association*. Edinburgh and London, E. and S. Livingstone, Ltd., 1959.

MADISON, CHARLES A.: *American Labor Leaders*. New York, Unger Publishing Co., 1962.

MANCHESTER, HARLAND: *Trail Blazers of Technology*. New York, Charles Scribner's Sons, 1962.

MARTIN, FRANKLIN H.: *The Joy of Living, An Autobiography*. 2 vols. Garden City, N. Y., Doubleday, Doran and Co., 1933.

MILL, JOHN STUART: *Autobiography*. New York, Columbia University Press, 1944.

OWEN, ROBERT: *Autobiography, The Life of Robert Owen*. New York, Alfred A. Knopf, Inc., 1920.

SCHWEITZER, ALBERT: *Out of My Life and Thought*. New York, Henry Holt and Co., 1949.

SIGERIST, H. E.: *The Great Doctors*. Trans. by E. and C. Paul from the 2nd German edition. New York, W. W. Norton and Co., 1933.

TAUSSIG, FRANK WILLIAM: *American Business Leaders; A Study in Social Origins and Social Stratification*. New York, The Macmillan Co., 1932.

WARNER, W. LLOYD, and ABEGGLEN, JAMES C.: *Big Business Leaders in America*. New York, Harper and Brothers, 1955.

WHITE, WILLIAM ALLEN: *The Autobiography of William Allen White.* New York, The Macmillan Co., 1946.

WINSLOW, CHARLES-EDWARD AMORY: *The Life of Hermann M. Biggs.* Philadelphia, Lea and Febiger, 1929.

WINSLOW, WALKER: *The Menninger Story,* Garden City, N. Y., Doubleday and Co., 1956.

YOUNG, AGATHA: *The Men Who Made Surgery.* New York, Hillman Books, 1961. Original title, *Scalpel,* Random House, 1956.

ZINSSER, HANS: *As I Remember Him—The Biography of R. S.* New York, Little, Brown and Co. and Atlantic Monthly Press, 1940.

BUSINESS, INDUSTRY, FINANCE

AMERICAN MANAGEMENT ASSOCIATION: *Insurance Costs and Controls; a Reappraisal.* New York, The Association, 1958.

ARNOLD, THURMAN W.: *The Folklore of Capitalism.* New Haven, Yale University Press, 1959.

AYRES, C. E.: *Toward a Reasonable Society: The Values of Industrial Civilization.* Austin, Texas, University of Texas Press, 1962.

BRADY, ROBERT A.: *Organization, Automation and Society.* Berkeley, University of California Press, 1961.

BUCKINGHAM, WALTER: *Automation: Its Impact on Business and People.* New York, Harper and Row, 1961.

CHILDS, MARQUIS W., and CATER, DOUGLASS: *Ethics in a Business Society.* New York, Harper and Brothers, 1954.

CHURCH, DAVID M.: *So—You're Going to Raise Funds.* New York, National Publicity Council for Health and Welfare Services, 1957.

COMMISSION ON FINANCING OF HOSPITAL CARE: *Financing Hospital Care in the United States.* 3 vols. Philadelphia, The Blakiston Company, Inc., 1954.

FELLOWS, MARGARET M., and KOENIG, STELLA A.: *Tested Methods of Raising Money.* New York, Harper and Brothers, 1959.

FORRESTER, J. W.: *Industrial Dynamics.* Cambridge, M.I.T. Press, 1961.

GLOVER, JOHN G., and CORNELL, WILLIAM B., eds.: *Development of American Industry.* New York, Prentice-Hall, 1955.

GORDON, ROBERT AARON: *Business Fluctuations,* 2nd ed. New York, Harper and Brothers, 1961.

HALACY, D. S., JR.: *Computers: The Machines We Think With.* New York, Harper and Brothers, 1962.

HOWARD, RONALD A.: *Dynamic Programming and Markov Processes.* Cambridge, M.I.T. Press, 1960.

JOHNSON, ROBERT WOOD: *Or Forfeit Freedom.* Garden City, N. Y., Doubleday and Co., 1947.

KORNHAUSER, WILLIAM: *Scientists in Industry.* Berkeley, University of California Press, 1962.

MC GREGOR, D.: *The Human Side of Enterprise.* New York, McGraw-Hill Book Co., 1960.

PASK, GORDON: *An Approach to Cybernetics.* New York, Harper and Row, 1961.

WIEBE, ROBERT H.: *Businessmen and Reform: A Study of the Progressive Movement.* Cambridge, Harvard University Press, 1962.

WIENER, NORBERT: *Cybernetics: Or Control and Communication in the Animal and the Machine,* rev. Cambridge, M.I.T. Press, 1961.

WORTHY, JAMES C.: *Big Business and Free Men.* New York, Harper and Brothers, 1959.

COMMUNICATION; PUBLIC RELATIONS

ASSOCIATION OF BRITISH SCIENCE WRITERS: *A Guide to Press Arrangements for Scientific, Medical and Technical Conferences.* London, Spottiswoode, Ballantyne and Co., 1960.

BENTLEY, GARTH: *Editing the Company Magazine.* New York, Harper and Brothers, 1953.

BERNAYS, EDWARD L.: *Public Relations.* Norman, University of Oklahoma Press, 1952.

—— *The Engineering of Consent.* Norman, University of Oklahoma Press, 1955.

BRISTOL, LEE, JR.: *Developing the Corporate Image.* New York, Charles Scribner's Sons, 1960.

CUTLIP, SCOTT M., and CENTER, ALLEN H.: *Effective Public Relations: Pathways to Public Favor.* Englewood Cliffs, N. J., Prentice-Hall, 1952.

GRISWOLD, GLENN, and GRISWOLD, DENNY: *Your Public Relations.* New York, Funk and Wagnalls Co., 1950.

HANEY, WILLIAM W.: *Communication: Patterns and Incidents.* Homewood, Ill., Richard D. Irwin, Inc., 1960.

HARLOW, REX F.: *Social Science in Public Relations.* New York, Harper and Brothers, 1957.

HARRAH, DAVID: *Communication: A Logical Model.* Cambridge, M.I.T. Press, 1963.

KRIEGHBAUM, HILLIER: *When Doctors Meet Reporters.* New York, New York University Press, 1957.

LESLEY, PHILIP, ed.: *Public Relations Handbook,* rev. Englewood Cliffs, New Jersey, Prentice-Hall, 1963.

MEIER, RICHARD L.: *A Communications Theory of Urban Growth,* Cambridge, M.I.T. Press, 1962.

MERRIHUE, WILLARD V.: *Managing by Communication.* New York, McGraw-Hill Book Co., 1960.

MILLS, ALDEN B.: *Hospital Public Relations.* Chicago, Physicians' Record Co., 1939.

MOTT, FRANK LUTHER: *American Journalism: A History of Newspapers.* New York, The Macmillan Co., 1941.

NEAL, HELEN, ed.: *Better Communications for Better Health.* New York, National Health Council and Columbia University Press, 1962.

PETERSON, THEODORE: *Magazines in the Twentieth Century.* Urbana, Ill., University of Illinois Press, 1956.

PUBLIC RELATIONS SOCIETY OF AMERICA. *The Organization of Public Relations in Health and Welfare Organizations.* New York, The Society, 1954.

REDFIELD, CHARLES E.: *Communications in Management,* rev. Chicago, University of Chicago Press, 1958.

STEINBERG, CHARLES S.: *The Mass Communicators: Public Relations, Public Opinion, Mass Media.* New York, Harper and Brothers, 1958.

WHYTE, WILLIAM H., JR., and editors of *Fortune: Is Anybody Listening?* New York, Simon and Schuster, 1952.

EDUCATION AND RESEARCH

AMERICAN MEDICAL ASSOCIATION: *A Guide Regarding Objectives and Basic Principles of Postgraduate Medical Education Programs.* Chicago, The Association, 1957.

ASSOCIATION OF PREVENTIVE MEDICINE, COMMITTEE ON MEDICAL CARE TEACHING: *Readings in Medical Care.* Durham, N. C., University of North Carolina Press, 1958.

BROWN, RAY E., and FORSMAN, VERNON W.: *Student Selection: A Study of Criteria for Selection of Students for Graduate Education in Hospital Administration.* Chicago, University of Chicago Press, 1958.

BROWN, RAY E., ed.: *Graduate Education for Hospital Administration.* Chicago, University of Chicago, Graduate Program in Hospital Administration, 1959.

CANADIAN NURSES' ASSOCIATION: *Spotlight on Nursing Education.* Ottawa, Canada, The Association, 1960.

COMMISSION ON UNIVERSITY EDUCATION IN HOSPITAL ADMINISTRATION: *University Education for Hospital Administration.* Washington, D.C., American Council on Education, 1954.

DEITRICK, JOHN E.: *Medical Schools in United States at Mid-Century.* New York, McGraw-Hill Book Co., 1953.

FLAGLE, CHARLES D., *et al.,* eds.: *Operations Research and Systems Engineering.* Baltimore, Johns Hopkins University Press, 1960.

FLEXNER, ABRAHAM: *Medical Education in the United States and Canada.* Boston, Merrymount Press, 1910.

FRENCH, SIDNEY J., ed.: *Accent on Teaching.* New York, Harper and Brothers, 1954.

GOLDWIN, ROBERT A., and NELSON, CHARLES A., eds.: *Toward the Liberally Educated Executive.* New York, a Mentor Book, 1960. (The Fund for Adult Education, 1957.)

GORDON, ROBERT AARON, and HOWELL, JAMES EDWIN: *Higher Education for Business*. New York, Columbia University Press, 1959.

GREGG, ALAN: *Group Practice and Medical Education*. New York, Medical Administration Service, Inc., 1949.

—— *For Future Doctors*. Chicago, University of Chicago Press, 1957.

HAMMOND, KENNETH R., *et al*.: *Teaching Comprehensive Medical Care: A Psychological Study of a Change in Medical Education*. (A Commonwealth Fund book.) Cambridge, Harvard University Press, 1959.

HENLE, ROBERT J., and KAHLER, CAROL: *A Doctoral Program in Health Organization Research*. St. Louis, Missouri, St. Louis University Press, 1958.

JOINT COMMISSION ON EDUCATION: *The College Curriculum in Hospital Administration*. Chicago, Physicians' Record Co., 1948.

LAMBERTSEN, ELEANOR C.: *Education for Nursing Leadership*. Philadelphia, J. B. Lippincott Co., 1958.

LIEBERMAN, M.: *Education as a Profession*. Englewood Cliffs, N. J., Prentice-Hall, 1956.

MC GLOTHLIN, WILLIAM JOSEPH: *Patterns of Professional Education*. New York, G. P. Putnam's Sons, 1960.

MONTAGUE, M.: *Community College Education for Nursing*. New York, McGraw-Hill Book Co., 1959.

MULLANE, MARY KELLY: *Education for Nursing Service Administration*. Battle Creek, Michigan, W. K. Kellogg Foundation, 1959.

PIERSON, FRANK COOK, *et al*.: *The Education of American Businessmen: A Study of University-College Programs in Business Administration*. New York, McGraw-Hill Book Co., Inc., 1959.

ROBINSON, GEORGE CANBY: *Adventures in Medical Education*. Cambridge, Harvard University Press, 1957.

ROGERS, MARTHA E.: *Educational Revolution in Nursing*. New York, The Macmillan Co., 1961.

SHEPS, CECIL G.: *Needed Research in Health and Medical Care*. Chapel Hill, University of North Carolina Press, 1954.

SWEENEY, STEPHEN B.: *Education for Administrative Careers in Government Service*. Philadelphia, University of Pennsylvania Press, 1958.

TYLER, RALPH W., ed.: *Social Forces Influencing American Education*. Chicago, University of Chicago Press, 1961.

UNITED STATES PUBLIC HEALTH SERVICE: *Resources for Medical Research; Federal Expenditures for Medical and Health-related Research, 1960–63*. Washington, D.C., U.S. Government Printing Office, 1962.

UNIVERSITY OF TORONTO, DEPARTMENT OF HOSPITAL ADMINISTRATION: *Practical Studies in Education for Hospital Administration*. Toronto, University of Toronto Press, 1960.

WEATHERFORD, WILLIS D., JR., ed.: *The Goals of Higher Education*. Cambridge, Harvard University Press, 1960.

WHITEHEAD, ALFRED NORTH: *The Aims of Education.* New York, The Macmillan Co., 1929. (Republished as a Mentor Book, 1953.)

WORLD HEALTH ORGANIZATION: Report of a Study Group: *Internationally Acceptable Minimum Standards of Medical Education.* Geneva, W.H.O. Technical Report Series, No. 239, 1962.

GOVERNMENT

ACTON SOCIETY TRUST: *Hospitals and the State.* 3 vols. London, The Trust, 1955–1957.

BARTHOLOMEW, PAUL C.: *An Outline of Public Administration.* Paterson, New Jersey, Littlefield, Adams and Co., 1959.

CONSERVATIVE POLITICAL CENTRE, LONDON: *The Future of the Welfare State.* London, The Centre, 1958.

DIMOCK, MARSHALL EDWARD: *Business and Government,* 3rd ed. New York, Henry Holt and Co., 1957.

—— *Administrative Vitality: The Conflict with Bureaucracy.* New York, Harper and Brothers, 1959.

—— *The New American Political Economy: A Synthesis of Politics and Economics.* New York, Harper and Row, 1962.

GEMMILL, PAUL F.: *Britain's Search for Health: The First Decade of the National Health Service.* Philadelphia, University of Pennsylvania Press, 1960.

GOLDMANN, FRANZ: *Public Medical Care.* New York, Columbia University Press, 1945.

HARRISON, GLADYS A.: *Government Controls and the Voluntary Nonprofit Hospital; An Exploratory Study, with a Supplementary Statement on the External Voluntary Controls Affecting Hospitals.* Chicago, American Hospital Association, 1961.

HENSEY, BRENDAN: *The Health Services of Ireland.* Dublin, Institute of Public Administration, 1959.

JEWKES, JOHN, and JEWKES, SYLVIA: *Genesis of the British National Health Service.* Basil Blackwell and Mott, Ltd., 1961.

KILGOUR, D. E.: *Canadian Health Insurance: Observations from the Ringside.* New York, Health Insurance Institute, 1962.

LEES, D. S.: *Health Through Choice: An Economic Study of the British National Health Service.* (Hobart Paper 14.) London, Institute of Economic Affairs, 1961.

MORGAN, MURRAY: *Doctors to the World (W.H.O.).* New York, The Viking Press, 1958.

MUND, VERNON A.: *Government and Business.* 3rd ed. New York, Harper and Brothers, 1960.

MUSTARD, HARRY S.: *Government in Public Health.* New York, The Commonwealth Fund, 1945.

NEWSHOLME, SIR ARTHUR: *Medicine and the State.* London, George Allen and Unwin, 1960.

PETERSON, WALLACE C.: *The Welfare State in France.* Lincoln, University of Nebraska Press, 1960.

RIVLEN, ALICE M.: *The Role of the Federal Government in Financing Higher Education.* Washington, D.C., The Brookings Institute, 1961.

SIMON, H. A.; SMITHBURG, D. W.; and THOMPSON, V. A.: *Public Administration.* 4th ed. New York, Alfred A. Knopf, Inc., 1958.

STAHL, O. GLENN: *Public Personnel Administration,* 5th ed. New York, Harper and Row, 1962.

UNITED STATES PUBLIC HEALTH SERVICE: *Final Report of the Study Group on Mission and Organization of the Public Health Service.* Washington, D.C., United States Government Printing Office, 1960.

VASEY, WAYNE: *Government and Social Welfare.* New York, Henry Holt and Co., 1958.

History

ADAMS, GEORGE WORTHINGTON: *Doctors in Blue, The Medical History of the Union Army in the Civil War.* New York, Henry Schuman, Inc., 1952.

ALLBUTT, SIR T. C.: *Greek Medicine in Rome.* London, The Macmillan Co., 1921.

AMERICAN COLLEGE OF HOSPITAL ADMINISTRATORS: *A Venture Forward.* Chicago, The College, 1955.

ARRINGTON, GEORGE E., JR.: *History of Ophthalmology.* New York, M. D. Publications, 1959.

BARBER, MARY T., ed.: *History of the American Dietetic Association.* Philadelphia, J. B. Lippincott Co., 1959.

BEARD, MIRIAM: *A History of the Business Man.* New York, The Macmillan Co., 1938.

BROMBERG, WALTER: *Man Above Humanity; History of Psychotherapy.* Philadelphia, J. B. Lippincott Co., 1954.

BULLOCH, WILLIAM: *The History of Bacteriology.* London, Oxford University Press, 1938.

BURDETT, SIR HENRY CHARLES: *Hospitals and Asylums of the World.* 4 vols. London, J. and A. Churchill, 1891–1893.

CANADIAN NURSES' ASSOCIATION: *The First Fifty Years.* Ottawa, Canada, The Association, 1958.

CANNIFF, WILLIAM: *The Medical Profession in Upper Canada (1783–1850).* Toronto, W. Briggs, 1894.

CASTIGLIONI, ARTURO: *The Origin and Development of the Anatomical Theater to the End of the Renaissance.* Summit, N. J., Ciba Symposia, May, 1941.

—— *A History of Medicine.* Trans. by E. B. Krumbhaar. New York, Alfred A. Knopf, Inc., 1941.

CHAMBERLAIN, JOHN: *The Story of American Business.* New York, Harper and Row, 1962.

CHANDLER, ALFRED D., JR.: *Strategy and Structure; Chapters in the History of the Industrial Enterprise.* Cambridge, M.I.T. Press, 1962.

CLARK, MARGUERITE: *Medicine Today: A Report on a Decade of Progress.* New York, Funk and Wagnalls, 1960.

CLAY, ROTHA MARY: *Mediaeval Hospitals of England.* London, Methuen and Co., 1909.

COPE, ZACHARY: *History of the Royal College of Surgeons of England.* Springfield, Ill., Charles C Thomas, 1959.

DAINTON, COURTNEY: *The Story of England's Hospitals.* Springfield, Ill., Charles C Thomas, 1962.

DAVIS, LOYAL C.: *Fellowship of Surgeons.* Springfield, Ill., Charles C Thomas, 1960.

EATON, LEONARD K.: *New England Hospitals, 1790–1833.* Ann Arbor, University of Michigan Press, 1957.

GALDSTON, I. A.: *Progress in Medicine; A Critical Review of the Last Hundred Years.* New York and London: Alfred A. Knopf, Inc., 1940.

GARRISON, FIELDING H.: *An Introduction to the History of Medicine,* 4th ed. Philadelphia, W. B. Saunders Co., 1929.

GIBBON, JOHN MURRAY, and MATHEWSON, MARY S.: *Three Centuries of Canadian Nursing.* New York, The Macmillan Co., 1948.

GIDE, CHARLES, and RIST, CHARLES: *A History of Economic Doctrines.* London, G. G. Hamp and Co., 1948.

GOODNOW, MINNIE: *Nursing History,* 10th ed., Josephine A. Dolan, ed. Philadelphia, W. B. Saunders Co., 1958.

GORDON, BENJAMIN LEE: *Medieval and Renaissance Medicine.* London, Peter Owen, Ltd., 1959.

HARTLEY, SIR HAROLD, ed.: *The Royal Society: its Origins and Founders.* London, Royal Society of London, 1960.

HAEGERTY, J. J.: *Four Centuries of Medical History in Canada and a Sketch of the Medical History of Newfoundland.* 2 vols. Toronto, The Macmillan Co., 1928.

HEATON, HERBERT: *Economic History of Europe,* rev. New York, Harper and Brothers, 1958.

HERRICK, JAMES B.: *A Short History of Cardiology.* Springfield, Ill., Charles C Thomas, 1942.

HOLBROOK, STEWART H.: *The Golden Age of Quackery.* New York, The Macmillan Co., 1959.

HORRAX, GILBERT: *Neurosurgery: An Historical Sketch.* Springfield, Ill., Charles C Thomas, 1952.

KELLOGG, W. K., FOUNDATION: *The First Twenty-Five Years—The Story of a Foundation.* Battle Creek, Mich., The Foundation, 1955.

KREMERS, EDWARD, and URDANG, GEORGE: *History of Pharmacy.* 2nd ed. Philadelphia, J. B. Lippincott Co., 1951.

LEFF, SAMUEL, and LEFF, VERA: *From Witchcraft to World Health.* New York, The Macmillan Co., 1957.

MC CLUGGAGE, ROBERT W.: *A History of the American Dental Association.* Chicago, The Association, 1959.

MAJOR, RALPH H.: *A History of Medicine.* 2 vols. Springfield, Ill., Charles C Thomas, 1954.

MEANS, JAMES HOWARD: *Association of American Physicians: Its First 75 Years.* London, New York, Toronto, McGraw-Hill Book Co., 1961.

MOLL, A. A.: *Aesculapius in Latin America.* Philadelphia, W. B. Saunders Co., 1944.

NEUBURGER, MAX: *History of Medicine.* Trans. by Ernest Playfair. 2 vols. London, H. Frowde, 1910–1925.

PACKARD, F. R.: *History of Medicine in the United States,* 2nd ed. 2 vols. New York, Paul B. Hoeber, Inc., 1931.

PAVEY, A. E.: *The Story of the Growth of Nursing.* London, Faber and Faber, 1938.

RICCI, JAMES V.: *The Genealogy of Gynaecology.* Philadelphia, Blakiston Co., 1944.

RIESMAN, DAVID: *The Story of Medicine in the Middle Ages.* New York, Paul B. Hoeber, Inc., 1931.

RISLEY, MARY (DAVIS): *House of Healing; the Story of the Hospital.* Garden City, N. Y., Doubleday and Co., 1961.

ROBERTS, M. M.: *American Nursing, History and Interpretation.* New York, The Macmillan Co., 1954.

ROBINSON, VICTOR: *Syllabus of Medical History.* New York, Froben Press, 1933.

ROSEN, GEORGE: *History of Public Health.* New York, M. D. Publications, 1958.

SHRYOCK, R. H.: *The Development of Modern Medicine.* Philadelphia, University of Pennsylvania Press, 1936.

—— *Medicine and Society in America,* 1660–1860. New York, New York University Press, 1960; reissue, Cornell University Press, 1962.

—— *The History of Nursing; an Interpretation of the Social and Medical Factors Involved.* Philadelphia, W. B. Saunders Co., 1959.

SIGERIST, HENRY ERNEST: *On the History of Medicine.* New York, M. D. Publications, 1960.

STARR, JOHN: *Hospital City: The Story of the Men and Women of Bellevue.* New York, Crown Publishers, 1957.

STEWART, ISABEL MAITLAND, and AUSTIN, ANNE L.: *A History of Nursing.* New York, G. P. Putnam's Sons, 1962.

STILES, M. A.: *History of the American Association of Medical Social Workers.* Washington, D.C., The Association, 1955.

THATCHER, V. S.: *History of Anesthesia.* Philadelphia, J. B. Lippincott Co., 1953.

TOYNBEE, ARNOLD J.: *A Study of History: Volume XII, Reconsiderations.* Oxford, Oxford University Press, 1961.

WELLS, H. G.: *The Outline of History.* New York, The Macmillan Co., 1921.

ZIMMERMAN, LEO M., and VEITH, ILZA: *Great Ideas in the History of Surgery.* Baltimore, Williams and Wilkins Co., 1961.

Hospitals and Related Institutions and Organizations

AMERICAN ACADEMY OF GENERAL PRACTICE: *Manual on General Practice Departments in Hospitals.* Kansas City, Mo., The Academy, 1961.

AMERICAN ACADEMY OF PEDIATRICS: *Standards and Recommendations for Hospital Care of Newborn Infants, Full-term and Premature.* Evanston, Ill., The Academy, 1957, amended 1960.

AMERICAN ASSOCIATION OF HOMES FOR THE AGING: *Directory of Nonprofit Homes for the Aged.* New York, The Association, 1962.

AMERICAN COLLEGE OF HOSPITAL ADMINISTRATORS: *Hospital Administration: A Life's Profession.* Chicago, The College, 1948.

AMERICAN COLLEGE OF SURGEONS: *A Model of a Hospital Emergency Department.* Chicago, The College, 1961.

AMERICAN HOSPITAL ASSOCIATION: See current *Publications Catalogue.*

AMERICAN MEDICAL ASSOCIATION: See current list of publications.

AMERICAN NURSING HOME ASSOCIATION: *Code of Professional Ethics and Principles for the Nursing Home.* Washington, D.C., The Association, 1960.

AMERICAN PSYCHIATRIC ASSOCIATION: *Current Practices in Mental Hospital Administration.* Washington, D.C., The Association, 1957.

BACHMEYER, ARTHUR C., and HARTMAN, GERHARD, eds.: *Hospital Trends and Developments, 1940–1946.* New York, The Commonwealth Fund, 1948.

BAILEY, NORMAN D.: *Hospital Personnel Administration,* 2nd ed. Berwyn, Ill., Physicians' Record Co., 1959.

BARNES, ELIZABETH: *People in Hospital.* London and New York, The Macmillan Co., 1961. (A World Mental Health Year Publication.)

BELL, GEORGE H., ed.: *Hospital and Medical School Design.* 2 vols. Edinburgh, E. and S. Livingstone, 1962.

BENNETT, ADDISON C.: *Methods Improvement in Hospitals.* Philadelphia, J. B. Lippincott Co., 1963.

BILLINGTON, GEORGE F.: *Cases in Hospital Administration.* New York, Columbia University Press, 1959.

BROWN, ESTHER LUCILE: *Newer Dimensions of Patient Care.* 2 vols. New York, Russell Sage Foundation, Part I, 1961, Part II, 1962.

BROWN, RAY E., and JOHNSON, RICHARD L.: *Hospitals Visualized.* Chicago, American College of Hospital Administrators, 1957.

BURLING, TEMPLE; LENTZ, EDITH M.; and WILSON, ROBERT N.: *The Give and Take in Hospitals.* New York, G. P. Putnam's Sons, 1956.

CANADIAN COUNCIL ON HOSPITAL ACCREDITATION: *Standards for Accreditation of Canadian Hospitals.* Toronto, The Council, 1959; *Accreditation Guide,* 1960.

CATHOLIC HOSPITAL ASSOCIATION: *Administration of Long Term Care Facilities; Nursing Homes, Homes for the Aged, Chronic and Convalescent Homes.* St. Louis, The Association, 1960 and 1962.

CHAPMAN, FRANK E.: *Hospital Organization and Operation.* New York, The Macmillan Co., 1924.

CHARITABLE RESEARCH FOUNDATION, INC.: *Effective Standards for Institutional Care of the Infirm Aged.* Wilmington, Delaware, The Foundation, 1962.

COLBECK, J. C.: *Control of Infections in Hospitals.* Chicago, American Hospital Association, 1962.

COMMISSION ON HOSPITAL CARE: *Hospital Care in the United States.* New York, The Commonwealth Fund, 1947.

CORWIN, E. H. L.: *The American Hospital.* New York, The Commonwealth Fund, 1946.

CUNNINGHAM, ROBERT MARIS: *Hospitals, Doctors, and Dollars; Reports and Opinions on Our Good Samaritans, Who Are Having Some Bad Times.* New York, F. W. Dodge Corp., 1961.

DAVIS, MICHAEL M.: *Clinics, Hospitals and Health Centers.* New York and London, Harper and Brothers, 1927.

DODD, JOHN: *Hospitals and Health Services in Britain and the United States of America.* Bristol, England, British Hospitals Contributory Schemes Association, 1961.

FARNDALE, JAMES: *The Day Hospital Movement in Great Britain.* Oxford, England, The Pergamon Press, 1961.

FAXON, NATHANIEL W.: *The Hospital in Contemporary Life.* Cambridge, Harvard University Press, 1949.

GEORGE, F., and KUEHN, R.: *Patterns of Patient Care.* New York, The Macmillan Co., 1955.

GEORGOPOULOS, BASIL SPYROS, and MANN, FLOYD C.: *The Community General Hospital.* New York, The Macmillan Co., 1962.

GERLETTI, JOHN D.; CRAWFORD, C. C.; and PERKINS, DONOVAN J.: *Nursing Home Administration.* Downey, California, The Attending Staff Association, 1961.

GINZBERG, ELI, and ROGATZ, PETER: *Planning for Better Hospital Care.* New York, King's Crown Press, 1961.

GOLDWATER, S. S.: *On Hospitals.* New York, The Macmillan Co., 1947.

GREENBLATT, MILTON, *et al.,* eds.: *Mental Patients in Transition; Steps in Hospital-Community Rehabilitation.* Springfield, Ill., Charles C Thomas, 1961.

GUNN, SELSKAR M., and PLATT, PHILIP S.: *Voluntary Health Agencies.* New York, Ronald Press Co., 1945.

HAMILTON, JAMES ALEXANDER, *et al.*: *Patterns of Hospital Ownership and Control.* Minneapolis, University of Minnesota Press, 1961.

HOSPITAL COUNCIL OF PHILADELPHIA: *Structure, Financing and Activities of*

Twenty Metropolitan Hospital Councils in the United States. Philadelphia, The Council, 1958.

JOINT COMMISSION ON ACCREDITATION OF HOSPITALS: *Standards for Hospital Accreditation,* rev. Chicago, The Commission, 1960.

KELLOGG, W. K., FOUNDATION: *Planning and Operation of an Intensive Care Unit.* Battle Creek, Mich., The Foundation, 1961.

KLARMAN, HERBERT E.: *Hospital Care in New York City: The Roles of Voluntary and Municipal Hospitals.* New York, Columbia University Press, 1963.

LA BELLE, A. M., and BARTON, J. P.: *Administrative Housekeeping.* New York, G. P. Putnam's Sons, 1951.

LETOURNEAU, CHARLES U.: *Hospital Trusteeship.* Chicago, Starling Publications, 1959.

LINN, LOUIS, ed.: *Frontiers in General Hospital Psychiatry.* New York, International Universities Press, 1961.

LITTAUER, DAVID; FLANCE, I. JEROME; and WESSEN, ALBERT F.: *Home Care.* Chicago, American Hospital Association, 1961.

DE LOURDES, MOTHER M. BERNADETTE, and STAFF OF MARY MANNING WALSH HOME: *Where Somebody Cares.* New York, G. P. Putnam's Sons, 1960.

MAC EACHERN, MALCOLM T.: *Hospital Organization and Management,* 3rd ed. Berwyn, Ill., Physicians' Record Co., 1963.

MC GIBONY, JOHN R.: *Principles of Hospital Administration.* New York, G. P. Putnam's Sons, 1952.

MC NERNEY, WALTER J., and study staff: *Hospital and Medical Economics.* 2 vols. Chicago, Hospital Research and Educational Trust, 1962.

MC NERNEY, WALTER J., and RIEDEL, DONALD C.: *Regionalization and Rural Health Care.* Ann Arbor, University of Michigan, 1962.

MAHAFFEY, THOMAS E.: *Proprietary Nursing Homes; A Report on Interviews With 35 Nursing Home Operators in Detroit.* Chicago, Health Information Foundation, 1961.

MARTIN, T. LEROY: *Hospital Accounting Principles and Practice,* 3rd ed. Berwyn, Illinois, Physicians' Record Co., 1958.

MOTT, BASIL J. F.: *Financing and Operating Rehabilitation Centers and Facilities.* Chicago, National Society for Crippled Children and Adults, Inc., 1960.

NATIONAL FIRE PROTECTION ASSOCIATION: *Standard for Essential Hospital Electrical Service,* rev. Boston, The Association, 1963.

NICHOLSON, EDNA: *Planning New Institutional Facilities for Long Term Care.* New York, G. P. Putnam's Sons, 1956.

OWEN, JOSEPH KARLTON, ed.: *Modern Concepts of Hospital Administration.* Philadelphia and London, W. B. Saunders Co., 1962.

PONTON, THOMAS R.: *The Medical Staff in the Hospital,* 2nd ed., rev. by Malcolm T. MacEachern. Chicago, Physicians' Record Co., 1955.

PRALL, C. E.: *Problems of Hospital Administration.* Chicago, Physicians' Record Co., 1948.

REDKEY, HENRY: *Rehabilitation Centers Today.* Washington, D.C., United States Department of Health, Education and Welfare, 1959.

ROBINSON, GEOFFREY A.: *Hospital Administration.* Toronto, Canada, Butterworth and Co. (Canada), 1962.

SEAWELL, L. VANN: *Principles of Hospital Accounting.* Berwyn, Ill., Physicians' Record Co., 1960.

SLOAN, RAYMOND P.: *This Hospital Business of Ours.* New York, G. P. Putnam's Sons, 1952.

SOLON, JERRY, *et al.*: *Nursing Homes, Their Patients and Their Care.* (A joint project of the Commission on Chronic Illness and the Public Health Service.) Washington, D.C., United States Government Printing Office, 1957.

STAGEMAN, ANNE, and BANEY, ANNA MAE: *Hospital–Nursing Home Relationships:* Selected references annotated. Washington, D.C. United States Public Health Service Publication No. 930-G-2, June, 1962.

STANTON, ALFRED H., and SCHWARTZ, MORRIS S.: *The Mental Hospital.* New York, Basic Books, 1954.

STONE, J. E.: *Hospital Organization and Management,* 4th ed. London, Faber and Faber, 1956.

UNITED STATES DEPARTMENT OF HEALTH, EDUCATION AND WELFARE: *Areawide Planning for Hospitals and Related Health Facilities.* Washington, D.C., United States Government Printing Office, 1962.

UNITED STATES DEPARTMENT OF STATE, AGENCY FOR INTERNATIONAL DEVELOPMENT: *Training for Leadership and Service: Proceedings of the National Conference on the International Training Programs of A.I.D., June 25–26, 1962.* Washington, D.C., The Agency, 1962.

UNITED STATES PUBLIC HEALTH SERVICE: *Elements of Progressive Patient Care.* Washington, D.C., United States Government Printing Office, 1962.

WASSERMAN, CLARA, and WASSERMAN, PAUL: *Health Organizations of the United States and Canada, National, Regional and State.* Ithaca, N. Y., Cornell University Press, 1961.

WILLIAMS, RALPH C., and ASSOCIATES: *Nursing Home Management.* New York, F. W. Dodge Corp., 1959.

WORLD HEALTH ORGANIZATION: *Role of Hospitals in Programmes of Community Health Protection.* Geneva, W.H.O., 1957.

WRIGHT, MARION J.: *The Improvement of Patient Care.* New York, G. P. Putnam's Sons, 1954.

Law

BENTHAM, JEREMY: *An Introduction to the Principles of Morals and Legislation.* Oxford, England, Clarendon Press, 1907.

BROWN, ESTHER LUCILE: *Lawyers, Law Schools, and the Public Service.* New York, Russell Sage Foundation, 1948.

CANADA, DEPARTMENT OF JUSTICE: *Report of the Restrictive Trade Practices Commission Concerning the Manufacture, Distribution and Sale of Drugs.* Ottawa, Canada, The Department, 1963.

CARLSTON, KENNETH S.: *Law and Structures of Social Action.* New York, Columbia University Press, 1956.

CLARK, G. L.: *Summary of American Law.* Rochester, New York, The Lawyers Cooperative Publishing Co., 1949.

COHEN, MORRIS R.: *Law and the Social Order.* New York, Harcourt, Brace and Co., 1933.

CUSUMANO, CHARLES L.: *Malpractice Law Dissected for Quick Grasping.* New York, Medicine-Law Press, 1962.

DICKINSON, JOHN: *Administrative Justice and the Supremacy of Law in the United States.* Cambridge, Harvard University Press, 1927.

GRADWOHL, R. B. H.: *Legal Medicine.* St. Louis, Mo., C. V. Mosby Co., 1954.

HAYT, EMANUEL; HAYT, LILLIAN R.; GROESCHEL, AUGUST H.; and MC MULLAN, DOROTHY: *Law of Hospital and Nurse.* New York, Hospital Textbook Co., 1958.

HEALTH LAW CENTER, UNIVERSITY OF PITTSBURGH: *Hospital Law Manual and Quarterly Service.* (Administrator's volume and attorney's volume.) Pittsburgh, The Center, 1959. (Also a Canadian supplement.)

LESNIK, M. J., and ANDERSON, B. E.: *Nursing Practice and the Law,* 2nd ed. New York, J. B. Lippincott Co., 1955.

LOUISELL, DAVID W., and WILLIAMS, HAROLD: *The Parenchyma of Law.* Rochester, N. Y., Professional Medical Publications, 1960.

LUDLAM, J. E.: *Consent Manual.* San Francisco, California Hospital Association, 1960.

MACDONALD, R. ST. J., ed.: *Current Law and Social Problems.* Toronto, University of Toronto Press, 1960.

MANN, G. T.: *Principals of Legal Medicine.* Richmond, Va., Medical College of Virginia, 1960.

NORTH, FRANCIS N., S.J.: *Canon Law for Hospitals,* 2nd ed. St. Louis, Mo., Catholic Hospital Association, 1962.

POUND, ROSCOE: *An Introduction to the Philosophy of Law.* New Haven, Conn., Yale University Press (Yale paperbound edition), 1959.

REGAN, L., JR.: *Doctor and Patient and Law,* 3rd ed. St. Louis, C. V. Mosby Co., 1956.

Medicine and Allied Professions

ABDELLAH, F. G.; BELAND, I. L.; MARTIN, A.; and MATHENEY, R. V.: *Patient-Centered Approaches to Nursing.* New York, The Macmillan Co., 1960.

THE AMERICAN FOUNDATION, INC.: *American Medicine—Expert Testimony Out of Court.* New York, The Foundation, 1937.

AMERICAN HOSPITAL ASSOCIATION: *Careers in Hospitals.* Chicago, The Association, 1963.

AMERICAN MEDICAL ASSOCIATION: *Health Aspects of Aging.* Chicago, The Association, 1958.

AMERICAN RECREATION SOCIETY: *Basic Concepts in Hospital Recreation.* Washington, D.C., The Society, 1957.

BAEHR, GEORGE: *The Role of Medical Group Practice in the Changing Order.* New York, Medical Administration Service, Inc., 1949.

BAKER, F. J., ed.: *Progress in Medical Laboratory Technique.* Toronto, Canada, Butterworth and Co., 1962.

BARTLETT, H. M.: *Fifty Years of Social Work in the Medical Setting.* New York, National Association of Social Workers, 1956.

BELL, ENID HESTER CHATAWAY MOBERLY: *The Story of Hospital Almoners.* London, Faber and Faber, 1961.

Blakiston's New Gould Medical Dictionary, 2nd ed. New York, McGraw-Hill, Blakiston Division, 1956.

BOYD, WILLIAM: *An Introduction to the Study of Disease,* 5th ed. Philadelphia, Lea and Febiger, 1962.

BROWN, ESTHER LUCILE: *Nursing for the Future.* New York, Russell Sage Foundation, 1948.

BROWN, FRANCIS J.: *Sociology—with Application to Nursing and Health Education.* Englewood Cliffs, N. J., Prentice-Hall, 1957.

BURROW, JAMES G.: *AMA, Voice of American Medicine.* Baltimore, Johns Hopkins Press, 1963.

CABOT, RICHARD C.: *Social Work: Essays on the Meeting-Ground of Doctor and Social Worker.* Boston and New York, Houghton Mifflin Co., 1919.

CANNON, IDA MAUD: *Social Work in Hospitals.* New York, Russell Sage Foundation, 1923.

——— *On the Social Frontier of Medicine.* Cambridge, Harvard University Press, 1952.

CLARE, SISTER MARY AGNES (FRENAY): *Understanding Medical Terminology,* 2nd ed. St. Louis, Mo., Catholic Hospital Association, 1962.

CLUTE, KENNETH F.: *The General Practitioner.* Toronto, Canada, University of Toronto Press, 1963.

COMMISSION ON CHRONIC ILLNESS: *Chronic Illness in the United States.* 4 vols. Cambridge, published for the Commonwealth Fund by Harvard University Press, 1956–1959.

DAVIES, J. O. F., et al.: *Towards a Measure of Medical Care: Operational Research in the Health Services.* (Published for the Nuffield Provincial Hospitals Trust.) Fair Lawn, N. J., Oxford University Press, 1962.

DAVIS, MICHAEL M.: *America Organizes Medicine.* New York, Harper and Brothers, 1941.

——— *Medical Care for Tomorrow.* New York, Harper and Brothers, 1955.

DOE, JANET; IDOLE, J.; and MARSHALL, M. L., eds.: *A Handbook of Medical Library Practice,* 2nd ed. Chicago, American Library Association, 1956.

DONALD, DONNA M.: *Survey of the Paramedical Field.* Berkeley, University of California Press, 1954.

DORLAND, W. A. NEWMAN, *et al.*: *Dorland's Illustrated Medical Dictionary,* 23rd ed. (1st ed. 1900). Philadelphia and London, W. B. Saunders Co., 1957.

ECKSTEIN, HARRY: *Pressure Group Politics: The Case of the British Medical Association.* Stanford, Calif., Stanford University Press, 1960.

EMERSON, CHARLES PHILLIPS, JR., and BRAGDON, JANE SHERBURN: *Essentials of Medicine,* 18th ed. Philadelphia, J. B. Lippincott Co., 1959.

EMERSON, HAVEN, ed.: *Administrative Medicine.* Edinburgh and New York, Thomas Nelson and Sons, 1951.

EVANG, KARL: *Health Service, Society and Medicine; Present Day Health Services in Their Relation to Medical Science and Social Structures.* London, New York and Toronto, Oxford University Press, 1960.

FIELD, MINNA: *Patients Are People; a Medical-Social Approach to Prolonged Illness.* New York, Columbia University Press, 1958.

FINER, HERMAN: *Administration and the Nursing Services.* New York, The Macmillan Co., 1952.

FINK, ARTHUR EMIL; WILSON, EVERETT E.; and CONOVER, MERRILL B.: *The Field of Social Work,* 3rd ed. New York, Henry Holt and Co., 1955.

FORSYTH, G., and LOGAN, R.: *The Demand for Medical Care.* London, Oxford University Press, 1960.

GOODHART, ROBERT S., and WOHL, MICHAEL G.: *Modern Nutrition in Health and Disease,* 2nd ed. Philadelphia, Lea and Febiger, 1960.

GOODMAN, LOUIS S., and GILMAN, ALFRED: *The Pharmacological Basis of Therapeutics,* 2nd ed. New York, The Macmillan Co., 1955.

GREGG, ALAN: *Challenges to Contemporary Medicine.* New York, Columbia University Press, 1956.

GREGOR, REX H., and MICKEY, HAROLD C.: *Procurement and Materials Management for Hospitals.* Springfield, Ill., Charles C Thomas, 1960.

HEYMAN, MARGARET M.: *Effective Utilization of Social Workers in a Hospital Setting.* Chicago, American Hospital Association, 1962.

HOLMES, OLIVER WENDELL: *The Autocrat of the Breakfast Table* (reprint). New York, Sagamore Press, 1957.

HUFFMAN, EDNA K.: *Medical Records in Nursing Homes.* Berwyn, Ill., Physicians' Record Co., 1962.

———*Manual for Medical Record Librarians,* 5th ed. Berwyn, Ill., Physicians' Record Co., 1963.

HUGHES, EVERETT C., *et al.*: *Twenty Thousand Nurses Tell Their Story.* Philadelphia, J. B. Lippincott Co., 1958.

KELLOGG, W. K., FOUNDATION: *Medical Diagnostic Services for Small Communities.* Battle Creek, Mich., The Foundation, not dated.

KELLY, CORDELIA W.: *Dimensions of Professional Nursing.* New York, The Macmillan Co., 1962.

KESSLER, H.: *Rehabilitation of the Physically Handicapped*. New York, Columbia University Press, 1953.

LE VESCONTE, HELEN P.: *Guideposts of Occupational Therapy*. Toronto, Canada, University of Toronto Press, 1959.

LOVE, R. D.: *Medical Care of the Aged*. New York, National Association of Manufacturers, 1960.

MACDONALD, E. M. *et. al.*: *Occupational Therapy in Rehabilitation*. London, Bailliere, Tindall and Cox, Ltd., 1960.

MACGREGOR, FRANCES COOKE: *Social Science in Nursing*. New York, Russell Sage Foundation, 1960.

MAHONEY, T.: *The Merchants of Life* (Pharmacy). New York, Harper and Brothers, 1959.

MAINLAND, DONALD: *Elementary Medical Statistics (The Principles of Quantitative Medicine)*. Philadelphia, W. B. Saunders Co., 1952.

MASSIE, WILLMAN A.: *Medical Services for Rural Areas*. Cambridge, Harvard University Press, 1957.

MOSER, ROBERT H.: *Diseases of Medical Progress*. Springfield, Ill., Charles C Thomas, 1959.

NATIONAL LEAGUE FOR NURSING: *How to Organize and Extend Community Nursing Services*. New York, The League, 1962.

NEW YORK ACADEMY OF MEDICINE: *Medicine in a Changing Society*. New York, Columbia University Press, 1956.

PAGE, SIR EARLE: *What Price Medical Care? A Preventive Prescription for Private Medicine* (Australia). Philadelphia, J. B. Lippincott Co., 1960.

PERRODIN, CECILIA M.: *Supervision of Nursing Service Personnel*. New York, The Macmillan Co., 1954.

PLUNKETT, R. J., and HAYDEN, ADALINE C.: *Textbook and Guide to the Standard Nomenclature of Diseases and Operations,* 4th ed. New York, Blakistan Co., 1961.

QUIMBY, E. H.: *Safe Handling of Radioactive Isotopes in Medical Practice*. New York, The Macmillan Co., 1960.

REITZES, DIETRICH C.: *Negroes and Medicine*. Cambridge, Harvard University Press, 1958.

ROSS, FRANK XAVIER: *The World of Medicine*. New York, Lothrop, Lee and Shepard, 1963.

RUSK, HOWARD A.: *Rehabilitation Medicine; A Textbook on Physical Medicine and Rehabilitation*. St. Louis, Mo., C. V. Mosby Co., 1958.

SAND, RENÉ: *The Advance to Social Medicine*. London and New York, Staples Press, 1952.

SHEPARD, WILLIAM P.: *Physicians in Industry*. New York, Toronto, London, McGraw-Hill Book Co., 1961.

SILVERMAN, MILTON: *Magic in a Bottle,* 2nd ed. New York, The Macmillan Co., 1948.

SOMERS, HERMAN MILES, and SOMERS, ANNE RAMSAY: *Doctors, Patients and Health Insurance: The Organization and Financing of Medical Care.* Washington, D.C., The Brookings Institute, 1961.

SPENCER, STEVEN M.: *Wonders of Modern Medicine.* New York, McGraw-Hill Book Co., 1953.

STEDMAN, THOMAS L.: *Medical Dictionary,* 19th ed. Baltimore, Williams and Wilkins Co., 1957.

UNITED STATES PUBLIC HEALTH SERVICE: *International Classification of Diseases, Adapted for Indexing Hospital Records by Diseases and Operations.* Publication No. 719 (revised). 2 vols. Washington, D.C., United States Government Printing Office, 1963. (Prepared by a special committee of the National Office of Vital Statistics; contains codes used in the Professional Activity Study and the Medical Audit Program.)

WOOLMER, RONALD: *The Conquest of Pain.* New York, Alfred A. Knopf, 1961.

WORLD HEALTH ORGANIZATION: *W.H.O. and Mental Health, 1949–1961.* Geneva, W.H.O., 1962.

PUBLIC HEALTH AND PREVENTIVE MEDICINE

AMERICAN PUBLIC HEALTH ASSOCIATION: *Control of Communicable Disease in Man.* New York, The Association, 1955.

—— *Guide to a Community Health Study.* New York, The Association, 1960.

EMORY, FLORENCE H. M.: *Public Health Nursing in Canada.* New York, The Macmillan Co., 1953.

ESSEX-CRATER, A. J.: *Synopsis of Public Health and Social Medicine.* Bristol, England, John Wright and Sons, 1960.

FOLKS, HOMER (SAVEL ZIMAND, ed.) *Public Health and Welfare: The Citizen's Responsibility.* New York, The Macmillan Co., 1958.

FREEMAN, RUTH B., and HOLMES, EDWARD M., JR.: *Administration of Public Health Services.* Philadelphia and London, W. B. Saunders Co., 1960.

HOBSON, W.: *Theory and Practice of Public Health.* London, Oxford University Press, 1961.

MUSTARD, HARRY S., and STEBBINS, ERNEST L.: *Introduction to Public Health,* 4th ed. New York and London, The Macmillan Co., 1959.

ROEMER, M. I.: *Medical Care in Relation to Public Health.* Geneva, W.H.O., 1956.

ROSENAU, MILTON J.: *Preventive Medicine and Hygiene,* 6th ed. reprinted 1944. New York, D. Appleton-Century Co., 1944.

STIEGLITZ, EDWARD J.: *A Future for Preventive Medicine.* New York, The Commonwealth Fund, 1945.

WINSLOW, C.-E. A.: *The Evaluation and Significance of the Modern Public Health Campaign.* New Haven, Conn., Yale University Press, 1923.

(See also the references under "History")

RELIGION

BURSK, EDWARD C.: *Business and Religion: A New Depth Dimension in Management.* New York, Harper and Brothers, 1959.

CABOT, RICHARD C., and DICKS, RUSSELL L.: *The Art of Ministering to the Sick.* New York, The Macmillan Co., 1945.

DICKS, RUSSELL L.: *Thy Health Shall Spring Forth.* New York, The Macmillan Co., 1945.

DRUMM, WILLIAM MARTIN: *Hospital Chaplains—An Historical Synopsis and Commentary.* Washington, D.C., The Catholic University of America Press, 1943.

ELLIS, JOHN TRACY: *American Catholicism.* Chicago, University of Chicago Press, 1959.

EVERETT, JOHN RUTHERFORD: *Religion in Economics, a Study of John Bates Clark, Richard T. Ely and Simon N. Patten.* New York, King's Crown Press, 1946.

GALDSTON, IAGO, ed.: *Ministry and Medicine in Human Relations.* New York, International University Press, 1953.

GLAZER, NATHAN: *American Judaism.* Chicago, University of Chicago Press, 1959.

HARNEY, MARTIN P.: *The Jesuits in History* (reissue). Chicago, Loyola University Press, 1962.

HERBERG, WILL: *Protestant—Catholic—Jew.* New York, Doubleday and Co., 1955.

HUDSON, WINTHROP S.: *American Protestantism.* Chicago, University of Chicago Press, 1961.

HUME, EDGAR ERSKINE: *Medical Work of the Knights Hospitallers of Saint John of Jerusalem.* Baltimore, Johns Hopkins University Press, 1940.

JAKOBOVITS, IMMANUEL: *Jewish Medical Ethics; a Comparative and Historical Study of the Jewish Religious Attitude to Medicine and Its Practice.* New York, Philosophical Library, 1959.

JAMES, WILLIAM: *The Varieties of Religious Experience.* New York, Modern Library, 1902.

LASSWELL, HAROLD D., and CLEVELAND, HARLAN, eds.: *The Ethic of Power: The Interplay of Religion, Philosophy, and Politics.* New York, Harper and Row, 1962.

SCHERZER, CARL J.: *The Church and Healing.* Philadelphia, The Westminster Press, 1940.

SMITH, JAMES WARD, and JAMISON, A. LELAND, eds.: *Religion in American Life.* 2 vols. Princeton, N. J., Princeton University Press, 1961.

TAWNEY, R. H.: *Religion and the Rise of Capitalism.* New York, Harcourt, Brace and Co., 1952.

WEBER, MAX: *The Protestant Ethic and the Spirit of Capitalism.* London, George Allen and Unwin, 1930.

WESTBERG, GRANGER: *Nurse, Pastor, and Patient.* Rock Island, Ill., Augustana Press, 1955.
—— *Minister and Doctor Meet.* New York, Harper and Row, 1961.
YOUNG, RICHARD K., and MEIBURG, ALBERT L.: *Spiritual Therapy.* New York, Harper and Row, 1960.

SCIENCE, PHYSICAL

BATES, RALPH S.: *Scientific Societies in the United States,* 2nd ed. Cambridge, M.I.T. Press, 1958.
BEECHER, HENRY K., ed.: *Disease and the Advancement of Basic Science.* Cambridge Harvard University Press, 1960.
BROOKS, STEWART M.: *Integrated Basic Science.* St. Louis, Missouri, C. V. Mosby Co., 1962.
DAMPIER, WILLIAM CECIL: *A Shorter History of Science.* Cambridge, England, Cambridge University Press, 1944; New York, Meridian Books, 1957.
HOGBEN, LANCELOT: *Science for the Citizen.* New York, W. W. Norton and Co., 1951.
LWOFF, ANDRÉ: *Biological Order.* Cambridge, M.I.T. Press, 1962.
MARCSON, SIMON: *The Scientist in American Industry.* New York, Harper and Brothers, 1960.
PALTER, ROBERT M.: *Whitehead's Philosophy of Science.* Chicago, University of Chicago Press, 1960.
PRIOR, MOODY E.: *Science and the Humanities.* Evanston, Ill., Northwestern University Press, 1962.
RABI, ISIDOR I.: *Science, Education, and Society.* Cambridge, M.I.T. Press, 1963.
DE SANTILLANA, GIORGIA: *The Origins of Scientific Thought: From Anaximander to Proclus, 600 B.C. to 300 A.D.* Chicago, University of Chicago Press, 1961.
WHITEHEAD, ALFRED: *Science and the Modern World.* New York, The Macmillan Co., 1925.

THE SOCIAL SCIENCES

ABEL-SMITH, BRIAN, and TITMUSS, RICHARD M.: *The Cost of the National Health Service in England and Wales.* Cambridge, England, National Institute of Economic and Social Research, Cambridge University Press, 1956.
AD HOC CITIZENS COMMITTEE: *Voluntary Health and Welfare Agencies in the United States.* New York, The Schoolmasters' Press, 1961.
ALLAN, W. SCOTT: *Rehabilitation: A Community Challenge.* New York, John Wiley and Sons, 1958.
ANDERSON, ODIN, and SEACAT, MILVOY S.: *An Analysis of Personnel in Medical Sociology.* Chicago, Health Information Foundation, 1962.

ANDREWS, FRANK M.: *Study of Company-sponsored Foundations.* New York, Russell Sage Foundation, 1960.

APPLE, DORRIAN, ed.: *Sociological Studies of Health and Sickness.* New York, McGraw-Hill Book Co., 1960.

ARMYTAGE, W. H. G.: *Heavens Below: Utopian Experiments in England, 1560–1960.* Toronto, University of Toronto Press, 1962.

BERNARD, JESSIE: *American Community Behavior.* New York, Dryden Press, 1949.

BEVERIDGE, LORD: *Voluntary Action, A Report on Methods of Social Advance.* London, George Allen and Unwin, 1948.

BLACK, EUGENE R.: *The Diplomacy of Economic Development.* Cambridge, Harvard University Press, 1961.

BLACK, MAX, ed.: *The Social Theories of Talcott Parsons.* Englewood Cliffs, N. J., Prentice-Hall, 1961.

BOEK, WALTER E., and BOEK, JEAN K.: *Society and Health.* New York, G. P. Putnam's Sons, 1956.

BOLLENS, JOHN C., ed.: *Exploring the Metropolitan Community.* Berkeley, University of California Press, 1961.

BORNET, VAUGHAN DAVIS: *Welfare in America.* Norman, Oklahoma University Press, 1960.

BOSSARD, JAMES H. S.: *Social Change and Social Problems,* rev. New York, Harper and Brothers, 1938.

BREMNER, ROBERT H.: *American Philanthropy.* Chicago, University of Chicago Press, 1960.

BUELL, BRADLEY: *Community Planning for Human Services.* New York, Columbia University Press, 1952.

BURGESS, ERNEST W.: *Aging in Western Societies.* Chicago, University of Chicago Press, 1960.

CARREL, ALEXIS: *Man, the Unknown.* New York, Harper and Brothers, 1935.

CARTER, RICHARD: *The Gentle Legions.* (A study of the major national voluntary health organizations.) New York, Doubleday and Co., 1961.

CHASE, STUART: *Men and Machines.* New York, The Macmillan Co., 1929.

CLARK, S. D., ed.: *Urbanism and the Changing Canadian Society.* Toronto, Canada, University of Toronto Press, 1961.

COHEN, NATHAN E.: *The Citizen Volunteer: His Responsibility, Role and Opportunity in Modern Society.* New York, Harper and Brothers, 1960.

COLCORD, JOANNA C.: *Your Community: Its Provision for Health, Education, Safety, Welfare.* New York, Russell Sage Foundation, 1947.

COLE, G. D. H.: *World in Transition: A Guide to the Shifting Political and Economic Forces of Our Time.* London and New York, Oxford University Press, 1949.

COMMONS, JOHN ROGERS: *Institutional Economics: Its Place in the Political Economy.* 2 vols. Madison, University of Wisconsin Press, 1959.

DAHL, ROBERT A.; HAIRE, MASON; and LAZARFELD, PAUL: *Social Science Research on Business: Product and Potential.* New York, Columbia University Press, 1959.

DE HUSZAR, GEORGE B., ed.: *Fundamentals of Voluntary Health Care.* Caldwell, Idaho, Caxton Printers, 1962.

DOBRINER, WILLIAM: *The Suburban Community.* New York, G. P. Putnam's Sons, 1958.

DUNCAN, OTIS DUDLEY, *et al.: Metropolis and Region.* Baltimore, Johns Hopkins University Press, 1960.

DURANT, WILL: *The Story of Philosophy.* Garden City, N. Y., Garden City Publishing Co., 1927.

EELLS, RICHARD: *Corporation Giving in a Free Society.* New York, Harper and Brothers, 1956.

FISHER, ROBERT MOORE, ed.: *The Metropolis in Modern Life.* Garden City, N. Y. Doubleday and Co., 1955.

FREEMAN, RALPH E., ed.: *Postwar Economic Trends.* New York, Harper and Brothers, 1960.

GALBRAITH, JOHN K.: *American Capitalism, The Concept of Countervailing Power.* Boston, Houghton Mifflin Co., 1952.

GALDSTON, IAGO, ed.: *The Meaning of Social Medicine.* Cambridge, Harvard University Press, 1954.

GLASSER, MELVIN A.: *What Makes a Volunteer?* New York, Public Affairs Committee, 1955.

HAGEN, EVERETT E.: *How Economic Growth Begins.* Homewood, Ill., Dorsey Press, 1962.

HAMMOND, KENNETH R., and HOUSEHOLDER, JAMES E.: *Introduction to the Statistical Method; Foundations and Use in the Behavorial Sciences.* New York, Alfred A. Knopf, Inc., 1962.

HERSKOVITS, MELVILLE JEAN: *Man and His Works: The Science of Cultural Anthropology.* New York, Alfred A. Knopf, Inc., 1948.

HIGGINS, BENJAMIN: *Economic Development.* New York, W. W. Norton and Co., 1961.

HIRSCHMAN, ALBERT: *The Strategy of Economic Development.* New Haven, Conn., Yale University Press, 1961.

HISCOCK, IRA V.: *Community Health Organization.* New York, the Commonwealth Fund, 1939.

HOOVER, EDGAR M., and VERNON, RAYMOND: *Anatomy of a Metropolis.* Cambridge, Harvard University Press, 1959.

HUNTER, FLOYD; SCHAFFER, RUTH CONNOR; and SHEPS, CECIL G.: *Community Organization: Action and Inaction.* Chapel Hill, N. C., University of North Carolina Press, 1956.

INTERNATIONAL LABOUR OFFICE: *The Cost of Medical Care.* Geneva, The Office, 1959.

KOENIG, SAMUEL: *Man and Society.* New York, Barnes and Noble, 1957.

KOOS, EARL L.: *The Sociology of the Patient.* New York, McGraw-Hill Book Co., 1959.

LEBENSTEIN, HARVEY: *Economic Theory and Organizational Analysis.* New York, Harper and Brothers, 1960.

LORWIN, LEWIS L.: *The International Labor Movement.* New York, Harper and Brothers, 1953.

LUNDBERG, GEORGE A.; SCHRAG, CLARENCE C.; and LARSON, OTTO N.: *Sociology.* New York, Harper and Brothers, 1958.

MAC INTYRE, DUNCAN M.: *Voluntary Health Insurance and Rate Making.* Ithaca, N. Y., Cornell University Press, 1962.

MARSHALL, ALFRED: *Principles of Economics.* New York, The Macmillan Co., 1948.

MAYO, ELTON: *The Social Problems of an Industrial Civilization.* Cambridge, Harvard University Press, 1945.

MERCER, BLAINE E.: *The Study of Society.* New York, Harcourt, Brace and Co., 1958.

MIAL, DOROTHY, and MIAL, CURTIS: *Our Community.* New York, New York University Press, 1960.

MUMFORD, LEWIS: *The City in History.* New York, Harcourt, Brace and Co., 1961.

NATIONAL HEALTH ASSEMBLY: *America's Health.* New York, Harper and Brothers, 1949.

PARKINSON, C. NORTHCOTE: *The Evolution of Political Thought.* New York, The Viking Press, Compass Books ed., 1960; Houghton Mifflin Co., 1958.

POLYANI, KARL: *The Great Transformation* (rise of capitalism). New York, Farrar and Rinehart, 1944.

ROREM, C. RUFUS: *Economic Aspects of Medical Group Practice.* New York, Medical Administration Service, Inc., 1949.

SCHLESINGER, A. M.: *The American As Reformer.* Cambridge, Harvard University Press, 1950.

SCHOECK, HELMUT, ed.: *Financing Medical Care, an Appraisal of Foreign Programs.* Caldwell, Idaho, Caxton Printers, 1962.

SCHUMPETER, JOSEPH A.: *Capitalism, Socialism and Democracy.* New York, Harper and Brothers, 1950.

—— *History of Economic Analysis.* New York, Oxford University Press, 1955.

SEIPP, CONRAD, ed.: *Health Care for the Community; Selected Papers of Dr. John B. Grant.* Baltimore, Johns Hopkins Press, 1963.

SELLECK, HENRY B.: *Occupational Health in America.* Detroit, Wayne State University Press, 1962.

SELYE, HANS: *The Stress of Life.* New York, McGraw-Hill Book Co., 1956.

SELZNICK, PHILIP: *Leadership in Administration: A Sociological Interpretation.* New York, Harper and Brothers, 1957.

SIEVERS, ALLEN M.: *General Economics, An Introduction.* New York, J. B. Lippincott Co., 1952.

SIGERIST, HENRY E. (MILTON I. ROEMER, ed.): *On the Sociology of Medicine.* New York, M.D. Publications, 1960.

SILLS, DAVID L.: *The Volunteers.* Glencoe, Ill., Free Press, 1960.

SIMMONS, LEO WILLIAM, and WOLFF, HAROLD G.: *Social Science in Medicine.* New York, Russell Sage Foundation, 1954.

SMOLENSKY, JACK, and HAAR, FRANKLIN B.: *Principles of Community Health.* Philadelphia and London, W. B. Saunders Co., 1961.

SOULE, GEORGE: *Ideas of the Great Economists.* New York, The Viking Press, and Mentor Books, 1959.

SPIEGELMAN, MORTIMER: *Ensuring Medical Care for the Aged.* Homewood, Ill., R. D. Irwin, Inc., 1960.

STEIN, MAURICE R.: *The Eclipse of Community: An Interpretation of American Studies.* Princeton, N. J., Princeton University Press, 1960.

STERN, BERNHARD J.: *Society and Medical Progress.* Princeton, N. J., Princeton University Press, 1941.

STEWART, GEORGE R.: *Man: An Autobiography.* New York, Random House, 1960.

TIBBITTS, CLARK: *Handbook of Social Gerontology.* Chicago, University of Chicago Press, 1960.

TRIPP, L. REED: *Labor Problems and Processes: A Survey.* New York, Harper and Row, 1961.

VEBLEN, THORSTEIN: *The Theory of the Leisure Class: An Economic Study of Institutions.* New York, The Modern Library, 1934.

VELIE, LESTER: *Labor, U.S.A.* New York, Harper and Brothers, 1959.

VICKERS, SIR GEOFFREY: *The Undirected Society, Essays on the Human Implications of Industrialism in Canada.* Toronto, Canada, University of Toronto Press, 1959.

VIDICH, ARTHUR J., and BENSMAN, JOSEPH: *Small Town in Mass Society: Its Class, Power and Religion.* Princeton, N.J., Princeton University Press, 1958.

VON MISES, LUDWIG: *Theory and History: An Interpretation of Social and Economic Evolution.* New Haven, Conn., Yale University Press, 1957.

WAGNER, DONALD O.: *Social Reformers.* New York, The Macmillan Co., 1934.

WARREN, ROLAND L.: *Studying Your Community.* New York, Russell Sage Foundation, 1955.

WHITE, MORTON, ed.: *The Age of Analysis—Twentieth Century Philosophers.* New York, Mentor Books, 1961.

WILENSKY, HAROLD L.: *Industrial Society and Social Welfare.* New York, Russell Sage Foundation, 1958.

WINSLOW, C-E. A.: *The Cost of Sickness and the Price of Health.* Geneva, W.H.O., 1951.

YOUNG, ROLAND, ed.: *Approaches to the Study of Politics.* Evanston, Ill., Northwestern University Press, 1962.

INDEX